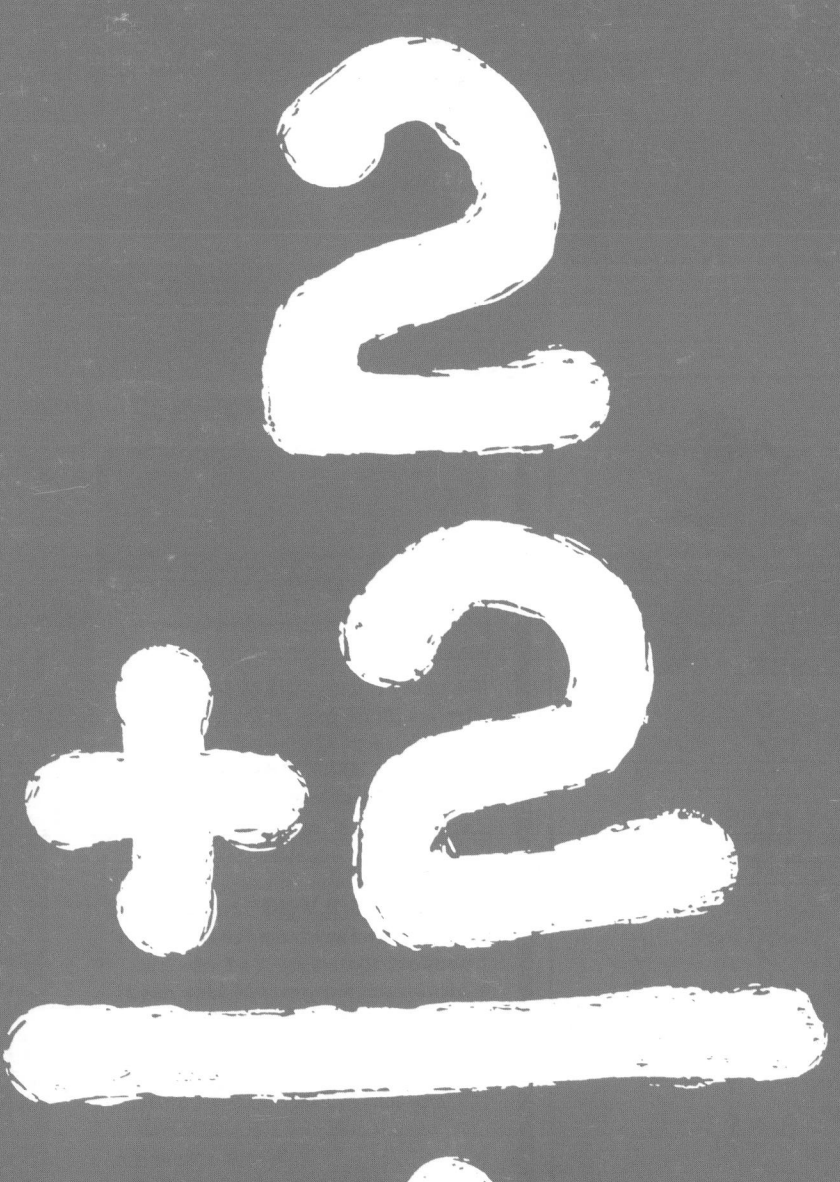

Pages of Support for Each Student Lesson.

Why choose anything less?

Success

- **Student Editions K-8 (K-6 Spanish*)**
These editions include a broad range of topics, stimulating lessons that help motivate students for learning mathematics, plus ample practice and application lessons to build success.

- **Teacher's Edition K-8 (K-6 Spanish*)**
They provide maximum support and options that save time through program manageability and teaching flexibility.

• Supplements

"I think it's an outstanding program. My rep is great and he's only a phone call away. I can always get the materials or information I need."

(Middle School Teacher)

Practice Workbook*
Extra practice pages that provide reinforcement for mastery of concepts and computational competence

Reteaching Workbook*
Opportunities to reteach and review concepts to ensure student success before moving to new ideas.

Challenges Workbook*
Mathematical situations for all students that motivate students to have fun with mathematics.

Building Thinking Skills Workbook*
Opportunities to build critical thinking and mathematical reasoning power which foster independent decision-making abilities.

Family Math Letters*
Positive communication with students' families that provide information and math experiences for families to be enjoyed at home.

Transparency Package - Teaching Aids
Items such as geometric shapes and graph paper to help make teaching and learning concepts easier in transparency and blackline master formats.

Kindergarten Big Book
Enlarged format to facilitate interactive whole group teaching.

Storybooks (K, 1, 2)
Beautifully illustrated stories for each chapter in a 17" x 22" format that deepens under-standing of concepts through the mathematics and language arts connection.

Computer-Assisted Problem Solving Software
Exciting software that allows students to enter the variables in a word problem and have the computer compute the correct answer.

Manipulative Kits
Ample materials in a convenient, easy to manage fomat. The pack-age is designed for ease in storing, distributing, and retrieving materials.

Overhead Manipulatives
These frequently requested overhead materials save teaching time by making classroom demonstrations colorful, exciting, and easy for all students to see.

Assessment Options*
A variety of options from which to choose for easy and efficient assessment of understanding and computational competence.
-Multiple Choice Test Booklets*
-Free Response Test Booklets*
-Alternative tests to use with manipulatives and critical thinking situations.

Record Keeping
Blackline masters, including Observation Checklists, that provide efficient and time-saving record keeping devices.

Cumulative Record Card
An easy to use record card that makes recording students' math progress from grades K-8 practical and easy to review and store.

Calculator Kits
Conveniently packaged calculators and resourse materials.

*Available in Spanish K-6
Las Matemáticas de Addison-Wesley ©1991

Two pages of lesson options preceed every lesson.

The options include:

Quick Review	Problem of the Day	Practice Supplement
Prior Knowledge	Subject Integration	Reteaching Supplement
Communication	Life Skills	Challenge Supplement
Explore and Connect	Math Connection	Building Thinking Skills Supplement
	Creative Thinking	Options for Individual Needs

CONTENTS · Grade 2

> **Two pages of lesson options preceed every lesson.**

The options include:	**Problem of the Day**	**Practice Supplement**
Quick Review	**Subject Integration**	**Reteaching Supplement**
Prior Knowledge	**Life Skills**	**Challenge Supplement**
Communication	**Math Connection**	**Building Thinking Skills Supplement**
Explore and Connect	**Creative Thinking**	**Options for Individual Needs**

CHAPTER 5 More Subtraction Facts

CONTENTS

CONTENTS   Grade 2

> **Two pages of lesson options preceed every lesson.**

The options include:	Problem of the Day	Practice Supplement
Quick Review	Subject Integration	Reteaching Supplement
Prior Knowledge	Life Skills	Challenge Supplement
Communication	Math Connection	Building Thinking Skills Supplement
Explore and Connect	Creative Thinking	Options for Individual Needs

Grade 2 CONTENTS

CONTENTS   Grade 2

> **Two pages of lesson options preceed every lesson.**

The options include:	Problem of the Day	Practice Supplement
Quick Review	Subject Integration	Reteaching Supplement
Prior Knowledge	Life Skills	Challenge Supplement
Communication	Math Connection	Building Thinking Skills Supplement
Explore and Connect	Creative Thinking	Options for Individual Needs

Grade 2 — CONTENTS

Robert E. Eicholz
Addison-Wesley Author
Woodinville, Washington

Phares G. O'Daffer
Professor Emeritus of Mathematics
Illinois State University
Normal, Illinois

Charles R. Fleenor
Addison-Wesley Author
Sunnyvale, California

Sharon L. Young
Addison-Wesley Author
Palm Harbor, Florida

Randall I. Charles
Associate Professor and Chairperso
Department of Mathematics and
Computer Science
San Jose State University
San Jose, California

Carne S. Barnett
Principle Investigator and
Program Director
Far West Laboratory for Educationa
Research and Development
San Francisco, California

Stanley R. Clemens
Professor of Mathematics
Bluffton College
Bluffton, Ohio

Andy Reeves
Elementary Mathematics Consultant
Florida Department of Education
Tallahassee, Florida

Carol A. Thornton
Professor, Department of Mathematics
Illinois State University
Normal, Illinois

Joan E. Westley
Addison-Wesley Author
San Francisco, California

John A. Dossey
Professor of Mathematics
Illinois State University
Bloomington, Illinois

David C. Brummett
Educational Consultant
Palo Alto, California

Betty C. Lee
Assistant Principal
Ferry Elementary School
Detroit, Michigan

Rosalie Whitlock
Educational Consultant
Stanford, California

Freddy Renfro
K-12 Mathematics Coordinator
La Porte Independent School District
La Porte, Texas

William J. Driscoll
Mathematics Education Consultant.
Burlington, Connecticut

Irene Medima
Mathematics Coordinator
Tom Brown Middle School
Corpus Christi, Texas

Contributing Writers

Betsy Franco

Mary Heinrich

Penny Holland

Marilyn Jacobson

Michael E. Jay

Judit N. Moschkovich

Ann Muench

Gini Shimabukuro

Julie Sitomer

Marny Sorgen

Connie Thorpe

Sandra Ward

Judith K. Wells

TEACHER REVIEWERS AND CONSULTANTS

Michele Acker-Hopevar
New Port Richey, Florida

Gerald Alford
Bellingham, Washington

Mary Altieri
Shrub Oak, New York

Carol Ballentine
Jacksonville, Florida

Gini Bergstresser
Fort Myers, Florida

Donna Bibbins
Watertown, New York

Beth Bishop
Houston, Texas

Janet Boatman
Tampa, Florida

Teresa Bonderson
Euless, Texas

Inga Borowski
Hoffman Estates, Illinois

Kathryn Bowden
Palo Alto, California

Linda Braham
Seattle, Washington

Mary Ann Bravo
San Mateo, California

Richard Breen
Soring Lake, Michigan

Virginia Burdick
San Antonio, Texas

Lynn Callahan
Melbourne, Florida

Linda Cantrell
Seattle, Washington

Jeanne Cantu
San Antonio, Texas

Bernie Capuano
Greenwich, Connecticut

Norm Carter
Santa Clara, California

Ginger Cartwright
Grand Prairie, Texas

Richard Caulfield
Westfield, Indiana

Holly Cavanaugh
St. Petersburg, Florida

Darlene Choe
Tampa, Florida

Toni Coclin
Winchester, Massachusetts

Laura Cohen
Palo Alto, California

Howard Cohn
Jacksonville, Florida

Anna Corbett
Zebulon, North Carolina

Elizabeth Correll
Hanahan, South Carolina

Cathy J. Davenport
San Antonio, Texas

Robert Davies
Stamford, Connecticut

Bill Davis
Dallas, Texas

Linda Deal
Kent, Washington

Leola Deboise
Dallas, Texas

Paul Dillenberger
Minneapolis, Minnesota

Nancy Diorio
Liverpool, New York

Candace Doherty
Palm Harbor, Florida

Nancy Doll-Ugrin
Fort Bragg, California

Joan Drennan
San Antonio, Texas

Patty Dunham
Pembroke Pines, Florida

Peggy Eddy
San Antonio, Texas

Dawn Lynn Eibel
Virginia Beach, Virginia

Barbara Elliott
El Cajon, California

Margaret Erdman
Hingham, Massachusetts

Lynda Evans
Houston, Texas

Carol Farr
Bonne Terre, Missouri

Floyd Flack
Temple City, California

Joseph Floyd
Opa Locka, Florida

Jim Foley
Anoka, Minnesota

Anne Franzmann
Bellingham, Washington

Pat Freda
Zephyrhills, Florida

George Frye
East Bridgewater, Massachusetts

Jean Fuhrman
Dolton, Illinois

Eileen Fukunaga
Santa Clara, California

Ponzella Fuller
Birmingham, Alabama

Deborah Gerretsen
Tinley Park, Illinois

Sylvia Geshell
Missoula, Montana

Patty J. Gillentine
Grand Prairie, Texas

Richard Giuliano
Hamilton, Ohio

Deborah Glynn
Largo, Florida

Cara Gordon
Mount Airy, North Carolina

Patricia Guzylak
Rochester, New York

Mary Gwinn
Covington, Virginia

Barbara Hackney
Madison, Tennessee

Sylvia Hale
South Daytona, Florida

Sandra Hall
Largo, Florida

Polly C. Hamm
Zephyrhills, Florida

Aida Haro
Houston, Texas

Mary Alice Harrington
Hingham, Massachusetts

Don Hastings
Stratford, Connecticut

Francis Hernandez
San Antonio, Texas

Nancy Hildebrand
Bellingham, Washington

Shyoko Hiraga
Seattle, Washington

Hector Hirigoyen
Miami, Florida

Beverly Horne
San Antonio, Texas

Catherine Howard
Palo Alto, California

Carole Ireland
Chicago, Illinois

Roberta Irwin
South San Francisco, California

Brenda Jacobs
Port Charlotte, Florida

Helen Jacobson
Kent, Washington

JoAnn Jeffreys
Darien, Illinois

Cora Johns
Lancaster, Texas

Cynthia Johnson
Hollywood, Florida

Marianne Johnson
Palo Alto, California

Cheryl Johnson
Reno, Nevada

Marcia A. Jones
Springfield, Ohio

Ellenore Mary Jordon
Bloomfield, Connecticut

Beva Karay
Palm Harbor, Florida

Lelo Kassel
Nanuet, New York

Rosemary Kavner
Reno, Nevada

Vicki Kayusa
Fort Myers, Florida

Janet King
Tampa, Florida

Michelle Klupchak
Chicago Heights, Illinois

Debra Knowles
Hayward, California

Charles LaBarbera
Liverpool, New York

Annette LaLonde
Kent, Washington

Esther A. Lamb
Park Forest, Illinois

Susan Lapworth
Indianapolis, Indiana

Susan Larson
Elk Grove, California

Virgina Lazidis
San Antonio, Texas

Josephine Leece
Tampa, Florida

Peggy Leftakis
Orlando, Florida

a Leonard
Katy, Texas

othy Ling
Lansing, Michigan

ty Looney
Grand Prairie, Texas

nne MacAdam
Tampa, Florida

a Madonia
Liverpool, New York

rilyn Majer
Clearwater, Florida

ra L. Martins
Cincinnati, Ohio

ry Martocci
Burlingame, California

bara Mathers
St. Petersburg, Florida

issa Mathews
Orlando, Florida

Mattioli
Elk Grove Village, Illinois

an McCartney
Rockledge, Florida

ureen McClain
Natick, Massachusetts

bie McCleskey
Palo Alto, California

et McGregor
Port Charlotte, Florida

endolyn McMullen
St. Louis, Missouri

en Mead
South San Francisco, California

ki Meredith
argo, Florida

ol Midgett
Southport, North Carolina

ice Miller
Fairport, New York

ricia Miller
St. Petersburg, Florida

go Morrison
San Mateo, California

Mosier
Tampa, Florida

ol Newman
Lauderdale Lakes, Florida

ores Norris
Port Charlotte, Florida

ricia O'Brien
Liverpool, New York

onne Oaldon
Orlando, Florida

enia Oeser
Arcadia, California

ty Olson
Olympia, Washington

en Opsomer
Ballwin, Missouri

an Ormiston
Hoffman Estates, Illinois

icent Osburn
Varico, Florida

lys J. Otis
White Bear Lake, Minnesota

rick Page
Oneida, New York

Beverly Peterson
Hingham, Massachusetts

Paula Phelps
Plano, Texas

Claire M. Piccinelle
Redway, California

Laura Pitts
Mexico, Missouri

Michael Pomara
Lake Grove, New York

Diana Price-Stone
Philomath, Oregon

Susan Pulisci
Palo Alto, California

Violet T. Pullara
Tampa, Florida

Michael Rapalje
Shrub Oak, New York

Jeanie Reed
Houston, Texas

Ann Reimer
Rochester, New York

Donna Ritchie
Elk Grove, Illinois

Linda S. Rittle
Tampa, Florda

Kathleen Roberson
Chicago Heights, Illinois

Martha Rosewell
East Bridgewater, Massachusetts

Beverly Saylor
South San Francisco, California

Philip Schmidt
Maple Grove, Minnesota

Mark Schumacher
Ballwin, Missouri

Margaret Scordias
Richmond Heights, Missouri

Michele Scott
Palo Alto, California

Jody Scott
Silverdale, Washington

Mary Sessler
Cupertino, California

John D. Shea
East Bridgewater, Massachusetts

Susan K. Skeiber
East Bridgewater, Massachusetts

Pearl Solomon
Pearl River, New York

Lynn Spadaccini
Melbourne, Florida

Karen Stafford
Garland, Texas

Les Steinberger
Plainview, New York

Jerry Stenson
San Bruno, California

Mary Ann Stine
Kennewick, Washington

Tom Stone
Eugene, Oregon

Lydia Stoopenkoff
San Francisco, California

Biruta Strausser
Menlo Park, California

Nancy Strodtbeck
Fairfield, Ohio

Maggie Sullivan
Chicago, Illinois

Linda Talford
Houston, Texas

Joyce Tarowsky
Indianapolis, Indiana

Elizabeth Travis
Seattle, Washington

Marie Trevino
San Antonio, Texas

Susan Troutman
Sugarland, Texas

Gloria Valenti
Tampa, Florida

Debbie Valentine
Houston, Texas

Elizabeth Von Rotz
Centralia, Washington

Karen Wade
Dade City, Florida

Anne Walters
Fort Meyers, Florida

Mary Ann Ward
Pontiac, Michigan

Edna Wayne
Sparks, Nevada

Christine West
Sullivan's Island, South Carolina

Mildred Wester
Indio, California

Sylvia White
Chicago, Illinois

Susan Widsten
San Antonio, Texas

Pat Wiemann
Kent, Washington

Joyce Wiley
Seminole, Florida

Gloria Williams
Palo Alto, California

Jo Helen Williams
Dayton, Ohio

Tamara L. Wilson
Hoffman Estates, Illinois

May Wiza
Park Forest, Illinois

Susan Wolfe
Easley, South Carolina

Dorothy Wood
Larkspur, California

Jean Worsh
Marshfield, Massachusetts

Bonnie Wrazien
Strousburg, Pennsylvania

Huretta Wright
Daytona Beach, Florida

Jane Wright
San Mateo, California

Sister Marla Yeck
St. Louis, Missouri

Jane Zarate
San Antonio, Texas

Mary Ann Zatlikal
West Nyack, New York

Margaret Zehnder
Bellingham, Washington

CHAPTER 1   Understanding Addition and Subtraction

To count on and back with numbers to 20 — **1-1**
To model and write addition sentences — **1-2**
To model and write subtraction sentences — **1-3**
To use the 6-point checklist to solve problems; to use critical thinking to identify missing numbers — **1-4**
To show different ways to name a sum — **1-5**
To model and write related addition and subtraction sentences — **1-6**

To model and finish related subtraction facts
To model and write fact families
To solve problems by finding missing data; to solve problems using the strategy Choose the Operation

CHAPTER 2   Addition Facts Sums to 18

To use the mental math techniques of counting on 1, 2, or 3 to find sums; to use the identity property of addition — **2-1**
To use the mental math technique of doubles to find sums — **2-2**
To use the mental math technique of doubles plus one to find sums — **2-3**
To practice the mental math techniques learned to find sums — **2-4**
To understand the operations of addition and subtraction by putting together or by taking away; to take a survey using tally marks — **2-5**

To use the mental math technique of finding sums of 10
To use the mental math technique of adding with 9 to find sums
To use the mental math technique of making 10 and adding extra to find sums
To practice the mental math techniques learned to find sums
To add three numbers
To understand the question in a problem; to solve problems using the strategy Make a List

CHAPTER 3   Patterns and Graphs

To model, identify, and continue odd and even patterns — **3-1**
To model, identify, and continue growing patterns — **3-2**
To identify and continue color patterns — **3-3**
To understand the operations of addition and subtraction by putting together or by taking away; to use critical thinking to continue patterns — **3-4**

To make and read bar graphs
To take and graph data from a survey
To read pictographs
To solve problems by retelling a story; to solve problems using the strategy Look for a Pattern

CHAPTER 4   Management

To use the mental math technique of counting back 1, 2, or 3 and subtracting with zero to find differences — **4-1**
To use the mental math technique of subtraction doubles to find differences — **4-2**
To use the mental math techniques of subtracting from 9 and 10 to find differences — **4-3**
To understand the operation of subtraction by comparing; to tell which event is more, less, or equally likely to occur — **4-4**

To use the mental math technique of counting up to find differences
To practice the mental math techniques learned to find differences
To model and finish related subtraction facts
To model and finish fact families
To solve problems by showing the data; to solve problems using the strategy Guess and Check

CHAPTER 9   Time and Money

To count 5-minute intervals on the clock   **9-1**

To tell and write time to 15-minute intervals   **9-2**

To tell and write time to 5-minute intervals   **9-3**

To write elapsed time   **9-4**

To read a calendar   **9-5**

To understand the operations of addition and subtraction by putting together or by comparing; to tell which event is more likely to occur   **9-6**

To count dimes, nickels, and pennies   **9-7**

To count quarters, dimes, nickels, and pennies

To count collections of coins including half dollars

To show different ways to pay an exact amount; to identify coins needed to pay an exact amount

To solve problems using data from a chart; to solve problems using the strategy Make a Table

CHAPTER 10 Understanding 2-Digit Addition

To model and add a 2-digit and a 1-digit number by counting on by ones   **10-1**

To model and add decade numbers; to use the commutative property of addition   **10-2**

To model and add a 2-digit and a decade number by counting on by tens   **10-3**

To model and add 2- digit numbers; to decide if trading is needed   **10-4**

To understand the operations of addition and subtraction by identifying which operation is needed; to estimate sums as more or less than 50—

To show different ways to name the same sum

To solve problems by writing a number sentence; to solve problems using the strategy Make a List

CHAPTER 11 Adding 2-Digit Numbers

To trade 10 ones for 1 ten   **11-1**

To add two 2-digit numbers using models   **11-2**

To add two 2-digit numbers using pictures   **11-3**

To add two 2-digit numbers using symbols   **11-4**

To estimate sums using front-end estimation   **11-5**

To practice adding two 2-digit numbers   **11-6**

To understand the operations of addition and subtraction by putting together or by taking away; to use a calculator to find two and three 2-digit sums   **11-7**

To choose an appropriate method of calculation

To add three 2-digit numbers

To solve problems using estimation; to solve problems using the strategy Guess and Check

CHAPTER 12   Geometry

To identify and sort solid figures   **12-1**

To make a solid figure; to count the number of corners, edges, or faces   **12-2**

To identify plane shapes on solids   **12-3**

To make plane shapes using a geoboard; to count the number of sides and corners; to find points inside, outside, and on   **12-4**

To understand the operation of subtraction by finding the missing part; to use critical thinking to make visual predictions   **12-5**

To make symmetric figures

To identify and make congruent figures

To solve problems using data from a number pair graph; to solve problems using the strategy Look for a Pattern

CHAPTER 13   Understanding 2-Digit Subtraction

To model and subtract a 1-digit from a 2-digit number by counting back by ones   **13-1**

To model and subtract decade numbers   **13-2**

To model and subtract a decade number from a 2-digit number by counting back by tens   **13-3**

To show different ways to name the same difference   **13-4**

To understand the operation of subtraction by comparing or by finding the missing part; to estimate differences as more or less than 50°

To subtract two 2-digit numbers using models; to decide if trading is needed

To solve problems by finding missing data; to solve problems using the strategy Draw a Picture

This pacing chart will help you plan your school year. It gives a suggested amount of time to spend on each chapter. You can adjust the times suggested to meet the needs of the students in your class.

Chapter	Pages	Number of Days
1 Understanding Addition and Subtraction	1-22	10
2 Addition Facts: Sums to 18	23-48	12
3 Patterns and Graphs	49-68	9
4 Subtraction Facts	69-90	10
5 More Subtraction Facts	91-110	9
6 Measurement	111-136	12
7 Place Value: Numbers to 100	137-158	10
8 Number Relationships and Counting Patterns	159-180	10
9 Time and Money	181-206	12
10 Understanding 2-Digit Addition	207-224	8
11 Adding 2-Digit Numbers	225-248	11
12 Geometry	249-268	9
13 Understanding 2-Digit Subtraction	269-286	8
14 Subtracting 2-Digit Numbers	287-312	12
15 Fractions	313-330	8
16 Understadning Multiplication and Division	331-352	10
17 Place Value: Numbers to 1,000	353-374	10
18 Adding and Subtracting 3-Digit Numbers	375-396	10

Total number of days: 180

	Chapter																	
	1	2	3	4	5	6	7	8	9	10	11	12	13	14	15	16	17	18
Balance scale and weights							▓											
Numeral cards						▓		▓						▓	▓			
Judy Clock														▓				
Small clocks														▓				
2-color counters*		▓	▓	▓	▓	▓		▓		▓					▓	▓	▓	▓
Cube-a-links*	▓		▓			▓					▓	▓						
Cup, pint, quart set										▓								
Fraction circles*																		▓
Geoboard*									▓									
Geometric solids*									▓									
Money coin set	▓	▓									▓							
Money bill set					▓													
Pattern blocks									▓									
Place value materials*											▓	▓					▓	
Ruler*							▓	▓	▓									
Spinners*	▓	▓			▓						▓	▓						
Ten frame*		▓				▓				▓					▓	▓	▓	

*This item can be found in the Addison-Wesley Manipulative Kit.

SCOPE AND SEQUENCE

Addison-Wesley Mathematics (©1991) fully integrates *motivation, understanding, problem solving, math reasoning, communication, subject integra*, *strand integration, group work* and *use of manipulatives* with all mathematical topics in the Scope and Sequence chart.

Algebra	K	1	2	3	4	5	6	7	8
Missing numbers and number sentences									
Variables and equations									
Patterns, functions, and relations									
Expressions									
Formulas									
Inequalities									
Informal proof									

Calculator Skills	K	1	2	3	4	5	6	7	8
Counting									
Whole numbers									
Decimals									
Fractions									
Integers									
Order of operations									
Constant key									
Memory key									
Error messages									
Ratio, proportion, percent									
Powers and roots									
Patterns									

Computer Technology	K	1	2	3	4	5	6	7	8
Computer programs									
Computer software									

Concepts & Computation	K	1	2	3	4	5	6	7	8
Number, Number Properties, Numeration, Number Sense									
Numbers and counting									
Compare and order									
whole numbers									
decimals									
fractions									
integers									
rational numbers									
Ordinal numbers									
Whole number place value									
Decimal place value									
Roman numerals									
Exponents									
Prime and composite numbers									
Scientific notation									
Square numbers and square roots									

 **TEACH**   **REINFORCE**

Note: Red type indicates that a topic is being introduced for the first time.

Grade 2

Algebra

Missing numbers and number sentences 21, 33, 1█ 224, 340

Calculator Skills

Counting 6, 170, 354, 401, 404
Whole numbers 30, 170, 238, 239-240, 278, 294, 300, 303-304, 309, 354, 363, 381, 391, 401, 40█ 403, 404
Constant key 170, 354, 401, 404
Choose a calculation method 239-240, 246, 303-3█ 363, 381, 430

Computer Technology

Computer programs 405, 406, 407, 408
Computer software 6, 12, 36, 44, 56, 64, 73, 80, 9█ 102, 114, 123, 143, 146, 169, 176, 186, 200, 215, 218, 233, 242, 256, 260, 262, 272, 281, 294, 3█ 318, 324, 340, 344, 358, 370, 381, 388

Concepts & Computation

Number, Number Properties, Numeration, Number Sense
Numbers and counting 1-2, 12, 16, 19, 20, 22, 23-█ 34, 48, 49-50, 66, 69-70, 77-78, 90, 109, 152, 163-164, 166, 169-170, 171-172, 173-174, 177, 1█ 179, 193-194, 195-196, 197-198, 204, 206, 207-█ 211-212, 214, 224, 236, 269-270, 273-274, 296, 320, 346, 359-360, 361-362, 364, 396, 401, 404 409, 411, 417, 418, 430
Compare and order whole numbers 3, 6, 19, 24, 3█ 57-58, 109, 146, 159-160, 165-166, 177, 178, 20█ 206, 224, 361-362, 365-366, 371, 372, 382, 39█ 417, 431
Ordinal numbers 173-174, 177, 178, 224, 370, 418
Whole number place value 137-138, 139-140, 141-1█ 134-144, 147-148, 149-150, 151-152, 155, 156, 1█ 206, 354, 355-356, 357-358, 362, 372, 396, 416, 417, 429
Roman numerals 109

...son-Wesley Mathematics (©1991) fully integrates *motivation, understanding, problem solving, math reasoning, communication, subject integration,* ...d integration, group work and *use of manipulatives* with all mathematical topics in the Scope and Sequence chart.

oncepts & Computation	K	1	2	3	4	5	6	7	8
hole Number Properties									
Properties of addition		T	T	R	R	R	R	R	R
Properties of subtraction		T	T	R	R	R	R	R	R
Properties of multiplication				T	T	R	R	R	R
Properties of division					T	T	R	R	R
dding Whole Numbers									
Understand addition concept	T	T	R	R	R				
Concrete and pictorial models	T	T	R	R	R				
Fact strategies		T	T	R					
Basic facts and fact families		T	T	R	R				
Problem solving	T	T	R	R	R	R	R	R	R
Estimate sums			T	R	R	R	R		
2- and 3-digit numbers			T	T	R	R	R		
3- and 4-digit numbers				T	T	R	R	R	
Larger numbers					T	R	R	R	R
ubtracting Whole Numbers									
Understand subtraction concept	T	T	R	R	R	R	R	R	R
Concrete and pictorial models	T	T	R	R	R	R	R		
Fact strategies		T	T	R					

TEACH ░   REINFORCE ▓

Grade 2

Concepts & Computation

Whole Number Properties
Properties of addition 9-10, 19, 22, 23-24, 26, 29, 30, 34, 38, 39-40, 41-42, 46, 48, 62, 68, 90, 128, 209-210, 214, 218, 221, 267
Properties of subtraction 69-70, 72, 74, 78, 79, 84, 88, 104, 110, 412
Properties of multiplication 332, 334, 337-338, 427
Properties of division 342

Adding Whole Numbers
Understand addition concept 1-2, 3-4, 9-10, 11-12, 15-16, 207-208, 225-226
Concrete models 1-2, 3, 7, 9, 11, 15-16, 21, 23-24, 31, 33, 35-36, 37-38, 42, 55, 72, 83-84, 86, 94, 103, 207-208, 211-212, 213-214, 217-218, 219, 221, 225-226, 227-228, 375-376, 377, 379-380, 384, 388, 389-390, 391, 394
Pictorial models 4, 9-10, 11-12, 16, 25, 68, 85, 209-210, 211-212, 214, 229-230, 234, 246, 248, 268, 376, 409
Fact strategies 23-24, 25-26, 27-28, 29-30, 33-34, 35-36, 37-38, 39-40, 45, 46, 48, 62, 68, 84, 90, 104, 128, 200, 218, 240, 362, 364, 410
Fact families 15-16, 19, 20, 48, 83-84, 88, 103-104, 107, 108, 110, 136, 413
Problem solving 7, 17, 18, 22, 31, 36, 43, 48, 55, 60, 63, 68, 85, 86, 90, 117, 167, 175, 191, 201, 204, 208, 219, 222, 232, 237, 240, 242, 243, 244, 246, 248, 263, 268, 281, 286, 292, 307, 336, 339, 363, 369, 376, 381391, 394, 430
Estimate sums 216, 222, 233-234, 243, 246, 268286, 307, 422
2-digit numbers 201, 207-208, 209-210, 211-212, 213-214, 217-218, 221, 222, 227-228, 229-230, 231-232, 233-234, 235-236, 237-238, 239-240, 241-242, 243, 244, 245, 246, 247, 248, 263, 267, 268, 276, 281, 286, 297-298, 304, 305-306, 307, 309, 311, 336, 346, 352, 368, 377-378, 380, 384, 393, 402, 421, 422
3-digit numbers 239, 363, 375-376, 379-380, 381, 384, 388, 389-390, 391, 393, 394, 402, 431, 432

Subtracting Whole Numbers
Understand subtraction concept 1-2, 5-6, 11-12, 13-14, 15-16, 269-270
Concrete models 1-2, 5, 7, 11, 13-14, 15-16, 21, 31, 40, 55, 69-70, 72, 73-74, 75, 81-82, 83-84, 91-92, 94, 97, 103, 145, 219, 269-270, 273-274, 275-276, 277, 279-280, 287-288, 289, 299, 383-384, 385-386, 387-388, 389-390, 391, 394
Pictorial models 6, 11-12, 14, 16, 20, 48, 85, 271-272, 274, 284, 291-292, 298310, 312, 383, 387, 409
Fact strategies 69-70, 71-72, 73-74, 77-78, 79-80, 84, 87, 88, 91-92, 93-94, 95-96, 99-100, 101-102, 104, 108, 110, 128, 136, 172, 200, 218, 240, 273-274

Red type indicates that a topic is being introduced for the first time.

Addison-Wesley Mathematics (©1991) fully integrates *motivation, understanding, problem solving, math reasoning, communication, subject integra[tion], strand integration, group work* and *use of manipulatives* with all mathematical topics in the Scope and Sequence chart.

Concepts & Computation cont.	K	1	2	3	4	5	6	7	8
Basic facts and fact families									
Problem solving									
Estimate differences									
2- and 3-digit numbers									
3- and 4-digit numbers									
Larger numbers									
Multiplying Whole Numbers									
Understand multiplication concept									
Concrete and pictorial models									
Basic facts and fact families									
Problem solving									
Estimating products									
2- and 3-digit numbers									
3- and 4-digit numbers									
Larger numbers									
Dividing Whole Numbers									
Understand division concept									
Concrete and pictorial models									
Basic facts and fact families									
Problem solving									
Estimating quotients									
1-digit divisors									
With remainders									
2-digit divisors									
Zero in quotients									
3-digit divisors									
2-digit quotients									
3-digit quotients									
Fraction Concepts									
Understand fractions									
Concrete and pictorial models									
Compare and order									
Equivalent fractions									
Lowest-terms fractions									
Greatest common factor									
Least common multiple/denominator									
Convert improper fractions and mixed numbers									
Reciprocals									
Computation with Fractions and Mixed Numbers									
Estimate									
Problem solving									
Add fractions									
like denominators									

■ TEACH ■ REINFORCE

Note: Red type indicates that a topic is being introduced for the first time.

Grade 2

Concepts & Computation cont.

Fact families 15-16, 19, 20, 48, 83-84, 88, 103-104, 107, 108, 110, 136, 413

Problem solving 7, 14, 17, 18, 20, 31, 40, 43, 46, 55,63, 75, 82, 85, 88, 97, 102, 105, 108, 110, 13[?], 145, 148, 156, 162, 167, 175, 178, 180, 191, 219, ·224, 237, 257, 262, 277, 280, 281, 299, 302, 303-304, 306, 307, 310, 330, 336, 352, 363, 38[?], 391, 394

Estimate differences 278, 295-296, 298, 307, 310, 330, 425

2-digit numbers 271-272, 273-274, 275-276, 277, 278, 279-280, 281, 283, 284, 289-290, 291-292, 293-294, 295-296, 297-298, 299, 300, 301-302, 303-304, 305-306, 307, 309, 310, 312, 330, 336, 346, 352, 363, 368, 381, 403, 424, 425

3-digit numbers 303, 383-384, 387-388, 389-390, 391, 393, 394, 403, 431, 432

Multiplying Whole Numbers

Understand multiplication concept 331-332, 333-3[?]

Concrete models 331-332, 333-334, 335-336, 337-338, 339, 344, 345, 347

Pictorial models 336, 338, 346, 350, 374, 396, 42[?]

Basic facts 333-334, 335-336, 337-338, 339, 343, 345-346, 347, 349, 350, 351, 374, 396, 404

Problem solving 339, 344, 347, 348, 350, 363, 39[?], 427, 430

Dividing Whole Numbers

Understand division concept 341-342, 343-344

Concrete models 341-342, 343, 345

Pictorial models 344, 346, 350, 396, 428

Problem solving 348

Fraction Concepts

Understand fractions 313-314, 315-316, 317-318, 3[?], 323-324, 327, 328, 426

Concrete models 313-314, 315, 319, 321, 323-324, 325, 326, 328

Pictorial models 316, 318, 320, 327, 328, 329, 352, 368, 374, 390, 426

Estimate 316, 322, 328

Problem solving 321, 324, 325, 326, 328, 374, 42[?]

...son-Wesley Mathematics (©1991) fully integrates *motivation, understanding, problem solving, math reasoning, communication, subject integration,* ...d integration, *group work* and *use of manipulatives* with all mathematical topics in the Scope and Sequence chart.

Concepts & Computation cont.	K	1	2	3	4	5	6	7	8
unlike denominators					■	■	■	■	■
Subtract fractions									
like denominators				■	■	■	■	■	■
unlike denominators					■	■	■	■	■
Multiply							■	■	■
Divide							■	■	■
Convert decimals, fractions				■	■	■	■	■	■
Convert decimals, fractions, and percents						■	■	■	■
Add mixed numbers					■	■	■	■	■
Subtract mixed numbers					■	■	■	■	■
Multiply mixed numbers							■	■	■
Divide mixed numbers							■	■	■
Decimal Concepts									
Understand decimals				■	■	■	■	■	■
Models				■	■	■	■		
Place value				■	■	■	■	■	■
Compare and order				■	■	■	■	■	■
Round decimals				■	■	■	■	■	■
Relate decimals to money concepts				■	■	■	■	■	■
Convert decimals, fractions				■	■	■	■	■	■
Convert decimals, fractions, and percents						■	■	■	■
Terminating and repeating decimals								■	■
Non-repeating decimals									■
Computation with Decimals									
Estimate				■	■	■	■	■	■
Problem solving				■	■	■	■	■	■
Add				■	■	■	■	■	■
Subtract				■	■	■	■	■	■
Multiply						■	■	■	■
Divide									
with whole number divisors						■	■	■	■
with decimal divisors							■	■	■
repeating quotients								■	■
Integers, Rational Numbers, and Real Numbers									
Negative numbers				■	■		■	■	■
Understand integers							■	■	■
Problem solving							■	■	■
Integers on a number line							■	■	■
Compare and order							■	■	■
Properties of integers							■	■	■
Models							■	■	■
Integer Operations							■	■	■

■ TEACH   ▦ REINFORCE

Red type indicates that a topic is being introduced for the first time.

Addison-Wesley Mathematics (©1991) fully integrates *motivation, understanding, problem solving, math reasoning, communication, subject integra..., strand integration, group work* and *use of manipulatives* with all mathematical topics in the Scope and Sequence chart.

Concepts & Computation cont.	K	1	2	3	4	5	6	7	8
Absolute value							T	T	T
Solve linear equations							T	T	T
Graph							T	T	T
Rational numbers							T	T	T
compute with rational numbers									T
scientific notation							T	T	T
Scientific notation							T	T	T
Exponents							T	T	T
Irrational numbers									T

Consumer Math	K	1	2	3	4	5	6	7	8
Problem solving	T	T	T	T	T	T	T	R	R
Consumer information sources	T	T	T	T	T	T	T	R	R
Decision making			T	T	T	T	T	R	R
Purchasing			T	T	T	T	T	R	R
Travel			T	T	T	T	T	R	R
Percent applications						T	T	R	R
Misleading statistics						T	T	T	R
Checking account/savings account/credit cards							T	T	T
Discounts							T	T	T

Critical Thinking & Logic	K	1	2	3	4	5	6	7	8
Compare or contrast	T	T	T	T	T	T	T	T	T
Classify and sort	T	T	T	T	T	T	T	T	T
Patterns	T	T	T	T	T	T	T	T	T
Spatial visualization	T	T	T	T	T	T	T	T	T
Logical reasoning	T	T	T	T	T	T	T	T	T
Reasoning from graphs	T	T	T	T	T	T	T		
Explain your reasoning		T	T	T	T	T	T	T	T
Predict and verify		T	T	T	T	T	T	T	T
Evaluate evidence and conclusions		T	T	T	T	T	T	T	T
Make generalizations	T	T	T	T	T	T	T	T	T

■ TEACH   ■ REINFORCE

Grade 2

Consumer Math

Problem solving 10, 14, 22, 36, 45, 82, 86, 102, 13...
147-148, 153, 175, 193-194, 195-196, 197-198,
199-200, 201, 202, 204, 205, 216, 222, 232,
233-234, 243, 245, 248, 263, 278, 281, 283, 28...
295, 299, 335-336, 349, 367-368, 376, 381,
389-390, 391, 392, 393, 394, 402, 416, 420, 42...
432
Consumer information sources 36, 45, 102, 147-14...
153, 193-194, 198, 199-200, 201, 202, 204, 216,
232, 233, 246, 248, 263, 283, 295, 336, 349, 3...
376, 389, 391, 392, 393, 394, 402, 416, 420, 43...

Critical Thinking & Logic

Compare or contrast 50, 56, 146, 179, 230, 250, 25...
Classify and sort 249
Patterns 49-50, 51-52, 53-54, 56, 58, 64, 65, 66, 9...
106, 110, 135, 152, 158, 169-170, 171-172, 174, 17...
190, 247, 264, 266, 282, 301-302, 311, 359-360,
411, 425
Spatial visualization 56, 110, 258
Logical reasoning 4, 8, 10, 14, 19, 24, 36, 45, 74, 8...
92, 96, 107, 155, 160, 177, 182, 203, 221, 228, 24...
290, 309, 327, 332, 349, 371, 386, 393
Explain your reasoning 4, 56, 92, 112, 163, 169, 170...
192, 230, 250, 255, 267, 334, 380
Predict and verify 67, 192, 258
Evaluate evidence and conclusions 146, 153, 192
Make generalizations 285

Note: Red type indicates that a topic is being introduced for the first time.

...son-Wesley Mathematics (©1991) fully integrates *motivation, understanding, problem solving, math reasoning, communication, subject integration,* ...d integration, *group work* and *use of manipulatives* with all mathematical topics in the Scope and Sequence chart.

Data Collection & Analysis	K	1	2	3	4	5	6	7	8
Collect and record data	■	■	■	■	■	■	■	■	■
Make a graph	■	■	■	■	■	■	■	■	■
Make a survey	■	■	■	■	■	■	■	■	■
Make a tally chart	■	■	■	■	■	■	■	■	■
Predict and verify				■	■	■	■	■	■
Generalize from data				■	■	■	■	■	■
Summarize results				■	■	■	■	■	■
Make a questionnaire				■	■	■	■	■	■
Conduct a simulation					■	■	■	■	■
Sampling						■	■	■	■

Estimation	K	1	2	3	4	5	6	7	8
Strategies									
Visual	■	■	■	■	■	■	■	■	■
Front-end			■	■	■	■	■	■	■
Use reference point or benchmark	■	■	■	■	■	■	■	■	■
Round whole numbers				■	■	■	■	■	■
Significant digits								■	■
Compatible numbers				■	■	■	■	■	■
Underestimates and overestimates					■	■	■		
Clustering						■	■	■	■
Adjusting an estimate				■	■	■	■	■	■
Round decimals					■	■	■	■	■
Sampling						■	■	■	■
Applications									
Problem solving	■	■	■	■	■	■	■	■	■
Measurement	■	■	■	■	■	■	■	■	■
Geometry				■	■	■	■	■	
Determine reasonable answers		■	■	■	■	■	■	■	■
Time	■	■	■	■	■	■	■	■	■
Decide when to estimate				■	■	■	■	■	■
Decimals and fractions					■	■	■	■	■
Percents						■	■	■	■
Algebra						■	■	■	■

	TEACH		REINFORCE

Grade 2

Data Collection & Analysis

Collect and record data 6, 32, 59, 80, 101, 114, 115, 164, 186, 232, 302, 336, 366
Make a graph 57-58, 59-60, 66, 101, 115, 382
Take a survey 32, 59
Make a tally chart 32, 59, 101, 121, 182
Data Bank 6, 80, 186, 232, 302, 336
Data Hunt 114, 164, 366

Estimation

Strategies
Visual estimation 28, 111-112, 113-114, 118, 119-120, 121, 122, 123, 124, 125-126, 127-128, 129, 130, 131, 133, 134, 152, 158, 172, 180, 184, 226, 316, 322, 328
Front-end 216, 222, 233-234, 243, 246, 268, 286, 295-296, 298, 307, 310, 422, 425
Use reference point or benchmark 157, 216, 268, 278, 322, 328, 330
Applications
Problem solving 7, 131, 134, 243, 286, 307, 325, 328, 415, 422
Measurement 111-112, 113-114, 118, 119-120, 121, 122, 123, 124, 125-126, 127-128, 129, 130, 131, 133, 134, 152, 157, 158, 172, 180, 414, 415
Determine reasonable answers 131, 134, 325, 328, 415
Time 28, 184, 223
See also CONCEPTS AND COMPUTATION, Add Whole Numbers, Estimate sums; Subtract Whole Numbers, Estimate differences.

Red type indicates that a topic is being introduced for the first time.

Addison-Wesley Mathematics (©1991) fully integrates *motivation, understanding, problem solving, math reasoning, communication, subject integrati[on],* *strand integration, group work* and *use of manipulatives* with all mathematical topics in the Scope and Sequence chart.

Geometry	K	1	2	3	4	5	6	7	8
Explore geometry	Teach	Teach	Teach	Teach	Teach/Reinforce	Teach/Reinforce	Reinforce	Reinforce	Reinforce
Concrete models	Teach	Teach	Teach	Teach	Teach/Reinforce	Teach/Reinforce	Reinforce	Reinforce	Reinforce
Identify plane figures	Teach	Teach	Teach	Teach	Teach/Reinforce	Teach/Reinforce	Reinforce	Reinforce	Reinforce
Identify space figures	Teach	Teach	Teach	Teach	Teach/Reinforce	Teach/Reinforce	Reinforce	Reinforce	Reinforce
Relate plane figures to space figures	Teach	Teach	Teach	Teach/Reinforce	Teach/Reinforce	Reinforce	Reinforce	Reinforce	Reinforce
Patterns	Teach	Teach	Teach	Teach	Teach/Reinforce	Teach/Reinforce	Reinforce	Reinforce	Reinforce
Symmetry	Teach	Teach	Teach	Teach	Teach	Teach/Reinforce	Reinforce	Reinforce	Reinforce
Congruent figures	Teach	Teach	Teach	Teach	Teach/Reinforce	Teach/Reinforce	Reinforce	Reinforce	Reinforce
Sides and corners		Teach	Teach	Reinforce	Reinforce	Reinforce	Reinforce	Reinforce	Reinforce
Inside, outside, and on		Teach	Teach	Reinforce	Reinforce	Reinforce	Reinforce	Reinforce	Reinforce
Points, lines, and segments				Teach	Teach	Teach	Teach/Reinforce	Teach/Reinforce	Reinforce
Classify angles				Teach	Teach	Teach	Teach/Reinforce	Teach/Reinforce	Reinforce
Classify polygons				Teach	Teach	Teach	Teach/Reinforce	Teach/Reinforce	Reinforce
Classify polyhedrons									Teach
Measure/estimate angles						Teach	Teach	Teach	Teach
Coordinate geometry				Teach	Teach	Teach	Teach/Reinforce	Teach/Reinforce	Reinforce
Similar figures					Teach	Teach	Teach	Teach/Reinforce	Teach/Reinforce
Formulas									
perimeter						Teach	Teach	Teach/Reinforce	Teach/Reinforce
circumference						Teach	Teach	Teach	Teach/Reinforce
area						Teach	Teach	Teach/Reinforce	Teach/Reinforce
volume						Teach	Teach	Teach/Reinforce	Teach/Reinforce
surface area						Teach	Teach	Teach/Reinforce	Teach/Reinforce
Pythagorean relationship								Teach	Teach
translations (slides)				Teach	Teach	Teach	Teach	Teach	Teach
rotations (turns)				Teach	Teach	Teach	Teach	Teach	Teach
reflections (flips)				Teach	Teach	Teach	Teach	Teach	Teach
Circles, radius and diameter						Teach	Teach	Teach/Reinforce	Reinforce
Circles, circumference and area						Teach	Teach	Teach/Reinforce	Teach/Reinforce
Constructions						Teach	Teach	Teach	Teach/Reinforce
Build/draw geometric solids				Teach	Teach	Teach	Teach	Teach	Teach
Central angles							Teach	Teach	Teach
Tangent, sine, and cosine ratios									Teach
Topology									Teach
Applications				Teach	Teach	Teach	Teach	Teach/Reinforce	Teach/Reinforce

TEACH **REINFORCE**

Grade 2

Geometry

Explore geometry 249-250, 251-252, 253, 254, 255-256, 258, 259-260, 261
Concrete models 249-250, 251-252, 253, 254, 255-256, 258, 259-260, 261, 265
Identify plane figures 253-254, 255-256, 265, 266, 423
Identify space figures (geometric solids) 249-250, 254, 265, 266, 286, 312, 423
Relate plane figures to space figures 253-254, 266, 286, 423
Patterns 51-52, 58, 65, 106, 110, 135, 411
Symmetry 259-260, 286, 424
Congruent figures 261-262, 266, 312
Sides and corners 255-256, 266, 286, 312
Inside, outside, and on 256, 265, 312

Note:

...dison-Wesley Mathematics (©1991) fully integrates *motivation, understanding, problem solving, math reasoning, communication, subject integration,* ...*and integration, group work* and *use of manipulatives* with all mathematical topics in the Scope and Sequence chart.

Graphs & Graphing	K	1	2	3	4	5	6	7	8
Pictographs									
Bar graphs									
Line graphs									
Circle graphs									
Double bar graphs									
Multiple line graphs									
Divided bar graphs									
Scattergrams									
Reasoning from a graph									
Stem and leaf plots									
Box and whisker graphs									
Frequency tables and histograms									
Graphing ordered pairs									
Graphing linear equations									
Graphing inequalities									

Measurement	K	1	2	3	4	5	6	7	8
Explore using concrete objects									
Problem solving									
Precision in measurement									
Estimation									
Non-standard units									
Length									
customary units									
metric units									
Perimeter									
Area									
Area/perimeter relationships									
Surface area									
Weight (mass)									
Volume									
Capacity									
Circumference									
Convert units									
Temperature									
Indirect measurement									
use scale drawings									
use geometric relationships									

■ TEACH   ■ REINFORCE

Grade 2

Graphs & Graphing

Bar graphs 6, 57-58, 59-60, 65, 66 67, 80, 90, 101, 115-116, 133, 382
Pictographs 61-62, 110, 153, 164, 206, 347
Coordinate graphs 263

Measurement

Explore using concrete objects 111-112, 113-114, 115, 117, 118, 119-120, 121, 122, 123, 124, 125-126, 127-128, 129, 130, 152
Problem solving 117, 130, 132, 135, 237, 307
Estimation 112, 113-114, 118, 119-120, 121, 122, 123, 124, 125-126, 127-128, 129, 130, 131, 133, 134, 152, 157, 158, 172, 180
Nonstandard units 47, 111-112, 121, 123, 180
Length
   customary 113-114, 115-116, 117, 118, 119-120, 124, 133, 135, 152, 158, 257, 307, 414, 423
   metric 125-126, 127-128, 134, 158, 172, 180, 415
Area 131, 134, 322, 415
Weight/Mass
   customary 124, 133, 135, 180, 237, 307
   metric 130, 134
Capacity
   customary 122, 124, 133, 180, 329, 415
   metric 129, 134, 158
Perimeter 47, 117, 133
Temperature
   Fahrenheit 373
   Celsius 157

...e: Red type indicates that a topic is being introduced for the first time.

SCOPE AND SEQUENCE

Addison-Wesley Mathematics (©1991) fully integrates *motivation, understanding, problem solving, math reasoning, communication, subject integration, strand integration, group work* and *use of manipulatives* with all mathematical topics in the Scope and Sequence chart.

Time & Money	K	1	2	3	4	5	6	7	8
Time									
Calendar									
Tell and show time									
to the hour									
to the half hour									
to the quarter hour									
to 5-minute intervals									
to 1-minute intervals									
Estimate time									
Problem solving									
Elapsed time									
a.m. or p.m.									
Time zones									
Money									
Count and show amounts of money									
Problem solving									
Add									
Subtract									
Multiply									
Divide									
Estimate									
Relate to decimals									

Mental Math	K	1	2	3	4	5	6	7	8
Count on or back									
Skip counting									
Basic fact patterns and strategies									
special sums and differences									
doubles									
special products									
special quotients									
Use properties									
Break apart									
Compatible numbers									
Compensation									
Multiply/divide decimals by 10, 100, 1,000									
Find a fraction of a number									
Find a percent of a number									
Algebraic expressions, equations									
Measurement									

■ TEACH **■ REINFORCE**

Grade 2

Time & Money

Time
Calendar 189-190, 224
Tell and show time to the hour 183-184, 185-186
Tell and show time to the half hour 183-184, 185-186, 204, 256, 419
Tell and show time to the quarter hour 183-184, 194, 204, 224, 248, 419
Tell and show time to 5-minute intervals 181-182, 185-186, 194, 204, 224, 248, 256, 419
Estimate 28, 184, 223, 243
Problem solving 186, 191, 202, 224, 240, 242, 243, 308, 330
Elapsed time 187-188, 194, 204, 224

Money
Count and show amounts of money 10, 14, 30, 36, 45, 82, 86, 147-148, 156, 180, 193-194, 195-196, 197-198, 199-200, 203, 204, 205, 224, 248, 256, 320, 367-368, 372, 396, 416, 420
Problem solving 10, 14, 36, 82, 86, 102, 148, 175, 193-194, 201, 202, 204, 243, 246, 248, 263, 286, 391, 394, 402, 432
Add 14, 33, 36, 45, 86, 90, 175, 201, 204, 205, 216, 222, 233-234, 236, 263, 283, 286, 298, 336, 389-390, 391, 393, 394, 402, 422, 432
Subtract 14, 82, 102, 148, 278, 294, 295, 299, 310, 330, 336, 389-390, 391, 393, 394, 432
Multiply 335-336, 338, 349, 374
Estimate 216, 222, 233-234, 243, 268, 278, 286, 295, 298, 310, 330

Mental Math

Count on or back by ones 1-2, 12, 16, 20, 22, 23-24, 34, 48, 69-70, 77-78, 146, 161-162, 166, 177, 178, 206, 208, 214, 236, 269-270, 274, 284, 312, 359-360, 362, 396, 409, 430
Count on or back by tens 163-164, 166, 177, 178, 206, 210, 211-212, 214, 236, 273-274, 284, 296, 360, 364
Counting patterns
  by twos 50, 58, 61-62, 66, 152, 169-170, 177, 178, 179, 401, 411
  by threes 169-170, 177, 178, 179, 206, 346, 401, 418
  by fours 169-170, 177, 418
  by fives 171-172, 178, 179, 182, 193-194, 320, 401
  by tens 163-164, 166, 177, 178, 212, 214, 236, 272, 273-274, 296, 360, 364, 372
  by twenty-fives 171-172, 178, 195, 401
  by hundreds 354, 362, 401
Basic fact patterns and strategies
  special sums 209-210, 222, 236, 304, 369, 378, 388
  special differences 272, 273-274, 303, 403
  doubles 25-26, 27-28, 29-30, 34, 36, 38, 39-40, 45, 46, 68, 71-72, 74, 78, 79-80, 87, 88, 90, 98
Use properties 24, 34, 38, 39-40, 70, 209-210, 214, 221, 267, 304

Note: Red type indicates that a topic is being introduced for the first time.

...son-Wesley Mathematics (©1991) fully integrates *motivation, understanding, problem solving, math reasoning, communication, subject integration,* ...nd integration, *group work* and *use of manipulatives* with all mathematical topics in the Scope and Sequence chart.

Patterns, Relations & Functions	K	1	2	3	4	5	6	7	8
Number patterns									
Spatial/positional/geometric patterns									
Color patterns									
Exponents									
Problem solving strategies									
find a pattern									
make a table									
Functions									
Make a generalization									
Ordered pairs									
Graph functions									
Geometric progressions									
Pascal's triangle									
Harmonic triangle									
Fibonacci sequence									
Napier's Bones									

Problem Solving	K	1	2	3	4	5	6	7	8
Strategy and Skill Lessons									
Act it out									
Use objects									
Choose the operation									
Draw a picture									
Make an (organized) list									
Guess and check									
Make a table									
Look for a pattern									
Use logical reasoning									
Solve a simpler problem									
Work backwards									
Write/use equations									
Understand the operations									
Tell or write a story									
Determine reasonable answers									
Estimate the answer									
Decide when to estimate									
Find related problems									
Interpret remainders									
Multiple-step problems									

■ **TEACH**   ■ **REINFORCE**

Grade 2

Patterns, Relations & Functions

Number patterns 49-50, 51-52, 58, 64, 65, 66, 90, 106, 135, 152, 158, 169-170, 171-172, 179, 190, 202, 247, 264, 266, 301-302, 311, 359, 401, 411, 425
Spatial/positional/geometrical patterns 51-52, 58, 65, 106, 110, 135, 411
Color patterns 53-54, 56, 58, 66, 90, 174, 179, 282
Problem solving strategies
  look for a pattern 64, 264, 266
  make a table 202, 264, 266, 392, 395
Functions 64, 202, 264, 266, 285, 392
Make a generalization 285, 311

Problem Solving

Strategy and Skill Lessons
Act it out 176, 370
Use objects 31, 40, 55, 82, 86, 154, 220, 221, 264, 280, 292, 310, 321, 324, 325, 326, 344, 358, 395
Choose the operation 18, 20, 22, 48, 68, 348, 396
Draw a picture 106, 282, 284, 312, 395, 424
Make (an organized) list 44, 220
Guess and check 86, 130, 244, 292, 358, 376
Make a table 64, 202, 264, 266, 285, 392, 395
Look for a pattern 64, 106, 158, 190, 264, 266
Use logical reasoning 14, 36, 132, 162, 292, 308, 370, 376
Understand the operations 31, 40, 55, 69, 75, 82, 90, 97, 108, 110, 117, 133, 136, 145, 148, 156, 162, 167, 178, 180, 191, 208, 215, 224, 237, 242, 257, 262, 268, 277, 280, 286, 299, 306, 310, 321, 324, 330, 339, 344, 350, 352, 363, 372, 374, 381, 410, 412, 427, 428, 430
Determine reasonable answers 131, 134, 325, 328, 415
Use estimation 243, 307, 422
Missing data 17, 281
Extra data 175, 206, 418
Ask a question 43, 46, 411
Retell a story 63
Write a story 105, 369, 414
Problems with two questions 391, 394, 432
Write number sentences 219, 222, 421
Choose a calculation method 239-240, 246, 303-304, 363, 381, 430

Red type indicates that a topic is being introduced for the first time.

Addison-Wesley Mathematics (©1991) fully integrates *motivation, understanding, problem solving, math reasoning, communication, subject integratio strand integration, group work* and *use of manipulatives* with all mathematical topics in the Scope and Sequence chart.

Problem Solving cont.	K	1	2	3	4	5	6	7	8
Problems with more than one answer									
Problems with two or more questions									
Problems without solutions									
Use/write a number sentence									
Use a calculator									
Use data sources									
from a story									
from a chart or table									
from a graph									
from other data sources									
Choose/use strategies									
Computational Methods									
choose a calculation method									
use objects									
mental math									
calculators									
computers									
Estimation									
decide when to estimate									
determine reasonable answers									
use estimation									
Six-Point Checklist									
Introduction to the checklist									
1. UNDERSTAND THE SITUATION									
understand the question									
understand the operation									
finish/write a problem									
2. FIND DATA NEEDED/ANALYZE DATA									
missing data									
extra data									
use data									
3. PLAN WHAT TO DO									
understand the operations									
develop a plan									
decide when to estimate									
choose a calculation method									
find related problems									
4. ESTIMATE THE ANSWER									
estimate the answer									
determine reasonable answers									

■ TEACH   ■ REINFORCE

Grade 2

Problem Solving cont.

Show the data 85, 88, 413
Data from a chart or table 6, 80, 102, 186, 201, 204, 232, 248, 302, 307, 336, 352, 382, 402
Data from a graph 6, 57-58, 59-60, 61-62, 67, 80, 90, 101, 110, 115-116, 133, 153, 164, 206, 263, 34
Data from a data bank 6, 80, 186, 232, 302, 336
Data from a data hunt 114, 164, 366

Computational Methods
Choose a calculation method 239-240, 246, 303-304 363, 381, 430
Use objects 31, 40, 55, 82, 86, 154, 220, 221, 264, 280, 292, 310, 321, 324, 325, 326, 344, 363, 381 358, 395, 430
Mental math 208, 239-240, 246, 303-304, 363, 381, 430
Calculators 239-240, 246, 303-304, 363, 381, 430
Computers 405, 406, 407, 408

Estimation
Determine reasonable answers 131, 134, 325, 328, 415
Use estimation 243, 307, 422

Six-Point Checklist
Introduction to the checklist 7

UNDERSTAND THE PROBLEM
Ask a question 43, 46, 411
Write a story 105, 369, 414

FIND THE DATA
Missing data 17, 281
Extra data 175, 206, 418
Show the data 85, 88, 413
Retell a story 63
Use data
  from a graph 6, 57-58, 59-60, 61-62, 67, 80, 90, 101, 110, 115-116, 133, 153, 164, 206, 263, 347, 382
  from a chart or table 6, 80, 102, 186, 201, 204, 232, 248, 302, 307, 336, 352, 382, 402
  from a data bank 6, 80, 186, 232, 302, 336
  from a data hunt 114, 164, 366

PLAN WHAT TO DO
Understand the operations 31, 40, 55, 69, 75, 82, 90, 97, 108, 110, 117, 133, 136, 145, 148, 156, 162 167, 178, 180, 191, 208, 215, 224, 237, 242, 257, 262, 268, 277, 280, 286, 299, 306, 310, 321, 324 330, 339, 344, 350, 352, 363, 372, 374, 381, 410 412, 427, 428, 430
Choose a calculation method 239-240, 246, 303-30 363, 381, 430
See also PROBLEM SOLVING: Strategy and Skill Lessons.

ESTIMATE THE ANSWER
Use estimation 243, 307, 422
Determine reasonable answers 131, 134, 325, 328, 415

Note: Red type indicates that a topic is being introduced for the first time.

...ison-Wesley Mathematics (©1991) fully integrates *motivation, understanding, problem solving, math reasoning, communication, subject integration,* ...*nd integration, group work* and *use of manipulatives* with all mathematical topics in the Scope and Sequence chart.

Problem Solving cont.	K	1	2	3	4	5	6	7	8
5. SOLVE THE PROBLEM									
solve/use number sentences/equations		▨	▨	▨	▨	▨	▨	▨	▨
use a calculator		▨	▨	▨	▨	▨	▨	▨	▨
use formulas						▨	▨	▨	▨
more than one answer			▨	▨	▨	▨	▨	▨	▨
problems without solutions					▨	▨	▨	▨	▨
interpret remainders				▨	▨	▨	▨	▨	▨
6. CHECK/EXAMINE THE ANSWER									
determine reasonable answers		▨	▨	▨	▨	▨	▨	▨	▨
think/talk/write about the solution		▨	▨	▨	▨	▨	▨	▨	▨
Applications									
applied problem solving lessons				▨	▨	▨	▨	▨	▨
data collection and analysis lessons	▨	▨	▨	▨	▨	▨	▨	▨	▨

Ratio, Proportion, & Percent	K	1	2	3	4	5	6	7	8
Understand concept or ratio						▨	▨	▨	▨
Equal ratios						▨	▨	▨	▨
Tangent ratio									▨
Problem solving						▨	▨	▨	▨
Estimate ratio						▨	▨	▨	▨
Cross products							▨	▨	▨
Similar figures						▨	▨	▨	▨
Understand concept of proportion							▨	▨	▨
Solve proportions							▨	▨	▨
Unit price						▨		▨	▨
Understand concept of percent						▨	▨	▨	▨
Interest								▨	▨
Discounts and sales prices							▨	▨	▨
Commission								▨	▨
Circle graphs							▨	▨	▨
Estimate percent							▨	▨	▨
Convert fractions, decimals, percents							▨	▨	▨
Find a percent of a number							▨	▨	▨
Calculator, using percent key							▨	▨	▨
Find what percent one number is of another							▨	▨	▨
Find a number when a percent is known								▨	▨
Percent of increase or decrease							▨	▨	▨

☐ **TEACH**   ▨ **REINFORCE**

Grade 2

Problem Solving cont.

SOLVE THE PROBLEM
Problems with two questions 391, 394, 432
Write number sentences 219, 222, 421
CHECK THE ANSWER
Determine reasonable answers 131, 134, 325, 328, 415
Applications
Use data sources *See* PROBLEM SOLVING, Six-Point Checklist: Find the Data.
Data collection and analysis *See* DATA COLLECTION AND ANALYSIS.
Consumer math and life skills *See* CONSUMER MATH.

Red type indicates that a topic is being introduced for the first time.

Addison-Wesley Mathematics (©1991) fully integrates *motivation, understanding, problem solving, math reasoning, communication, subject integration, strand integration, group work* and *use of manipulatives* with all mathematical topics in the Scope and Sequence chart.

Statistics & Probability	K	1	2	3	4	5	6	7	8
Collect and organize data									
Present data graphically									
Tally charts									
Graphs									
Charts and tables									
Misleading statistics/biased representation									
Mean, median, mode, range									
Statistical sampling									
Scattergrams									
Stem and leaf plots									
Box and whisper graphs									
Frequency tables and histograms									
Understand probability									
Equally likely outcomes									
Probability and prediction									
Fair and unfair games									
Mathematical and experimental probabilities									
Compound events and tree diagrams									
Permutations and combinations									
Simulations									

Cooperative Group Learning Skills	K	1	2	3	4	5	6	7	8
Listen to others									
Encourage and respect others									
Explain and summarize									
Disagree in an agreeable way									
Check for understanding									

■ TEACH   ■ REINFORCE

Grade 2

Statistics & Probability

Collect and organize data 32, 114, 164, 366, 382
Present data graphically 57-58, 59-60, 101-102, 382
Make or interpret tally charts 59-60, 382
Make or interpret graphs 6, 57-58, 59-60, 61-62, 67, 80, 153, 201, 263, 336, 347, 382, 402
Make or interpret charts and tables 102, 201, 232, 264, 382, 392
Understand probability 76, 89, 192, 220, 305
Equally likely outcomes 76, 192
Probability and predictions 76, 192
See also DATA COLLECTION AND ANALYSIS; GRAPHS AND GRAPHING.

Note: Red type indicates that a topic is being introduced for the first time.

Addison-Wesley Mathematics

Teacher's Edition

Grade 2

▲▲ Addison-Wesley Publishing Company

Menlo Park, California ■ *Reading, Massachusetts* ■ *New York*
Don Mills, Ontario ■ *Wokingham, England* ■ *Amsterdam* ■ *Bonn*
Sydney ■ *Singapore* ■ *Tokyo* ■ *Madrid* ■ *San Juan*

STAFF ACKNOWLEDGMENTS

Diane Fernández, *Executive Editor*
Judith Vandegrift, *Managing Editor*
Ken Shue, *Design Manager*

STUDENT EDITION

Kelly Stewart, *Senior Editor*
Ellen Kwan, *Design Production Coordinator*

TEACHER'S EDITION AND SUPPLEMENTS

Mary Fraser, *Senior Editor*
Mark Askew, *Project Editor*
Dennis Horan, *Design Production Coordinator*

ISBN 0-201-27201-6   ISBN 0-201-27224-5 TEXAS EDITION

ABCDEFGHIJKL-BA- 943210

Dear Girls and Boys,

What will you do inside this book?

2   +   4   =   6   6   -   2   =   4

You will see how numbers work together.

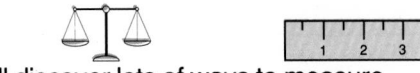

You will look for patterns and make graphs.

You will work in groups or with a partner.

You will discover lots of ways to measure.

You will see how math can be used everyday.

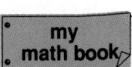

You will talk about shapes and fractions.

You will make your own math book.

We know you will like your book.

From your friends at Addison-Wesley.

OVERVIEW

Lesson	Pages	Objectives	Subject Integration	Strand Integration
Counting On and Back	1-2	1-1 To count on and back with numbers to 20	health and fitness: playground skills	mental math
Addition Sentences	3-4	1-2 To model and write addition sentences	health and fitness: trampoline	computation
Subtraction Sentences	5-6	1-3 To model and write subtraction sentences	health and fitness: swimming	graphing
Introduction to Problem Solving/Using Critical Thinking	7-8	1-4 To use the checklist to solve problems; to identify missing numbers	health and fitness: swimming	measurement, money, time
Different Ways to Name a Sum	9-10	1-5 To show different ways to name a sum	health and fitness: swings	critical thinking
Relating Addition and Subtraction	11-12	1-6 To model and write related addition and subtraction sentences	health and fitness: balance beam	number sense
Related Subtraction Facts	13-14	1-7 To model and finish related subtraction facts	health and fitness: chin-ups	problem solving
Fact Families	15-16	1-8 To model and write fact families	health and fitness: exercise	computation
Problem Solving: Finding Missing Data/Problem Solving Strategy: Choose the Operation	17-18	1-9 To find missing data; to use the strategy Choose the Operation	health and fitness: bicycle riding	computation, operations sense

MATHEMATICAL BACKGROUND

Addition and Subtraction
The concept of addition has one interpretation: Two or more groups are put together to find a total (sum). Subtraction has several interpretations. Two of the most common are *take away* and *comparison*. Since students are most familiar with the *take away* interpretation of subtraction, it is the only one introduced in this initial chapter. Other real-world interpretations of subtraction are introduced later in Book 2.

Addition and Subtraction Facts
This chapter reviews the concepts of addition and subtraction to help students memorize facts for fast and easy recall. Most students will have learned the concepts and have already committed the addition and subtraction facts to memory.

Fact Families
Understanding fact families will help students remember addition and subtraction facts. A fact family is formed by 3 numbers used in all 4 possible combinations of addition and subtraction equations.

Problem Solving
In this chapter, students use the strategy *Choose the Operation* and find missing data in problems.

TIPS FROM TEACHERS

Have students use crayons to color strips to show various fact families. For example: 4 + 3 = 7, 3 + 4 = 7, 7 − 3 = 4, 7 − 4 = 3.

Students can write the number sentences for the fact family on the back of the strip.

**Peggilee Barry
Lincroft School
Middletown, NJ**

ASSESSMENT

Pretest — Chapter 1, page 1
Multiple-Choice Format

Name _____

1. Count on. Choose the number.

11, 12, ? (A) 13
B 10
C 15

2. Count back. Choose the number.

19, 18, ? A 20
B 15
(C) 17

3. What does the picture show?

(A) 3 + 3 = 6
B 3 + 4 = 7
C 4 + 4 = 8

4. What does the picture show?

A 3 + 3 = 6
(B) 2 + 4 = 6
C 3 + 2 = 5

5. Cross out to take away. Then subtract.

4
−3
A 4
B 3
(C) 1

6. Cross out to take away. Then subtract.

5
−1
A 5
(B) 4
C 3

7. Read the picture story. What action does it show?

(A) put together
B take away

MCT 2   1

Pretest — Chapter 1, page 2
Multiple-Choice Format

Name _____

8. Add. Choose the turnaround fact.

1
+7
(A) 7
+1
8

B 6
+1
7

9. Choose the related subtraction sentence.

1 + 8 = 9

A 8 − 1 = 7
(B) 9 − 1 = 8

10. Choose the related subtraction sentence.

A 6
−1
5

(B) 7
−6
1

11. Choose the fact that belongs to the family.

3   2
+2 +3
5   5

5
−2
3

A 3
−1
2

(B) 5
−3
2

12. Read the picture story. Would you add or subtract?

(A) add
B subtract

2   MCT 2

Posttest — Chapter 1, page 1
Multiple-Choice Format

Name _____

1. Count on. Choose the number.

9, 10, ? (A) 11
B 10
C 8

2. Count back. Choose the number.

18, 17, ? A 20
B 15
(C) 16

3. What does the picture show?

A 1 + 2 = 3
(B) 3 + 2 = 5
C 4 + 1 = 5

4. What does the picture show?

A 4 + 3 = 7
(B) 5 + 2 = 7
C 1 + 6 = 7

5. Cross out to take away. Then subtract.

4
−1
A 4
(B) 3
C 1

6. Cross out to take away. Then subtract.

6
−3
A 6
B 5
(C) 3

7. Read the picture story. What action does it show?

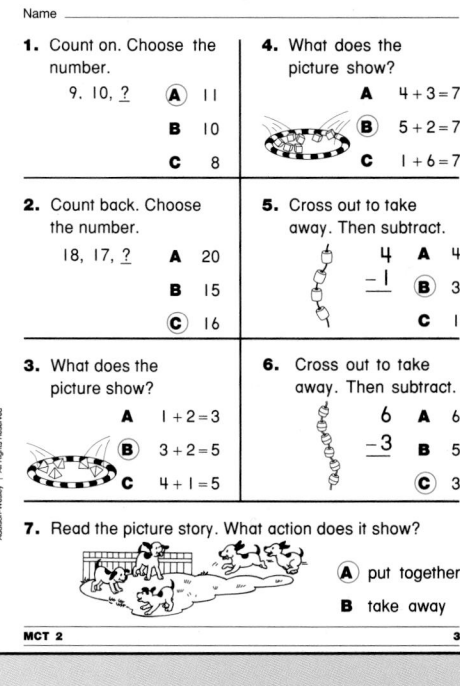

(A) put together
B take away

MCT 2   3

Posttest — Chapter 1, page 2
Multiple-Choice Format

Name _____

8. Add. Choose the turnaround fact.

1
+5
6
(A) 5
+1
6

B 4
+1
5

9. Choose the related subtraction sentence.

1 + 6 = 7

(A) 7 − 1 = 6
B 6 − 1 = 5

10. Choose the related subtraction sentence.

(A) 5
−2
3

B 3
−1
2

11. Choose the fact that belongs to the family.

5   2
+2 +5
7   7

7
−2
5

(A) 7
−5
2

B 5
−2
3

12. Read the picture story. Would you add or subtract?

(A) add
B subtract

4   MCT 2

ITEM ANALYSIS

Items	Objectives
1, 2	1-1
3, 4	1-2
5, 6	1-3
7	1-4
8	1-5
9	1-6
10	1-7
11	1-8
12	1-9

Note: The item analysis is the same for all pretests and posttests for this chapter.

ALSO AVAILABLE

► Free Response Tests
► Alternative Tests
► Thinking Strategies
► Concrete Materials

PROJECT AND BULLETIN BOARD

Play indoor basketball. Tape a shooting line on the floor and place a wastebasket 8 ft from the line. Write numbers 1-10 on beanbags and place them in a paper bag. Divide students into 2 teams. Direct players, one at a time, to pull out 2 beanbags without looking and add the numbers on the bags. When the answer is correct, the player tosses the bags, one at a time, into the basket. Keep a tally of the baskets made by each team. Then have both teams count the number of baskets they made in all. Give 1 point to the team with the fewest baskets and 2 points to the team with the most. Write the score on the scoreboard under Day 1 and under TOTAL. Continue the game for the next week, adding each day's score to the TOTAL score from the previous days. For subtraction lessons, have students subtract the numbers on the bean bags.

SCOREBOARD

	1	2	3	4	5	6	7	8	Total
A Team	1	2	2						5
B Team	2	1	1						4

COOPERATIVE LEARNING

Explain that a *couplet* is one of the simplest kinds of poetry. It has two lines that rhyme. Have students listen as you read an addition couplet.
> *Bite, and chew, and swallow seven,*
> *Eat four more and that's eleven.*

Ask students to identify the rhyming words. (seven, eleven) Then, write a number sentence for the poem.

Divide the class into 5 or 6 groups. Identify the group skill: taking turns. Direct groups to write couplets about addition facts to 18. Ask them to brainstorm rhyming words to use with the fact. When brainstorming, remind students to take turns naming pairs of rhyming words that are associated with the facts. Have a recorder list the words on a chart. Individual students should then: create 2 rhyming lines using the fact and the listed words, write the poem on chart paper, illustrate the poem, and present the poem to the class.

You will find grouping suggestions and cooperative learning activities in most lessons throughout this chapter. *Cooperative Learning in Mathematics: A Handbook for Teachers,* (Menlo Park: Addison-Wesley, 1990) contains many suggestions for organizing cooperative learning groups specifically for mathematics.

LITERATURE

Burningham, John. *The Shopping Basket.* New York: Thomas Y. Crowell, 1980.

> In this amusing story Steven goes to the store for his mother with a long list of things to buy. He remembers everything in spite of many distractions along the way. What happens to Steven when he leaves the store will surprise and delight.

Encourage students to use the events in the story to write number sentences and to count on and back with numbers to 20.

de Paola, Tomie. *Pancakes for Breakfast.* New York: Harcourt Brace Jovanovich, 1978.

Galdone, Paul. *Henny Penny.* New York: Seabury Press, 1968

ENGLISH AS A SECOND LANGUAGE

As students begin work in addition and subtraction, remember that ESL students will differ in their natural abilities to acquire the English language, in the length of time they have been in the United States, and in the experiences they have already had in American schools. They need extra attention and time to develop the language tools necessary to understand and talk about the math being learned. In general, engage them in preparatory activities to ensure that they understand the vocabulary used. Involve them in small group work and show them how to use other students as resources to clarify or expand their language.

In this chapter, explain the potentially confusing *sums* as opposed to *some*. Stress synonyms such as *total* or *in all*. In the problem solving activities, use overhead projectors, pictures, or games to focus on the vocabulary before doing the problems. Explain specific phrases such as *the swim meet,* and the comparative and superlative forms (greater, greatest).

GIFTED

Mathematically talented students may already understand how addition and subtraction are related. They will nevertheless be interested in many of the strategies presented in this chapter. After they have completed their Student Edition work, you may wish to challenge these students to list as many names as they can for a number between 5 and 10. For example, after Lesson 5 on different ways to name a sum, write 8 on the chalkboard, then ask what addition and subtraction sentences give an answer of 8 (10 − 2, 5 + 3, 9 − 1, among others). Students may write their own magic number in the center section of a practagon and complete the wheel with addition and subtraction sentences. Offer a language arts connection by challenging students to write riddles for their magic number. These may include, *If you add me to 2 you get 10. What am I?* If this appeals to your verbally gifted students, you may wish to use the technique throughout the chapter.

STUDENTS AT RISK

Two important counting materials, are a large hundred chart and a hundred number line. These may serve as wall posters during the year. The hundred poster is a 20″ square divided into 10 rows of 10 squares each, and numbered in order. TA6 may be used as an individual worksheet. The hundred number line is a drawn on a continuous 2″ strip of oak tag. Place circular stickers at regular intervals, about 2″ apart and label ten in order. The number line may wrap around the walls of the classroom, and will provide an important visual reference for students who have trouble with the numbers greater than 20, or who need concrete representation of *before, after,* and *between.* The number line worksheet may be reproduced on one page, and students can cut the strips apart to make the line continuous.

For students who have difficulty counting on without starting at 1, display a small number of counters. Then cover them with your hand, saying *4 here*. Add 2 more: *5, 6.* Model this procedure until students can do it themselves. Next, show how 4 and 2 more can be represented on the hundred chart and on the number line. Repeat for counting back.

You may also use the Reteaching Supplements and the specific Reteaching Tips from each lesson in this chapter.

Chapter 1 Optional Chapter Activities

1D

PICTURE

These pictures and accompanying stories and poems are available as storybooks.

You may want to read and discuss this story with your students before starting the chapter. The first lesson in this chapter includes a question about the story. Lessons 1, 5, 6 and 9 in this chapter have questions in the informal Assessment that refer to the story.

Six Little Ones

"Where are those rascals?" Mama Chipmunk wondered. It was quiet in the burrow, and she knew that her six little children must have gone to the park. She stopped sorting her winter supply of seeds and nuts and scampered over to the park to check.

"Have you seen my six little ones?" she asked old Mrs. Tiddlebit, who was sitting on a log watching the children play in the park.

"No, I haven't seen six little chipmunks, but I did see five chipmunks on the swings and one on the slide," she responded. "But don't worry. I'll keep an eye out for them."

Mama Chipmunk noticed three young raccoons jumping rope. They were counting each jump, 13, 14, 15....They stopped for a moment when the jumper's tail got caught in the rope, and Mama Chipmunk asked, "Have you seen my six little ones?"

"No, but we did see two little chipmunks on the bars and four doing tumbling exercises," the oldest one said. "Have you looked over by the jogging trail?"

Mama Chipmunk scurried over to the jogging trail and asked one of the gardeners, "Have you seen my six little ones?"

The gardener leaned on her rake for a minute and replied, "No, but I did watch three chipmunks doing jumping jacks and three doing sit-ups on the trail."

Just then six little chipmunks came sprinting out of the woods. "Hi, Mom!" they said.

The gardener was puzzled. The six little chipmunks looked awfully familiar. "Are you the same children I saw doing exercises?" she asked. The chipmunks nodded and scampered around their mother, who smiled proudly. "Yes, these are my six little ones," she said. And before she could introduce them, they darted across the grass—1, 2, 3, 4, 5, and 6.

Counting On and Back

OBJECTIVE 1-1 To count on and back with numbers to 20

PREBOOK ACTIVITIES

QUICK REVIEW

Fill in the blanks with the numbers that come before and the numbers that come after.

 (1) , 2, (3)   (5) , 6, (7)
 (12) , 13, (14)   (9) , 10, (11)
 (18) , 19, (20)   (7) , 8, (9)
 (14) , 15, (16)   (4) , 5, (6)

PRIOR KNOWLEDGE

You are trying to save 20 pennies. Listen to what happened. Tell whether you would add to your pennies or subtract from your pennies for each thing that happens.
1. You lose 3 pennies at school. (subtract)
2. You give 5 pennies to your brother. (subtract)
3. You find 4 pennies on the ground. (add)
4. Your father gives you 6 pennies. (add)

COMMUNICATION

Reading and Writing in Math   Write the terms **counting on** and **counting back** on the chalkboard, and explain that these words refer to different ways of counting. *When you add numbers, you are counting on. When you take away numbers, you are counting back.* You may wish to copy and distribute Math Journal pages (TA1 and 2). Give students folders in which they can collect the Math Journal pages they create and have them write *My Math Journal* on the cover and decorate it if they wish. Ask students to write these sentences and fill in the blanks:
Adding 1 number at a time is called (counting on) .
Taking away 1 number at a time is called (counting back) .

EXPLORE AND CONNECT

Materials: counters, 10-frames
Grouping Suggestions: pairs
Have 1 partner choose a number less than 10 and fill a 10-frame with that number of counters. Ask that student to count on from that number by adding 1 counter at a time and say the number for the total. After the 10-frame is filled, the next counter goes in the partner's 10-frame and is called 1 extra. For 12, there will be 10 and 2 extra. The partner continues the counting-on process for the extra counters. *What kind of counting is this?* (counting on) Have partners repeat th activity starting with different numbers less than 10. Then hav students start with a number greater than 10 and remove 1 counter at a time while calling out the number. *Identify this kind of counting.* (counting back)

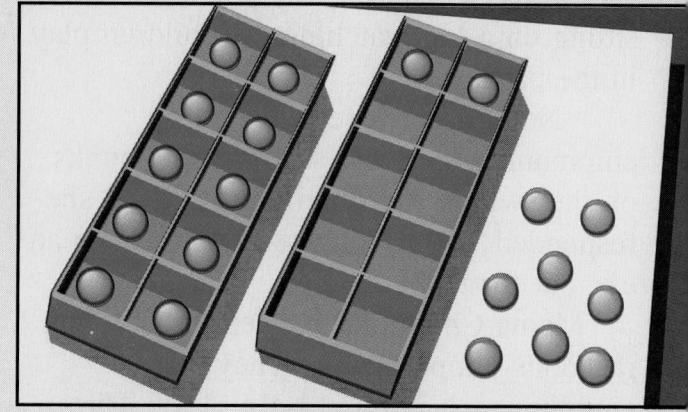

CONNECTIONS   Use these anytime.

Problem of the Day
Counting On and Counting Back
Read the story. Ring whether you would count on or count back to find the answer.
Keith had 9 model airplanes. He gave 1 to his brother. How many models did he have then?
count on   count back

Math Connection
Counting Game   Write *count on* and *count back* on each of several slips of paper. Take turns. One person rolls a number cube and picks one slip of paper Begin at 8. Count on or count back the number you rolled according to what it says on the paper. Play until you have counted to 20.

Counting Patterns
On or Back   Look at each pattern. Tell whether you would count on or count back to continue the pattern.
4, 5, 6, 7, 8, . . . (count on)
2, 4, 6, 8, 10, . . . (count on)
20, 19, 18, 17, 16, . . . (count back)
13, 15, 17, 19, . . . (count on)
12, 10, 8, 6, . . . (count back)

CLASSWORK AND HOMEWORK SUPPLEMENTS

Practice

Skills Maintenance   1-1

Name _____

Counting On and Back

Count on.

1. 15, _16_ , _17_ , _18_ , _19_ , _20_

2. 5, _6_ , _7_ , _8_ , _9_ , _10_

3. 12, _13_ , _14_ , _15_ , _16_ , _17_

4. 9, _10_ , _11_ , _12_ , _13_ , _14_

5. 2, _3_ , _4_ , _5_ , _6_ , _7_

Count back.

6. 16, _15_ , _14_ , _13_ , _12_ , _11_

7. 7, _6_ , _5_ , _4_ , _3_ , _2_

8. 18, _17_ , _16_ , _15_ , _14_ , _13_

9. 6, _5_ , _4_ , _3_ , _2_ , _1_

10. 10, _9_ , _8_ , _7_ , _6_ , _5_

PS-2   Use with text pages 1 – 2.   1

Building Thinking Skills

Number Sense   1-1

Name _____

Framed Numbers

Match the clue to the 10-frame pictures.
Count on or back to solve.

1. I more than 13

2. 3 less than 8

3. 2 more than 7

4. 4 less than 20

Write your own clues.
Draw counters on the 10-frames.   Answers will vary.

5. _____ more than _____

6. _____ less than _____

TS-2   Use with text pages 1 – 2.   1

Reteaching

Skills Review   1-1

Name _____

Counting On and Back

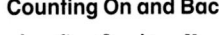

Start   Stop

Counting on means
adding I to
each number.

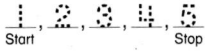
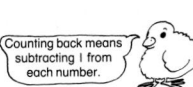
Start   Stop

Counting back means
subtracting I from
each number.

Count on.

1. _4_ , _5_ , _6_ , _7_ , _8_ , _9_
    Start   Stop

2. 13 , _14_ , _15_ , _16_ , _17_ , _18_

3. 11 , _12_ , _13_ , _14_ , _15_ , _16_

Count back.

4. 19 , _18_ , _17_ , _16_ , _15_ , _14_
    Start   Stop

5. 8 , _7_ , _6_ , _5_ , _4_ , _3_

6. 14 , _13_ , _12_ , _11_ , _10_ , _9_

RS-2   Use with text pages 1 – 2.   1

Challenges

Mental Math   1-1

Name _____

Space Math

Draw the space creature. Use mental math.

1. The space creature has I less than 2 heads.

2. It has 2 more than I eye.

3. It has 5 less than 6 noses.

4. It has 2 more than 4 arms.

5. It has 6 more than 2 ears.

6. It has 9 less than 11 smiling mouths.

7. It has 8 less than 14 legs.

8. It has 3 more than 4 tails.

Accept all drawings of space person with: 1 head,
3 eyes, 1 nose, 6 arms, 8 ears, 2 smiling mouths,
6 legs, and 7 tails.

CS-2   Use with text pages 1 – 2.   1

OPTIONS FOR INDIVIDUAL NEEDS

Basic

Exercises All
More Practice, p. 409, set A

Supplements
Reteaching 1 or
Practice 1

Average

Exercises All
More Practice, p. 409, set A

Supplements
Practice 1
Challenges 1 or
Thinking Skills 1

Extended

Exercises All

Supplements
Challenges 1
Thinking skills 1

Other Resources:
Mathematics Their Way, pp. 93-111
Explorations, pp. 7, 42, 100

OBJECTIVE 1-1
To count on and back with numbers to 20

Materials: counters

Grouping Suggestions: pairs, small groups

---

1. MOTIVATE AND TEACH

LEARN ABOUT IT

As students look at page 1, read the chapter story about the chipmunks. *Pretend that you see 5 chipmunks on the swings. Place 5 counters on the 10-frame. Then count on to show how many chipmunks were on the slide. How many counters did you put in the 10-frame?* (1)

▶ **In the story, some chipmunks were jumping rope and counting. If the jumper's tail had not gotten caught in the rope as they counted 15, what are the next 3 numbers they would have counted?** (16, 17, 18)

▶ **How would you show counting on from 13 to 20 on the 10-frame?** (Possible answer: Fill up the 10-frame with 10 counters and then show 3 extra counters on your partner's 10-frame to make 13. Then add one at a time until you have 10 extra, or 20.)

▶ **Pretend that 2 of the 6 chipmunks did not go to the park. How would you use your counters and the 10-frame to show how many chipmunks did go to the park?** (Possible answer: Place 6 counters in the 10-frame. Then take a counter away as you count back 2. You will have 4 counters left.)

▶ **Compare how you use counters to show counting on and counting back.** (Possible answer: When you count on, you add counters as you count. When you count back, you take counters away as you count.)

2. CHECK UNDERSTANDING

ERROR ALERT Forgetting to add or take away counters in counting on or counting back.

I
Understanding Addition and Subtraction

TEACHING OPTIONS

RETEACHING TIPS Draw 2 large 10-frames. Have students pick a 1-digit number and draw that many circles in the 10-frame. Ask them to count on and draw a circle for each number to 20. Repeat for counting back, erasing circles as they count. Assign Reteaching Supplement 1.

ENRICHMENT With a partner watching, students count on or count back while jumping rope, bouncing a ball, shooting baskets, or hopping on one leg. The partner keeps a record of how many actions were counted for each event. Students can practice and try to go farther each time.

...me _____

...ounting On and Back

9, 10, . . .

...ork with a partner.
...ace counters on your
...0-frame punchout to match
...ch start number.

Add I counter at a time to
count on. Write the numbers.

Start | 9 | 10 | 11 | 12 | 13 | 14

15 | 16 | 17 | 18 | 19 | 20 | Stop

Take away I counter at a time to count back.
Write the numbers.

Start | 12 | 11 | 10 | 9 | 8 | 7

6 | 5 | 4 | 3 | 2 | 1 | Stop

...E MENTAL MATH

Solve.

The number on Pepe's back is 3 less than 15.

What is the number? Count back to solve.

15, 14 , 13 , 12

...he number on Pepe's back is 12 .

---

3. PRACTICE AND APPLY

Basic	All
Average	All
Extended	All

PRACTICE

Why do you need to work with a partner on this page? (You need two 10-frames to hold your counters as you count on or count back.) *How do you know how many counters to start with?* (Look at the number in the box that says start.)

APPLY

USE MENTAL MATH ▶ **Why is it important to clear your 10-frames before you start a new problem?** (Possible answer: You might count on incorrectly because counters were left on the frame.)
▶ **Explain how you know whether this problem involves counting on or counting back.** (Possible answer: counting back, because the number on Pepe's back is *less* than 15)

...LOSE AND ASSESS

...HOW WHAT YOU KNOW

...ave students start with 5 and write
...ch number as they count on to 20.
...ncourage them to use their counters
...d 10-frames if they need help. Then
...ll them you are thinking of a number
...at is 2 less than 18. Have students
...ount back and circle 16. Repeat,
...ying you are thinking of a number
...at is 1 less than 10. Have them
...ount back 1 and place a square
...round 9.

QUICK QUIZ

Count on or count back.
Start　　　　　　　　　　　Stop
3, (4) , (5) , (6) , (7) , 8
17, (16) , (15) , (14) , 13
15, (16) , (17) , (18) , 19

OBJECTIVE 1-2   To model and write addition sentences

PREBOOK ACTIVITIES

QUICK REVIEW

Name the number that is 1 more than each number below.

2 (3)   6 (7)   3 (4)   0 (1)   5 (6)
1 (2)   7 (8)   4 (5)

PRIOR KNOWLEDGE

Discuss with students what they already know about addition. *Bill has 2 marbles in a box. Tom added 3 marbles to a box. What does it mean to add two groups of objects?* (Possible answer: to put the two groups together to find how many in all) *Who can describe a time when you had to add two groups of objects to find how many in all?* (Answers will vary.)

COMMUNICATION

Discussing Math   Use a set of 2-color counters to demonstrate the addition sentence $2 + 3 = 5$. Write the sentence on the chalkboard and point to the appropriate parts as students say the following terms: **addition sentence, addend, equal,** and **sum.** Have students place counters on a table to show the following numbers: 2, 5, 6, 8. Write these numbers on the board. Ask students to show which number is **greatest** and which number is **least.** (8, 2)

EXPLORE AND CONNECT

Materials: four 2-color counters for each student, one numbe cube for each pair
Alternative Materials: blocks or squares of paper in 2 color
Grouping Suggestion: pairs
Label the faces of the number cubes 1, 2, 2, 3, 4, and 4. As partners to take turns rolling the cube. Each one displays the number shown on the cube in counters of one color. At the e of each round, ask students to write an addition sentence usin these two numbers. Repeat to find different sums.
What is the greatest sum you can get? Why (8; because the greatest numbers you can add are $4 + 4$.) *What is the least sum you can get? Why?* (2; because the least numbers you ca add are $1 + 1$.)

CONNECTIONS   Use these anytime.

Problem of the Day

Logic   Use counters to help you write an addition sentence to show this riddle: I have 12 counters. Some are red and some are yellow. I have 2 more red than yellow counters. ($7 + 5 = 12$)

Creative Thinking

Flower Arranging   How many different ways can you arrange 6 flowers in 2 vases? Draw a picture and write an addition sentence to show each one.
(7 ways: $6 + 0 = 6$, $5 + 1 = 6$, $4 + 2 = 6$, $3 + 3 = 6$, $2 + 4 = 6$, $1 + 5 = 6$, $0 + 6 = 6$)

Number Sense

Estimation   About how many brand-new pencils laid end-to-end would it take to go across the length of the chalkboard? Guess and check. (Answers will vary.)

CLASSWORK AND HOMEWORK SUPPLEMENTS

Practice

Skills Maintenance   1-2

Name _____

Addition Sentences

Add.

1. $3 + 3 = \underline{6}$ $2 + 3 = \underline{5}$
2. $4 + 1 = \underline{5}$ $2 + 6 = \underline{8}$
3. $1 + 3 = \underline{4}$ $4 + 3 = \underline{7}$
4. $6 + 2 = \underline{8}$ $7 + 1 = \underline{8}$

Practice.

5. $\dfrac{5}{+3} \rightarrow 8$ $\dfrac{1}{+4} \rightarrow 5$ $\dfrac{2}{+5} \rightarrow 7$ $\dfrac{3}{+3} \rightarrow 6$ $\dfrac{6}{+2} \rightarrow 8$

6. $\dfrac{1}{+1} \rightarrow 2$ $\dfrac{2}{+3} \rightarrow 5$ $\dfrac{3}{+3} \rightarrow 6$ $\dfrac{5}{+1} \rightarrow 6$ $\dfrac{2}{+2} \rightarrow 4$

7. $\dfrac{7}{+1} \rightarrow 8$ $\dfrac{3}{+4} \rightarrow 7$ $\dfrac{5}{+2} \rightarrow 7$ $\dfrac{1}{+6} \rightarrow 7$ $\dfrac{4}{+3} \rightarrow 7$

8. $\dfrac{4}{+4} \rightarrow 8$ $\dfrac{4}{+3} \rightarrow 7$ $\dfrac{7}{+1} \rightarrow 8$ $\dfrac{3}{+3} \rightarrow 6$ $\dfrac{1}{+3} \rightarrow 4$

2   Use with text pages 3–4.   **PS-2**

Reteaching

Skills Review   1-2

Name _____

Addition Sentences

$$5 + 3 = 8$$

Say the larger number.
Count on to find the sum.

1. $4 + 3 = \underline{7}$ $3 + 2 = \underline{5}$
   (4, 5, 6, 7)   (3, 4, 5)

2. $4 + 2 = \underline{6}$ $6 + 2 = \underline{8}$
   (4, 5, 6)   (6, 7, 8)

3. $3 + 5 = \underline{8}$ $3 + 2 = \underline{5}$

4. $5 + 2 = \underline{7}$ $1 + 6 = \underline{7}$

5. $\dfrac{1}{+2} \rightarrow 3$ $\dfrac{4}{+3} \rightarrow 7$ $\dfrac{2}{+3} \rightarrow 5$ $\dfrac{1}{+5} \rightarrow 6$ $\dfrac{6}{+1} \rightarrow 7$

2   Use with text pages 3–4.   **RS-2**

Building Thinking Skills

Mental Math   1-2

Name _____

Going Shopping

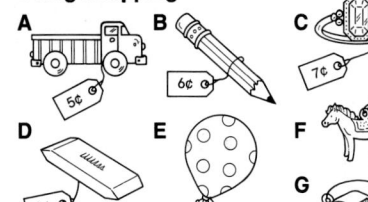

Which two did the person buy?

1. Lee spent 8¢.   2. Lana spent 5¢.

He bought 1 **B** and 1 $\underline{G}$.   She bought 1 **E** and 1 $\underline{F}$.

3. Tom spent 7¢.   4. Pam spent 4¢.

He bought 1 **B** and 1 $\underline{F}$.   She bought 1 **F** and 1 $\underline{D}$.

5. Sue spent 6¢.   6. Ted spent 8¢.

She bought 1 **G** and 1 $\underline{E}$.   He bought 1 **D** and 1 $\underline{A}$.

2   Use with text pages 3–4.   **TS-2**

Challenges

Reading Math   1-2

Name _____

Addition Riddles

Complete the addition sentences in the box.

$3 + 1 = \underline{4}$ riddles	$2 + 3 = \underline{5}$ is
$6 + 2 = \underline{8}$ I	$1 + 2 = \underline{3}$ adding
$1 + 1 = \underline{2}$ doing	$2 + 4 = \underline{6}$ like
$5 + 2 = \underline{7}$ fun	

Look at the words next to your answers.
Each word matches a number.
Write these words under the numbers below.
What do the addition riddles say? Read them to a friend.

8	6	2	4
I	like	doing	riddles

3	5	7
Adding	is	fun

8	6	3
I	like	adding

2	4	5	7
Doing	riddles	is	fun

2   Use with text pages 3–4.   **CS-2**

OPTIONS FOR INDIVIDUAL NEEDS

Basic

Exercises All
More Practice, p. 409, set B

Supplements
Reteaching 2 or
Practice 2

Average

Exercises All
More Practice, p. 409, set B

Supplements
Practice 2
Challenges 2 or
Thinking Skills 2

Extended

Exercises All

Supplements
Challenges 2
Thinking Skills 2

Other Resources:
Explorations, pp. 50-55, 65-67
Workjobs, pp. 194-197, 200-211
WorkjobsII, pp. 14, 16, 18-19, 103, 107, 110
Workjobs for Parents, pp. 104-105, 114-115
Developing Number Concepts with Unifix Cubes, pp. 76-111
Mathematics Book A, pp. 13-14

OBJECTIVE 1-2
To model and write addition sentences

Materials 8 two-color counters for each pair of students

Grouping Suggestions: pairs, individual work

---

1. MOTIVATE AND TEACH

LEARN ABOUT IT

Read this story aloud: *Two students are jumping on a trampoline. Three more students decide to join them.*
▶ **How many students are jumping on the trampoline?** (5)
Have students look at the picture of the trampoline on page 3.
▶ **How can you use the counters to act out this story?** (Possible answer: Use counters as jumpers.)
▶ **Do you need to use all of your 8 counters for this story?** (no)
▶ **How could you write an addition sentence to show the jumpers in this story?** (2 + 3 = 5)
Have each pair of students place their 8 counters on the trampoline and write an addition sentence in Exercise 1.
▶ **What plan can you think of to help you complete Exercises 2–6?** (Possible answer: Use a different number of counters each time. Write an addition sentence to match.)
▶ **Why will the greatest sum you can make not be greater than 8?** (Because there are 8 counters in all.)
▶ **How did you find the total number of counters on the trampoline each time?** (Possible answers: count on; use addition facts; count)

2. CHECK UNDERSTANDING

ERROR ALERT Counting on or adding from the wrong number. For example, in 5 + 3 = 8, the student may begin with 5, but in counting on 3, say *five, six, seven.*

Name _____

Addition Sentences

Work with a partner.
Share 9 two-color counters.

Place some counters of one color on the trampoline. Your partner places some counters of the other color on the trampoline. Write the addition sentence below. Try it again. Use a different number of counters.

Answers may vary

Addend	Addend	Sum
1. ____ ⊕	____ ▦	____ ☐
3. ____ ◯	____ ☐	
5. ____ ◯	____ ☐	

Addend	Addend	Sum
2. ____ ◯	____ ☐	
4. ____ ◯	____ ☐	
6. ____ ◯	____ ☐	

7. The greatest sum above is ____.

8. The least sum above is ____.

Answers may vary, but should not be greater than 9.

Answers may vary, but should not be less than 2.

Chapter 1   (three)

TEACHING OPTIONS

RETEACHING TIPS Place 4 counters on the table and have students count them. Then place 3 more counters on the table, counting aloud *four, five, six, seven.* Repeat, focusing on the counting procedure each time. Use Reteaching Supplement 2 for further help in addition.

ENRICHMENT **Family Math** Have students work with a family member to find 2 addends that will give each of the following sums: 5, 8, 7, 6, 4, 1 (Answers will vary.) They may use raisins or dried beans to check their sums.

$$\underline{3} + \underline{2} = \underline{5}$$

$$\begin{array}{r} 3 \\ +2 \\ \hline 5 \end{array}$$

rite what the picture shows.

1.
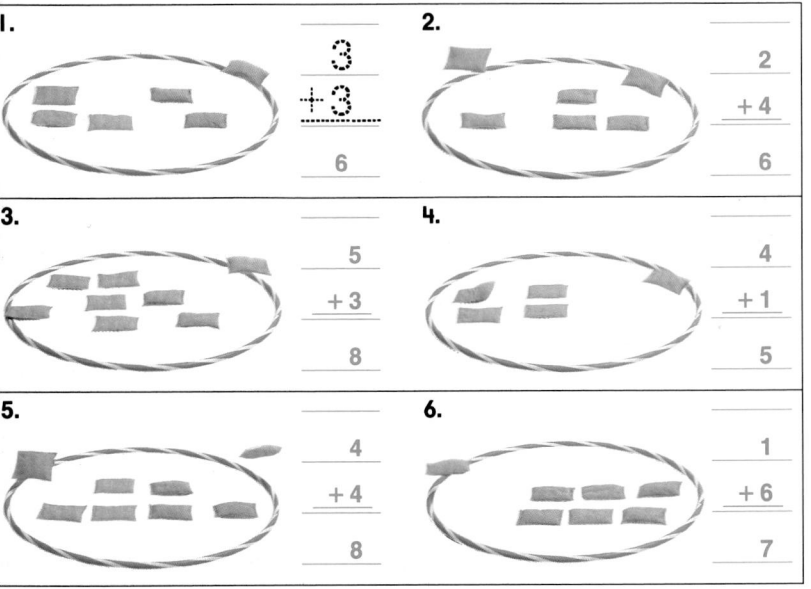
$$\begin{array}{r} 3 \\ +3 \\ \hline 6 \end{array}$$

2.
$$\begin{array}{r} 2 \\ +4 \\ \hline 6 \end{array}$$

3.
$$\begin{array}{r} 5 \\ +3 \\ \hline 8 \end{array}$$

4.
$$\begin{array}{r} 4 \\ +1 \\ \hline 5 \end{array}$$

5.
$$\begin{array}{r} 4 \\ +4 \\ \hline 8 \end{array}$$

6.
$$\begin{array}{r} 1 \\ +6 \\ \hline 7 \end{array}$$

LK ABOUT IT

Which addition fact will have
the greater sum? Tell why.   5 + 2, because 2 is greater than 1

 5 + 1    5 + 2

3. PRACTICE AND APPLY

Basic	All
Average	All
Extended	All

PRACTICE

*How can you check your addition
sentences in the exercises on page 4?*
(Possible answer: Count the number of
counters in each set to make sure it
matches the addend. Count the total
number of counters to make sure it
matches the sum.)

APPLY

**TALK ABOUT IT ▶ If one of the
addends in two addition sentences is
the same, which sentence will have
the greater sum? Why?** (Possible
answer: the one whose second addend is
greater; the total will be greater)

CLOSE AND ASSESS

HOW WHAT YOU KNOW
ave each student use 2-color
unters to model problems such as
e following. Then have them write
addition sentence to match.
*ou have 3 toy cars. A friend gives
u 4 more.* How many cars do you
ave? (3 + 4 = 7)

QUICK QUIZ

Use + and = to write 3 different
addition sentences with sums of 8.
1. __(Answers will vary.)__
2. _____
3. _____

Subtraction Sentences

OBJECTIVE 1-3   To model and write subtraction sentences

PREBOOK ACTIVITIES

QUICK REVIEW

What is 1 less than each of these numbers?
4, 6, 2, 7, 5   (3, 5, 1, 6, 4)
What is 2 less than each of these numbers?
5, 3, 6, 2, 4   (3, 1, 4, 0, 2)

PRIOR KNOWLEDGE

Pose the following situation: There are 7 days in the week. You go to school 5 of the days. How can we find out how many days you do not go to school? (Possible answers: Count back 5 from 7; take away 5 from 7; subtract 5 from 7.)

COMMUNICATION

Reading and Discussing Math   Write the word **difference** on the chalkboard and ask students to say it. Ask what they think the word means. (Possible answers: it is like *different*; when things are different) Write 7 and 5 on the chalkboard and ask what the difference is between them. (Possible answers: they look different; 7 is greater than 5; 5 is less than 7; 2) Remind students of your discussion of how many days in the week they do not go to school. Work together to write the subtraction sentence: $7 - 5 = 2$. Explain that the answer when we subtract is called the difference. Have students identify the difference in the subtraction sentence. (2)

EXPLORE AND CONNECT

Materials: 9 counters for each pair of students
Grouping Suggestion: pairs
Pair students and provide each pair with 9 counters. Suggest that the students' tables or desks represent swimming pools a that their counters represent people at the pool. Invite the partners, in turn, to make up a story about people going in ar out of the pool, using the counters to represent the people. Have them determine the **difference** between the number of people inside and outside the pool. Then ask them to draw a picture to illustrate the story. Stress that students take turns doing the various tasks: one partner tells a story while the oth shows the story with counters; one partner draws the picture, then the other checks it.

CONNECTIONS   Use these anytime.

Problem of the Day

How Many Left?   Draw a picture to illustrate the story. Eddie had a 6-pack of juice. He drank 2 cans and gave 2 to his friend Paul. How many cans were left?
(2)

Math Connection

Calculator   Use a calculator to find the differences:
$8 - 5 =$ _(3)_ $7 - 3 =$ _(4)_
$8 - 6 =$ _(2)_ $6 - 1 =$ _(5)_
When you are done, try some of your own subtraction sentences.

Subject Integration

Science   Make a class weather calendar. Write the number of sunny and cloudy days for a week. Then compare. What is the difference between the number of sunny and cloudy days?

CLASSWORK AND HOMEWORK SUPPLEMENTS

Practice

Skills Maintenance   1-3

Name _____

Subtraction Sentences

Subtract.

1. $8 - 1 = \underline{7}$ $3 - 2 = \underline{1}$

2. $4 - 2 = \underline{2}$ $7 - 1 = \underline{6}$

3. $6 - 1 = \underline{5}$ $5 - 2 = \underline{3}$

4. $7 - 2 = \underline{5}$ $8 - 3 = \underline{5}$

5.
$\begin{array}{r} 4 \\ -3 \\ \hline 1 \end{array}$
$\begin{array}{r} 8 \\ -5 \\ \hline 3 \end{array}$
$\begin{array}{r} 7 \\ -6 \\ \hline 1 \end{array}$
$\begin{array}{r} 6 \\ -4 \\ \hline 2 \end{array}$
$\begin{array}{r} 5 \\ -1 \\ \hline 4 \end{array}$

6.
$\begin{array}{r} 6 \\ -5 \\ \hline 1 \end{array}$
$\begin{array}{r} 7 \\ -2 \\ \hline 5 \end{array}$
$\begin{array}{r} 8 \\ -6 \\ \hline 2 \end{array}$
$\begin{array}{r} 4 \\ -2 \\ \hline 2 \end{array}$
$\begin{array}{r} 6 \\ -3 \\ \hline 3 \end{array}$

7.
$\begin{array}{r} 4 \\ -1 \\ \hline 3 \end{array}$
$\begin{array}{r} 5 \\ -3 \\ \hline 2 \end{array}$
$\begin{array}{r} 6 \\ -2 \\ \hline 4 \end{array}$
$\begin{array}{r} 8 \\ -7 \\ \hline 1 \end{array}$
$\begin{array}{r} 7 \\ -4 \\ \hline 3 \end{array}$

8.
$\begin{array}{r} 7 \\ -3 \\ \hline 4 \end{array}$
$\begin{array}{r} 8 \\ -2 \\ \hline 6 \end{array}$
$\begin{array}{r} 3 \\ -1 \\ \hline 2 \end{array}$
$\begin{array}{r} 5 \\ -2 \\ \hline 3 \end{array}$
$\begin{array}{r} 5 \\ -4 \\ \hline 1 \end{array}$

PS-2   Use with text pages 5–6.   **3**

Building Thinking Skills

Mental Math   1-3

Name _____

Leaving the Cage

How many flew away?

1. Start with 8. $\underline{7}$ flew away.

2. Start with 6. $\underline{2}$ flew away.

3. Start with 5. $\underline{3}$ flew away.

4. Start with 7. $\underline{5}$ flew away.

5. Start with 6. $\underline{4}$ flew away.

6. Start with 7. $\underline{4}$ flew away.

TS-2   Use with text pages 5–6.   **3**

Reteaching

Skills Review   1-3

Name _____

Subtraction Sentences

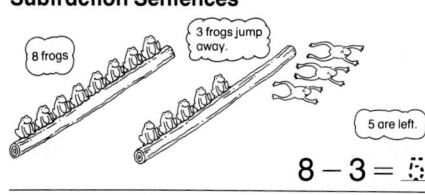

8 frogs   3 frogs jump away.   5 are left.

$$8 - 3 = 5$$

Cross out and subtract.

1. $6 - 3 = \underline{3}$ $5 - 3 = \underline{2}$

2. $7 - 3 = \underline{4}$ $4 - 3 = \underline{1}$

Subtract.

3. $5 - 2 = \underline{3}$ $6 - 4 = \underline{2}$

4. $7 - 2 = \underline{5}$ $8 - 2 = \underline{6}$

5. $4 - 3 = \underline{1}$ $5 - 4 = \underline{1}$

6.
$\begin{array}{r} 5 \\ -1 \\ \hline 4 \end{array}$
$\begin{array}{r} 4 \\ -2 \\ \hline 2 \end{array}$
$\begin{array}{r} 7 \\ -4 \\ \hline 3 \end{array}$
$\begin{array}{r} 8 \\ -6 \\ \hline 2 \end{array}$

RS-2   Use with text pages 5–6.   **3**

Challenges

Family Math   1-3

Name _____

Three in a Row

> Dear Family,
> We have just completed a lesson on subtraction facts. As you play this game with your child, say the subtraction sentences aloud.

Take turns subtracting.
Find three 3s in a row to win.
Draw a line.

$8 - 5 = 3$	$7 - 2 = 5$	$4 - 2 = 2$
$5 - 4 = 1$	$6 - 3 = 3$	$8 - 7 = 1$
$7 - 3 = 4$	$8 - 2 = 6$	$5 - 2 = 3$

Play again.
Find three differences in a row that are the same to win. Draw a line.

$6 - 3 = 3$	$4 - 3 = 1$	$8 - 3 = 5$
$7 - 4 = 3$	$7 - 2 = 5$	$8 - 6 = 2$
$6 - 1 = 5$	$8 - 6 = 2$	$6 - 4 = 2$

CS-2   Use with text pages 5–6.   **3**

OPTIONS FOR INDIVIDUAL NEEDS

Basic

Exercises All
Data Bank, p. 398
More Practice, p. 409, set C

Supplements
Reteaching 3 or
Practice 3

Average

Exercises All
Data Bank, p. 398
More Practice, p. 409, set C

Supplements
Practice 3
Challenges 3 or
Thinking Skills 3

Extended

Exercises All
Data Bank, p. 398

Supplements
Challenges 3
Thinking Skills 3

Other Resources:
Problem-Solving Experiences In Mathematics, pp. 15, 26
Workjobs, pp. 198-199
WorkjobsII, pp. 15, 17, 20-21, 104
Workjobs for Parents, pp. 104-105, 114-115
Developing Number Concepts with Unifix cubes, pp. 76-111
Mathematics Book A, p. 25

LESSON PLAN 1-3

OBJECTIVE 1-3
To model and write subtraction sentences

> **Materials:** 9 counters for each pair of students, flannelboard and up to 9 felt objects, 9 Cube-A-Links for each student
>
> **Alternative Materials:** punchout tiles
>
> **Grouping Suggestion:** pairs

1. MOTIVATE AND TEACH

LEARN ABOUT IT

Have students use counters to make up stories about people going in and out of a pool and work together to write subtraction sentences to show those stories.
▶ **In Exercises 1-4, how did you know which number to put first in the subtraction sentence?** (Possible answers: It is the number of people in the pool to begin with; it is the bigger number.)
▶ **In Exercises 5-6, what does the difference stand for?** (the children waiting to jump into the pool)

2. CHECK UNDERSTANDING

ERROR ALERT Not making the transfer from the representation of objects to the symbolic notation.

Name _____

Subtraction Sentences

Work with a partner. Share 9 counters.

Place some counters in the swimming pool.
Your partner takes away some counters.
Write the subtraction sentence below.
Try it again. Use a different number of counters.

Answer may var[y]

1. ___ ◯ ___ ▢

2. ___ ◯ ___ ▢

3. ___ ◯ ___ ▢

4. ___ ◯ ___ ▢

Write the difference. Then write the subtraction sentence the other way.

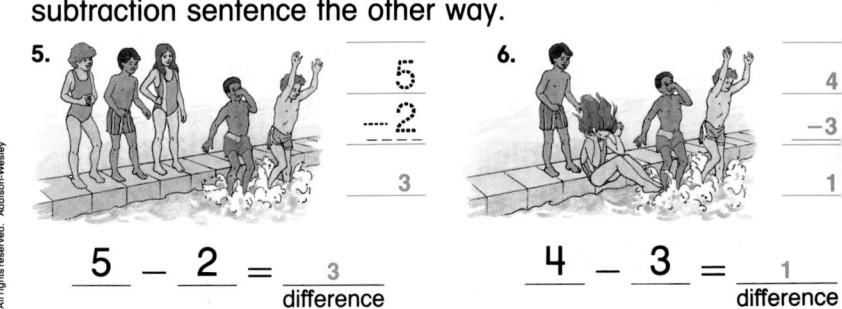

5.
$$\begin{array}{r} 5 \\ -\ 2 \\ \hline 3 \end{array}$$

$$5 - 2 = \underset{\text{difference}}{3}$$

6.
$$\begin{array}{r} 4 \\ -3 \\ \hline 1 \end{array}$$

$$4 - 3 = \underset{\text{difference}}{1}$$

Chapter 1

(five)

TEACHING OPTIONS

RETEACHING TIPS Pose the problem of 6 − 4 and put 6 objects on the flannelboard. Have a student take away the 4 objects as the rest of the group counts. Ask how many are left. Write 6 − 4 = 2. Repeat for other subtraction sentences. Use Reteaching Supplement 3 to provide additional help.

COMPUTER Learning About Numbers, C & C Software © 1983 Subtraction practice for all students. In *Arithmetic Fun*, students use a story to practice single-digit subtraction. They should begin with difficulty Level 1 and continue to Level 2. The lesson requires 10-15 minutes.

oss out to take away. Then subtract.
mber of objects left uncrossed should match answers.

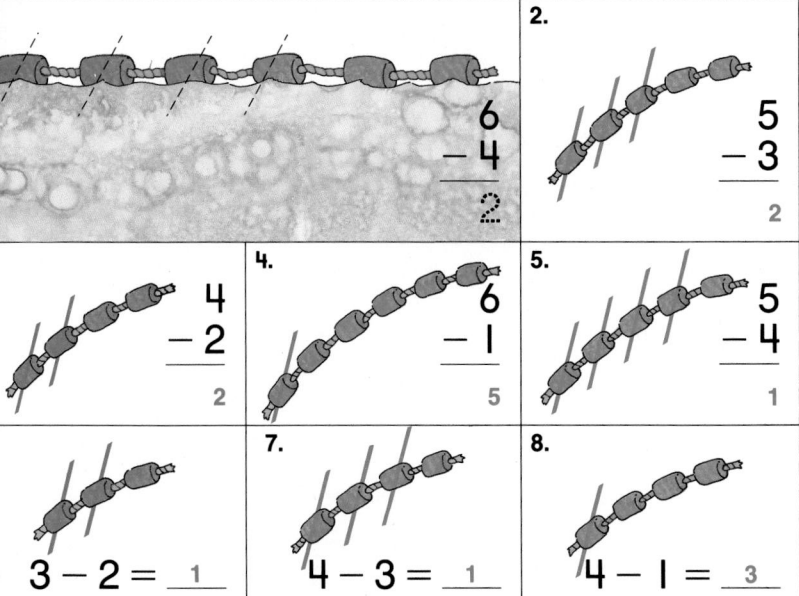

1.	2.
$\begin{array}{r} 6 \\ -4 \\ \hline 2 \end{array}$	$\begin{array}{r} 5 \\ -3 \\ \hline 2 \end{array}$
3.	4. 5.

3.
$\begin{array}{r} 4 \\ -2 \\ \hline 2 \end{array}$

4.
$\begin{array}{r} 6 \\ -1 \\ \hline 5 \end{array}$

5.
$\begin{array}{r} 5 \\ -4 \\ \hline 1 \end{array}$

6. $3 - 2 = \underline{1}$

7. $4 - 3 = \underline{1}$

8. $4 - 1 = \underline{3}$

ND THE DATA DATA BANK

How many events was Ali in? _4_ events

How many events was Sonia in? _3_ events

Who was in the least number of events? **Larry**

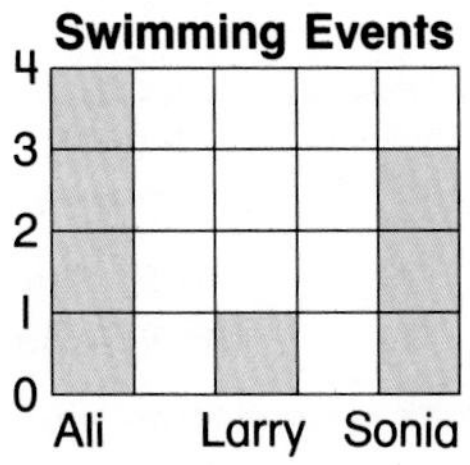

Data Bank Who won the greatest number of ribbons in the swim meet? (See page 398.) **Ali**

Swimming Events

(Bar graph with y-axis labeled 0, 1, 2, 3, 4 and x-axis labeled Ali, Larry, Sonia)

(six)   More Practice, page 409, set C   Chapter 1

---

3. PRACTICE AND APPLY

Basic	All
Average	All
Extended	All

1-3

PRACTICE

How are Exercises 1-8 on page 6 like those on page 5? (They start with a number of things, then take some away.) *What does the difference stand for in these exercises?* (the number of corks left)

APPLY

FIND THE DATA Review how to read a bar graph.
▶ **What does the graph tell you?** (how many events each person was in) Show students how to use the Data Bank.
▶ **Who tied for third place in winning ribbons?** (Rosa and Peter)
▶ **How did you figure this out?** (found who came in second, then third)

LOSE AND ASSESS

HOW WHAT YOU KNOW
ve students work in pairs, using erlocking cubes to make stacks of to 9 cubes. Then have them break e stacks apart at different points to resent the whole and the number ing taken away. Ask them to take ns writing the subtraction sentences t result.

QUICK QUIZ

Circle the 3 exercises that have the same difference.
7 − 5 = _(2)_   5 − 1 = _(4)_
6 − 3 = _(3)_   8 − 7 = _(1)_
4 − 1 = _(3)_   7 − 4 = _(3)_

Problem Solving: Introduction/Use Thinking Skills

OBJECTIVE 1-4 To use the 6-point checklist to solve problems; to use critical thinking to identify missing number

PREBOOK ACTIVITIES

QUICK REVIEW

Add or subtract.

$5 - 3 = \underline{(2)}$ $4 - 1 = \underline{(3)}$ $6 + 2 = \underline{(8)}$ $3 + 5 = \underline{(8)}$
$4 + 4 = \underline{(8)}$ $3 - 2 = \underline{(1)}$ $5 - 4 = \underline{(1)}$ $1 + 7 = \underline{(8)}$

3	1	8	7	4	8	2
+ 3	+ 6	− 3	− 3	+ 1	− 4	+ 4
(6)	(7)	(5)	(4)	(5)	(4)	(6)

PRIOR KNOWLEDGE

Listen to the action in each sentence. Does the action involve something being put together or something being taken away?
Read each sentence and invite students to act out the actions.
1. 1 bird left 3 others in a tree. (take away)
2. 2 dogs joined 1 dog running. (put together)
3. Jerry ate 3 of the 6 carrots he had. (take away)
4. 7 fish swam over to be with 1 big fish. (put together)

COMMUNICATION

Writing and Reading Math Write the words **understand, find data, plan, estimate, solve,** and **check** in a column on the chalkboard. Read the words in order and explain that these are the 6 steps students should follow to solve story problems. Discuss the meaning of each step. Then ask volunteers to use each word in a complete sentence.
Write the words **thinking skills** on the chalkboard. *To use thinking skills means to use what you know to help you solve a problem.* On the board write: *Jane had 6¢. She found 3¢ more. 6 − 3 = 3 or 6 + 3 = 9? What do you know that will help you decide which number sentence to choose?* (The words *had* and *found...more* mean addition.)

EXPLORE AND CONNECT

COOPERATIVE ACTIVITY

Grouping Suggestion: small groups
5 people were waiting for a bus.
1 more person joined them.
How many people were waiting for the bus then?

TEACHING ACTIONS

Hold up a card showing each point from the 6-point checklist—Understand, Find Data, Plan, Estimate, Solve, and Check—as you explain what it means.

▶ **What does the problem ask you to do?**
(Possible answer: Find out how many people wer waiting for the bus all together.)
▶ **What data can help you solve this problem?** (Possible answer: the number of people who were first waiting and number of people who joined them)

▶ **What plan would you use to solve the problem—put together or take away? Why?**
(Possible answer: put together; because *joined* is a word that means *came together*)
▶ **Estimate how large the sum will be. Why do you think so?** (Possible answer: more than 5, since there were 5 people and more joined them)

▶ **How might you check your answer?**
(Possible answer: Act out the actions in the story using people or counters or draw a picture.) Have small groups of students act out the story. Then have each group make up a new story and act it out.

CONNECTIONS   Use these anytime.

Problem of the Day
Using the Checklist Read the problem. Use the checklist to help you write a number sentence.
There were 6 apples on the tree.
4 apples fell off.
How many apples were left on the tree?
$(6 - 4 = 2)$

Number Sense
Reasoning Tell which number makes sense in each of the situations.
number of days in a month 3 or 30 (30)
number of wheels on a car 4 or 40 (4)
number of boys in your class 12 or 120 (12)
weight (in pounds) of a baby 7 or 70 (7)
length (in inches) of a pencil 6 or 60 (6)

Subject Integration
Physical Education Working in groups, show put-together and take-away number sentences. First, divide your group into 2 smaller groups. Join groups and strike a pose. Then have some members leave the pose. Say the number sentence that matches each action.

sing Critical Thinking

use critical thinking to identify missing numbers

CLASSWORK AND HOMEWORK SUPPLEMENTS

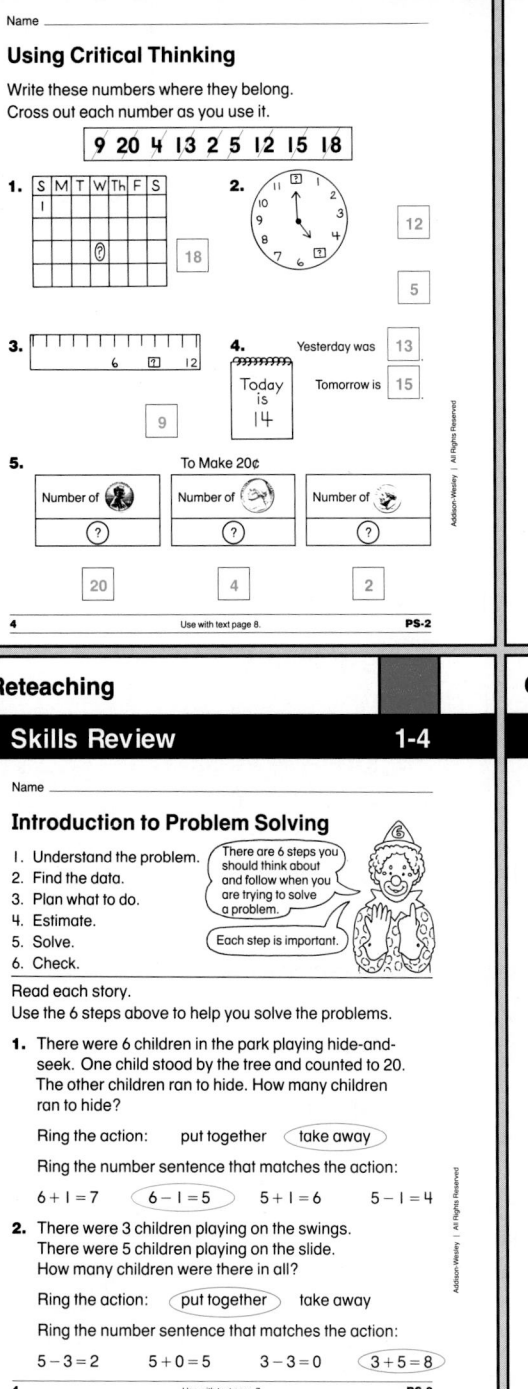

Practice

Critical Thinking — 1-4

Name

Using Critical Thinking

Write these numbers where they belong.
Cross out each number as you use it.

9 20 4 13 2 5 12 15 18

1. S M T W Th F S
2. 12 5
3. 6 12
4. Yesterday was 13 / Today is 14 / Tomorrow is 15 / 9
5. To Make 20¢
    Number of ( ) ? 20
    Number of ( ) ? 4
    Number of ( ) ? 2

4   Use with text page 8.   PS-2

Reteaching

Skills Review — 1-4

Name

Introduction to Problem Solving

1. Understand the problem.
2. Find the data.
3. Plan what to do.
4. Estimate.
5. Solve.
6. Check.

There are 6 steps you should think about and follow when you are trying to solve a problem.

Each step is important.

Read each story.
Use the 6 steps above to help you solve the problems.

1. There were 6 children in the park playing hide-and-seek. One child stood by the tree and counted to 20. The other children ran to hide. How many children ran to hide?

   Ring the action: put together   (take away)

   Ring the number sentence that matches the action:

   6 + 1 = 7   (6 − 1 = 5)   5 + 1 = 6   5 − 1 = 4

2. There were 3 children playing on the swings. There were 5 children playing on the slide. How many children were there in all?

   Ring the action: (put together)   take away

   Ring the number sentence that matches the action:

   5 − 3 = 2   5 + 0 = 5   3 − 3 = 0   (3 + 5 = 8)

4   Use with text page 7.   RS-2

Building Thinking Skills

Problem Solving — 1-4

Name

The Sleepover Party

Read the story.
Look at the picture.
Write a number sentence
to answer each question.

Nan and Fran are twins.
They invited some friends to sleep over.

1. How many friends did they invite?
   8 ⊖ 2 = 6

Six girls at the party have stuffed animals.

2. How many are teddy bears?
   6 ⊖ 1 = 5

Two girls with short hair wear glasses and two girls with long hair wear glasses.

3. How many girls in all wear glasses?
   2 ⊕ 2 = 4

Seven of the girls are watching TV.

4. How many of them are sitting up?
   7 ⊖ 3 = 4

4   Use with text page 7.   TS-2

Challenges

Family Math — 1-4

Name

My Birthday

Dear Family,
   Your child is learning to use thinking skills and to make inferences. Complete this page this page together to help reinforce these skills.

Look at a calendar. Finish these sentences.

1. My birthday is _____ _____
   (month)   (number)

2. My birthday is on the _____
   day of the month.   (ordinal number)

3. Right now, I am _____ years old.
   (number)

4. This year, my birthday is on a _____
   (day of the week)

5. I will be _____ years old.
   (number)

6. On the Sunday after my birthday, I will be _____ years and _____ days old.
   (number)   (number)

7. There are _____ days in the month
   (number)
   before my birthday.

8. There are _____ days in the month
   (number)
   after my birthday.

4   Use with text page 8.   CS-2

OPTIONS FOR INDIVIDUAL NEEDS

1-4

Basic

Exercises All

Supplements
Reteaching 4 or
Practice 4

Average

Exercises All

Supplements
Practice 4
Challenges 4 or
Thinking Skills 4

Extended

Exercises All

Supplements
Challenges 4
Thinking Skills 4

Other Resources:
Mathematics Their Way, pp. 204-205, 207-208
Explorations, pp. 56-59, 67, 71
Problem-Solving Experiences In Mathematics, pp. 13-14, 19-20, 25-26
WorkjobsII, pp. 15, 17, 20-21
Mathematics Book A, pp. 15-16

LESSON PLAN 1-4

OBJECTIVE 1-4
To use the 6-point checklist to solve problems; to use critical thinking to identify missing numbers

1. MOTIVATE AND TEACH

LEARN ABOUT IT

Read Story 1 aloud to students and go through each of the questions on this page. Do the same for Story 2.

Story 1: *At the swim meet, there were 6 people waiting to use the high dive. 2 people climbed the ladder and dove into the pool. How many people were still waiting to use the high dive?*

Story 2: *2 swimmers sat in chairs by the pool while they waited for the race. 4 other swimmers waited in the pool. How many swimmers were waiting for the race?*

 **BEFORE** ▶ **How will you know which data to use?** (Listen to the numbers in the story and match them to the data in Exercise 2.)

▶ **Why is it important to listen carefully to each story?** (Information from the stories is needed to answer the questions.)

 **DURING** ▶ **How will you plan what to do?** (Decide whether the action is putting together or taking away.)

▶ **Why is there a 6-point checklist?** (The checklist gives you steps to follow to solve story problems.)

 **AFTER** ▶ **What other method could you use to check your answers?** (Possible answer: Draw a picture to match the data and the action in the story. See if it matches your number sentence.)

2. CHECK UNDERSTANDING

ERROR ALERT   Page 7   Not listening to the clues and data in each story.

Page 8   Inserting numbers that do not make sense in the exercise.

Name _____

Introduction to Problem Solving

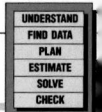

Listen to the stories.
Use ◁▨▣▥ for Story 1 and ◁▨▣▥ for Story 2.

1. **Understand** the problem. Ring the picture that shows the story.

Story 1   Story 2

2. **Find** the **data**. Ring the data to match the story.

   6 divers   2 swimmers out of pool   6 divers
   4 dove in   4 swimmers in pool   2 dove in
                     Story 2   Story 1

3. **Plan** what to do. Ring the action in the story.

   put together Story 2   take away Story 1

4. **Estimate.** Ring the better estimate.

   more than 5 Story 2   less than 5 Story 1

5. **Solve.** Ring the number sentence that matches the plan.

                              Story 1   Story 2
   $6 - 4 = 2$ $6 - 2 = 4$ $4 + 2 = 6$
                                        See teaching notes.

6. **Check.** Use counters to act out Story 1 and Story 2.

Chapter 1   (seven)

TEACHING OPTIONS

RETEACHING TIPS   Write a number pattern such as 2, 4, 6, ___, 10 on the chalkboard. Ask students to choose a number between 8 and 12 to complete and explain their answers. Repeat with other number patterns. Assign Reteaching Supplement 4.

ENRICHMENT   Have students write a silly number sentence, such as *Dogs have 14 legs*, illustrate it, and display it for the class. Ask the class to decide if a sensible number would be greater than or less than the silly number. Have a student read the sentence, substituting the correct number.

Using Critical Thinking

Write these numbers where they belong.
Cross out each number as you use it.

| ~~1~~ | 2 | 3 | ~~6~~ | ~~7~~ | ~~10~~ | ~~14~~ | ~~16~~ |

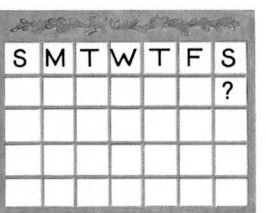

 7 days in one week

2.

?

1

6

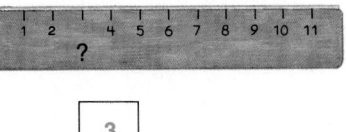

?

3 inches

4. Yesterday was

14 .

Tomorrow is

16 .

 TODAY IS 15

To Make 10¢		
Number of 🪙	Number of 🪙	Number of 🪙
?	?	I

10 pennies

2 nickels

(eight)

Chapter 1

3. PRACTICE AND APPLY

Basic	All
Average	All
Extended	All

1-4

Why is it important to cross out each number after you use it? (so that you do not use a number more than once) *What should you do if you see that you need to use a crossed-out number?* (Go back to where you used that number and find a different number that makes more sense.)

▶ **How will thinking skills help you do the exercises on this page?** (Possible answer: Only 1 number in the box will make sense in each exercise. Use what you know to decide which number fits.)

▶ **How might you use estimation to help you plan which number fits?** (Possible answer: Without looking at the numbers in the box, estimate what you think the number will be. Then look at the box to see if there is a number that is close to the estimate.)

▶ **What is one way to check your answers?** (Possible answer: As you use each number, cross it out so you do not use it again. If the numbers left fit the exercises that are left, you can be sure your answers are correct.)

CLOSE AND ASSESS

SHOW WHAT YOU KNOW

Have small groups of students make up put-together or a take-away stories. Ask one student to record the story and another to identify the type of story it is. Invite groups to act out their stories and write number sentences to match. Remind students to use the checklist when solving their stories.

QUICK QUIZ

Ring the action for this story.
8 children were playing baseball.
2 left to go home.
How many children were left?
put together   take away

LESSON OPTIONS 1-5

Different Ways to Name a Sum

OBJECTIVE 1-5   To show different ways to name a sum

PREBOOK ACTIVITIES

Find the sums.

4 + 1 = __(5)__   2 + 2 = __(4)__   3 + 4 = __(7)__   1 + 5 = __(6)__
0 + 7 = __(7)__   3 + 3 = __(6)__   1 + 2 = __(3)__   6 + 2 = __(8)__

PRIOR KNOWLEDGE

Write the number sentences 3 + 2 = 5 and 2 + 3 = 5 on the chalkboard. *How are these addition sentences alike?* (Possible answers: Both have a sum of 5; both have the same 3 numbers.) *How are these addition sentences different?* (Possible answer: The numbers 3 and 2 change places in the second sentence.)

COMMUNICATION

Reading and Discussing Math   Write the following addition sentences on the chalkboard: 3 + 4 = 7, 4 + 3 = 7. Point to the appropriate parts of the addition sentences as you say each of the following math terms: **addition sentence, addend, sum, turnaround fact.** Have students explain what might happen if they had a turnaround day. (Possible answer: eat dinner in the morning and breakfast at night) *What happens to addends when they are turned around in an addition sentence?* (Possible answer: They change places with each other.)

Materials: 5 two-color counters for each student
Alternative Materials: punchout square tiles
Grouping Suggestion: pairs
Pair students and help them use their counters as **addends** to show **addition sentences** with the **sum** of 5. *Can anyone use the counters to find a different way to make a sum of 5?* (Possible answer: Change the order of the addends by moving the counters.) Have students use the counters to show the addition sentences and match up the **turnaround facts.** *How are turnaround facts alike?* (Possible answers: They have the same addends; they have the same sum.) *What happens to the sum when you turn the addends around?* (It stays the same.) Then have pairs of students take turns writing their turnaround facts on the chalkboard.

CONNECTIONS   Use these anytime.

Problem of the Day

Reasoning   Jill has 3 red balloons and 2 green ones. Peter has 2 blue balloons and 3 yellow ones. Peter said, "I have more balloons than Jill." Is he right? What do you think? (No; they both have 5 balloons.)

Subject Integration

Art   Put 4 drops of red food coloring in a glass of water. What will you get if you add blue? (purple) Do it. Now start with blue. What will you get if you add red? (purple) Do it. Does it matter in what order you add the colors? (no)

Counting Patterns

Skip Counting   Say a number between one and ten. Try 3. Ask your partner to skip a number and say the next one. (5) Count on in this pattern to see how high you can go. (7, 9 . . .) Then skip count backward from there.

CLASSWORK AND HOMEWORK SUPPLEMENTS

Practice

Skills Maintenance   1-5

Name _____

Different Ways to Name a Sum   Answers will vary.

Use 2 colors. Show different ways to make a sum of 8.
Write both turnaround facts.

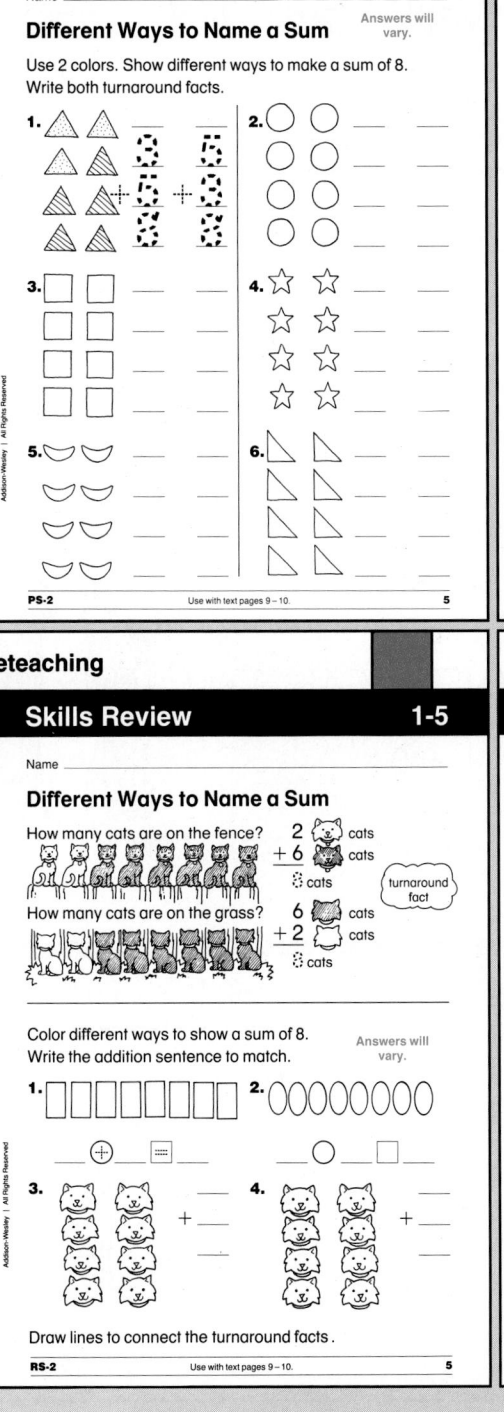

PS-2   Use with text pages 9 – 10.   5

Reteaching

Skills Review   1-5

Name _____

Different Ways to Name a Sum

How many cats are on the fence?   2 cats
+ 6 cats
⋮ cats   turnaround fact

How many cats are on the grass?   6 cats
+ 2 cats
⋮ cats

Color different ways to show a sum of 8.
Write the addition sentence to match.   Answers will vary.

1. 2.

3. 4.

Draw lines to connect the turnaround facts.

RS-2   Use with text pages 9 – 10.   5

Building Thinking Skills

Math Reasoning   1-5

Name _____

What's My Number?

How many different names can you find for a sum?
Make a list to help you predict.

SUM	DIFFERENT NAMES	NUMBER OF NAMES
1	0 + 1 1 + 0	2
2	0 + 2 1 + 1 2 + 0	3
3	0 + 3 1 + 2 3 + 0 2 + 1	4
4	0 + 4, 1 + 3, 2 + 2, 3 + 1, 4 + 0	5
5	0 + 5, 1 + 4, 2 + 3, 3 + 2, 4 + 1, 5 + 0	6
6	0 + 6, 1 + 5, 2 + 4, 3 + 3, 4 + 2, 5 + 1, 6 + 0	7

PREDICT

How many ways can you name each sum?

the sum of 8   9 names

the sum of 9   10 names

the sum of 10   11 names

5   Use with text pages 9 – 10.   TS-2

Challenges

Cooperative Activities   1-5

Name _____

Color Cube Patterns

Play this game with a partner. Take turns.
Use 16 cubes of 4 colors. Arrange them in a 4-by-4 square.
Cubes of the same color
should not touch each other.
If you choose red, blue, white,
and yellow, your square
might look like this.

R	B	R	B
Y	W	Y	W
R	B	R	B
Y	W	Y	W

Ask your partner to look away.

1. Remove 1 cube from a
   corner of the square.
   Ask your partner to tell what color is missing.
   Take away 2 or 3 cubes.
   Can your partner put them back in the right place?

2. Snap 2 side-by-side cubes together.
   Take them both away. Turn them around.
   Put them back.
   Can your partner find the turned-around
   cubes and turn them back?
   Try this with 4 cubes snapped together.

3. Think up your own color cube game.
   Try using 36 cubes of 4 colors in a 6-by-6 square.

CS-2   Use with text pages 9 – 10.   5

OPTIONS FOR INDIVIDUAL NEEDS

Basic

Exercises All

Supplements
Reteaching 5 or
Practice 5
Thinking Skills 5

Average

Exercises All

Supplements
Practice 5
Challenges 5 or
Thinking Skills 5

Extended

Exercises All

Supplements
Challenges 5
Thinking Skills 5

Other Resources:
Math In Stride, pp. 13-17,
24-26, 103-106
Explorations, pp. 50-51,
54-55, 63
*Developing Number Concepts
with Unifix Cubes*, pp.
115-118, 120, 124

LESSON PLAN 1-5

OBJECTIVE 1-5
To show different ways to name a sum

Materials: 6 two-color counters for each student

Alternative Materials: punchout square tiles

Grouping Suggestions: whole group, individual work

---

1. MOTIVATE AND TEACH

LEARN ABOUT IT

Read this story aloud: *Two children wearing red shirts each sat on a swing. Then four children wearing blue shirts each sat on the swings that were left. How many children were swinging in all?*
▶ **How can you use your counters to act out the story?** (Possible answer: Use different colors to show the two groups of children.)
▶ **What are two addition sentences that match the counters on the swings?** (2 + 4 = 6, 4 + 2 = 6)
Have students use their counters to model two different addends that have a sum of 6, then use two crayons to shade in the swings in Exercise 1. Explain that they should color the swings for the first addend and then color the swings for the second addend. Make sure that students write over the dashed plus and equal signs as they write the addition sentence that matches their coloring.
▶ **What turnaround facts did you use to complete the exercises?** (Answers will vary.)

2. CHECK UNDERSTANDING

ERROR ALERT Forgetting that the sum always stays the same and that only the addends change places when writing turnaround facts.

Name _____

Different Ways to Name a Sum

Use 6 two-color counters. Act out the story.

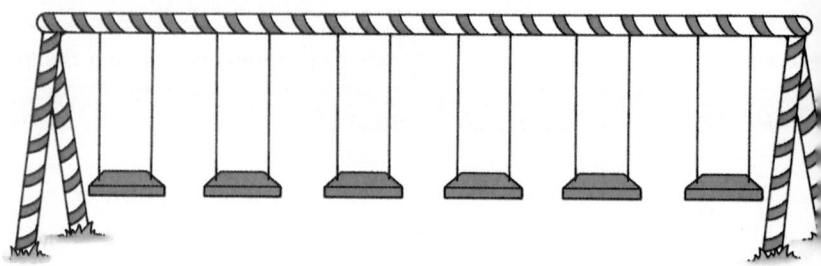

Color different ways to show a sum of 6.
Write the addition sentence to match.　**Answers may vary.**

1. ___ ⊕ ___ ☐
   ____ addend   ____ addend   sum

2. ___ ○ ___ ☐
   ____ addend   ____ addend   sum

3. ___ ○ ___ ☐
   ____ addend   ____ addend   sum

4. ___ ○ ___ ☐
   ____ addend   ____ addend   sum

Add. Write the turnaround fact.
Use counters to check.

5.
```
  4      2
+ 2    + 4
  6      6
```

6.
```
  6      0
+ 0    + 6
  6      6
```

Chapter 1   (nine)

TEACHING OPTIONS

RETEACHING TIPS Have students use two-color counters to model a fact and its turnaround for the sum 5. Then ask them to write the addition sentences that match the counters. Repeat for other sums. They also may follow this process as they complete Reteaching Supplement 5.

ENRICHMENT Copy these turnaround facts and fill in the missing addends.
(3) + 4 = 7   4 + (3) = 7
(2) + 5 = 7   5 + (2) = 7
(6) + 1 = 7   1 + (6) = 7
(0) + 7 = 7   7 + (0) = 7

...se two colors.
...ow different ways to make a sum of 7.
...rite the turnaround facts. Answers may vary.

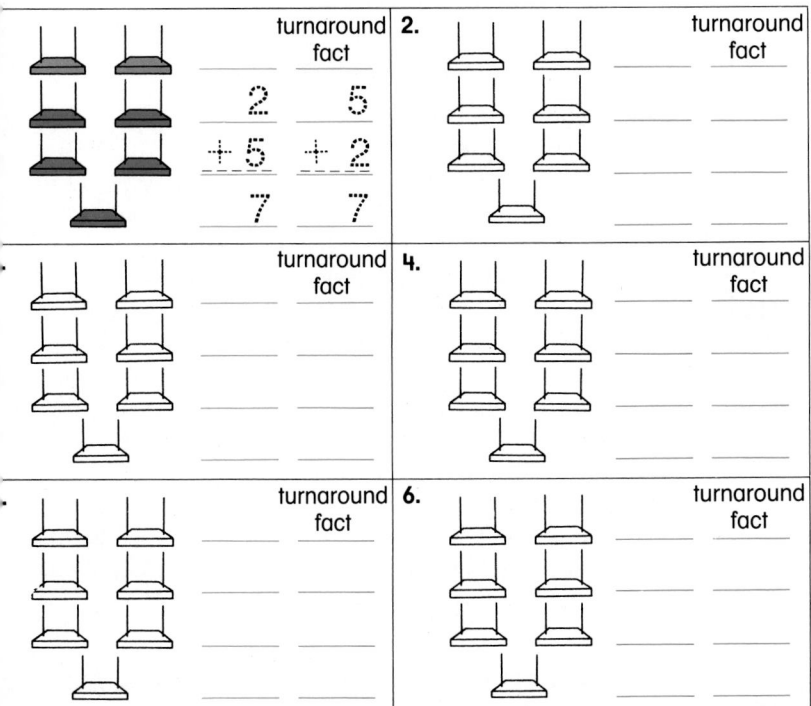

		turnaround fact
	2	5
	+5	+2
	7	7

2. turnaround fact

turnaround fact | **4.** turnaround fact

turnaround fact | **6.** turnaround fact

...E CRITICAL THINKING

Jenny shook out 3 coins
from her bank. One was
a penny. In all, there was 7¢.
Show the other 2 coins.

1 penny

1 nickel

(ten)

Chapter 1

3. PRACTICE AND APPLY

Basic	All
Average	All
Extended	All

PRACTICE

How can you show the two addends in each exercise? (Possible answer: Color the swings for each addend in a different color.) *How will each set of turnaround facts be the same?* (Possible answer: They have the same addends and the same sum.)

APPLY

USING THINKING SKILLS ▶ **How much more money does Jenny need to make 7¢?** (6¢)
▶ **What coins could she use?** (Possible answers: 6 pennies; 1 nickel, 1 penny)
▶ **How many coins does she have?** (3)
▶ **Explain how you could use the addition sentences in Exercise 1 to help you.** (Possible answer: The 5 could stand for a nickel and the 2 for two pennies.)

...LOSE AND ASSESS

...RITE WHAT YOU KNOW

...eread *Six Little Ones* to students. ...sk them to think about how many ...fferent ways the number of little ...ipmunks add up to 6. Then have ...em work in small groups, using ...ounters to show the different ...ombinations of numbers that make ...e same sum and writing them as ...ey discover them.

QUICK QUIZ

Add. Write the turnaround fact to match.

2	(3)	5	(2)	4	(2)
+ 3	+(2)	+ 2	+(5)	+ 2	+(4)
5	(5)	7	(7)	6	(6)

Relating Addition and Subtraction

OBJECTIVE 1-6 To model and write related addition and subtraction sentences

---

QUICK REVIEW

I am thinking of the number 5. What two numbers added together make a sum of 5? (4 + 1, 1 + 4, 3 + 2, 2 + 3, 0 + 5, 5 + 0)

PRIOR KNOWLEDGE

Present a situation such as the following to help students recall adding and subtracting.
3 children are running in a playground.
2 more children join them.
How many children in all? (5)
3 children go inside.
How many children are left? (2)

COMMUNICATION

Reading and Discussing Math List the following words on the chalkboard: **part, whole.** Read the words to the students, then have students read the words together. Encourage students to describe what they know about the words as they are used every day. (Possible responses: *Part* means *some, not the entire thing. Whole* means *everything, all.*) Ask students to explain how these meanings are the same when they are working with addition and subtraction sentences. (Possible answers: You add parts together to get a whole; you break up a whole to get parts.)

EXPLORE AND CONNECT

Materials: paper, pencils
Grouping Suggestion: pairs
Give students the following directions: *Put one hand behind your back with 0, 1, 2, 3, 4, or all your fingers out. When I say* Go! *show your fingers to your partner. Count your fingers and your partner's fingers. Write an addition sentence telling how many fingers each of you extended and how many in all. Now, one of you can take away your fingers. How many fingers are left? Write a subtraction sentence telling how many were in the whole group, what part was taken away, and what part was left.* Play this game many times and have students take turns taking away their fingers.

When students have completed the activity, have them share their addition and subtraction sentences with the class. List the sentences on the chalkboard, focusing on **parts** and **whole** in each pair.

CONNECTIONS Use these anytime.

Problem of the Day

Logic You have a 2-pound weight in one hand and a 5-pound weight in the other. How many pounds do you have in all? (7) You put down the 2-pound weight. How many pounds are you now holding? (5) When did you add or subtract? (added 2 + 5; subtracted 7 − 2)

Math Connection

Number Sense In an addition or subtraction sentence, would the *part* or the *whole* number be the largest? (whole) Will it always be that way? (Yes, unless 0 is one of the parts.) Why? (The whole is the sum of the parts.)

Subject Integration

Physical Fitness Do 4 jumping jacks before lunch. Do 5 jumping jacks after lunch. How many jumping jacks will you do in all? (9) What parts did you add together to find the whole? (4 and 5)

CLASSWORK AND HOMEWORK SUPPLEMENTS

Practice

Skills Maintenance   1-6

Name _____

Relating Addition and Subtraction

Complete the number sentences.

1. $6 + 1 = \underline{7}$ 2. $4 + 2 = \underline{6}$
   $7 - 1 = \underline{6}$ $6 - 2 = \underline{4}$

3. $1 + 4 = \underline{5}$ 4. $7 + 1 = \underline{8}$
   $5 - 4 = \underline{1}$ $8 - 1 = \underline{7}$

5. $2 + 6 = \underline{8}$ 6. $4 + 3 = \underline{7}$
   $8 - 6 = \underline{2}$ $7 - 3 = \underline{4}$

7. $2 + 3 = \underline{5}$ 8. $3 + 1 = \underline{4}$
   $5 - 3 = \underline{2}$ $4 - 1 = \underline{3}$

9. $5 + 2 = \underline{7}$ 10. $5 + 1 = \underline{6}$
   $7 - 5 = \underline{2}$ $6 - 1 = \underline{5}$

11. $2 + 2 = \underline{4}$ 12. $3 + 3 = \underline{6}$
    $4 - 2 = \underline{2}$ $6 - 3 = \underline{3}$

6   Use with text pages 11 – 12.   PS-2

Building Thinking Skills

Math Reasoning   1-6

Name _____

Changing Rings

Look at the rings.   ◯◯◯◯◯◯◯
How many are there? $\underline{7}$
Predict how many addition sentences with 2 addends you
can show with these rings. ___ Now write them.
Next to each addition sentence you write,
draw and color the rings to match.

$6 + 1 = 7$
$1 + 6 = 7$
$5 + 2 = 7$
$2 + 5 = 7$
$4 + 3 = 7$
$3 + 4 = 7$
$0 + 7 = 7$
$7 + 0 = 7$

Look at the rings.   ◯◯◯◯◯
How many are there? $\underline{5}$
Predict how many subtraction sentences you can show
with these rings. ___ Now write them.
Next to each subtraction sentence you write,
draw and color the rings to match.

$5 - 1 = 4$
$5 - 4 = 1$
$5 - 2 = 3$
$5 - 3 = 2$
$5 - 0 = 5$
$5 - 5 = 0$

6   Use with text pages 11 – 12.   TS-2

Reteaching

Skills Review   1-6

Name _____

Relating Addition and Subtraction

Count the beads.
◯◯◯◯◯◯◯◯

Write the addition sentence.
part   part   whole

Count the beads.
◯◯◯◯◯◯◯

Write the subtraction sentence.
whole   part   part

Count the beads.
Complete the number sentences.

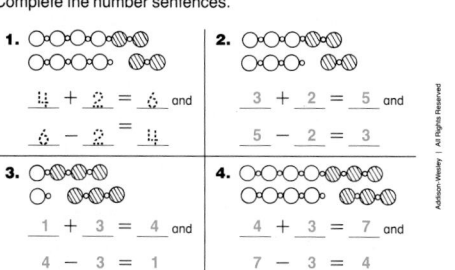

1.
   $\underline{4} + \underline{2} = \underline{6}$ and
   $\underline{6} - \underline{2} = \underline{4}$

2.
   $\underline{3} + \underline{2} = \underline{5}$ and
   $\underline{5} - \underline{2} = \underline{3}$

3.
   $\underline{1} + \underline{3} = \underline{4}$ and
   $\underline{4} - \underline{3} = \underline{1}$

4.
   $\underline{4} + \underline{3} = \underline{7}$ and
   $\underline{7} - \underline{3} = \underline{4}$

6   Use with text pages 11 – 12.   RS-2

Challenges

Cooperative Activities   1-6

Name _____

Bingo!

Work with a friend to make 16 cards for this game.
Write one subtraction fact on each card.

$6 - 3 = 3$ $7 - 3 = 4$ $6 - 1 = 5$ $6 - 2 = 4$
$7 - 5 = 2$ $7 - 1 = 6$ $6 - 0 = 6$ $5 - 4 = 1$
$8 - 8 = 0$ $8 - 1 = 7$ $5 - 2 = 3$ $5 - 5 = 0$
$8 - 6 = 2$ $8 - 3 = 5$ $8 - 4 = 4$ $4 - 2 = 2$

Complete the addition facts on the game board below.

You need 2 players, counters, the game cards you made.
Mix up the cards and put them facedown.
Pick a card. Find the matching addition fact.
Cover the addition fact with a counter.
Play until someone has four in a row.

$3 + 3 = \underline{6}$	$4 + 3 = \underline{7}$	$5 + 1 = \underline{6}$	$4 + 2 = \underline{6}$
$5 + 2 = \underline{7}$	$6 + 1 = \underline{7}$	$6 + 0 = \underline{6}$	$1 + 4 = \underline{5}$
$8 + 0 = \underline{8}$	$7 + 1 = \underline{8}$	$3 + 2 = \underline{5}$	$0 + 5 = \underline{5}$
$2 + 6 = \underline{8}$	$5 + 3 = \underline{8}$	$4 + 4 = \underline{8}$	$2 + 2 = \underline{4}$

6   Use with text pages 11 – 12.   CS-2

OPTIONS FOR INDIVIDUAL NEEDS

Basic

Exercises All

Supplements
Reteaching 6 or
Practice 6
Challenges 6

Average

Exercises All

Supplements
Practice 6
Challenges 6 or
Thinking Skills 6

Extended

Exercises All

Supplements
Challenges 6
Thinking Skills 6

Other Resources:
Math In Stride, pp. 18-20
Explorations, pp. 50-51

LESSON PLAN 1-6

OBJECTIVE 1-6
To model and write related addition and subtraction sentences

Material: Cube-A-Links, two-color counters, TA 3 (Graph Paper)

Alternative Materials: colored blocks, punchout square tiles

Grouping Suggestions: pairs, individual work

1. MOTIVATE AND TEACH

LEARN ABOUT IT

Have students practice working with cubes by making trains. Begin by asking students to make 2 one-color trains with 5 or fewer cubes. Have students join them for addition and snap them apart for subtraction.

▶ **In Exercise 1, why are the red cubes next to each other?** (Colors are grouped together so they can be added as an entire part.)

▶ **How do the number sentences describe the cubes?** (Possible answer: The addition sentence joins the red and blue cubes and tells the whole amount. The subtraction sentence tells how the whole is separated into one part and then another.)

▶ **What number will be the same in Exercise 2 for each pair of sentences?** (6; the whole)

▶ **How will each addition and subtraction sentence in each exercise be the same?** (They will use the same numbers.)

▶ **What will be different?** (the order of the numbers; the operation signs)

2. CHECK UNDERSTANDING

ERROR ALERT Adding when they should write a subtraction sentence.

Name _____

Relating Addition and Subtraction

Work with a partner. Use cubes of two different colors to make a train. Color to show your train. Write the addition sentence to match. Snap off a part. Write a subtraction sentence about it. **Answers may vary.**

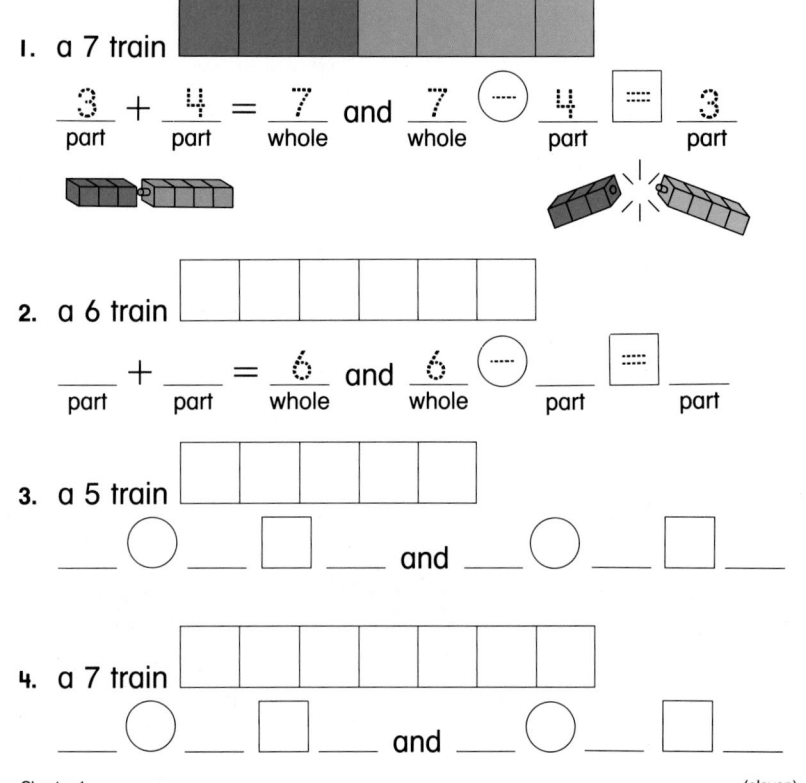

1. a 7 train

$$\underset{\text{part}}{3} + \underset{\text{part}}{4} = \underset{\text{whole}}{7} \text{ and } \underset{\text{whole}}{7} \bigcirc \underset{\text{part}}{4} \boxed{} \underset{\text{part}}{3}$$

2. a 6 train

$$\underset{\text{part}}{\rule{1cm}{0.4pt}} + \underset{\text{part}}{\rule{1cm}{0.4pt}} = \underset{\text{whole}}{6} \text{ and } \underset{\text{whole}}{6} \bigcirc \underset{\text{part}}{\rule{1cm}{0.4pt}} \boxed{} \underset{\text{part}}{\rule{1cm}{0.4pt}}$$

3. a 5 train

_____ ◯ _____ ☐ _____ and _____ ◯ _____ ☐ _____

4. a 7 train

_____ ◯ _____ ☐ _____ and _____ ◯ _____ ☐ _____

Chapter 1   (eleven)

TEACHING OPTIONS

RETEACHING TIPS Supply students with grid paper. Have them color 1 to 4 squares with two colors. Then ask them to write an addition sentence describing the train, cover one color, and write a subtraction sentence. Use Reteaching Supplement 6 to provide help in relating addition and subtraction.

COMPUTER Math Blaster!, Davidson & Associates © 1983 For students who require extra practice. Students play an arcade-style game to practice their + and − skills. Begin at the first level of difficulty with *Look and Learn*, and then *Build Your Skill*. Each game requires 15-20 minutes.

nish the number sentences.

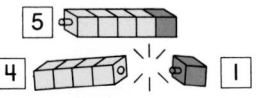
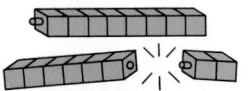

$4 + 1 = \underline{5}$ and $5 - 1 = \underline{4}$

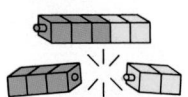

$6 + 2 = \underline{8}$ and $8 - 2 = \underline{6}$

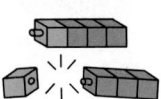

$3 + 2 = \underline{5}$ and $5 - 2 = \underline{3}$

$1 + 3 = \underline{4}$ and $4 - 3 = \underline{1}$

MIDCHAPTER REVIEW/QUIZ

unt on or back.

13, 14, 15, $\underline{16}$, $\underline{17}$ 2. 15, 14, 13, $\underline{12}$, $\underline{11}$

rite what the picture shows.

$$\begin{array}{r} 3 \\ + 1 \\ \hline 4 \end{array}$$

4.

$$\begin{array}{r} 2 \\ + 4 \\ \hline 6 \end{array}$$

oss out to take away. Then subtract.

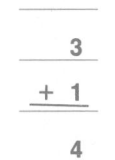

$$\begin{array}{r} 5 \\ - 2 \\ \hline 3 \end{array}$$

6.

$$\begin{array}{r} 3 \\ - 1 \\ \hline 2 \end{array}$$

(twelve)   Chapter 1

3. PRACTICE AND APPLY

Basic	All, Midchapter Review/Quiz
Average	All, Midchapter Review/Quiz
Extended	All, Midchapter Review/Quiz

1-6

PRACTICE

How will you find the answers to the exercises on page 12? (Add parts; take away from the whole.) *How do the cubes help you?* (They describe the sentences and show you what to do; you can count them to prove your answer.)

APPLY

▶ **Why do the addition and subtraction sentences in these exercises have the same numbers?** (Possible answer: They each have the same whole and the same parts.)

MIDCHAPTER REVIEW/QUIZ

ITEM ANALYSIS The following table correlates the Midchapter Review/Quiz items with lesson objectives.

Items	Objectives
1, 2	1-1
3, 4	1-2
5, 6	1-3

LOSE AND ASSESS

RITE WHAT YOU KNOW
emind students of events in the apter story. Then have them make situations similar to the following d use cubes to show the subtraction ntence and the related addition ntence. *There were 6 little ipmunks. Two were on a seesaw d the rest were on the erry-go-round.* $(6 - 2 = 4; 2 + 4$ 6)

QUICK QUIZ

Copy and complete the number sentences.
$3 + 5 = \underline{(8)}$ and $8 - 5 = \underline{(3)}$
$6 + 1 = \underline{(7)}$ and $7 - 1 = \underline{(6)}$
$4 + 2 = \underline{(6)}$ and $6 - 2 = \underline{(4)}$

Related Subtraction Facts

OBJECTIVE 1-7   To model and finish related subtraction facts

PREBOOK ACTIVITIES

QUICK REVIEW

Find the sums.

3 + 2 = (5)	2 + 3 = (5)	4 + 3 =
3 + 4 = (7)	6 + 0 = (6)	0 + 6 =
1 + 3 = (4)	3 + 1 = (4)	5 + 2 =
2 + 5 = (7)	4 + 2 = (6)	2 + 4 =

PRIOR KNOWLEDGE

Visualize a number sentence for this story.
5 children are running.
1 child stops.
How many children are still running? (5 − 1 = 4) *Who can tell another story that shows 5 − 1 = 4? Who can tell a story that shows 5 − 4 = 1?* (Answers will vary.)

COMMUNICATION

Reading and Discussing Math   Write this sentence on the chalkboard: _____ is **related to** _____. Read the phrase **related to** to students and ask them to describe what it means to be related to someone. (Possible answers: to be connected in some way, to be part of a family) Ask volunteers to fill in the blanks in the sentence with their name and the name of someone to whom they are related and to read the sentence aloud. *How are the number sentences 6 − 1 = 5 and 6 − 5 = 1 related to each other?* (Possible answer: They both have the same numbers but two of the numbers change places.)

EXPLORE AND CONNECT

Materials: subtraction flashcards, 10 Cube-A-Links for each pair of students
Alternative Materials: punchout square tiles
Grouping Suggestion: pairs
Provide each pair of students with one train of cubes. Place a flashcard such as 8 − 5 = _____ on the chalkledge. *How ca you find the answer using your cubes?* (Possible answer: Start with 8 cubes, then break off 5 cubes to see how many are lef When partners agree, ask them to find another subtraction fac that has the same numbers. Have students use their cubes to find the answer. *How are these two number sentences related* (Possible answer: Both sentences have the same numbers, but two of the numbers switch places.) Have partners take turns using the cubes to explore other related subtraction facts. One student models a subtraction fact and the partner models the related fact.

CONNECTIONS   Use these anytime.

Problem of the Day

Logic   Draw a picture to show the answer to this problem.
There are 8 birds.
There are 6 nests.
How many birds do not have their own nest? (2)

Subject Integration

Language Arts   Work with a partner to identify objects in the room that are related to one another. For example: a pen is related to paper. Draw a picture to show the related pairs of objects.

Counting Patterns

Bingo   Have the first person in a circle say *1*. Continue counting with the next person, but when a 2 or a number containing 2 comes up, say *Bingo* instead of the number. Repeat this game counting backward.

CLASSWORK AND HOMEWORK SUPPLEMENTS

Practice

Skills Maintenance   1-7

Name _____

Related Subtraction Facts

How many are there in each part?
Subtract.

1.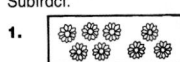
   5   3   4   3
   8 − 3 = 5   7 − 3 = 4
   8 − 5 = 3   7 − 4 = 3

2.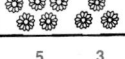
   5   2   7   1
   7 − 2 = 5   8 − 1 = 7
   7 − 5 = 2   8 − 7 = 1

Subtract.

3.
8	8	8	8	8
−4	−7	−2	−5	−3
4	1	6	3	5

4.
7	7	7	7	7
−5	−1	−3	−6	−2
2	6	4	1	5

PS-2   Use with text pages 13–14.   7

Building Thinking Skills

Family Math   1-7

Name _____

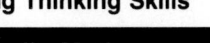
> Dear Family,
> We are learning about subtraction facts in our math class. You may enjoy doing this activity with your child to provide additional experiences with subtraction. Use a clothes hanger and clothespins to model subtraction facts shown below.

You need: 2 clothes hangers and 16 clothespins or paper clips.

Take turns.
Think of a subtraction fact.
Show it with clothespins.
Say it out loud.
Write the subtraction fact.
Then show, say, and
write the related fact.

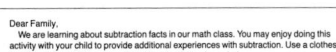
5 − 2 = 3

5 − 3 = 2

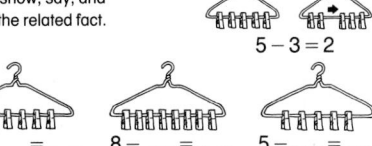
6 − ___ =   8 − ___ =   5 − ___ =

Show and write the related facts here.

6 − ___ =   8 − ___ =   5 − ___ =

TS-2   Use with text pages 13–14.   7

Reteaching

Skills Review   1-7

Name _____

Related Subtraction Facts

Subtract from 8.

1.
   8 − 1 = 7
   8 − 7 = 1

2. 8 − 2 = 6
   8 − 6 = 2

Subtract from 7.

3.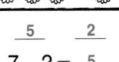
   7 − 2 = 5
   7 − 5 = 2

4.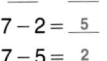
   7 − 3 = 4
   7 − 4 = 3

Subtract.

5.
8	8	6	6	7	7
−3	−5	−2	−4	−1	−6
5	3	4	2	6	1

6.
7	7	8	8	5	5
−3	−4	−2	−6	−3	−2
4	3	6	2	2	3

RS-2   Use with text pages 13–14.   7

Challenges

Creative Thinking   1-7

Name _____

Look! Up in the Sky!

Write the answers in the circles.
Put your pencil on the words "Start here."
Draw a line between the related subtraction facts.

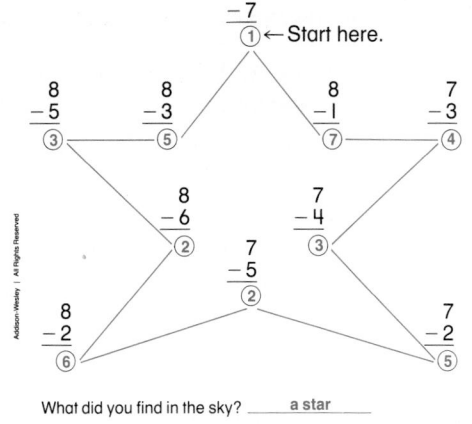

What did you find in the sky? ___ a star ___

CS-2   Use with text pages 13–14.   7

Addison-Wesley / All Rights Reserved

OPTIONS FOR INDIVIDUAL NEEDS

Basic

Exercises All

Supplements
Reteaching 7 or
Practice 7
Thinking Skills 7

Average

Exercises All

Supplements
Practice 7
Challenges 7 or
Thinking Skills 7

Extended

Exercises All

Supplements
Challenges 7
Thinking Skills 7

Other Resources:
Math in Stride, pp. 18-20
Workjobs, pp. 198-199
Workjobs for Parents, pp. 114-115
Mathematics Book A, p. 28

LESSON PLAN 1-7

OBJECTIVE 1-7
To model and finish related subtraction facts

> **Materials:** 10 Cube-A-Links for each student, penny punchouts, blank flashcards
>
> **Alternative Materials:** punchout square tiles
>
> **Grouping Suggestions:** individual work, cooperative learning groups of 3

1. MOTIVATE AND TEACH

LEARN ABOUT IT

Write the following subtraction facts on the chalkboard: $8 - 1 = 7$, $7 - 2 = 5$, $7 - 5 = 2$, $9 - 6 = 3$, $8 - 7 = 1$, $9 - 3 = 6$. Ask volunteers to draw lines to connect the related facts. *How do you know which facts are related?* (Possible answer: Related subtraction facts have the same three numbers, but the last two numbers in the sentence trade places.)
▶ **How do the cubes show the related facts?** (Possible response: They show 7 as the whole with 3 and 4 as the parts that make up the whole.)
▶ **How could you use your cubes to show the facts in Exercise 1?** (Possible answer: Snap off 2 of 6 cubes to get 4; snap off 4 of 6 cubes to get 2.) Make sure students use their cubes to complete the exercises.

2. CHECK UNDERSTANDING

ERROR ALERT Writing the same problem twice instead of writing the related fact.

Name _____

Related Subtraction Facts

Whole, take away part, another part is left.

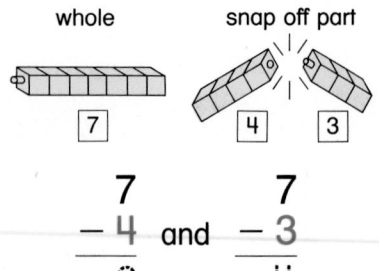

whole   snap off part

7   4   3

$$7 - 4$$ and $$7 - 3$$
3   4

Use cubes. Make a train for the top number in each exercise. Snap off the number shown in green. Write the number that is left.

1. $6 - 2$ and $6 - 4$	2. $8 - 1$ and $8 - 7$
4 2	7 1
3. $5 - 4$ and $5 - 1$	4. $7 - 2$ and $7 - 5$
1 4	5 2
5. $8 - 3$ and $8 - 5$	6. $6 - 1$ and $6 - 5$
5 3	5 1

Chapter 1   (thirteen)

TEACHING OPTIONS

RETEACHING TIPS Write $6 - 4 = 2$ on the chalkboard. Ask students to show that number sentence using a train of cubes and its related fact with another train. Then have students use their cubes to show other related facts. For further practice, use Reteaching Supplement 7.

ENRICHMENT Have students write the related subtraction facts that can be made with each group of numbers.
1, 6, 7 ($7 - 1 = 6$, $7 - 6 = 1$)
1, 8, 9 ($9 - 8 = 1$, $9 - 1 = 8$)
2, 3, 5 ($5 - 3 = 2$, $5 - 2 = 3$)

ubtract. Use cubes to help.

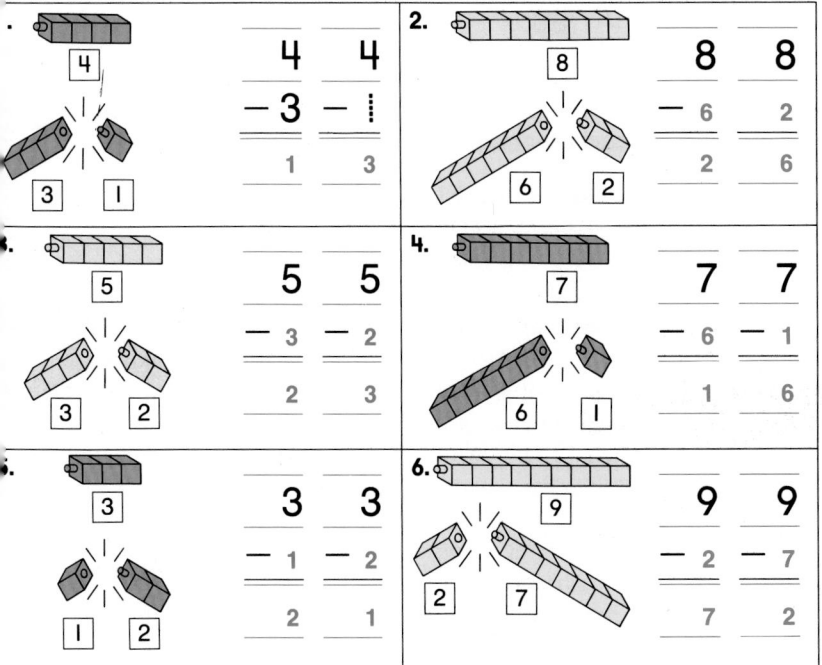

	4 4	2.	8 8
	-3 $-$		-6 2
3 1	1 3	6 2	2 6

	5 5	4.	7 7
5	-3 -2	7	-6 -1
3 2	2 3	6 1	1 6

	3 3	6.	9 9
3	-1 -2	9	-2 -7
1 2	2 1	2 7	7 2

ROBLEM SOLVING

Leah had 7
She gave 2 away. Did she
have enough pennies left
to trade for ?

Ring your answer.   (yes)   no

(fourteen)   Chapter 1

---

3. PRACTICE AND APPLY

Basic	All
Average	All
Extended	All

PRACTICE

*Why is the cube train the same as the top
number in each subtraction exercise?*
(The cube train and the top number
represent the whole.) *What do the bottom
sets of cubes and the bottom numbers
represent?* (the parts)

APPLY

**PROBLEM SOLVING ▶ How can
you use the penny punchouts to help
you find the answer?** (Possible answer:
Count out 7 pennies, then take away 2.)
**▶ How do you know Leah can trade
for a nickel?** (5 pennies is the same as 1
nickel.)

LOSE AND ASSESS

HOW WHAT YOU KNOW
ovide each cooperative group of 3
th blank flashcards. Ask one student
write a subtraction fact on one
rd. Another student writes the
lated fact on another card, and a
ird uses counters to check the
lated facts. Remind students to take
rns at each job.

QUICK QUIZ

Draw lines to match the related facts.
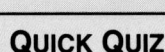
$6 - 1 = 5$ $9 - 6 = 3$ $9 - 1 = 8$
$9 - 3 = 6$ $6 - 5 = 1$ $9 - 8 = 1$

Fact Families

OBJECTIVE 1-8   To model and write fact families

PREBOOK ACTIVITIES

QUICK REVIEW

Add or subtract.

3 + 2 = _____ (5)	6 + 2 = _____ (8)
2 + 3 = _____ (5)	6 − 2 = _____ (4)
5 + 3 = _____ (8)	7 − 3 = _____ (4)
5 − 3 = _____ (2)	4 + 3 = _____ (7)

PRIOR KNOWLEDGE

Tell this story to help students recall the concept of addition and subtraction: *You have 5 blocks. A friend gives you 3 more. How many blocks do you have?* (8) *You decide to give 3 of your blocks to another friend. How many blocks do you have now?* (5) *Can you tell about a time when you shared something in this way or someone shared with you?* (Answers will vary.)

COMMUNICATION

Discussing Math   Write the word **family** on the chalkboard. *What does it mean to be a part of a family?* (Possible answers: to be related to people, to have parents, brothers, sisters, cousins) Write 4 + 3 = 7, 3 + 4 = 7, 7 − 3 = 4, and 7 − 4 = 3 on the board. *Why do you think we call these facts a family?* (Possible answer: The same numbers are used in all the facts, but they are arranged in different ways.) *What numbers are used in this fact family?* (4, 3, 7)

EXPLORE AND CONNECT

Materials: Cube-A-Links in 2 colors for each pair
Alternative Materials: punchout square tiles
Grouping Suggestion: pairs
Tell this story: *A family of 5 shiny robots went for a walk. Suddenly, rain began to fall. Two robots rusted and could no move. The others walked to the nearest town for he* Have pairs of students use cubes of one color to show the rus robots and cubes of another color to show the ones that went for help. Then have them model the following situations and write number sentences for each.
All the robots together. (2 + 3 = 5 or 3 + 2 = 5)
The number of robots left after some went away. (5 − 3 = 2
The number of robots that did not rust. (5 − 2 = 3)
How are the number sentences alike? (All use the same 3 numbers.) *How are they different?* (Numbers are in different order; some use addition, and others use subtraction.)

CONNECTIONS   Use these anytime.

Problem of the Day

Count by Twos   6 panda bears are looking for food at the pond. They all got their front feet wet. How many feet got wet? (12)

Counting Patterns

Show this pattern with cubes: 2, 4, 6. What is the pattern? (skip counting by 2s) Use these numbers to write four addition and subtraction sentences. (2 + 4 = 6, 4 + 2 = 6, 6 − 2 = 4, 6 − 4 = 2)

Math Connection

Money   Sally had some pennies. Tom gave her 3 more pennies. Now Sally has 8 pennies. How many pennies did Sally have in the beginning? (5)

CLASSWORK AND HOMEWORK SUPPLEMENTS

Practice

Skills Maintenance   1-8

Name _____

Fact Families

Count the apples on the tree.
Count the apples in the basket.
Count how many apples in all.
Finish the apple fact family. Color the apples.

1.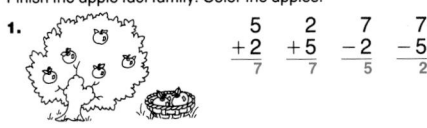

$$\begin{array}{r} 5 \\ +2 \\ \hline 7 \end{array} \quad \begin{array}{r} 2 \\ +5 \\ \hline 7 \end{array} \quad \begin{array}{r} 7 \\ -2 \\ \hline 5 \end{array} \quad \begin{array}{r} 7 \\ -5 \\ \hline 2 \end{array}$$

Pears and bananas grow on trees, too.
Finish each fact family.
Color the fruits.

2.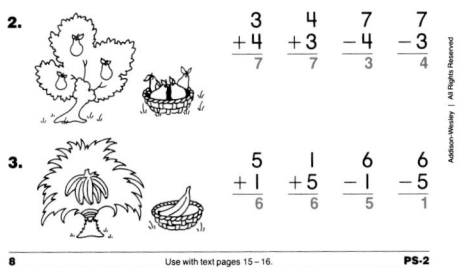

$$\begin{array}{r} 3 \\ +4 \\ \hline 7 \end{array} \quad \begin{array}{r} 4 \\ +3 \\ \hline 7 \end{array} \quad \begin{array}{r} 7 \\ -4 \\ \hline 3 \end{array} \quad \begin{array}{r} 7 \\ -3 \\ \hline 4 \end{array}$$

3.

$$\begin{array}{r} 5 \\ +1 \\ \hline 6 \end{array} \quad \begin{array}{r} 1 \\ +5 \\ \hline 6 \end{array} \quad \begin{array}{r} 6 \\ -1 \\ \hline 5 \end{array} \quad \begin{array}{r} 6 \\ -5 \\ \hline 1 \end{array}$$

8   Use with text pages 15–16.   **PS-2**

Building Thinking Skills

Math Reasoning   1-8

Name _____

Flying Kites

Look at the tail on kite 1.
How many bows are shaded? __1__ How many are
white? __4__ Write the fact family that matches the bows
on the kite. Do the same for kites 2 and 3.
For kite 4, decide how many bows to draw.
Shade some. Leave some white.
Give your page to a friend to write the fact family.

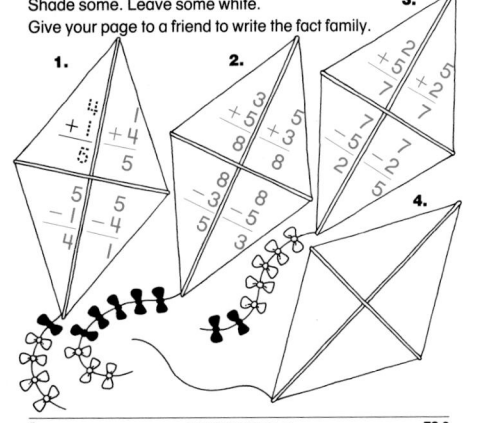

8   Use with text pages 15–16.   **TS-2**

Reteaching

Skills Review   1-8

Name _____

Fact Families

$$\begin{array}{r} 5 \\ +3 \\ \hline \end{array} \quad \begin{array}{r} 3 \\ +5 \\ \hline \end{array} \quad \begin{array}{r} 8 \\ -3 \\ \hline \end{array} \quad \begin{array}{r} 8 \\ -5 \\ \hline \end{array}$$

Add or subtract.
Ring each fact family.

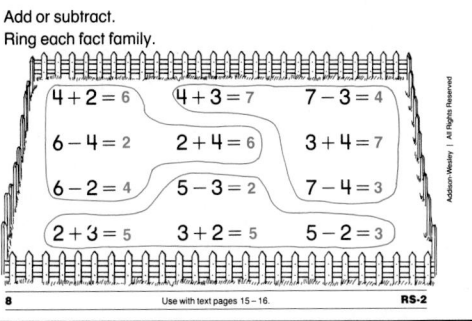

$4+2=6$ $4+3=7$ $7-3=4$

$6-4=2$ $2+4=6$ $3+4=7$

$6-2=4$ $5-3=2$ $7-4=3$

$2+3=5$ $3+2=5$ $5-2=3$

8   Use with text pages 15–16.   **RS-2**

Challenges

Data Analysis   1-8

Name _____

Amazing Fact Families

Complete the fact families in the six boxes below.
Then trace the path from one part of each fact
family to the other part. Use a different color
crayon to connect each fact family.

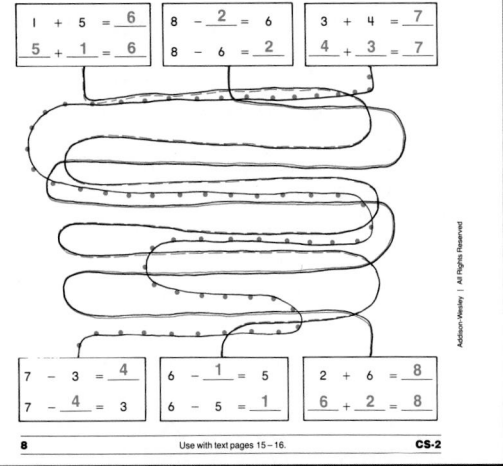

$1 + 5 = 6$ $8 - 2 = 6$ $3 + 4 = 7$
$5 + 1 = 6$ $8 - 6 = 2$ $4 + 3 = 7$

$7 - 3 = 4$ $6 - 1 = 5$ $2 + 6 = 8$
$7 - 4 = 3$ $6 - 5 = 1$ $6 + 2 = 8$

8   Use with text pages 15–16.   **CS-2**

OPTIONS FOR INDIVIDUAL NEEDS

1-8

Basic

Exercises All

Supplements
Reteaching 8 or
Practice 8
Challenges 8

Average

Exercises All

Supplements
Practice 8
Challenges 8 or
Thinking Skills 8

Extended

Exercises All

Supplements
Challenges 8
Thinking Skills 8

Other Resources:
Math In Stride, pp. 28-29
Mathematics Book A, p. 28

LESSON PLAN 1-8

OBJECTIVE 1-8
To model and write fact families

Materials: 18 Cube-A-Links divided equally, 2 colors per pair

Alternative Materials: punchout square tiles

Grouping Suggestions: whole group, pairs

1. MOTIVATE AND TEACH

LEARN ABOUT IT

Write this fact family on the chalkboard: $4 + 2 = 6$, $2 + 4 = 6$, $6 - 4 = 2$, $6 - 2 = 4$. Have students model the number sentences with cubes.
▶ **Which facts are the turnaround addition facts?** ($4 + 2 = 6$, $2 + 4 = 6$)
▶ **Which are the related subtraction facts?** ($6 - 4 = 2$, $6 - 2 = 4$)
▶ **How are the turnaround addition facts related to the subtraction facts?** (Possible answers: They are part of the same fact family; they all use the same 3 numbers.)
Have students use their cubes to model the fact family at the top of page 15. *How many numbers are there in a fact family?* (3)
▶ **Why do you need only 3 numbers to make a fact family?** (Possible answer: Two numbers stand for the parts; one number stands for the whole.)
▶ **Think about the addition sentence $4 + 4 = 8$. How many facts are in this fact family? Why?** (2; the parts are the same.)
▶ **If you know that $4 + 3 = 7$, what other facts can you write?** ($3 + 4 = 7$, $7 - 4 = 3$, $7 - 3 = 4$)

2. CHECK UNDERSTANDING

ERROR ALERT Confusing addition and subtraction by not paying attention to signs.

Name _____

Fact Families

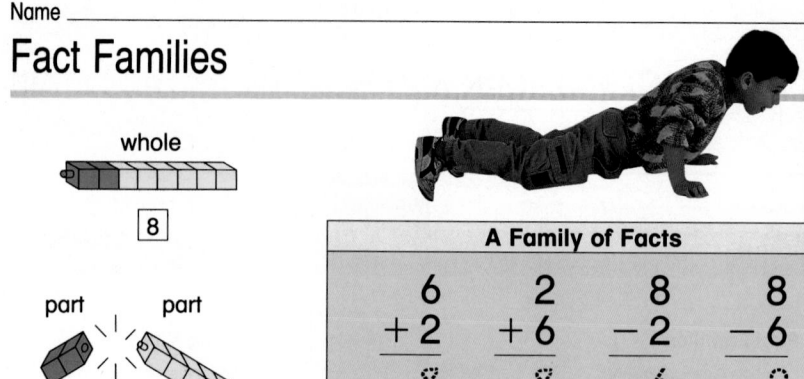

whole

8

part   part

2   6

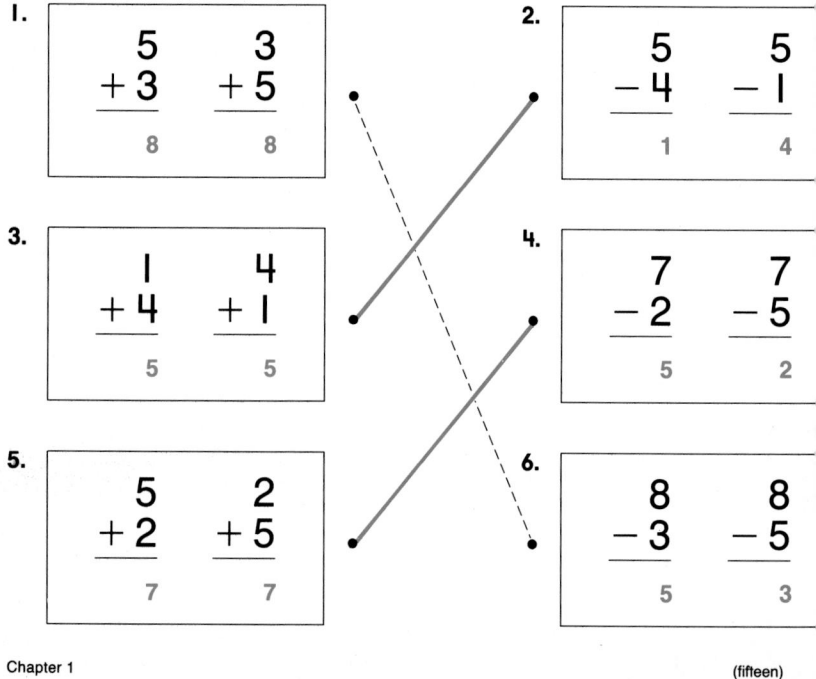

A Family of Facts

6	2	8	8
$+2$	$+6$	-2	-6
8	8	6	2

Add or subtract. Draw lines to show the fact family. Use cubes to check.

1.
5	3
$+3$	$+5$
8	8

2.
5	5
-4	-1
1	4

3.
1	4
$+4$	$+1$
5	5

4.
7	7
-2	-5
5	2

5.
5	2
$+2$	$+5$
7	7

6.
8	8
-3	-5
5	3

Chapter 1

(fifteen)

TEACHING OPTIONS

RETEACHING TIPS Discuss the meaning of *addition* and *subtraction:* part + part = whole; whole − part = part. Have students model fact families with cubes and write the matching number sentences, paying special attention to the addition and subtraction signs. Assign Reteaching Supplement 8.

ENRICHMENT Provide each student with 8 counters. Have them use the counters to help find the missing sign.
$6 + 2 = 5 \square 3$ (+)
$8 - 2 = 5 \square 1$ (+)
$7 - 3 = 6 \square 2$ (−)
$2 + 1 = 8 \square 5$ (−)

inish the fact families.
se cubes to help.

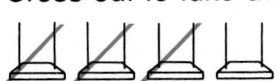 [7] [3] [4]	3 4 +4 +3 —— —— 7 7	7 7 −4 −3 —— —— 3 4
[6] [1] [5]	1 5 +5 +1 —— —— 6 6	6 6 −1 −5 —— —— 5 1
[9] [2] [7]	2 7 +7 +2 —— —— 9 9	9 9 −2 −7 —— —— 7 2

MIXED REVIEW

Count on from 7.

7, _8_ , _9_ , _10_

5. Count back from 17.

17, _16_ , _15_ , _14_

Cross out to take away. Then subtract.

4 − 3 = _1_
difference

6 (sixteen)   Chapter 1

3. PRACTICE AND APPLY

Basic	All, Mixed Review
Average	All, Mixed Review
Extended	All, Mixed Review

1-8

PRACTICE

For page 16, have students model the fact families with cubes. *How can turnaround facts help you find the difference for the related subtraction facts?* (They are all part of the same fact family.)

APPLY

▶ **Why is the sum of the 2 addition sentences always the same?** (Possible answer: The addends are the same.)

▶ **Why are the answers for the subtraction sentences different?** (Possible answer: A different part is being subtracted each time.)

MIXED REVIEW *How is Exercise 1 different from Exercise 2?* (Exercise 1 is counting on by 1s; Exercise 2 is counting back by 1s.)

CLOSE AND ASSESS

HOW WHAT YOU KNOW

rovide each pair of students with ubes. Write 3 numbers in a fact mily, such as 3, 5, and 8, on the halkboard. Have students take turns odeling the facts with cubes, writing e matching addition and subtraction entences, and checking the answers. epeat with 3 and 6.

QUICK QUIZ

Write each fact family.
1, 5, 6,   (1 + 5 = 6, 5 + 1 = 6,
           6 − 1 = 5, 6 − 5 = 1)
3, 5, 8   (3 + 5 = 8, 5 + 3 = 8,
           8 − 3 = 5, 8 − 5 = 3)

LESSON OPTIONS 1-9

Problem Solving: Finding Missing Data

OBJECTIVE 1-9   To solve problems by finding missing data

PREBOOK ACTIVITIES

QUICK REVIEW

Write the 2 addition sentences and 2 subtraction sentences for each group of numbers.

2, 3, 5   (2 + 3 = 5, 3 + 2 = 5, 5 − 3 = 2, 5 − 2 = 3)
7, 3, 4   (3 + 4 = 7, 4 + 3 = 7, 7 − 3 = 4, 7 − 4 = 3)
1, 8, 7   (1 + 7 = 8, 7 + 1 = 8, 8 − 1 = 7, 8 − 7 = 1)
4, 2, 6   (4 + 2 = 6, 2 + 4 = 6, 6 − 4 = 2, 6 − 2 = 4)

PRIOR KNOWLEDGE

Draw a sign on the chalkboard and write *Fun Fair, Friday Night, Come One Come All!* Ask students to read the sign. *Pretend that you want to go to the Fun Fair. Does the sign tell you all the information you need to know? What information is missing?* (time and place) Rewrite the sign together, asking students to supply the missing information.

COMMUNICATION

Reading and Discussing Math   Write the word **data** on the chalkboard. Read the word and explain that another word for *data* is *information*. Write the following sentence on the board. Have students read it and fill in the blank:
An important piece of data about me is _____. (Answers will vary.)
Tell students that math word problems often have different actions in them. *Name some actions that you know.* (Possible answers: running, throwing, swimming) List some actions on the board and invite students to act them out.

EXPLORE AND CONNECT

COOPERATIVE ACTIVITY

Grouping Suggestion: small groups
Listen to the story. Make up the missing data. Write the number sentence. *Jay's dog had puppies. She had 3 brown ones and some black ones. How many puppies did she have in all?* (Possible answer: She had 2 black puppies. 3 + 2 = 5)

TEACHING ACTIONS

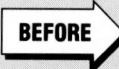 **BEFORE**
▶ **Describe the data in this story.** (Possible answer: A dog had 3 brown and some black puppies.)
▶ **What question does the story ask?** (How many puppies did the dog have in all?)
▶ **Explain what data is missing and why it is needed to solve the problem.** (Possible answer: The missing data is the number of black puppies. You need that number to add to the number of brown puppies.)

 **DURING**
▶ **How will you add the missing data to the story?** (Possible answer: Add a number that makes sense before *black ones*.)
▶ **What can you use to help you find the answer?** (Possible answer: Use counters to show the number of brown and black puppies; add the counters to find the answer.)

 **AFTER**
▶ **How can you check your answer?** (Possible answer: Draw a picture of 3 brown puppies and your number of black puppies. Count to see if your answer matches the answer in your number sentence.)
Have groups illustrate their data for the problem and write the matching number sentence.

CONNECTIONS   Use these anytime.

Problem of the Day

Missing Data   Read the story. Make up the missing data. Write the number sentence.
Mary had 6 drawings. She gave some to her grandmother. How many drawings does she have left? (Answers will vary. For example: She gave 2 to her grandmother. 6 − 2 = 4)

Subject Integration

Art   Read the story. Decide if it has a put-together action or a take-away action. Draw a picture of what happens in the story.
Sue builds birdhouses. She built 3 small ones, and now she is making 1 large one. How many birdhouses will she have? (put together)

Life Skills

Data for Jobs   Match the data to the person who would use it.
doctor — 29 Spruce Ave.
mail carrier — launch time 9:00 a.m.
astronaut — 2 cups of flour
cook — temperature of 101°F
race-car driver — 200 laps

Problem Solving Strategy: Choose The Operation

• solve problems using the strategy Choose the Operation

CLASSWORK AND HOMEWORK SUPPLEMENTS

Practice

Critical Thinking   1-9

Name _____

Problem Solving Strategy: Choose the Operation

Read the story. Think about the action. Then write the number sentence.

1. Cheryl mailed 3 letters on Monday. She mailed 5 letters on Friday. How many letters did she mail in all?

   3 ⊕ 5 = 8

2. Randy wanted to mail 9 letters at the post office. But he lost 2 letters on the way. How many letters did he mail?

   9 ⊖ 2 = 7

3. Corrie mailed 4 packages at the post office. She mailed 5 letters, too. How many more letters than packages did she mail?

   5 ⊖ 4 = 1

4. Matt mailed 6 letters first class. He sent 3 letters air mail. How many letters did he mail in all?

   6 ⊕ 3 = 9

PS-2   Use with text page 18.   9

Building Thinking Skills

Critical Thinking   1-9

Name _____

What Is Wrong with This Picture?

Look at each picture.
Ring the things that are wrong. Count them.
Write an addition or subtraction sentence to show what should be in each picture.

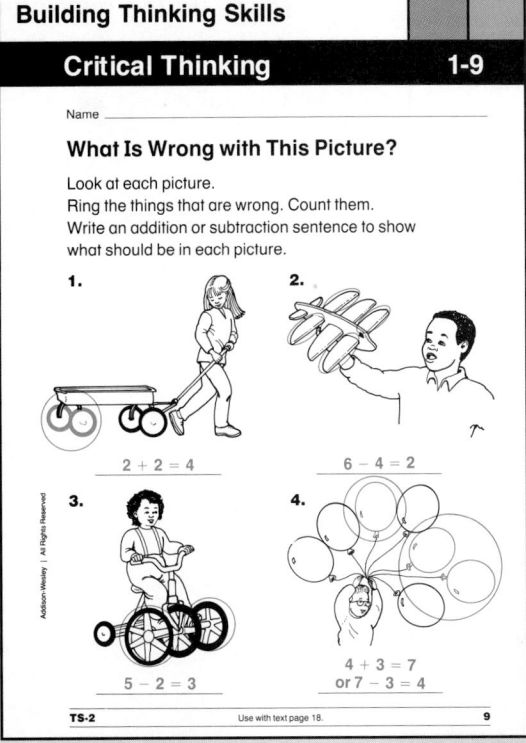

1.   2 + 2 = 4

2.   6 − 4 = 2

3.   5 − 2 = 3

4.   4 + 3 = 7 or 7 − 3 = 4

TS-2   Use with text page 18.   9

Reteaching

Problem Solving   1-9

Name _____

Finding Missing Data

9 children rode their pink and blue scooters in the park.

_2_ of the scooters were pink. How many scooters were blue?

9 ⊖ 2 = 7

Read the story.
Think carefully about it.
Make up the missing data.
Write the number sentence.

1. The club members rode their bikes to the meeting. 3 boys

   and ____ girls came to the meeting. How many club members were there in all?

   3 ⊕ ____ = ____

2. 6 children were taking turns riding in the wagon.

   ____ children already had turns. How many children were waiting for turns?

   6 ⊖ ____ = ____

RS-2   Use with text page 17.   9

Challenges

Creative Thinking   1-9

Name _____

Playground Problems

Finish the picture below.
Draw some boys and girls on the swings and seesaws.
Then finish the number sentences so they describe the picture.

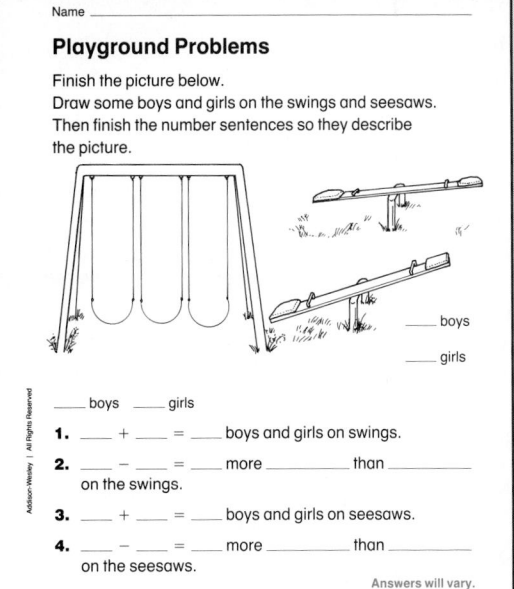

____ boys

____ girls

____ boys   ____ girls

1. ____ + ____ = ____ boys and girls on swings.

2. ____ − ____ = ____ more _____ than _____ on the swings.

3. ____ + ____ = ____ boys and girls on seesaws.

4. ____ − ____ = ____ more _____ than _____ on the seesaws.

Answers will vary.

CS-2   Use with text page 17.   9

OPTIONS FOR INDIVIDUAL NEEDS

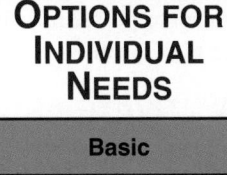

1-9

Basic

Exercises All

Supplements
Reteaching 9 or
Practice 9

Average

Exercises All

Supplements
Practice 9
Challenges 9 or
Thinking Skills 9

Extended

Exercises All

Supplements
Challenges 9
Thinking Skills 9

Other Resources:
Mathematics Their Way, pp. 204-205, 207-208
Explorations, pp. 56-59, 67, 71
Mathematics Book A, p. 17

OBJECTIVE 1-9

To solve problems by finding missing data; to solve problems using the strategy Choose the Operation

1. MOTIVATE AND TEACH

LEARN ABOUT IT

Read each of these stories to the class. Ask students what data is missing. Have them make up the missing data and use counters to solve each problem.

Story 1: *Maria rode her bike to Denise's house. On her way, Maria saw 3 black dogs and some spotted dogs. How many dogs did Maria see?*

Story 2: *Kai delivers newspapers after school. Kai had 8 newspapers in her pack. She delivered some newspapers to homes on State Street. How many newspapers are left in Kai's pack?*

Story 3: *Daryl and Tim rode their bikes to the park. At the pond, they saw some ducks in the water. They also saw 6 ducks on the grass. How many ducks did Daryl and Tim see?*

 **BEFORE** ▶ **How will you know what data is missing from the story?** (Listen carefully to find out what information is needed to find the answer.)

 **DURING** ▶ **Look at the space for the number sentences. What information is shown that will help you solve the problem?** (The operation signs are given so you know whether to add or to subtract.)

 **AFTER** ▶ **How can the pictures help you?** (They help you see what is happening in each story.)

▶ **How can you check your answer?** (Use counters; draw a picture to show your number sentence.)

2. CHECK UNDERSTANDING

ERROR ALERT **Page 17** Making up data that is not useful.

Page 18 Not being able to identify the story action.

Name _____

Problem Solving
Finding Missing Data

Listen to the stories.
Make up the missing data.
Write the number sentences. Answers may vary.

1.

___ 3 ___ ⊕ ___ ___ ▭

2.
___ 8 ___ ⊟ ___ ___ ▭

3.

___ ⊕ ___ 6 ___ ▭

Chapter 1 (seventeen)

TEACHING OPTIONS

RETEACHING TIPS Have students use felt shapes to model addition and subtraction stories on a flannelboard. Make 2 columns and have them place the shapes under the correct operation. For help use Reteaching Supplement 9.

ENRICHMENT Have students look through magazines to find pictures that show the actions of putting together or taking away. Ask them to write or tell a story about each picture. Challenge their classmates to identify the action in the story.

roblem Solving Strategy
hoose the Operation

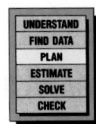

UNDERSTAND
FIND DATA
PLAN
ESTIMATE
SOLVE
CHECK

sten to the stories. Think about the action.
hen paste the pictures where they belong.

Addition	Subtraction
Put together	Take away
marble picture; horseshoes picture	bowling pins picture; wooden trees picture

 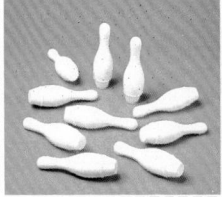  

(eighteen)   Chapter 1

3. PRACTICE AND APPLY

Basic	All
Average	All
Extended	All

Ask students to listen for the action in each story and paste the appropriate picture under *Addition* or *Subtraction*. Tony's story: *Tony and some friends were playing marbles. After a while, there were still 4 red marbles and 5 blue marbles left in the ring. How many marbles are still in the ring?* Gina's story: *Gina went bowling with her father. On her first try, she knocked down 8 of the 10 bowling pins. How many pins were left standing?* Marcia's story: *Marcia played horseshoes with her brother and sister. On one turn, 3 of her horseshoes hit the stake, but 2 others missed. How many horseshoes did she throw in that turn?* Glenn's story: *Glenn went to the fair. At one booth, he knocked down 2 out of 5 wooden trees. How many trees were left standing?* *What action shows addition?* (the action of putting together) *What action shows subtraction?* (the action of taking away)

LOSE AND ASSESS

RITE WHAT YOU KNOW

emind students of the chapter story, *x Little Ones. At the park, the ipmunks saw 3 gray squirrels and me brown squirrels. How many quirrels did they see in all?* Have udents identify and make up missing ata to solve the problem. Then ask em to write the number sentence.

QUICK QUIZ

Read the story. Circle the action.
Cher had 7 golf balls. She hit 3 balls into the water. How many golf balls did she have then?
put together   take away

Chapter 1 Lesson 9   **18**

CHAPTER 1

WRAP UP

INTRODUCTION
The Wrap Up provides activities emphasizing math language and thinking skills for the chapter.

USING PAGE 19
Word Meaning ▶ What is the difference between counting on and counting back? (Possible answer: When you count on, you are adding. When you count back, you are subtracting.)

Math Reasoning ▶ What do addition and subtraction turnaround facts have in common? (Possible answer: They are 4 facts that have the same 3 numbers in different places.)
▶ Describe the parts of an addition sentence. (Possible answer: An addition sentence has 2 parts, or addends which equal the answer, or sum.)

Name _____

WRAP UP

MATH WORDS

Ring the answer.

1. When you add 2, you count ____ . (on) bac

2. When you subtract 2, you count ____ . on (bac)

3. The number 3 is the greater addend in ____ . $4 + 3 = 7$ $(3 + 1 =$

4. The sum of $4 + 4$ is the same as the sum of ____ . $(5 + 3)$ $4 +$

5. The turnaround fact for $2 + 5 = 7$ is ____ . $(5 + 2 = 7)$ $1 + 6 =$

MATH REASONING

Write the missing numbers so that the sentence makes sense. Use turnaround facts and fact families.

6. If I know that $2 + 3 = 5$,

   then I know that $\underline{3} + \underline{2} = 5$.

7. If I know that $8 - 3 = 5$,

   then I know that $8 - \underline{5} = \underline{3}$.

8. If I know that $2 + 4 = 6$, then I know that

   $\underline{4} + \underline{2} = \underline{6}$,

   $\underline{6} - \underline{4} = \underline{2}$, and $\underline{6} - \underline{2} = \underline{4}$.

Chapter 1 Wrap Up   (nineteen)

TEACHING OPTIONS

ENRICHMENT Write the numbers 1 and 5 on the chalkboard and ask students to use these numbers and a third number of their choice to write a set of addition and subtraction sentences that are a fact family. There will be different results depending on the third number that the students choose.

Then ask students to write another set of 4 number sentences that will have the same sum as the fact family they used in the previous activity. Allow time for students to finish and then compare their results. Have volunteers list the combinations of numbers they used to get the same sum.

Name _____

CHAPTER REVIEW/TEST

Count on or back.

13, 14, __15__, __16__   19, 18, __17__, __16__

12, 11, __10__, __9__   7, 8, __9__, __10__

Add or subtract.

1 + 4 = __5__   2 + 6 = __8__   6 − 2 = __4__

$$\begin{array}{r} 2 \\ +4 \\ \hline 6 \end{array} \qquad \begin{array}{r} 1 \\ +3 \\ \hline 4 \end{array} \qquad \begin{array}{r} 6 \\ +1 \\ \hline 7 \end{array} \qquad \begin{array}{r} 5 \\ -4 \\ \hline 1 \end{array} \qquad \begin{array}{r} 4 \\ -2 \\ \hline 2 \end{array} \qquad \begin{array}{r} 6 \\ -4 \\ \hline 2 \end{array}$$

$$\begin{array}{r} 5 \\ +3 \\ \hline 8 \end{array} \qquad \begin{array}{r} 8 \\ -3 \\ \hline 5 \end{array} \qquad \begin{array}{r} 2 \\ +1 \\ \hline 3 \end{array} \qquad \begin{array}{r} 3 \\ -1 \\ \hline 2 \end{array} \qquad \begin{array}{r} 9 \\ -4 \\ \hline 5 \end{array} \qquad \begin{array}{r} 9 \\ -5 \\ \hline 4 \end{array}$$

Finish this fact family.

4 + 3 = __7__   7 − __4__ = __3__

3 + __4__ = __7__   __7__ − __3__ = __4__

Ring the action you see in the picture.

put together

(take away)

(twenty)

Chapter 1   Review/Test

CHAPTER 1

CHAPTER REVIEW/TEST

INTRODUCTION   The Review/Test is provided to review and evaluate the skills and concepts presented in Chapter 1.

USING PAGE 20
If you prefer to use this page for review, you may want to use the **Multiple-Choice Posttest** (pages 3-4) or the **Free-Response Posttest** (pages 3-4) to evaluate mastery of chapter objectives.

ITEM ANALYSIS   The table below correlates the Chapter Review/Test items with the lesson objectives for the chapter.

Items	Objectives
1	1-1
2, 3	1-2, 1-3
4	1-6, 1-7
5	1-5, 1-8
6	1-4

INFORMAL ASSESSMENT

Using Manipulatives   Tell each student a problem that involves counting on, counting back, fact families, addition or subtraction facts to 8, or put-together and take-away actions. Have each write the problem on the chalkboard and explain how to solve it. Later, work with students on their needs.

Communication   ▶ Explain what is meant by showing different ways to name a sum. Show 2 ways to make the sum of 6. (Possible answer: There are many different pairs of numbers that have the same sum. For the sum of 6: 1 + 5, 2 + 4, 3 +3, 5 + 1, 4 + 2, 6 + 0)

Critical Thinking   ▶ Why is it important to look for action in a math problem? (Possible answer: Identifying an action of either putting together or taking away will tell you what operation to use to solve the problem.)

CHAPTER 1

ENRICHMENT

INTRODUCTION
The Enrichment page provides an extension to addition and subtraction sentences by having students identify missing parts of each kind of number sentence.

USING PAGE 21
This Enrichment page is provided for all students. You may wish to use it after they have completed the Chapter Review/Test on page 20.

▶ **Show how to use counters to find the missing addend in an addition sentence.** (Possible answers: Count out the number of counters for the addend given; count out the number of counters for the sum; find the difference. Show one addend and then keep adding counters until you reach the sum.)

▶ **How might a number line help you find the missing numbers?** (Possible answer: You could start on the number you know and then jump forward or backward to the sum or difference. The number of jumps will be the missing number.)

EXTENSIONS
Continue addition and subtraction activities that have a theme of camping. Ask students to give reasons they might use addition and subtraction when they camp. (Possible answers: Add to see whether they have enough food for everyone; subtract to see how many miles they need to drive or hike.) Together, write 2 stories about camping—1 that has a put-together action and 1 that has a take-away action. Ask students to identify a number sentence to match each story.

Name _____

ENRICHMENT
Missing Addends

Rainy Day Activity
Find the missing number.

Write the missing number.
Use counters to help.

$3 + \underline{1} = 4$

$\underline{2} + 3 = 5$

$\underline{3} + 4 = 7$

$3 + \underline{6} = 9$

$8 - \underline{1} = 7$

$\underline{5} - 2 = 3$

$\underline{7} - 2 = 5$

$6 - \underline{3} = 3$

Chapter 1   Enrichment: Missing Addends

(twenty-one)

Name _____

ЈMULATIVE REVIEW

Count on.

3, 4, 5, ____

- ○ 5
- ● 6
- ○ 7

Count back.

18, 17, 16, ____

- ● 15
- ○ 14
- ○ 13

Which is the turnaround fact for 3 + 2 = 5?

- ○ 3 + 1 = 4
- ● 2 + 3 = 5
- ○ 4 + 1 = 5

If 4 + 3 = 7, then

- ○ 3 + 7 = 10
- ● 7 − 3 = 4
- ○ 7 − 2 = 5

Add or subtract.

5.
$$\begin{array}{r} 3 \\ + 5 \\ \hline \end{array}$$
- ○ 4
- ● 8
- ○ 6

6.
$$\begin{array}{r} 6 \\ - 3 \\ \hline \end{array}$$
- ○ 1
- ○ 2
- ● 3

7.
$$\begin{array}{r} 6 \\ + 1 \\ \hline \end{array}$$
- ● 7
- ○ 8
- ○ 9

8.
$$\begin{array}{r} 9 \\ - 2 \\ \hline \end{array}$$
- ○ 8
- ○ 5
- ● 7

Jill had 7 balloons. She bought 2 more balloons. How many balloons did she have then? Choose the number sentence to match.

- ○ 7 − 2 = 5
- ● 7 + 2 = 9
- ○ 7 − 5 = 2

CUMULATIVE REVIEW

INTRODUCTION The purpose of this Cumulative Review is to maintain previously taught skills and concepts. The emphasis in this Cumulative Review is on understanding addition and subtraction, Chapter 1.

ITEM ANALYSIS The table below correlates the Cumulative Review items with the lesson objectives.

Items	Objectives
1, 2	1-1
3, 4	1-5, 1-6, 1-7
5, 7	1-2
6, 8	1-3
9	1-4

CHAPTER 2 ADDITION FACTS; SUMS TO 18

Chapter Management

Lesson	Pages	Objectives	Subject Integration	Strand Integration
Count Ons and Zeros	23-24	2-1 To use the mental math techniques of counting on.	science-endangered animals	number line
Doubles	25-26	2-2 To use the mental math technique of doubles.	science-doubles patterns	patterns
Doubles Plus One	27-28	2-3 To use the mental math technique of doubles plus one.	science-animals	estimation, time
Fact Practice	29-30	2-4 To practice mental math techniques to find sums.	science-animals	calculator, money
Problem Solving: Understanding the Operations	31-32	2-5 To understand operations; to collect data.	science-animals	operations sense, data analysis
Sums of 10	33-34	2-6 To use the mental math technique of finding sums of 10.		reasoning, patterns, money
Adding with 9	35-36	2-7 To use the mental math technique of adding with 9.	science-animals	logic
Making 10, Adding Extra	37-38	2-8 To use mental math techniques.	science-mammals	patterns
Fact Practice	39-40	2-9 To practice mental math techniques to find sums.	science-animals	problem solving
Adding Three Numbers	41-42	2-10 To add three numbers.	science-animals	math reasoning
Problem Solving: Asking a Question/Problem Solving Strategy: Make a List	43-44	2-11 To understand the question in a problem; to use the strategy Make a List.	social studies-map reading	logic

MATHEMATICAL BACKGROUND

Addition and Subtraction Facts

The three steps for teaching basic facts are shown in this figure.

Teach the concept of addition.   Get students ready to memorize the addition facts.   Help students memorize the addition facts.

1st Stage   2nd Stage   3rd Stage

The first stage, teaching the concept of addition, was done in Chapter 1. The third stage, fast and accurate recall of addition facts, is the ultimate goal of teaching the facts.

Stage 2 bridges the gap from understanding the meaning of addition to memorizing the addition facts. Students are introduced to *thinking strategies* that help move them beyond understanding the concept, where all sums are found using objects (counters or fingers), to finding sums mentally.

Problem Solving

Plan is the focus in this chapter as students learn how to use models, to ask a question, and to use the strategy Make a List to solve problems. They also learn to collect, record, and analyze data from a survey.

TIPS FROM TEACHERS

As part of the calendar activity each morning, have fun exploring the day. Put up a blank sheet of paper with the date at the top. Have students submit problems using the date as their answer. Record their suggestions.

**Linda Cantrell
Lake Forest Park School
Seattle, WA**

September
18

ASSESSMENT

Pretest — Chapter 2, page 1

Name _____

Multiple-Choice Format

1. Add.

$3 + 4$

A 6
(B) 7
C 8

2. Add.

$8 + 8$

A 12
B 18
(C) 16

3. Add.

$7 + 8$

(A) 15
B 13
C 16

4. Add.

$6 + 5$

A 13
B 12
(C) 11

5. 3 puppies were sleeping. I woke up. How many were still sleeping?

A 4
B 1
(C) 2

6. Add.

$6 + 4$

(A) 10
B 2
C 5

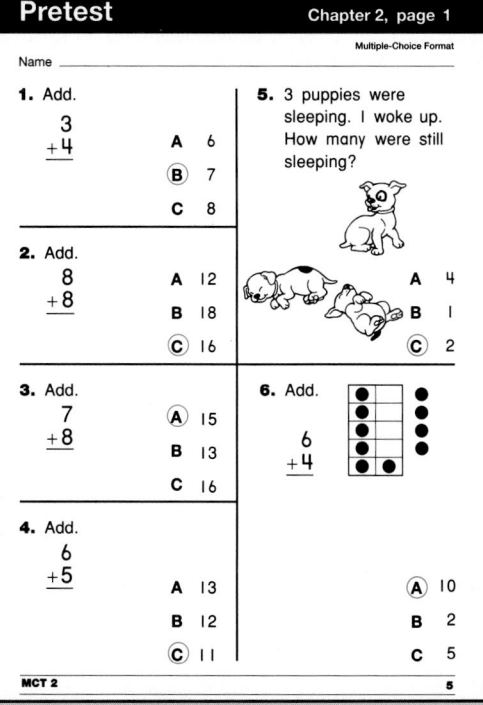

MCT 2   5

Pretest — Chapter 2, page 2

Name _____

Multiple-Choice Format

7. Add.

$9 + 7$

A 18
(B) 16
C 14

8. Add.

$8 + 4$

A 4
B 10
(C) 12

9. Add.

$7 + 4$

A 13
B 14
(C) 11

10. Add.

$4 + 6 + 5$

A 9
B 10
(C) 15

11. Choose the better question for the story.

6 kittens were in Jane's yard.
2 more kittens came to join them.

A How many kittens were left?

(B) How many kittens were in Jane's yard then?

6   MCT 2

Posttest — Chapter 2, page 1

Name _____

Multiple-Choice Format

1. Add.

$3 + 5$

A 6
B 7
(C) 8

2. Add.

$7 + 7$

A 12
(B) 14
C 16

3. Add.

$6 + 7$

A 15
(B) 13
C 16

4. Add.

$8 + 7$

A 16
B 15
C 14

5. 4 kittens were sleeping. 3 woke up. How many were still sleeping?

A 4
(B) 1
C 0

6. Add.

$3 + 7$

(A) 10
B 2
C 5

MCT 2   7

Posttest — Chapter 2, page 2

Name _____

Multiple-Choice Format

7. Add.

$9 + 4$

A 15
(B) 13
C 11

8. Add.

$8 + 5$

A 3
B 10
(C) 13

9. Add.

$1 + 4$

A 3
B 4
(C) 5

10. Add.

$8 + 2 + 6$

A 10
B 14
(C) 16

11. Choose the better question for the story.

6 birds were in Jane's yard.
2 more birds came to join them.

A How many birds were left?

(B) How many birds were in Jane's yard then?

8   MCT 2

ITEM ANALYSIS

Items	Objectives
1	2-1
2	2-2
3	2-3
4	2-4
5	2-5
6	2-6
7	2-7
8	2-8
9	2-9
10	2-10
11	2-11

Note: The item analysis is the same for all pretests and posttests for this chapter.

ALSO AVAILABLE

► **Free Response Tests**
► **Alternative Tests**
► **Thinking Strategies**
► **Concrete Materials**

Addison-Wesley | All Rights Reserved

Optional Chapter Activities

PROJECT AND BULLETIN BOARD

Help students learn interesting facts about three famous Americans, such as Helen Keller, John Glenn, and Clara Barton. Write information about the men and women on separate pieces of chart paper. Below each paragraph, write the code puzzles, using addition facts with answers that correspond to the code letters. On the bulletin board, post the title and code. During each session, post a chart about one of the people. Have students read about the person and then find the sums and use the code to discover the person's name. Follow up by having students draw or cut out pictures of the person and attach them to the bottom of each chart.

FAMOUS AMERICANS

He was the first American astronaut to orbit the Earth. He flew on the spacecraft Friendship 7.

K	J	G	A	T	E	N	R	O	C	B	L	H
1	3	4	6	8	9	10	12	14	15	16	17	18

1 +2	7 +7	9 +9	9 +1
3	14	18	10
J	O	H	N

3 +1	9 +8	2 +7	7 +3	8 +2
4	17	9	10	10
G	L	E	N	N

COOPERATIVE LEARNING

Divide the class into groups of 5 or 6. Identify the group skill: listening to each other. Ask each group to write riddles and create codes for solving them. Individual tasks include the following:
1. Write the riddle and its answer on chart paper.
2. Make up a secret code using one number from 2 to 18 for each letter in the answer to the riddle.
3. Write facts using addition doubles and doubles plus one. Match sums to code letters.
4. Illustrate a chart with a picture that gives visual clues to the answer.
5. Display the riddle, picture, and code. Ask students in other groups to solve the riddle.

Encourage students working on each task to listen carefully to decisions made about codes and letters so that the corresponding letters and numbers will match.

You will find grouping suggestions and cooperative learning activities in most lessons throughout this chapter.

LITERATURE

Quackenbush, Robert, *Too Many Lollipops,* New York: Golden Press, 1987.

Henry has a lot of accidents and children will love the remedy, lollipops.
Have students use dried beans or counters to practice finding sums to 10 and adding with 9.

Gerstein, Mordicai, *Roll Over,* New York: Crown Publishers, 1984.

Korr, David, *The Day the Count Stopped Counting,* New York: Golden Press, 1977.

ENGLISH AS A SECOND LANGUAGE

Students are given a number of strategies for finding and remembering sums to 18 in this chapter.

Use active rather than passive voice when working with students with limited English proficiency. Encourage all students to verbalize the strategies they use to solve problems. If ESL students are not yet ready to describe their strategies, assign a letter to each strategy so that they can still identify them.

Since the chapter theme is endangered animals, help students identify each animal. In problem-solving, the past continuous (*6 were eating*) is used with the simple past (*2 ran away*). If this poses a comprehension problem, have them act out the stories and draw pictures to be sure the action is understood.

In the data analysis lesson, give ESL students the more active role of survey taker, to practice formulating questions.

GIFTED

Mathematically talented students may already know their addition facts to 18. They will nevertheless likely be interested in many of the strategies presented in this chapter. You may wish to challenge these students, after they have completed their student book work, by showing them how to add numbers of tens instead of ones to find 2- and 3-digit sums. For example, after Lesson 2 on doubles, write $4 + 4 = 8$ on the chalkboard, then ask what 4 tens + 4 tens would equal. (8 tens) Write 8 tens and ask students if they know another way to say and write 8 tens. (eighty, 80) Use place value models to demonstrate, if necessary. Then challenge students to complete the exercises in their books using tens instead of ones and reading the new number sentences to a friend. ($40 + 40 = 80$; forty plus forty equals eighty.) Equations that result in sums over one hundred should be especially challenging and satisfying. If this appeals to your students, you may wish to use the technique throughout the chapter.

STUDENTS AT RISK

Many learning disabled students are effective thinkers but poor memorizers. It is very important to give these students strategies for remembering their addition facts.

Before these strategies can be developed, however, students do need to memorize the doubles facts and the sums that make 10. There are simple games that will aid students in achieving both of these goals. First, create a standard game board from an opened-out file folder. Use circular stickers or draw steps to create a winding trail with a clearly marked Start and Finish. To practice doubles facts, students roll a number cube marked 1-6 or 4-9 and advance **twice** the number they roll. To practice sums of 10, students spin a spinner marked with the digits 1-9 and advance the number of steps it would take to reach 10 from the number on the spinner.

To practice these and other addition fact thinking strategies, have each student create a set of cards for the addition facts through 18. Have them practice using thinking strategies in pairs, so that they can help each other by explaining which strategy they used.

You may also use the Reteaching Supplements and the specific Reteaching Tips from each lesson in this chapter.

Storybook

PICTURE

These pictures and accompanying stories and poems are available as storybooks.

You may want to read and discuss this poem with your students before starting the chapter. The first lesson in this chapter is introduced with a question about the poem. Lessons 2, 3, 6, and 10 in this chapter have questions in the informal Assessment that refer to the poem.

POEM

Have You Seen an Eagle?

Have you ever seen an eagle fly?
It soars high, crossing the sky,
wheeling around the trees and down
toward the water, where its food can be found.

One eagle has two wings, big things
it spreads to glide through the air.
Two eagles have more than two wings.
Together, two eagles have four.

Two eagles return to their nest,
a very big place where they rest.
In the nest are two eggs that will hatch
into eaglets, each with two wings.
The family, four eagles, will fly
on eight wings through the sky.

If four eagles met five more,
the sky would be quite a sight,
filled with eagles in flight.

But there aren't many eagles left to soar.
The bald eagle, a bird our country calls its own,
is almost gone.

Scientists work to help the birds,
keeping track of how and where they live,
trying to give them a chance to grow.
We'd like them to double, you know.
From two to four to eight to even more,
so that everywhere eagles will soar.

Past mountains and forests and rivers
the birds will glide,
proud and free, way up in the sky.
Wouldn't you like to see an eagle fly?

Count Ons and Zeros

OBJECTIVE 2-1 To use the mental math techniques of counting on 1, 2, or 3 to find sums; to use the

PREBOOK ACTIVITIES

QUICK REVIEW

Fill in the blanks.

0, 1, 2, __(3)__, 4, 5, 6, __(7)__, 8, 9, 10, 11, __(12)__, 13, 14, 15

0, 2, __(4)__, 6, 8, __(10)__, 12, 14, 16, __(18)__, 20

0, 3, 6, __(9)__, 12, 15, __(18)__, 21, __(24)__

0, 5, __(10)__, 15, __(20)__, 25, 30, __(35)__, __(40)__, 45

PRIOR KNOWLEDGE

Read the following sentences aloud. Ask students to ask a question and say an addition sentence to answer each one. Have volunteers write the addition facts on the chalkboard. *Liz had 1 orange. Then she bought 2 more.* (How many did she have then? 1 + 2 = 3) *Bill found 6 pennies. Then he found 3 more.* (How many did he find in all? 6 + 3 = 9)

COMMUNICATION

Reading and Discussing Math Write the words **count ons** and **zero** on the chalkboard and read the words aloud. Explain that count ons are numbers that you can add quickly by counting on from another number without using pencil and paper. *What does a zero look like?* Have a volunteer write a zero on the board and then count aloud to 10 starting with 0. *When might you want to count quickly in your head?* (Possible answer: You might need to know an answer in a hurry. You might not have a pencil and paper handy.) *Tell a story about an addition fact with zero as an addend.* (Possible answer: My brother has 2 hamsters. I do not have any. How many hamsters do we have in all? 2 + 0 = 2)

EXPLORE AND CONNECT

Materials: addition flashcards, counters
Grouping Suggestion: pairs
Show students a flashcard that has a 0, 1, 2, or 3 as an addend. *Look at the number fact and find the greater numbe. Then count on from this number to find the total.* Practice **count ons:** display a flashcard; have one student say the greater number, then have the partner continue counting to t total. Have students imagine that their hand is a cave and th counters are lion cubs. Write a number fact on the chalkboa (with the greater addend not always first) and have one stude place counters/lion cubs for the greater number inside the ca The other partner then counts on as he or she places more (0 1, 2, or 3) counters/lion cubs outside the cave. *What happer to an addend when you add zero to it?* (It stays the same.)

CONNECTIONS   Use these anytime.

Problem of the Day

Finding Missing Data Read the story. Make up a number for the missing data. Write a number sentence and solve it.
Mia has 6 dolls.
She goes to the store.
How many dolls does she have in all?
(Answers will vary. Possible answer: She buys 1 doll. 6 + 1 = 7; 7 dolls)

Subject Integration

Health and Fitness Work with a small group. Have one person be the caller who says a count-on number fact, such as 5 + 3. Take giant steps for the greater addend. Then take baby steps to count on to the total. The caller then chooses a new person to say number fact.

Number Sense

Zero Describe what would happen in each situation.
A firefighter has zero buckets of water to put out a fire.
A baker has zero bowls of dough to bake bread.
A baseball team has zero hits.
A student has zero cavities.

entity property of addition

CLASSWORK AND HOMEWORK SUPPLEMENTS

OPTIONS FOR INDIVIDUAL NEEDS

Basic

Exercises All

Supplements
Reteaching 10 or
Practice 10

2-1

Average

Exercises All

Supplements
Practice 10
Challenges 10 or
Thinking Skills 10

Extended

Exercises All

Supplements
Challenges 10
Thinking Skills 10

Other Resources:
Mathematics Their Way, pages 236-240
Problem Solving Experiences In Mathematics, page 33

Practice

Skills Maintenance　　2-1

Name _____

Count Ons and Zeros

Add.

1. $0 + 4 = \underline{4}$　$0 + 3 = \underline{3}$　$7 + 0 = \underline{7}$

2. $3 + 6 = \underline{9}$　$2 + 0 = \underline{2}$　$1 + 9 = \underline{10}$

3. $0 + 7 = \underline{7}$　$8 + 3 = \underline{11}$　$1 + 5 = \underline{6}$

4. $9 + 2 = \underline{11}$　$2 + 2 = \underline{4}$　$5 + 0 = \underline{5}$

5.
$\begin{array}{r}0\\+1\\\hline 1\end{array}$　$\begin{array}{r}1\\+6\\\hline 7\end{array}$　$\begin{array}{r}3\\+9\\\hline 12\end{array}$　$\begin{array}{r}6\\+0\\\hline 6\end{array}$　$\begin{array}{r}8\\+2\\\hline 10\end{array}$

6.
$\begin{array}{r}3\\+4\\\hline 7\end{array}$　$\begin{array}{r}0\\+9\\\hline 9\end{array}$　$\begin{array}{r}8\\+1\\\hline 9\end{array}$　$\begin{array}{r}9\\+1\\\hline 10\end{array}$　$\begin{array}{r}7\\+3\\\hline 10\end{array}$

7.
$\begin{array}{r}0\\+8\\\hline 8\end{array}$　$\begin{array}{r}2\\+3\\\hline 5\end{array}$　$\begin{array}{r}4\\+1\\\hline 5\end{array}$　$\begin{array}{r}3\\+8\\\hline 11\end{array}$　$\begin{array}{r}2\\+6\\\hline 8\end{array}$

10　　Use with text pages 23-24.　　PS-2

Building Thinking Skills

Mental Math　　2-1

Name _____

Add in Your Head

Ring the expression that has the greater sum.

1. $6 + 1$ or $(6 + 2)$?　2. $5 + 0$ or $(5 + 2)$?

3. $2 + 7$ or $(7 + 3)$?　4. $(9 + 1)$ or $0 + 9$?

Ring the expressions that have the same sum.

5. $(2 + 5)$　$6 + 0$　$4 + 1$　$(4 + 3)$

6. $9 + 0$　$(7 + 3)$　$(2 + 8)$　$0 + 8$

7. $(3 + 6)$　$9 + 1$　$(7 + 2)$　$7 + 1$

8. $5 + 3$　$5 + 2$　$(8 + 1)$　$(0 + 9)$

Write 0, 1, 2, or 3 in the blank to make the sentence true.

9. $6 + 2 = 7 + \underline{1}$

10. $3 + 8 = \underline{2} + 9$

11. $4 + 3 = \underline{0} + 7$

12. $2 + 7 = 6 + \underline{3}$

10　　Use with text pages 23-24.　　TS-2

Reteaching

Skills Review　　2-1

Name _____

Count Ons and Zeros

Say the larger number.
Count on to find the sum.

1. $8 + 1 = \underline{9}$　$2 + 6 = \underline{8}$　$3 + 5 = \underline{8}$
(8, 9)　(6, 7, 8)　(5, 6, 7, 8)

2. $1 + 7 = \underline{8}$　$6 + 3 = \underline{9}$　$8 + 2 = \underline{10}$

3. $2 + 9 = \underline{11}$　$4 + 1 = \underline{5}$　$3 + 9 = \underline{12}$

4. $7 + 3 = \underline{10}$　$1 + 5 = \underline{6}$　$2 + 4 = \underline{6}$

Add zero.

5. $3 + 0 = \underline{3}$ (still 3)　$0 + 2 = \underline{2}$ (still 2)　$0 + 4 = \underline{4}$ (still 4)

6. $1 + 0 = \underline{1}$　$8 + 0 = \underline{8}$　$0 + 9 = \underline{9}$

7.
$\begin{array}{r}0\\+7\\\hline 7\end{array}$　$\begin{array}{r}2\\+0\\\hline 2\end{array}$　$\begin{array}{r}0\\+6\\\hline 6\end{array}$　$\begin{array}{r}5\\+0\\\hline 5\end{array}$　$\begin{array}{r}9\\+0\\\hline 9\end{array}$

10　　Use with text pages 23-24.　　RS-2

Challenges

Family Math　　2-1

Name _____

Math Bingo

Dear Family Member:
Your child has just learned about counting on to add 1, 2, and 3 to a number, and about how to add zero. Play this game with your child to reinforce these addition facts.

Play with a family member. Each player chooses a game board. Toss a bean or a paper clip on the answer board. Color an expression on your game board that has that sum. Say **Bingo** when all your squares are colored.

Answer Board

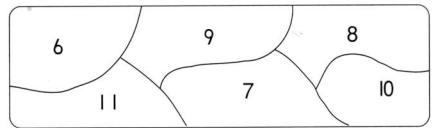

6　　9　　8
11　　7　　10

Game Board

6+0	1+8	8+3
9+2	2+6	0+7
5+3	2+8	7+3
7+1	0+9	1+6

Game Board

2+4	9+1	3+5
5+1	6+3	1+10
0+8	1+8	2+9
5+2	7+0	3+8

10　　Use with text pages 23-24.　　CS-2

Chapter 2 Lesson 1　　**23H**

OBJECTIVE 2-1

To use the mental math techniques of counting on 1, 2, or 3 to find sums; to use the identity property of addition

---

Materials: counters, Cube-A-Links, small cards

Grouping Suggestions: individual work, small groups

---

1. MOTIVATE AND TEACH

LEARN ABOUT IT

As students look at page 23, reread the poem about the eagles. Then, as you read the following question, have 7 students pretend to be eagles flying and have 2 more join them. Have the class count on to find how many in all.
7 eagles soar high above the river.
2 more eagles join them.
How many eagles are there in all? (9)
Direct students' attention to the picture on page 23.
What do you see in the cave picture? (a cave with 2 lion cubs outside) *Pretend your counters are lion cubs. How can you use them to make the picture show a count-on fact?* (Possible answer: There are 2 cubs outside the cave. Place 5 counters/cubs inside the cave. Start with the 5 and count on 2 more to get 7.)
▶ **What will always stay the same even if we change the number of cubs in the cave?** (Possible answer: The number of cubs outside will always be 2. We will always count on 2 more from the number in the cave.)

2. CHECK UNDERSTANDING

ERROR ALERT Beginning with the smaller number instead of the greater number to count on.

2
Addition Facts
Sums to 18

TEACHING OPTIONS

RETEACHING TIPS Draw a house on the chalkboard and write 6 + 2 = 8. Draw 2 people outside the house and ask a volunteer to draw 6 people inside. Demonstrate how to count on by starting with the larger number. Assign Reteaching Supplement 10.

ENRICHMENT Write number facts with the count-on addend missing—for example, 6 + _____ = 9. Have students draw a number line and show how many jumps are needed to get from 6 to 9. Then have them write the complete number fact and identify the count-on addend.

‐ount Ons and Zeros

‐se cubes.
‐ount on to add.

Cover the greater addend.

Count on with the other addend.

4, 5, 6

$6 + 2 = \underline{8}$

$3 + 7 = \underline{10}$

$8 + 1 = \underline{9}$

‐ing the greater number. Add zero or count on.

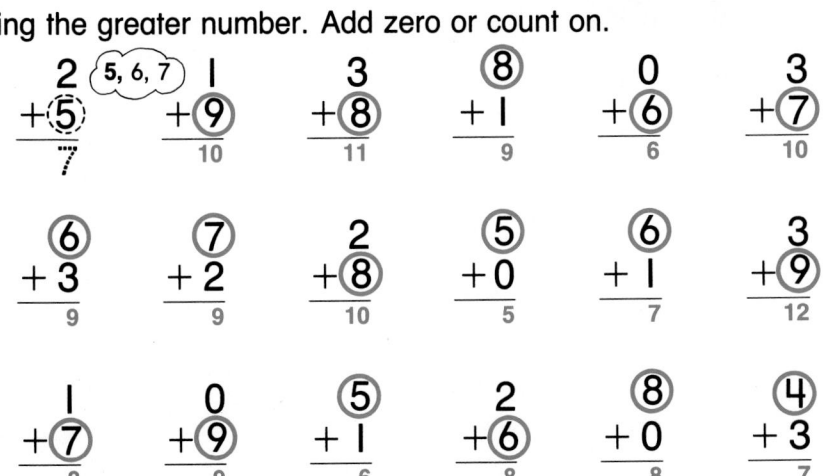

$\begin{array}{r} 2 \\ +\underline{5} \\ \hline 7 \end{array}$ (5, 6, 7) $\begin{array}{r} 1 \\ +\underline{9} \\ \hline 10 \end{array}$ $\begin{array}{r} 3 \\ +\underline{8} \\ \hline 11 \end{array}$ $\begin{array}{r} \underline{8} \\ +1 \\ \hline 9 \end{array}$ $\begin{array}{r} 0 \\ +\underline{6} \\ \hline 6 \end{array}$ $\begin{array}{r} 3 \\ +\underline{7} \\ \hline 10 \end{array}$

$\begin{array}{r} \underline{6} \\ +3 \\ \hline 9 \end{array}$ $\begin{array}{r} \underline{7} \\ +2 \\ \hline 9 \end{array}$ $\begin{array}{r} 2 \\ +\underline{8} \\ \hline 10 \end{array}$ $\begin{array}{r} \underline{5} \\ +0 \\ \hline 5 \end{array}$ $\begin{array}{r} \underline{6} \\ +1 \\ \hline 7 \end{array}$ $\begin{array}{r} 3 \\ +\underline{9} \\ \hline 12 \end{array}$

$\begin{array}{r} 1 \\ +\underline{7} \\ \hline 8 \end{array}$ $\begin{array}{r} 0 \\ +\underline{9} \\ \hline 9 \end{array}$ $\begin{array}{r} \underline{5} \\ +1 \\ \hline 6 \end{array}$ $\begin{array}{r} 2 \\ +\underline{6} \\ \hline 8 \end{array}$ $\begin{array}{r} \underline{8} \\ +0 \\ \hline 8 \end{array}$ $\begin{array}{r} \underline{4} \\ +3 \\ \hline 7 \end{array}$

‐SE CRITICAL THINKING

Make jumps on the number line to show $9 + 3$.

Start here.
↓

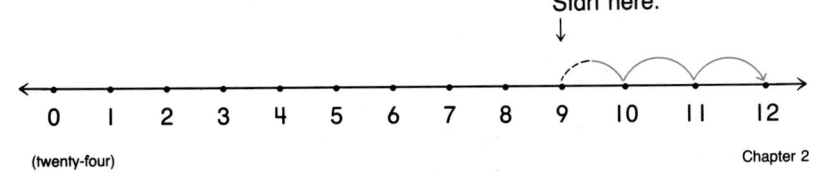

0 1 2 3 4 5 6 7 8 9 10 11 12

‐4 (twenty-four) Chapter 2

3. PRACTICE AND APPLY

Basic	All
Average	All
Extended	All

2-1

PRACTICE

What objects can you use to help you count on for these exercises? (Possible answer: cubes) *What number will you ring in Exercises 3-5?* (the greater addend)

APPLY

USING THINKING SKILLS *In Exercise 6, why can you start at 9 on the number line without showing 9 jumps?* (Possible answer: You start on 9 because it is the greater addend; show the count-on jumps from there.)

▶ **How can you use the number line to help you show other count-on facts?** (Possible answer: Start on the number for the greater addend. Jump the number of times you need to count on from the greater addend.)

‐LOSE AND ASSESS

‐HOW WHAT YOU KNOW

‐ave students work in small groups. ‐sk one student to write the numbers ‐-9 on small cards. Have another ‐udent make count-on cards for the ‐umbers 0-3. Have group members ‐hoose a card from each set, say the ‐umber fact, and demonstrate how to ‐ount on from the greater addend to ‐nd the total. The other students ‐erify the answer using counters.

QUICK QUIZ

Ring the greater number. Add zero or count on.

$\begin{array}{r} 1 \\ +8 \\ \hline (9) \end{array}$ $\begin{array}{r} \underline{7} \\ +0 \\ \hline (7) \end{array}$ $\begin{array}{r} \underline{6} \\ +3 \\ \hline (9) \end{array}$ $\begin{array}{r} 2 \\ +4 \\ \hline (6) \end{array}$ $\begin{array}{r} 3 \\ +8 \\ \hline (11) \end{array}$

Doubles

OBJECTIVE 2-2 To use the mental math technique of doubles to find sums

PREBOOK ACTIVITIES

QUICK REVIEW

As I call out an addition problem, hold up the number card that shows the sum.

6 + 1	4 + 0	3 + 2	1 + 5	2 + 7	0 + 8
(7)	(4)	(5)	(6)	(9)	(8)

PRIOR KNOWLEDGE

Ask students to think of things that come in pairs or rows of 2. Help students brainstorm by offering topics such as a pair of hands—5 fingers on each hand; 2 rows of eggs in a carton—6 eggs in a row. Have students listen to each other's examples as you write each doubles addition expression on the chalkboard.

COMMUNICATION

Listening and Writing in Math Write the word **doubles** on the chalkboard. Read the word to students, then have them read the word together. Encourage students to describe what they know about the word **doubles** as it is used every day. (Possible responses: It means two of something, twice as much.) Write the following number expressions on the chalkboard and explain that they are number doubles.

5 + 5 6 + 6 7 + 7 8 + 8 9 + 9

Ask students to listen to the following riddles and identify the number double on the chalkboard that describes each one. *We are 2 feet. How many toes?* (5 + 5) *We are 2 weeks. How many days?* (7 + 7) *We are 2 octopuses. How many legs?* (8 + 8)

EXPLORE AND CONNECT

Materials: Cube-A-Links of 2 different colors
Alternative Materials: counters
Grouping Suggestions: pairs
Provide each student pair with 18 cubes. Each student should have 9 cubes of one color. Have one student begin by displaying a train of up to 9 cubes. The partner makes a train using the same number of cubes. *What* **doubles** *addition expression tells about your trains?* (5 + 5, 6 + 6, 7 + 7, 8 + 8, or 9 + 9) Allow time for students to show their trains to the class and listen to each other's answers. Ask students to change roles and repeat the activity.

CONNECTIONS   Use these anytime.

Problem of the Day

Logic How would fact families for doubles be different from other fact families? (They have no turnaround facts, so there would be only two, not four, facts.)

Math Connection

Patterns Write the doubles and sums for 1 + 1 through 3 + 3. Read the sums aloud. What pattern do you hear? (Every other counting number is said.) What do you think the sum will be for the next double, 4 + 4? (8)

Subject Integration

Science Place up to 3 small objects in front of a mirror so that you can see all of them in the mirror. What happens to the number of objects? (They double.) How many do you see now? (doubles from 2 to 6)

CLASSWORK AND HOMEWORK SUPPLEMENTS

Practice

Skills Maintenance   2-2

Name _____

Doubles

Add. Ring the doubles facts.

1. (4 + 4 = 8)   5 + 6 = 11
2. 8 + 2 = 10   (7 + 7 = 14)
3. (5 + 5 = 10)   3 + 5 = 8
4. (8 + 8 = 16)   (9 + 9 = 18)
5. 7 + 2 = 9   8 + 1 = 9

6. 6   (7)   2   (6)   5
   +5   +7   +9   +6   +4
   ---   ---   ---   ---   ---
   11   14   11   12   9

7. (6)   2   (5)   3   (9)
   +6   +7   +5   +4   +9
   ---   ---   ---   ---   ---
   12   9   10   7   18

8. (8)   6   4   (7)   2
   +8   +2   +4   +7   +5
   ---   ---   ---   ---   ---
   16   8   8   14   7

PS-2   Use with text pages 25-26.   11

Reteaching

Skills Review   2-2

Name _____

Doubles

Match the picture with the fact.
Then add.

8 + 8 = 16
6 + 6 = 12
9 + 9 = 18
7 + 7 = 14

Add. Ring doubles.

1. 7   (6)   8   2   (9)
   +1   +6   +8   +8   +9
   ---   ---   ---   ---   ---
    8   12   16   10   18

2. (5)   3   7   7   6
   +5   +9   +7   +1   +2
   ---   ---   ---   ---   ---
   10   12   14   8   8

3. 3   8   3   (6)   5
   +4   +1   +6   +6   +3
   ---   ---   ---   ---   ---
    7   9   9   12   8

4. (8)   (7)   9   (4)   (8)
   +8   +7   +3   +4   +8
   ---   ---   ---   ---   ---
   16   14   12   8   16

RS-2   Use with text pages 25-26.   11

Building Thinking Skills

Number Sense   2-2

Name _____

Doubles Riddles

Choose a number 1 through 9.

1. My double is 6. Who am I? 3	**2.** My double has two digits. It ends in 0. Who am I? 5
3. My double is between 6 and 10. Who am I? 4	**4.** Double me and you get two digits. One of them is 8. Who am I? 9
5. My double is 14. Who am I? 7	**6.** My double is between 10 and 14. Who am I? 6
7. When you double me, you get 8. Who am I? 4	**8.** Double me and you get 16. Who am I? 8

TS-2   Use with text pages 25-26.   11

Challenges

Cooperative Activities   2-2

Name _____

Crazy Caterpillar

You need: one or more friends,
          a spinner with numbers 4 to 9,
          a marker for each player.

Rules: Put the markers on **Start**.
          Spin the spinner.
          Double the number on the spinner.
          Move your marker that number of spaces
          on the caterpillar.
          Now it is your friend's turn.
          The first one to get to the leaf wins.

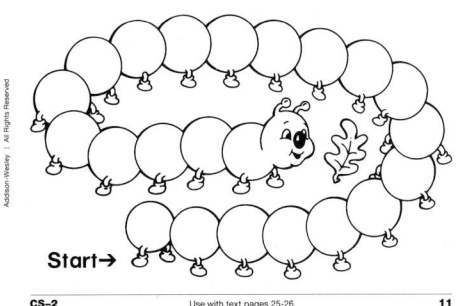

Start→

CS-2   Use with text pages 25-26.   11

OPTIONS FOR INDIVIDUAL NEEDS

2-2

Basic

Exercises All

Supplements
Reteaching 11 or
Practice 11

Average

Exercises All

Supplements
Practice 11
Challenges 11 or
Thinking Skills 11

Extended

Exercises All

Supplements
Challenges 11
Thinking Skills 11

Other Resources:
Explorations, pages 52-55, 69, 189, 193

LESSON PLAN 2-2

OBJECTIVE 2-2
To use the mental math technique of doubles to find sums

> **Materials:** scissors, paste, doubles flipover punchouts, paper clips, counters, 10-frames
>
> **Grouping Suggestions:** individual work, pairs

1. MOTIVATE AND TEACH

LEARN ABOUT IT

Practice working with doubles by having students use the doubles flipover punchouts. Ask students to place each card number side down. As students draw a card, have them count the objects for each part of the double and think of the written numbers that describe the picture. Students may then flip the card over to check.

▶ **What is the same about all of the pictures on the page?** (They each show two addends of the same amount; they show doubles.)

▶ **How will you know which fact matches each picture?** (Count the objects in half of the picture and match it to the addends.)

2. CHECK UNDERSTANDING

ERROR ALERT Computing the sums incorrectly.

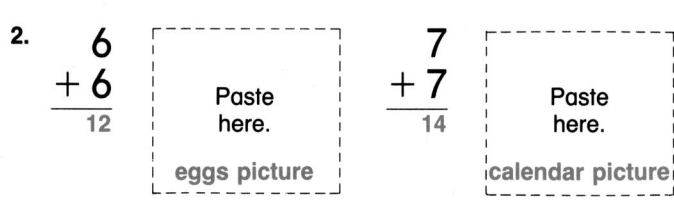

Name _____

Doubles

Cut out the double pictures.
Paste to match the double facts.
Then add.

1.
$\begin{array}{r} 4 \\ +4 \\ \hline 8 \end{array}$
⌐ Paste here. ¬
spider picture

$\begin{array}{r} 5 \\ +5 \\ \hline 10 \end{array}$
⌐ Paste here. ¬
gloves picture

2.
$\begin{array}{r} 6 \\ +6 \\ \hline 12 \end{array}$
⌐ Paste here. ¬
eggs picture

$\begin{array}{r} 7 \\ +7 \\ \hline 14 \end{array}$
⌐ Paste here. ¬
calendar picture

3.
$\begin{array}{r} 8 \\ +8 \\ \hline 16 \end{array}$
⌐ Paste here. ¬
crayons picture

$\begin{array}{r} 9 \\ +9 \\ \hline 18 \end{array}$
⌐ Paste here. ¬
dominos picture

Add. Think of the double picture.

4.
$\begin{array}{r} 6 \\ +6 \\ \hline 12 \end{array}$
$\begin{array}{r} 8 \\ +8 \\ \hline 16 \end{array}$
$\begin{array}{r} 5 \\ +5 \\ \hline 10 \end{array}$
$\begin{array}{r} 9 \\ +9 \\ \hline 18 \end{array}$
$\begin{array}{r} 4 \\ +4 \\ \hline 8 \end{array}$
$+$

5. $9 + 9 =$ __18__ $7 + 7 =$ __14__ $6 + 6 =$ __12__

Chapter 2   (twenty-five)

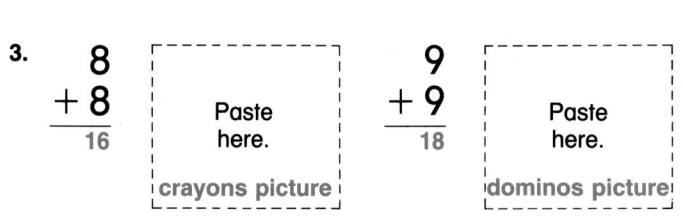

TEACHING OPTIONS

RETEACHING TIPS Provide students with paper clips or other counters. Have students add 5 + 5, 7 + 7, and 9 + 9 by making a paper-clip chain to show each addend. Then have them combine the chains and count to find the sum. Assign Reteaching Supplement 11.

ENRICHMENT Have students use 10-frames and counters to show doubles from 4 + 4 through 9 + 9. *For which doubles do you need only 1 10-frame?* (4 + 4 and 5 + 5) *For which doubles do you need 2 10-frames?* (6 + 6 through 9 + 9) *How many frames do you need for 10 + 10?* (2)

Add. Ring the double facts.

1.
$$\begin{array}{r} 8 \\ +8 \\ \hline 16 \end{array}$$ (ringed)
$$\begin{array}{r} 7 \\ +2 \\ \hline 9 \end{array}$$
$$\begin{array}{r} 9 \\ +0 \\ \hline 9 \end{array}$$
$$\begin{array}{r} 6 \\ +1 \\ \hline 7 \end{array}$$
$$\begin{array}{r} 5 \\ +5 \\ \hline 10 \end{array}$$ (ringed)

2.
$$\begin{array}{r} 6 \\ +6 \\ \hline 12 \end{array}$$ (ringed)
$$\begin{array}{r} 0 \\ +5 \\ \hline 5 \end{array}$$
$$\begin{array}{r} 4 \\ +4 \\ \hline 8 \end{array}$$ (ringed)
$$\begin{array}{r} 3 \\ +9 \\ \hline 12 \end{array}$$
$$\begin{array}{r} 8 \\ +2 \\ \hline 10 \end{array}$$

3.
$$\begin{array}{r} 3 \\ +5 \\ \hline 8 \end{array}$$
$$\begin{array}{r} 7 \\ +7 \\ \hline 14 \end{array}$$ (ringed)
$$\begin{array}{r} 9 \\ +9 \\ \hline 18 \end{array}$$ (ringed)
$$\begin{array}{r} 2 \\ +6 \\ \hline 8 \end{array}$$
$$\begin{array}{r} 6 \\ +3 \\ \hline 9 \end{array}$$

4.
$$\begin{array}{r} 8 \\ +0 \\ \hline 8 \end{array}$$
$$\begin{array}{r} 1 \\ +9 \\ \hline 10 \end{array}$$
$$\begin{array}{r} 0 \\ +4 \\ \hline 4 \end{array}$$
$$\begin{array}{r} 3 \\ +3 \\ \hline 6 \end{array}$$ (ringed)
$$\begin{array}{r} 1 \\ +1 \\ \hline 2 \end{array}$$ (ringed)

5.
$$\begin{array}{r} 1 \\ +7 \\ \hline 8 \end{array}$$
$$\begin{array}{r} 2 \\ +2 \\ \hline 4 \end{array}$$ (ringed)
$$\begin{array}{r} 3 \\ +8 \\ \hline 11 \end{array}$$
$$\begin{array}{r} 9 \\ +1 \\ \hline 10 \end{array}$$
$$\begin{array}{r} 6 \\ +3 \\ \hline 9 \end{array}$$

6. (9 + 9 = 18) (ringed)   7 + 1 = 8

7. 2 + 9 = 11   (8 + 8 = 16) (ringed)

8. (4 + 4 = 8) (ringed)   (5 + 5 = 10) (ringed)

9. (6 + 6 = 12) (ringed)   0 + 6 = 6

10. (7 + 7 = 14) (ringed)   7 + 0 = 7

3. PRACTICE AND APPLY

Basic	All
Average	All
Extended	All

PRACTICE

Which exercises are like those on page 25? (the doubles) *How can the doubles pictures help you with sums?* (They help you see a sum—such as 12 eggs— quickly so you do not have to add or count 6 + 6.)

APPLY

Look at the doubles pictures and use them to create names for doubles facts.
▶ **What would you call:**
4 + 4? (the *spider* fact)
5 + 5? (the *fingers* fact)
6 + 6? (the *dozen eggs* fact)
7 + 7? (the *two-week* fact)
8 + 8? (the *crayon* fact)
9 + 9? (the *double-nine domino* fact)

CLOSE AND ASSESS

SHOW WHAT YOU KNOW
...read the chapter poem. Have ...dents solve this problem: *How ...ny eagles were there after 2 eagles ...ubled in number?* (4 eagles) *After 4 ...gles doubled?* (8 eagles)

QUICK QUIZ

Copy the doubles pattern from the chalkboard. Find the sums. Add one more double to the pattern and solve.
4 + 4   5 + 5   6 + 6   (7 + 7)
(8)   (10)   (12)   (14)

Doubles Plus One

OBJECTIVE 2-3   To use the mental math technique of doubles plus one to find sums

PREBOOK ACTIVITIES

Add.

$2 + 2 = \underline{(4)}$ $3 + 3 = \underline{(6)}$ $4 + 4 = \underline{(8)}$
$5 + 5 = \underline{(10)}$ $6 + 6 = \underline{(12)}$ $7 + 7 = \underline{(14)}$
$8 + 8 = \underline{(16)}$

PRIOR KNOWLEDGE

Review the doubles introduced in the previous lesson. Draw two pairs of socks on the chalkboard (or use real socks) and write $2 + 2 = 4$. Then draw one more sock near one of the pairs and write $2 + 3$. *How can we use doubles to help us add some other combinations of numbers?* (Possible answer: When one of the numbers is one more than the other, we can just double the smaller number and then add one more.)

COMMUNICATION

Reading and Discussing Math   Write the following sentence on the chalkboard: *I estimate that there are about 25 people in this classroom.* Underline the words **estimate** and **about.** Read the sentence aloud and ask students to tell what they think it means to estimate. (Possible answer: to guess; to tell about how many) Ask questions such as the following. *About how tall are you? About how many students have pets? About what time is it now?* Have students give estimates; then ask for examples of other things they might estimate. Have them list their estimates in their Math Journals.

EXPLORE AND CONNECT

Materials: Cube-A-Links of one color for each student, doubles pictures from Lesson 2, one extra picture of each obje
Alternative Materials: colored blocks or counters
Grouping Suggestion: pairs

Pair students, giving one partner 9 cubes of one color and the other partner 9 cubes of another color. Display pictures or rea objects, and invite students to represent the doubles you show them with their cubes. Show a picture of a dozen eggs and as each partner to snap 6 cubes together to represent each of the rows of 6. Then add 1 egg to the group and have the partners represent it with one of their cubes and add it to one of their rows. Then ask them to snap the two rows together. *How ma cubes do you have all together?* (13) Have the partners work together to write the addition facts and remind them to listen t each other's ideas. Continue the activity, referring to the doubles pictures in the previous lesson.

CONNECTIONS   Use these anytime.

Problem of the Day

Too Much Information   Craig is carrying 4 books. Fran is carrying 5 books. They can walk to the library in 8 minutes. How many books are there all together? (9) What information did you not need? (that it took 8 minutes to walk to the library)

Number Sense

Mental Math   Do this in your head and then check your answer on paper: If you are 7 years old now, how old will you be in 8 years? (15) How did you do it? ($7 + 8 = 15$ or $7 + 7 + 1 = 15$)

Subject Integration

Language Arts   Get together with several other students and think of phrases we use that have the word *double* in them, such as *double trouble*. Write them down and discuss what they mean.

CLASSWORK AND HOMEWORK SUPPLEMENTS

Practice

Skills Maintenance   2-3

Name _____

Doubles Plus One

Add. Ring the doubles-plus-one facts.

1. (7 +6 = 13)   5 +5 = 10   (8 +7 = 15)   9 +2 = 11   3 +4 = 7

2. (4 +5 = 9)   8 +2 = 10   3 +5 = 8   (6 +5 = 11)   7 +3 = 10

3. (7 +8 = 15)   9 +1 = 10   (6 +6 = 12)   (5 +4 = 9)   2 +7 = 9

4. 2 +6 = 8   (8 +9 = 17)   7 +0 = 7   9 +9 = 18   (6 +7 = 13)

5. (5 +6 = 11)   3 +3 = 6   (8 +9 = 17)   5 +2 = 7   7 +7 = 14

12   Use with text pages 27-28.   PS-2

Building Thinking Skills

Life Skills   2-3

Name _____

Doubles-Plus-One Coin Count

Ring the coins to show the doubles.
Then write a doubles-plus-one number sentence.
How much money is in each box? 5¢ , 11¢, 13¢, 15¢

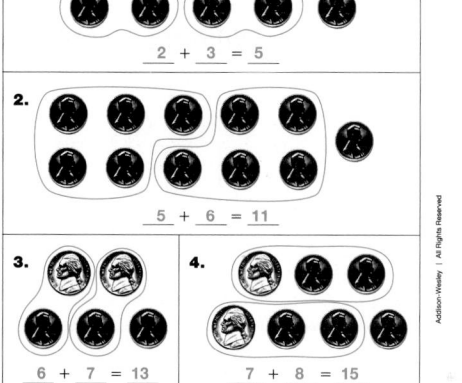

1. __2__ + __3__ = __5__

2. __5__ + __6__ = __11__

3. __6__ + __7__ = __13__   4. __7__ + __8__ = __15__

12   Use with text pages 27-28.   TS-2

Reteaching

Skills Review   2-3

Name _____

Doubles Plus One

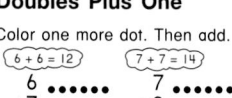

(Use the doubles!)

Color one more dot. Then add.

6 + 6 = 12   7 + 7 = 14   8 + 8 = 16

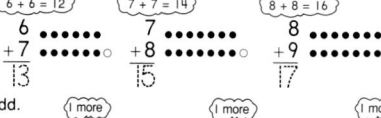

6 +7 = 13   7 +8 = 15   8 +9 = 17

Add. (1 more)

1. [6 +6 = 12] [6 +7 = 13]   [7 +7 = 14] [7 +8 = 15]   [8 +8 = 16] [8 +9 = 17]

2. 7 +6 = 13   8 +9 = 17   6 +5 = 11   7 +7 = 14   5 +5 = 10

3. 5 +4 = 9   8 +8 = 16   9 +9 = 18   9 +8 = 17   6 +3 = 9

4. 6 +7 = 13   3 +4 = 7   2 +3 = 5   6 +6 = 12   9 +9 = 18

12   Use with text pages 27-28.   RS-2

Challenges

Cooperative Activities   2-3

Name _____

Doubles-Plus-Ones Game

You need: one or more friends,
a spinner with numbers 1 to 8,
lots of markers.

Rules: Spin the spinner.
Double the number and add 1.
Cover a number that matches the sum.
Now it is your friend's turn.
The first one to get 5 markers in a row
wins.

17	5	13	9	13
9	3	15	11	7
7	11	13	17	15
3	5	9	13	3
15	17	11	7	5

12   Use with text pages 27-28.   CS-2

OPTIONS FOR INDIVIDUAL NEEDS

Basic

Exercises All
More Practice, p. 410, set A

Supplements
Reteaching 12 or
Practice 12
Challenge 12

Average

Exercises All
More Practice, p. 410, set A

Supplements
Practice 12
Challenges 12 or
Thinking Skills 12

Extended

Exercises All

Supplements
Challenges 12
Thinking Skills 12

Other Resources:
Mathematics Their Way, pages 103-104
Explorations, pages 42-43, 110-113

LESSON PLAN 2-3

OBJECTIVE 2-3
To use the mental math technique of doubles plus one to find sums

---

Materials: 20 counters for each pair of students; demonstration clock; tagboard

Alternative materials: punchout clock

---

1. MOTIVATE AND TEACH

LEARN ABOUT IT

Have students use counters to represent doubles such as 3 + 3, 4 + 4, 5 + 5, and 6 + 6. Ask them to add 1 counter to each double and to write the addition sentence that matches the new fact. Have students look at the sample example at the top of page 27.

▶ **In what way is 8 + 9 similar to 8 + 8?** (Possible answers: It is almost the same; it is close to 8 + 8; it is just one more.)

▶ **In what way is it different?** (It is one more.)

▶ **Why is 8 + 8 a good helper double for 8 + 9?** (Possible answers: because 8 + 8 is easy to remember; because 8 + 9 is only 1 more)

▶ **What is a good way to tell which addend to use as the double to help?** (Possible answer: Use the smaller addend.)

▶ **Why should you not double the greater addend when you are using a double to help?** (Possible answer: because the sum will be too big)

2. CHECK UNDERSTANDING

ERROR ALERT Being unsure of which addend to double and increase by one. Using the greater addend instead of the lesser.

Name _____

Doubles Plus One

Write the double that helps. Add.

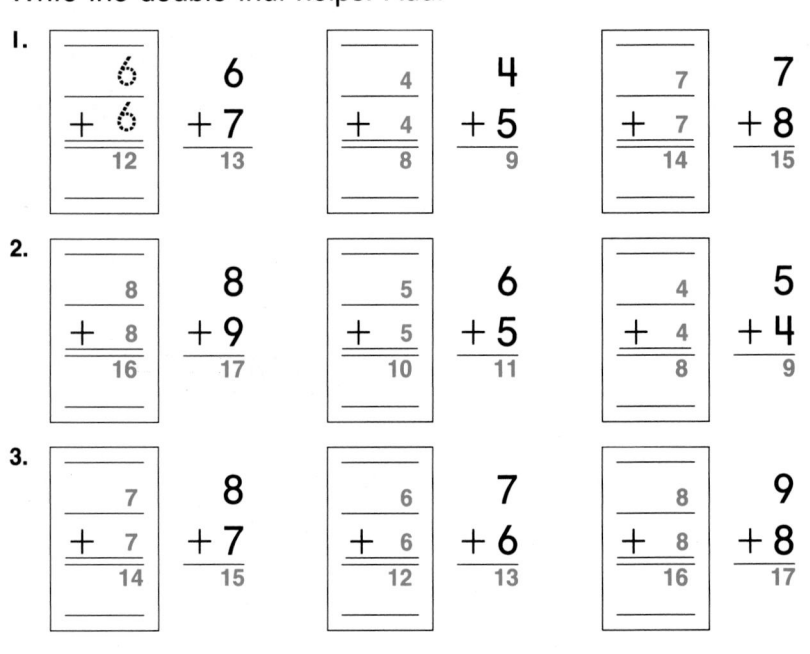

Chapter 2

(twenty-seven)

TEACHING OPTIONS

RETEACHING TIPS Write 4 + 4, 4 + 5 = 9, and 5 + 5 on the board. Have students use counters to model 4 + 4 and 5 + 5. Have them choose the group that yields 9 when you add one more. Continue with other problems. Assign Reteaching Supplement 12.

ENRICHMENT Write 1 + 3, 2 + 4, and 3 + 5 on the chalkboard. *How are they alike?* (The counting number between the two addends is missing.) *Add 1 + 3 and 2 + 2.* (4) *Add 2 + 4 and 3 + 3.* (6) *What pattern do you see?* (The missing number doubled has the same sum as the other two numbers.)

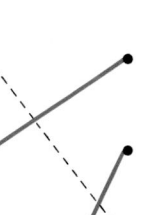

aw a line to the double that helps.
en add.

$6 + 7 = 13$	$4 + 4 = 8$
$5 + 4 = 9$	$8 + 8 = 16$
$8 + 7 = 15$	$6 + 6 = 12$
$5 + 6 = 11$	$7 + 7 = 14$
$8 + 9 = 17$	$5 + 5 = 10$

d. Ring double-plus-one facts.

$\begin{array}{r}7\\+8\\\hline 15\end{array}$ $\begin{array}{r}2\\+9\\\hline 11\end{array}$ $\begin{array}{r}8\\+7\\\hline 15\end{array}$ $\begin{array}{r}7\\+6\\\hline 13\end{array}$ $\begin{array}{r}6\\+5\\\hline 11\end{array}$ $\begin{array}{r}1\\+8\\\hline 9\end{array}$

$\begin{array}{r}5\\+6\\\hline 11\end{array}$ $\begin{array}{r}6\\+7\\\hline 13\end{array}$ $\begin{array}{r}3\\+3\\\hline 6\end{array}$ $\begin{array}{r}9\\+8\\\hline 17\end{array}$ $\begin{array}{r}4\\+5\\\hline 9\end{array}$ $\begin{array}{r}8\\+9\\\hline 17\end{array}$

KE AN ESTIMATE

Look at the time.
Ring the correct answer. It is closer to

12 o'clock   (I o'clock)

(twenty-eight)   More Practice, page 410, set A   Chapter 2

LOSE AND ASSESS

HOW WHAT YOU KNOW

ve pairs of students use tagboard to
ake two sets of doubles-plus-one
ct cards and two sets of answer
rds. Have them shuffle and place
e cards face down. Players take
ns drawing fact and answer cards,
eping the ones that match.
emind students of the chapter poem.
ow many eagles are there in all if
e 4 eagles meet 5 more eagles? (9
gles)

QUICK QUIZ

Write the doubles-plus-one
expressions that produce these sums:
7, 13, 9, 11, 5, 17
$(3 + 4, 6 + 7, 4 + 5, 5 + 6, 2 + 3,$
$8 + 9)$

---

3. PRACTICE AND APPLY

Basic	All
Average	All
Extended	All

2-3

PRACTICE

*How are Exercises 1-5 on page 28
similar to those on page 27?* (They use
doubles to help with adding.) *How will
you show the answers in rows 6 and 7?*
(by adding, then circling the
doubles-plus-one facts)

APPLY

MAKE AN ESTIMATE   Review the
meaning of estimation. Ask students
when it might be important to know the
exact time and when an estimate would
be enough. Model 12:50 on a real or
punchout clock.
▶ **Explain how you decided that the
time is closer to 1:00 than to 12:00.**
(Possible answer: The short hand is
closer to one.)

Fact Practice

OBJECTIVE 2-4 To practice the mental math techniques learned to find sums

PREBOOK ACTIVITIES

QUICK REVIEW

Add.

6 + 1 = (7)	0 + 3 = (3)
8 + 2 = (10)	2 + 3 = (5)
4 + 4 = (8)	6 + 7 = (13)
4 + 5 = (9)	9 + 0 = (9)

PRIOR KNOWLEDGE

Have students describe, in their own words, some of the strategies they have learned to help them add two numbers. (Possible answers: counting on, adding zeros, doubles, doubles-plus-one, any strategies of their own devising) Discuss these strategies, with examples, making sure they are understood clearly and correctly.

COMMUNICATION

Reading and Listening in Math On the chalkboard, write the names of the addition strategies discussed in the previous lessons. Then say aloud several addition expressions, such as 4 + 4, one at a time. After you say each one, point to two or three of the listed strategies and ask the students to raise their hands when you point to the one that would be most useful for that problem.

EXPLORE AND CONNECT

Materials: addition flashcards for each group of students, counters
Grouping Suggestion: cooperative learning groups
Distribute counters and a set of addition flashcards to each group of students. Make sure each group receives four kinds of facts in the card set: zeros, count ons, doubles, and doubles plus one. Have students in each group take turns choosing a card, modeling the fact with counters, and telling the strategy for remembering the fact, while the rest of the group listens to their ideas. After all the facts have been reviewed, have students summarize the addition strategies they know so far.

CONNECTIONS Use these anytime.

Problem of the Day

Ask a Question Give a question you could answer for this story. Then answer it.
There were 4 birds in a tree.
5 more birds flew into the tree.
(Possible answer: How many birds were there in all? 9)

Math Connection

Money Take 12 punchout pennies and place them on the table. Record all the combinations of heads and tails that make 12 and write those addition facts. Share your answers with a partner.

Subject Integration

Fine Arts Make a poster about one number from 1-9, using designs, magazine pictures, and other materials. When you are finished, join another student and find the sum of the numbers for the two posters.

CLASSWORK AND HOMEWORK SUPPLEMENTS

2-4

Practice

Skills Maintenance   2-4

Name ____

Fact Practice

Find the sums.

1. 7 + 6 = 13   5 + 5 = 10   2 + 3 = 5

2. 8 + 2 = 10   4 + 0 = 4   7 + 7 = 14

3. 3 + 3 = 6   6 + 2 = 8   8 + 9 = 17

4. 5 + 3 = 8   9 + 9 = 18   5 + 4 = 9

5. 9 + 1 = 10   8 + 8 = 16   3 + 9 = 12

6.
| 8 +7 = 15 | 4 +4 = 8 | 6 +5 = 11 | 7 +3 = 10 | 0 +9 = 9 |

7.
| 9 +8 = 17 | 7 +2 = 9 | 3 +8 = 11 | 6 +6 = 12 | 5 +2 = 7 |

8.
| 9 +3 = 12 | 4 +2 = 6 | 7 +8 = 15 | 3 +6 = 9 | 2 +9 = 11 |

PS-2   Use with text pages 29-30.   13

Building Thinking Skills

Number Sense   2-4

Name ____

To the Top

This building has 17 floors.
Pretend that you live on the 5th floor.

1. You start on your floor. You go up 5 floors. What floor are you on? __10__

2. Go up 5 more floors. What floor are you on? __15__

3. You visit a friend on the 11th floor. How many floors do you go up from your floor? __6__

4. You are on floor 7. How many floors to the top? __10__

Fill in the table.

You are on floor	2	3	9	10	13	11	16
How many to the top?	15	14	8	7	4	6	1

TS-2   Use with text pages 29-30.   13

Reteaching

Skills Review   2-4

Name ____

Fact Practice

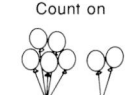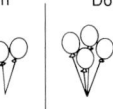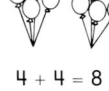

Count on	Doubles	Doubles plus one
5 + 2 = 7	4 + 4 = 8	4 + 5 = 9

Count on to add.

1.
| 7 +3 = 10 | 8 +2 = 10 | 3 +2 = 5 | 5 +1 = 6 | 2 +1 = 3 |

Add. Use doubles and doubles plus one.

2.
| 5 +5 = 10 | 3 +3 = 6 | 6 +7 = 13 | 7 +7 = 14 | 7 +8 = 15 |

Find the sums.

3. 6 + 6 = 12   5 + 6 = 11   6 + 3 = 9

4. 9 + 9 = 18   7 + 1 = 8   8 + 9 = 17

RS-2   Use with text pages 29-30.   13

Challenges

Math Reasoning   2-4

Name ____

What Is the Question?

Make your own addition problems that have the given answers. Answers will vary. Possible answers are given.

1.
| 8 +1 = 9 | 7 +2 = 9 | 6 +3 = 9 | 5 +4 = 9 | 9 +0 = 9 |

2.
| 8 +2 = 10 | 7 +3 = 10 | 5 +5 = 10 | 1 +9 = 10 | 10 +0 = 10 |

3.
| 8 +3 = 11 | 9 +2 = 11 | 5 +6 = 11 | 3 +8 = 11 | 10 +1 = 11 |

CS-2   Use with text pages 29-30.   13

OBJECTIVE 2-4
To practice the mental techniques learned to find sums

> **Materials:** addition flashcards, 20 two-color counters or tiles, calculators, punchout coins
>
> **Grouping Suggestions:** individual work; pairs

1. MOTIVATE AND TEACH

LEARN ABOUT IT

On the chalkboard, write addition expressions such as 4 + 5, 6 + 6, 8 + 0, 6 + 7, and 5 + 3. Have students give the sums orally and tell which addition strategy they used.

Go over the first exercise on page 29. Remind students to color the oval for the sum that is *different* from the other two.

▶ **What were some exercises in which the strategies we have discussed helped you add?** (Possible answers: all of them; any individual exercise numbers; none, I know all of them by memory)

▶ **Who can classify the facts by the addition strategy they used?** (count ons: 2 + 9, 7 + 3, 2 + 7, 8 + 1, and so on; doubles: 6 + 6, 7 + 7, 9 + 9, 5 + 5, 4 + 4, 8 + 8; doubles plus one: 5 + 6, 6 + 7, 6 + 5, 9 + 8)

2. CHECK UNDERSTANDING

ERROR ALERT   Not remembering how to apply the addition strategies discussed.

Name _____

Fact Practice

Add. Two have the same sum.
Color ⬭ for the one that is different.

1.
⬭ 2 + 9 = 11
⬭ 5 + 6 = 11
⬤ 7 + 3 = 10

2.
⬭ 2 + 7 = 9
⬭ 8 + 1 = 9
⬤ 6 + 6 = 12

3.
⬤ 6 + 7 = 13
⬭ 9 + 3 = 12
⬭ 6 + 6 = 12

4.
⬭ 0 + 8 = 8
⬤ 7 + 7 = 14
⬭ 3 + 5 = 8

5.
⬭ 3 + 8 = 11
⬤ 9 + 9 = 18
⬭ 6 + 5 = 11

6.
⬤ 7 + 2 = 9
⬭ 5 + 5 = 10
⬭ 2 + 8 = 10

7.
⬭ 4 + 4 = 8
⬤ 9 + 8 = 17
⬭ 1 + 7 = 8

8.
⬭ 3 + 7 = 10
⬤ 8 + 8 = 16
⬭ 1 + 9 = 10

Chapter 2   (twenty-nine)

TEACHING OPTIONS

RETEACHING TIPS   Have partners quiz each other with flashcards and set aside the ones they miss. Have them work together to model the missed facts with two-color counters and to remind each other of the appropriate thinking strategies. Assign Reteaching Supplement 13.

ENRICHMENT   Have students use the grid to add and ring pairs, across or down, that add to 11.

(7	4)	3	4	(8
0	4	(6	5)	3)
(9	2)	(4	6	0
1	9)	7	3)	8

dd.

$$\begin{array}{r}5\\+4\\\hline 9\end{array}\qquad\begin{array}{r}3\\+6\\\hline 9\end{array}\qquad\begin{array}{r}7\\+7\\\hline 14\end{array}\qquad\begin{array}{r}8\\+2\\\hline 10\end{array}\qquad\begin{array}{r}9\\+8\\\hline 17\end{array}$$

$$\begin{array}{r}3\\+9\\\hline 12\end{array}\qquad\begin{array}{r}9\\+9\\\hline 18\end{array}\qquad\begin{array}{r}8\\+7\\\hline 15\end{array}\qquad\begin{array}{r}0\\+6\\\hline 6\end{array}\qquad\begin{array}{r}4\\+4\\\hline 8\end{array}$$

$$\begin{array}{r}7\\+6\\\hline 13\end{array}\qquad\begin{array}{r}4\\+5\\\hline 9\end{array}\qquad\begin{array}{r}5\\+6\\\hline 11\end{array}\qquad\begin{array}{r}9\\+2\\\hline 11\end{array}\qquad\begin{array}{r}8\\+8\\\hline 16\end{array}$$

$$\begin{array}{r}1\\+9\\\hline 10\end{array}\qquad\begin{array}{r}2\\+7\\\hline 9\end{array}\qquad\begin{array}{r}8\\+3\\\hline 11\end{array}\qquad\begin{array}{r}5\\+5\\\hline 10\end{array}\qquad\begin{array}{r}5\\+3\\\hline 8\end{array}$$

$$\begin{array}{r}6\\+6\\\hline 12\end{array}\qquad\begin{array}{r}7\\+8\\\hline 15\end{array}\qquad\begin{array}{r}9\\+0\\\hline 9\end{array}\qquad\begin{array}{r}2\\+8\\\hline 10\end{array}\qquad\begin{array}{r}6\\+7\\\hline 13\end{array}$$

TRY A CALCULATOR

. Write as you add.

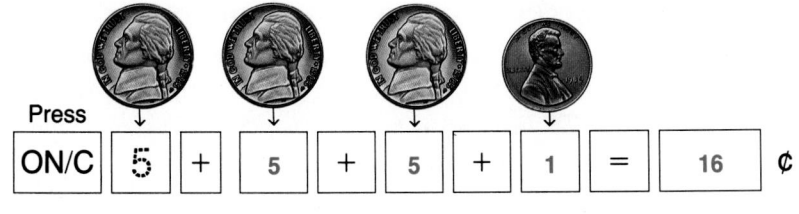

Press

| ON/C | 5 | + | 5 | + | 5 | + | 1 | = | 16 | ¢ |

Chapter 2

3. PRACTICE AND APPLY

Basic	All
Average	All
Extended	All

PRACTICE

How are the addition facts in Exercises 1-5 on page 30 different from those on page 29? (Possible answer: They are in vertical form.)

APPLY

TRY A CALCULATOR Review the use of the calculator as necessary. After students complete the exercise, have them place punchout coins over those pictured as they count the money: 5, 10, 15, 16¢.
► **How does this exercise compare with any of our adding strategies?** (Possible answers: It is like doubles plus one with triples; it has counting on by 5s to 15 and then adding one more.)

CLOSE AND ASSESS

SAY WHAT YOU THINK Pair students, giving each student a set of 10 flashcards. Have partners take turns finding the sums and telling how they did the addition. Encourage students to listen carefully to their partners' answers and explanations and to discuss any errors or differences in strategies used.

QUICK QUIZ

Find the sums.

$7 + 6 = \underline{(13)}\qquad 9 + 0 = \underline{(9)}$

$$\begin{array}{r}9\\+8\\\hline (17)\end{array}\qquad\begin{array}{r}6\\+5\\\hline (11)\end{array}\qquad\begin{array}{r}7\\+7\\\hline (14)\end{array}\qquad\begin{array}{r}2\\+8\\\hline (10)\end{array}$$

Chapter 2 Lesson 4   **30**

Problem Solving: Understanding the Operations/Data Analysis

OBJECTIVE 2-5   To understand the operations of addition and subtraction by putting together or by taking away;

PREBOOK ACTIVITIES

QUICK REVIEW

Add or subtract.

6	9	3	7	2	1	6	5
$-\ 3$	$-\ 2$	$+\ 7$	$+\ 7$	$-\ 1$	$+\ 9$	$+\ 0$	$-\ 3$
(3)	(7)	(10)	(14)	(1)	(10)	(6)	(2)

$5 + 6 =$ _(11)_ $8 - 6 =$ _(2)_ $9 - 3 =$ _(6)_ $4 + 5 =$ _(9)_

PRIOR KNOWLEDGE

Ask students to imagine that they have 10 pennies in each hand. *Pretend that each of the following situations happens to you and your pennies. Decide whether each situation would cause you to subtract pennies from your total or add pennies to your total.*
You lose 2 pennies.   (subtract)
You find 5 pennies on the ground.   (add)
Your mother gives you a penny.   (add)
You spend 6 of your pennies.   (subtract)

COMMUNICATION

Reading and Discussing Math   Write the words **plan** and **data** on the chalkboard. Read the words aloud and explain that to plan something means to think about something before you do it. Then write *We need to collect some information.* Explain that another word for *information* is *data.* Ask students to read the sentence and substitute the word *data* for *information.* *Suppose you want to collect data about the families of your class members. How might you plan to get this information?* (Possible answer: Make a list of people and questions to ask.)

EXPLORE AND CONNECT

COOPERATIVE ACTIVITY

Grouping Suggestion: small groups
Finish the number sentence.
5 dogs were barking.
2 others joined them.
How many dogs were barking together?
5 + _(2)_ = _(7)_

TEACHING ACTIONS

▶ **What is happening in this story?** (Possible answer: A group of dogs is barking. More dogs come to join them.)
▶ **Can you identify important data in this story?** (Possible answer: the number of dogs to begin; the number that join them.)

▶ **How might you plan whether to subtract or add to find the answer?** (Possible answers: Think about what the question asks you. The question might tell you whether to join or separate groups.)
▶ **How could you plan a way to solve this problem?** (Possible answer: Act out each step of the problem with other people or use counters to represent each group of dogs. Then write a number sentence that fits the problem.)

AFTER ▶ **How could you check your answer?** (Possible answer: Read it over to make sure the answer makes sense. Add again.) Have groups use counters to model the action in the problem.

CONNECTIONS   Use these anytime.

Problem of the Day
Understanding the Operations
Circle the addition question for this story.
6 blue birds are in the tree.
4 red birds are in the tree.
How many birds are left?
How many birds are there altogether?

Subject Integration
Language Arts   Write an addition or subtraction story that has your name in it. Trade your story with a friend and write number sentences to match each other's stories. Discuss the answers together. Draw a picture to show your story.

Life Skills
Careers   Tell what kind of data the following people might need to collect to help them do their jobs:
mail carrier   (addresses, names)
pilot   (weather forecast, type of plane)
doctor   (data about how you are feeling)
waiter   (the menu, your order)
referee   (rules of the sport)

take a survey using tally marks

CLASSWORK AND HOMEWORK SUPPLEMENTS

Practice

Problem Solving 2-5

Name _____

Understanding the Operations

Solve.

1. 8 birds were on the fence.
5 flew away.
How many are left? __3__ birds
8 ⊖ 5 ⊟ 3

2. 7 flowers are in one vase.
4 flowers are in another vase.
How many are there in all? __11__ flowers
7 ⊕ 4 ⊟ 11

3. 6 apples were under a tree.
A horse ate 2 apples.
How many are left? __4__ apples
6 ⊖ 2 ⊟ 4

4. 4 horses were in the field.
2 horses joined them.
How many were in the field? __6__ horses
4 ⊕ 2 ⊟ 6

14   Use with text page 31.   PS-2

Building Thinking Skills

Problem Solving 2-5

Name _____

Blowing Away

Read the story.
Fill in the number sentences as you read.

Doug needs 10 balloons for
his birthday party.

He blew up 3 red balloons.
Then he blew up 4 more.   3 ⊕ 4 = ⑦
Then he blew up 3 yellow balloons.   7 ⊕ 3 = ⑩
4 balloons popped.   10 ⊖ 4 = ⑥
3 balloons blew away.   6 ⊖ 3 = ③
Bonnie came to help.
She gave Doug 5 green balloons.   3 ⊕ 5 = ⑧
Then she blew up 3 more green   8 ⊕ 3 = ⑪
balloons, but 3 balloons blew away.   11 ⊖ 3 = ⑧
Bonnie blew up 4 more balloons,   8 ⊕ 4 = ⑫
but 5 balloons popped.   12 ⊖ 5 = ⑦
Doug had a rest.
Then he blew up 4 more balloons.   7 ⊕ 4 = ⑪
Does he have enough balloons?   yes

14   Use with text pages 31-32.   TS-2

Reteaching

Data Analysis 2-5

Name _____

Collecting Data

I		2 II	3 III	4 IIII
(number) (tally)				

5 卌   6 卌 I   7 卌 II
8 卌 III   9 卌 IIII   10 卌 卌

Make tally marks for each kind of pet.

1.    **2.**

3.   **4.**

Write the totals.

5.  7   **6.** 5   **7.** 9   **8.** 4

14   Use with text page 32.   RS-2

Challenges

Data Analysis 2-5

Name _____

Birthday Survey

Take a survey. Find out the birthday of each
classmate. Tally the birthdays by month. Answers will vary.

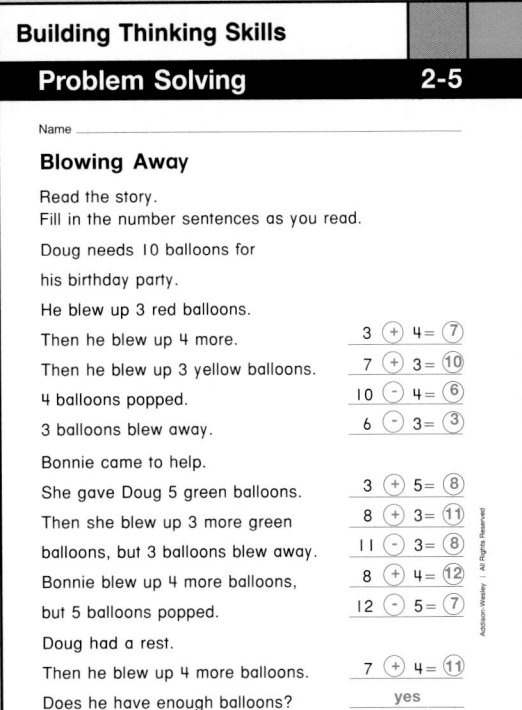

January	February	March	April
May	June	July	August
September	October	November	December

Which month has the most birthdays? _____

Which month has the fewest birthdays? _____
How many students have their birthday in the same

month as you do? _____
Share the data with your classmates.

14   Use with text page 32.   CS-2

Basic

Exercises All
More Practice, p. 410, set B

Supplements
Reteaching 14 or
Practice 14

Average

Exercises All
More Practice, p. 410, set B

Supplements
Practice 14
Challenges 14 or
Thinking Skills 14

Extended

Exercises All

Supplements
Challenges 14
Thinking Skills 14

Other Resources:
Explorations, pages 6, 42,
196-200
*Problem-Solving Experiences
In Mathematics*, page 33
Workjobs, pages 222-223
Workjobs II, pages 111-115
*Developing Number Concepts
with Unifix Cubes*, pages
129-131

OBJECTIVE 2-5

To understand the operations of addition and subtraction by putting together or by taking away; to take a survey using tally marks

1. MOTIVATE AND TEACH

LEARN ABOUT IT

 **BEFORE** ▶ **Describe what is happening in Exercise 1.** (Possible answer: A group of pandas was eating. Two pandas ran away.)

 **DURING** ▶ **How can you use counters to help you plan whether to add or subtract?** (Possible answer: Act out what happens. Show 6 counters and take 2 away to find how many pandas were still eating.)

AFTER ▶ **Suggest a way that you can check your number sentence.** (Possible answer: Draw a picture to show what happened in the story. Write the number sentence under it to make sure it fits.)

2. CHECK UNDERSTANDING

ERROR ALERT **Page 31** Not organizing parts of number sentences in the correct order.

Page 32 Not writing the appropriate number of tally marks for the number that they represent.

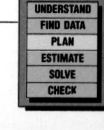

UNDERSTAND / FIND DATA / PLAN / ESTIMATE / SOLVE / CHECK

Name _____

Problem Solving
Understanding the Operations

Use counters to show the stories.
Finish the number sentences.

1. 6 pandas were eating bamboo.
   2 ran away.
   How many pandas were still eating?

   6  _2_ ▦ _4_   _4_ pandas

2. 2 blue whales were swimming together. 7 others swam over to them. How many blue whales were swimming together then?

   2 ⊕ _7_ = _9_   _9_ blue whales

3. 4 cougars were hunting in the mountains. 3 joined the hunt. How many cougars were hunting then?

   4 ⊕ _3_ = _7_   _7_ cougars

4. 9 gorillas were sleeping 3 woke up and began to play. How many gorillas were still sleeping?

   9 ⊖ _3_ = _6_   _6_ gorillas

Chapter 2   More Practice, page 410, set B   (thirty-one)

TEACHING OPTIONS

RETEACHING TIPS Place objects, numbers, and operation signs on a flannelboard. Write a story problem on the chalkboard. Ask pairs to show the action in the story. Then ask them to arrange a number sentence to match. Assign Reteaching Supplement 14.

ENRICHMENT Have students conduct their own survey. Topics might include a favorite food, a favorite day of the week, or a favorite color. Have them prepare a survey sheet and then ask classmates and family members for their opinions. Have students share their results with the class.

...ata Analysis

...ke a survey. Find out which endangered ...imal your classmates like best.

Make a **tally mark** for each vote. Then write the totals.

> | means I vote.
> |||| means 5 votes.

Answers may vary.

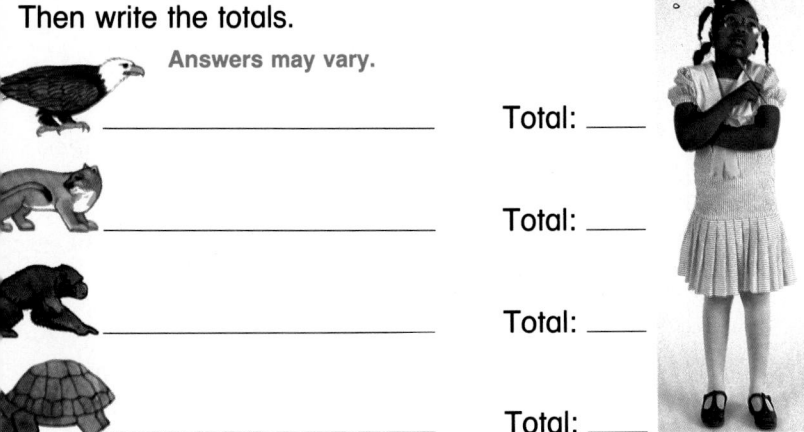

Total: ____

Total: ____

Total: ____

Total: ____

...Ring the animal that got the greatest number of votes.

Answers may vary.

...Ring the animal that got the least number of votes.

Answers may vary.

Count to find how many more votes the animal in ⟨2⟩ got than the animal in ⟨3⟩ ____ more votes

Answers may vary.

(thirty-two)

Chapter 2

---

3. PRACTICE AND APPLY

Basic	All
Average	All
Extended	All

You can see how 5 tally marks are written. How would you write 6 tally marks? (|||| |) *How will you determine which animal was the favorite among your classmates?* (Look at the total for each animal. The one with the greatest number is the favorite.)

▶ **What is a tally mark?** (Possible answer: a line used to count things; you write tally marks in groups of 5)

▶ **What is the purpose of a survey?** (Possible answer: Sometimes it is used to find out people's opinions.)

▶ **What is one way to take a survey of your classmates to see which endangered animal they like best? How will you show your answers?** (Possible answer: Ask students to raise their hands when they hear their favorite animal's name. Count the hands and record the number using tally marks.)

▶ **What can you do with the results of your survey?** (Possible answer: Find out the most and least popular animal in your class. Compare your results with those of another class.)

...LOSE AND ASSESS

...AY WHAT YOU THINK Write 7 ... 3 = 4 and 3 + 4 = 7 on the ...alkboard. Ask students for story ...eas that will match each number ...entence. As they tell a story, write it ...n the board. Have them identify ...hich number sentence it goes with ...nd then use pictures to prove that the ...umber sentence fits. If time allows, ...sk students to write their own stories ...r two different number sentences ...d display them in the classroom.

QUICK QUIZ

Find the total for each object. Ring the object with the most tally marks.

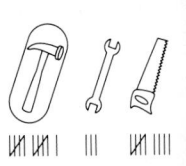

|||| |||| | ||| |||| ||||

Chapter 2 Lesson 5   **32**

Sums of 10

OBJECTIVE 2-6   To use the mental math technique of finding sums of 10

PREBOOK ACTIVITIES

QUICK REVIEW

As I write a number on the chalkboard (use numbers 1-5), hold up the number of fingers that shows the sum of the number doubled. As I write a number on the chalkboard (use numbers 1-4), hold up the number of fingers that shows the sum of the number doubled plus one.

PRIOR KNOWLEDGE

What coins can you put together to come up with 10 cents? (Possible answers: 1 dime; 2 nickels; 10 pennies; 1 nickel, 5 pennies.) *What number sentences would show these coin combinations?* ($10 + 0 = 10$, $5 + 5 = 10$)

COMMUNICATION

Reading and Discussing Math   Write the word *ten* on the chalkboard. Read the word to the students, then have students read the word together. Next, write 10 on the chalkboard. Call on students to draw sets of 10 shapes. *What do you already know about the number 10?* (Possible answers: It comes after 9 and before 11 when you count; it is the number of pennies for a dime.)

EXPLORE AND CONNECT

Materials: 10 penny punchouts and 10-frame punchout for each student, Basic Facts Chart
Grouping Suggestions: individual work, pairs
How are the sides of a penny different? (One side is called heads, the other side is called tails.) Have students fill the 10-frame with pennies. *How many pennies is a fair trade for dime?* (10) *How can you show sums of 10 using pennies?* (Us heads to represent one addend and tails to represent the other Have students experiment with different addends and write their findings on the board. Continue until all 10 sums have been identified. Then have students work in pairs to THINK, PAIR, and SHARE sums of 10. Write a 1-digit number on th chalkboard. Have one student THINK and then tell the partne what number added to the number on the board gives a sum 10. When the PAIR agree, they raise a hand to signal they a ready to SHARE with the class.

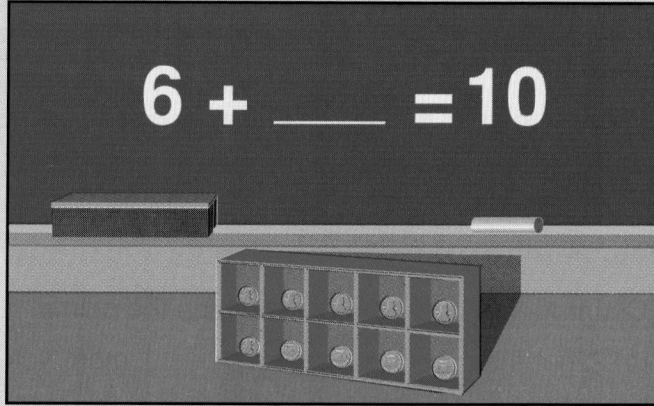

CONNECTIONS   Use these anytime.

Problem of the Day
Reasoning   Write a question about this story. Answer your question. 2 red buttons are in a jar. 8 blue buttons are in a jar. (Accept reasonable responses.)

Subject Integration
Physical Education   Let's see how far we get when we take 10 tiny steps . . . 10 giant steps . . . 10 regular steps. Be careful not to touch anyone else.

Counting Patterns
Skip Counting   Start with 0. Count by 10s up to 100. Then count back to 0.

CLASSWORK AND HOMEWORK SUPPLEMENTS

Practice

Skills Maintenance 2-6

Name

Sums of 10

Find the sums.
Color four 10 sums in a row.

2 +6 8	5 +5 10	4 +5 9	6 +6 12
8 +2 10	6 +4 10	1 +9 10	7 +3 10
6 +1 7	2 +9 11	9 +9 18	5 +6 11
7 +8 15	0 +10 10	8 +8 16	2 +8 10

PS-2   Use with text pages 33-34.   15

Building Thinking Skills

Data Analysis 2-6

Name

Buying Toys

SALE PRICES
Train 1¢
Car   9¢
Boat   5¢
Plane 4¢
Bike   3¢

Use the sign at the store.
Write what each person bought.

1. Ellen bought 2 toys.
She spent 10¢.
She bought a __train__
and a __car__.

2. Peter bought 2 toys.
He spent 8¢.
He bought a __boat__
and a __bike__.

3. Chris spent 7¢.
He bought 2 toys.
He bought a __bike__
and a __plane__.

4. Carmen spent 6¢.
She bought 2 toys.
She bought a __boat__
and a __train__.

5. You have 10¢.
What can you buy? __Answers will vary.__
Will you have change? _____ How much? _____

TS-2   Use with text pages 33-34.   15

Exercises All

Supplements
Reteaching 15 or
Practice 15

Exercises All

Supplements
Practice 15
Challenges 15 or
Thinking Skills 15

Reteaching

Manipulatives 2-6

Name

Sums of 10

6
+4
10

1. Use the 10-frame and counters.
Make sums of 10.

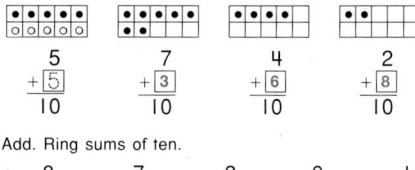

5
+5
10   7
+3
10   4
+6
10   2
+8
10

Add. Ring sums of ten.

2. 8
+2
(10)   7
+1
8   3
+7
(10)   9
+3
12   1
+9
(10)

3. 6 + 4 = (10)   4 + 4 = 8   7 + 0 = 7

RS-2   Use with text pages 33-34.   15

Challenges

Cooperative Activities 2-6

Name

Target Ten

Play with a friend.
Player 1 puts a marker on a number.
Player 2 puts a marker on the number needed to make 10.

5	9	6	1
3	7	8	10
0	2	4	5

Play again.
This time player 2 goes first.
Play until you cover all the numbers.

Now try **Target Twelve**.

4	0	3	6	10
5	1	8	7	6
6	9	11	12	2

CS-2   Use with text pages 33-34.   15

Extended

Exercises All

Supplements
Challenges 15
Thinking Skills 15

Other Resources:
Math in Stride, pages 25-26
Explorations, pages 43-44,
52-55, 176-183

LESSON PLAN 2-6

OBJECTIVE 2-6
To use the mental math technique of finding sums of 10

Materials: 10 punchout pennies per student, magazines

Grouping Suggestions: pairs, cooperative learning groups of 3

1. MOTIVATE AND TEACH

LEARN ABOUT IT

Draw 3 circles on the chalkboard. Then ask a volunteer to draw the number of circles needed to make a sum of 10. (7) Write the number sentence 3 + 7 = 10.
▶ **How do the pennies at the top of page 33 help you find the answer?** (Possible answers: The heads stand for 6, and the tails stand for 4; they help us picture the sum.)
▶ **What strategy can you use to find the missing addends?** (Possible answer: Put pennies to match one addend in the 10-frame; count on to find the other addend.)
▶ **How are the first exercise in Row 3 and Exercise 4 related?** (Possible answers: They are turnaround facts; they have the same addends.)

2. CHECK UNDERSTANDING

ERROR ALERT Miscounting addends when placing pennies in the 10-frame, causing mistakes in computation.

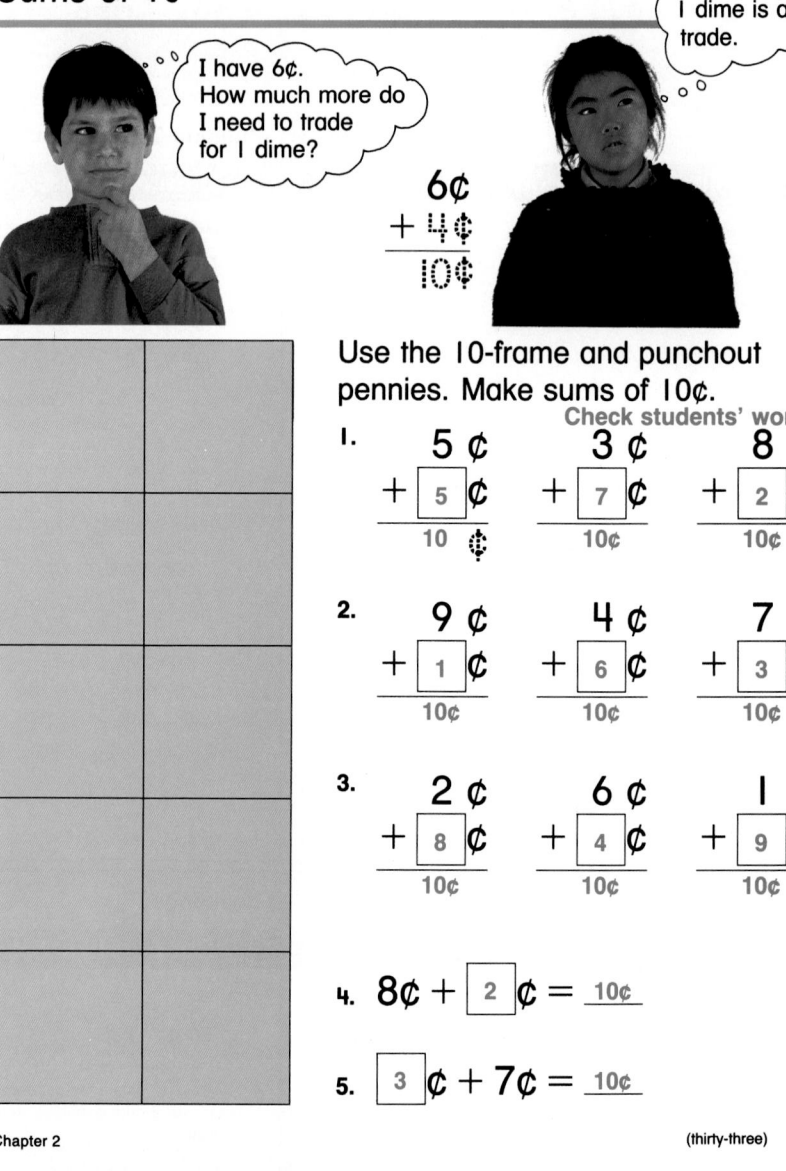

Name _____

Sums of 10

I have 6¢. How much more do I need to trade for 1 dime?

Remember— 10 pennies [...] I dime is a [...] trade.

$$\begin{array}{r} 6¢ \\ + 4¢ \\ \hline 10¢ \end{array}$$

Use the 10-frame and punchout pennies. Make sums of 10¢.

Check students' work

1. $\begin{array}{r} 5¢ \\ + \boxed{5}¢ \\ \hline 10¢ \end{array}$ $\begin{array}{r} 3¢ \\ + \boxed{7}¢ \\ \hline 10¢ \end{array}$ $\begin{array}{r} 8¢ \\ + \boxed{2}¢ \\ \hline 10¢ \end{array}$

2. $\begin{array}{r} 9¢ \\ + \boxed{1}¢ \\ \hline 10¢ \end{array}$ $\begin{array}{r} 4¢ \\ + \boxed{6}¢ \\ \hline 10¢ \end{array}$ $\begin{array}{r} 7¢ \\ + \boxed{3}¢ \\ \hline 10¢ \end{array}$

3. $\begin{array}{r} 2¢ \\ + \boxed{8}¢ \\ \hline 10¢ \end{array}$ $\begin{array}{r} 6¢ \\ + \boxed{4}¢ \\ \hline 10¢ \end{array}$ $\begin{array}{r} 1¢ \\ + \boxed{9}¢ \\ \hline 10¢ \end{array}$

4. $8¢ + \boxed{2}¢ = \underline{10¢}$

5. $\boxed{3}¢ + 7¢ = \underline{10¢}$

Chapter 2   (thirty-three)

TEACHING OPTIONS

RETEACHING TIPS Have students use 2-color counters to model sums of 10. Encourage them to use a different color to show each addend and to count carefully. Then have them write addition sentences to match the models. Use Reteaching Supplement 15 for help in finding sums of 10.

ENRICHMENT Have students work with a partner. One claps hands 1 to 9 times. The partner claps the number that would add to 10. Trade roles often.

ld. Use 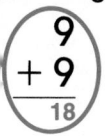 to color sums of 10.

$\begin{array}{r} 2 \\ +8 \\ \hline 10 \end{array}$	$\begin{array}{r} 4 \\ +4 \\ \hline 8 \end{array}$	$\begin{array}{r} 7 \\ +3 \\ \hline 10 \end{array}$	$\begin{array}{r} 8 \\ +7 \\ \hline 15 \end{array}$	$\begin{array}{r} 4 \\ +6 \\ \hline 10 \end{array}$	$\begin{array}{r} 6 \\ +3 \\ \hline 9 \end{array}$
$\begin{array}{r} 5 \\ +6 \\ \hline 11 \end{array}$	$\begin{array}{r} 9 \\ +1 \\ \hline 10 \end{array}$	$\begin{array}{r} 7 \\ +0 \\ \hline 7 \end{array}$	$\begin{array}{r} 5 \\ +5 \\ \hline 10 \end{array}$	$\begin{array}{r} 7 \\ +6 \\ \hline 13 \end{array}$	$\begin{array}{r} 6 \\ +4 \\ \hline 10 \end{array}$
$\begin{array}{r} 8 \\ +2 \\ \hline 10 \end{array}$	$\begin{array}{r} 2 \\ +6 \\ \hline 8 \end{array}$	$\begin{array}{r} 4 \\ +6 \\ \hline 10 \end{array}$	$\begin{array}{r} 8 \\ +3 \\ \hline 11 \end{array}$	$\begin{array}{r} 3 \\ +7 \\ \hline 10 \end{array}$	$\begin{array}{r} 4 \\ +5 \\ \hline 9 \end{array}$

Ring the pattern
you made.

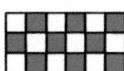 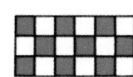 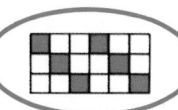

MIDCHAPTER REVIEW/QUIZ

ld zero or count on.

$\begin{array}{r} 8 \\ +3 \\ \hline 11 \end{array}$	$\begin{array}{r} 2 \\ +9 \\ \hline 11 \end{array}$	$\begin{array}{r} 0 \\ +7 \\ \hline 7 \end{array}$	$\begin{array}{r} 2 \\ +8 \\ \hline 10 \end{array}$	$\begin{array}{r} 1 \\ +6 \\ \hline 7 \end{array}$	$\begin{array}{r} 9 \\ +0 \\ \hline 9 \end{array}$

ld. Ring the double facts.

$\begin{array}{r} 9 \\ +9 \\ \hline 18 \end{array}$	$\begin{array}{r} 5 \\ +6 \\ \hline 11 \end{array}$	$\begin{array}{r} 4 \\ +4 \\ \hline 8 \end{array}$	$\begin{array}{r} 4 \\ +5 \\ \hline 9 \end{array}$	$\begin{array}{r} 8 \\ +8 \\ \hline 16 \end{array}$	$\begin{array}{r} 6 \\ +7 \\ \hline 13 \end{array}$

(thirty-four)

Chapter 2

3. PRACTICE AND APPLY

Basic	All, Midchapter Review/Quiz
Average	All, Midchapter Review/Quiz
Extended	All, Midchapter Review/Quiz

PRACTICE

How can you use pennies and a 10-frame to help you find the answers in Exercises 1-3? (Possible answer: Use pennies for the addends. Place them on the 10-frame to show if the sum is 10 or more or less than 10.)

APPLY

▶ **Did you use turnaround facts to help you find sums of 10?** (Possible answer: Yes, the first exercise is 2 + 8 = 10; you know 8 + 2 also is 10, so you can find it quickly.)

MIDCHAPTER REVIEW/QUIZ

ITEM ANALYSIS The table correlates the Midchapter Review/Quiz with lesson objectives.

Items	Objectives
1	2-1
2	2-2

LOSE AND ASSESS

HOW WHAT YOU KNOW

read the chapter poem. Have
dents use mental math and a
-frame to answer the question.
ppose there are 4 eagles soaring
ove the forest and 6 eagles soaring
ove the cliffs. How many are there
all? (10 eagles)

QUICK QUIZ

Ring the sums of 10.
| 6 + 4 | 5 + 3 | 7 + 2 | 5 + 5 |
| 9 + 1 | 3 + 6 | 2 + 8 | 4 + 5 |

Adding with 9

OBJECTIVE 2-7   To use the mental math technique of adding with 9 to find sums

PREBOOK ACTIVITIES

QUICK REVIEW

As I say each number, add 10 and say the sum together.
4 (14), 3 (13), 5 (15), 6 (16), 2 (12), 1 (11)

PRIOR KNOWLEDGE

Help students recall adding to make a sum of 10. *You want to buy a toy that costs $10 but you have only $9. How much more money do you need?* ($1)

COMMUNICATION

Listening and Discussing Math   Read the following story: Tanya saw 9 zebras in the African Veldt at the zoo. Then she saw the zookeeper bring 4 more in. She said, "I see 13 zebras." Her mother asked, "How did you add so quickly?" Tanya answered, "I counted 9 zebras. When the zookeeper brought in 4 more, I thought, 1 more makes 10. Then I added the 3 extras." *Why did Tanya make 10 and add the extras?* (Possible answer: It made it easier to add.)

EXPLORE AND CONNECT

Materials: 10-frame, 18 two-color counters for each pair of students
Grouping Suggestion: pairs
Pair students and have them place 9 counters of one color inside the 10-frame for the entire activity. Students take turns saying a number from 1 to 9 and using counters of the second color to show that number outside of the frame. Then they move 1 counter inside the 10-frame to fill it, mentally add to 10 the number of counters left outside the frame, and tell their partner the sum. *What happens each time you fill up your 10-frame to help you find the total?* (Possible answer: I always get 10 to add to.) *Why is it easier to add 10 + 4 than 9 + 5?* (Possible answer: You add the extras to the zero.)

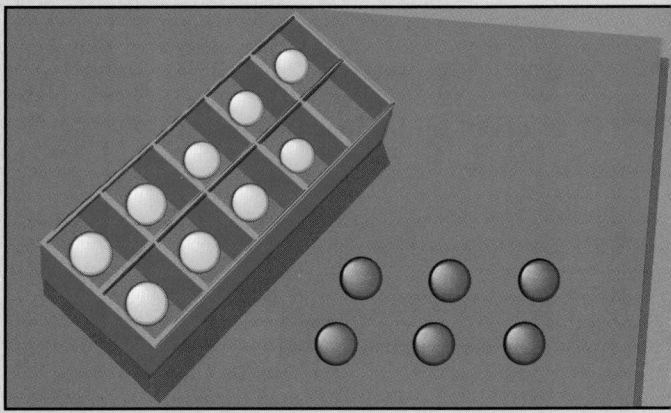

CONNECTIONS   Use these anytime.

Problem of the Day

Logic   A = 9¢, T = 4¢, S = 8¢, N = 6¢ You may use a calculator to do this. Which of the following 3 words costs the most? Which costs the least?
AS   AT   AN
(AS = 17¢, most expensive; AT = 13¢, least expensive)

Number Sense

Mental Math   Name the number that is
2 more than 9.   (11)
5 more than 9.   (14)
8 more than 9.   (17)
3 more than 9.   (12)

Math Connection

Consumer Math   You have 3 bags of coins with values of 7¢, 6¢, and 9¢ each. Which two bags will add up to 16¢? (9¢ and 7¢)

CLASSWORK AND HOMEWORK SUPPLEMENTS

Basic

Exercises All

Supplements
Reteaching 16 or
Practice 16

Practice

Skills Maintenance   2-7

Name _____

Adding with 9

Add.

1.	6 +9 15	9 +2 11	3 +9 12	9 +8 17	5 +9 14
2.	9 +7 16	4 +9 13	1 +9 10	9 +6 15	7 +9 16
3.	8 +9 17	9 +9 18	9 +5 14	6 +6 12	8 +7 15
4.	6 +5 11	7 +6 13	8 +8 16	9 +8 17	7 +7 14
5.	9 +4 13	9 +3 12	7 +8 15	2 +9 11	7 +9 16

16   Use with text pages 35-36.   PS-2

Addison-Wesley / All Rights Reserved

Building Thinking Skills

Mental Math   2-7

Name _____

What Number Am I?

Read each clue.
Write the number.

1. I am between 12 and 15.
I am not equal to 9 + 5.
What number am I?   _13_

2. I am between 8 and 12.
I am less than 5 + 6.
When you double me you get 18.
What number am I?   _9_

3. I am more than 9 + 3.
I am less than 9 + 7.
I am not an odd number.
What number am I?   _14_

4. I am between 10 and 17.
When you add my two digits
you get 6.
What number am I?   _15_

5. Make up your own clues.
First pick a number. Then write the clues.
Ask a friend to guess your number.

16   Use with text pages 35-36.   TS-2

Addison-Wesley / All Rights Reserved

Average

Exercises All

Supplements
Practice 16
Challenges 16 or
Thinking Skills 16

Reteaching

Skills Review   2-7

Name _____

Adding with 9

10 + 5 = 15   (14 is 1 less than 15.)
9 + 5 = 14

10 + 7 = 17   (16 is 1 less than 17.)
9 + 7 = 16

10 + 8 = 18   (Write the ones digit.)
9 + 8 = 17

10 + 6 = 16   (Write the ones digit.)
9 + 6 = 15

Add.

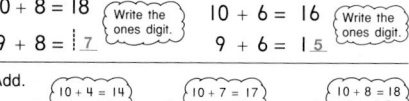

1.	9 +4 13 (10 + 4 = 14 1 less is?)	9 +7 16 (10 + 7 = 17 1 less is?)	8 +9 17 (10 + 8 = 18 1 less is?)

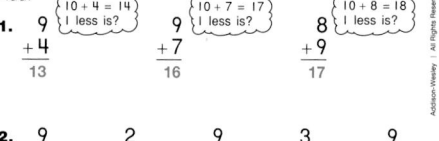

2.	9 +6 15	2 +9 11	9 +1 10	3 +9 12	9 +9 18

16   Use with text pages 35-36.   RS-2

Addison-Wesley / All Rights Reserved

Challenges

Math Reasoning   2-7

Name _____

Spin to Add

Use your spinner.
Add 9 to the number
you spin.
Keep your score on the
scorecard below.
Put a √ for each sum.
Answers will vary.

Scorecard

Sums of	13	14	15	16	17	18

1. Write numbers on this spinner so that when you add 9, you can make only sums of 13, 15, and 17.

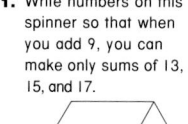

2. Write numbers on this spinner so that when you add 9, you can make only sums of 14, 16, and 18.

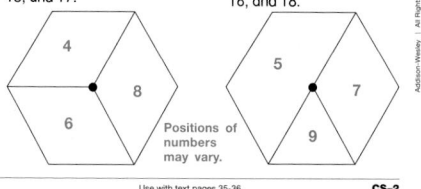

Positions of numbers may vary.

16   Use with text pages 35-36.   CS-2

Addison-Wesley / All Rights Reserved

Extended

Exercises All

Supplements
Challenges 16
Thinking Skills 16

Other Resources:
Mathematics Their Way, pages 237-240.
Problem-Solving Experiences In Mathematics 27, 33, 63
Explorations 68, 177-184
Mad Minute, pages 91-94, 151-155

LESSON PLAN 2-7

OBJECTIVE 2-7
To use the mental math technique of adding with 9 to find sums

> **Materials:** 18 two-color counters and one 10-frame per pair
>
> **Grouping Suggestions:** pairs, cooperative learning groups of 3

1. MOTIVATE AND TEACH

LEARN ABOUT IT

Have pairs of students use counters to do the example on page 35. *How many counters are inside the 10-frame?* (9) *How many counters should be outside the 10-frame?* (6)

▶ **How can you use the 10-frame to add with 9?** (Possible answer: Put 1 counter in the frame to make 10. Add the counters that are left.)

▶ **What pattern do you notice when you are adding with 9?** (Possible answer: The sum always ends in a number that is 1 less than the number you are adding to 9.)

▶ **How could you use this pattern to help you check your answers when you add with 9?** (Possible answer: You could check to see that the ones digit in the sum is 1 less than the number you added to 9.)

2. CHECK UNDERSTANDING

ERROR ALERT In an addition sentence such as 9 + 6 = 15, putting one counter inside the 10-frame but still adding 6 to 10.

Name _____

Adding with 9

Work with a partner.
Use the 10-frame and
two-color counters to add.
Then write the sums.
Check students' work.

I have 10 and 5 extra That makes 15.

$$\begin{array}{r} 9 \\ + 6 \\ \hline 15 \end{array}$$

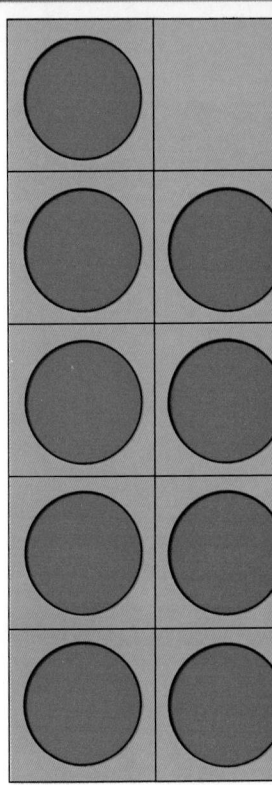

> Start with 9 counters in the 10-frame. Place counters for the other addend outside.

> Move 1 counter to fill the 10-frame.

> Add the extra counters to 10.

1.
$$\begin{array}{r} 9 \\ + 6 \\ \hline 15 \end{array} \quad \begin{array}{r} 3 \\ + 9 \\ \hline 12 \end{array} \quad \begin{array}{r} 9 \\ + 1 \\ \hline 10 \end{array}$$

2.
$$\begin{array}{r} 9 \\ + 2 \\ \hline 11 \end{array} \quad \begin{array}{r} 9 \\ + 4 \\ \hline 13 \end{array} \quad \begin{array}{r} 8 \\ + 9 \\ \hline 17 \end{array}$$

3.
$$\begin{array}{r} 9 \\ + 9 \\ \hline 18 \end{array} \quad \begin{array}{r} 5 \\ + 9 \\ \hline 14 \end{array} \quad \begin{array}{r} 9 \\ + 7 \\ \hline 16 \end{array}$$

Chapter 2

(thirty-five)

TEACHING OPTIONS

RETEACHING TIPS Have students use counters to demonstrate another strategy for adding with 9: To add 9 + 6, subtract 1 from 6, then add the 1 to 9 and find the sum of 10 + 5.
Use Reteaching Supplement 16.

COMPUTER Addition Magician, Learning Company, © 1984 Difficulty level one is for all students. Students practice addition facts by using problem solving skills. The object is to group numbers to add up to the target. Students should select two addends. The game requires 15-20 minutes.

dd. Use your 10-frame punchout to help.

$$\begin{array}{r} 4 \\ +\,9 \\ \hline 13 \end{array}$$

$$\begin{array}{r} 3 \\ +\,9 \\ \hline 12 \end{array}$$
$$\begin{array}{r} 8 \\ +\,1 \\ \hline 9 \end{array}$$
$$\begin{array}{r} 9 \\ +\,8 \\ \hline 17 \end{array}$$
$$\begin{array}{r} 6 \\ +\,7 \\ \hline 13 \end{array}$$
$$\begin{array}{r} 5 \\ +\,9 \\ \hline 14 \end{array}$$
$$\begin{array}{r} 7 \\ +\,7 \\ \hline 14 \end{array}$$

$$\begin{array}{r} 6 \\ +\,9 \\ \hline 15 \end{array}$$
$$\begin{array}{r} 7 \\ +\,3 \\ \hline 10 \end{array}$$
$$\begin{array}{r} 6 \\ +\,6 \\ \hline 12 \end{array}$$
$$\begin{array}{r} 1 \\ +\,9 \\ \hline 10 \end{array}$$
$$\begin{array}{r} 0 \\ +\,8 \\ \hline 8 \end{array}$$
$$\begin{array}{r} 9 \\ +\,7 \\ \hline 16 \end{array}$$

$$\begin{array}{r} 9 \\ +\,9 \\ \hline 18 \end{array}$$
$$\begin{array}{r} 2 \\ +\,8 \\ \hline 10 \end{array}$$
$$\begin{array}{r} 7 \\ +\,9 \\ \hline 16 \end{array}$$
$$\begin{array}{r} 6 \\ +\,5 \\ \hline 11 \end{array}$$
$$\begin{array}{r} 9 \\ +\,4 \\ \hline 13 \end{array}$$
$$\begin{array}{r} 5 \\ +\,5 \\ \hline 10 \end{array}$$

$9 + 5 = \underline{14}$ $4 + 6 = \underline{10}$ $2 + 9 = \underline{11}$

$6 + 9 = \underline{15}$ $8 + 9 = \underline{17}$ $3 + 7 = \underline{10}$

ROBLEM SOLVING

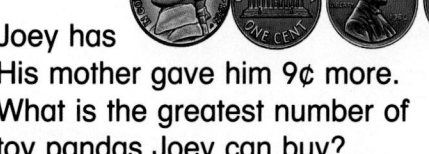

Joey has
His mother gave him 9¢ more.
What is the greatest number of
toy pandas Joey can buy?

7¢

$\underline{2}$ toy pandas

(thirty-six)

Chapter 2

Basic	All
Average	All
Extended	All

2-7

PRACTICE

How many counters will be left outside after you fill up your 10-frame when you are adding 4 + 9? (3) *Find an exercise in which you do not need to use the 10-frame.* (Possible answer: 8 + 1 = 9)

APPLY

PROBLEM SOLVING ▶ **How much money does Joey have left if he buys 2 pandas?** (3¢)
▶ **How much more would Joey need to buy 3 pandas?** (4¢)

LOSE AND ASSESS

HOW WHAT YOU KNOW

ovide each cooperative learning
oup of 3 with a 10-frame and 18
o-color counters. Have students take
ns at the following tasks: One
dent says 9 and a second number.
e second student uses the counters
add the 2 numbers on the 10-frame,
d the third student writes an
dition sentence to match. Remind
dents to listen to each other as they
rk.

QUICK QUIZ

Add.
$9 + 5 = \underline{(14)}$ $3 + 9 = \underline{(12)}$
$9 + 0 = \underline{(9)}$ $2 + 9 = \underline{(11)}$
$9 + 4 = \underline{(13)}$ $7 + 9 = \underline{(16)}$
$6 + 9 = \underline{(15)}$ $9 + 9 = \underline{(18)}$

Making 10, Adding Extra

OBJECTIVE 2-8   To use the mental math technique of making 10 and adding extra to find sums

PREBOOK ACTIVITIES

QUICK REVIEW

Use your counters to find the sums for the following addition sentences:

$2 + \underline{(8)} = 10$ $6 + \underline{(4)} = 10$ $\underline{(7)} + 3 = 10$

$5 + \underline{(5)} = 10$ $\underline{(9)} + 1 = 10$ $\underline{(0)} + 10 = 10$

PRIOR KNOWLEDGE

Have students use a drawing to help them answer these questions: *If you have 13 baby gerbils and you can put only 10 in a cage, how many gerbils will you have inside the cage?* (10) *How many gerbils will you need to put in another cage?* (3)

COMMUNICATION

Discussing Math   Write $10 + 4 = 14$ on the chalkboard and read it aloud. *What extra number was added to 10 to get the sum of 14?* (4) Write $10 + 6 = 16$ on the board. *What extra was added to 10 to get the sum of 16?* (6) Discuss the ease or difficulty of adding numbers to 10.

EXPLORE AND CONNECT

Materials: 10-frames and 18 two-color counters for each pair
Grouping Suggestions: pairs
Pair students. On the chalkboard, write $8 + 4$ and tell students to show each addend with different-colored counters. Have them decide which addend is greater. (8) Then have them place counters for the greater addend inside the 10-frame and counters to show the other addend outside the 10-frame. (4) *How many counters can you take from outside the 10-frame to fill it up?* (2) *How many are left outside?* (2) *How many counters in all?* (12) *What did you do to add the counters?* (Possible answer: made a 10, added the extra 1s) *How would making 10 and adding extra help you know that $7 + 4 = 11$?* (Possible answer: Take 3 from 4, add the 3 to 7 to get a sum of 10; the extra 1 can be added to 10 to get a sum of 11.) *Use counters to show and explain to your partner how to make 10 and add extra to find the sum of $7 + 5$.*

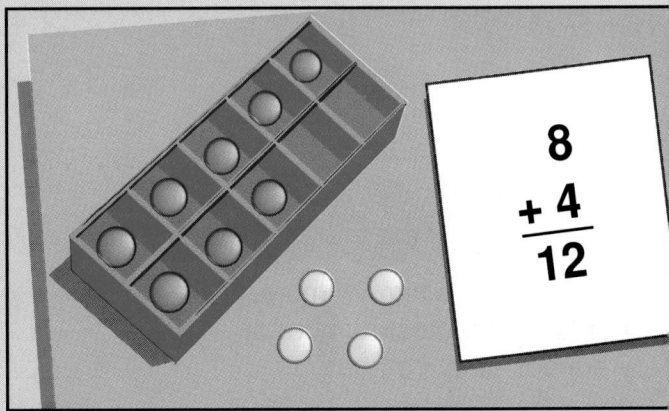

CONNECTIONS   Use these anytime.

Problem of the Day

Life Skills   You want to buy a postage stamp that costs 16¢. You have a dime and pennies. How many pennies must you add to the dime in order to buy the stamp? (6)

Subject Integration

Science   I have a circus train with 11 cars. I have these animals: a horse, a zebra, a lion, a giraffe, a tiger, and an elephant. How many more animals do I need to have one in each car? (5) Name the animals. (Answers will vary.)

Counting Patterns

Can you complete this pattern? 4, 7, 10, _____, _____ (13, 16) Now explain the pattern. (Add 3.)

CLASSWORK AND HOMEWORK SUPPLEMENTS

Practice

Skills Maintenance 2-8

Name _____

Making 10, Adding Extra

Add.

1. $\begin{array}{r} 8 \\ +5 \\ \hline 13 \end{array}$ $\begin{array}{r} 7 \\ +7 \\ \hline 14 \end{array}$ $\begin{array}{r} 7 \\ +4 \\ \hline 11 \end{array}$ $\begin{array}{r} 8 \\ +6 \\ \hline 14 \end{array}$ $\begin{array}{r} 5 \\ +7 \\ \hline 12 \end{array}$

2. $\begin{array}{r} 7 \\ +5 \\ \hline 12 \end{array}$ $\begin{array}{r} 8 \\ +4 \\ \hline 12 \end{array}$ $\begin{array}{r} 9 \\ +4 \\ \hline 13 \end{array}$ $\begin{array}{r} 8 \\ +8 \\ \hline 16 \end{array}$ $\begin{array}{r} 4 \\ +7 \\ \hline 11 \end{array}$

3. $\begin{array}{r} 8 \\ +5 \\ \hline 13 \end{array}$ $\begin{array}{r} 5 \\ +8 \\ \hline 13 \end{array}$ $\begin{array}{r} 7 \\ +5 \\ \hline 12 \end{array}$ $\begin{array}{r} 4 \\ +8 \\ \hline 12 \end{array}$ $\begin{array}{r} 8 \\ +6 \\ \hline 14 \end{array}$

4. $\begin{array}{r} 6 \\ +5 \\ \hline 11 \end{array}$ $\begin{array}{r} 7 \\ +6 \\ \hline 13 \end{array}$ $\begin{array}{r} 8 \\ +8 \\ \hline 16 \end{array}$ $\begin{array}{r} 9 \\ +8 \\ \hline 17 \end{array}$ $\begin{array}{r} 7 \\ +7 \\ \hline 14 \end{array}$

5. $\begin{array}{r} 5 \\ +7 \\ \hline 12 \end{array}$ $\begin{array}{r} 5 \\ +8 \\ \hline 13 \end{array}$ $\begin{array}{r} 7 \\ +4 \\ \hline 11 \end{array}$ $\begin{array}{r} 4 \\ +9 \\ \hline 13 \end{array}$ $\begin{array}{r} 5 \\ +7 \\ \hline 12 \end{array}$

PS-2   Use with text pages 37-38.   17

Building Thinking Skills

Critical Thinking 2-8

Name _____

Mystery Addends

Make the sums.
Use each number 2 times.
Make number cards and move them around to help.
Answers will vary. Possible answers given.

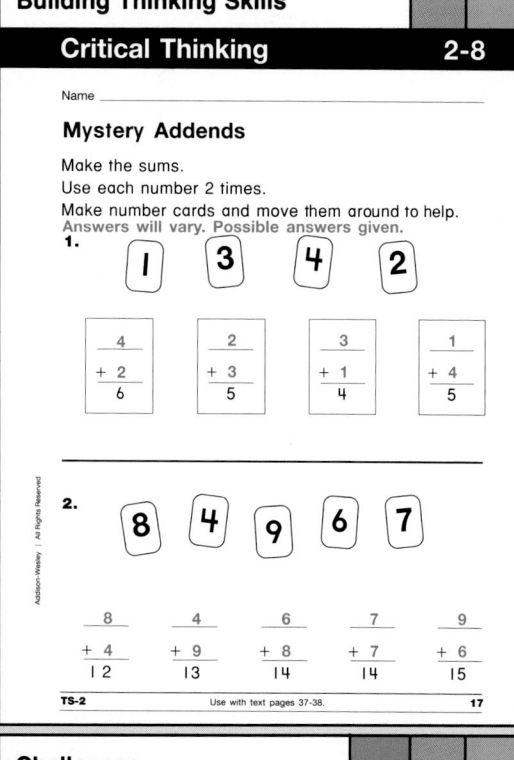

1. cards: 1 3 4 2

$\begin{array}{r} 4 \\ +2 \\ \hline 6 \end{array}$ $\begin{array}{r} 2 \\ +3 \\ \hline 5 \end{array}$ $\begin{array}{r} 3 \\ +1 \\ \hline 4 \end{array}$ $\begin{array}{r} 1 \\ +4 \\ \hline 5 \end{array}$

2. cards: 8 4 9 6 7

$\begin{array}{r} 8 \\ +4 \\ \hline 12 \end{array}$ $\begin{array}{r} 4 \\ +9 \\ \hline 13 \end{array}$ $\begin{array}{r} 6 \\ +8 \\ \hline 14 \end{array}$ $\begin{array}{r} 7 \\ +7 \\ \hline 14 \end{array}$ $\begin{array}{r} 9 \\ +6 \\ \hline 15 \end{array}$

TS-2   Use with text pages 37-38.   17

Average

Exercises All

Supplements
Practice 17
Challenges 17 or
Thinking Skills 17

Reteaching

Skills Review 2-8

Name _____

Making 10, Adding Extra

Add.

1. $\begin{array}{r} 8 \\ +5 \\ \hline 13 \end{array}$ (8 + 2 = 10, so 8 + 5 is 3 more.) $\begin{array}{r} 7 \\ +5 \\ \hline 12 \end{array}$ (5 + 5 = 10, so 5 + 7 is 2 more.)

2. $\begin{array}{r} 7 \\ +4 \\ \hline 11 \end{array}$ (7 + 3 = 10, so 7 + 4 is 1 more.) $\begin{array}{r} 8 \\ +4 \\ \hline 12 \end{array}$ (8 + 2 = 10, so 8 + 4 is 2 more.)

3. $\begin{array}{r} 5 \\ +8 \\ \hline 13 \end{array}$ $\begin{array}{r} 7 \\ +4 \\ \hline 11 \end{array}$ $\begin{array}{r} 8 \\ +4 \\ \hline 12 \end{array}$ $\begin{array}{r} 7 \\ +5 \\ \hline 12 \end{array}$ $\begin{array}{r} 8 \\ +5 \\ \hline 13 \end{array}$

4. $\begin{array}{r} 8 \\ +6 \\ \hline 14 \end{array}$ $\begin{array}{r} 9 \\ +4 \\ \hline 13 \end{array}$ $\begin{array}{r} 4 \\ +8 \\ \hline 12 \end{array}$ $\begin{array}{r} 4 \\ +7 \\ \hline 11 \end{array}$ $\begin{array}{r} 5 \\ +8 \\ \hline 13 \end{array}$

5. $\begin{array}{r} 6 \\ +8 \\ \hline 14 \end{array}$ $\begin{array}{r} 5 \\ +7 \\ \hline 12 \end{array}$ $\begin{array}{r} 4 \\ +9 \\ \hline 13 \end{array}$ $\begin{array}{r} 4 \\ +8 \\ \hline 12 \end{array}$ $\begin{array}{r} 4 \\ +9 \\ \hline 13 \end{array}$

6. $\begin{array}{r} 4 \\ +7 \\ \hline 11 \end{array}$ $\begin{array}{r} 9 \\ +4 \\ \hline 13 \end{array}$ $\begin{array}{r} 5 \\ +7 \\ \hline 12 \end{array}$ $\begin{array}{r} 8 \\ +6 \\ \hline 14 \end{array}$ $\begin{array}{r} 8 \\ +5 \\ \hline 13 \end{array}$

RS-2   Use with text pages 37-38.   17

Challenges

Math Reasoning 2-8

Name _____

Try This Make Ten Machine!

MAKE TEN MACHINE — In: 8 + 4 — Out: 8 4 / 10 2 — 10 + 2 — 12 Sum

Complete the out cards. Then find the sums.

1. 8+6 10+ 4 14

2. 4+9 10+ 3 13

3. 7+4 10+ 1 11

4. 7+5 10+ 2 12

5. 6+8 10+ 4 14

6. 9+5 10+ 4 14

7. 5+8 10+ 3 13

8. 8+5 10+ 3 13

9. 6+7 10+ 3 13

10. 5+9 10+ 4 14

CS-2   Use with text pages 37-38.   17

Extended

Exercises All

Supplements
Challenges 17
Thinking Skills 17

Other Resources:
Mathematics Their Way, pages 76-77, 237-240
Explorations, pages 188-195
Problem-Solving Experiences In Mathematics, page 33

OBJECTIVE 2-8

To use the mental math technique of making 10 and adding extra to find sums

> **Materials** 10-frames, 18 two-color counters per group
>
> **Grouping Suggestions:** pairs, groups of 3

1. MOTIVATE AND TEACH

LEARN ABOUT IT

Write the addition expression 8 + 6 on the chalkboard. Have one student in each pair place 8 counters of one color inside a 10-frame and 6 of the other color outside the 10-frame.

▶ **How can you use the counters and the 10-frame to help you add 8 + 6?** (Possible answer: Place 2 of the 6 counters inside the 10-frame and add them to the 8 to get 10. Then add the 4 extras to it to get 14.)

Have students look at the sample exercise at the top of page 37.

▶ **How are the two addition sentences 8 + 5 = 13 and 5 + 8 = 13 alike?** (Possible answer: They are turnaround facts.)

▶ **Why do you think it is easier to add a number to 10?** (Possible answer: because it is easy to add a number to the zero in the ones place)

▶ **Why do you think you put counters for the greater addend in the 10-frame?** (Possible answer: You do not have so many counters to count when you add the extras.)

2. CHECK UNDERSTANDING

ERROR ALERT In adding 8 + 4 = 12, for example, making a ten by taking 2 from 4, but still adding 4 extras to 10 instead of the remaining 2.

Name _____

Making 10, Adding Extra

Work with a partner.
Use the 10-frame and
two-color counters to add.
Then write the sums.

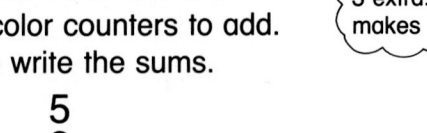

I have 10 and 3 extra. That makes 13.

$$\begin{array}{r} 8 \\ +5 \\ \hline 13 \end{array} \qquad \begin{array}{r} 5 \\ +8 \\ \hline 13 \end{array}$$

Check students' work.

> Place counters for the greater addend inside the 10-frame.
>
> Place counters for the other addend outside the 10-frame.
>
> Move counters to fill the 10-frame.
>
> Add the extra counters to 10.

1. $\begin{array}{r} 8 \\ +5 \\ \hline 13 \end{array}$ $\begin{array}{r} 7 \\ +4 \\ \hline 11 \end{array}$ $\begin{array}{r} 5 \\ +7 \\ \hline 12 \end{array}$ $\begin{array}{r} 4 \\ +8 \\ \hline 12 \end{array}$

2. $\begin{array}{r} 6 \\ +8 \\ \hline 14 \end{array}$ $\begin{array}{r} 8 \\ +4 \\ \hline 12 \end{array}$ $\begin{array}{r} 4 \\ +7 \\ \hline 11 \end{array}$ $\begin{array}{r} 5 \\ +8 \\ \hline 13 \end{array}$

Chapter 2

(thirty-seven)

TEACHING OPTIONS

RETEACHING TIPS Have students use 10-frames and counters to proceed step-by-step with making 10 and adding extra as shown.

$$\begin{array}{r} 8 \\ +4 \end{array} \to \begin{array}{r} +2 \\ -2 \end{array} \to \begin{array}{r} 10 \\ 2 \\ \hline 12 \end{array}$$

Assign Reteaching Supplement 17.

ENRICHMENT Family Math Have students and family members make a 10-frame from an egg carton. They should use their 10-frames and addends of beans or macaroni to find sums of 11, 12, 13, and 14 and glue the items to construction paper to show the sums they found.

dd. Use your 10-frame punchout to help.

$$\begin{array}{r} 7 \\ +4 \\ \hline 11 \end{array}$$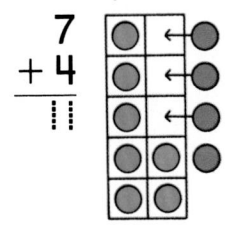

$$\begin{array}{r} 8 \\ +6 \\ \hline 14 \end{array}$$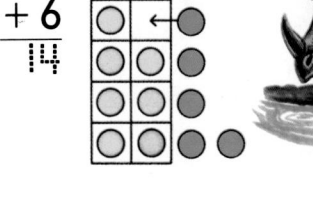

$$\begin{array}{r} 6 \\ +8 \\ \hline 14 \end{array} \quad \begin{array}{r} 5 \\ +8 \\ \hline 13 \end{array} \quad \begin{array}{r} 8 \\ +4 \\ \hline 12 \end{array} \quad \begin{array}{r} 4 \\ +9 \\ \hline 13 \end{array} \quad \begin{array}{r} 7 \\ +5 \\ \hline 12 \end{array} \quad \begin{array}{r} 4 \\ +7 \\ \hline 11 \end{array}$$

$$\begin{array}{r} 7 \\ +5 \\ \hline 12 \end{array} \quad \begin{array}{r} 4 \\ +8 \\ \hline 12 \end{array} \quad \begin{array}{r} 7 \\ +4 \\ \hline 11 \end{array} \quad \begin{array}{r} 5 \\ +7 \\ \hline 12 \end{array} \quad \begin{array}{r} 8 \\ +6 \\ \hline 14 \end{array} \quad \begin{array}{r} 8 \\ +5 \\ \hline 13 \end{array}$$

$4 + 7 = \underline{11}$ $8 + 4 = \underline{12}$ $5 + 8 = \underline{13}$

$6 + 8 = \underline{14}$ $9 + 4 = \underline{13}$ $7 + 5 = \underline{12}$

MIXED REVIEW

dd. Write the turnaround fact.

$$\begin{array}{r} 3 \\ +7 \\ \hline 10 \end{array} \quad \begin{array}{r} 7 \\ +3 \\ \hline 10 \end{array} \qquad \begin{array}{r} 6 \\ +0 \\ \hline 6 \end{array} \quad \begin{array}{r} 0 \\ +6 \\ \hline 6 \end{array} \qquad \begin{array}{r} 4 \\ +5 \\ \hline 9 \end{array} \quad \begin{array}{r} 5 \\ +4 \\ \hline 9 \end{array}$$

Add.

$9 + 9 = \underline{18}$ $6 + 7 = \underline{13}$ $4 + 6 = \underline{10}$

    Chapter 2

---

3. PRACTICE AND APPLY

Basic	All, Mixed Review
Average	All, Mixed Review
Extended	All, Mixed Review

2-8

PRACTICE

Describe how you would make 10 and add extra for the first exercise on page 38. (Possible response: Move 3 counters into the 10-frame to make 10 and add the extra 1 to get the sum 11.)

APPLY

▶ **How would you tell a friend how to add by making a 10 and adding extra?** (Possible answer: Take away from one number enough to make the other become 10. Then add the remainder to 10. Check the answer with counters.)

MIXED REVIEW *How will you write the turnaround facts in row 6?* (Change the order of the addends.)

LOSE AND ASSESS

HOW WHAT YOU KNOW

ovide each cooperative group of 3
udents with one 10-frame and 18
o-color counters. Write addition
ntences such as 7 + 5 = 12 and 8
6 = 14 on the chalkboard. Have
udents take turns with the following
ree tasks: One student uses the
ounters and 10-frame to show the
ddition sentence; the second writes
e addition sentence; the third tells a
ory using the numbers.

QUICK QUIZ

8 + 5 = (13)	4 + 8 = (12)
7 + 4 = (11)	5 + 7 = (12)
4 + 9 = (13)	8 + 6 = (14)

LESSON OPTIONS 2-9

Fact Practice

OBJECTIVE 2-9   To practice the mental math techniques learned to find sums

PREBOOK ACTIVITIES

QUICK REVIEW

As I write a number on the chalkboard (use numbers 9-18), think of addition sentences that have this number as their sum. (Make a list of students' sentences on the chalkboard.)

PRIOR KNOWLEDGE

Ask students to tell stories about how they use addition at home. Help students brainstorm by offering topics such as setting the dinner table (3 plates + 4 plates = 7 plates), putting groceries away (5 boxes + 3 boxes = 8 boxes), or reading stories (4 pages + 5 pages = 9 pages). Have students listen to each other's stories, pointing out how addition is used in each situation.

COMMUNICATION

Listening and Discussing Math   Write the following number sentences on the chalkboard: 3 + 4 = 7, 5 + 1 = 6, 2 + 3 = 5, 4 + 2 = 6. *3 and 4 are parts in the first sentence. 5 and 1 are parts in the second sentence. What are the parts for the next two sentences?* (2 + 3; 4 + 2). *The sums for the first two sentences are 7 and 6. What is the sum for the third sentence?* (5) *for the fourth sentence?* (6) *Is the greatest number in each sentence the sum or one of the parts?* (the sum)

EXPLORE AND CONNECT

Materials: punchout number cards 0-9 for each student
Grouping Suggestion: pairs
Provide each student pair with number cards. Have students shuffle their number cards and place them face down on the table. Tell both students in each pair to turn over their top cards. Then have them write an addition sentence, using the numbers on their cards as addends and writing the sum. Ask them to continue the activity until all the cards have been used. *What is the greatest sum that you made with your number pairs? What is the least sum?* Allow time for students to listen to each other's answers.

CONNECTIONS   Use these anytime.

Problem of the Day

Logic   If Carrie is 7 years old now, in how many years will she be 10? (3) How did you find your answer? (Possible answer: counted on from 7)

Math Connection

Number Sense   Use two 10-frames and 13 counters. How many ways can you make 13? Can you fill both 10-frames with the same amount of counters? Why or why not? (No; it is an odd number.)

Subject Integration

Language Arts   Cut out newspaper ads that show different foods. Glue them to a sheet of paper under the headings *Foods I Like* and *Foods I Don't Like*. What addition sentence describes your paper? (Answers will vary.)

CLASSWORK AND HOMEWORK SUPPLEMENTS

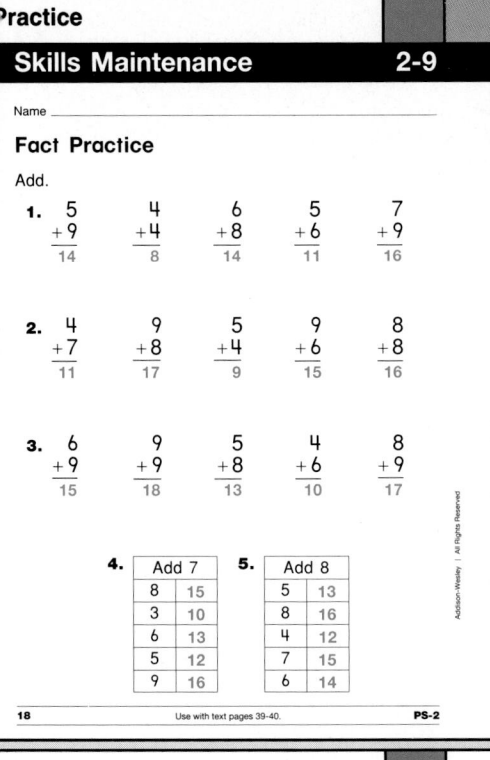

Practice

Skills Maintenance 2-9

Name _____

Fact Practice

Add.

1.
$\frac{5}{+9} = 14$ $\frac{4}{+4} = 8$ $\frac{6}{+8} = 14$ $\frac{5}{+6} = 11$ $\frac{7}{+9} = 16$

2.
$\frac{4}{+7} = 11$ $\frac{9}{+8} = 17$ $\frac{5}{+4} = 9$ $\frac{9}{+6} = 15$ $\frac{8}{+8} = 16$

3.
$\frac{6}{+9} = 15$ $\frac{9}{+9} = 18$ $\frac{5}{+8} = 13$ $\frac{4}{+6} = 10$ $\frac{8}{+9} = 17$

4. Add 7

8	15
3	10
6	13
5	12
9	16

5. Add 8

5	13
8	16
4	12
7	15
6	14

18   Use with text pages 39-40.   PS-2

Building Thinking Skills

Math Reasoning 2-9

Name _____

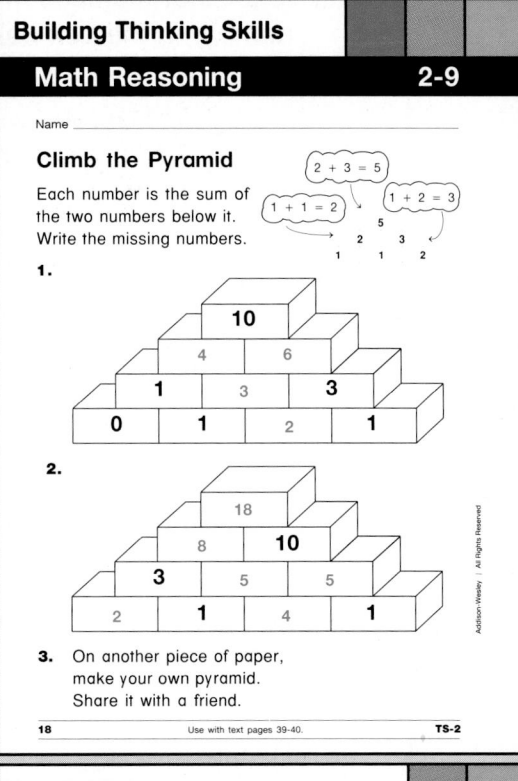

Climb the Pyramid

Each number is the sum of the two numbers below it. Write the missing numbers.

2 + 3 = 5
1 + 1 = 2   1 + 2 = 3
1   2   3   2

1.

		10		
	4		6	
1		3		3
0	1	2	1

2.

	18	
8		10
3	5	5
2	1	4	1

3. On another piece of paper, make your own pyramid. Share it with a friend.

18   Use with text pages 39-40.   TS-2

Reteaching

Skills Review 2-9

Name _____

Fact Practice

(doubles) (doubles plus one) (sums of 10) (adding 9) (making 10, adding extra)

$\frac{4}{+4} = 8$ $\frac{4}{+5} = 9$ $\frac{6}{+4} = 10$ $\frac{9}{+4} = 13$ $\frac{4}{+8} = 12$

Add.

1.
$\frac{7}{+7} = 14$ $\frac{6}{+6} = 12$ $\frac{8}{+8} = 16$ $\frac{9}{+9} = 18$

2.
$\frac{5}{+6} = 11$ $\frac{8}{+7} = 15$ $\frac{9}{+8} = 17$ $\frac{7}{+6} = 13$

3.
$\frac{7}{+3} = 10$ $\frac{9}{+1} = 10$ $\frac{8}{+2} = 10$ $\frac{4}{+6} = 10$

4.
$\frac{7}{+9} = 16$ $\frac{9}{+5} = 14$ $\frac{8}{+5} = 13$ $\frac{5}{+7} = 12$ $\frac{6}{+8} = 14$

18   Use with text pages 39-40.   RS-2

Challenges

Mental Math 2-9

Name _____

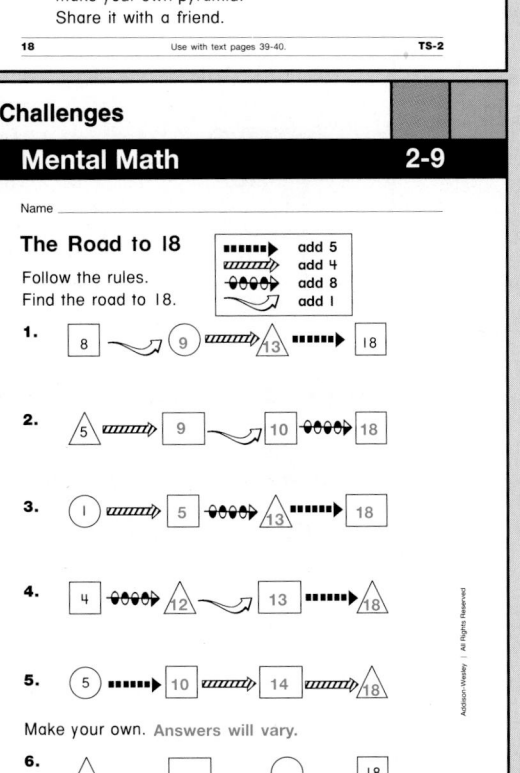

The Road to 18

Follow the rules. Find the road to 18.

▬▬▶ add 5
▬▬▶ add 4
▬▬▶ add 8
↝ add 1

1. 8 ↝ 9 ▬▶ 13 ▬▶ 18

2. 5 ▬▶ 9 ↝ 10 ▬▶ 18

3. 1 ▬▶ 5 ▬▶ 13 ▬▶ 18

4. 4 ▬▶ 12 ↝ 13 ▬▶ 18

5. 5 ▬▶ 10 ▬▶ 14 ▬▶ 18

Make your own. Answers will vary.

6. △ ▢ ○ 18

18   Use with text pages 39-40.   CS-2

OPTIONS FOR INDIVIDUAL NEEDS

Basic

Exercises All

Supplements
Reteaching 18 or
Practice 18
Thinking Skills 18

Average

Exercises All

Supplements
Practice 18
Challenges 18 or
Thinking Skills 18

Extended

Exercises All

Supplements
Challenges 18
Thinking Skills 18

Other Resources:
Problem-Solving Experiences In Mathematics, pages 35, 39, 45, 69
Explorations, pages 188-195
Workjobs II, 102-110
Mad Minute, pages 6-15

2-9

OBJECTIVE 2-9

To practice the mental math techniques learned to find sums

Materials: counters, Cube-A-Links, chart paper, markers, index cards

Grouping Suggestions: individual work, cooperative learning groups of 3

1. MOTIVATE AND TEACH

LEARN ABOUT IT

Have students work in groups of 3. Practice addition-fact recall by having each student write a number from 0 through 5 on an index card. Have two of the students hold up their cards and the third student give the sum of the two numbers. Have students repeat the activity several times, exchanging roles. Direct students' attention to the sample exercise on page 39. *What is the sum of 8 + 9?* (17) *What letter does it match in the riddle's answer?* (s)

▶ **What strategy can you use to find sums to match the same letter?** (Possible answer: Look for different names for that sum.)

▶ **What are some other strategies you used to find the sums?** (Possible answers: doubles, doubles plus one, zero, count on)

2. CHECK UNDERSTANDING

ERROR ALERT Difficulty recalling facts with accuracy.

Name _____

Fact Practice

Why is it possible for an ostrich to go without water for a long time?

Add. Then write the code letter that matches the number in the box below.

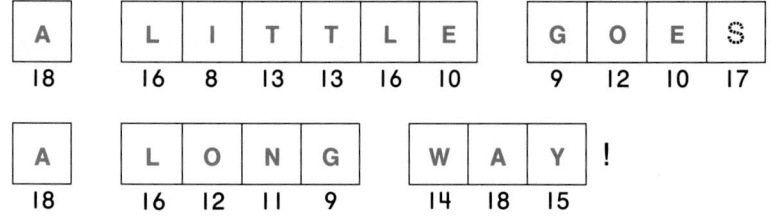

S	9 + 8 = 17		W	7 + 7 = 14
G	0 + 9 = 9		N	7 + 4 = 11

S	8 + 9 = 17	I	6 + 2 = 8	T	5 + 8 = 13
E	6 + 4 = 10	O	7 + 5 = 12	Y	9 + 6 = 15
G	7 + 2 = 9	N	8 + 3 = 11	T	7 + 6 = 13
I	5 + 3 = 8	L	9 + 7 = 16	W	6 + 8 = 14
O	6 + 6 = 12	O	8 + 4 = 12	A	9 + 9 = 18

Because

A	L	I	T	T	L	E		G	O	E	S
18	16	8	13	13	16	10		9	12	10	17

A	L	O	N	G		W	A	Y	!
18	16	12	11	9		14	18	15	

Chapter 2   (thirty-nine)

TEACHING OPTIONS

RETEACHING TIPS Provide students with cubes of two different colors. Have students complete addition exercises by modeling each addend with a different-colored cube train and joining the trains to find the sum. Use Reteaching Supplement 18 to provide help in practicing addition facts.

ENRICHMENT Have students copy and complete the pattern:

5	5	5	5	(5)
+ 5	+ 6	+ 7	+ (8)	+ (9)
(10)	(11)	(12)	(13)	(14)

What would happen if you continued the pattern? Why? (The second addend would increase by 1 and so would the sum.)

.dd.

$$\begin{array}{r} 4 \\ +7 \\ \hline 11 \end{array}$$
$$\begin{array}{r} 7 \\ +8 \\ \hline 15 \end{array}$$
$$\begin{array}{r} 8 \\ +2 \\ \hline 10 \end{array}$$
$$\begin{array}{r} 5 \\ +3 \\ \hline 8 \end{array}$$

$$\begin{array}{r} 3 \\ +4 \\ \hline 7 \end{array}$$
$$\begin{array}{r} 9 \\ +9 \\ \hline 18 \end{array}$$
$$\begin{array}{r} 1 \\ +5 \\ \hline 6 \end{array}$$
$$\begin{array}{r} 8 \\ +5 \\ \hline 13 \end{array}$$
$$\begin{array}{r} 5 \\ +2 \\ \hline 7 \end{array}$$
$$\begin{array}{r} 3 \\ +8 \\ \hline 11 \end{array}$$

.
4 + 8 = 12

3 + 3 = 6

4.
9 + 7 = 16

4 + 5 = 9

5 + 0 = 5

5.
6 + 8 = 14

9 + 4 = 13

4 + 4 = 8

7 + 3 = 10

ROBLEM SOLVING

There were 6 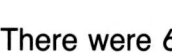 playing in the field.

Then 2 ran to the river. How many were still playing?

Use counters to help. Then finish the number sentence.

 6 $\bigcirc$ 2 $\boxed{=}$ 4   4 jaguars were still playing.

CLOSE AND ASSESS

HOW WHAT YOU KNOW

rovide each group of 3 students with 5 index cards and 3 markers. Have ach student write 5 addition facts ith sums from 10 to 18 on one side f the cards. On the other side of the ards, have them write the answers. Vhen all have finished, have them ke turns using their flashcards to uiz each other. Encourage students to sten to each other's questions and nswers.

QUICK QUIZ

Find the sums.
5 + 6 = (11)   4 + 9 = (13)

$$\begin{array}{r} 8 \\ +3 \\ \hline (11) \end{array}$$
$$\begin{array}{r} 9 \\ +8 \\ \hline (17) \end{array}$$
$$\begin{array}{r} 4 \\ +6 \\ \hline (10) \end{array}$$
$$\begin{array}{r} 3 \\ +5 \\ \hline (8) \end{array}$$
$$\begin{array}{r} 7 \\ +4 \\ \hline (11) \end{array}$$

3. PRACTICE AND APPLY

Basic	All
Average	All
Extended	All

PRACTICE

For which exercises do you think the sums will be greater than 10? What makes you think so? How can you check your guesses? (Possible answers: One or both addends are greater than 5; you can use counters or 10-frames.)

APPLY

PROBLEM SOLVING ► **Estimate your answer. Will it be larger or smaller than 6? Explain.** (smaller; some of the jaguars are leaving, and there are 6 to start)
► **How will you find the answer?** (Subtract 6 − 2.)
► **How can you check to see if your answer is reasonable?** (Use counters; reread the problem and see if the answer makes sense.)

2-9

Adding Three Numbers

OBJECTIVE 2-10   To add three numbers

PREBOOK ACTIVITIES

QUICK REVIEW

I am going to say some addition facts. If the sum is 10, point your thumb up. If it is not 10, point your thumb down.

$$\begin{array}{cccccccc} 3 & 2 & 4 & 9 & 7 & 8 & 1 & 5 \\ +\,7 & +\,6 & +\,4 & +\,1 & +\,3 & +\,0 & +\,8 & +\,5 \\ (10) & (8) & (8) & (10) & (10) & (8) & (9) & (10) \end{array}$$

PRIOR KNOWLEDGE

Pose the following situation to help students recall addition with more than two addends.
You and 2 friends are collecting stickers.
You have 2 stickers.
Your friends each have 3 stickers.
How will you find out how many stickers you have altogether?
(Possible answer: Write down how many each one has. Add them in order.)
How many stickers do you have in all? (8)

COMMUNICATION

Listening and Discussing Math   Write the following exercise on the chalkboard in column form: 3 + 6 + 4. Read the exercise to students. Encourage them to tell what they know about adding two numbers. *How can you use what you know about adding two numbers to find sums for three numbers?* (Find the sum for the first two numbers; add the third number to that sum.) Call on students to describe how they would find the sum. Encourage them to produce more than one plan for a solution. (Possible responses: Add up; add down; look for sums of ten; look for doubles.)

EXPLORE AND CONNECT

Materials: Cube-A-Links of 3 colors
Grouping Suggestion: pairs
Provide each pair with cubes. On the chalkboard, write sets of three vertical addends with a double or 10 sum as adjacent addends. Have students join cubes to add, using a different color for each addend. Begin with 4 + 3 + 7. *Which numbers should you add first?* (Possible answer: the bottom 2 numbers) Have one student hold 4 cubes for the top addend as the other joins 3 + 7 cubes. *What is the sum of the bottom 2 addends?* (10) Have the first student attach the 4 cubes for the top addend. *What is the sum now?* (14)
Do you think the sum will be the same if we add the top two addends first and add down? Why? Use cubes to check. Have students find the remaining sums. Direct one student to add up as the other adds down. Then ask them to compare answers. *Which way is easier? Why?*

CONNECTIONS   Use these anytime.

Problem of the Day

Counting Patterns   How can you use a pattern to find the sum of three addends when the addends are all the same? (skip count)

Math Connection

Number Sense   Spin a spinner 3 times. Write down the number you get on each spin. Then use the numbers to write an addition exercise. Estimate. Will the sum be less than 10, 10, or greater than 10? Add. Was your guess correct?

Subject Integration

Reading   (Write the following on the chalkboard.)
Add the words in each line of this sentence to find the total number of words.
(6 + 5 + 5 = 16)
How did you find the answer? (adding, counting each word)

CLASSWORK AND HOMEWORK SUPPLEMENTS

Practice

Skills Maintenance   2-10

Name _____

Adding Three Numbers

Match.

1. 1 + 5 + 5 ⟋ 5	**2.** 7 + 0 + 7 ⟍ 14
3 + 0 + 2 ⟋⟍ 11	8 + 1 + 2 ⟋ 12
6 + 4 + 2 —— 12	4 + 2 + 6 ⟋⟍ 11
3. 5 + 2 + 4 ⟍ 11	**4.** 9 + 2 + 1 —— 12
4 + 5 + 4 ⟋⟍ 14	2 + 7 + 2 ⟍ 13
8 + 0 + 6 ⟋ 13	3 + 3 + 7 ⟋ 11

Add.

5.
3	4	3	6	2	5
2	1	4	4	1	2
+3	+1	+7	+3	+8	+2
8	6	14	13	11	9

6.
4	3	0	6	5	6
2	2	2	1	2	2
+4	+8	+5	+6	+5	+1
10	13	7	13	12	9

PS-2   Use with text pages 41-42.   19

Reteaching

Skills Review   2-10

Name _____

Adding Three Numbers

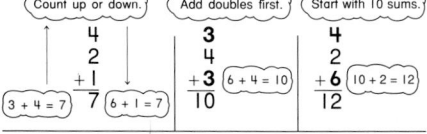

(Count up or down.)
4
2
+1
(3 + 4 = 7) 7

(Add doubles first.)
3
4
+3 (6 + 4 = 10)
10

(Start with 10 sums.)
4
2
+6 (10 + 2 = 12)
12

1. Count up or down to add.

5	2	3	4	1
2	1	6	3	2
+3	+7	+0	+2	+6
10	10	9	9	9

Add. Start with doubles or 10 sums.

2.
5	4	6	1	3
2	3	4	8	7
+5	+3	+3	+2	+2
12	10	13	11	12

3. 4 + 2 + 4 = __10__   8 + 0 + 2 = __10__

4. 4 + 1 + 6 = __11__   3 + 5 + 5 = __13__

RS-2   Use with text pages 41-42.   19

Building Thinking Skills

Critical Thinking   2-10

Name _____

Path to a Prize

Choose the correct path.
Draw it.

1. 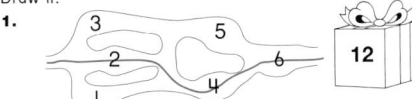 12

2.  13

3.  14

4. 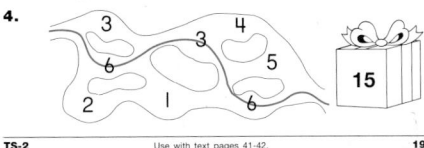 15

TS-2   Use with text pages 41-42.   19

Challenges

Calculators   2-10

Name _____

Across and Down

Each ⊞ has the same sum when you add across and down. Write the missing numbers. Make some of your own.
Use a calculator to help you.   **Answers will vary.**

1.
	2	
3	5	0	8
	1	
	8	

2.
	7	
6	2	8	16
	7	
	16	

3.
5	
6	14
3	
14	

4.
3	11
4	
11	

5.
	12
12	

6.
	7
7	

CS-2   Use with text pages 41-42.   19

Basic

Exercises All
More Practice, p. 410, set C

Supplements
Reteaching 19 or
Practice 19

Average

Exercises All
More Practice, p. 410, set C

Supplements
Practice 19
Challenges 19 or
Thinking Skills 19

Extended

Exercises All

Supplements
Challenges 19
Thinking Skills 19

Other Resources:
Mathematics Their Way, pages 220, 234, 242
Explorations, pages 177-183
Developing Number Concepts with Unifix Cubes, pages 120-121, 123-124

Chapter 2 Lesson 10   **41B**

LESSON PLAN 2-10

OBJECTIVE 2-10
To add three numbers

Materials: counters, punchout number cards 0–5

Grouping Suggestions: pairs, cooperative learning groups of 3

1. MOTIVATE AND TEACH

LEARN ABOUT IT

Practice adding three numbers by having groups of 1, 2, and 3 students stand in front of the class. Ask others to tell the sum. Repeat by changing groups of students and the order of the addends. Direct students' attention to the example at the top of page 41.

▶ **What is different about the way the sum is found each time?** (The numbers are added down the first time, up the second time.)

▶ **What do you know about addition that could help you predict that the answer would be the same?** (The numbers can be added in any order without changing the sum.)

▶ **How can doubles and 10 sums help you find sums with 3 addends?** (You can add the third number to a sum you already know.)

▶ **How can you add 3 addends when there are no 10 sums or doubles?** (Add 2 numbers, then add the third number to that sum.)

2. CHECK UNDERSTANDING

ERROR ALERT Forgetting to add one of the addends when adding three numbers.

Name _____

Adding Three Numbers

You could add **down**.
9 + 2 = 11

You cou add **up**.
8 + 3 =

If you see a double, add it first.

It's easy when you start with 10 sums!

Add.

1.
2	3	1	3	2
5	5	9	1	3
+1	+4	+1	+6	+6
	12	11	10	11

2.
5	4	3	2	3
2	5	3	7	6
+5	+4	+7	+2	+3
12	13	13	11	12

3.
4	3	8	9	6
2	7	1	0	4
+6	+2	+2	+1	+3
12	12	11	10	13

Chapter 2 · · · · · · · · · · · · · · · · · (forty-one) 41

TEACHING OPTIONS

RETEACHING TIPS Provide pairs with 15 counters. Write exercises with 3 addends on the chalkboard. Have students arrange the counters to match the 3 addends and look for doubles or for sums of 10. Guide them as they combine the counters to find the total. Assign Reteaching Supplement 19.

ENRICHMENT Have students complete the magic square. Use each digit 0-8 exactly once. All columns, rows, and diagonals equal 12.

5	6	1
0	4	8
7	2	3

Id. Start with doubles or
sums when you can.

$$\begin{array}{r} 7 \\ 1 \\ +3 \\ \hline 11 \end{array} \qquad \begin{array}{r} 5 \\ 2 \\ +5 \\ \hline 12 \end{array} \qquad \begin{array}{r} 4 \\ 3 \\ +2 \\ \hline 9 \end{array}$$

$$\begin{array}{r} 8 \\ 2 \\ +3 \\ \hline 13 \end{array} \quad \begin{array}{r} 4 \\ 4 \\ +1 \\ \hline 9 \end{array} \quad \begin{array}{r} 1 \\ 9 \\ +0 \\ \hline 10 \end{array} \quad \begin{array}{r} 2 \\ 7 \\ +3 \\ \hline 12 \end{array} \quad \begin{array}{r} 3 \\ 3 \\ +5 \\ \hline 11 \end{array} \quad \begin{array}{r} 6 \\ 0 \\ +4 \\ \hline 10 \end{array}$$

$$\begin{array}{r} 4 \\ 6 \\ +3 \\ \hline 13 \end{array} \quad \begin{array}{r} 2 \\ 8 \\ +2 \\ \hline 12 \end{array} \quad \begin{array}{r} 2 \\ 5 \\ +5 \\ \hline 12 \end{array} \quad \begin{array}{r} 6 \\ 1 \\ +3 \\ \hline 10 \end{array} \quad \begin{array}{r} 0 \\ 7 \\ +2 \\ \hline 9 \end{array} \quad \begin{array}{r} 4 \\ 3 \\ +1 \\ \hline 8 \end{array}$$

$8 + 2 + 2 = \underline{12}$ $\qquad$ $9 + 0 + 1 = \underline{10}$

OW WITH CUBES

Add. Use cubes to show that each
set of addends has the same sum.

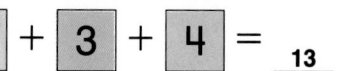

$\underline{} + \boxed{6} + \boxed{3} = \underline{13}$

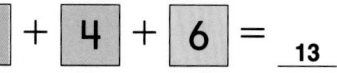

$\underline{} + \boxed{3} + \boxed{4} = \underline{13}$

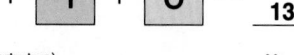

$\underline{} + \boxed{4} + \boxed{6} = \underline{13}$

(forty-two) $\qquad$ More Practice, page 410, set C $\qquad$ Chapter 2

---

3. PRACTICE AND APPLY

Basic	All
Average	All
Extended	All

PRACTICE

Direct students' attention to page 42.
*Which exercises in Row 1 have 10 sums?
doubles? How can they help you find the
sum?* (10 sums: first, second, fourth;
doubles: second; they can be added
together first to find the sums more
easily.)

APPLY

SHOW WITH CUBES ▶ **Why are
the sums the same for all three
exercises?** (The addends are the same.)
▶ **Who can make up a rule to explain
what this exercise proves?** (Possible
answer: Three addends can be added in
any order and the sum will be the same.)
Allow time for students to listen to each
other's rules.

LOSE AND ASSESS

HOW WHAT YOU KNOW
vide each group with 3 sets of
nchout number cards 0-5 and
nters. Reread the chapter poem.
ve students use cards and counters
solve this problem. *Scientists
unted 2 eggs in one nest, 2 in
other, and 3 eggs in a third. How
ny eggs did they count in all?* (7)

QUICK QUIZ

Copy the numbers from the chalkboard.
Write them in any order to make an
addition sentence and solve it.
4 5 6 (15)
3 2 3 (8)

Problem Solving: Asking a Question/Make a List

OBJECTIVE 2-11   To understand the question in a problem; to solve problems using the strategy Make a List

PREBOOK ACTIVITIES

QUICK REVIEW

Write + or − for each exercise.
1. $5 \bigcirc 3 = 8$ (+)   2. $9 \bigcirc 4 = 5$ (−)
3. $5 \bigcirc 2 = 3$ (−)   4. $8 \bigcirc 8 = 16$ (+)
5. $10 \bigcirc 5 = 5$ (−)   6. $7 \bigcirc 5 = 12$ (+)
7. $8 \bigcirc 9 = 17$ (+)   8. $6 \bigcirc 6 = 0$ (−)
9. $6 \bigcirc 2 = 4$ (−)   10. $7 \bigcirc 6 = 1$ (−)

PRIOR KNOWLEDGE

Why do we ask questions? (Possible answer: We ask questions to find information.) *Listen to my story. Then think of a question that you could ask about the story.* Substitute names of children in the class before you read the story.
Jill made 6 mud pies.
Jack made 7 mud pies.
What are some questions you could ask about this story?
(Possible answers: How many mud pies did they make in all? How many more pies did Jack make than Jill?)

COMMUNICATION

Reading and Discussing Math   Write the words **understand** and **list** on the chalkboard. Read the words aloud. Explain that to understand something means to know what it is about. Write this sentence on the board and ask students to fill in the blank and read it:

   Asking questions helps me _____ things. (understand)
What kinds of lists do you or your family make? (Possible answers: grocery lists, lists of things to do) *Explain how a list helps you.* (Possible answer: A list shows you what you need or what you must do so that you will not forget.)

EXPLORE AND CONNECT

COOPERATIVE ACTIVITY

Grouping Suggestion: small groups
Circle the best question for this story. Then write a number sentence about the question.
3 kittens were playing.
2 other kittens joined them.
How many kittens were left?
How many kittens were playing then? (3) + (2) = (5)

TEACHING ACTIONS

▶ **Describe the action going on in this story.** (Possible answer: Some kittens are playing and more kittens come and join them.)

▶ **What data in this story will help you solve it?** (Possible answer: the number of kittens; the phrase *joined them*)

▶ **What plan might help you decide which question makes sense for this story?** (Possible answer: First, reread the data in the story to see what action takes place; then, decide whether the action tells you to try addition or subtraction.)

▶ **How might you plan a way to solve this problem?** (Possible answer: Draw a picture to represent what each question asks about the problem. See which one makes sense. Then write a number sentence to fit the problem.)

▶ **How will you know if your answer is correct?** (Possible answer: It will make sense; you can check the addition or subtraction with counters.) Have students work in small cooperative learning groups and use counters to show the action in the story.

CONNECTIONS   Use these anytime.

Problem of the Day

Asking a Question   Write a question for the story. Then write a number sentence.
7 children were swimming.
4 children went home.
(Possible answer: How many children were still swimming? 7 − 4 = 3)

Math Connection

Making a List   Choose a number between 6 and 9. Make a list of addition and subtraction facts that have your number as the answer. Compare your list with a friend's. Which of your numbers has a greater number of facts? (Answers will vary. 9 has the most facts.)

Creative Thinking

Storytelling   With a partner, make up an addition or subtraction story. Let your partner ask a number question. Then you answer the question. Trade jobs and share your stories with the class.

CLASSWORK AND HOMEWORK SUPPLEMENTS

Practice

Problem Solving 2-11

Name _____

Asking a Question

Ring the better question for each story.
Then write the number sentence.

1. 6 children were at the park.
3 more children came.

(How many children were at the park in all?)

How many children were left?

6 (+) 3 (=) 9

2. 7 children were on the swings.
2 got off.

How many children got off the swings?

(How many children were still on the swings?)

7 (−) 2 (=) 5

3. 5 children ran to the sandbox.
4 children were already playing there.

(How many children are at the sandbox now?)

How many children left the sandbox?

5 (+) 4 (=) 9

20   Use with text page 43.   PS-2

Addison-Wesley | All Rights Reserved

Building Thinking Skills

Family Math 2-11

Name _____

Animals at the Zoo

Dear Family,
    Your child has learned how to ask a question for addition and subtraction stories. Use the picture to tell story problems. Begin a story, such as, "There are 4 monkeys in the trees. There are 3 monkeys on the ground." Have your child ask a question, such as, "How many monkeys are there in all?" Then have your child write the number sentence and solve.

1. ◯ — ▢
2. ◯ — ▢
3. ◯ — ▢
4. ◯ — ▢

20   Use with text pages 43-44.   TS-2

Addison-Wesley | All Rights Reserved

Reteaching

Problem Solving 2-11

Name _____

Make a List

List the ways to go from the start to the end.

(Start)

A   C   B

D   E

(End)

1. First A then D .   **3.** First B then D .
2. First A then E .   **4.** First B then E .
        5. First C then D .
        6. First C then E .

20   Use with text page 44.   RS-2

Addison-Wesley | All Rights Reserved

Challenges

Critical Thinking 2-11

Name _____

What Is for Lunch?

Lunch Menu
Sandwiches   Drinks 🥛
tuna 🥪   milk
cheese   apple juice
ham   grape drink

Pick I sandwich and I drink.
Write 9 different lunches you can have.
Order may vary.

1. ___tuna___ and ___milk___
2. ___tuna___ and ___apple juice___
3. ___tuna___ and ___grape drink___
4. ___cheese___ and ___milk___
5. ___cheese___ and ___apple juice___
6. ___cheese___ and ___grape drink___
7. ___ham___ and ___milk___
8. ___ham___ and ___apple juice___
9. ___ham___ and ___grape drink___

20   Use with text pages 43-44.   CS-2

Addison-Wesley | All Rights Reserved

OPTIONS FOR INDIVIDUAL NEEDS

2-11

Basic

Exercises All
More Practice, p. 411, set A

Supplements
Reteaching 20 or
Practice 20

Average

Exercises All
More Practice, p. 411, set A

Supplements
Practice 20
Challenges 20 or
Thinking Skills 20

Extended

Exercises All

Supplements
Challenges 20
Thinking Skills 20

Other Resources:
Problem-Solving Experiences In Mathematics, pages 4, 27
Mathematics Book A, pages 22-23

LESSON PLAN 2-11

OBJECTIVE 2-11
To understand the question in a problem; to solve problems using the strategy Make a List

1. MOTIVATE AND TEACH

LEARN ABOUT IT

 **BEFORE** ▶ **Describe the action taking place in Exercise 1.** (Possible answer: One group of rhinos joins another.)

 **DURING** ▶ **How can the action help you decide which question fits?** (Possible answer: Groups that join each other show addition. Groups that leave show subtraction.)
▶ **Why should you decide which question fits best before you write the number sentence?** (Clues in the question and the story will help you decide how to show the data in the number sentence.)

 **AFTER** ▶ **How can you can check your number sentence?** (Possible answer: Use counters to act out the story. Match your number sentence to the counters.)

2. CHECK UNDERSTANDING

ERROR ALERT **Page 43** Difficulty matching the action with the correct operation.
Page 44 Listing a path twice.

Name _____

Problem Solving
Asking a Question

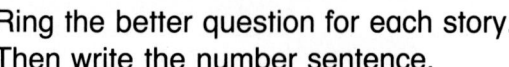

Ring the better question for each story.
Then write the number sentence.

1. 5 big rhinos were in the water.
    6 baby rhinos came in to join them.

    (How many rhinos were in the water then?)

    How many rhinos were left?

    <u>5</u> (+) <u>6</u> [=] <u>11</u>   <u>11</u> rhinos

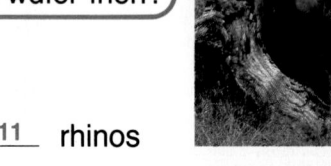

2. 9 condors were in a tree.
    2 condors flew away.

    (How many condors were in the tree then?)

    How many condors flew to the tree?

    <u>9</u> (−) <u>2</u> [=] <u>7</u>   <u>7</u> condors

3. 4 young tigers raced to the water.
    4 other tigers were already at the water.

    (How many tigers were at the water in all?)

    How many tigers were left?

    <u>4</u> (+) <u>4</u> [=] <u>8</u>   <u>8</u> tigers

Chapter 2   More Practice, page 411, set A   (forty-three)

TEACHING OPTIONS

RETEACHING TIPS Write a story with 1 addition and 1 subtraction question on the chalkboard. Have pairs move figures on a flannelboard to show action. Have one student circle a question and the other write a number sentence to match. Assign Reteaching Supplement 20.

COMPUTER **Conservation and Counting, Hartley Courseware © 1985** Three levels of play for all students. In *Bunny Hop*, students use estimation skills to select the number and types of steps for the bunny to get to the tree. Use paper and pencil to make a list. The game requires about 15 minutes.

oblem Solving Strategy
ke a List

sten to the story.
st the 8 ways the tortoise
n return to the sea.

| UNDERSTAND |
| FIND DATA |
| PLAN |
| ESTIMATE |
| SOLVE |
| CHECK |

Ways to the Sea

. First _A_ then _C_ .	5. First _B_ then _F_ .
. First _A_ then _D_ .	6. First _B_ then _E_ .
. First _A_ then _E_ .	7. First _B_ then _D_ .
. First _A_ then _F_ .	8. First _B_ then _C_ .

(forty-four)   Chapter 2

---

3. PRACTICE AND APPLY

Basic	All
Average	All
Extended	All

Read the following story to students:
Tony Tortoise wandered into the jungle looking for food. When it was time to go home to the sea, Tony could not remember which path to take. He needs your help to get home. Look at the picture. How do you know where to begin? (The picture of the tortoise shows the starting point.) *Which two paths are the only ones that the tortoise can start traveling on?* (paths A and B)

▶ **Describe the jungle trails.** (6 lettered trails)

▶ **Starting with path A, what different routes might Tony take?** (Possible answer: Trace a path with your finger. Start with A, then follow another path to the sea. Write this path letter down.)

▶ **What can you do to be sure you have listed every path that Tony might take?** (Possible answer: Color each path a different color after you have traced it to be sure you do not use the same path twice.)

LOSE AND ASSESS

HOW WHAT YOU KNOW   Ask
e student to write the beginning of a
ory that tells about joining or
parating. Another student writes a
btraction question for the story and
hird student writes an addition
estion. Invite students to work
gether to decide which question best
s the story. Have them write a
mber sentence for the story and
aw a picture to illustrate it.

QUICK QUIZ

Ring the question that fits the story.
9 feathers were on the table.
6 feathers blew away.
How many feathers were left?
How many feathers were added?

CHAPTER 2

WRAP UP

INTRODUCTION The Wrap Up provides activities emphasizing math language and thinking skills for the chapter and an enrichment activity that integrates those skills with other math strands.

USING PAGE 45

▶ **How can you use the fact you write for Exercise 1 to help you write a fact for Exercise 2?** (Possible answer: Remember to use a doubles fact to write a doubles-plus-one fact.)

▶ **How might you model the problem in Exercise 5?** (Possible answer: First, different combinations of 3 punchout pennies and nickels could be arranged to find the answer to the first question. Then coins could be added to make 16¢ and counted in different ways to see what Jose could buy at the fair.)

Name _____

WRAP UP

MATH WORDS

Write an addition fact. Answers may vary. Sample answers are shown.

1. This is a double fact.
   5 (+) 5 [=] 10

2. This is a double-plus-one fact.
   4 (+) 5 [=] 9

3. This fact has a sum of 10.
   7 (+) 3 [=] 10

4. This fact has a sum of 10 and 2 extra.
   8 (+) 4 [=] 12

MATH REASONING

5. José had 7¢. He had 3 coins.
   What coins did José have?   _1_   _2_

   His mother gave him 9¢ more.
   How much money does José have now?   _16¢_

   José went to the fair. He saw these things.

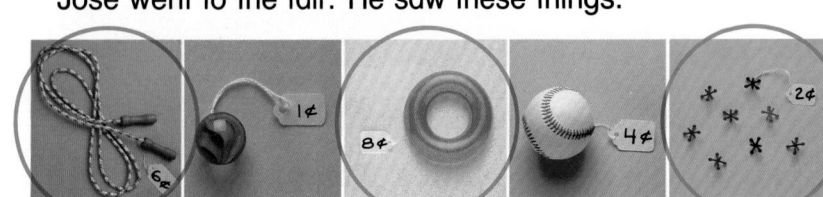

6¢   1¢   8¢   4¢   2¢

   What is the greatest number of hoops José can buy?   _2_ hoops

   José spent all his money buying 3 things. Ring the 3 things he bought.

Chapter 2 Wrap Up   (forty-five)   45

TEACHING OPTIONS

ENRICHMENT Have pairs of students set up make believe booths at the fair and display small objects or pictures of objects with price tags of less than 10¢ on them. Have one student work at the booth while the other student uses 16¢ in punchout money to shop at other booths in the class.

Students should try to buy as many items as they can for the money they have. When the shoppers have spent their money, they change places with the shopkeepers. Have students discuss the experience and show their purchases.

Name _____

CHAPTER REVIEW/TEST

Add.

4 +4 — 8	6 +6 — 12	3 +3 — 6	5 +5 — 10	4 +5 — 9	7 +6 — 13
8 +7 — 15	2 +2 — 4	7 +7 — 14	8 +9 — 17	9 +9 — 18	8 +8 — 16
9 +1 — 10	8 +5 — 13	6 +0 — 6	4 +9 — 13	7¢ +3¢ — 10¢	2¢ +8¢ — 10¢
2 2 +3 — 7	5 3 +1 — 9	6 2 +5 — 13	4 7 +2 — 13	5 4 +3 — 12	2 3 +6 — 11

Ring the better question for the story.
Then write the number sentence.

Ann found 5  .

She gave 2  to Joe.

How many feathers did she have in all?

⟨ How many feathers did she have left? ⟩

 _5_ ⊖ _2_ ☐= _3_   _3_ feathers

(forty-six)   Chapter 2 Review/Test

INTRODUCTION The Review/Test is provided to review and evaluate the skills and concepts presented in Chapter 2.

USING PAGE 46
If you prefer to use this page for review, you may want to use the **Multiple-Choice Posttest** (pages 7-8) or the **Free-Response Posttest** (pages 7-8) to evaluate mastery of chapter objectives.

ITEM ANALYSIS The table below correlates the Chapter Review/Test items with the lesson objectives for the chapter.

Items	Objectives
1	2-1, 2-2, 2-4, 2-9
2	2-1, 2-3, 2-4, 2-9
3	2-1, 2-4, 2-6, 2-7, 2-8, 2-9
4	2-10
5	2-11

INFORMAL ASSESSMENT

Using Manipulatives Provide small groups with flashcards for the addition facts studied in this chapter. Have a student in each group use cubes or counters to model an exercise on a flashcard as others take turns giving the sum. Have groups trade sets of flashcards for more practice.

Communication *Explain why it is a good idea to look for sums of 10 when you are adding numbers.* (Possible answers: Numbers that add up to 10 are important facts to know in your head, especially if you are adding more than 2 numbers; because 10 ends in a zero it is an easy number to add another number to.)

Critical Thinking ▶ How can you decide when you need to add to find the answer to a story problem? (Possible answer: Look for clues that indicate putting something together; for example, *How many in all?* or *How many joined them?*)

CHAPTER 2

ENRICHMENT

INTRODUCTION
Students will begin to understand the concept of measuring the perimeter by adding the measurements of the sides of different shapes in nonstandard units.

USING PAGE 47
This Enrichment page is provided for all students. You may wish to use it after they have completed the Chapter Review/Test on page 46.

▶ **Look at the opposite sides of each shape. What do the opposite sides have in common?** (Possible answer: The opposite sides will measure the same number of paper clips because they look as if they are the same length.)

▶ **Explain why following the colored lines is a good way to record the number of paper clips used.** (Possible answer: By measuring the sides of a shape in order, you can make sure that you write down all of the numbers without missing any.)

EXTENSIONS
Have pairs of students explore and measure small classroom objects shaped like squares, rectangles, or triangles. First, have them use paper clips to measure the item and add the measures of the sides. Then let them explore what happens when they use different sizes of paper clips to measure around an item. *Are the numbers that are added smaller or larger? Does it take a greater number of large paper clips to measure the item than small paper clips?* (Possible answer: No; since the clips are larger, it takes fewer of them to measure the same distance.) *How many paper clips might it take to measure around the room? Would it be possible just to measure two sides of certain objects and know what the other sides measure? Why?* Allow students to discuss their findings.

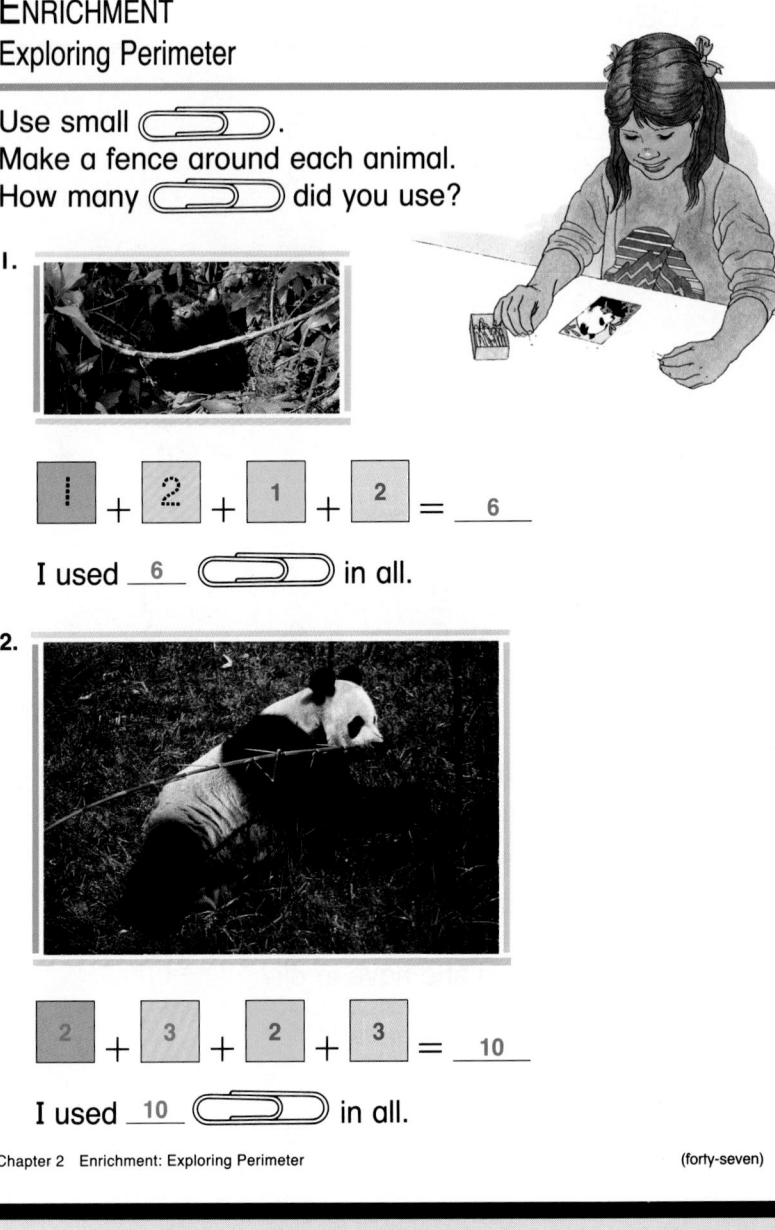

Name

ENRICHMENT
Exploring Perimeter

Use small ⬭.
Make a fence around each animal.
How many ⬭ did you use?

1.

$1 + 2 + 1 + 2 = \underline{6}$

I used $\underline{6}$ ⬭ in all.

2.

$2 + 3 + 2 + 3 = \underline{10}$

I used $\underline{10}$ ⬭ in all.

Chapter 2 Enrichment: Exploring Perimeter   (forty-seven)

Name _____

CUMULATIVE REVIEW

Add or subtract.

1.
$$5 + 0$$
○ 0
● 5
○ 3

2.
$$8 - 5$$
○ 13
○ 2
● 3

3.
$$9 + 1$$
● 10
○ 11
○ 8

4.
$$4 \\ 5 \\ +3$$
○ 13
○ 14
● 12

5. Finish the fact family.

$7 + 2 = 9$ ○ $4 + 3 = 7$
$2 + 7 = 9$ ● $9 - 2 = 7$
$9 - 7 = 2$ ○ $9 + 0 = 9$

Count on or back.

6. 15, 16, _____
○ 14
● 17
○ 18

7. _____, 4, 5
● 3
○ 4
○ 6

8. Which is a double-plus-one fact?
● $7 + 8$
○ $4 + 4$
○ $4 + 6$

9. 8 birds were in a tree.
3 more flew to the tree.
How many birds were in
the tree? Choose a number
sentence to match.

○ $8 - 3 = 5$
● $8 + 3 = 11$
○ $3 + 8 = 12$

CUMULATIVE REVIEW

INTRODUCTION The purpose of this Cumulative Review is to maintain previously taught skills and concepts. The emphasis in this Cumulative Review is on understanding addition and subtraction, Chapter 1, and on addition facts, Chapter 2.

ITEM ANALYSIS The table below correlates the Cumulative Review items with the lesson objectives.

Items	Objectives
1	2-1
2	1-3
3	2-7
4	2-10
5	1-8
6, 7	1-1
8	2-3
9	2-5

CHAPTER 3 PATTERNS AND GRAPHS

Chapter Management

OVERVIEW

Lesson	Pages	Objectives	Subject Integration	Strand Integration
Odd and Even Number Patterns	49-50	3-1 To model, identify, and continue odd and even patterns	fine arts: Asian crafts	critical thinking
Growing Patterns	51-52	3-2 To model, identify, and continue growing patterns	fine arts: cut & paste	number patterns
My Pattern Book	53-54	3-3 To identify and continue color patterns	fine arts: color patterns	logic
Problem Solving: Understanding the Operations/Using Critical Thinking	55-56	3-4 To add and subtract by putting together or by taking away; to continue patterns	fine arts: kites	critical thinking
Bar Graphs	57-58	3-5 To make and read bar graphs	fine arts: origami	data analysis
Graphing Data from a Survey	59-60	3-6 To take and graph data from a survey	language arts: writing	data analysis
Pictographs	61-62	3-7 To read pictographs	fine arts: drawing pictures	data analysis
Problem Solving: Retelling a Story/Problem Solving Strategy: Look for a Pattern	63-64	3-8 To retell a story; to use the strategy Look for a Pattern	fine arts: origami	computation, logic

MATHEMATICAL BACKGROUND

Patterns

The concept of patterns is basic to all of mathematics. Throughout elementary school, students will be using and identifying number patterns. The following pattern concepts are introduced in this chapter: odd and even patterns, growing patterns, and color patterns. Students learn to recognize and continue patterns and to make their own patterns.

Graphing

In Book 1, students were introduced to bar graphs and pictographs. They also learned to read tally marks for data. In Book 2, these skills are reviewed in detail and are extended to require that students write and total tally marks to obtain data for a graph. Students should know that every graph must have a descriptive title. Pictographs, like bar graphs, are best for comparing totals for groups of data. Students are introduced to pictographs with each picture representing 2 objects. Later on, students will be using pictographs in which each picture represents a greater number of objects. This progression of pictures in pictographs from a 2-to-1 relationship to a many-to-1 relationship is an important instructional concept.

Problem Solving

In this chapter, students solve problems by retelling a story and by using the Look for a Pattern strategy.

TIPS FROM TEACHERS

Use the following graphing topics with your class:
(1) types of shoes
(2) favorite color, fruit, cereal, and holiday
(3) birthday months
(4) number of people in family
(5) weather

Eileen Fukunaga
Sutter School
Santa Clara, CA

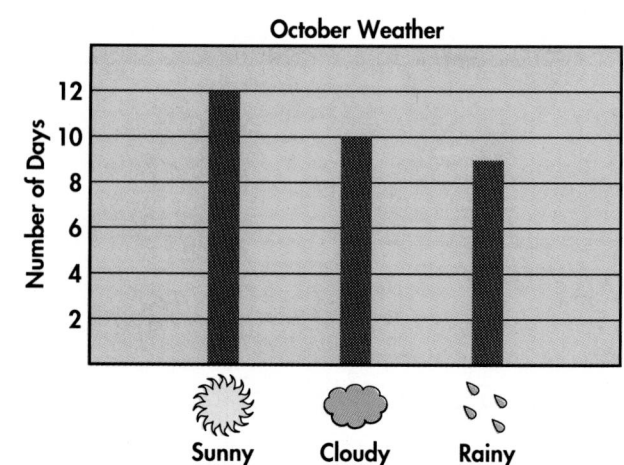

October Weather

ASSESSMENT

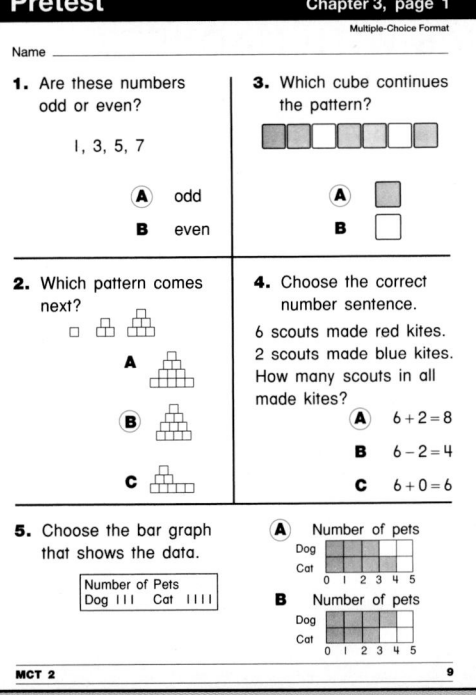

Pretest — Chapter 3, page 1

Multiple-Choice Format

Name _____

1. Are these numbers odd or even?

1, 3, 5, 7

- (A) odd
- B even

2. Which pattern comes next?

- A
- (B)
- C

3. Which cube continues the pattern?

- (A)
- B

4. Choose the correct number sentence.

6 scouts made red kites.
2 scouts made blue kites.
How many scouts in all made kites?

- (A) 6 + 2 = 8
- B 6 − 2 = 4
- C 6 + 0 = 6

5. Choose the bar graph that shows the data.

| Number of Pets |
| Dog III   Cat IIII |

- (A) Number of pets
- B Number of pets

MCT 2   9

Pretest — Chapter 3, page 2

Multiple-Choice Format

Name _____

6. Kathleen took a survey to find what color bikes her friends had. She made this bar graph. What color bike did most students have?

Bike Colors
Yellow
Black
Blue
0 1 2 3 4 5

- A yellow
- (B) black
- C blue

7. Use the pictograph to answer the question.

How many more boxes did George decorate than Rod?

Decorated Boxes
Each 🔲 stands for 2.
Lani
George
Rod

- (A) 2 boxes
- B 4 boxes
- C 1 box

8. Look for a pattern. Use the table to answer the question.

The class started a garden.
Row 1 had 1 plant.
Row 2 had 3 plants.
Row 3 had 5 plants.
How many plants were in Row 5?

| Row | 1 | 2 | 3 | 4 | 5 |
| Plants | 1 | 3 | 5 | 7 | ? |

- A 8 plants
- (B) 9 plants
- C 6 plants

10   MCT 2

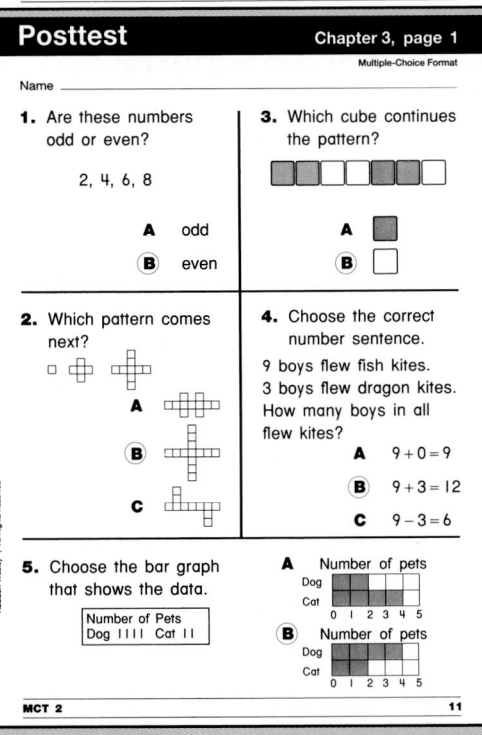

Posttest — Chapter 3, page 1

Multiple-Choice Format

Name _____

1. Are these numbers odd or even?

2, 4, 6, 8

- A odd
- (B) even

2. Which pattern comes next?

- A
- (B)
- C

3. Which cube continues the pattern?

- (A)
- B

4. Choose the correct number sentence.

9 boys flew fish kites.
3 boys flew dragon kites.
How many boys in all flew kites?

- A 9 + 0 = 9
- (B) 9 + 3 = 12
- C 9 − 3 = 6

5. Choose the bar graph that shows the data.

| Number of Pets |
| Dog IIII   Cat II |

- A Number of pets
- (B) Number of pets

MCT 2   11

Posttest — Chapter 3, page 2

Multiple-Choice Format

Name _____

6. Ricardo took a survey to find what color pencils his friends had. He made this bar graph. What color pencil did most students have?

Pencil Colors
Red
Blue
Yellow
0 1 2 3 4 5

- A red
- (B) blue
- C yellow

7. Use the pictograph to answer the question.

How many more cards did Glenda color than Sid?

Colored Cards
Each 🔲 stands for 2.
Alysia
Glenda
Sid

- (A) 2 cards
- B 1 card
- C 3 cards

8. Look for a pattern. Use the table to answer the question.

The class started a garden.
Row 1 had 2 plants.
Row 2 had 4 plants.
Row 3 had 6 plants.
How many plants were in Row 6?

| Row | 1 | 2 | 3 | 4 | 5 | 6 |
| Plants | 2 | 4 | 6 | 8 | 10 | ? |

- A 10 plants
- (B) 12 plants
- C 6 plants

12   MCT 2

ITEM ANALYSIS

Items	Objectives
1	3-1
2	3-2
3	3-3
4	3-4
5	3-5
6	3-6
7	3-7
8	3-8

Note: The item analysis is the same for all pretests and posttests for this chapter.

ALSO AVAILABLE

- ▶ Free Response Tests
- ▶ Alternative Tests
- ▶ Thinking Strategies
- ▶ Concrete Materials

Chapter 3 Chapter Management   **49B**

PROJECT AND BULLETIN BOARD

Provide a large horseshoe magnet and display a box of common objects, the majority of which are magnetic. Have students investigate to discover which objects are attracted to the magnet and which are not. Label a prepared bulletin board graph: *Discoveries with Magnets.* Label the columns: *Will Attract, Will Not Attract.* Have students show the results by drawing a picture of each object in the appropriate graph box. Compare the results. *Did the magnet attract or repel most of the objects? How can you tell?*

Use the same objects in subsequent sessions to investigate and discover whether more sink or float and whether more are smooth or rough. Students may think of other ways to classify and graph information about the objects.

DISCOVERIES WITH MAGNETS

Will Attract		Will Not Attract	
	6		6
	5		5
	4		4
	3		3
	2		2
	1		1

COOPERATIVE LEARNING

Divide the class into groups of 5. Identify the group skill: treating each other with respect. Direct each group to survey 20 people about their favorite sport and then graph the results. Have students divide the following tasks: make a survey sheet listing several sports; ask 8 boys, 8 girls, and 4 teachers which of the listed sports is their favorite; tally the results on the survey sheet; and graph the results. Display the graphs prepared by each group. Compare the results. Are the graphs identical? Ask students to explain why or why not. (Each group will probably come up with different results.) Remind students to treat the members of other groups with respect when comparing graphs and to remember that there is more than 1 correct way to accomplish most tasks.

You will find grouping suggestions and cooperative learning activities in most lessons throughout this chapter.

Survey Sheet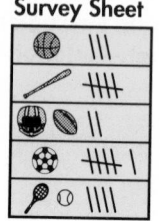

Graph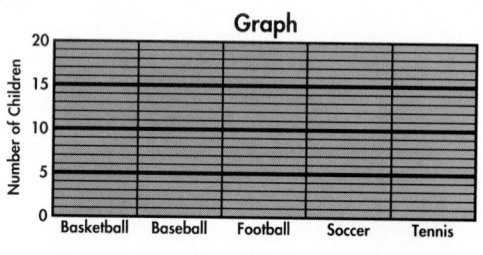

LITERATURE

Rockwell, Anne. *The Old Woman and Her Pig.* New York: Thomas Y. Crowell, 1979.

An old woman sets out to buy a pig with a crooked sixpence she found while sweeping her house. The purchase of the pig is only the beginning of this charming story told in repetitive patterns.
Ask students to create repetitive story patterns of their own. They might also graph the numbers of times different animals and objects appear in the story.

Emberley, Barbara. *Drummer Hoff.* New York: Simon & Schuster, 1967.

Shaw, Charles G. *It Looked Like Spilt Milk.* New York: Harper & Row, 1947.

Zemach, Margot. *It Could Always Be Worse.* New York: Farrar, Straus & Giroux, 1976.

ENGLISH AS A SECOND LANGUAGE

The theme of this chapter is Asian crafts. Have Asian students bring in objects, or invite parents into the classroom to demonstrate the crafts. Include crafts from other cultures as well to raise students' multicultural awareness.

Review the necessary vocabulary—*alike, different, more, less, fewer, greatest, least, odd,* and *even*—by demonstrating visually, paraphrasing, and having students act out. For example, give each student in a line a number and then ask them to group themselves according to whether their number is odd or even.

Review question forms—such as *How many kites did they make?*—paying particular attention to the negative questions, such as *How many did **not** fly their kites?* In addition, introduce the idea of estimating with *about how many.* For the more complex questions about bar graphs—such as *How many more people plan to come at 1:00 than at 2:30?*—break the questions into parts to simplify.

GIFTED

Mathematically gifted students may already be able to identify patterns and complete graphs. They will nevertheless be interested in many of the strategies presented in this chapter. You may wish to challenge these students by asking them to create and graph patterns. For example, after students complete Lesson 3 on patterns and Lesson 5 on bar graphs, provide students with a collection of attribute blocks. Ask them to create a growing pattern using the blocks, then make a bar graph or pictograph showing the total number of each block. For musically gifted students, you may wish to have student pairs create and continue musical patterns using xylophones, music blocks, or other classroom instruments.

STUDENTS AT RISK

Graphing is a series of abstractions. It is a sound practice to reintroduce graphing with concrete objects. Soon, most students will be ready to represent objects with pictures in a picture graph.

Conduct a survey in the class and have students graph the results. For example, you might ask what kind of pets students have, what their favorite color is, or what the number of people in their family is. Have students make pictures of the actual person or thing they are representing. Then they can replace these pictures with symbols that they have chosen to represent each category. Have them prepare the picture symbols and mount them as a picture graph. At this point, 1 picture should represent only 1 item. Repeat the survey on another topic and eventually have students interview members of another class. Discuss the results of each survey or growth graph to make sure students practice the language associated with this activity. Write their conclusions and observations on a large chart to provide a reading experience in a mathematical context.

You may also use the Reteaching Supplements and the specific Reteaching Tips from each lesson in this Chapter.

PICTURE

These pictures and accompanying stories and poems are available as storybooks.

You may want to read and discuss this story with your students before starting the chapter. The first lesson in this chapter includes a question about the story. Lessons 1, 2, 4, 5 and 8 in this chapter have questions in the informal Assessment that refer to the story.

The Ginger Jar Painter

"Have you ever wondered where butterflies got the elegant patterns on their wings?" the old Chinese storyteller began. His long grey beard was no wider than a piece of rope. He was the oldest and best-liked storyteller in the village. He continued:

All of the butterflies used to be just plain yellow, orange, white, or blue. They were graceful and colorful, but not exceptionally beautiful. Then, one day, a young village girl noticed an unusual butterfly. Its orange wings were delicately outlined in black, and the beautiful pattern on one wing was perfectly matched on the other wing. "Where could it have come from?" she wondered. "Perhaps another part of the world."

That evening she told her mother, father, and brother about the butterfly. Her brother said that he too had seen a butterfly with an unusual pattern flying high in a magnolia tree. Its bright blue wings were strikingly patterned in black, and there was a little spot of yellow on each wing. "How lovely it was," he said. "I believe that someone may be painting the butterflies. I wonder who it could be."

The next day, as the little girl and her brother walked the narrow streets of the village, they found many people asking the same question. "Where are the magnificent patterns on the butterflies coming from?"

The little girl and her brother thought and thought. "Who in the village loves to make patterns? Perhaps the stone layer," the little girl said. "He makes beautiful patterns." The little girl and her brother visited the stone layer. He knew nothing about the butterflies.

"Maybe the gardener painted the butterflies," the brother said. "He plants flowers in patterns." They stopped by to ask the gardener, but he did not know about the butterflies.

Then the little girl had an idea. "Who loves patterns and loves to paint?" She and her brother cried out together, "The ginger jar painter!"

They hurried over to the ginger jar painter's studio and peeked through the bamboo shade. They saw shelf after shelf of neatly arranged ginger jars. The painter was working on a jar that had pink butterflies rimming the tops of cabbage leaves in a pattern. It was beautiful.

The little girl and her brother watched at a distance as a plain yellow butterfly flew into the studio and settled on the edge of the work table. The ginger jar painter dabbed a bit of black paint on her brush and swirled it lightly into a pattern on the butterfly's left wing. The butterfly carefully closed its wings, transferring the exact design to the other wing. Then he flew away.

"Thus the boy and girl learned the secret of the patterns on butterflies' wings," said the old Chinese storyteller. He stroked his beard and smiled. "And the next time you see a butterfly, study him carefully. You will see that the ginger jar painter is still very hard at work."

Patterns and Graphs

OBJECTIVE 3-1   To model, identify, and continue odd and even patterns

PREBOOK ACTIVITIES

QUICK REVIEW

Complete each pattern.

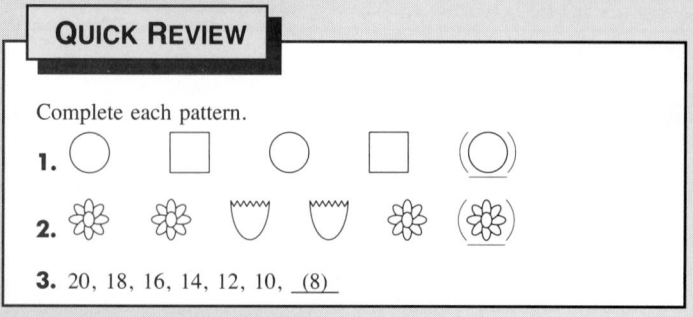

1. ○ □ ○ □ (○)

2. ✿ ✿ ⬱ ⬱ ✿ (✿)

3. 20, 18, 16, 14, 12, 10, <u>(8)</u>

PRIOR KNOWLEDGE

How many things are in a pair? (2) *Name some things that you buy in pairs.* (Possible answers: gloves, shoes, socks) Ask a student to draw a pair of items on the chalkboard. Write the number 2 under the items. *What would your picture look like if you lost 1 of the items? What would your picture look like if you found an extra 1 to go with your pair?* Encourage students to notice that the single or odd items do not have a mate as the paired items do.

COMMUNICATION

Reading and Writing in Math   Write the words **even numbers** and **odd numbers** on the chalkboard. Have students read the words aloud. Explain that to show an even number, students can draw pairs and that an odd number will always have an extra item that does not have a partner.

Write these 2 sentences on the board. Have students copy them in their Math Journals and fill in the blanks. They may draw a picture to help them find the answer.

2 is an <u>(even)</u> *number*.

3 is an <u>(odd)</u> *number*.

EXPLORE AND CONNECT

Materials: cubes
Grouping Suggestions: small groups
Provide each group with several cubes. Have each student take a handful of cubes and pair them. *Do all your cubes have a partner?* If so, explain that they have shown an even number. Ask students to count their cubes and write the number. *Do you have a cube left over? What kind of number did you show* (odd) Have students practice skip counting by 2s, starting with 0 (for even numbers) and then with 1 (for odd numbers). As you count, have group members take turns displaying sets of cubes; 2 cubes, 4 cubes, 6 cubes; or 1 cube, 3 cubes, 5 cubes. *What do you notice about the odd numbers of cubes?* (Possible answer: They do not end with a pair. Each set has 2 more than the last set.) *What do you notice about the even number of cubes?* (Possible answer: Even numbers end with a pair. Each set has 2 more than the last set.)

CONNECTIONS   Use these anytime.

Problem of the Day

Choosing a Question   Ring the question that fits the story.
7 roosters were crowing.
2 more roosters joined in.
How many roosters stopped crowing?
<u>How many roosters were crowing then?</u>

Mental Math

Even/Odd Riddles   Say the answer.
I am an odd number.
I am greater than 5.
I am less than 9.
What number am I? <u>(7)</u>
I am an even number.
Add me to 8 and you will get a number between 11 and 13.
What number am I? <u>(4)</u>

Subject Integration

Music   Have a leader clap a rhythm. Listen to the rhythm and count the number of claps. The first person to clap the rhythm correctly and say whether it is an even or odd number of claps gets to be the next leader. Limit the number of claps to less than 10.

CLASSWORK AND HOMEWORK SUPPLEMENTS

Practice

Patterns 3-1

Name _____

Odd and Even Number Patterns

Count on or back to continue the pattern.
Write whether the numbers are **odd** or **even**.

1. 2, 4, _6_, _8_, _10_ even

2. 1, 3, _5_, _7_, _9_ odd

3. 18, 16, _14_, _12_, 10 even

4. 9, 11, _13_, _15_, 17 odd

Put a ☐ around the even numbers.
Put a ○ around the odd numbers.

6   9   16   11   4
0   12   1   18   20   5
17   7   3   14
2   13   8   10   19   15

PS-2   Use with text pages 49 – 50.   21

Building Thinking Skills

Family Math 3-1

Name _____

Patterns to See

> Dear Family,
> Your child has just completed a lesson on odd and even number patterns. Complete these problems with your child. Then help him or her describe the patterns that appear.

Add.

1	2	3	4	5	6
+1	+2	+3	+4	+5	+6
2	4	6	8	10	12

What is the pattern of the addends? ___Add one each time.___
What is the pattern of the sums? ___2, 4, 6, 8, 10, 12; count by 2s___
Are the sums odd or even? ___even___
What happens when you add two even numbers? ___The sum is even.___
What happens when you add two odd numbers? ___The sum is even.___

Add these. Talk about the patterns in the addends and the sums.

4	5	6	7	8	9
+5	+6	+7	+8	+9	+10
9	11	13	15	17	19

What happens when you add one even number and one odd number? ___The sum is odd.___

Try some on your own. See what happens.

TS-2   Use with text pages 49 – 50.   21

Reteaching

Manipulatives 3-1

Name _____

Odd and Even Number Patterns

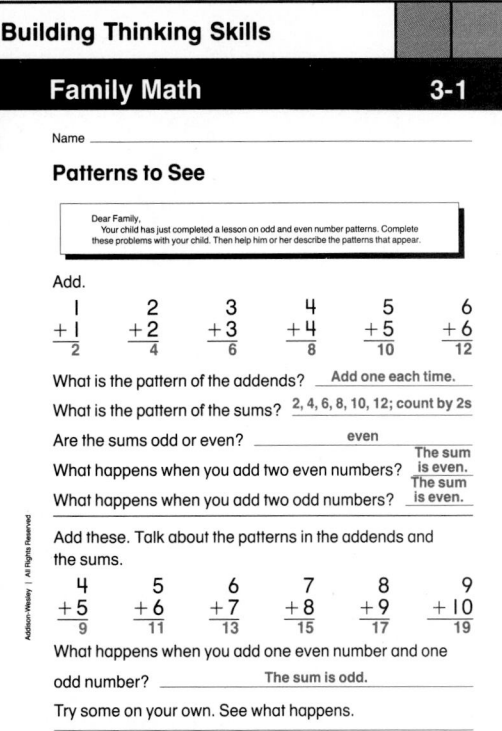

2 even (1 pair)   3 odd (1 pair, 1 left over)
4 even (2 pairs)   5 odd (2 pairs, 1 left over)

Numbers you can make with pairs are **even**.
Numbers that have one left over are **odd**.

Use counters to make each number.
Color even numbers red.
Color odd numbers blue.
Tell about the pattern.

1	2	3	4	5	6	7	8	9	10
11	12	13	14	15	16	17	18	19	20

Color 1, 3, 5, 7, 9, 11, 13, 15, 17, 19 blue.
Color 2, 4, 6, 8, 10, 12, 14, 16, 18, 20 red.

RS-2   Use with text pages 49 – 50.   21

Challenges

Number Sense 3-1

Name _____

Turtle Race

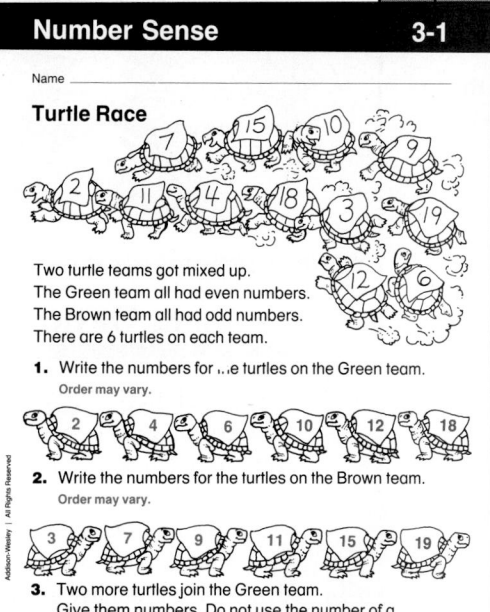

Two turtle teams got mixed up.
The Green team all had even numbers.
The Brown team all had odd numbers.
There are 6 turtles on each team.

1. Write the numbers for the turtles on the Green team.
   Order may vary.
   2   4   6   10   12   18

2. Write the numbers for the turtles on the Brown team.
   Order may vary.
   3   7   9   11   15   19

3. Two more turtles join the Green team.
   Give them numbers. Do not use the number of a turtle above.
   Answers may vary, but should be even.

CS-2   Use with text pages 49 – 50.   21

OPTIONS FOR INDIVIDUAL NEEDS

Basic

Exercises All
Calculator Bank, p. 401
More Practice, p. 411, set B

Supplements
Reteaching 21 or
Practice 21

Average

Exercises All
Calculator Bank, p. 401
More Practice, p. 411, set B

Supplements
Practice 21
Challenges 21 or
Thinking Skills 21

Extended

Exercises All
Calculator Bank, p. 401

Supplements
Challenges 21
Thinking Skills 21

Other Resources:
Math in Stride, pp. 7-8, 11-12, 44-45
Mathematics Their Way, pp. 328-329
Explorations, pp. 100, 112-116, 132-133, 144, 173, 204-205, 235, 245-244
Mathematics Book A, pp. 8-11

3-1

OBJECTIVE 3-1
To model, identify, and continue odd and even patterns

Materials: cubes or counters, attribute blocks, flannelboard, felt numbers and pieces, number cards 1-10

1. MOTIVATE AND TEACH

LEARN ABOUT IT

Read the chapter story to the class. *Look at the picture that goes with this story. What patterns do you see?* (Possible answers: patterns on the ginger jars; patterns in the way the ginger jars are arranged on the shelves)

▶ **What do you notice about the beginning of the first pattern on page 49?** (Possible answers: The pattern shows even numbers; 2 more masks are added each time.)

▶ **How can this information help you continue the pattern?** (Possible answer: The next number has to be even, and it has to be 2 more than the number before it.)

▶ **How are the patterns in the first and second exercises different?** (Possible answer: The pattern in the second exercise starts with an odd number; the groups of teapots in this exercise do not form pairs.)

▶ **Compare the third exercise to the first exercise. How are they alike? How are they different?** (Possible answer: They both show a pattern with even numbers and pairs or items; you count on in the first exercise and count back in the third exercise.)

Have students lay counters or cubes over the objects and then continue each pattern.

2. CHECK UNDERSTANDING

ERROR ALERT Forgetting that even numbers form pairs while odd numbers do not.

3
Patterns and Graphs

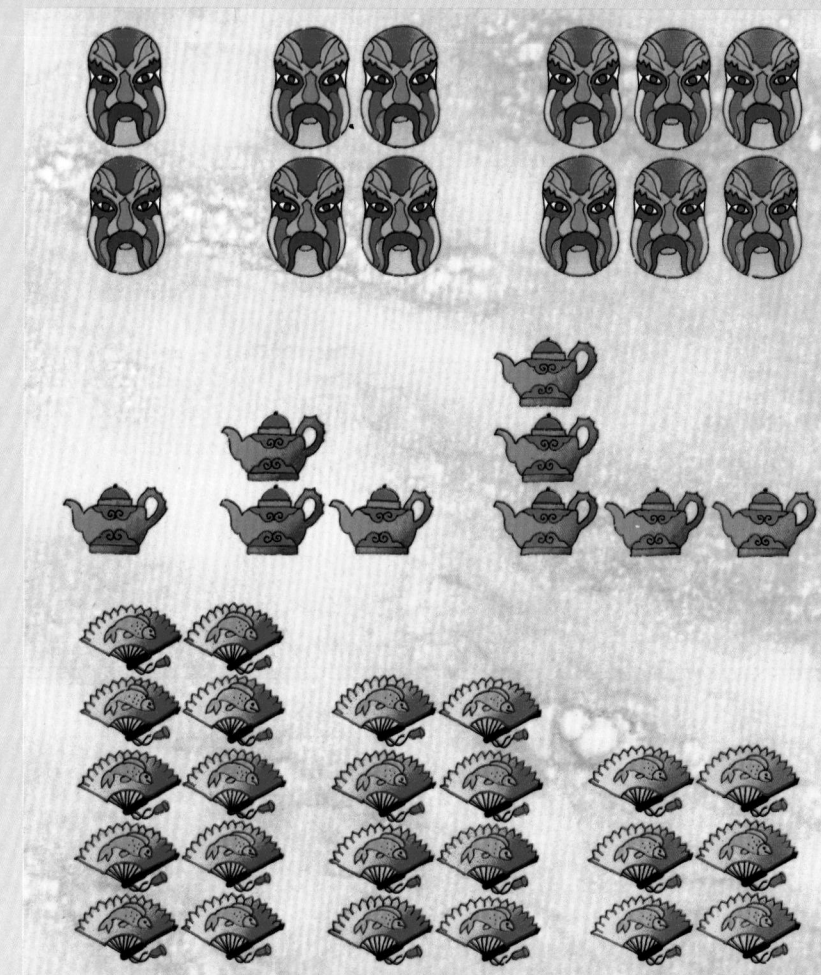

TEACHING OPTIONS

RETEACHING TIPS Display numbers on a flannelboard. Next to each, have students group small felt pieces to match. *How can you tell which are the odd numbers?* (They have 1 piece left over.) Have them identify each number as even or odd and tell why. Assign Reteaching Supplement 21.

ENRICHMENT Have students experiment with addition and subtraction facts to determine whether each of the following sums would always be odd or always be even: even number + even number, odd number + odd number, even number + odd number. (even; even; odd)

...dd and Even Number Patterns

...me _____

...se cubes to continue each pattern.
...rite the numbers. Are the numbers
...dd or **even**? Ring your answer.

_2_ , _4_ , 6 , _8_ , _10_   odd **(even)**

_1_ , _3_ , 5 , _7_ , _9_   **(odd)** even

...ount on or count back to continue
...ch pattern. Write the numbers.
...ng odd or even.

6, 8, 10, _12_ , _14_ , _16_ , _18_   odd **(even)**

5, 7, 9, _11_ , _13_ , _15_ , _17_   **(odd)** even

20, 18, 16, _14_ , _12_ , _10_ , _8_   odd **(even)**

19, 17, 15, _13_ , _11_ , _9_ , _7_   **(odd)** even

...E CRITICAL THINKING

...ng the words that tell how the blocks are different.

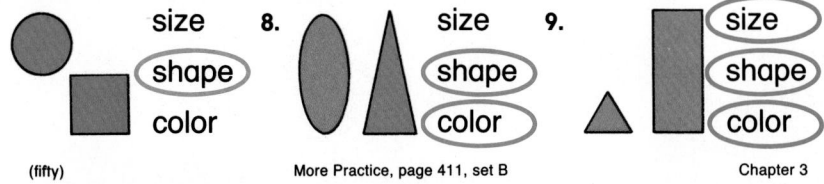

size   **8.**   size   **9.**   **(size)**
(shape)   **(shape)**   **(shape)**
color   **(color)**   **(color)**

(fifty)   More Practice, page 411, set B   Chapter 3

...LOSE AND **ASSESS**

...HOW WHAT YOU KNOW

...ovide number cards labeled 1–10.
...ve each student choose a number
...thout looking. Ask each to write a
...mber pattern starting with the
...mber and continuing to 19 or 20.
...e pattern will be odd or even
...pending on the starting number.
...hen each student is finished, have
...m or her show the number, read the
...ttern, and tell whether the numbers
...the pattern are even or odd.

QUICK QUIZ

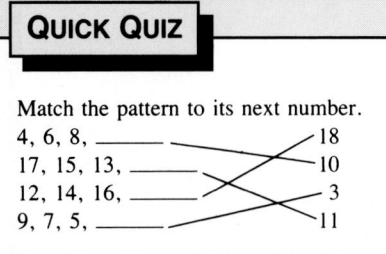

Match the pattern to its next number.
4, 6, 8, _____   18
17, 15, 13, _____   10
12, 14, 16, _____   3
9, 7, 5, _____   11

---

3. PRACTICE AND APPLY

Basic	All
Average	All
Extended	All

PRACTICE

How will using cubes to continue each pattern help you decide if the pattern shows odd or even numbers? (You will see whether the cubes form pairs or have 1 left over.) *How are Exercises 5 and 6 different from Exercises 1-4?* (You are counting back in Exercises 5 and 6.)

APPLY

USE CRITICAL THINKING
▶ **What rule can you make up about all even numbers?** (Possible answer: They all end in 0, 2, 4, 6, or 8.)
▶ **What rule can you make up about all odd numbers?** (Possible answer: They all end in 1, 3, 5, 7, or 9.)
▶ **Name a question you can ask yourself as you try to identify how each pair of blocks is different.**
(Possible answer: How are the 2 blocks alike? Are they the same size? color? shape? If not, then you know to circle that word.)

3-1

Growing Patterns

OBJECTIVE 3-2 To model, identify, and continue growing patterns

PREBOOK ACTIVITIES

QUICK REVIEW

Count by 2s. Begin at 2. Count to 10.
Count by 3s. Begin at 3. Count to 15.
Count by 5s. Begin at 5. Count to 20.

PRIOR KNOWLEDGE

Present a situation such as the following to help students recall and notice number patterns.

Jack has 5 stickers.

Each day he gets 2 more stickers at school.

How many stickers will he have after 5 days? (15)
How did you find the answer? (Possible answer: added 2 for 5 days to get 10; added that sum to the first 5 stickers) *What pattern do you see in the addition for the 5 days?* (adding 2 each time)

COMMUNICATION

Discussing Math Write these patterns on the chalkboard:

1 2 1 2 1 2 1 2 1 2 1 2 1 2 1 2 1 2
1 1 2 1 2 3 1 2 3 4 1 2 3 4 5

How would you describe the first pattern? (Possible answer: The numbers 1 and 2 are repeated.) *What is different about the second pattern?* (Another number is being added each time; the pattern is growing.) *What numbers will come next in the first pattern?* (1, 2) *In the second pattern?* (1, 2, 3, 4, 5, 6)

EXPLORE AND CONNECT

Materials: cubes, punchout number cards 1 through 5
Grouping Suggestion: pairs
Provide each pair of students with cubes and number cards. Number cards should be shuffled and placed face down on the table. Begin by putting 1 cube on the table. One student draws a number card and, without looking, shows it to the partner. The partner adds that number of cubes to the first cube. The first student must determine what number was on the card and continue the pattern by adding the same number of cubes. The partner turns the number card over to show if the guess was correct. Students change roles and repeat the activity.

CONNECTIONS   Use these anytime.

Problem of the Day

Logic Sam puts a penny in his bank one day. The next day he puts 2 pennies in the bank. He puts 3 pennies in the third day. How much money will he have in 5 days if he continues this pattern? (15 cents)

MathConnection

Operations Would addition or subtraction be used to make patterns that grow? (addition) Why? (Addition makes things get bigger, or grow.) Use cubes to show that your answer is correct.

Subject Integration

Fine Arts You buy 1 bunch of pink flowers, 2 bunches of red flowers, and 3 bunches of purple flowers. Each bunch has 3 flowers. Draw a design for mixing the flowers so there is a growing pattern.

CLASSWORK AND HOMEWORK SUPPLEMENTS

OPTIONS FOR INDIVIDUAL NEEDS

3-2

Basic

Exercises All
More Practice, p. 411, set C

Supplements
Reteaching 22 or
Practice 22

Average

Exercises All
More Practice, p 411, set C

Supplements
Practice 22
Challenges 22 or
Thinking Skills 22

Extended

Exercises All

Supplements
Challenges 22
Thinking Skills 22

Other Resources:
Math in Stride, pp. 7-8
Mathematics Their Way, pp. 328-337, 359
Explorations, pp. 29-32, 205
Developing Number Concepts With Unifix Cubes, pp. 31-44
Workjobs, pp. 40-41

Practice

Patterns 3-2

Name

Growing Patterns

Ring the one that comes next.

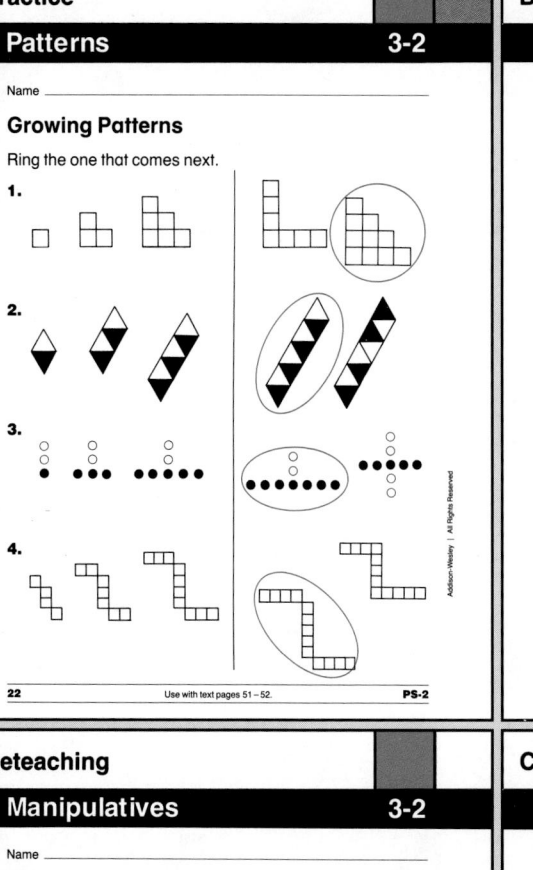

22   Use with text pages 51 – 52.   PS-2

Building Thinking Skills

Number Sense 3-2

Name

Finding Patterns

Read each question.
Find the pattern.
Write the number.

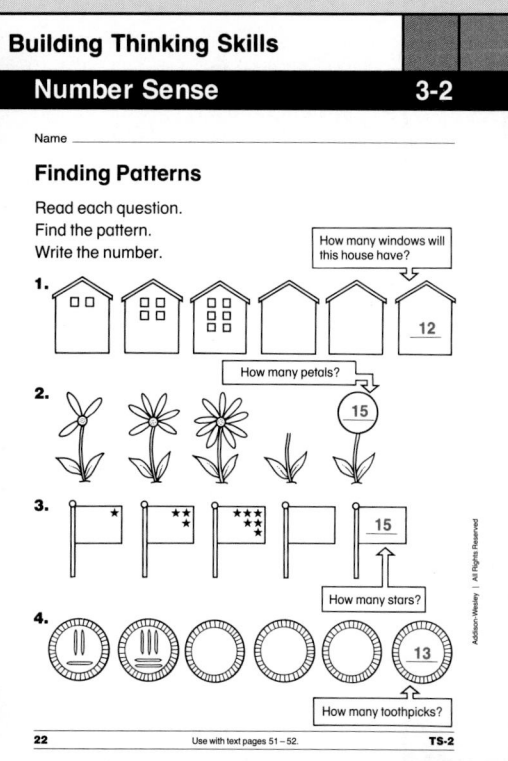

22   Use with text pages 51 – 52.   TS-2

Reteaching

Manipulatives 3-2

Name

Growing Patterns

Use counters to show each pattern.
Draw what comes next. Write the numbers.

22   Use with text pages 51 – 52.   RS-2

Challenges

Cooperative Activities 3-2

Name

Make Your Own Pattern

Work with a partner.
Color squares to show a growing pattern.
Decide on a rule. Take turns.
Use one of these rules or make up your own.

Patterns will vary. Check students' work.

- Color 1 more each time.
- Color 4 more each time.
- Color 2 more, then 3 more, then 4 more. . . .

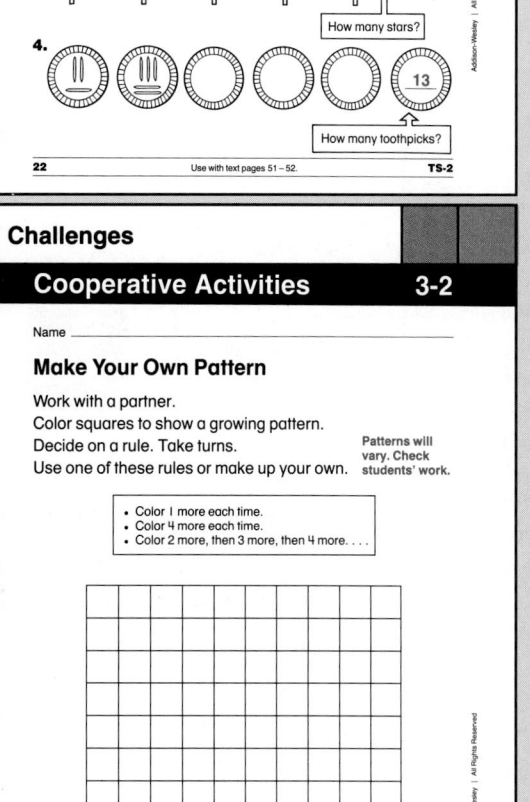

22   Use with text pages 51 – 52.   CS-2

LESSON PLAN 3-2

OBJECTIVE 3-2
To model, identify, and continue growing patterns

Materials: Cube-A-Links in 4 colors, paper, markers, scissors, paste, TA 3 (Graph Paper)

Alternative Materials: counters or other manipulatives in 4 colors

Grouping Suggestions: individual work, pairs

1. MOTIVATE AND TEACH

LEARN ABOUT IT

Practice recognizing number patterns by reviewing already learned number sequences. Write the following on the chalkboard: 1, 3, 5, 7. Ask students to read the sequence aloud. *What number comes next?* (9) *How do you know?* (Possible answers: The numbers are odd; they are skip counted by twos.) Repeat with 10, 15, and 20. (25)
In the example at the top of Page 51, how many cubes are added as you move from one part of the pattern to the next? (4)
▶ **Besides a number pattern, what other pattern do you see?** (Possible answers: The cubes are being added to the ends of the design each time; the cubes look like an *X* that grows bigger.)
▶ **How would you describe the shape the cubes are making in Exercise 1?** (Possible answer: They look like steps.)
▶ **How many cubes are being added to the pattern each time?** (2, 3, 4)
▶ **How are the patterns in Exercises 1 and 2 alike? How are they different?** (Possible answer: The number pattern is the same; the shape of the pattern is different.)

2. CHECK UNDERSTANDING

ERROR ALERT Choosing a design with the right shape but an incorrect number of cubes for the next picture in the pattern.

Name _____

Growing Patterns

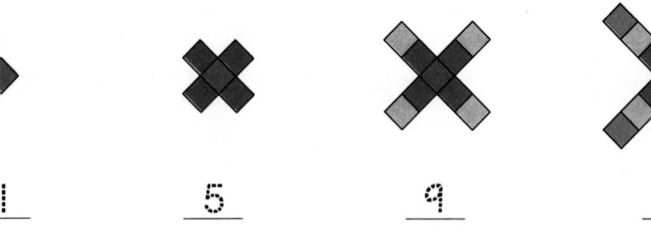

Use cubes to show each pattern. Cut and paste what comes next. Write the number of cubes.

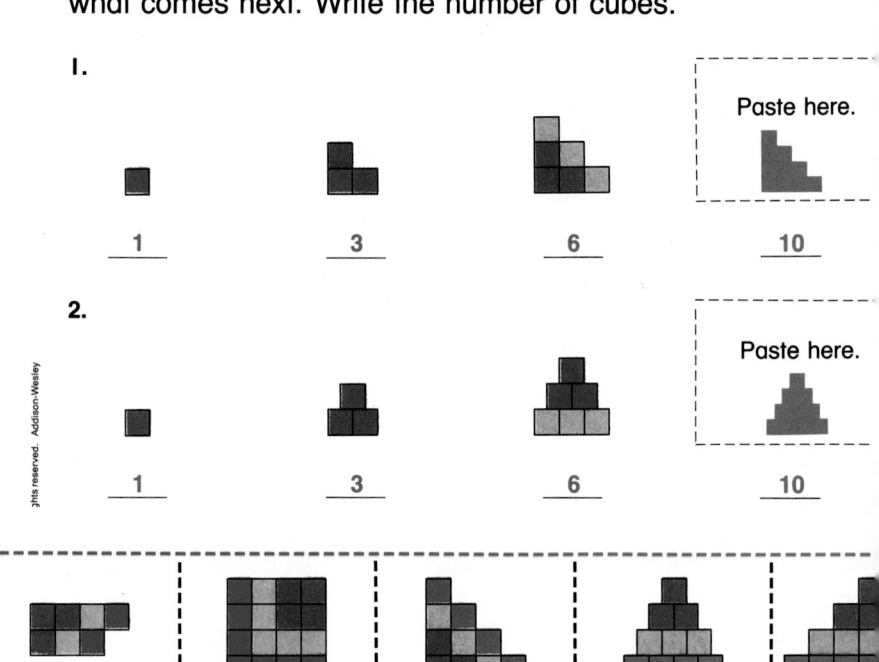

1.

   1   3   6   Paste here.   10

2.

   1   3   6   Paste here.   10

Chapter 3   (fifty-one)

TEACHING OPTIONS

RETEACHING TIPS Have students use cubes in 4 colors to create a step pattern with 1 red cube, 2 blue cubes, and 3 yellow cubes. Ask how many green cubes they will put in the next row and tell why. (4; each row increases by 1.) Assign Reteaching Supplement 22.

ENRICHMENT Have students use markers of different colors and graph paper to show a pattern that has this number sequence: 2, 6, 12. *How many cubes were added each time?* (4, 6) Have them tell the next number in the pattern (20) and draw their own design for this sequence.

---

51   Chapter 3 Lesson 2

e cubes to show each
tern. Cut and paste
at comes next. Write
number of cubes.

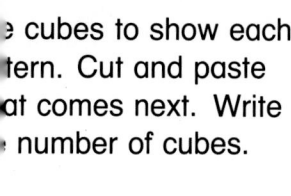   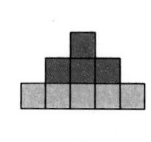   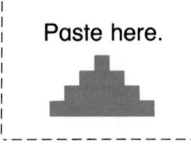   Paste here.

1   4   9   16

      Paste here.

1   3   5   7

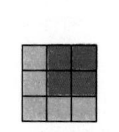      Paste here.

1   4   9   16

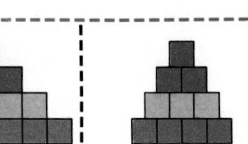   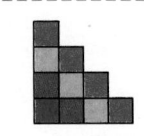      

3. PRACTICE AND APPLY

Basic	All
Average	All
Extended	All

PRACTICE

Before students complete page 52, have
them look carefully at the patterns. *How
will you show the answers?* (Possible
answers: Use cubes to build the patterns;
paste the correct picture in the box; write
the number on the line.)

APPLY

▶ **What order remains the same in all
the patterns on pages 51 and 52?** (the
color order of the cubes: blue, red,
yellow, green)
▶ **Describe what you did, step by
step with cubes, to build one of the
patterns on page 52.** (Answers will
vary.)
▶ **Which pattern was the easiest to
build? Which was the hardest?
Explain your answer.**

OSE AND ASSESS

OW WHAT YOU KNOW
iew with students the chapter
y, *The Ginger Jar Painter. Can
make your own pattern of ginger
sitting on shelves?* Have students
k in small groups to create
erns using counters or drawings.
nind them to treat each other with
ect as they view each other's
gns.

QUICK QUIZ

Copy the pattern and write the
numbers. Draw the next picture in the
pattern.

□□ □□□ □□□□ □□□□□

Chapter 3 Lesson 2   **52**

LESSON OPTIONS 3-3

My Pattern Book

OBJECTIVE 3-3   To identify and continue color patterns

PREBOOK ACTIVITIES

QUICK REVIEW

Sally's color pattern has 1 red block, 2 blue blocks, and 3 green blocks. How many orange blocks should she add to her pattern? (4)

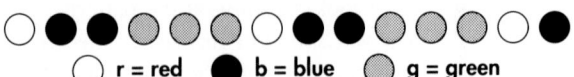

○ r = red   ● b = blue   ◉ g = green

PRIOR KNOWLEDGE

Ask students to think of places where they have seen color or number patterns. Help students brainstorm by offering topics such as floor tile patterns, patterns on clothing, wallpaper patterns, or color patterns in the produce section of the grocery store. Have students listen to each other's stories, showing respect for individual opinions.

COMMUNICATION

Discussion Math   Use colored chalks to show the following pattern on the chalkboard:

○○●◎◎◎○○●◎◎◎○○●◎◎◎

○ r = red   ● b = blue   ◉ g = green

Ask students to describe the shapes and colors that they see. (Possible answer: red, blue, and green circles in a pattern) *What pattern can you identify?* (Possible answer: There is one more of each color than the color before; the circles repeat from 1 red, 2 blue, and 3 green.) *What do you think comes next in the pattern?* (1 more blue) *Explain how you got your answer*. (Possible answer: counted the circles of each color from the beginning of the pattern)

EXPLORE AND CONNECT

Materials: 6 punchout triangles, 6 red and 6 yellow square tiles for each group

Grouping Suggestion: groups of 4

Provide each group with 6 punchout triangles and 12 square tiles. Have one student begin by placing up to 3 triangles on table. The next student places up to 3 yellow square tiles beside the triangles. The third student places up to 3 red square tiles next. The fourth student continues the pattern by repeating the triangles, yellow squares, and red squares placed by the first 3 students. Encourage students to respect each other's ideas and make corrections only when necessary. Allow time for students to change roles and repeat the activity.

CONNECTIONS   Use these anytime.

Problem of the Day

Logic   Wayne wants to use 1 circle, 2 triangles, and 4 squares again and again to make a pattern. Can you make three different patterns for Wayne? (Answers may include CTTSSSS; CSSTTSS; CSSTSST.)

Math Connection

Number Sense   Can you continue this pattern: blue, red, green, red, blue, red, green, red? (brgr) Write a sentence explaining the pattern and how you found it. (Blue and green alternate; red is every other color.)

Subject Integration

Language Arts   *Haiku* are poems written in a pattern. Each haiku has only 3 lines. The lines have 5, 7, and 5 syllables, in order. For example:
   Little birds chirping
   Sitting on newly grown twigs
   It must be springtime.
Write your own haiku and draw a picture to illustrate it.

CLASSWORK AND HOMEWORK SUPPLEMENTS

Practice

Patterns 3-3

Name

My Pattern Book

Color to continue the patterns.

Use these colors:

R = Red
Y = Yellow
B = Blue
G = Green

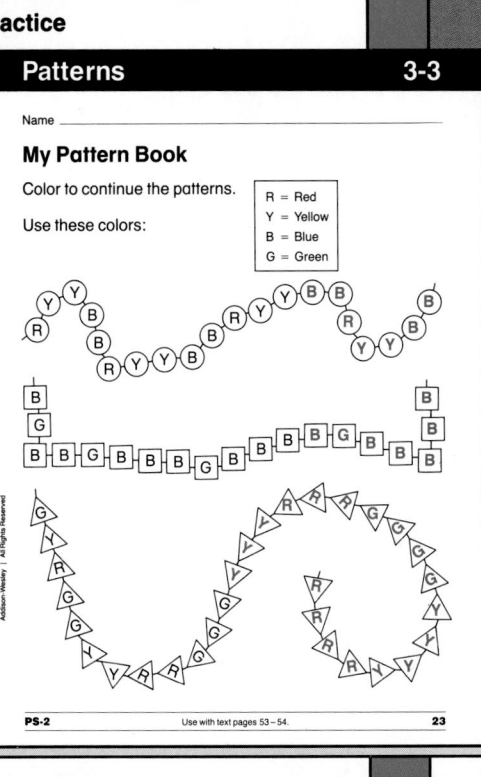

PS-2 Use with text pages 53–54. 23

Reteaching

Patterns 3-3

Name

My Pattern Book

Say the pattern.

white, black, black, white, black, black . . .

Read each pattern.
Ring the shape that comes next.

1.
2.
3.
4.

RS-2 Use with text pages 53–54. 23

Building Thinking Skills

Patterns 3-3

Name

Colorful Ways

Color the boxes.
Can you finish the pattern?
Use the same colors.

R = Red
O = Orange
P = Purple

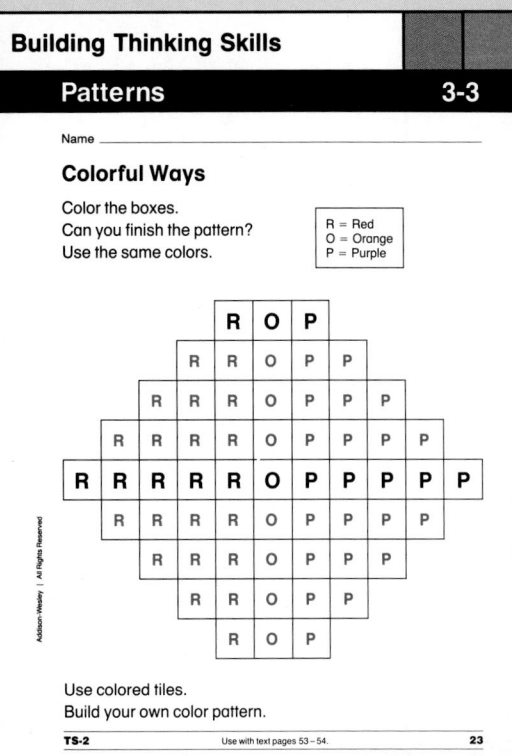

Use colored tiles.
Build your own color pattern.

TS-2 Use with text pages 53–54. 23

Challenges

Patterns 3-3

Name

Follow the Pattern

Color the circles to make a pattern.
Start in the middle. Use two or three colors.
Read your pattern to a friend. **Patterns will vary.**

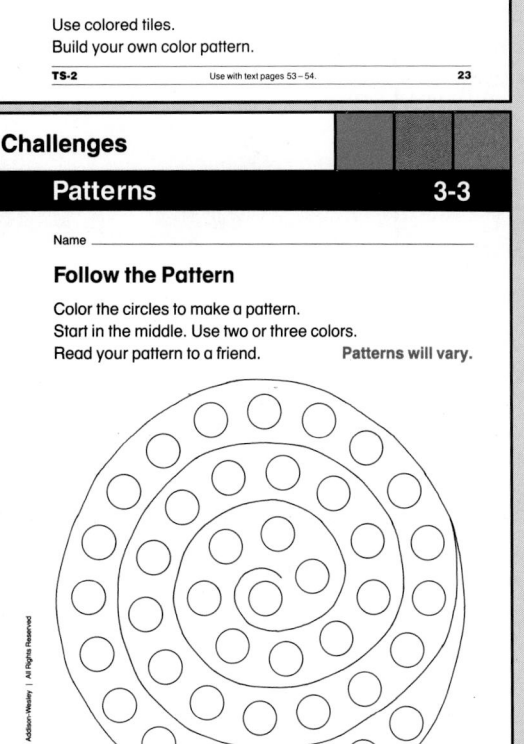

CS-2 Use with text pages 53–54. 23

OPTIONS FOR INDIVIDUAL NEEDS

Basic

Exercises All

Supplements
Reteaching 23 or
Practice 23
Challenges 23

Average

Exercises All

Supplements
Practice 23
Challenges 23 or
Thinking Skills 23

Extended

Exercises All

Supplements
Challenges 23
Thinking Skills 23

Other Resources:
Math in Stride, pp. 9-10, 30-31
Mathematics Their Way, pp. 34, 172-173
Explorations, pp. 32-34

3-3

Chapter 3 Lesson 3 **53B**

OBJECTIVE 3-3
To identify and continue color patterns

Materials: crayons, Cube-A-Links, paper clips, counters

Grouping Suggestions: individual oork, pairs

1. MOTIVATE AND TEACH

LEARN ABOUT IT

Practice working with color patterns by displaying a train made up of the following cubes: 2 red, 2 green, 3 yellow, 2 red, 2 green, 3 yellow. Point to each colored section as the class counts and says the color aloud. Ask students to tell how the pattern can be continued. (2 red, 2 green, 3 yellow) Give students time to study the color patterns on page 53.
► **How are all the patterns on the page similar?** (They all involve repeating color designs.)
► **How is the middle pattern different?** (It is a growing pattern.)
► **What color is repeated most often in the third pattern?** (blue) **How can you tell?** (It occurs after red *and* yellow.)

2. CHECK UNDERSTANDING

ERROR ALERT   Not being able to identify the patterns on the page.

Name _____

My Pattern Book

Color to continue the patterns.

Dear Family: Ask your child to read each pattern and tell what comes next.

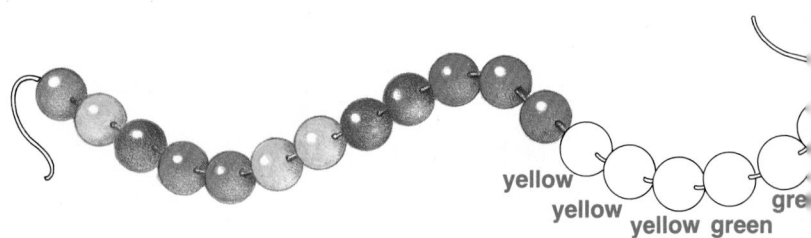

red   yellow

red   red   y(

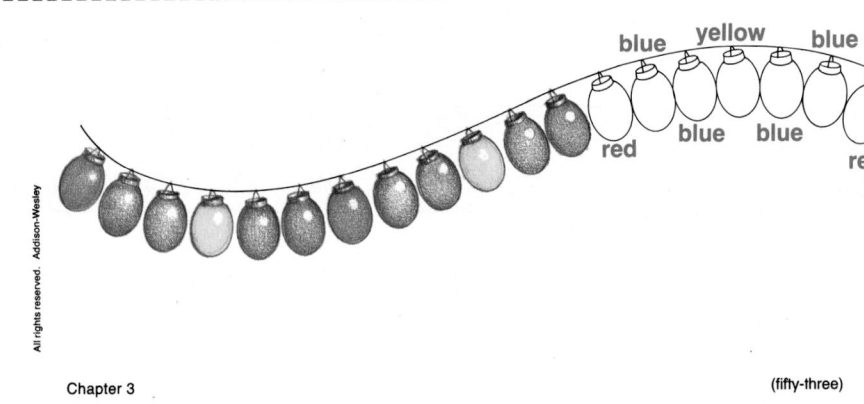

yellow
yellow   gre
yellow green

blue   yellow   blue

red   blue   blue

re

Chapter 3

(fifty-three)

TEACHING OPTIONS

RETEACHING TIPS   Provide students with counters of several different colors. Model a pattern, such as the following:
R B B R B B R B B R B B
Have students copy the pattern and extend it. Repeat with a pattern of 3 colors. Use Reteaching Supplement 23 to provide additional help.

ENRICHMENT   Have students use crayons, cubes, paper clips, or other manipulatives to make a repeating pattern. Have them trade patterns with a partner and continue each other's patterns.

...lor to continue the patterns.

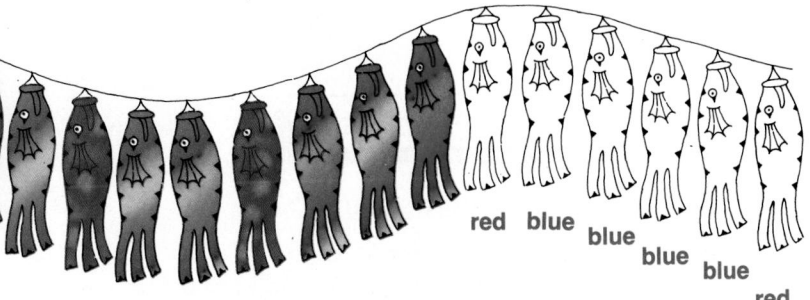

red blue blue
blue
blue
red

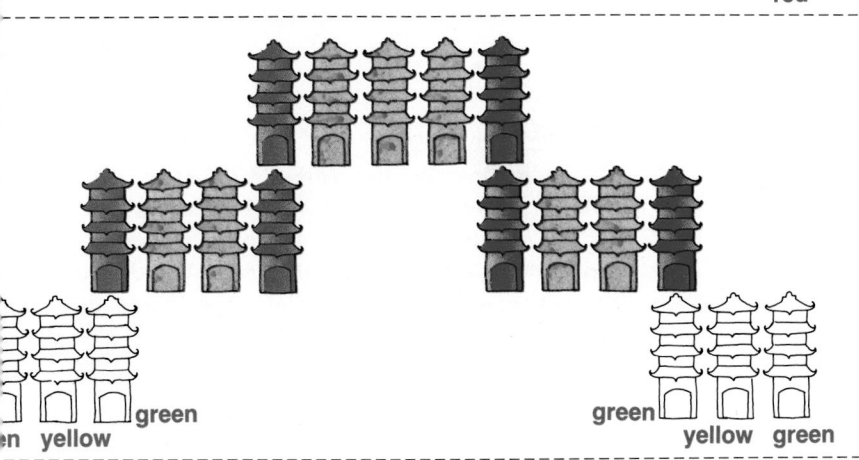

...green
...n yellow

green
yellow green

...ake your own pattern with cubes.
...olor it below. **Answers may vary.**

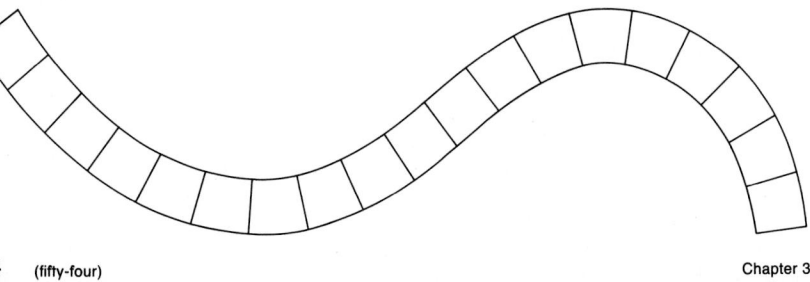

Chapter 3

3. PRACTICE AND APPLY

Basic	All
Average	All
Extended	All

PRACTICE

How will you continue the first pattern? (Color in 1 red, 4 blues, 1 red.) *In how many places will you continue the second pattern?* (two places; both ends)

APPLY

► **Identify in the classroom or at home objects that have patterns.** (Possible answers: the flag, a shell, a woven basket, a border on a bookcover, a plate, a blanket, a sheet, a shirt, a tie, a dress)
► **How can you tell whether the pattern on an object is repeated or growing?** (Answers will vary.)

CLOSE AND ASSESS

HOW WHAT YOU KNOW

...ovide each student pair with an ...sortment of red, blue, and yellow ...bes. Ask one student to make a ...ttern using some of each color cube. ...he partner identifies the pattern and ...ses more cubes to continue it. ...ncourage pairs to treat each other's ...sponses with respect.

QUICK QUIZ

Copy the pattern, Continue the pattern by making more circles and coloring them.

○○●○○○○○○●○○○○○○●○●○○○●
○ r = red ● b = blue ◎ g = green

Chapter 3 Lesson 3   **54**

Problem Solving: Understanding Addition and Subtraction

OBJECTIVE 3-4   To understand the operations of addition and subtraction by putting together or by taking away

PREBOOK ACTIVITIES

QUICK REVIEW

Read the number sequences. Tell which number is missing.

1, 2, 4, 5 (3)	8, 7, 5, 4, 3, 2 (6)
6, 8, 9, 10 (7)	6, 5, 4, 2, 1, 0 (3)
3, 4, 6, 7, 8 (5)	10, 11, 13, 14, 15, 16 (12)
19, 18, 16, 15, 14 (17)	9, 11, 12, 13, 14, 15 (10)

PRIOR KNOWLEDGE

Pretend that you and 5 of your friends are together. Think about what would happen to your group in each of the following situations. Would you end up with more friends or less friends?
1. 1 friend gets sick and has to go home.   (less)
2. 2 new friends join you.   (more)
3. 1 friend brings along her little sister.   (more)

COMMUNICATION

Reading and Discussing Math   Write **clockwise** and **counterclockwise** on the chalkboard. Read the words aloud and explain that these terms show direction. Draw circular clock faces on the board and trace the direction for each term. *How can the numbers on the clock help you remember the direction for clockwise?* (*Clockwise* means the direction the numbers are written in.) *What does the term* **put together** *mean?* (Possible answer: When things are put together, they are added.) *What does the term* **take away** *mean?* (Possible answer: When you take away something, you subtract it.) *Tell a put-together story and a take-away story.* (Answers will vary.)

EXPLORE AND CONNECT

COOPERATIVE ACTIVITY

Grouping Suggestion: small groups
Beth made food for the picnic. She made 3 ham sandwiches and 4 cheese sandwiches. How many sandwiches did she make in all? 3 + 4 = _____   4 − 3 = _____   She made _____ sandwiches.

TEACHING ACTIONS

BEFORE

▶ **Describe the action in the story.** (Possible answer: Beth made 2 kinds of sandwiches that she will put together to take to the picnic.)
▶ **What data is important to this story? The data can be both numbers and words.** (Possible answer: She made 3 of one sandwich and 4 of another. The question asks *how many . . . in all?*)

DURING

▶ **How can you use this data to choose the number sentence that goes with the story?** (Possible answer: Put all the data together. Then decide whether it makes more sense to add or subtract.)
▶ **Model this story with counters. Did the story suggest you put out more counters or take away counters? Why?** (Possible answer: Show a group of 3 counters. Then put out 4 more because there are no words to suggest taking away.)

AFTER

▶ **How can you use the model to write a number sentence?** (Possible answer: Match the action shown by the counters: 3 + 4 = 7.) Have students in small groups use counters to show other addition and subtraction stories.

CONNECTIONS   Use these anytime.

Problem of the Day
Understanding the Operations
Circle the subtraction question for this story. Dad bought 5 bags of ice for the picnic. 2 bags melted in the hot sun. How many bags of ice were left? How many bags did Dad buy?

Subject Integration
Music   Use your voice to start a pattern. Combine high notes and low notes or start and stop your voice. Sing your pattern. Then have the rest of the class repeat or finish the pattern.

Math Connection
Choosing the Operation   Have a partner give a question from a story problem, such as *How many dogs were left?* or *How many girls joined in?* Then make up a story to go with the question and tell it to your partner. Together, write the number sentence to match your story problem and share them with the class.

Using Critical Thinking

o use critical thinking to continue patterns

CLASSWORK AND HOMEWORK SUPPLEMENTS

Practice

Patterns 3-4

Name _____

Using Critical Thinking

Finish the last figure in each row to continue the pattern.

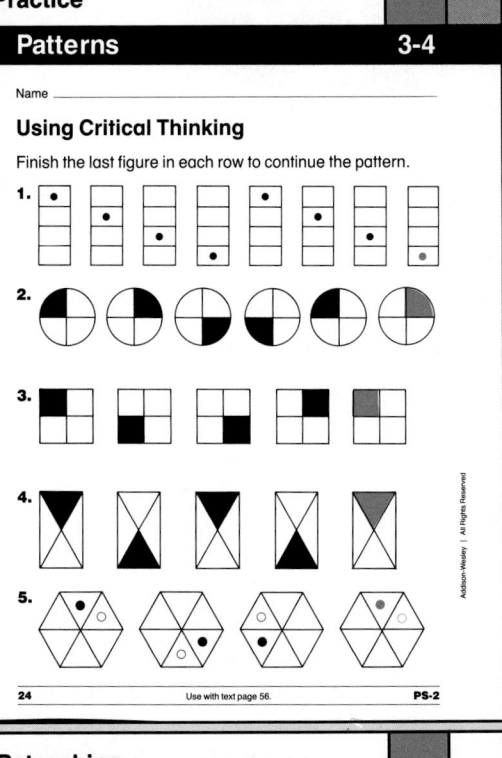

24   Use with text page 56.   PS-2

Building Thinking Skills

Problem Solving 3-4

Name _____

Pet Problems

Write two number sentences to solve the problem.

1. 2 girls are playing with pets.
2 friends join them.
How many friends in all? $2 + 2 = 4$
They meet 2 more friends.
How many are there now? $4 + 2 = 6$

2. Barbara had 8 kittens.
2 ran away.
How many kittens are left? $8 - 2 = 6$
Barbara sells 3 kittens.
How many does she have now? $6 - 3 = 3$

3. Greg has 10 goldfish.
He gives 4 to his brother.
How many does he have now? $10 - 4 = 6$
He gives 2 to his friend.
How many does Greg keep? $6 - 2 = 4$

4. Rico has 4 gerbils.
He gets 5 more.
How many does he have now? $4 + 5 = 9$
2 gerbils escape.
How many are left? $9 - 2 = 7$

24   Use with text pages 55–56.   TS-2

Reteaching

Problem Solving 3-4

Name _____

Understanding the Operations

Ring the correct fact. Use the picture to help. Complete the answer.

1. 7 clowns were in the tent.
3 ran out of the tent.
How many clowns were still in the tent?
$7 - 3 = 4$
$7 + 3 = 10$
__4__ clowns were still in the tent.

2. One juggler has 9 balls. (Find the total.)
Another juggler has 4 balls.
How many balls do the two jugglers have?
$9 - 4 = 5$
$9 + 4 = 13$
They have _13_ balls.

3. 8 elephants were in line.
2 of them sat down.
How many did not sit down?
$8 + 2 = 10$
$8 - 2 = 6$
__6__ elephants did not sit down.

24   Use with text pages 55–56.   RS-2

Challenges

Cooperative Activities 3-4

Name _____

Pattern Talk

Work with a partner.

1. Color the small squares to make a pattern.
Use two or three colors.

Ask your partner to tell what pattern you made.

2. Have your partner color the small triangles to make a pattern. Use two or three colors.

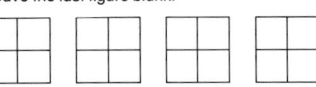

Tell what pattern your partner made.

3. This time color the small squares to start a pattern. Leave the last figure blank.

Ask your partner to finish the pattern.

24   Use with text pages 55–56.   CS-2

OPTIONS FOR INDIVIDUAL NEEDS

Basic

Exercises All
Computer Bank, pp. 405-406
More Practice, p. 412, set A

Supplements
Reteaching 24 or
Practice 24

Average

Exercises All
Computer Bank, pp. 405-406
More Practice, p. 412, set A

Supplements
Practice 24
Challenges 24 or
Thinking Skills 24

Extended

Exercises All
Computer Bank, pp. 405-406

Supplements
Challenges 24
Thinking Skills 24

Other Resources:
Problem-Solving Experiences In Mathematics, pp. 39, 45, 57, 63, 69, 75, 81, 92, 98-99
Mathematics Their Way, pp. 27-36

3-4

Chapter 3 Lesson 4   **55B**

OBJECTIVE 3-4

To understand the operations of addition and subtraction by putting together or by taking away; to use critical thinking to continue patterns

Materials: counters, copies of figures on page 56

1. MOTIVATE AND TEACH

LEARN ABOUT IT

 **BEFORE** ▶ **Look at Exercise 1. What action takes place in this story?** (Possible answer: 1 group made fish kites, and 1 group made dragon kites.)

▶ **What do you need to do to answer the story question?** (You need to put the 2 groups together to see how many kites they made.)

 **DURING** ▶ **How can you be sure that this story shows addition?** (Possible answer: A take-away action would have a question such as *How many kites would not fly?* or *How many kites did they sell?*)

 **AFTER** ▶ **How can you check your number sentence?** (Possible answer: Use counters to act out the story. Write the number sentence under the counters to see if it makes sense.)

2. CHECK UNDERSTANDING

ERROR ALERT **Page 55** Being unable to identify the action presented in each story.
Page 56 Being unable to visualize how a pattern changes position.

Name _____

Problem Solving
Understanding the Operations

Use counters to show each story. Ring and finish the correct number sentence. Write the answer.

1. Everyone in Seth's family made kites. 3 people made fish kites. 2 people made dragon kites. How many kites did they make?

   $(3 + 2 = \underline{5})$

   $3 - 2 = \underline{}$

   They made __5__ kites.

2. In Alice's class, 6 students brought kites to school. 3 of them flew kites at lunchtime. How many did not fly kites?

   $6 + 3 = \underline{}$

   $(6 - 3 = \underline{3})$

   __3__ did not fly kites.

3. In the kite-building contest, 4 kites won blue ribbons. 2 kites won red ribbons. How many kites won ribbons?

   $(4 + 2 = \underline{6})$

   $4 - 2 = \underline{}$

   __6__ kites won ribbons.

4. After school, students were flying 5 kites. Then 2 of the kites got stuck in a tree. How many kites were still flying?

   $5 + 2 = \underline{}$

   $(5 - 2 = \underline{3})$

   __3__ were still flying.

Chapter 3   More Practice, page 412, set A   (fifty-five) 5

TEACHING OPTIONS

RETEACHING TIPS Have students place 4 different-colored triangles to form a square and explore ways that the triangles can change position. Have them record their findings by drawing a picture each time they change a triangle's position. For additional help use Reteaching Supplement 24.

COMPUTER **Moptown Parade, Learning Company © 1985** For use with all levels of students. In *Moptown Parade*, students practice pattern recognition by creating a parade of muppets, each successive muppet only one attribute different from the one before. The lesson takes 15 minutes.

sing Critical Thinking

olor the last shape
continue the pattern.

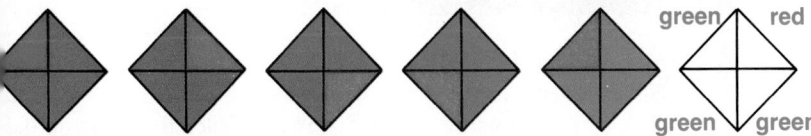

green / red

green \ green

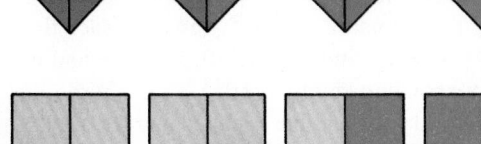

yellow yellow

red   yellow

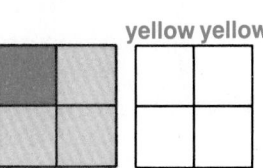

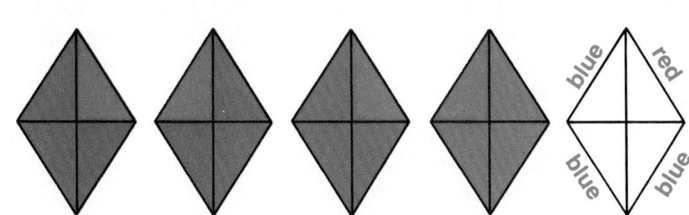

blue red

blue blue

How are the shapes and
patterns above alike?
How are they different?

Answers may vary. See teaching notes.

3. PRACTICE AND APPLY

Basic	All
Average	All
Extended	All

How are the shapes and patterns on page 56 alike? (All have 4 sides and 4 equal parts; all patterns begin with a red section; all have straight lines.) *How are they different?* (Figures 1 and 2 are the same shape and size; figure 3 is not. Figures 1 and 3 are divided into triangles; figure 2 is divided into squares.)

Provide students with copies of the 3 figures on this page to manipulate as they discuss the following questions.

▶ **Compare how the shapes in Exercise 1 and 2 must be turned to match the patterns on this page. How are their rotations different?** (Possible answer: Exercise 1 is turned clockwise. Exercise 2 is turned counterclockwise.)

▶ **How is Exercise 3 different from the other patterns?** (Possible answer: You cannot turn it to match the pattern. You need to flip the figure.)

▶ **How can you check your answer in Exercise 3?** (Possible answer: Before you flip it, color both sides to get an accurate picture of the pattern.)

3-4

CLOSE AND ASSESS

SHOW WHAT YOU KNOW

Remind students of the butterflies in the chapter story. *Two of the butterflies in the magnolia tree had plain wings. The other 5 had beautiful designs on their wings. How many butterflies were in the tree altogether?* (7) Ask students to draw a picture and write the matching number sentence for this problem.

QUICK QUIZ

Ring the correct number sentence.
Ken walked 5 dogs at once. Later, he returned 2 to their owners. How many dogs did he have then?
$5 + 2 = 7$ $\underline{5 - 2 = 3}$

Bar Graphs

OBJECTIVE 3-5   To make and read bar graphs

PREBOOK ACTIVITIES

QUICK REVIEW

Write the following numbers from least to greatest.

6, 3, 14, 0, 15, 9, 2, 12

(0, 2, 3, 6, 9, 12, 14, 15)

27, 8, 16, 32, 13, 1, 19, 50

(1, 8, 13, 16, 19, 27, 32, 50)

PRIOR KNOWLEDGE

List the following pets on the chalkboard: dog, cat, fish, bird, hamster, gerbil. Have students select one as their favorite pet. Place a tally mark under each student's choice. *Which pet was chosen as favorite by the greatest number of students? How do you know?* (Answers will vary. The favorite has the greatest number of tallies.) *What is the least favorite pet? How do you know?* (Answers will vary. It has the least number of tallies.)

COMMUNICATION

Discussing Math   Use cubes to construct a 3-column bar graph by placing 2 green cubes in the first column, 5 red cubes in the second column, and 7 yellow cubes in the third column. *Which column has the most cubes?* (yellow) *Which column has the least?* (green) *Why is this called a bar graph?* (Possible answer: It shows data by the height of the bars.) *Why do you think we use bar graphs to show data?* (Possible answer: They are easy to read.)

EXPLORE AND CONNECT

Materials: 3-by-5 cards

Have students look at the color of their shoes. Draw a shoe in each of the colors on a 3-by-5 card and place the cards on the floor. Have each student take off one shoe and place it next to the corresponding color, forming a row. Write the shoe colors on the chalkboard and have students make a tally mark next to their shoe color. *How do the tally marks match the rows of shoes?* (Possible answer: They are the same as the number of shoes of each color.) Attach the shoe pictures to chart paper or to the chalkboard and draw the outline of a bar graph. Have volunteers fill in squares for the number of shoes of each color and explain to students that they have made a bar graph. *How many columns does our graph have? How many rows? If we owned a shoe store, what color should we have more of in our store?* (Possible answer: the most popular color; the color with the longest bar)

CONNECTIONS   Use these anytime.

Problem of the Day

Apple juice Ⅲ I

Orange juice Ⅲ II

Grape juice Ⅲ III

Cranberry juice II

Which juice has the greatest number of votes? (grape) Which juice has the least number of votes? (cranberry)

How many tallies are there in all? (23)

Life Skill

Nutrition   Write down the names of 8 friends in your Math Journal. Ask each friend which of these 3 vegetables they like the best: celery, carrots, or potatoes. Place a tally mark in front of their choice. Which of the 3 vegetables was chosen most? (Answers will vary.)

Minute Math

Write only the answers. How many can you do in 1 minute?

16	11	6	7	5	12
− 7	− 8	+ 7	+ 8	+ 9	− 8
(9)	(3)	(13)	(15)	(14)	(4)

14	8	17	18	6	9
− 7	+ 5	− 8	− 9	+ 8	+ 4
(7)	(13)	(9)	(9)	(14)	(13)

CLASSWORK AND HOMEWORK SUPPLEMENTS

OPTIONS FOR INDIVIDUAL NEEDS

Basic

Exercises All

Supplements
Reteaching 25 or
Practice 25

Average

Exercises All

Supplements
Practice 25
Challenges 25 or
Thinking Skills 25

Extended

Exercises All

Supplements
Challenges 25
Thinking Skills 25

3-5

Practice

Data Analysis   3-5

Name _____

Bar Graphs

Tally the number of each kind of flower.
Write the total.

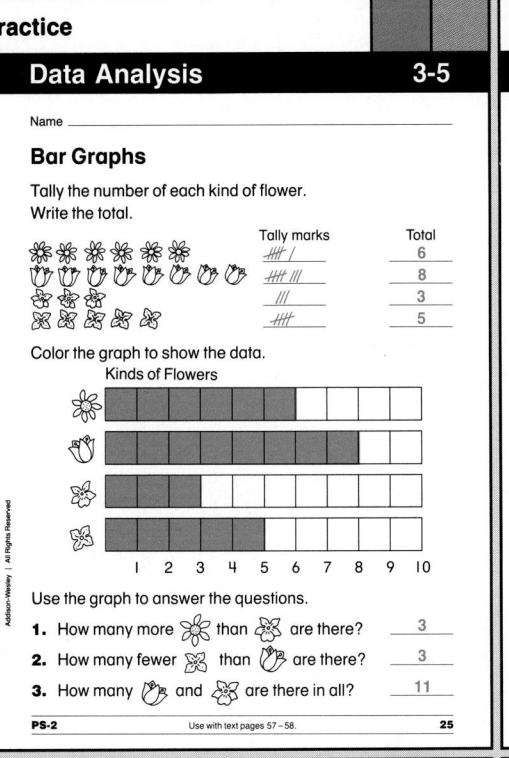

Color the graph to show the data.
Kinds of Flowers

Use the graph to answer the questions.

1. How many more 🌼 than 🌸 are there?   3

2. How many fewer 🌼 than 🌷 are there?   3

3. How many 🌺 and 🌸 are there in all?   11

PS-2   Use with text pages 57 – 58.   25

Building Thinking Skills

Data Analysis   3-5

Name _____

Sports Special

Pretend that you work in a sports store.
You keep track of all the things you sell on one Saturday.

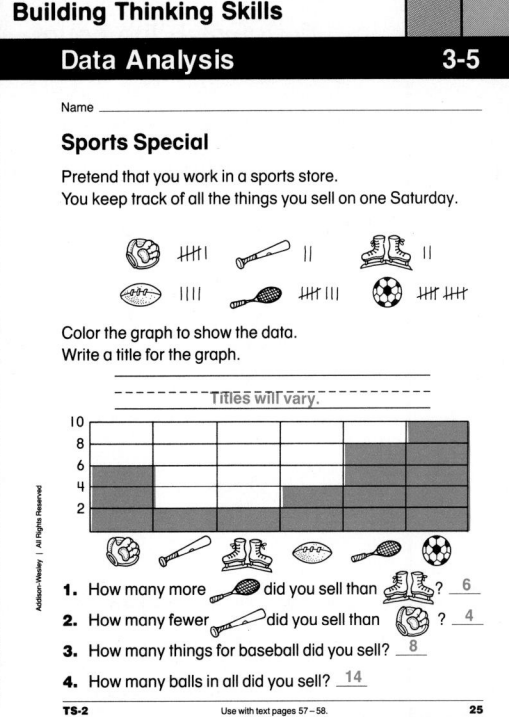

Color the graph to show the data.
Write a title for the graph.

_____ Titles will vary. _____

1. How many more 🎾 did you sell than ⛸? 6

2. How many fewer ⚾ did you sell than ⚽? 4

3. How many things for baseball did you sell? 8

4. How many balls in all did you sell? 14

TS-2   Use with text pages 57 – 58.   25

Reteaching

Data Analysis   3-5

Name _____

Bar Graphs

A group of children counted the number of pets they had.

1. Count the tally marks for each pet.
Then color the graph to match.

Dogs	Cats	Fish	Birds
5	5	4	5
5	+4		+2
+2	9		7
12			

Total: 12   Total: 9   Total: 4   Total: 7

Pet Graph

(Shade 9)
(12 blocks)

2. How many more children have dogs than cats?   3

3. How many more children have birds than fish?   3

RS-2   Use with text pages 57 – 58.   25

Challenges

Life Skills   3-5

Name _____

A Time to Vote

Color the graph to show the votes.

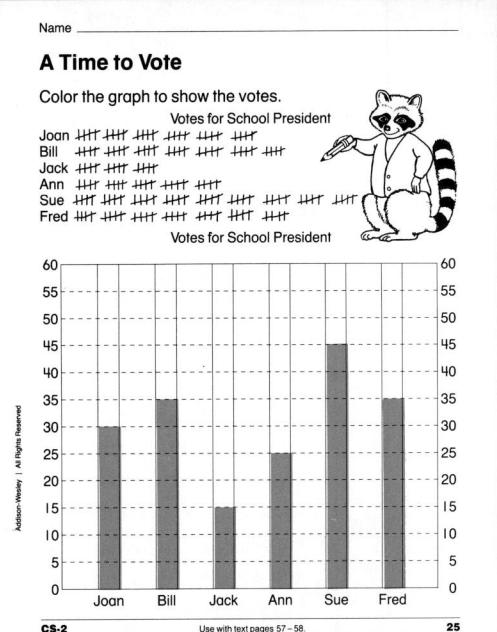

Votes for School President

CS-2   Use with text pages 57 – 58.   25

Other Resources:
Explorations, pp. 6, 74,
91-95, 196-200, 328-329
Workjobs II, pp. 29-31
Mathematics Book A, pp.
34-38, 67
Mathematics Their Way, pp.
142-163, 311-312

LESSON PLAN 3-5

OBJECTIVE 3-5
To make and read bar graphs

Materials: Cube-A-Links (red, yellow, blue, green), TA 000 (Graph Paper)

1. MOTIVATE AND TEACH

LEARN ABOUT IT

Focus students' attention on the word *origami* and explain that it is an oriental art of paper folding. Point out the origami birds on the page.
What do the tally marks tell us?
(Possible answer: how many origami birds Ann's class made in each color)
Why do you think the title of the graph is Origami Bird Colors? (Possible answer: It tells what the graph is about.)
▶ **Can you think of another title for the graph?** (Answers may vary.)
▶ **What do the birds along the left side of the graph tell us?** (what colors were used)
▶ **What do the numbers at the bottom of the graph tell us?** (Possible answer: the number of birds that were made)
▶ **What color was used most often? least often?** (green, yellow)
▶ **How do you know this?** (by looking at the length of the bars; by reading the number at the end of each bar)
▶ **How many origami birds did Ann's class make?** (22) **How did you get the answer?** (count; add)

2. CHECK UNDERSTANDING

ERROR ALERT   Not understanding the words or phrases *more than, less than, least, most, fewest*.

Name _____

Bar Graphs

1. Ann's class made origami birds. They used tally marks to count the birds by color. Finish the count.

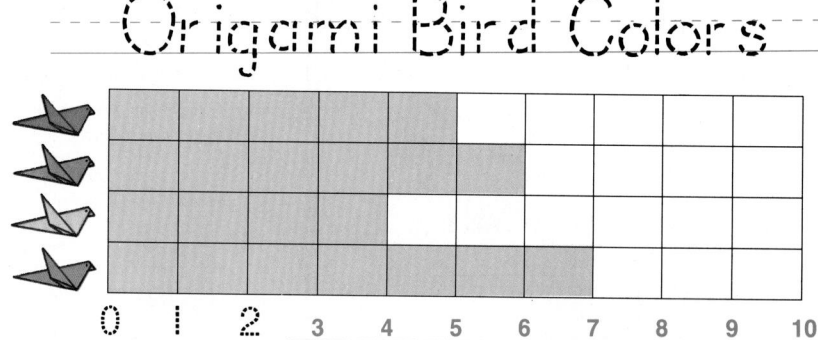

Make a bar graph to show the data.
2. Write a title for the graph.

Origami Bird Colors

0   1   2   3   4   5   6   7   8   9   10

3. Write numbers across the bottom of the graph.
4. Color the graph. Show how many birds of each color the class made.

Use the graph to answer the questions.
5. Which has more? Ring it.   6. Which has less? Ring it.

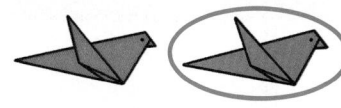      

How many more? __1__ more   How many less? __3__ less

Chapter 3   (fifty-seven)   5

TEACHING OPTIONS

RETEACHING TIPS   Have students use colored cubes to make a model of the graph on page 57. Have students count the cubes to answer questions about the graph involving *how many more?, how many less?, which color has most?*, and so on. Assign Reteaching Supplement 25.

ENRICHMENT   **Family Math**
Have students ask family members to choose their favorite color: blue, red, purple, or green. Ask them to work together to make a tally chart for this information, then draw a bar graph. Have students write a sentence about their family's favorite and least favorite color.

Todd's class made origami animals. Finish the bar graph. Write a title. Then fill in the missing numbers. Color the graph to match the tally.

Titles may vary.

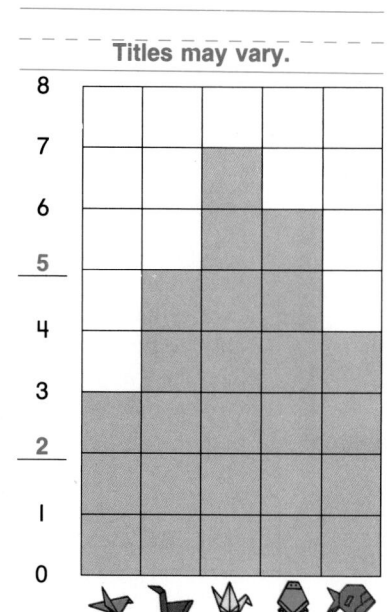

Origami Tally

Robin		III
Duck		IIII
Crane		IIIIII
Frog		IIIII
Fish		IIII

Ring 🖍 the one made the greatest number of times.
Ring 🖍 the one made the least number of times.

MIDCHAPTER REVIEW/QUIZ

Write the next three numbers in the pattern. Are they odd or even? Ring your answer.

13, 11, 9, <u>7</u>, <u>5</u>, <u>3</u>   (odd)   even

Ring the cube that comes next in the pattern.

(fifty-eight)

Chapter 3

3. PRACTICE AND APPLY

Basic	All, Midchapter Review/Quiz
Average	All, Midchapter Review/Quiz
Extended	All, Midchapter Review/Quiz

3-5

PRACTICE

Where will you find the data to complete the graph? (in the tally chart) *What is the difference between the greatest and least number of tallies?* (4) *How many more cranes did the class make than fish?* (3)

APPLY

How can you explain how many squares should be colored on the graph? (Possible answer: Count the number of tally marks.)
► **Can you find a way to sort these animals?** (Possible answer: by number of legs or where they live)

MIDCHAPTER REVIEW/QUIZ

ITEM ANALYSIS The table correlates the Midchapter Review/Quiz items with lesson objectives.

Items	Objectives
1	3-1
2	3-3

QUICK QUIZ

Favorite Subject in School
Science IIII I   Math   IIII II
Reading IIII   Social Studies III
What subject is liked the least? the most? (social studies; math)

Graphing Data from a Survey

OBJECTIVE 3-6 To take and graph data from a survey

PREBOOK ACTIVITIES

QUICK REVIEW

Write the greatest number in each pair:

17, 14 (17)   12, 5 (12)   13, 12 (13)
23, 32 (32)   49, 94 (94)   62, 26 (62)

Write the least number in each pair:

49, 26 (26)   33, 88 (33)   28, 20 (20)
47, 74 (47)   93, 39 (39)   81, 18 (18)

PRIOR KNOWLEDGE

Ask how many students have bought frozen yogurt from a frozen yogurt stand. *Suppose there is a stand outside of school. How could we find out the most popular flavor?* (Possible answer: Keep a tally of the flavors bought.)

COMMUNICATION

Discussing Math Write the word **survey** on the chalkboard and have students say it aloud. Explain what it means to take a survey. *What kinds of information might you want to find by taking a survey?* (Possible answers: what people like, how they vote, what they think) *How can we record the results of the survey?* (Possible answer: in a tally chart) *How can you show this information in another way?* (Make a bar graph.) *Why might the results of a survey be different if you surveyed a different group of people?* (Possible answer: Different people would make different choices.)

EXPLORE AND CONNECT

List the following on the chalkboard: hockey, soccer, baseball, basketball. Add any other sports students may suggest. *How can we find out which sport the class likes best?* (Possible answer: Have students vote.) Have students come to the board and place a tally mark next to their choice. Draw a bar graph grid on the chalkboard. Write the names of the sports at the bottom and the numbers up the left side, beginning with 0. *How can we show the result of our votes on this bar graph?* (Possible answer: Color in the same number of boxes as tally marks for each sport.) Have volunteers color in the appropriate boxes. *What do you think is an appropriate title for our graph?* (Titles may vary.) *How can you tell which sport the class likes best?* (Possible answers: The sport with the longest bar is the favorite; the one with the shortest bar is least favorite.)

CONNECTIONS   Use these anytime.

Problem of the Day

Favorite Subjects 17 students chose math as their favorite subject. 9 students liked reading best, and 11 students liked art best. How many more students liked math than liked reading? (8)

Math Connection

Geometry and Probability

Predict which geometric shape the class likes the best—square, triangle, or circle. Take a survey to find out. Make a tally chart to record the information. Compare your prediction to your results. Did anything surprise you? (Answers may vary.)

Subject Integration

Reading Take a survey to find out how many of each vowel there are in your classmates' first names. Record your information on a tally chart. Make a bar graph to show your data. What did you learn from this graph? (Possible answer: The vowel *e* had the most tallies.)

CLASSWORK AND HOMEWORK SUPPLEMENTS

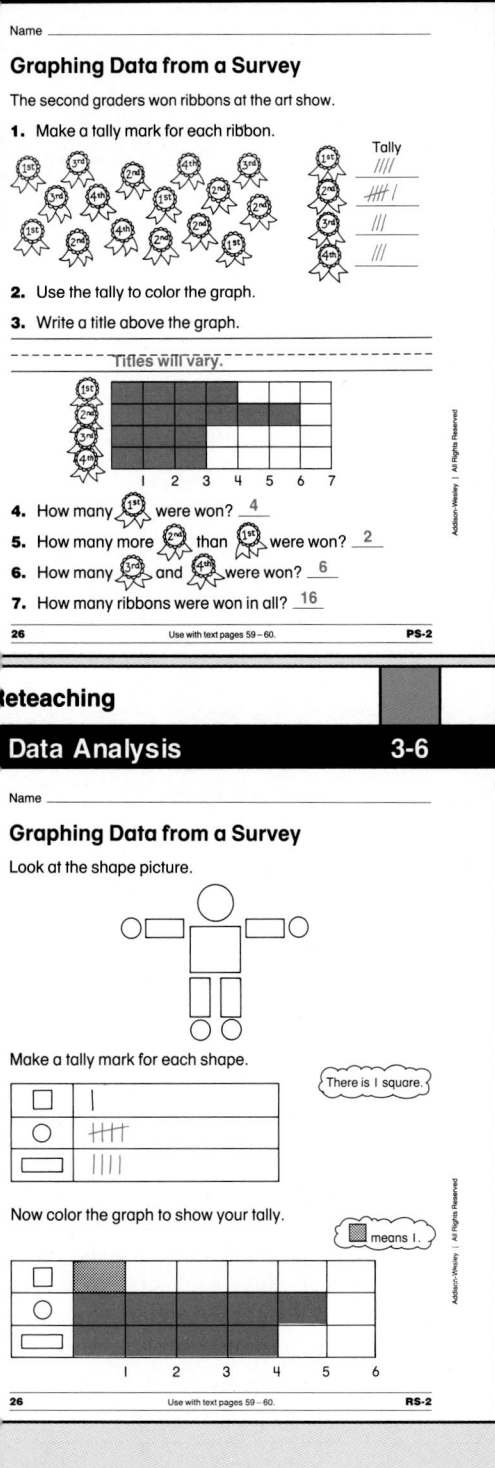

Practice

Data Analysis   3-6

Name _____

Graphing Data from a Survey

The second graders won ribbons at the art show.

1. Make a tally mark for each ribbon.

	Tally
1st	////
2nd	//// /
3rd	///
4th	///

2. Use the tally to color the graph.

3. Write a title above the graph.

Titles will vary.

4. How many 1st were won? _4_

5. How many more 2nd than 1st were won? _2_

6. How many 3rd and 4th were won? _6_

7. How many ribbons were won in all? _16_

26   Use with text pages 59–60.   PS-2

Building Thinking Skills

Math Reasoning   3-6

Name _____

Taking a Survey

Matt took a survey.
He asked 25 people which fruit they like best.
Matt made a graph to show the data.

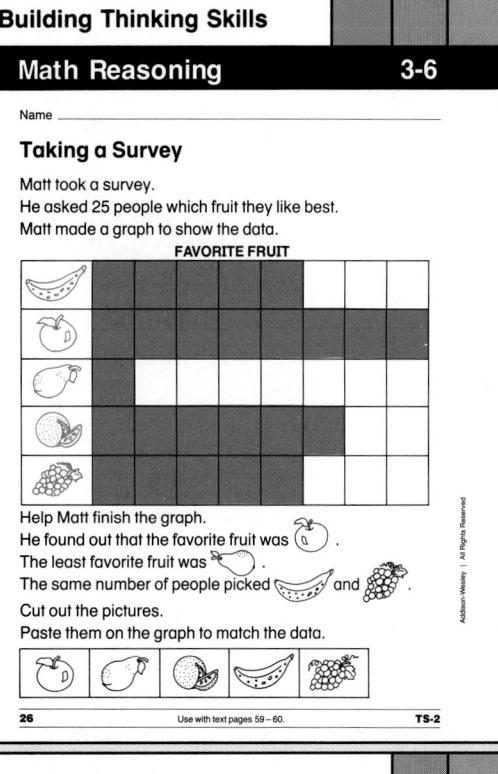

FAVORITE FRUIT

Help Matt finish the graph.
He found out that the favorite fruit was 🍎.
The least favorite fruit was 🍐.
The same number of people picked 🍌 and 🍇.
Cut out the pictures.
Paste them on the graph to match the data.

26   Use with text pages 59–60.   TS-2

Reteaching

Data Analysis   3-6

Name _____

Graphing Data from a Survey

Look at the shape picture.

Make a tally mark for each shape.

□	\
○	////
▭	////

There is 1 square.

Now color the graph to show your tally.

▨ means 1.

26   Use with text pages 59–60.   RS-2

Challenges

Cooperative Activities   3-6

Name _____

Graph the Sums

Play with a partner.
You will need 2 cubes numbered 1 to 6.
Roll the cubes and name the sum.
Color a space next to that sum.
Take turns. Stop when one column is full.

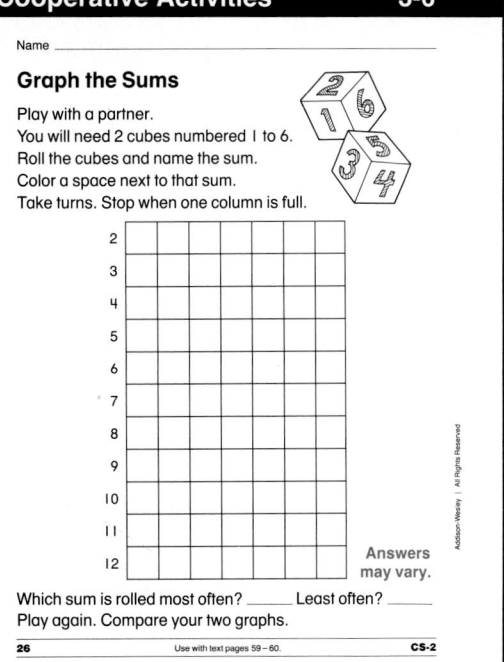

Answers may vary.

Which sum is rolled most often? _____ Least often? _____
Play again. Compare your two graphs.

26   Use with text pages 59–60.   CS-2

OPTIONS FOR INDIVIDUAL NEEDS

Basic

Exercises All

Supplements
Reteaching 26 or
Practice 26
Thinking Skills 26

Average

Exercises All

Supplements
Practice 26
Challenges 26 or
Thinking Skills 26

Extended

Exercises All

Supplements
Challenges 26
Thinking Skills 26

Other Resources:
Explorations, pp. 6, 74, 91-95, 196-200, 328-329
Workjobs II, pp. 29-31
Mathematics Book A, pp. 34-38

3-6

OBJECTIVE 3-6
To take and graph data from a survey

Materials: Cube-A-Links in 3 colors

Alternative Materials: counters

---

1. MOTIVATE AND TEACH

LEARN ABOUT IT

Explain that papercuts are a traditional Chinese art form and that Chinese people use pictures of flowers, animals, and simple geometric shapes to make papercuts. *On page 59, where do you record the tally marks for each vote?* (on the line beside each papercut) *How can you make sure you record the data on the bar graph correctly?* (Possible answer: Count the number of tally marks for each paper cut.)
▶ **Why do you think we use tally marks instead of numbers to keep track of votes in a survey as we count them?** (Possible answer: We can add to tally marks easily as we count.)
▶ **Why do you think we show the data from the survey in a bar graph instead of leaving it in the form of a tally chart?** (Possible answer: You can read the data more quickly and easily in the bar graph; you would have to count tallies to find the same information in a tally chart.)

2. CHECK UNDERSTANDING

ERROR ALERT Miscounting tally marks when making the bar graph.

Name _____

Graphing Data from a Survey

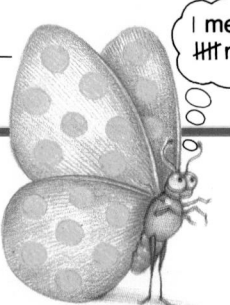

I means 1 v
Hfl means 5

1. Take a survey. Find out which papercut your class likes best. Make a tally mark for each vote.
Answers may vary.

 Rooster    Butterfly   Flow

_____   _____   _____

2. Finish the bar graph. First write the title. Then color the graph to show your data.

Titles may vary.

	0	1	2	3	4	5	6	7	8	9	10	11	12	13	14	15	16

3. Which papercut did your class like best?

_____
Answers may vary.

4. Which papercut got the least number of votes?

_____
Answers may vary.

Chapter 3   (fifty-nine)

TEACHING OPTIONS

RETEACHING TIPS Have students use cubes in 3 colors to construct a bar graph from the tallies they counted in their survey. Have them count the tally and add a cube to the column for each tally mark. Then have them count to check the totals. Use Reteaching Supplement 26 for additional help.

ENRICHMENT Have students take a survey to find out the months in which their classmates have their birthdays. Have them record the data in a tally chart, then make a bar graph. Have each student write a question about their graph, then exchange questions with a partner, and answer the question.

arlos is helping at an art show. He took a
rvey of the times his friends would come.

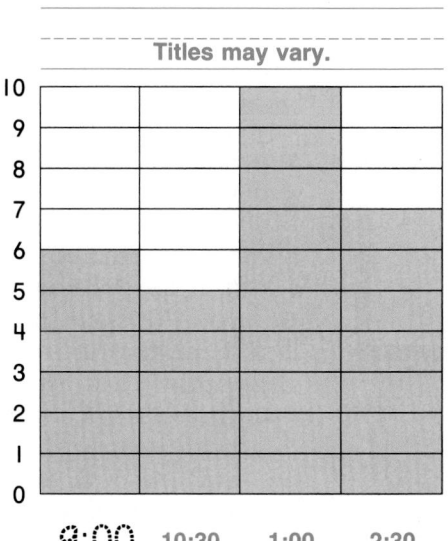

Morning

ꓱꓱꓱ I   ꓱꓱꓱ

Afternoon

ꓱꓱꓱ ꓱꓱꓱ   ꓱꓱꓱ II

Titles may vary.

10
9
8
7
6
5
4
3
2
1
0

9:00   10:30   1:00   2:30

nish the bar graph.

Write a title.
Fill in the times.
Color the graph to
match the tally.

e the graph to answer the questions.

At which time are the most people coming? __1:00__

How many more people plan
to come at 1:00 than at 2:30? __3__ more people

OBLEM SOLVING

How many people are coming in the morning?

Finish the number sentence.
Then answer the question.   6 (+) _5_ [=] _11_

__11__ people are coming in the morning.

(sixty)   Chapter 3

3. PRACTICE AND APPLY

Basic	All
Average	All
Extended	All

PRACTICE

*According to the clocks on page 60, how
many people are planning to come to the
art show at 10:30 a.m.? (5)
Compare the two morning times. When
are more people are coming? (9:00 a.m.)*

APPLY

PROBLEM SOLVING   ▶ **How can
you find out how many people are
planning to come in the morning?**
(Possible answer: Add.)
▶ **Are more people coming in the
morning or in the afternoon?**
(afternoon)
▶ **What other number sentence could
you write about the data in the
survey?** (Possible answer: 10 + 7 =
17)

3-6

LOSE AND ASSESS

IOW WHAT YOU KNOW

ve students work in small groups.
ve one student think of a survey
estion such as *What is your favorite
or?* A second student records the
ults using tallies. A third student
s the data to make a bar graph. All
up members should check the
ph for accuracy.

QUICK QUIZ

Write a question about the data on the
tally chart and answer it.
Number of Boys and Girls in Rm. 507
Boys   ꓱꓱꓱ   ꓱꓱꓱ   III
Girls   ꓱꓱꓱ   ꓱꓱꓱ   ꓱꓱꓱ   I

Pictographs

OBJECTIVE 3-7   To read pictographs

PREBOOK ACTIVITIES

QUICK REVIEW

Count by 1s to 20.
Count by 2s to 20.
How is counting by twos different from counting by ones?
(Possible answers: It is quicker; every other number is left out.)

PRIOR KNOWLEDGE

What data is given in this survey?
Left-handed students: ⴸⵁ ⵏ
Right-handed students: ⴸⵁ ⴸⵁ ⵏⵏⵏ
(6 students are left-handed, 13 students are right-handed.) *How else might this data be shown?* (in a bar graph)

COMMUNICATION

Reading and Discussing Math   Write **pictograph** on the chalkboard. Read the word aloud. *What two words are combined to make up the word pictograph?* (picture, graph) *How would you expect a pictograph to be different from a bar graph?* (Possible answer: It would use pictures instead of bars to show information.) *How is a pictograph like a bar graph?* (Possible answer: It is a way of showing information.)

EXPLORE AND CONNECT

Materials: 20 cubes per pair
Grouping Suggestion: pairs
Give students the following information: Nan has 6 nickels, ⵏ has 4 nickels, and Lee has 8 nickels. Write the names in a column on the chalkboard. *What picture could we use to show the nickels?* (Possible answer: circles) Pair students and ask them to use their cubes to show what each row in the pictograph will look like. *How can we show this information using fewer pictures or cubes?* (Let one cube or picture stand for two.) *In what way is using one cube or one picture to stand for two a more useful way of showing the information?* (Possible answer: It is easier and quicker to read.) Above the pictograph write *Each ○ stands for two nickels.* Allow time ⵏ students to recreate the rows by letting one cube stand for two. Invite volunteers to finish the pictograph on the chalkboard. Discuss the results.

CONNECTIONS   Use these anytime.

Problem of the Day

Reading a Map   Use the picture to find the distance from Bigtown to Littletown.   (15 miles)

```
                              Littletown
                          7 miles
   8 miles      Midville
Bigtown
```

Life Skills

Following Directions   Listen carefully and visualize the answer for each step. Raise your hand when you know the final answer.
1. 6 + 6   **2.** −5
3. +2   **4.** −3   (6)

Subject Integration

Social Studies   What pictures could these workers use in a pictograph about their jobs?
  mail carrier (letters, stamps)
  florist (flowers, pots)
  veterinarian (dogs, cats)
  grocer (shopping cart, vegetable)

CLASSWORK AND HOMEWORK SUPPLEMENTS

Basic

Exercises All

Supplements
Reteaching 27 or
Practice 27
Challenges 27

3-7

Practice

Data Analysis 3-7

Name _____

Pictographs

Ms. Frank's class is making a pictograph to show the number of students absent from Grove School.

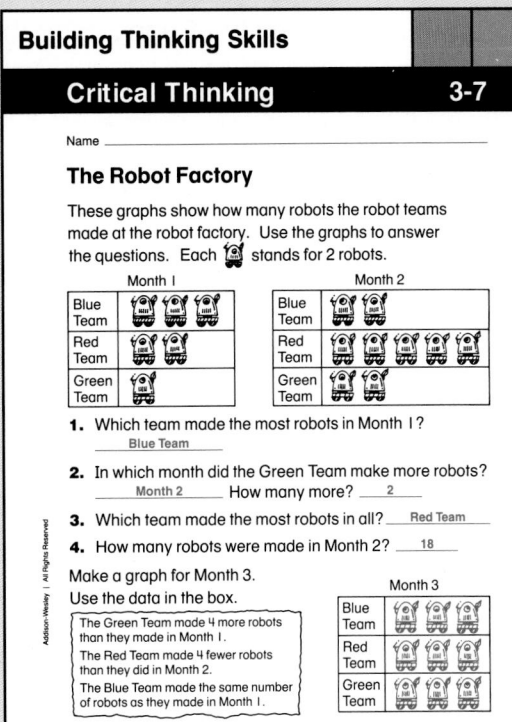

Draw 3 faces for Wednesday. _6_ students absent

Draw 5 faces for Thursday. _10_ students absent

Draw 8 faces for Friday. _16_ students absent

1. On what day were the most students absent? _Friday_

2. How many fewer students were absent on Tuesday than on Monday? _4_

PS-2 Use with text pages 61–62. 27

Building Thinking Skills

Critical Thinking 3-7

Name _____

The Robot Factory

These graphs show how many robots the robot teams made at the robot factory. Use the graphs to answer the questions. Each 🤖 stands for 2 robots.

1. Which team made the most robots in Month 1? _Blue Team_

2. In which month did the Green Team make more robots? _Month 2_ How many more? _2_

3. Which team made the most robots in all? _Red Team_

4. How many robots were made in Month 2? _18_

Make a graph for Month 3.
Use the data in the box.

The Green Team made 4 more robots than they made in Month 1.
The Red Team made 4 fewer robots than they did in Month 2.
The Blue Team made the same number of robots as they made in Month 1.

TS-2 Use with text pages 61–62. 27

Average

Exercises All

Supplements
Practice 27
Challenges 27 or
Thinking Skills 27

Reteaching

Data Analysis 3-7

Name _____

Pictographs

This **pictograph** shows how many family members from each class attended the school play.

Each 🧍 means 2 family members.

Count by twos!

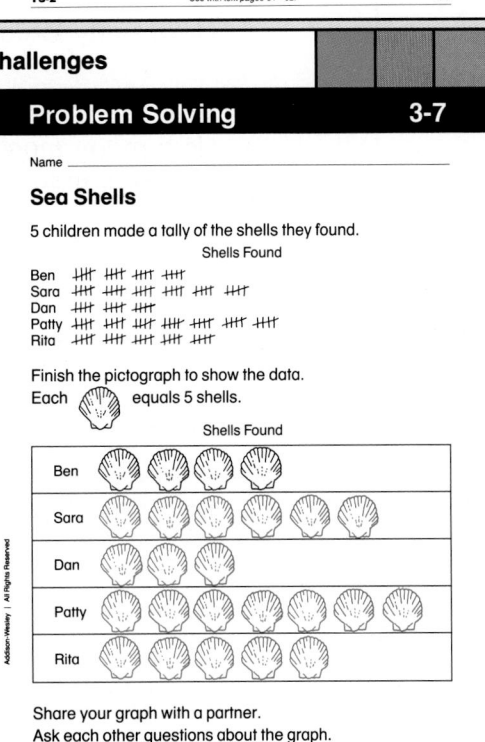

Family Members at the Play

1. Tell how many family members from each room attended the play.

Room 5 _12_ Room 8 _10_ Room 10 _6_

Room 6 _8_ Room 9 _14_

2. How many more family members came from room 8 than from room 10? _4_

RS-2 Use with text pages 61–62. 27

Challenges

Problem Solving 3-7

Name _____

Sea Shells

5 children made a tally of the shells they found.

Shells Found

Ben ⊬⊬ ⊬⊬ ⊬⊬ ⊬⊬
Sara ⊬⊬ ⊬⊬ ⊬⊬ ⊬⊬ ⊬⊬ ⊬⊬
Dan ⊬⊬ ⊬⊬ ⊬⊬
Patty ⊬⊬ ⊬⊬ ⊬⊬ ⊬⊬ ⊬⊬ ⊬⊬ ⊬⊬ ⊬⊬
Rita ⊬⊬ ⊬⊬ ⊬⊬ ⊬⊬ ⊬⊬

Finish the pictograph to show the data.
Each 🐚 equals 5 shells.

Shells Found

Share your graph with a partner.
Ask each other questions about the graph.

CS-2 Use with text pages 61–62. 27

Extended

Exercises All

Supplements
Challenges 27
Thinking Skills 27

Other Resources:
Mathematics Their Way, pp. 148-149, 151-152, 311-312
Explorations, pp. 91-95, 196-200

OBJECTIVE 3-7
To read pictographs

Materials: 18 cubes per student

Grouping Suggestions: whole class, individual work, cooperative learning groups of 4

---

1. MOTIVATE AND TEACH

LEARN ABOUT IT

On the chalkboard, write:
Each ⚲ means 2 people. Draw 3 rows of ⚲ so that each row has a different number of pictures. Have the class practice counting aloud by 2s as you point to each picture in the first row. *How can you find how many people are represented in the other rows?* (Count by 2s.)

▶ **How do you know what each lamp stands for?** (The sentence, or key, at the top of the graph tells you.)

▶ **Describe how you would count the red lanterns.** (Possible answer: Point to each picture in that row and count by 2 as you go.)

▶ **How could you use your cubes to help find the answer to Exercise 1?** (Possible answer: Line up 2 cubes for every lantern in the row. Add to find the total.)

2. CHECK UNDERSTANDING

ERROR ALERT Forgetting that each picture in the pictograph stands for 2 lanterns instead of 1.

Name _____

Pictographs

Tam's class made paper lanterns. They used a **pictograph** to show how many of each color they made.

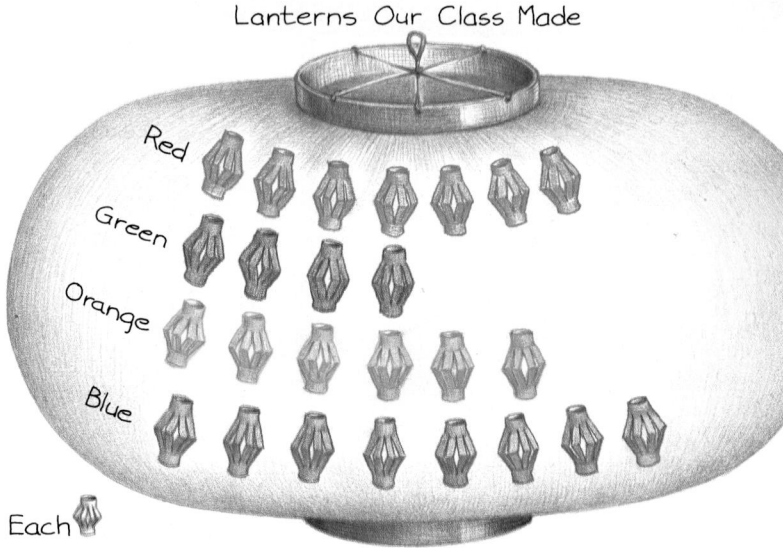

Lanterns Our Class Made

Red
Green
Orange
Blue

Each 🏮 means 2 lanterns.

Use the graph to answer the questions.

1. How many lanterns of each color were there?

   red __14__ green __8__ orange __12__ blue __16__

2. How many more blue lanterns than orange lanterns were there?

   __4__ more blue lanterns

Chapter 3   (sixty-one)

TEACHING OPTIONS

RETEACHING TIPS Create a pictograph by taping paper cups to the chalkboard. Place 2 cubes in each cup. Have students count the cubes to find the number represented by the cups. Then have students count by 2s to find the answers. For further help, use Reteaching Supplement 27.

ENRICHMENT **Family Math** Have students ask a family member to help them cut out a pictograph from a newspaper or magazine and then to write 2 questions that can be answered by reading the graph. Display the graphs in the classroom and discuss the questions.

Juan's class sold fans every Saturday
for 4 weeks. They made a pictograph
to show how many fans they sold.

2, 4, 6, 8, 10....

Fan Sales

Each ⌘ means 2 fans sold.

Week 1

Week 2

Week 3

Week 4

Use the graph to answer the questions.
How many fans did the class sell each week?

Week 1 __10__   Week 2 __12__   Week 3 __8__   Week 4 __14__

How many fewer fans did the class sell
during Week 3 than during Week 2?   __4__ fewer fans

MIXED REVIEW

Add.

$8 + 3 = $ __11__ $2 + 0 = $ __2__ $5 + 6 = $ __11__

$8 + 8 = $ __16__ $6 + 4 = $ __10__ $1 + 9 = $ __10__

$6 + 8 = $ __14__ $7 + 1 = $ __8__ $3 + 3 = $ __6__

(sixty-two)   Chapter 3

3. PRACTICE AND APPLY

Basic	All, Mixed Review
Average	All, Mixed Review
Extended	All, Mixed Review

PRACTICE

Ask students to describe what they see in
the pictograph on page 62. (Possible
answers: Each picture means two fans
sold; it shows the fan sales for four
weeks.)

APPLY

▶ **If you make a pictograph to show
how many books you read in a
week, what information would you
have to include?** (a key, days of the
week, pictures to show the number of
books read each day)
▶ **How does a pictograph help you
visualize the data?** (Possible answers:
It shows at a glance which row has more
or less; it lets you compare data quickly.)

MIXED REVIEW *Will you add or
subtract to complete these exercises?*
(add)

3-7

CLOSE AND ASSESS

SHOW WHAT YOU KNOW
Have small groups pretend to be
zookeepers who will make a
pictograph showing 4 animals at the
zoo. Have one student decide what the
graph will show, a second student
write the key, a third draw the graph.
Have groups show their graphs and
ask questions about them for others to
answer.

QUICK QUIZ

Make a pictograph from this data.
Miles We Drive Each Day
Each 🚗 means 2 miles.
Monday: 6 miles   Tuesday: 10 miles
Wednesday: 14 miles

Problem Solving: Retelling a Story/Look for a Pattern

OBJECTIVE 3-8 To solve problems by retelling a story; to solve problems using the strategy Look for a Pattern

PREBOOK ACTIVITIES

QUICK REVIEW

Finish each pattern.
84, 86, 88, __(90)__, __(92)__, __(94)__, __(96)__, __(98)__, __(100)__
39, 41, 43, __(45)__, __(47)__, __(49)__, __(51)__, __(53)__, __(55)__
21, 19, 17, __(15)__, __(13)__, __(11)__, __(9)__, __(7)__, __(5)__
20, 18, 16, __(14)__, __(12)__, __(10)__, __(8)__, __(6)__, __(4)__
45, 40, 35, __(30)__, __(25)__, __(20)__, __(15)__, __(10)__, __(5)__

PRIOR KNOWLEDGE

Ask students whether they have ever written a story, read it, and then changed some of the facts in the story. *How did changing the facts change your story?* (Possible answers: It might affect what the characters did; it might cause the ending to be different.)

COMMUNICATION

Reading and Discussing Math Write this sentence on the chalkboard: Retell the story exactly as I said it. Underline **Retell** and ask students to read the sentence. *What does it mean to retell something?* (Say it again.) *What are some things people might retell?* (Possible answers: messages, stories, recipes, events) Explain that sometimes when people retell a story, some of the information in the story might get changed. Show students several examples of graphs and tables. *How might a graph be used to show a pattern?* (Possible answer: You might see a pattern in the bars of a bar graph or in the pictures on a pictograph.) Explain that a table, like a graph, often can be completed by finding a pattern.

EXPLORE AND CONNECT

COOPERATIVE ACTIVITY

Grouping Suggestion: small groups
3 white rabbits and 2 brown rabbits are in the pet shop. How many rabbits are there in all? 3 _____ 2 = _____ *There are* _____ *rabbits in all.* Number sentence for your story:
_____ _____ = _____

TEACHING ACTIONS

BEFORE ► **Describe what you know about this story.** (Possible answer: There are 2 kinds of rabbits. I need to find how many there are in all.)
► **What will help you find the answer?** (Possible answer: There are 3 rabbits of one color and 2 rabbits of another color.

DURING ► **Plan how you could change the data in this story in order to retell it.** (Possible answer: Change only the numbers; change the colors of the rabbits; change their location.)
► **How would you go about solving both this story and the one that you are retelling?** (Possible answer: They are both put-together stories. For each story add the data. The method would be the same; only the answers would be different.)

AFTER ► **What would be a good way to check whether your story makes sense?** (Possible answer: Retell the story to a friend and have that person try to solve it. Identify and discuss any changes between the first and second stories.) Have small groups of students make up a story, then change the data and retell it. Have them write number sentences to match both stories.

CONNECTIONS Use these anytime.

Problem of the Day

Retelling a Story Read the story. Change the data and tell the new story to a friend. Write a number sentence for your story. Brett made 8 napkin holders. He sold 4 of them. How many napkin holders were left?

_____ ○ _____ = _____

Subject Integration

Language Arts Retell a familiar story that has a number in it, such as *The Three Bears* or *The Three Little Pigs*. Change the data in it. Discuss how changing the number might affect the outcome of the story.

Math Connection

Patterns Continue the pattern.
Team 1 had 2 people.
Team 2 had 4 people.
Team 3 had 6 people.
Team 4 had __(8)__ people.
Team 5 had __(10)__ people.
Team 6 had __(12)__ people.
Team 7 had __(14)__ people.

CLASSWORK AND HOMEWORK SUPPLEMENTS

Exercises All

Supplements
Reteaching 28 or
Practice 28

3-8

Exercises All

Supplements
Practice 28
Challenges 28 or
Thinking Skills 28

Exercises All

Supplements
Challenges 28
Thinking Skills 28

Other Resources:
Math in Stride, p. 77
Problem-Solving Experiences in Mathematics, pp. 52-53, 58-59, 88-89
Mathematics Book A, pp. 57-62

Practice

Problem Solving   3-8

Name _____

Retelling a Story

Work with a partner.
Finish the number sentence.
Then change the data. Tell your story.
Write the number sentence for your story.

1. There were 6 brown rabbits in the pen.
   There were 4 white rabbits in the pen, too.
   How many rabbits were in the pen in all?

   $6 \oplus 4 = \underline{10}$ There were 10 rabbits.

   Answers may vary.
   Number sentence for your story: ___ $\oplus$ ___ $=$ ___

2. 9 rabbits were sitting in the field.
   2 rabbits went inside the hole.
   How many rabbits were left?

   $9 \ominus 2 = \underline{7}$ 7 rabbits were left.

   Answers may vary.
   Number sentence for your story: ___ $\ominus$ ___ $=$ ___

3. Fran gave carrots to 7 rabbits.
   She gave lettuce to 5 rabbits.
   How many rabbits did she feed?

   $7 \oplus 5 = \underline{12}$ She fed 12 rabbits.

   Answers may vary.
   Number sentence for your story: ___ $\oplus$ ___ $=$ ___

28   Use with text page 63.   PS-2

Building Thinking Skills

Problem Solving   3-8

Name _____

Missing Numbers

Fill in the missing data to tell the story.
Then tell the story a different way.   Answers will vary.

1. Ann has 7 baseball caps,   Ann has 7 baseball caps,
   some blue and some red.   some blue and some red.

   ____ are blue and   ____ are blue and

   ____ are red.   ____ are red.

2. One team beat the other   One team beat the other
   team by 4 points.   team by 4 points.

   The score was ___ to ___.   The score was ___ to ___.

3. Carol is in charge of 8 mitts.   Carol is in charge of 8 mitts.

   ____ are left-hand mitts.   ____ are left-hand mitts.

   ____ are right-hand mitts.   ____ are right-hand mitts.

4. Drew had cold drinks for   Drew had cold drinks for
   the 18 players.   the 18 players.

   ____ wanted orange juice.   ____ wanted orange juice.

   ____ wanted grape juice.   ____ wanted grape juice.

28   Use with text pages 63 – 64.   TS-2

Reteaching

Problem Solving   3-8

Name _____

Look for a Pattern

Do you see a pattern?

I	3	5	7	9

2 more 2 more 2 more 2 more

Read each story. Look for a pattern.
Finish each table. Then answer the question.

1. Each sticker cost 2¢. David bought 6 stickers.
   How much did he spend?

number of stickers	I	2	3	4	5	6
cost	2¢	4¢	6¢	8¢	10¢	12¢

David spent 12 ¢.

2. David put the stickers on his notebook in rows.
   Row I had I sticker. Row 2 had 2 stickers.
   Row 3 had 5 stickers.
   How many stickers were in row 6?

row	I	2	3	4	5	6
stickers	I	3	5	7	9	11

There were 11 stickers in row 6.

28   Use with text page 64.   RS-2

Challenges

Patterns   3-8

Name _____

At the Zoo

At the Children's Zoo you can
feed the llama for 5¢. Fill in the table.
Look for a pattern.

Cups of food	I	2	3	4	5	6	7	8	9
cost	5¢	10¢	15¢	20¢	25¢	30¢	35¢	40¢	45¢

Use the table to answer the questions.

1. Emily has 25¢. How many times can she feed
   the llama? 5

2. Two children have 10¢ each. How many times can
   they feed the llama? 4

3. How many times could you feed the llama with 30¢?
   6

4. Matthew has 37¢. He feeds the llama 7 times.
   How much money does he have left? 2¢

Think about the pattern.

5. How many times could you feed the llama with 50¢?
   10

28   Use with text pages 63 – 64.   CS-2

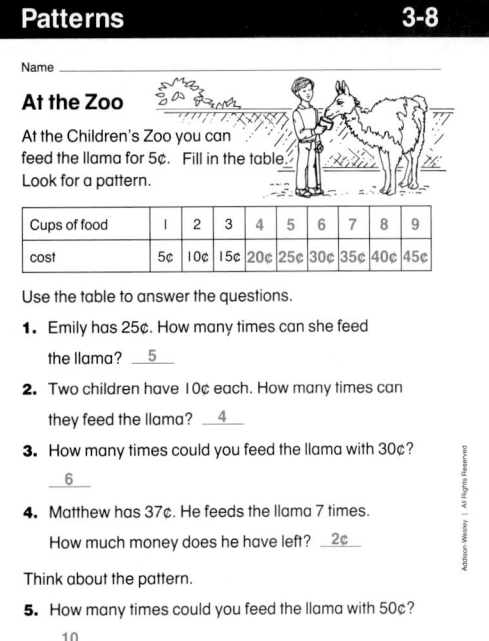

LESSON PLAN 3-8

OBJECTIVE 3-8
To solve problems by retelling a story; to solve problems using the strategy Look for a Pattern

1. MOTIVATE AND TEACH

LEARN ABOUT IT

Will the number sentences of the retold stories be different? Why? (Yes, because all students will be using different numbers when they retell the story.) *In a take-away story, what will you watch for when you change the data?* (The first number will need to be greater than the second so you can subtract from it.)

 **BEFORE** ► **How might you identify important data in these exercises as you read them?** (Possible answer: As you read, circle any numbers or words that give information. Then go back and identify the data that could be changed when retelling the story.)

 **DURING** ► **What should you think about as you are changing the data in your story?** (Possible answer: You need to make sure that the new data make sense in the story.)

 **AFTER** ► **Why is it a good idea to retell your story to a friend?** (Possible answer: A friend can listen and write a number sentence for the story. You can see if the number sentence matches the data you changed.)

2. CHECK UNDERSTANDING

ERROR ALERT **Page 63** Not understanding how to insert new data into a story.
Page 64 Not being able to identify a pattern within a table.

Name _____

Problem Solving
Retelling a Story

Work with a partner.
Finish the number sentence.
Then change the data. Tell your story. Write the number sentence for your story.

1. Chas made 8 big origami rabbits. He made 4 small rabbits. How many rabbits did he make in all?

   $8 \oplus 4 = \boxed{12}$ Chas made __12__ rabbits.

   number sentence for your story ____ ⊕ ____ $\boxed{=}$ ____
   Answers may vary.

2. Dawn made 5 origami birds. She gave away 2 of them. How many birds were left?

   $5 \ominus 2 = \boxed{3}$ __3__ birds were left.

   number sentence for your story ____ ⊕ ____ $\boxed{=}$ ____
   Answers may vary.

3. Stan made 9 origami deer. Hank made 7 deer. How many deer did Stan and Hank make together?

   $9 \oplus 7 = \boxed{16}$ Stan and Hank made __16__ deer.

   number sentence for your story ____ ⊕ ____ $\boxed{=}$ ____
   Answers may vary. (sixty-three)

Chapter 3

TEACHING OPTIONS

RETEACHING TIPS Have students identify and circle the data that can be changed in story problems. Then have them replace the circled data with new data, retell the stories and write a number sentence. For help in looking for a pattern, use Reteaching Supplement 28.

COMPUTER **Creative Creator, Designware © 1983** Three levels of difficulty for all levels. Students develop pattern recognition skills by identifying the movements of a dancing creature. They then instruct their own creature to duplicate the dance. The game requires 15-20 minutes.

Problem Solving Strategy
Look for a Pattern

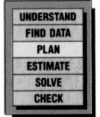

Read each story. Look for
a pattern. Finish the table.
Then answer the question.

For art class, each student
used 2 pieces of origami paper.
There were 9 students in the
class. How many pieces
of paper did the class use?

Students	1	2	3	4	5	6	7	8	9
Pieces of Paper	2	4	6	8	10	12	14	16	18

The class used __18__ pieces of paper.

The teacher put origami swans into rows.
Row 1 had 1 swan.
Row 2 had 3 swans.
Row 3 had 5 swans.
This pattern continued.
How many swans were in Row 7?

Rows	1	2	3	4	5	6	7
Swans	1	3	5	7	9	11	13

__13__ swans were in Row 7.

3. Practice and Apply

Basic	All
Average	All
Extended	All

*How do the dashed numbers help you
find the answer?* (They continue the
pattern farther to help you identify it.)
▶ **What can you do to show what is
happening in Exercise 1?** (Possible
answer: Draw a picture starting with 1
student and 2 pieces of paper and
continue until you show 9 students.)
▶ **How will drawing a picture help
you fill in the table?** (Possible answer:
You can count how many pieces of paper
there are for each student and fill in the
table at the appropriate place.)
▶ **Compare the numbers in the
second row of each table. How are
they different?** (Possible answer: The
first table shows even numbers; the
second table shows odd numbers.)

Close and Assess

SAY WHAT YOU THINK Reread
the chapter story, *The Ginger Jar
Painter*. Have pairs of students each
write an addition or a subtraction story
about butterflies and exchange papers.
Each student should read the partner's
story, change the data, and retell the
story to the partner. Then have both
students write the number sentence
that corresponds to each new story.

Quick Quiz

Look for a pattern. Finish the table.

Row	1	2	3	4	5	6
Vases	3	6	9	(12)	(15)	(18)

CHAPTER 3

WRAP UP

INTRODUCTION The Wrap up provides activities emphasizing math language and thinking skills for the chapter.

USING PAGE 65
Math Words ▶ **Look at the graph. How do you use the numbers and bars to find information?** (Possible answer: You match the height of the bars to the numbers to see how many of a certain color fish are in the tank.)

▶ **Compare the tally marks in Exercise 2 to the colored squares. How are they alike?** (Possible answer: They are both ways of showing a certain number of fish.)

Math Reasoning ▶ **Name 1 way to identify the even numbers in Exercise 6.** (Possible answer: Even numbers end in 0, 2, 4, 6, or 8.)

Name _____

WRAP UP

MATH WORDS

Look at the graph. Ring the answer.

1. This graph is a ____ .
   (bar graph)   pictograph

2. Which tally shows how many blue 🐟 ?
   ⅟⅟⅟⅟ I   (I I I I)

3. The greatest number of 🐟 are ____ .
   (red)   blue

4. There are 3 ____ yellow than red 🐟 .
   more   (fewer)

5. There is an even number of ____ 🐟 .
   yellow   (blue)

MATH REASONING

6. Cross out the odd numbers. Write the even numbers in order.

   | 4 | 6 | 8 | 10 | 12 |

7. Continue the pattern. Draw the next three groups.

   _1_   _3_   _5_   _7_   _9_   _11_

Chapter 3 Wrap Up

(sixty-five)

TEACHING OPTIONS

ENRICHMENT Have students make a pictograph showing the same information as the bar graph. To help them plan, have them ask questions such as *How can I arrange the information? What picture will I use to represent the fish? Is there any information I should add?*

Have small groups create a simple board game showing a path to a buried treasure. Outline squares on graph paper to make a path, and write special directions—such as *go ahead 2; go back 1*—in several spaces. Use a spinner labeled with even or odd numbers.

Name _____

CHAPTER REVIEW/TEST

Write the next two numbers in the pattern.
Are they odd or even? Ring your answer.

11, 13, 15, _17_ , _19_   (odd)   even

14, 12, 10, _8_ , _6_   odd   (even)

Color to continue the pattern.

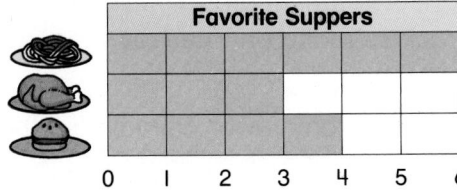

Color the next box to continue the pattern.

b	r	b
r	b	r

Color the graph to match the tally.

 ⌷⌷⌷⌷ |

 | | |

 | | | |

Favorite Suppers

0   1   2   3   4   5   6

Ring your answers.

Which supper did the most people like best?

Did more people like or  ?

(sixty-six)   Chapter 3 Review/Test

CHAPTER REVIEW/TEST

INTRODUCTION   The Review/Test is provided to review and evaluate the skills and concepts presented in Chapter 3.

USING PAGE 66
If you prefer to use this page for review, you may want to use the **Multiple-Choice Posttest** (pages 11-12) or the **Free-Response Posttest** (pages 11-12) to evaluate mastery of chapter objectives.

ITEM ANALYSIS   The table below correlates the Chapter Review/Test items with the lesson objectives for the chapter.

Items	Objectives
1	3-1
2	3-3
3	3-3
4, 5, 6	3-4

INFORMAL ASSESSMENT

Using Manipulatives   Ask pairs of students to use Cube-A-Links to make a color or number pattern. Have partners change places and continue each other's patterns for 1 or 2 more steps. Ask students to explain what they did to continue the patterns.

Communication   *If you were a TV weatherperson, how might you use a graph to look for a pattern in the weather?* (Possible answer: You might look at graphs that show the weather

for several weeks or months to see if there is a pattern of rainy days or of hot or cold weather.)

Critical Thinking ▶ How can you tell if a pattern is a growing pattern or if it has been made by turning it or flipping it? (Possible answer: A growing pattern has more parts to it each time; a pattern made by turning or flipping is always the same size and shape, but its position is different.)

CHAPTER 3

ENRICHMENT

INTRODUCTION Students will begin to understand how plotting information on a graph can help them make projections about future needs or events.

USING PAGE 67

The Enrichment page is provided for all students. You may wish to use it after they have completed the Chapter Review/Test on page 66.

▶ **Predict how this graph can help the class know the total amount of animals they will make for the fair.**
(Possible answer: The graph shows that each child can make about 1 animal a day. Knowing this, students can look ahead at days when they know some students will be out of school and estimate how many animals they will be able to make.)

▶ **Tell 2 different ways to find the answers to Exercises 3 and 4.**
(Possible answer: Subtract the lesser number from the greater number, or count back the number of squares from the greater amount to the lesser amount.)

EXTENSIONS Explain to students that many places of business use graphs to help them plan for their future needs. Read the following situations to students and then discuss how a graph would supply helpful information.

1. A bakery graphs how many cakes it sold during the week.

2. The post office graphs how many packages were sent during each month of the year.

3. A school graphs how many students are registered to attend the following year.

Invite individuals from local businesses to talk to the class about what they learn from their graphs and how they use this information.

Name _____

ENRICHMENT
Reading a Bar Graph

Debra's second grade class made origami animals.

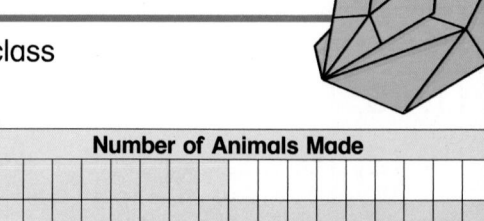

	Number of Animals Made
Monday	
Tuesday	
Wednesday	
Thursday	

0 1 2 3 4 5 6 7 8 9 10 11 12 13 14 15 16 17 1

1. How many animals did the class make on Wednesday?   __17__ animals

2. How many more animals did the class make on Tuesday than on Monday?   __9__ more animals

3. How many fewer animals did the class make on Thursday than on Wednesday?   __2__ fewer animals

4. On which day do you think half of the class was out sick?
_____
Monday

5. On Friday, half the students will be gone on a field trip. About how many animals do you think the class will make on Friday? Answers may vary.   about __9__ animals

Chapter 3 Enrichment: Reading a Bar Graph   (sixty-seven)

Name _____

UMULATIVE REVIEW

dd or subtract.

$$\begin{array}{r} 6 \\ +6 \\ \hline \end{array}$$
○ 9
● 12
○ 11

$5 + 3 =$ ___
○ 6
○ 7
● 8

$8 - 5 =$ ___
● 3
○ 2
○ 5

$$\begin{array}{r} 7 \\ -4 \\ \hline \end{array}$$
○ 1
○ 9
● 3

5. $$\begin{array}{r} 8 \\ +9 \\ \hline \end{array}$$
○ 16
○ 10
● 17

6. $$\begin{array}{r} 9 \\ +8 \\ \hline \end{array}$$
○ 14
○ 1
● 17

7. $6 + 0 =$ ___
○ 0
● 6
○ 7

8. $3 + 2 + 7 =$ ___
○ 15
● 12
○ 17

Li read 8 books. Jan read 4 books. How many books did they read in all? Choose a number sentence to match.

● $8 + 4 = 12$

○ $8 - 4 = 4$

○ $4 + 4 = 8$

CUMULATIVE REVIEW

INTRODUCTION   The purpose of this Cumulative Review is to maintain previously taught skills and concepts. The emphasis in this Cumulative Review is on addition and subtraction facts, Chapter 1; and on sums to 18, Chapter 2.

ITEM ANALYSIS   The table below correlates the Cumulative Review items with the lesson objectives.

Items	Objectives
1	2-2
2	1-2
3, 4	1-3
5, 6	2-7
7	2-1
8	2-10
9	2-5

Chapter Management

OVERVIEW

Lesson	Pages	Objectives	Subject Integration	Strand Integration
Count Backs and Zeros	69-70	4-1 To count back 1, 2, or 3 and to subtract zero	science: space shuttle	mental math
Subtraction Doubles	71-72	4-2 To use subtraction doubles to find differences	science: astronaut	logic
Subtracting from 9 and 10	73-74	4-3 To subtract from 9 and 10 to find differences	science: space ships	critical thinking
Problem Solving: Understanding the Operations/Probability	75-76	4-4 To compare to subtract; to predict events	science: moon rocks	probability
Counting Up to Subtract	77-78	4-5 To count up to find differences	science: space craft	number sense
Fact Practice	79-80	4-6 To use mental math to find differences	science: rocket	graphing
More Related Subtraction Facts	81-82	4-7 To model and finish related subtraction facts	science: parachutes	problem solving
Fact Families	83-84	4-8 To model and finish fact families	science: astronomy	computation
Problem Solving: Showing the Data/Problem Solving Strategy: Guess and Check	85-86	4-9 To show data; to use the strategy Guess and Check	science: astronomy	money, logic

MATHEMATICAL BACKGROUND

Subtraction

The *take away* method of subtraction involves taking objects away from a group. The number left is the answer. The *comparison* method of subtraction involves two groups of objects; the two groups are compared to determine how many more are in one group than the other.

Subtraction Facts

The goal of teaching subtraction facts to students is fast, accurate recall. To reach this goal, students learn strategies to help reason out answers. Lesson 4-1 reviews counting back 1, 2, or 3 by starting with the greater of the two numbers and counting back the number being subtracted. Lesson 4-2 reviews subtraction doubles, which are directly related to addition doubles. Lesson 4-5 reviews counting up to find differences. Related addition facts and fact families are also helpful fact strategies.

Mental Math

Students learn and practice subtraction fact strategies using counters and blocks, but the ultimate goal is to use the strategies as mental math techniques.

Problem Solving

In this chapter, students solve problems using the *take away* and the *comparison* methods of subtraction, by drawing pictures to show data, and by using the strategy *Guess and Check*.

TIPS FROM TEACHERS

Make a gameboard resembling a football field. Write team names at each end of the field. Use addition and subtraction fact cards with answers on the back. Each card should also include directions telling where to move the football if the correct answer is given. Students take turns playing until a touchdown is scored.

**Richard Wulf-McGrath
Sidecreek Elementary School
Aurora, CO**

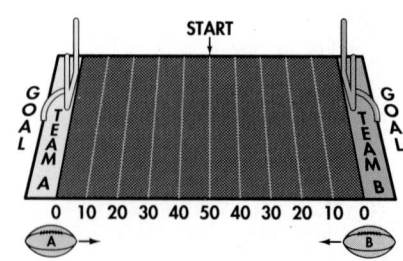

CORRECT ANSWER:
MOVE THE BALL 10 YD TOWARD THE OTHER TEAM'S GOAL.

INCORRECT ANSWER:
MOVE THE BALL 10 YD BACK TOWARD YOUR OWN GOAL.

ASSESSMENT

Pretest — Chapter 4, page 1

Multiple-Choice Format

Name _____

1. Count back to subtract.

$$6 - 2$$

  A 8
  (B) 4
  C 2

2. Subtract.

$$8 - 4$$

  A 3
  (B) 4
  C 5

3. Subtract.

$$10 - 6$$

  (A) 4
  B 5
  C 6

4. Think about pulling one counter from the box. Choose the true sentence.

  A Pulling ● or ○ is equally likely.
  (B) Pulling ● is more likely.
  C Pulling ● is less likely.

5. Count up to subtract.

$$9 - 7$$

  (A) 2
  B 3
  C 4

6. Choose the way to make a difference of 6.

  (A) 12 − 6
  B 10 − 6
  C 8 − 6

MCT 2   13

Pretest — Chapter 4, page 2

Multiple-Choice Format

Name _____

7. Subtract.

$$10 - 8$$

  A 1
  (B) 2
  C 3

8. Subtract. Choose the related subtraction fact.

$$11 - 4$$

  A 11 − 5
  B 11 − 6
  (C) 11 − 7

9. Choose the fact that belongs to the same fact family.

6 + 3 3 + 6 9 − 6

  A 3 + 3
  B 4 + 5
  (C) 9 − 3

10. Read the story. Choose the picture that shows the data.

Bess saw 3 stars. Raj saw 2 stars. How many did they see in all?

  (A) ☆☆☆ ☆☆ B ☆✕✕

11. Mary had 12¢. She had 3 coins. What were they?

  A
  (B)

14   MCT 2

ITEM ANALYSIS

Items	Objectives
1	4-1
2	4-2
3	4-3
4	4-4
5	4-5
6, 7	4-6
8	4-7
9	4-8
10, 11	4-9

Note: The item analysis is the same for all pretests and posttests for this chapter.

Posttest — Chapter 4, page 1

Multiple-Choice Format

Name _____

1. Count back to subtract.

$$5 - 3$$

  (A) 2
  B 3
  C 8

2. Subtract.

$$6 - 3$$

  (A) 3
  B 4
  C 5

3. Subtract.

$$9 - 5$$

  A 14
  B 5
  (C) 4

4. Think about pulling one counter from the box. Choose the true sentence.

  (A) Pulling ○ is less likely.
  B Pulling ○ is more likely.
  C Pulling ○ or ● is less likely.

5. Count up to subtract.

$$11 - 8$$

  A 7
  B 4
  (C) 3

6. Choose the way to make a difference of 2.

  (A) 8 − 6
  B 10 − 5
  C 5 − 4

MCT 2   15

Posttest — Chapter 4, page 2

Multiple-Choice Format

Name _____

7. Subtract.

$$10 - 3$$

  A 6
  (B) 7
  C 8

8. Subtract. Choose the related subtraction fact.

$$7 - 2$$

  A 11 − 3
  B 7 − 4
  (C) 7 − 5

9. Choose the fact that belongs to the same fact family.

9 + 1 1 + 9 10 − 9

  A 9 − 1
  B 10 + 9
  (C) 10 − 1

10. Read the story. Choose the picture that shows the data.

Alex saw 4 stars. A cloud covered 2 stars. Then how many did he see?

  A ☆☆☆☆ ☆☆ (B) ☆✕✕

11. Mary had 11¢. She had 3 coins. What were they?

  A
  (B)

16   MCT 2

ALSO AVAILABLE

▶ **Free Response Tests**
▶ **Alternative Tests**
▶ **Thinking Strategies**
▶ **Concrete Materials**

Optional Chapter Activities

PROJECT AND BULLETIN BOARD

Copy the riddle and the clues on a large piece of paper and attach it to the bulletin board. Draw and cut into 9 parts a picture of a space creature. Place the parts on squares of paper. Display pictures of other space objects on 9 other squares. Highlight the number in each clue. Have students use counters or cubes to model the highlighted number. Then, have them use the manipulatives to model fact families for the number. Each day, have students answer the question about the highlighted number. As questions are answered, assemble the pictures corresponding to the correct answers until the space creature is complete. Encourage students to group the counters to check names for the number. Remind them that the answer is *yes* only if EVERY fact listed is another name for the highlighted number.

WHO WILL HELP US LEARN THE FACTS?

Yes | No

Answer

1. Is 7 another name for
   10-3 16-9 14-7 15-8 and 4+3 ?

2. Is 12 another name for
   6+6 7+5 10-6 3+9 and 8+4 ?

3. Is 9 another name for
   3+6 8+1 12-3 18-9 and 16-7 ?

4. Is 5 another name for
   10-5 11-6 1+4 9-4 and 8-3 ?

5. Is 3 another name for
   10-7 12-9 11-6 9-6 and 8-5 ?

6. Is 6 another name for
   15-9 9-3 13-7 12-6 and 10-4 ?

COOPERATIVE LEARNING

Divide the class into 4 or 5 groups. Identify the group skill: summarizing and checking with others for agreement and understanding. Each group will make and use a subtraction wheel for practicing subtraction facts. Draw the subtraction wheel and a numberline on the chalkboard. Direct members of each group to copy the wheel and numberline on the floor or sidewalk. Members of the group should decide on the best way to copy them. Methods might include: draw with chalk, copy with masking tape, draw on posterboard. To play the subtraction game, two students toss beanbags onto the wheel. A third student names the greater number on which a beanbag landed. A fourth student steps onto the corresponding number on the numberline and then steps back the number of steps equal to the smaller number on which a beanbag landed. Then have a student record the subtraction sentence they enacted. Have members of the groups summarize the tasks, to be sure they understand what to do.

You will find grouping suggestions and cooperative learning activities in most lessons throughout this chapter.

LITERATURE

Brandenberg, Franz. "Flags for Sale," from *Leo and Emily's Big Ideas.* New York: Greenwillow Books, 1982.

Emily and Leo see an advertisement for flags in a newspaper: ten dollars for one hundred flags. They only need one, but decide to sell the other ninety-nine at a profit. Have students use events in the story to write number sentences.

Allen, Pamela. *Who Sank the Boat?* New York: Coward, McCann, 1982.

Burningham, *John. Mr. Grumpy's Outing.* New York: Thomas Y. Crowell, 1976.

ENGLISH AS A SECOND LANGUAGE

The problem solving stories in this chapter are long and complex. Familiarize the students with the vocabulary through pictures. Repeat and paraphrase the stories. Then have students retell the stories in their own words. Use this opportunity to help ESL students clarify their own language.

Focus on the language of subtraction: *How many more seas than oceans?* Have students create examples, filling in blanks to answer questions. Group ESL students with native speakers for linguistic support.

If ESL students are unable to follow the stories, explain that if they listen to the numbers and to the final sentence which signals the operation of subtraction, they will have understood enough to solve the problem.

For discussions of probability, the expressions *more likely* and *less likely* are confusing and should be demonstrated in concrete ways as well as paraphrased.

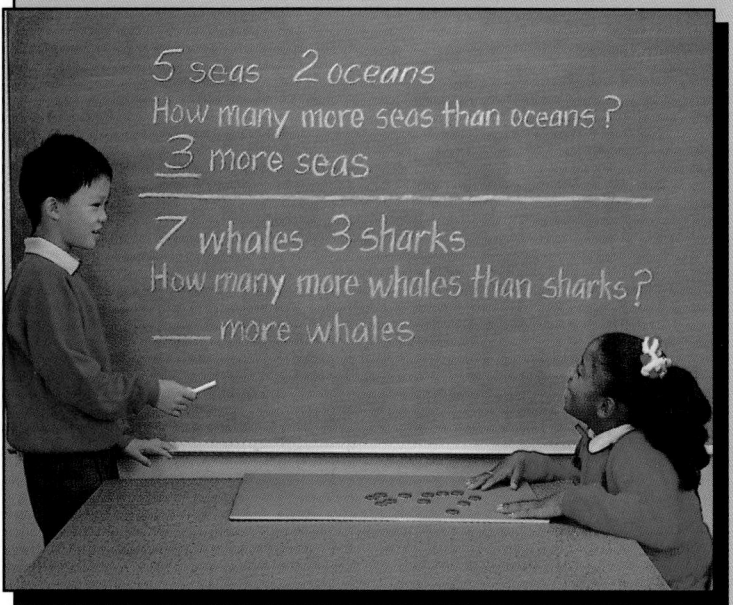

GIFTED

Mathematically talented students may already know subtraction facts to 12. Many of the strategies presented in this chapter may interest them, however. You may wish to challenge these students, after they have completed their student book work, by showing them how to make change by counting up. For example, after Lesson 5 on counting up, create a grocery store in the classroom. Attach price tags ranging from 1¢ to 12¢ to empty food containers. Introduce pennies, nickels, and dimes to students and have them group their punchout coins into like piles. Have students imagine that they have 12¢ and take turns purchasing items. They give 12¢ to the store clerk, who makes correct change by counting up from the price of the item. Have students check their change by subtracting on paper or by using a calculator. Students may use their store and punchout coins to illustrate other facts and strategies throughout the chapter.

STUDENTS AT RISK

Students must acquire basic subtraction facts in order to move on to subtraction with 2- and 3-digit numbers. Providing plenty of practice with activities such as the following will help them learn those facts so that they will no longer need to count the whole starting from 1. Give students a set of 10 or fewer counters. Have them count back aloud while dropping each counter into a cup. They say the amount left in their hands, without looking, and then check it. Take away amounts of 1, 2, or 3.

Pictures or objects will help students learn subtraction doubles. If you have introduced a set of pictures for addition doubles, continue to refer to them for subtraction. Otherwise, you might use the following pictures for subtraction doubles:

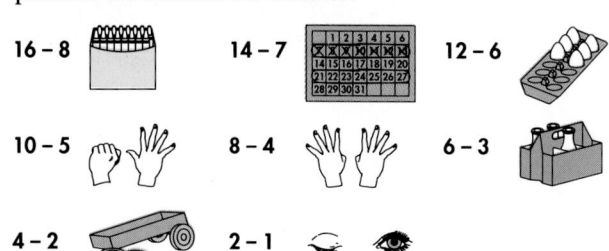

You may also use the Reteaching Supplements and the specific Reteaching Tips from each lesson in this chapter.

Storybook

PICTURE

These pictures and accompanying stories and poems are available as storybooks.

You may want to read and discuss this poem with your students before starting the chapter. The first lesson in this chapter includes a question about the poem. Lessons 1, 2, 3, and 5 in this chapter have questions in the informal Assessment that refer to the poem.

Space Creature

My dog and I traveled to outer space
To catch a glimpse of the nonhuman race.
We met a creature who looked quite weird;
He had ten eyes until three disappeared.

His six long tentacles waved in the air,
Then four retracted into his hair.
Eight gangling arms reached for a hug,
But two receded when I gave a tug.

Seven pointed ears were on his head,
Then five shriveled away into lumps instead.
This jelly-like body continued to change,
My dog sniffed up close, but I stayed out of range.

The creature began to steam and bubble,
And I wondered if maybe we were in trouble.
It ambled toward us and we were scared,
My dog barked loudly, we were prepared.

The creature turned and began to frown,
Then, as we watched, it melted down.
We stared at the pool that was on the floor,
And pretty soon there was no more.

Count Backs and Zeros

OBJECTIVE 4-1   To use the mental math technique of counting back 1, 2, or 3 and subtracting with zero

PREBOOK ACTIVITIES

QUICK REVIEW

Count on to complete the number pattern.
1. 50, 52, (54) , (56) , (58) , (60) , (62)
2. 12, 14, (16) , (18) , (20) , (22) , (24)
3. 33, 35, (37) , (39) , (41) , (43) , (45)
4. 26, 28, (30) , (32) , (34) , (36) , (38)
5. 85, 87, (89) , (91) , (93) , (95) , (97)

PRIOR KNOWLEDGE

Imagine that you are hiking in the woods. The leader of your group says "Go on" when you come to a small stream. What does the leader want you to do? (keep going in a forward direction) *When you reach a steep cliff, the leader says "Go back." What does the leader want you to do?* (turn around; go backward) Have students illustrate by walking the directions *go on* and *go back.*

COMMUNICATION

Reading and Discussing Math   Write **countback** on the chalkboard. Ask students to read the phrase and discuss what they think it means. Explain that counting back is one method for solving subtraction problems.
How do you think counting back is like going backward when you are walking? (Possible answer: They are alike because you do not go forward; you count or move backward.) *How is counting back different from counting on?* (Possible answer: When you count on, you count larger numbers than the number you start with. When you count back, you count smaller numbers than the number you start with.)

EXPLORE AND CONNECT

Materials: counters
Grouping Suggestions: small groups
Explain to students that when a subtraction problem has − 0, −1, −2, and −3 in it, they can count back to solve it. Write 12 − 3 on the chalkboard. Have students model the fact with you by showing 12 counters, then verbally counting back 3. Explain that the number students end on when they count back is the answer. Have students work in small groups using counters to model other subtraction count-back facts that you provide. *When you count back, with what number do you start?* (the whole number) Then have students model subtraction facts in which the whole is subtracted, such as 9 − 9. *What answer do you get when you subtract the whole number?* (0)

CONNECTIONS   Use these anytime.

Problem of the Day

Retell a Story   Solve the problem. Then change the data and retell the story to a partner. Solve the new problem. Fred wrote 9 letters. He mailed 2 of them. How many letters were left? (9 − 2 = 7; 7 letters were left. Answers for students' problems will vary.)

Subject Integration

Physical Education   Have everyone stand behind a line in the gym or playground. Have a caller give commands that involve counting back, such as *7 count back 3.* Find the answer and take that many steps. After each command, the caller says the number sentence that matches the command to check the steps. Take turns being caller.

Creative Thinking

Algebra   Imagine that you have 4 cards labeled A, B, C, and D. The backs of the cards are labeled with the numbers 2, 3, 7, and 8. Use these clues to find which number is on the back of each card.
B + B = 4   A − B = 6
B + C = 5   D − C = 4
(A = 8; B = 2; C = 3; D = 7)

find differences

CLASSWORK AND HOMEWORK SUPPLEMENTS

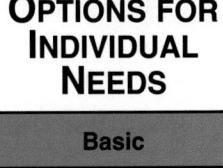

OPTIONS FOR INDIVIDUAL NEEDS

Basic

Exercises All
More Practice, p. 412, set B

Supplements
Reteaching 29 or
Practice 29

Average

Exercises All
More Practice, p. 412, set B

Supplements
Practice 29
Challenges 29 or
Thinking Skills 29

Extended

Exercises All

Supplements
Challenges 29
Thinking Skills 29

Other Resources:
Math in Stride, pp. 18-19, 27
Mathematics Their Way, pp. 103-104, 110-111, 180-183, 192-194, 248-249
Explorations, pp. 46-47, 56-59
Problem Solving Experiences in Mathematics, p. 45
Workjobs, pp. 210-211
Workjobs II, pp. 104-110, 114-115

Practice

Skills Maintenance   4-1

Name _____

Count Backs and Zeros

Subtract.

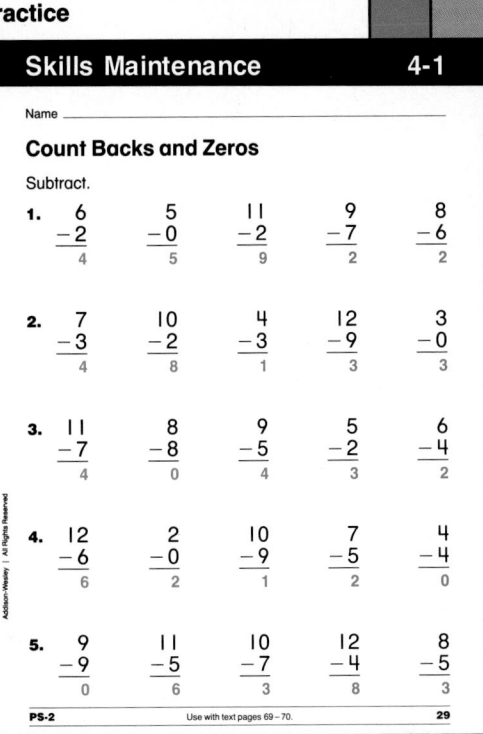

1.	6 −2 = 4	5 −0 = 5	11 −2 = 9	9 −7 = 2	8 −6 = 2
2.	7 −3 = 4	10 −2 = 8	4 −3 = 1	12 −9 = 3	3 −0 = 3
3.	11 −7 = 4	8 −8 = 0	9 −5 = 4	5 −2 = 3	6 −4 = 2
4.	12 −6 = 6	2 −0 = 2	10 −9 = 1	7 −5 = 2	4 −4 = 0
5.	9 −9 = 0	11 −5 = 6	10 −7 = 3	12 −4 = 8	8 −5 = 3

PS-2   Use with text pages 69 – 70.   29

Building Thinking Skills

Calculators   4-1

Name _____

Calculator Subtraction

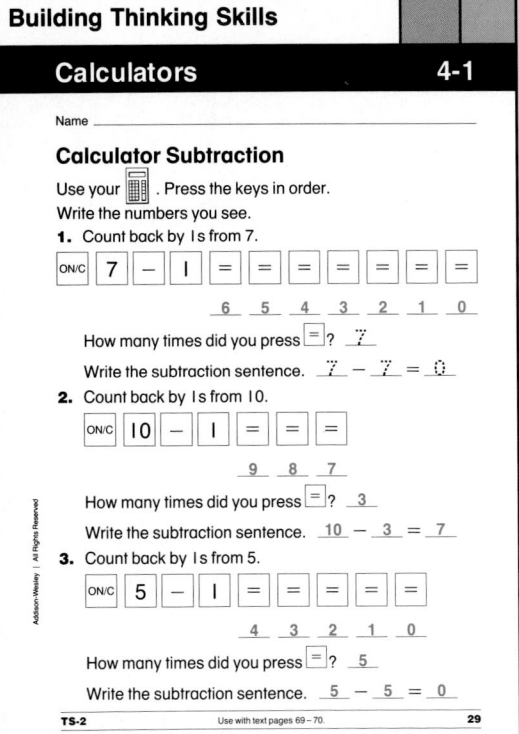

Use your [calculator]. Press the keys in order.
Write the numbers you see.

1. Count back by 1s from 7.

| ON/C | 7 | − | 1 | = | = | = | = | = | = | = |

    6   5   4   3   2   1   0

How many times did you press [=]? _7_

Write the subtraction sentence. _7_ − _7_ = _0_

2. Count back by 1s from 10.

| ON/C | 10 | − | 1 | = | = | = |

    9   8   7

How many times did you press [=]? _3_

Write the subtraction sentence. _10_ − _3_ = _7_

3. Count back by 1s from 5.

| ON/C | 5 | − | 1 | = | = | = | = |

    4   3   2   1   0

How many times did you press [=]? _5_

Write the subtraction sentence. _5_ − _5_ = _0_

TS-2   Use with text pages 69 – 70.   29

Reteaching

Skills Review   4-1

Name _____

Count Backs and Zeros (Count back as you subtract.)

$6 - 2 = 4$ (6, 5, 4)

$5 - 5 = 0$ (5, 4, 3, 2, 1, 0)

$4 - 0 = 4$ (4)

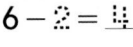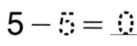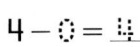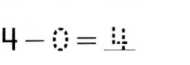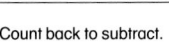

Count back to subtract.

1. $7 - 6 = 1$ $4 - 2 = 2$ $6 - 0 = 6$

2. $5 - 5 = 0$ $8 - 6 = 2$ $9 - 3 = 6$

3. $8 - 4 = 4$ $7 - 5 = 2$ $6 - 4 = 2$

4. $3 - 0 = 3$ $5 - 4 = 1$ $4 - 1 = 3$

5. $9 - 4 = 5$ $7 - 0 = 7$ $8 - 5 = 3$

RS-2   Use with text pages 69 – 70.   29

Challenges

Cooperative Activities   4-1

Name _____

Climb Down the Ladder

You need: a friend, a spinner with numbers 0 to 5, and 12 paper clips for each player.
Rules: Each player puts 1 paper clip on each step of the ladder. Take turns. Spin.

| 12 |
| 11 |
| 10 |
| 9 |
| 8 |
| 7 |
| 6 |
| 5 |
| 4 |
| 3 |
| 2 |
| 1 |

Subtract the number on the spinner from the number on the ladder. Start on step | 12 |. Remove the number of clips that matches the number on the spinner.

If you cannot subtract the number on the spinner from the number on the step, you lose your turn. The first player who lands exactly on step | 1 | wins.

| 12 |
| 11 |
| 10 |
| 9 |
| 8 |
| 7 |
| 6 |
| 5 |
| 4 |
| 3 |
| 2 |
| 1 |

CS-2   Use with text pages 69 – 70.   29

OBJECTIVE 4-1

To use the mental math technique of counting back 1, 2, or 3 and subtracting with zero to find differences

Materials: counters; number cubes labeled 3-8 and 1-2; number cards labeled − 0, − 1, − 2, − 3, and − all

Grouping Suggestions: small groups

1. MOTIVATE AND TEACH

LEARN ABOUT IT

Read the chapter story about the space creature. *The creature started with 8 gangling arms. Then 2 arms disappeared. How many did he have left?* (6) Have students use counters to show 8 arms and remove 2 counters as they count back. Then direct their attention to the space shuttle on page 69.

▶ **Imagine that there are 9 astronauts standing on the platform. How can you use counters to show how many astronauts are left after 3 astronauts board the shuttle?** (Possible answer: Put 9 counters on the platform; count back 3 from 9 and put 3 counters in the shuttle. 6 counters will be left.)

▶ **Why is counting back a good method to use when you are subtracting 3 or less?** (Possible answer: It is easy to count back 1, 2, or 3 without losing your place.)

▶ **Do you think counting back would be a good method to use when you are subtracting 7, 8, or 9? Why or why not?** (Probably not; you might lose track of numbers as you count back.)

▶ **Use counters to model a story in which none or all of the astronauts leave the platform. What number sentence would you write?** (Possible answer: *8 astronauts were on the platform. All of them boarded the shuttle. How many were left?* $8 - 8 = 0$)

2. CHECK UNDERSTANDING

ERROR ALERT Using the starting number as one of the count backs.

4
Subtraction Facts

TEACHING OPTIONS

RETEACHING TIPS Draw a number line on the chalkboard and present students with a count-back subtraction problem. As students use counters to find the difference, have a student count back aloud using the number line to show how far to count back. Assign Reteaching Supplement 29.

ENRICHMENT **Family Math**
Have students and a family member make 2 sets of cards—one numbered 4-12 and the other numbered 1-3—shuffle each pile separately, then turn over the top card of each pile. Take turns. Subtract the smaller number from the larger and give the difference.

ount Backs and Zeros

> Count back as you drop the number being subtracted.

$$\begin{array}{r} 7 \\ 2 \\ \hline 5 \end{array}$$

7, 6, 5

> Pick up cubes to match the starting number.

se cubes. Count back to subtract.

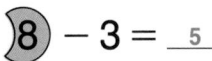

$8 - 3 = \underline{5}$ $6 - 2 = \underline{4}$

$6 - 3 = \underline{3}$ $7 - 1 = \underline{6}$

$7 - 3 = \underline{4}$ $5 - 2 = \underline{3}$

ubtract.

$$\begin{array}{r} 1 \\ -0 \\ \hline 1 \end{array} \qquad \begin{array}{r} 5 \\ -5 \\ \hline 0 \end{array} \qquad \begin{array}{r} 10 \\ -2 \\ \hline 8 \end{array}$$

| When you subtract all, you have 0 left. $6 - 6 = 0$ | When you subtract 0, you still have all. $6 - 0 = 6$ |

$$\begin{array}{r} 3 \\ -3 \\ \hline 0 \end{array} \quad \begin{array}{r} 5 \\ -3 \\ \hline 2 \end{array} \quad \begin{array}{r} 8 \\ -0 \\ \hline 8 \end{array} \quad \begin{array}{r} 6 \\ -3 \\ \hline 3 \end{array} \quad \begin{array}{r} 7 \\ -2 \\ \hline 5 \end{array} \quad \begin{array}{r} 11 \\ -2 \\ \hline 9 \end{array}$$

SE MENTAL MATH

What number am I? I am less than $9 - 3$.
I am greater than $1 + 2$. I am an even number.

My number is __4__.

---

3. PRACTICE AND APPLY

Basic	All
Average	All
Extended	All

PRACTICE

What do the numbers in the paws in Exercise 1 and 2 stand for? (the number you start with before you count back; the total number) *What happens when you subtract all?* (The difference is 0.) *What happens when you subtract 0?* (The difference is the number you started with.)

APPLY

USE MENTAL MATH

▶ **How are even numbers different from odd numbers?** (Possible answer: Even numbers end in either 2, 4, 6, 8, or 0; odd numbers end in 1, 3, 5, 7, or 9.)
▶ **How might you use punchout number cards to solve the riddle?** (Possible answer: As you read each clue, turn over any numbers that do not fit. You should have only 1 number showing after the last clue.)

4-1

LOSE AND ASSESS

HOW WHAT YOU KNOW

ave pairs of students choose a
mber between 4 and 8. Then have
em choose a card with − 0, − 1,
2, − 3, or − all written on it.
ave each pair draw a picture to
ustrate the subtraction exercise and
rite a number sentence to match.
fter students have finished, have
em describe their picture and
monstrate the counting back
volved in solving the problem.

| QUICK QUIZ |

Count back to subtract.

$$\begin{array}{ccccc} 8 & 6 & 7 & 4 & 5 \\ -2 & -6 & -0 & -1 & -3 \\ \hline (6) & (0) & (7) & (3) & (2) \end{array}$$

Subtraction Doubles

OBJECTIVE 4-2   To use the mental math technique of subtraction doubles to find differences

PREBOOK ACTIVITIES

QUICK REVIEW

Write the sum.

$3 + 3 = \underline{(6)}$ $4 + 4 = \underline{(8)}$ $5 + 5 = \underline{(10)}$

$2 + 2 = \underline{(4)}$ $7 + 7 = \underline{(14)}$ $1 + 1 = \underline{(2)}$

$9 + 9 = \underline{(18)}$ $6 + 6 = \underline{(12)}$ $8 + 8 = \underline{(16)}$

PRIOR KNOWLEDGE

What does the word double *mean?* (Possible answer: two of the same thing) *What kind of things do you think of when you hear the word* doubles? (Possible answers: twins, eyes, ears, fingers on two hands) List students' responses on the chalkboard.

COMMUNICATION

Discussing Math   Write the phrase **subtraction double** on the chalkboard. Show students 6 small counters and then cover them with one hand. Without lifting your hand, slide 3 counters into view. *How can you figure out how many counters are still under my hand?* (Possible answer: There were 6 counters all together. You moved 3 of them, so there must be 3 more under your hand.) Write $6 - 3 = 3$ on the board. *Explain why this is called a subtraction double.* (Two of the numbers are the same.) *How is a subtraction double like the add-to-check fact?* (Possible answer: The number being subtracted and the difference are the same as the two addends in the add-to-check fact.)

EXPLORE AND CONNECT

Materials: 10 Cube-A-Links in 2 colors for each pair
Alternative Materials: punchout square tiles
Grouping Suggestion: pairs

Write the following subtraction exercises on the chalkboard: $8 - 4, 6 - 3, 4 - 2, 10 - 5$. Have students take turns. One student uses the cubes to show the subtraction double and then writes the answer. The other student joins the cubes to show the add-to-check fact. Together they write an addition sentence for the subtraction double. *What do you notice about the numbers in subtraction doubles and add-to-check facts?* (Possible answer: 2 of the numbers are the same in each case. *Why are the subtraction doubles easier than other subtraction facts?* (Possible answer: The answer is always the same numb as the one being subtracted.)

CONNECTIONS   Use these anytime.

Problem of the Day

Logic   Sharon had 14 red and blue blocks. She had the same number of red blocks as she did blue ones. She gave her red blocks to a friend. How many red blocks did she give to her friend? (7) How many blue blocks did she keep? (7)

Counting Patterns

Use some cubes to help you complete the following pattern:

16, 8, 4, _____, _____ (2, 1)

What did you notice about the pattern? (Possible answer: The smaller of each two numbers is a subtraction double.)

Minute Math

Use doubles to find the answer. How many rabbits are there if there are 4 more legs than ears? (2 rabbits) How many more legs than ears do 3 rabbits have?   (6)

CLASSWORK AND HOMEWORK SUPPLEMENTS

Practice

Skills Maintenance   4-2

Name _____

Subtraction Doubles

Subtract.
Finish the add-to-check fact.

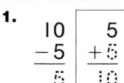

1.
10	5		8	4		16	8
−5	+5		−4	+4		−8	+8
5	10		4	8		8	16

2.
12	6		4	2		14	7
−6	+6		−2	+2		−7	+7
6	12		2	4		7	14

3.
2	1		18	9		6	3
−1	+1		−9	+9		−3	+3
1	2		9	18		3	6

Subtract. Finish the add-to-check fact.
Then ring the subtraction doubles.

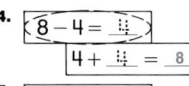

4. $8 - 4 = 4$ $10 - 5 = 5$
   $4 + 4 = 8$ $5 + 5 = 10$

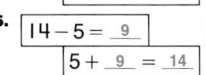

5. $14 - 5 = 9$ $16 - 8 = 8$
   $5 + 9 = 14$ $8 + 8 = 16$

30   Use with text pages 71–72.   PS-2

Building Thinking Skills

Number Sense   4-2

Name _____

Double Two = Four

Read each question.
Write the subtraction sentence.
Write the add-to-check fact.

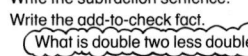

What is double two less double one?

$4 - 2 = 2$ $2 + 2 = 4$

1. What is double four less double two?

$8 - 4 = 4$ $4 + 4 = 8$

2. What is double six less double three?

$12 - 6 = 6$ $6 + 6 = 12$

3. What is double five less double two plus one?

$10 - 5 = 5$ $5 + 5 = 10$

4. What is double nine less double four plus one?

$18 - 9 = 9$ $9 + 9 = 18$

5. Make up your own. Give it to a friend to solve.

30   Use with text pages 71–72.   TS-2

Reteaching

Skills Review   4-2

Name _____

Subtraction Doubles

Subtract the doubles in the clouds. Finish the add-to-check
umbrellas. Draw a line between the clouds
and the matching umbrella facts.

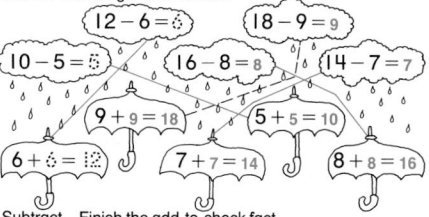

$12 - 6 = 6$ $18 - 9 = 9$
$10 - 5 = 5$ $16 - 8 = 8$ $14 - 7 = 7$
$9 + 9 = 18$ $5 + 5 = 10$
$6 + 6 = 12$ $7 + 7 = 14$ $8 + 8 = 16$

Subtract. Finish the add-to-check fact.

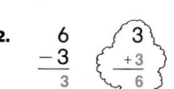 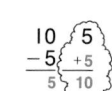 

1.
8	4		12	6		4	2
−4	+4		−6	+6		−2	+2
4	8		6	12		2	4

2.
6	3		10	5		18	9
−3	+3		−5	+5		−9	+9
3	6		5	10		9	18

30   Use with text pages 71–72.   RS-2

Challenges

Reading Math   4-2

Name _____

Subtraction Riddles

Complete the subtraction sentences in the box.
Look at the words next to your answers.
Each word matches a number.
Write these words under the numbers below.
What does the subtraction riddle say?
Read it to a friend.

$6 - 3 = 3$	your		$10 - 5 = 5$	What is
$16 - 8 = 8$	Ginger		$4 - 2 = 2$	name
$12 - 6 = 6$	bite		$2 - 1 = 1$	No
$8 - 4 = 4$	Does		$18 - 9 = 9$	snaps
$14 - 7 = 7$	dog's			

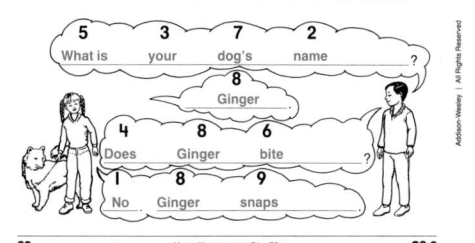

| 5 | 3 | 7 | 2 |
| What is | your | dog's | name | ? |

8
Ginger

| 4 | 8 | 8 |
| Does | Ginger | bite | ? |

| 1 | 8 | 9 |
| No | Ginger | snaps |

30   Use with text pages 71–72.   CS-2

OPTIONS FOR INDIVIDUAL NEEDS

Basic

Exercises All

Supplements
Reteaching 30 or
Practice 30
Thinking Skills 30

Average

Exercises All

Supplements
Practice 30
Challenges 30 or
Thinking Skills 30

Extended

Exercises All

Supplements
Challenges 30
Thinking Skills 30

Other Resources:
Mathematics Their Way, pp.
180-183, 192-194, 248-249
Workjobs II, pp. 104-105,
114-115
Workjobs For Parents, pp.
105-114
*Developing Number Concepts
with Unifix Cubes*, pp.
105-114
Mathematics Book A, pp.
29-30

4-2

LESSON PLAN 4-2

OBJECTIVE 4-2
To use the mental math technique of subtraction doubles to find differences

> **Materials:** 18 Cube-A-Links
>
> **Alternative Materials:** punchout square tiles
>
> **Grouping Suggestions:** pairs, individual work

1. MOTIVATE AND TEACH

LEARN ABOUT IT

Have students use cubes to model the example at the top of page 71.
▶ **What do you notice about two of the parts of the subtraction doubles?** (They are the same number.)
▶ **Why do you use add-to-check facts?** (to check subtraction facts)
▶ **Can you use an add-to-check fact when your subtraction fact is not a double?** (Yes, you can use an add-to-check fact to check any subtraction fact.)
Have students look at the add-to-check facts for subtraction doubles at the top of page 71.
▶ **What pattern do you notice in the sums of the add-to-check facts?** (Possible answer: They are skip counted by 2s; they are all even numbers.)

2. CHECK UNDERSTANDING

ERROR ALERT Using an incorrect difference to complete an add-to-check fact.

Name _____

Subtraction Doubles

The add-to-check fact helps you find the answer. Remember the double!

Subtract. Finish the add-to-check fact.

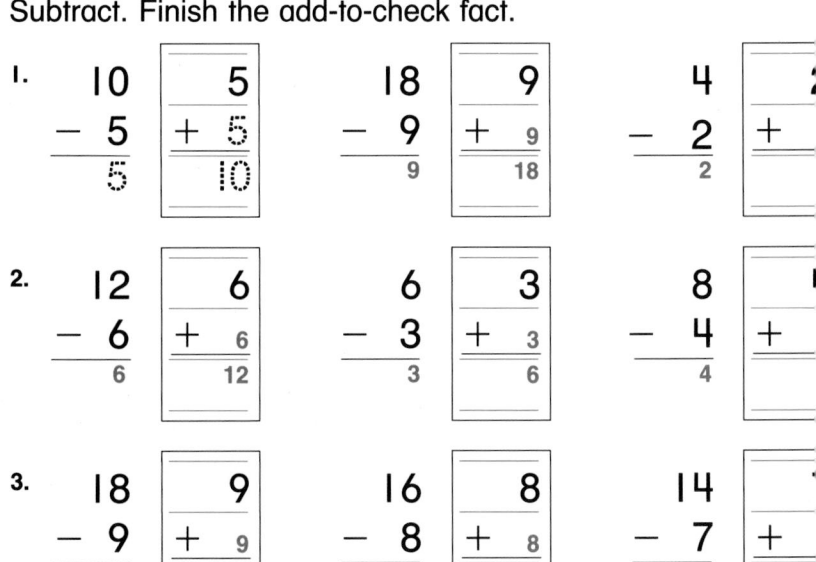

1.
$\begin{array}{r} 10 \\ -\ 5 \\ \hline 5 \end{array}$ $\begin{array}{r} 5 \\ +\ 5 \\ \hline 10 \end{array}$ $\begin{array}{r} 18 \\ -\ 9 \\ \hline 9 \end{array}$ $\begin{array}{r} 9 \\ +\ 9 \\ \hline 18 \end{array}$ $\begin{array}{r} 4 \\ -\ 2 \\ \hline 2 \end{array}$ $+$

2.
$\begin{array}{r} 12 \\ -\ 6 \\ \hline 6 \end{array}$ $\begin{array}{r} 6 \\ +\ 6 \\ \hline 12 \end{array}$ $\begin{array}{r} 6 \\ -\ 3 \\ \hline 3 \end{array}$ $\begin{array}{r} 3 \\ +\ 3 \\ \hline 6 \end{array}$ $\begin{array}{r} 8 \\ -\ 4 \\ \hline 4 \end{array}$ $+$

3.
$\begin{array}{r} 18 \\ -\ 9 \\ \hline 9 \end{array}$ $\begin{array}{r} 9 \\ +\ 9 \\ \hline 18 \end{array}$ $\begin{array}{r} 16 \\ -\ 8 \\ \hline 8 \end{array}$ $\begin{array}{r} 8 \\ +\ 8 \\ \hline 16 \end{array}$ $\begin{array}{r} 14 \\ -\ 7 \\ \hline 7 \end{array}$ $+$

Chapter 4   (seventy-one)

TEACHING OPTIONS

RETEACHING TIPS Review subtracting doubles using cubes. Have students separate cubes to form subtraction doubles and join them again to make the matching add-to-check facts. Then have them write the facts and use cubes to check their answers. Assign Reteaching Supplement 30.

ENRICHMENT Have students solve the following problem. Some birds were sitting on a fence. 4 of them flew away. Now there are half as many birds on the fence as there were at the beginning. How many birds were on the fence at first? How did you find the answer? (8; use subtraction doubles)

ubtract. Finish the
dd-to-check fact.
hen ring the subtraction
oubles.

$(10 - 5 = 5)$	$(16 - 8 = 8)$	$6 - 0 = 6$
$5 + 5 = 10$	$8 + 8 = 16$	$0 + 6 = 6$

$7 - 3 = 4$	$11 - 3 = 8$	$(18 - 9 = 9)$
$3 + 4 = 7$	$3 + 8 = 11$	$9 + 9 = 18$

$9 - 0 = 9$	$(12 - 6 = 6)$	$(14 - 7 = 7)$
$0 + 9 = 9$	$6 + 6 = 12$	$7 + 7 = 14$

HOW WITH CUBES

ubtract. Write the add-to-check fact.
se cubes to check.

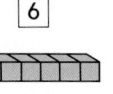   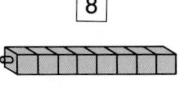

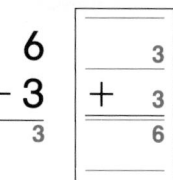

$$\begin{array}{r} 6 \\ -3 \\ \hline 3 \end{array} \quad \begin{array}{r} 3 \\ + 3 \\ \hline 6 \end{array}$$

5.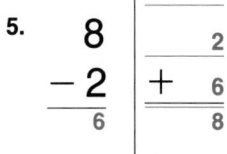

$$\begin{array}{r} 8 \\ -2 \\ \hline 6 \end{array} \quad \begin{array}{r} 2 \\ + 6 \\ \hline 8 \end{array}$$

6.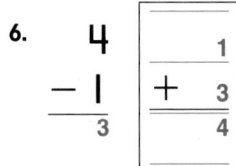

$$\begin{array}{r} 4 \\ -1 \\ \hline 3 \end{array} \quad \begin{array}{r} 1 \\ + 3 \\ \hline 4 \end{array}$$

3. PRACTICE AND APPLY

Basic	All
Average	All
Extended	All

PRACTICE

How many subtraction doubles did you find on page 72? (5)

APPLY

SHOW WITH CUBES ▶ **How can you use cubes to help you subtract?** (Possible answer: Snap off cubes for the number you are subtracting. Count how many are left to find the difference.)
▶ **Which add-to-check fact will have the greatest sum? Why?** (2 + 6 = 8; because you start with the greatest number of cubes)

4-2

LOSE AND ASSESS

HOW WHAT YOU KNOW

mind students of the chapter story, *ace Creature.* Suppose 8 creatures peared in the distance and then 4 sappeared. *How many creatures re left?* (4)? Have students work th partners and use cubes to model e action in similar subtraction ubles problems.

QUICK QUIZ

Subtract. Write the add-to-check fact.
$6 - 3 = (3)$ $14 - 7 = (7)$
$(3) + (3) = (6)$
$(7) + (7) = (14)$

Chapter 4 Lesson 2   **72**

Subtracting from 9 and 10

OBJECTIVE 4-3   To use the mental math techniques of subtracting from 9 and 10 to find differences

PREBOOK ACTIVITIES

QUICK REVIEW

As I call out a subtraction fact, hold up the number card that shows the answer.

7 − 1 (6)	5 − 2 (3)	8 − 0 (8)
6 − 3 (3)	7 − 2 (5)	4 − 3 (1)

PRIOR KNOWLEDGE

Ask students to tell stories about how they use subtraction at home. Help students brainstorm by offering topics such as clearing things off the dinner table, taking toys away from the toy shelf, and taking slices of bread away from the loaf. Have students listen and summarize each other's stories to make sure they understand how subtraction is involved in each instance.

COMMUNICATION

Writing in Math   In their Math Journals, have students copy and complete each sentence using one of the following words: **subtract, sentence, zero, all.**

1. When you add two parts, you find the number in __(all)__ .

2. When you __(subtract)__ , you can find a missing part.

3. You can add to check a subtraction __(sentence)__ .

4. When you subtract a number from itself, you get __(zero)__ .

EXPLORE AND CONNECT

Materials: Cube-A-Links
Alternative Materials: counters
Grouping Suggestions: pairs

Provide each pair of students with a 9-train of cubes, paper, and pencils. One student snaps the train so that it has 2 parts and hands one part to the partner. *How many cubes did you begin with?* (9) *How many cubes did you give away?* (Answer will vary.) *How many cubes do you have left?* (Answers will vary.) *Write a subtraction sentence describing what happened to your 9-train.* Encourage students to check with their partner for agreement. Ask students to change roles and repeat the activity. If time permits, have students work similarly with 10-trains.

CONNECTIONS   Use these anytime.

Problem of the Day

Delivering Books   You and Sue must deliver 10 books. You deliver 6. Sue finishes the job. How many books did she deliver? (4) Did you count on or back or add or subtract for the answer?

Math Connection

Number Sense   Yana has 10 pennies in her bank. How many can she give away and still keep at least 5 pennies? (She can give away up to 5 pennies and still keep 5.)

Subject Integration

Science   You are doing an experiment to find out whether objects sink or float. Of the 9 objects you have tested, only 4 float. How many sink? (5) Try it. Write a subtraction sentence to match the result.

CLASSWORK AND HOMEWORK SUPPLEMENTS

Practice

Skills Maintenance   4-3

Name _____

Subtracting from 9 and 10

Subtract.

1. 10 −5 =5   9 −4 =5   10 −4 =6   10 −1 =9   9 −3 =6

2. 10 −9 =1   9 −2 =7   9 −7 =2   9 −1 =8   10 −3 =7

3. 9 −8 =1   10 −3 =7   10 −6 =4   9 −4 =5   10 −9 =1

4. 10 −4 =6   9 −7 =2   9 −5 =4   10 −2 =8   9 −3 =6

5. 10 −8 =2   9 −5 =4   10 −3 =7   10 −1 =9   9 −8 =1

6. 9 −1 =8   10 −4 =6   9 −9 =0   10 −7 =3   9 −6 =3

PS-2   Use with text pages 73–74.   31

Building Thinking Skills

Patterns   4-3

Name _____

Make a Number Pattern

Subtract.

10 − 3 = 7   10 − 5 = 5   10 − 6 = 4
10 − 8 = 2   10 − 7 = 3   10 − 4 = 6

1. Write the exercises above in order from the smallest difference to the largest difference.

10 −8 =2   10 −7 =3   10 −6 =4   10 −5 =5   10 −4 =6   10 −3 =7

2. What pattern do you see? Check one.

Each time you take away one less, the difference is one less. ☐
Each time you take away one less, the difference is one more. ☑

3. Subtract from 9. Make the same pattern as the one in Exercise 1.

9 −7 =2   9 −6 =3   9 −5 =4   9 −4 =5   9 −3 =6   9 −2 =7

4. Look at the two sets of exercises. Talk about the patterns with a partner.

TS-2   Use with text pages 73–74.   31

Reteaching

Skills Review   4-3

Name _____

Subtracting from 9 and 10

How many are there in each part?
Subtract.

1. 7 3   6 2   6 2   8 2

10 − 7 = 3   10 − 8 = 2
10 − 3 = 7   10 − 2 = 8

2. 6 3   5 4

9 − 6 = 3   9 − 5 = 4
9 − 3 = 6   9 − 4 = 5

Subtract.

3. 10 −5 =5   10 −9 =1   10 −4 =6   10 −6 =4   10 −0 =10

4. 9 −2 =7   9 −7 =2   9 −9 =0   9 −8 =1   9 −1 =8

RS-2   Use with text pages 73–74.   31

Challenges

Critical Thinking   4-3

Name _____

Juggle the Numbers

Put each number in the correct place.
Use no other numbers.   Order may vary.

10 −7 =3 (3)
9 −5 =4
9 −3 =6
10 −9 =1
10 −2 =8

CS-2   Use with text pages 73–74.   31

OPTIONS FOR INDIVIDUAL NEEDS

Basic

Exercises All

Supplements
Reteaching 31 or
Practice 31
Challenges 31

Average

Exercises All

Supplements
Practice 31
Challenges 31 or
Thinking Skills 31

Extended

Exercises All

Supplements
Challenges 31
Thinking Skills 31

Other Resources:
Mathematics Their Way, pp. 221-224, 248-249.
Explorations, pp. 50-53
Workjobs II, pp. 104-110, 114-115
Workjobs For Parents, pp. 104-105, 114-115.
Mad Minute, pp. 16-20

4-3

LESSON PLAN 4-3

OBJECTIVE 4-3
To use the mental math techniques of subtracting from 9 and 10 to find differences

> **Materials:** 10-frames, counters, number lines
>
> **Grouping Suggestions:** pairs, individual work

1. MOTIVATE AND TEACH

LEARN ABOUT IT

Supply pairs of students with counters and 10-frames. Ask students to take turns finding facts with sums of 9 or 10, using the counters and 10-frames. Have them list their facts. Have students look at the sample at the top of page 73.

▶ **How does the 10-frame picture show the fact 10 − 4 = 6?** (There are 10 counters showing, 4 are being taken away, and 6 are left.)

▶ **What happens when you subtract 10 from 10 using 10-frames?** (Nothing would be left in the frames.)

▶ **How are the facts 9 − 4 and 10 − 5 the same?** (They both have a difference of 5.)

▶ **How can you use the 10-frame to help subtract from 9?** (Leave one section empty when you start.)

2. CHECK UNDERSTANDING

ERROR ALERT Miscounting the number of counters as they are removed from the 10-frame.

Name _____

Subtracting from 9 and 10

Take away 4 of the 10. That leaves 6.

$$\begin{array}{r} 10 \\ -\ 4 \\ \hline 6 \end{array}$$

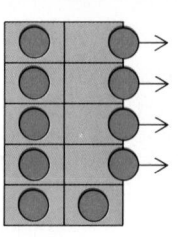

Work with a partner.
Use the 10-frame and counters.
Subtract. Write the differences.

Check students' work.

1. $\begin{array}{r} 10 \\ -\ 6 \\ \hline 4 \end{array}$ $\begin{array}{r} 10 \\ -\ 9 \\ \hline 1 \end{array}$ −

2. $\begin{array}{r} 10 \\ -\ 7 \\ \hline 3 \end{array}$ $\begin{array}{r} 10 \\ -\ 3 \\ \hline 7 \end{array}$ −

3. $\begin{array}{r} 9 \\ -\ 4 \\ \hline 5 \end{array}$ $\begin{array}{r} 10 \\ -\ 4 \\ \hline 6 \end{array}$ −

4. $9 - 5 = \underline{4}$ $10 - 4 = \underline{6}$

5. $10 - 9 = \underline{1}$ $9 - 4 = \underline{5}$

Chapter 4

(seventy-three)

TEACHING OPTIONS

RETEACHING TIPS Have students subtract by placing counters for the number in their 10-frames, then counting back aloud as they remove counters to be taken away. Have them write the subtraction sentence to match. Assign Reteaching Supplement 31.

COMPUTER Subtraction **Defenders, Gamco Industries ©** **1985** To review subtraction facts. Students race against the clock to solve subtraction problems. Difficulty Level 1 is subtracting from 6 or less. May be played at 5 different speed levels for about 10 minutes.

ubtract. Use the 10-frame to help.

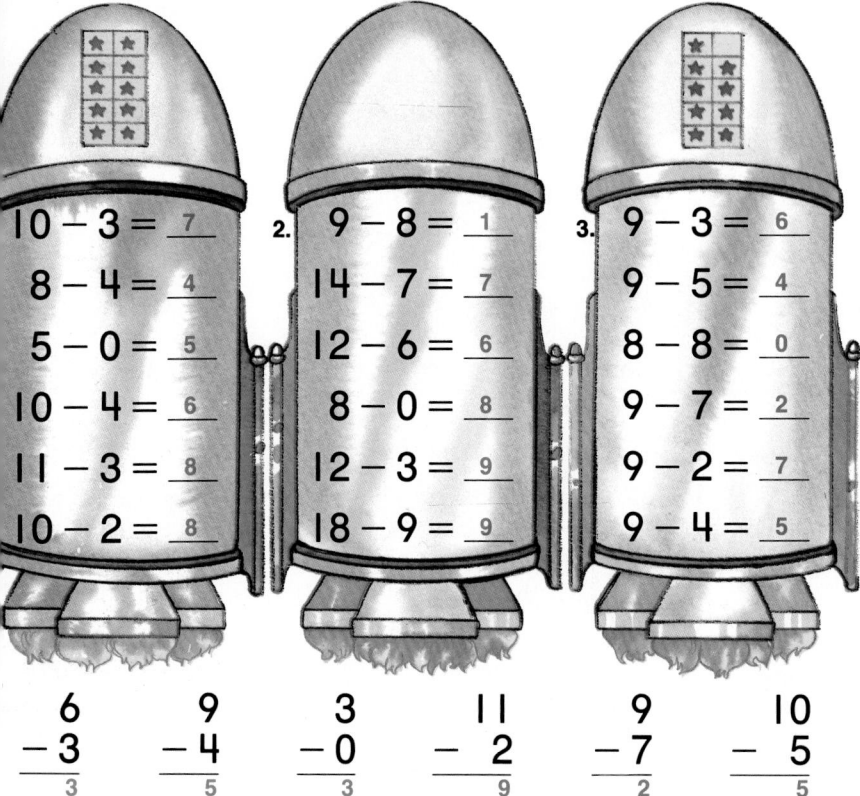

1. 10 − 3 = 7
8 − 4 = 4
5 − 0 = 5
10 − 4 = 6
11 − 3 = 8
10 − 2 = 8

2. 9 − 8 = 1
14 − 7 = 7
12 − 6 = 6
8 − 0 = 8
12 − 3 = 9
18 − 9 = 9

3. 9 − 3 = 6
9 − 5 = 4
8 − 8 = 0
9 − 7 = 2
9 − 2 = 7
9 − 4 = 5

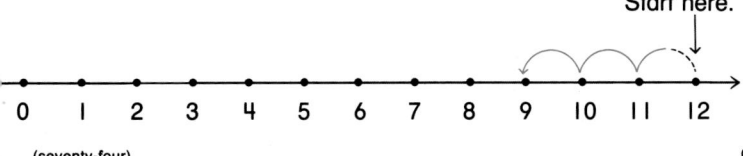

6
−3
‾‾
3

9
−4
‾‾
5

3
−0
‾‾
3

11
−2
‾‾
9

9
−7
‾‾
2

10
−5
‾‾
5

SE CRITICAL THINKING

Make jumps on the number line to show 12 − 3.

Start here.

0   1   2   3   4   5   6   7   8   9   10   11   12

(seventy-four)   Chapter 4

PRACTICE

Before students complete page 74, have them compare the exercises and the 10-frames in the rocket ships.
In Exercise 3, why does the 10-frame have only 9 stars? (All facts are subtraction from 9 or less.)

APPLY

USE CRITICAL THINKING
▶ **Explain how you will show 12 − 3 on the number line.** (Start at 12, show 3 jumps back.)
▶ **At what number do you start counting the jumps?** (11) **Why?** (Possible answer: You have not jumped yet when you are on 12; your first jump is from 12 to 11.)
▶ **Compare how subtraction and addition are shown on the number line.** (addition—move right; subtraction—move left)

4-3

LOSE AND ASSESS

RITE WHAT YOU KNOW Ask
udents to use the chapter story
cture to describe the creature in
*ace Creature. How many eyes did
e 10-eyed creature have after 3
sappeared?* (7) Have students make
before and after drawing of the
eature and then write a number
ntence for the problem.

QUICK QUIZ

Find the difference.

10	10	9	9	10	10
− 8	− 4	− 3	− 5	− 5	− 2
(2)	(6)	(6)	(4)	(5)	(8)

Chapter 4 Lesson 3   **74**

Problem Solving: Understanding the Operations/Probability

OBJECTIVE 4-4   To understand the operation of subtraction by comparing; to tell which event is more, less, or

PREBOOK ACTIVITIES

QUICK REVIEW

Subtract.

5	8	9	4	11	10	8	7	10
−3	−0	−5	−4	− 6	− 7	−3	−2	− 9
(2)	(8)	(4)	(0)	(5)	(3)	(5)	(5)	(1)

PRIOR KNOWLEDGE

Present the following story: *6 books were on the table. Paola took 2 books. How many books were left? Is this an addition story or a subtraction story? How do you know?* (a subtraction story; some part is being taken away; the question asks how many are left) *How can you solve the problem using counters?* (Put out 6 counters, then take away 2; 4 are left.) *Do we always subtract to solve a take-away story?* (yes) Tell students they will learn about another kind of story that is solved by subtracting.

COMMUNICATION

Reading and Discussing Math Write the words **probability, more likely, less likely,** and **equally likely** on the chalkboard. Read the words aloud and explain that the **probability** of something is the chance that it will happen. Give students an example: *If you have 5 pennies and 1 dime in your pocket and you pull out 1 coin, which coin is it more likely to be? Why?* (It is more likely to be a penny; since there are more pennies, your chances of pulling out a penny are greater.) Present similar situations to discuss the terms **less likely** and **equally likely.**

EXPLORE AND CONNECT

COOPERATIVE ACTIVITY

Grouping Suggestion: small groups
Finish the number sentence.
There were 7 puppies at the pet store.
There were 4 kittens at the pet store.
How many more puppies than kittens were there?
7 ◯ _____ ▢ _____   (7 − 4 = 3)

TEACHING ACTIONS

  ▶ **What are we trying to find out?** (how many more puppies there were than kittens)
  ▶ **What data do we need to solve the problem?** (the number of puppies; the number of kittens; 7 and 4)

  ▶ **In this story we are comparing, or finding the difference between the number of puppies and the number of kittens. Should your plan be to add or subtract?** (subtract)
▶ **How can you use counters to help you solve the problem?** (Show 7 counters for the puppies and 4 counters for the kittens. Compare the amounts by matching up the counters. Count how many more counters for puppies there are.)
▶ **What should you do next?** (Complete the number sentence.)

AFTER ▶ **How can you check your answer?** (Possible answer: Reread the story and see if the answer makes sense.)
Have students work in small groups to create another comparison subtraction story and to model it with counters.

CONNECTIONS   Use these anytime.

Problem of the Day

Understanding the Operation
Choose the number sentence that matches the story.
Sharon found 9 seashells.
Pele found 4 seashells.
How many more seashells did Sharon find?
9 + 4 = 13 9 − 4 = 5 (9 − 4 = 5)

Subject Integration

Language Arts Make up a subtraction story to compare the amounts of 2 kinds of objects in your desk. Show the objects to another student and tell your story. Ask your classmate to write the matching number sentence.

Creative Thinking

Probability Pretend that you tossed a coin 20 times. How many times do you think it will land heads up? Write your prediction. Now get a coin and try it. How many times did it land heads up? How close was your prediction?

ually likely to occur

CLASSWORK AND HOMEWORK SUPPLEMENTS

Practice
Problem Solving   4-4

Name _____

Understanding the Operations

Read the story.
Then subtract.

1. There were 9 players on the team. 2 players hit home runs. How many players did not hit home runs?

$$\begin{array}{r} 9 \\ -2 \\ \hline 7 \end{array}$$

2. There were 3 first graders who jumped rope. There were 8 second graders who jumped rope, too. How many more second graders were there?

$$\begin{array}{r} 8 \\ -3 \\ \hline 5 \end{array}$$

3. There were 10 children on the T-ball team. 7 were boys. How many were girls?

$$\begin{array}{r} 10 \\ -7 \\ \hline 3 \end{array}$$

4. There were 4 boys and 7 girls on the soccer team. How many more girls were there?

$$\begin{array}{r} 7 \\ -4 \\ \hline 3 \end{array}$$

32   Use with text page 75.   **PS-2**

Building Thinking Skills
Problem Solving   4-4

Name _____

Sea Story

Look at the picture.
Write a number sentence to answer each question.

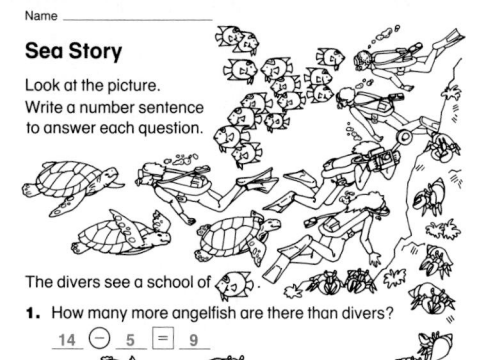

The divers see a school of 🐟.

1. How many more angelfish are there than divers?

$14 \ominus 5 = 9$

The 🐢 and the 🦀 have shells.

2. How many more hermit crabs are there than turtles?

$8 \ominus 3 = 5$

One diver has a 📷.

3. How many divers do not have cameras?

$5 \ominus 1 = 4$

4. How many more 🐟 are there than 🦀 ?

$14 \ominus 8 = 6$

32   Use with text page 75.   **TS-2**

Reteaching
Math Reasoning   4-4

Name _____

Probability

It is **more likely** to pull out a card with stripes.

It is **less likely** to pull out a card with dots.

It is **more likely** to pull out a card with dots.

It is **less likely** to pull out a card with stripes.

1. Draw 🔲 or ⬜ so you are **more likely** to pull a 🔲.

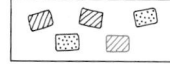

2. Draw 🔲 or ⬜ so you are **more likely** to pull a ⬜.

3. Draw 🔲 or ⬜ so you are **less likely** to pull a 🔲.

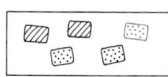

4. Draw 🔲 and ⬜ so you are **equally likely** to pull a 🔲 or a ⬜.

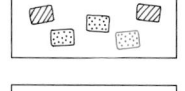

32   Use with text page 76.   **RS-2**

Challenges
Manipulatives   4-4

Name _____

Leapfrog

This is a game to play by yourself.
You need: a penny, a counter, and a pencil.

Rules: Put the counter on the middle frog.
Toss the penny.
If it lands **heads** up, make a tally mark under HEADS and move the counter one frog to the left.
If it lands **tails** up, make a tally mark under TAILS and move the counter one frog to the right.
Play until you reach one side or the other.
Predict whether you will toss heads or tails more often, or about the same number for each. Play 3 times.
Total the tallies. Was your prediction close?

	HEADS move left	Total	TAILS move right	Total
Game 1				
Game 2				
Game 3				

Heads   Answers will vary.   Tails

32   Use with text page 76.   **CS-2**

Addison-Wesley | All Rights Reserved

OPTIONS FOR INDIVIDUAL NEEDS

Basic

Exercises All

Supplements
Reteaching 32 or
Practice 32

Average

Exercises All

Supplements
Practice 32
Challenges 32 or
Thinking Skills 32

Extended

Exercises All

Supplements
Challenges 32
Thinking Skills 32

Other Resources:
Math in Stride, pp. 25-26
Mathematics Their Way, pp. 188-189

4-4

LESSON PLAN 4-4

OBJECTIVE 4-4
To understand the operation of subtraction by comparing; to tell which event is more, less, or equally likely to occur

---

Materials: 2-color counters; cubes of 2 colors, paper bags

---

1. MOTIVATE AND TEACH

LEARN ABOUT IT

Read the following stories. Have students use counters to act out the story and answer the *How many more?* question.

1. *Moon Rock story:* Two astronauts collected Moon rock samples. The first astronaut collected 9 samples; the second found 4. How many more rock samples did the first astronaut find than the second? (5)

2. *Sea story:* Back at their Moon base, the astronauts looked at Earth. They counted 5 seas and 2 oceans. How many more seas did they count? (3)

3. *Big City story:* Later, the astronauts saw lights from cities on Earth. One astronaut named 10 big cities; the other named 5. How many more cities did the first astronaut name? (5)

4. *Stars story:* One astronaut picked out 11 stars. The other astronaut picked 3. How many more stars did one astronaut pick than the other? (8)

▶ **Do we add or subtract to find out how many more? Why?** (Subtract, because we are comparing two numbers and finding the difference.

2. CHECK UNDERSTANDING

ERROR ALERT   Page 75   Adding instead of subtracting.
Page 76   Not understanding the terms *more, less,* and *equally likely.*

Name _____

Problem Solving
Understanding the Operations

Listen to each story. Use two-color counters to show it. Then subtract.

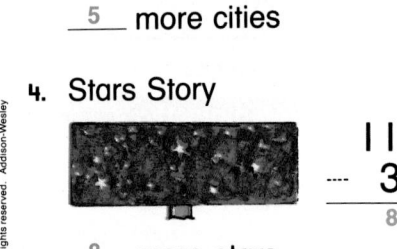

1. Moon Rock Story

$$\begin{array}{r} 9 \\ -\ 4 \\ \hline 5 \end{array}$$

___5___ more samples

2. Sea Story

$$\begin{array}{r} 5 \\ -\ 2 \\ \hline 3 \end{array}$$

___3___ more seas

3. Big City Story

$$\begin{array}{r} 10 \\ -\ 5 \\ \hline 5 \end{array}$$

___5___ more cities

4. Stars Story

$$\begin{array}{r} 11 \\ -\ 3 \\ \hline 8 \end{array}$$

___8___ more stars

Chapter 4

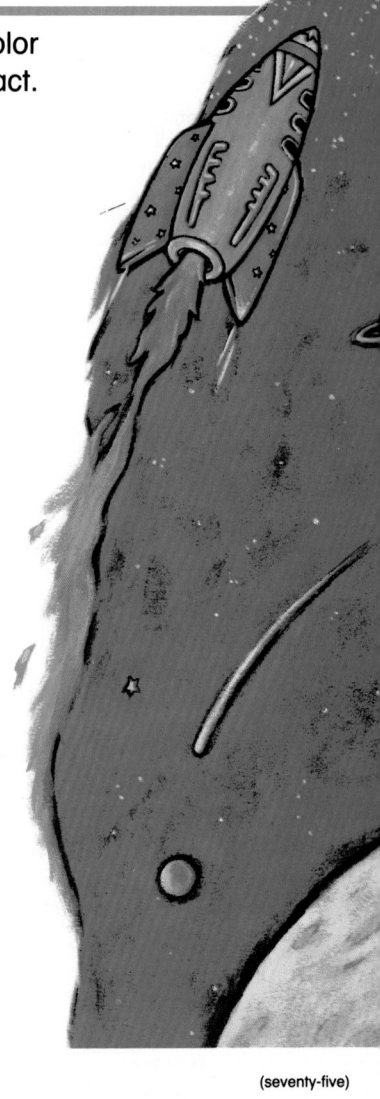

(seventy-five)

TEACHING OPTIONS

RETEACHING TIPS   Have pairs write two *How many more?* subtraction stories and exchange and solve them using counters. Then have them write the matching number sentences. For help with probability, assign Reteaching Supplement 32.

ENRICHMENT   Have students draw collections of red, blue, and yellow cubes on a bag so that the probability of pulling out a red cube is more likely and the probability of pulling out a yellow cube is less likely. Have them share pictures and experiment with cubes to match.

---

robability

Work with a partner.

Draw or so you

are **more likely** to

pull a .

Students must draw
at least 1 red cube.

Draw or so you

are **more likely** to

pull a .

Students must draw at
least 2 blue cubes.

Draw or so you

are **less likely** to

pull a .

Students must draw at
least 1 blue cube.

Draw or so you

are **equally likely** to

pull a or a .

Students must draw 2 red cubes.

Tell why you drew what you did in ⭐. See teaching notes.

(seventy-six)   Chapter 4

4-4

3. PRACTICE AND APPLY

Basic	All
Average	All
Extended	All

Have students look at the problems on page 76. *How can you check if your answers make sense?* (Possible answer: Put the red and blue cubes shown into a bag. Pull out a cube and record the color. Do this many times to check which cube is more or less likely to be pulled out or if the cubes are equally likely to be pulled out.)

▶ **What does *more likely* mean?** (Possible answer: It means that the chances of some things' happening are greater.)

▶ **What term means just the opposite?** *(less likely)*

▶ **What does *equally likely* mean?** (Possible answer: It means that the chances of either thing's happening are the same.)

▶ **Why did you draw 2 red cubes in Exercise 4?** (Possible answer: you must have the same number of cubes of each color to be equally likely to pull red or blue.)

CLOSE AND ASSESS

TELL WHAT YOU KNOW Have small groups of students create comparison subtraction stories for the number sentences $11 - 4 = 7$. Then ask them to create a situation where something is more, less, or equally likely to occur. Have groups present both ideas to the class for feedback on how they can be solved.

QUICK QUIZ

Use cubes of 2 colors to act out the problems. Then subtract.

$10 - 4$	(6)	$9 - 2$	(7)
$7 - 1$	(6)	$11 - 8$	(3)
$8 - 6$	(2)	$10 - 7$	(3)

Counting Up to Subtract

OBJECTIVE 4-5   To use the mental math technique of counting up to find differences

PREBOOK ACTIVITIES

QUICK REVIEW

Subtract.

7 − 4 = (3)	18 − 9 = (9)	8 − 2 = (6)
9 − 4 = (5)	10 − 5 = (5)	10 − 9 = (1)
6 − 3 = (3)	14 − 7 = (7)	16 − 8 = (8)
8 − 0 = (8)	12 − 4 = (8)	11 − 3 = (8)

PRIOR KNOWLEDGE

Present a situation such as the following to help students recall subtracting facts where the numbers are close together.
6 clowns are juggling.
4 clowns fall down.
How many clowns are still juggling?   (2)
What did you do to find the answer? (subtracted 4 from 6)

COMMUNICATION

Listening and Discussing Math   Draw a ladder on the chalkboard and number each rung 0 through 10. Write the words **count up** and explain that the answers to some subtraction facts can be found by counting up from the smaller number. Write 7 − 6 = _____. *What number would you start on to count up?* (6) Point to the sixth rung on the ladder and count up to 7. Then write 1 to complete the fact. *As I say a subtraction expression, listen for the number you would start on to count up. Show that number with your fingers: 8 − 6* (6), *10 − 7* (7), *9 − 6* (6). Allow time for students to use the ladder to complete the subtraction expressions.

EXPLORE AND CONNECT

Materials: flashcards, 1 cube train for each pair
Grouping Suggestions: whole group, pairs
Write the following on flashcards: 10 − 8, 7 − 4, 6 − 3, 9 − 6. *Why might these be called count-ups?* (Possible answers: because the numbers are close together; because you can count up to find the answer) Call on students to count up as you point to each of the subtraction expressions.
Have students work in pairs. On the chalkboard, write 8 − 5 = 3. Have them make a cube train for the *whole* of this expression (8), then stand the train on end and pretend it is an elevator. Ask them to imagine that they are on floor 5 and need to get to floor 8. Have one partner move a finger up the cubes to the fifth cube. *Close your eyes and imagine the floor numbers lighting up as the elevator moves up to floor 8. Count the floors.* Have the other partner say the subtraction sentence 8 − 5 = 3.

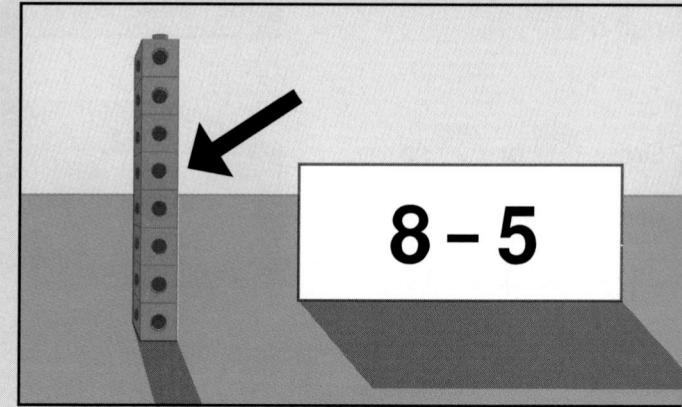

CONNECTIONS   Use these anytime.

Problem of the Day

Missing Data   Lisa had a bag of 9 marbles. The bag had a hole in it. Some of the marbles fell out. How many marbles does Lisa have now? What do you need to know to solve the problem? Supply the missing data and solve it. (how many marbles fell out)

Subject Integration

Physical Education   For each subtraction expression, jump the number of times you need to count up to find the answer.
12 − 9 (3),   5 − 2 (3),   10 − 9 (1),
7 − 5 (2),   11 − 9 (2),   8 − 5 (3)

Counting Patterns

Subtraction Patterns   Complete the patterns.
12, 10, 8,   (6)
14, 13, 12,   (11)
9, 6, 3,   (0)
11, 8, 5,   (2)

CLASSWORK AND HOMEWORK SUPPLEMENTS

OPTIONS FOR INDIVIDUAL NEEDS

Practice

Skills Maintenance 4-5

Name _____

Count Ups

Subtract.
Complete the add-to-check fact.

1.
$$\begin{array}{r} 10 \\ -7 \\ \hline 3 \end{array} \quad \begin{array}{r} 7 \\ +3 \\ \hline 10 \end{array} \qquad \begin{array}{r} 4 \\ -2 \\ \hline 2 \end{array} \quad \begin{array}{r} 2 \\ +2 \\ \hline 4 \end{array} \qquad \begin{array}{r} 9 \\ -6 \\ \hline 3 \end{array} \quad \begin{array}{r} 6 \\ +3 \\ \hline 9 \end{array}$$

2.
$$\begin{array}{r} 11 \\ -4 \\ \hline 7 \end{array} \quad \begin{array}{r} 4 \\ +7 \\ \hline 11 \end{array} \qquad \begin{array}{r} 12 \\ -9 \\ \hline 3 \end{array} \quad \begin{array}{r} 9 \\ +3 \\ \hline 12 \end{array} \qquad \begin{array}{r} 7 \\ -5 \\ \hline 2 \end{array} \quad \begin{array}{r} 5 \\ +2 \\ \hline 7 \end{array}$$

3.
$$\begin{array}{r} 8 \\ -5 \\ \hline 3 \end{array} \quad \begin{array}{r} 5 \\ +3 \\ \hline 8 \end{array} \qquad \begin{array}{r} 9 \\ -7 \\ \hline 2 \end{array} \quad \begin{array}{r} 7 \\ +2 \\ \hline 9 \end{array} \qquad \begin{array}{r} 6 \\ -5 \\ \hline 1 \end{array} \quad \begin{array}{r} 5 \\ +1 \\ \hline 6 \end{array}$$

4.
$$\begin{array}{r} 12 \\ -8 \\ \hline 4 \end{array} \quad \begin{array}{r} 8 \\ +4 \\ \hline 12 \end{array} \qquad \begin{array}{r} 5 \\ -4 \\ \hline 1 \end{array} \quad \begin{array}{r} 4 \\ +1 \\ \hline 5 \end{array} \qquad \begin{array}{r} 3 \\ -2 \\ \hline 1 \end{array} \quad \begin{array}{r} 2 \\ +1 \\ \hline 3 \end{array}$$

5.
$$\begin{array}{r} 11 \\ -5 \\ \hline 6 \end{array} \quad \begin{array}{r} 5 \\ +6 \\ \hline 11 \end{array} \qquad \begin{array}{r} 8 \\ -6 \\ \hline 2 \end{array} \quad \begin{array}{r} 6 \\ +2 \\ \hline 8 \end{array} \qquad \begin{array}{r} 10 \\ -4 \\ \hline 6 \end{array} \quad \begin{array}{r} 4 \\ +6 \\ \hline 10 \end{array}$$

6.
$$\begin{array}{r} 7 \\ -4 \\ \hline 3 \end{array} \quad \begin{array}{r} 4 \\ +3 \\ \hline 7 \end{array} \qquad \begin{array}{r} 6 \\ -2 \\ \hline 4 \end{array} \quad \begin{array}{r} 2 \\ +4 \\ \hline 6 \end{array} \qquad \begin{array}{r} 5 \\ -3 \\ \hline 2 \end{array} \quad \begin{array}{r} 3 \\ +2 \\ \hline 5 \end{array}$$

PS-2 Use with text pages 77 – 78. 33

Building Thinking Skills

Number Sense 4-5

Name _____

Which One?

When the number you are subtracting is 1 less, the difference is 1.

1. Ring facts with a difference of 1.
Tell how you know. Subtract to check.

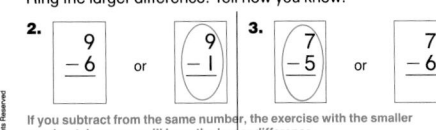

Ring the larger difference. Tell how you know.

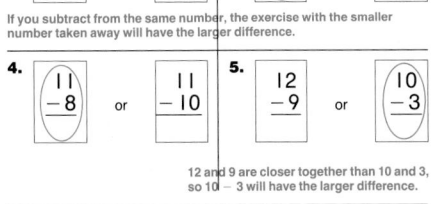

2. 9 − 6 or ⑨ − 1   3. ⑦ − 5 or 7 − 6

If you subtract from the same number, the exercise with the smaller number taken away will have the larger difference.

4. ⑪ − 8 or 11 − 10   5. 12 − 9 or ⑩ − 3

12 and 9 are closer together than 10 and 3, so 10 − 3 will have the larger difference.

TS-2 Use with text pages 77 – 78. 33

Reteaching

Skills Review 4-5

Name _____

Count Ups

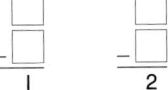

$$\begin{array}{r} 12 \\ -9 \\ \hline 3 \end{array} \quad \begin{array}{r} 9 \\ +3 \\ \hline 12 \end{array} \qquad \begin{array}{r} 11 \\ -9 \\ \hline 2 \end{array} \quad \begin{array}{r} 9 \\ +2 \\ \hline 11 \end{array}$$

Count up to subtract.

1.
$$\begin{array}{r} 11 \\ -8 \\ \hline 3 \end{array} \quad \begin{array}{r} 7 \\ -4 \\ \hline 3 \end{array} \quad \begin{array}{r} 10 \\ -8 \\ \hline 2 \end{array} \quad \begin{array}{r} 8 \\ -7 \\ \hline 1 \end{array} \quad \begin{array}{r} 9 \\ -6 \\ \hline 3 \end{array}$$

2.
$$\begin{array}{r} 6 \\ -3 \\ \hline 3 \end{array} \quad \begin{array}{r} 10 \\ -9 \\ \hline 1 \end{array} \quad \begin{array}{r} 5 \\ -2 \\ \hline 3 \end{array} \quad \begin{array}{r} 4 \\ -2 \\ \hline 2 \end{array} \quad \begin{array}{r} 2 \\ -1 \\ \hline 1 \end{array}$$

3.
$$\begin{array}{r} 3 \\ -1 \\ \hline 2 \end{array} \quad \begin{array}{r} 7 \\ -6 \\ \hline 1 \end{array} \quad \begin{array}{r} 8 \\ -6 \\ \hline 2 \end{array} \quad \begin{array}{r} 9 \\ -7 \\ \hline 2 \end{array} \quad \begin{array}{r} 6 \\ -4 \\ \hline 2 \end{array}$$

4.
$$\begin{array}{r} 8 \\ -5 \\ \hline 3 \end{array} \quad \begin{array}{r} 5 \\ -4 \\ \hline 1 \end{array} \quad \begin{array}{r} 10 \\ -7 \\ \hline 3 \end{array} \quad \begin{array}{r} 3 \\ -2 \\ \hline 1 \end{array} \quad \begin{array}{r} 4 \\ -1 \\ \hline 3 \end{array}$$

RS-2 Use with text pages 77 – 78. 33

Challenges

Creative Thinking 4-5

Name _____

It's a Fact

Write your own subtraction fact for each difference.

Answers will vary.

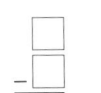
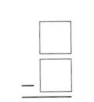
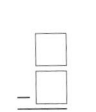
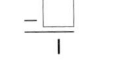
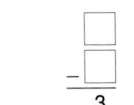

CS-2 Use with text pages 77 – 78. 33

OPTIONS FOR INDIVIDUAL NEEDS

Basic

Exercises All

Supplements
Reteaching 33 or
Practice 33
Challenges 33

Average

Exercises All

Supplements
Practice 33
Challenges 33 or
Thinking Skills 33

Extended

Exercises All

Supplements
Challenges 33
Thinking Skills 33

Other Resources:
Mathematics Their Way, pp. 103-104, 109-111, 182-185, 192-194
Explorations, pp. 50-53
Workjobs II, pp. 102-111
Mathematics Book A, pp. 29-30

4-5

LESSON PLAN 4-5

OBJECTIVE 4-5
To use the mental math technique of counting up to find differences

> **Materials:** 12 cubes per student, count-ups flipover punchouts, number cubes 1–6 and 5–12
>
> **Grouping Suggestions:** whole group, cooperative learning groups of 3

1. MOTIVATE AND TEACH

LEARN ABOUT IT

Write 5 − 3 on the chalkboard. Hold a stack of 5 cubes vertically. Call on a student to point to the third cube and count up to the fifth one. *What answer do you get?* (2)
▶ **When is it helpful to count up to solve a subtraction fact?** (Possible answers: when you do not know the answer; when the numbers of the fact are close together)
Repeat this activity with 9 − 6.
Have students solve the sample exercise on page 77 by using the spacecraft elevator.
▶ **How do you know where to begin counting in a count-up fact?** (Possible answer: Begin with the number that is less.)
▶ **How can you use cube trains to help complete the count-up facts?** (Possible answer: Build an elevator with the same number of cubes as the first number; start at the cube that matches the second number, count up to find the answer.)
▶ **How do you know when your add-to-check fact is correct?** (The answer is the same as the first number in your count-up fact.)

2. CHECK UNDERSTANDING

ERROR ALERT Including the starting number when counting up, so that the answer is one more than it should be.

Name _____

Counting Up to Subtract

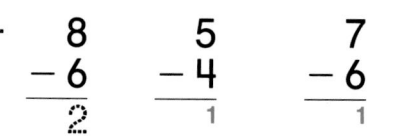

Add-to-Check Fact

Count up to subtract.

1.
$\begin{array}{r} 8 \\ -6 \\ \hline 2 \end{array}$
$\begin{array}{r} 5 \\ -4 \\ \hline 1 \end{array}$
$\begin{array}{r} 7 \\ -6 \\ \hline 1 \end{array}$
$\begin{array}{r} 11 \\ -8 \\ \hline 3 \end{array}$
$\begin{array}{r} 9 \\ -6 \\ \hline 3 \end{array}$

2.
$\begin{array}{r} 9 \\ -8 \\ \hline 1 \end{array}$
$\begin{array}{r} 6 \\ -4 \\ \hline 2 \end{array}$
$\begin{array}{r} 10 \\ -8 \\ \hline 2 \end{array}$
$\begin{array}{r} 8 \\ -5 \\ \hline 3 \end{array}$
$\begin{array}{r} 7 \\ -4 \\ \hline 3 \end{array}$

3.
$\begin{array}{r} 5 \\ -3 \\ \hline 2 \end{array}$
$\begin{array}{r} 8 \\ -7 \\ \hline 1 \end{array}$
$\begin{array}{r} 11 \\ -9 \\ \hline 2 \end{array}$
$\begin{array}{r} 9 \\ -8 \\ \hline 1 \end{array}$
$\begin{array}{r} 12 \\ -9 \\ \hline 3 \end{array}$

Answers may vary. Sample answers are shown

4. Write a count-up fact. Then write the add-to-check fact.

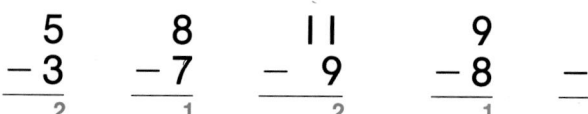

$\underline{11} - \underline{9} = \underline{2}$
$\underline{9} + \underline{2} = \underline{11}$

Chapter 4   (seventy-seven) 7

TEACHING OPTIONS

RETEACHING TIPS Draw and number 12 steps. Write *12 − 9 = ?* Have students count to find step 9 and use the steps to count to 12. Complete the fact. Students draw steps to count up as they use the count-ups flipovers. Use Reteaching Supplement 33.

ENRICHMENT Have pairs color paper strips to show count-up subtraction facts with the matching fact on the back. For example:

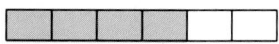

6 − 4 = 2
Use the strips to practice facts.

Subtract. Finish the add-to-check fact.

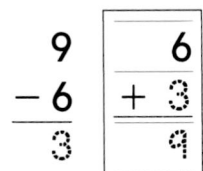
Look for count-up facts.

$$9 - 6 = 3 \qquad \begin{array}{r} 6 \\ + 3 \\ \hline 9 \end{array}$$

$$11 - 9 = 2 \qquad \begin{array}{r} 9 \\ + 2 \\ \hline 11 \end{array}$$

$$5 - 0 = 5 \qquad \begin{array}{r} 0 \\ + 5 \\ \hline 5 \end{array}$$

$$7 - 4 = 3 \qquad \begin{array}{r} 4 \\ + 3 \\ \hline 7 \end{array}$$

$$8 - 4 = 4 \qquad \begin{array}{r} 4 \\ + 4 \\ \hline 8 \end{array}$$

$$6 - 6 = 0 \qquad \begin{array}{r} 6 \\ + 0 \\ \hline 6 \end{array}$$

$$6 - 4 = \underline{2}$$

$$9 - 2 = \underline{7}$$

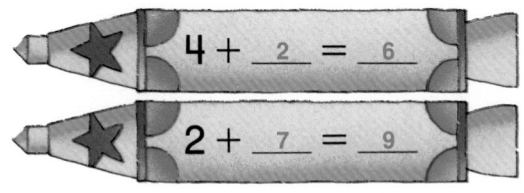

$$4 + \underline{2} = 6$$

$$2 + \underline{7} = 9$$

MIDCHAPTER REVIEW/QUIZ

Subtract.

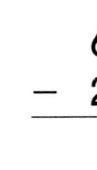

$$\begin{array}{r} 9 \\ - 1 \\ \hline 8 \end{array} \qquad \begin{array}{r} 8 \\ - 8 \\ \hline 0 \end{array} \qquad \begin{array}{r} 5 \\ - 0 \\ \hline 5 \end{array} \qquad \begin{array}{r} 10 \\ - 6 \\ \hline 4 \end{array} \qquad \begin{array}{r} 9 \\ - 4 \\ \hline 5 \end{array} \qquad \begin{array}{r} 10 \\ - 8 \\ \hline 2 \end{array}$$

Subtract. Finish the add-to-check fact.

$$\begin{array}{r} 8 \\ - 4 \\ \hline 4 \end{array} \qquad \begin{array}{r} 4 \\ + 4 \\ \hline 8 \end{array} \qquad \begin{array}{r} 6 \\ - 2 \\ \hline 4 \end{array} \qquad \begin{array}{r} 2 \\ + 4 \\ \hline 6 \end{array} \qquad \begin{array}{r} 10 \\ - 5 \\ \hline 5 \end{array} \qquad \begin{array}{r} 5 \\ + 5 \\ \hline 10 \end{array}$$

3. PRACTICE AND APPLY

Basic	All, Midchapter Review/Quiz
Average	All, Midchapter Review/Quiz
Extended	All, Midchapter Review/Quiz

PRACTICE

Explain what you are to do for Exercises 1 – 4. (Look for count-up facts; subtract; finish add-to-check facts.)

APPLY

▶ **Can you think of a way to add-to-check without rewriting the problem?** (Possible answer: Add the bottom number to the middle number to get the top number.)

MIDCHAPTER REVIEW/QUIZ

ITEM ANALYSIS The table correlates the Midchapter Review/Quiz items with lesson objectives.

Items	Objectives
1	4 – 1
2	4 – 2

4-5

CLOSE AND ASSESS

SHOW WHAT YOU KNOW

Review with students the chapter story, *Space Creature*. Seven pointed ears were on his head. Then 5 shriveled away into lumps instead. How would you find how many ears the creature had remaining? Have small groups work together to model the problem with cubes to find the answer.

QUICK QUIZ

Complete the count-up facts. Then add to check.

$$9 - 7 = \underline{(2)} \qquad 7 - 6 = \underline{(1)}$$
$$10 - 8 = \underline{(2)} \qquad 11 - 9 = \underline{(2)}$$
$$12 - 9 = \underline{(3)} \qquad 6 - 4 = \underline{(2)}$$

Fact Practice

OBJECTIVE 4-6   To practice the mental math techniques learned to find differences

PREBOOK ACTIVITIES

QUICK REVIEW

Subtract 3 from each number.
6, 8, 4, 9, 5   (3, 5, 1, 6, 2)
Subtract 4 from each number.
10, 7, 4, 6, 8   (6, 3, 0, 2, 4)

PRIOR KNOWLEDGE

Have students describe, in their own words, some of the strategies they have learned to help them subtract two numbers. (Possible responses: count back, subtract all or zero, count up, related subtraction facts and subtraction doubles) Discuss these, with examples, so that they are clearly understood.

COMMUNICATION

Listening and Writing in Math   Tell several subtraction stories such as the one below. After each, have students write the appropriate subtraction fact. Ask a volunteer to read the fact aloud and have the rest of the class check the answer. In other stories, vary the number of children playing, the number found, and the number still hiding. For the last number story, you might tell how many children had to go home.

10 children were playing hide and seek.
3 children were found.
How many were still hiding? $(10 - 3 = 7)$

EXPLORE AND CONNECT

Materials: subtraction flashcards, counters
Grouping Suggestion: cooperative learning groups of 3
Distribute to each group a set of subtraction flashcards that includes each of the following kinds of facts: count backs; zeros; 10-frame facts (10-facts, $9 - 5$, $9 - 4$); subtraction doubles; and count ups. Have one student read the flashcard aloud, a second student model the problem with counters, and a third lead a discussion of the subtraction strategy that might be used with that problem. After the discussion, the leader should summarize the group's ideas and check that each student agrees and understands the answer. Have students switch roles after every three or four flashcards. Collect the cards for later use.

CONNECTIONS   Use these anytime.

Problem of the Day

Logic   What number am I?
I am less than $7 - 2$.
I am more than $10 - 9$.
I am an odd number. (3)

Counting Patterns

What Is the Difference?   Subtract and find the pattern. Write 2 more facts to continue the pattern.

8	16	10	9
−3	−8	−5	−1
(5)	(8)	(5)	(8)

(Answers will vary.)

Subject Integration

Language Arts   Work with a partner. Write down your names. Add the vowels in the two names, then add the consonants. What is the difference between the number of vowels and consonants?

CLASSWORK AND HOMEWORK SUPPLEMENTS

Practice

Skills Maintenance 4-6

Name _____

Fact Practice

Write the differences.

1. 16 8 10 9 12
   −8 −4 −3 −6 −6
   ___ __ __ __ __
    8 4 7 3 6

2. 10 8 6 7 6
   −1 −3 −4 −6 −6
   __ __ __ __ __
    9 5 2 1 0

3. 9 12 5 7 9
   −3 −4 −2 −3 −2
   __ __ __ __ __
    6 8 3 4 7

4. 5 3 7 4 10
   −4 −3 −2 −0 −8
   __ __ __ __ __
    1 0 5 4 2

5. 14 8 4 6 5
   −7 −0 −1 −0 −1
   __ __ __ __ __
    7 8 3 6 4

6. 3 9 2 8 6
   −1 −5 −2 −7 −1
   __ __ __ __ __
    2 4 0 1 5

34   Use with text pages 79 – 80.   PS-2

Building Thinking Skills

Number Sense 4-6

Name _____

Subtraction Riddles

Can you find the mystery numbers?

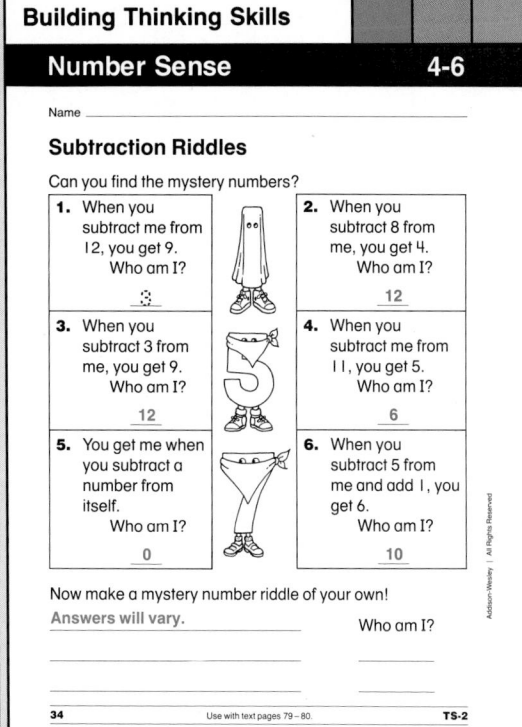

1. When you subtract me from 12, you get 9. Who am I? **3**

2. When you subtract 8 from me, you get 4. Who am I? **12**

3. When you subtract 3 from me, you get 9. Who am I? **12**

4. When you subtract me from 11, you get 5. Who am I? **6**

5. You get me when you subtract a number from itself. Who am I? **0**

6. When you subtract 5 from me and add 1, you get 6. Who am I? **10**

Now make a mystery number riddle of your own!
Answers will vary.   Who am I?

_____

34   Use with text pages 79 – 80.   TS-2

Reteaching

Skills Review 4-6

Name _____

Fact Practice

Match the puzzle pieces to complete the facts.

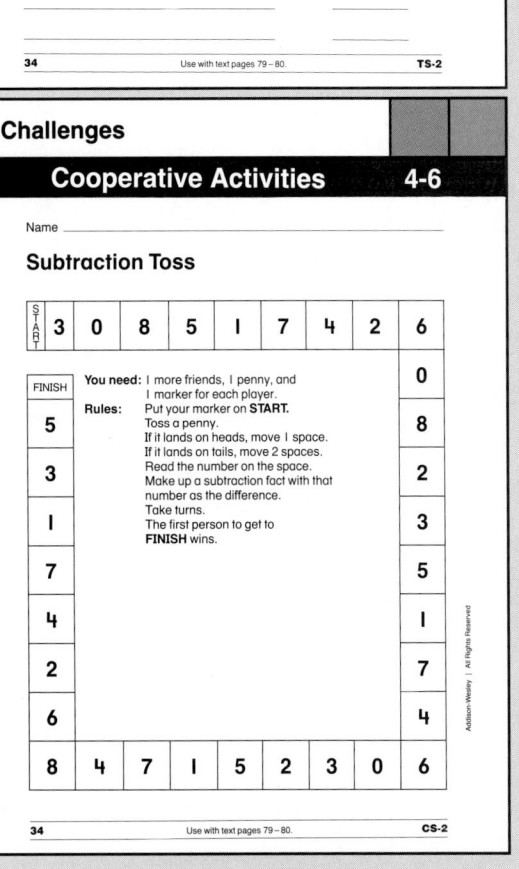

8 − 5   11 − 2   7 − 7   4   10 − 5
0   3   5   9 − 5   9

Write the differences.

1. 10 9 11 4 18
   −2 −4 −8 −4 −9
   __ __ __ __ __
    8 5 3 0 9

2. 8 12 7 11 10
   −0 −6 −4 −9 −6
   __ __ __ __ __
    8 6 3 2 4

3. 6 3 14 5 6
   −4 −0 −9 −4 −3
   __ __ __ __ __
    2 3 5 1 3

4. 16 10 9 12 8
   −8 −7 −6 −8 −6
   __ __ __ __ __
    8 3 3 4 2

34   Use with text pages 79 – 80.   RS-2

Challenges

Cooperative Activities 4-6

Name _____

Subtraction Toss

START	3	0	8	5	1	7	4	2	6

FINISH		0
5		8
3		2
1		3
7		5
4		1
2		7
6		4

8	4	7	1	5	2	3	0	6

You need: 1 more friends, 1 penny, and 1 marker for each player.

Rules: Put your marker on **START**. Toss a penny. If it lands on heads, move 1 space. If it lands on tails, move 2 spaces. Read the number on the space. Make up a subtraction fact with that number as the difference. Take turns. The first person to get to **FINISH** wins.

34   Use with text pages 79 – 80.   CS-2

OPTIONS FOR INDIVIDUAL NEEDS

Basic

Exercises All
Data Bank, p. 398

Supplements
Reteaching 34 or
Practice 34
Thinking Skills 34

Average

Exercises All
Data Bank, p. 398

Supplements
Practice 34
Challenges 34 or
Thinking Skills 34

Extended

Exercises All
Data Bank, p. 398

Supplements
Challenges 34
Thinking Skills 34

Other Resources:
Explorations, pp. 51, 63
Developing Number Concepts With Unifix Cubes, pp. 125-131
Mad Minute, pp. 16-20

4-6

OBJECTIVE 4-6
To practice the mental math techniques learned to find differences

Materials: TA 4 (Addition/Subtraction Mat), counters, subtraction flashcards, tape recorder

Grouping Suggestion: individual work, small groups

1. MOTIVATE AND TEACH

LEARN ABOUT IT

Write the following subtraction exercises on the chalkboard: $10 - 3 = \underline{(7)}$, $8 - 5 = \underline{(3)}$, $9 - 2 = \underline{(7)}$, $4 - 3 = \underline{(1)}$, and $9 - 6 = \underline{(3)}$. Ask students to find the differences; then ask volunteers to ring the exercises that have the same difference. ($10 - 3$ and $9 - 2$; $8 - 5$ and $9 - 6$)

Discuss how to complete rows 1 and 2 on page 79, using the worked-out exercise in row 1 as an example.

► **When did the doubles strategy help you in row 2?** ($16 - 8$, $10 - 5$)
► **When did the count ups strategy help in rows 1 and 2?** ($10 - 7$, $9 - 8$, $7 - 6$, $5 - 2$)
► **What is the pattern of the differences in row 3?** (0, 6, 4, 0, 6, 4)
► **Write a new subtraction fact that continues the pattern of differences in row 4.** (Possible responses: $4 - 1$, $5 - 2$, $9 - 6$, or $10 - 7$)

2. CHECK UNDERSTANDING

ERROR ALERT Using the wrong operation.

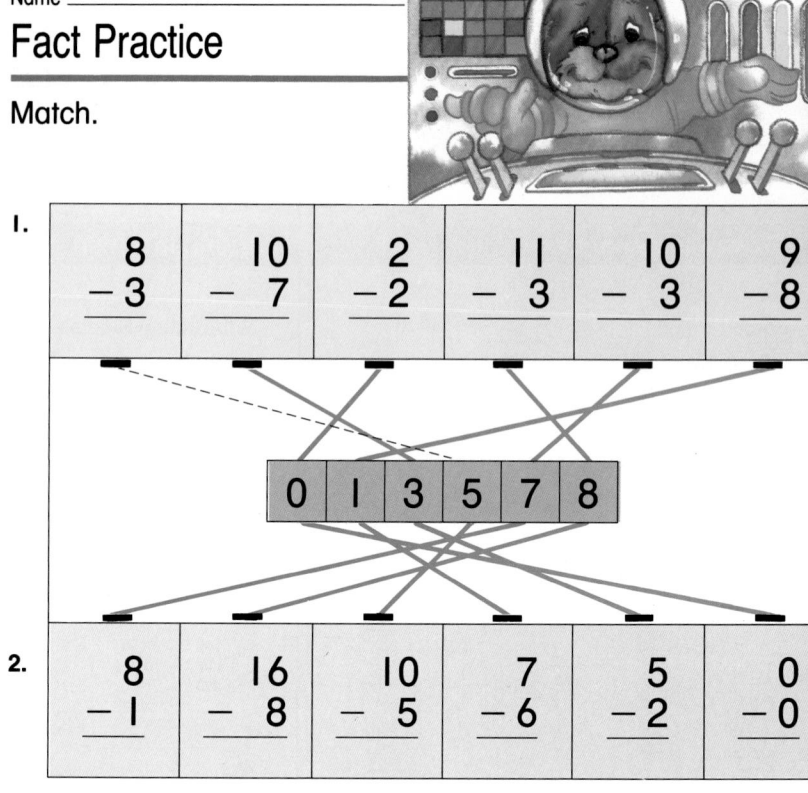

Name _____

Fact Practice

Match.

1.

| 8 -3 | 10 -7 | 2 -2 | 11 -3 | 10 -3 | 9 -8 |

| 0 | 1 | 3 | 5 | 7 | 8 |

2.

| 8 -1 | 16 -8 | 10 -5 | 7 -6 | 5 -2 | 0 -0 |

Write the differences.

3.

| 4 -4 | 9 -3 | 8 -4 | 3 -3 | 12 -6 | $-$ |
| 0 | 6 | 4 | 0 | 6 | |

4.

| 3 -0 | 6 -3 | 11 -2 | 8 -5 | 7 -4 | 1 $-$ |
| 3 | 3 | 9 | 3 | 3 | |

Chapter 4   (seventy-nine)

TEACHING OPTIONS

RETEACHING TIPS Discuss the meaning of addition and subtraction: parts given, total needed; total given, 1 part given, 1 part needed. Model $6 + 3 = 9$ and $9 - 6 = 3$ with counters and have students name the whole and the parts. Assign Reteaching Supplement 34.

COMPUTER Learning About Numbers, C & C Software © 1983 For practice in basic subtraction facts. In *Arithmetic Fun*, students use a story to practice single-digit subtraction. They should begin with Level 1 and advance to Level 2. The lesson requires 10-15 minutes.

ing all the ways to make each difference.

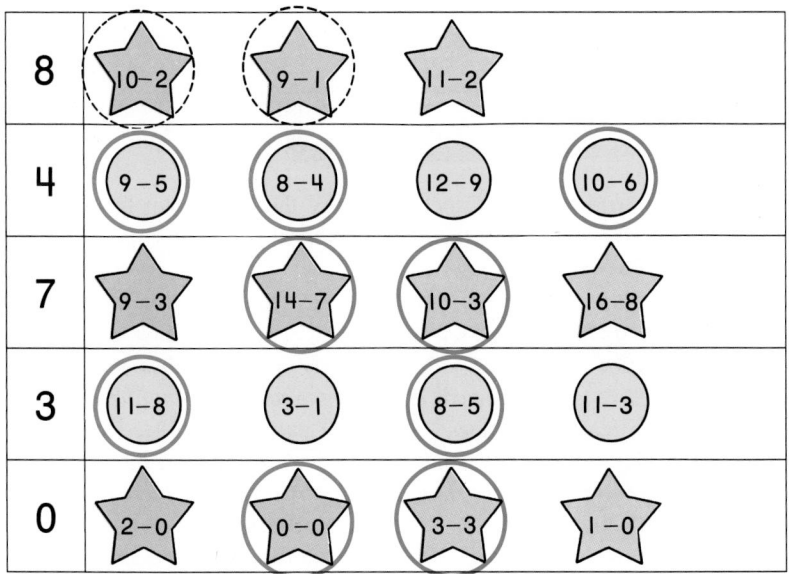

8	(10-2)	(9-1)	11-2	
4	(9-5)	(8-4)	(12-9)	(10-6)
7	9-3	(14-7)	(10-3)	16-8
3	(11-8)	(3-1)	(8-5)	(11-3)
0	2-0	(0-0)	(3-3)	1-0

ND THE DATA DATA BANK

How many days did the

3rd trip last? __9__ days

How many more days was the
2nd trip than the 1st trip?

__2__ more days

Data Bank How many
Americans in all have walked
on the moon? (See page 398.) __12__ Americans

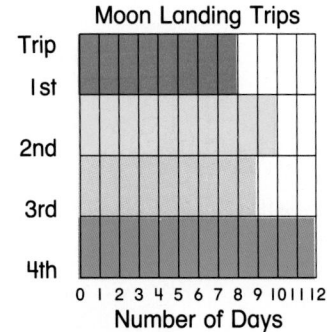

Moon Landing Trips

Trip
1st
2nd
3rd
4th

0 1 2 3 4 5 6 7 8 9 10 11 12
Number of Days

(eighty)

Chapter 4

3. PRACTICE AND APPLY

Basic	All
Average	All
Extended	All

PRACTICE

*How will you complete Exercises 1-6 on
page 80?* (Ring all the expressions that
have the difference shown at the
beginning of the row.)

APPLY

FIND THE DATA   Discuss what the
bar graph shows, and review the
meaning of ordinal numbers.
► **What was the difference in days
between the longest trip and the
shortest trip?** (4 days)
► **Using ordinal numbers, what will
you call the next moon landing trip?**
(the 5th)
► **Will you add or subtract to find the
answer to Exercise 9? Explain your
answer.** (Add; you put the numbers
together to find the total.)

LOSE AND ASSESS

AY WHAT YOU THINK   Give
oups of students a set of subtraction
ash cards for facts reviewed in this
sson. Have them practice these facts
y saying them and giving the
swers. Remind them to check with
assmates to make sure they
nderstand the facts. Then tape-record
udents as they give the facts.

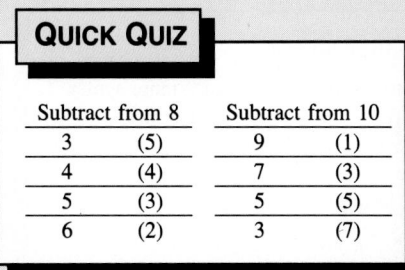

QUICK QUIZ

Subtract from 8		Subtract from 10	
3	(5)	9	(1)
4	(4)	7	(3)
5	(3)	5	(5)
6	(2)	3	(7)

More Related Subtraction Facts

OBJECTIVE 4-7 To model and finish related subtraction facts

PREBOOK ACTIVITIES

QUICK REVIEW

Subtract 2 from each number.

8	(6)	5	(3)	2	(0)	11	(9)
4	(2)	6	(4)	9	(7)	3	(1)
7	(5)	12	(10)	10	(8)		

PRIOR KNOWLEDGE

Write a number sentence for this story.
7 swans are swimming.
5 get out of the water.
How many swans are still swimming? $(7 - 5 = 2)$
Who will tell another story that shows $7 - 5 = 2$? (Answers will vary.) *Who will tell a story that shows $7 - 2 = 5$?*
(Answers will vary.)

COMMUNICATION

Reading and Disscussing Math Write the word *related* on the board and read it to the students. *How can two people be related?* (Possible answer: by having the same parents) *How can two animals be related?* (Possible answer: by being in the same family) Write this incomplete sentence on the chalkboard:
_____ and _____ are related because _____. Call on students to complete the sentence. *How can two subtraction facts be related?* (Possible answer: The numbers in the facts are the same, but two of the numbers trade places.) Write $10 - 3 = 7$, $10 - 4 = 6$, and $10 - 7 = 3$ on the chalkboard. *Identify the related subtraction facts.* $(10 - 3 = 7, 10 - 7 = 3)$

EXPLORE AND CONNECT

Materials: 12 Cube-A-Links of the same color for each pair
Alternative Materials: counters, blocks
Grouping Suggestion: pairs
Place a subtraction flashcard such as $11 - 3$ on the chalk ledge. Provide each pair with 12 cubes and have them make a cube train to show the whole. *How many cubes must your train have?* (11) *How can you find the answer using the cubes?* (Break off 3 cubes to see what part is left.) Place the flashcard $11 - 8$ on the chalk ledge. Have students use their cubes to find the answer. *How are these two number facts related?* (Both facts have the same numbers, but two of the numbers switch places.) Let students take turns telling each other a subtraction fact while their partner uses the cubes to show the related fact. Have them make a list of the related facts. Ask volunteers to read their related facts while other pairs raise their hands if these facts are on their lists.

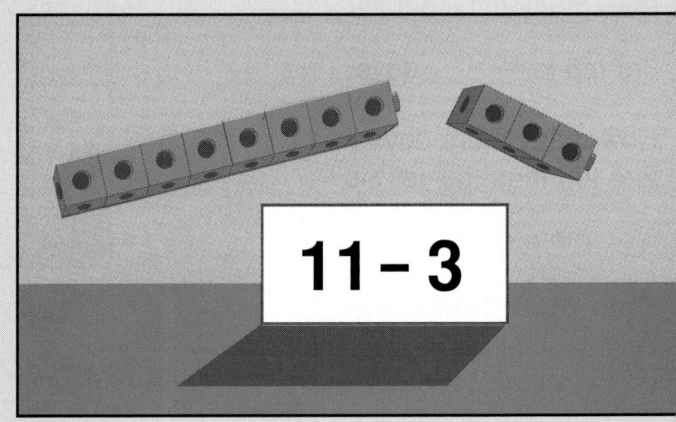

CONNECTIONS   Use these anytime.

Problem of the Day

Reasoning What question can you answer with this story? Show how you solved the problem.
Juan bought 10 flowers.
Jane planted 8 of the flowers.
(How many flowers are left?
$10 - 8 = 2$)

Number Sense

Comparing You need 2 more apples to have 1 dozen. If your friend had 3 fewer apples, he would have 7. Who has more apples—you or your friend? (You both have the same amount—10 apples.)

Math Connection

Money What coin combinations can you use to show 25 cents? (Possible answers: 1 quarter; 2 dimes, 1 nickel; 2 dimes, 5 pennies; 5 nickels; 25 pennies; 1 dime, 2 nickels, 5 pennies; 20 pennies, 1 nickel)

CLASSWORK AND HOMEWORK SUPPLEMENTS

Practice

Skills Maintenance 4-7

Name _____

More Related Subtraction Facts

Subtract.
Ring the related subtraction facts.

1. 9 − 6 = _3_
9 − 5 = _4_
9 − 3 = _6_

2. 11 − 4 = _7_
11 − 7 = _4_
11 − 9 = _2_

3. 7 − 4 = _3_
7 − 1 = _6_
7 − 6 = _1_

4. 5 − 2 = _3_
5 − 4 = _1_
5 − 3 = _2_

5. 12 − 4 = _8_
12 − 8 = _4_
12 − 6 = _6_

6. 8 − 2 = _6_
8 − 4 = _4_
8 − 6 = _2_

7. 6 − 5 = _1_
6 − 1 = _5_
6 − 6 = _0_

8. 10 − 5 = _5_
10 − 7 = _3_
10 − 3 = _7_

PS-2   Use with text pages 81–82.   **35**

Building Thinking Skills

Math Reasoning 4-7

Name _____

Relate the Facts

1. Write four subtraction sentences.
Use these numbers only.

| 4 | 5 | 7 | 11 | 12 |

11 − 4 = 7   12 − 5 = 7
11 − 7 = 4   12 − 7 = 5

2. Write five subtraction sentences.
Use these numbers only.

| 3 | 5 | 7 | 10 | 12 |

12 − 5 = 7   10 − 7 = 3
12 − 7 = 5   10 − 3 = 7
10 − 5 = 5

3. Write six subtraction sentences.
Use these numbers only.

| 4 | 5 | 9 | 13 | 14 |

14 − 9 = 5   13 − 9 = 4
14 − 5 = 9   13 − 4 = 9
9 − 4 = 5   9 − 5 = 4

TS-2   Use with text pages 81–82.   **35**

Reteaching

Skills Review 4-7

Name _____

More Related Subtraction Facts

Subtract.

1. 11 − 7 = 4
11 − 4 = 7

2. 10 − 6 = 4
10 − 4 = 6

3. 12 − 4 = 8
12 − 8 = 4

4. 9 − 6 = 3
9 − 3 = 6

Subtract.

5.
11 11 10 10 12 12
−2 −9 −7 −3 −9 −3
___ ___ ___ ___ ___ ___
 9   2   3   7   3   9

6.
9 9 7 7 8 8
−5 −4 −3 −4 −6 −2
__ __ __ __ __ __
 4 5 4 3 2 6

RS-2   Use with text pages 81–82.   **35**

Challenges

Cooperative Activities 4-7

Name _____

Doubles Bingo

You need: 1 friend, 2 number cubes, and 2 different-color crayons.
Rules: Choose a crayon. Color the FREE space on the game board.
Take turns tossing the cubes.
Use the numbers on the top of the cubes
to write a subtraction fact.

3 − 2 = 1
3 − 1 = 2

Find the related subtraction fact on the
game board and color that space.
If the space has been colored, you lose your turn.
If you roll 6 − 3, 4 − 2, or 2 − 1, color a **Doubles** space.
The first player to color 5 spaces in a row wins.

5 − 0 = 5	3 − 2 = 1	2 − 0 = 2	Doubles	4 − 0 = 4
Doubles	4 − 3 = 1	6 − 2 = 4	6 − 5 = 1	3 − 0 = 3
5 − 1 = 4	1 − 0 = 1	FREE	5 − 4 = 1	Doubles
5 − 3 = 2	Doubles	3 − 1 = 2	6 − 4 = 2	6 − 0 = 6
Doubles	6 − 1 = 5	4 − 1 = 3	5 − 2 = 3	Doubles

CS-2   Use with text pages 81–82.   **35**

OPTIONS FOR INDIVIDUAL NEEDS

Basic

Exercises All

Supplements
Reteaching 35 or
Practice 35
Challenges 35

Average

Exercises All

Supplements
Practice 35
Challenges 35 or
Thinking Skills 35

Extended

Exercises All

Supplements
Challenges 35
Thinking Skills 35

Other Resources:
Explorations, p. 68
*Problem Solving Experiences
in Mathematics*, p. 27
Workjobs II, pp. 224-227
Workjobs For Parents, pp.
107-109

4-7

OBJECTIVE 4-7
To model and finish related subtraction facts

Materials: Cube-A-Links, punchout coins, beans, Related Subtraction Facts Flipover Punchouts, related subtraction fact flashcards

Alternative Materials: counters, blocks

Grouping Suggestions: whole group, pairs

---

1. MOTIVATE AND TEACH

LEARN ABOUT IT

Write these facts on the chalkboard: $9 - 2 = 7$, $9 - 7 = 2$, $9 - 4 = 5$. Ask a student to circle the two related subtraction facts.

▶ **How do you know these facts are related?** (Possible answer: Related facts have the same three numbers, but the last two numbers in the sentence trade places.)

▶ **How do the cubes at the top of Page 81 help show the related facts?** (Possible answer: parts are broken off from the whole)

▶ **Describe how you can work with a partner to do Exercises 1–6.** (Possible answer: One student can use the cube train to show the first fact in each exercise and the partner can use the cube train to show the related fact.)

▶ **What must you do after you use the cubes to show the first subtraction fact?** (Possible answer: Make the train again before snapping off the part of the related fact.)

2. CHECK UNDERSTANDING

ERROR ALERT Writing the same answer for both of the related facts.

Name _____

More Related Subtraction Facts

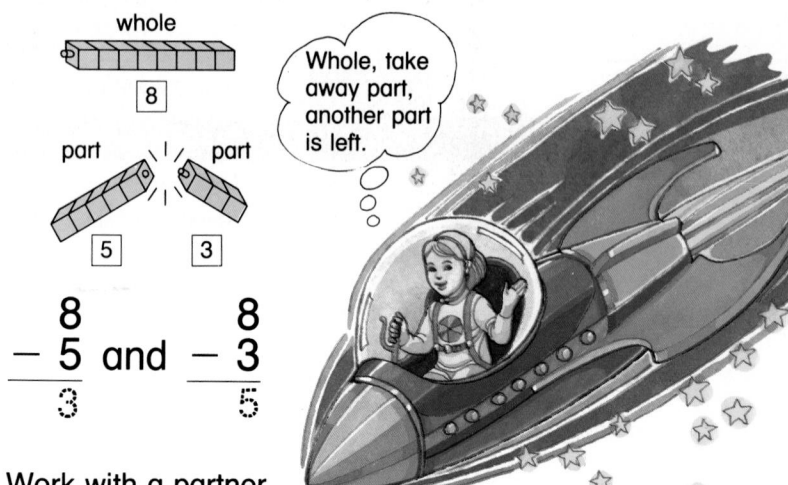

whole

8

part / part

5   3

$$\begin{array}{r} 8 \\ -5 \\ \hline 3 \end{array} \text{ and } \begin{array}{r} 8 \\ -3 \\ \hline 5 \end{array}$$

Whole, take away part, another part is left.

Work with a partner.
Subtract. Use cubes to help.

1. $\begin{array}{r}4\\-1\\\hline 3\end{array}$ and $\begin{array}{r}4\\-3\\\hline 1\end{array}$	**2.** $\begin{array}{r}11\\-8\\\hline 3\end{array}$ and $\begin{array}{r}11\\-3\\\hline 8\end{array}$
3. $\begin{array}{r}10\\-6\\\hline 4\end{array}$ and $\begin{array}{r}10\\-4\\\hline 6\end{array}$	**4.** $\begin{array}{r}7\\-2\\\hline 5\end{array}$ and $\begin{array}{r}7\\-5\\\hline 2\end{array}$
5. $\begin{array}{r}9\\-7\\\hline 2\end{array}$ and $\begin{array}{r}9\\-2\\\hline 7\end{array}$	**6.** $\begin{array}{r}12\\-9\\\hline 3\end{array}$ and $\begin{array}{r}12\\-3\\\hline 9\end{array}$

Chapter 4   (eighty-one)

TEACHING OPTIONS

RETEACHING TIPS Provide each student with dry beans and the Related Subtraction Facts Flipover Punchouts. Have students work with a partner to show these related facts by using beans to model the whole and then separating a part. For further help, use Reteaching Supplement 35.

ENRICHMENT Place 5 sets of related fact cards face down on a table. Have small groups of students play *Concentration* by picking up a fact and trying to find its related fact. The student with the most fact pairs wins.

---

ibtract. Ring the related subtraction
cts. Use cubes to help.

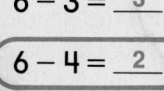

1. $7 - 2 = \underline{5}$
   $7 - 3 = \underline{4}$
   $7 - 4 = \underline{3}$

2. $9 - 5 = \underline{4}$
   $9 - 4 = \underline{5}$
   $9 - 7 = \underline{2}$

3. $6 - 2 = \underline{4}$
   $6 - 3 = \underline{3}$
   $6 - 4 = \underline{2}$

4. $5 - 1 = \underline{4}$
   $5 - 4 = \underline{1}$
   $5 - 3 = \underline{2}$

5. $10 - 7 = \underline{3}$
   $10 - 2 = \underline{8}$
   $10 - 8 = \underline{2}$

OBLEM SOLVING

Bing had 10¢. Lynn had a nickel.
How much more money did
Bing have than Lynn?

Use coin punchouts to help.
Finish the number sentence.

$10¢ \ominus \underline{5} ¢ \boxed{=} \underline{5} ¢$ Bing had $\underline{5}$ more cents.

3. PRACTICE AND APPLY

Basic	All
Average	All
Extended	All

PRACTICE

What can you do to help you subtract on page 82? (Possible answer: Use cube trains.) *How will you show related facts?* (Ring them.)

APPLY

PROBLEM SOLVING ▶ **What is a different way of writing how much money Lynn had?** (5 pennies, 5¢)
▶ **Tell why money punchouts can help you find the answer.** (Possible answer: You can use the money punchouts like cube trains.)
▶ **What coins can you use to show how much more money Bing had?** (5 pennies, 1 nickel)

4-7

LOSE AND ASSESS

RITE WHAT YOU KNOW On
board, write groups of numbers
ch as 10, 7, 3; 2, 4, 6. Ask one
dent in a pair to choose one set of
mbers and write a subtraction fact.
partner then writes the related
traction fact while the first student
ecks it. Have partners take turns
ing both jobs.

QUICK QUIZ

Write a subtraction fact that starts
with 5. Now write its related fact.
(Answers will vary.)

Fact Families

OBJECTIVE 4-8 To model and finish fact families

PREBOOK ACTIVITIES

QUICK REVIEW

Add or subtract.

3 + 6 = _(9)_	6 + 3 = _(9)_
7 − 2 = _(5)_	7 − 5 = _(2)_
11 − 8 = _(3)_	11 − 3 = _(8)_
8 + 7 = _(15)_	7 + 8 = _(15)_
10 − 4 = _(6)_	10 − 6 = _(4)_

PRIOR KNOWLEDGE

Help students recall what they know about fact families.
There are 12 months in the year.
Students are in school for 10 months of the year.
How many months are they not in school? (2) Ask a student to
write the fact on the chalkboard. (12 − 10 = 2) *How else can
we tell that number story?* (There are 12 months in the year.
Students are not in school for 2 months. How many months are
they in school?) *How would we write that story as a
subtraction fact?* (12 − 2 = 10) *What are the two addition
facts in this fact family?* (2 + 10 = 12, 10 + 2 = 12)

COMMUNICATION

Reading and Discussing Math Write the term **fact family**
on the chalkboard and have students read it aloud. Then write
these numbers: 2, 4, 6. *What addition fact can I write using
these numbers?* (2 + 4 = 6) *Can I write another addition fact
using these numbers?* (4 + 2 = 6) *What subtraction facts can I
write?* (6 − 2 = 4, 6 − 4 = 2) *How many facts are in this
fact family?* (4; 2 addition facts and 2 subtraction facts)

EXPLORE AND CONNECT

Materials: Cube-A-Links, 6 of one color per student
Grouping Suggestion: pairs
Have each student make a train of 1 to 6 cubes of one color,
each partner using a different color. Ask partners to combine
their trains and write the fact that shows what they did. Then
have them snap their trains apart and write that fact.
How can we write each of the facts in another way? (Possible
answer: Write the turnaround addition fact and the subtraction
fact that takes away the other part.) *What do we call these
related addition and subtraction facts?* (fact families) If any
pairs have used doubles, have them tell what is different about
their fact families. (There are only two facts.) Have students
model several other fact families, then summarize what they
know about fact families. (Possible answer: When you know
one fact, you know all the facts in the fact family.)

CONNECTIONS Use these anytime.

Problem of the Day

Number Families If 75 + 25 =
100, what other addition and subtraction
sentences do you know? Check your
answers with a partner. (25 + 75 = 100,
100 − 75 = 25, 100 − 25 = 75)

Math Connection

Operation Write + or − in each ○.

12 ○ 3 = 9 (−)	3 ○ 6 = 9 (+)
6 ○ 5 = 11 (+)	5 ○ 6 = 11 (+)
7 ○ 7 = 14 (+)	14 ○ 7 = 7 (−)
13 ○ 5 = 8 (−)	13 ○ 8 = 5 (−)
10 ○ 1 = 9 (−)	1 ○ 9 = 10 (+)

Subject Integration

Science Look at the weather calendar
you made earlier. Write the fact that tells
the total number of sunny days and
not-sunny days in the past 10 days. Then
write the rest of the facts in that fact
family.

CLASSWORK AND HOMEWORK SUPPLEMENTS

4-8 (side tab)

Practice

Skills Maintenance   4-8

Name _____

Fact Families

Add or subtract. Ring facts to make a family.

1. $8 + 4 = 12$
   $12 - 8 = 4$
   $6 + 6 = 12$
   $7 - 3 = 4$
   $4 + 8 = 12$
   $12 - 4 = 8$

2. $3 + 3 = 6$
   $4 + 2 = 6$
   $6 - 2 = 4$
   $3 + 6 = 9$
   $6 - 4 = 2$
   $2 + 4 = 6$

3. $8 + 3 = 11$
   $5 + 3 = 8$
   $11 - 8 = 3$
   $11 - 3 = 8$
   $5 - 3 = 2$
   $3 + 8 = 11$

4. $6 + 2 = 8$
   $2 + 4 = 6$
   $2 + 6 = 8$
   $2 + 2 = 4$
   $8 - 2 = 6$
   $8 - 6 = 2$

5. $5 + 5 = 10$
   $10 - 2 = 8$
   $10 - 5 = 5$
   $5 + 2 = 7$

6. $16 - 8 = 8$
   $10 - 8 = 2$
   $8 + 4 = 12$
   $8 + 8 = 16$

36   Use with text pages 83–84.   **PS-2**

Building Thinking Skills

Reading Math   4-8

Name _____

Fact Families

Read each story.
Think it through.
Write your answers on the lines.
Write the children's ages on the T-shirts below.

1. Ben is 2. Bob is 9 years older than Ben. Bill is 2 years younger than Bob.

   Think it through.
   Ben   2 years old
   Bob $9 + 2 = 11$
   Bill $11 - 2 = 9$

2. Jane is 7. Her sister Jill is 5 years older. Joy is 7 years younger than Jill.

   Think it through.
   Jane   7 years old
   Jill $5 + 7 = 12$
   Joy $12 - 7 = 5$

3. Bill's cat is 3 years old. Jane's rabbit is 3 years older than Bill's cat. Jill's dog is 3 years younger than Jane's rabbit.

   Think it through.
   cat   3 years old
   rabbit $3 + 3 = 6$
   dog $6 - 3 = 3$

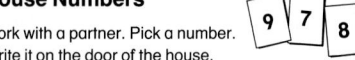

BEN 2   BOB 11   BILL 9   JANE 7   JILL 12   JOY 5

36   Use with text pages 83–84.   **TS-2**

Reteaching

Skills Review   4-8

Name _____

Fact Families

There are 4 facts in a fact family.

(10 / 4 6)

2 addition facts
$4 + 6 = 10$ and $6 + 4 = 10$

2 subtraction facts
$10 - 4 = 6$ and $10 - 6 = 4$

Write the missing number in each fact.

(11 / 8 3)
$8 + 3 = 11$ $3 + 8 = 11$
$11 - 3 = 8$ $11 - 8 = 3$

(12 / 5 7)
$5 + 7 = 12$ $7 + 5 = 12$
$12 - 7 = 5$ $12 - 5 = 7$

(9 / 7 2)
$7 + 2 = 9$ $2 + 7 = 9$
$9 - 2 = 7$ $9 - 7 = 2$

36   Use with text pages 83–84.   **RS-2**

Challenges

Cooperative Activities   4-8

Name _____

House Numbers

9 7 8 10

Work with a partner. Pick a number.
Write it on the door of the house.
In one part of the top window, write an addition sentence with the number as the sum.
In one part of the bottom window, have your partner write a sentence with different addends to make the same sum.
Finish each other's fact family by writing number sentences in the other parts of each window.
Take turns. Play again. Use your partner's sheet.
Pick a different number.

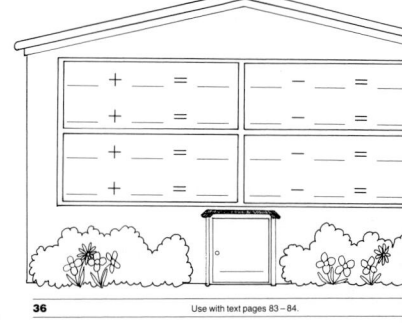

36   Use with text pages 83–84.   **CS-2**

Basic

Exercises All
Computer Bank, pp. 405-406
More Practice, p. 413, set A

Supplements
Reteaching 36 or
Practice 36
Thinking Skills 36

Average

Exercises All
Computer Bank, pp. 405-406
More Practice, p. 413, set A

Supplements
Practice 36
Challenges 36 or
Thinking Skills 36

Extended

Exercises All
Computer Bank, pp. 405-406

Supplements
Challenges 36
Thinking Skills 36

Other Resources:
Math in Stride, pp. 28-29, 46
Explorations, pp. 50-53, 64, 75, 188-190
Mathematics Book A, p. 28

LESSON PLAN 4-8

OBJECTIVE 4-8
To model and finish fact families

> **Materials:** up to 9 Cube-A-Links of 2 colors for each student, counters, tagboard, magic markers, TA 4 (Addition/Subtraction Mat)
>
> **Grouping Suggestion:** pairs

1. MOTIVATE AND TEACH

LEARN ABOUT IT

Have students use cubes of two colors to model an addition fact such as 5 + 3 and write the addition sentence to match. Then have them snap apart the cubes and write the related subtraction sentence. Ask volunteers to write their sentences on the chalkboard. Then have students name the turnaround fact and the related subtraction fact for each pair of sentences.

Discuss the fact family at the top of page 83.

▶ **How are the four members of each fact family alike?** (They are made up of the same numbers.)

▶ **Explain how you know how to fill in all the missing parts of each fact family.** (Possible answer: Once you know one fact in the family, you know all of them.)

▶ **How many numbers do you need to know in order to make a fact family?** (2)

2. CHECK UNDERSTANDING

ERROR ALERT Not recognizing the relationship between all the members of a fact family.

Name _____

Fact Families

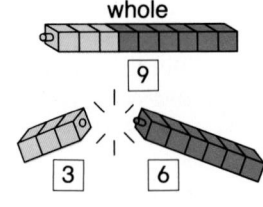
whole

A Family of Facts			
3	6	9	9
+6	+3	−6	−3
9	9	3	6

Work with a partner. Finish the fact family.
Add or subtract. Use cubes to check.

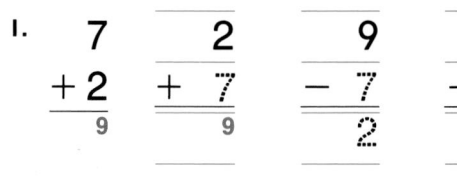
1.
7	2	9	9
+2	+7	−7	−2
9	9	2	7

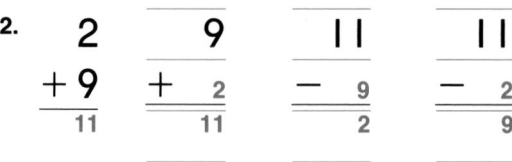
2.
2	9	11	11
+9	+2	−9	−2
11	11	2	9

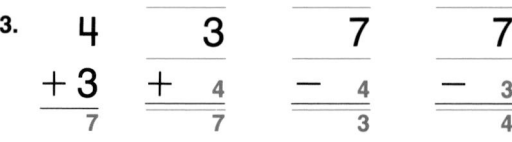
3.
4	3	7	7
+3	+4	−4	−3
7	7	3	4

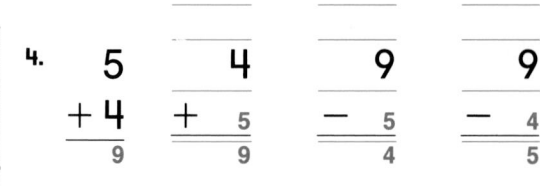
4.
5	4	9	9
+4	+5	−5	−4
9	9	4	5

Chapter 4

(eighty-three)

TEACHING OPTIONS

RETEACHING TIPS Have students use an addition mat and counters to show the relationship between addition and subtraction. Part + Part = Total: 5 + 4 = 9, 4 + 5 = 9. Total − Part = Part: 9 − 5 = 4, 9 − 4 = 5. Assign Reteaching Supplement 36.

ENRICHMENT Divide the class in half and make a YES/NO chart for each, headed *I'm wearing blue*. After students write their names in the appropriate column, partners use the data to write a fact family and discuss the information each fact shows.

dd or subtract. Ring facts to make
family. Use cubes to help.

$(2 + 8 = \underline{10})$ $(8 + 2 = \underline{10})$ $7 + 2 = \underline{9}$

$(10 - 2 = \underline{8})$ $10 - 3 = \underline{7}$ $(10 - 8 = \underline{2})$

$3 + 7 = \underline{10}$ $(3 + 8 = \underline{11})$ $(11 - 8 = \underline{3})$

$(8 + 3 = \underline{11})$ $11 - 9 = \underline{2}$ $(11 - 3 = \underline{8})$

$7 + 8 = \underline{15}$ $7 - 7 = \underline{0}$ $(7 + 7 = \underline{14})$

$8 + 8 = \underline{16}$ $(14 - 7 = \underline{7})$ $18 - 9 = \underline{9}$

$(3 + 9 = \underline{12})$ $6 + 4 = \underline{10}$ $(12 - 3 = \underline{9})$

$(9 + 3 = \underline{12})$ $9 - 4 = \underline{5}$ $(12 - 9 = \underline{3})$

$10 - 4 = \underline{6}$ $5 + 5 = \underline{10}$ $(6 + 6 = \underline{12})$

$(12 - 6 = \underline{6})$ $16 - 8 = \underline{8}$ $8 + 2 = \underline{10}$

Mixed Review

dd or subtract.

$16 - 8 = \underline{8}$ $8 - 3 = \underline{5}$ $7 + 9 = \underline{16}$

$6 - 0 = \underline{6}$ $7 + 7 = \underline{14}$ $9 - 4 = \underline{5}$

$12 - 9 = \underline{3}$ $8 + 6 = \underline{14}$ $3 + 5 + 4 = \underline{12}$

3. PRACTICE AND APPLY

Basic	All, Mixed Review
Average	All, Mixed Review
Extended	All, Mixed Review

PRACTICE

How are Exercises 1-5 on page 84 different from the exercises on page 83? (You have to ring facts to make a family.)

APPLY

▶ **What is the quickest way to tell if facts are in the same family?** (They are made up of the same three numbers.)
▶ **What kind of facts have only two facts in its fact family? Why?** (doubles facts, because there are only two different numbers in doubles facts, so the order cannot be switched)

MIXED REVIEW *Will you add or subtract to complete the exercises?* (both)

4-8

CLOSE AND ASSESS

SHOW WHAT YOU KNOW

ave each student make a number
mily card with a triangular piece of
gboard and markers, writing one
mber in each corner. Have small
oups of students share their cards
d work together to write all the
cts in the family of numbers that
pear on each card.

QUICK QUIZ

Complete the fact families.
1. 7 + 3 = 10
2. 6 + 6 = 12
3. 8 + 3 = 11
4. 5 + 2 = 7

LESSON OPTIONS 4-9

Problem Solving: Showing the Data

OBJECTIVE 4-9   To solve problems by showing the data; to solve problems using the strategy Guess and Check

PREBOOK ACTIVITIES

QUICK REVIEW

Copy and solve.

5	8	2	7	9	10	6	3	8	4	1
+4	−2	+3	+3	−4	− 5	+4	−1	−8	+4	+8
(9)	(6)	(5)	(10)	(5)	(5)	(10)	(2)	(0)	(8)	(9)

PRIOR KNOWLEDGE

Have 5 students stand at the front of the class. Ask 2 more students to join them. *Is this a put-together action or a take-away action? How do you know?* (put together; 2 students joined the 5 students) *What numbers can we add to find out how many students in all?* (Add 5 + 2 to get 7.) Now ask 3 of the 7 students to sit down. *What action is this?* (take-away action) *How many students are left?* (4) *Can we write an addition sentence or a subtraction sentence to show what happened?* (a subtraction sentence: 7 − 3 = 4)

COMMUNICATION

Reading and Discussing Math   Write **logical reasoning** on the chalkboard. Read the words and explain that we use logical reasoning when we use clues and pictures to **reason** the answer to a problem. Draw 2 circles on the board and tell students that they are mystery coins. *Suppose you want to find out what the mystery coins are. You know that the coins are worth 2¢. What are they?* (2 pennies) *How do you know?* (A penny is worth 1¢; all other coin combinations would be greater than 2¢.) *When you used the clues to rule out other coins and choose pennies, you used* logical reasoning.

EXPLORE AND CONNECT

COOPERATIVE ACTIVITY

Grouping Suggestion: small groups
Complete the number sentences.
1. Sharon had 6 oranges. She bought 3 more.
How many does she have now?   6 ◯ ____ = ____ (6 + 3 =
2. Sharon has 9 oranges. She gives 2 to Li.
How many does she have left?   9 ◯ ____ = ____ (9 − 2 =

TEACHING ACTIONS

 **BEFORE**   ▶ **What are we trying to find out in each story?** (How many oranges Sharon has.)
▶ **What is the data in the first story?** (6 and 3
What is the data in the second story? (9 and 2)

 **DURING**   ▶ **Is buying more oranges a put-together action or a take-away action?** (put together)
Should you plan to add or subtract? (add)
What kind of action is giving some oranges to Li? (take away) **Should you add or subtract?** (subtract)
▶ **You can draw pictures to help you solve the problems**
Draw 6 oranges for the first story. How can you show th
Sharon bought 3 more? (Draw 3 more oranges.) **How can you find out how many she has now?** (count)
▶ **How can you use a picture to solve the second story?** (Draw 9 oranges, cross out 2, count how many are left.)

 **AFTER**   ▶ **How can you check your answers?** (Match the number sentences to the pictures.) Have students work in groups to check each problem.

CONNECTIONS   Use these anytime.

Problem of the Day

Showing the Data   Copy the picture. Draw more or cross out some to solve.

   Jake had 7 marbles.
   2 rolled away.
   How many did he have left? (5)

(Students should cross out 2.)

Math Connection

Use Logical Reasoning   Use the clues to choose the mystery object.
1. It is pink.
2. It is made of rubber.
3. You might use it when you are writing.
a pink crayon   a ball   an eraser
(an eraser) Give reasons why the other answers cannot be right.

Creative Thinking

Make a List   How many different ways can you make a coin collection that is worth exactly 10¢. Make a list. Tell how many coins there are in each collection. Choose one collection and write a problem about it. For example: What coin collection is worth 10¢ and has 2 coins? (2 nickels) Give your problem to a classmate to solve.

roblem Solving Strategy: Guess and Check

CLASSWORK AND HOMEWORK SUPPLEMENTS

OPTIONS FOR
INDIVIDUAL
NEEDS

Basic

Exercises All
More Practice, p. 413, set B

Supplements
Reteaching 37 or
Practice 37

Average

Exercises All
More Practice, p. 413, set B

Supplements
Practice 37
Challenges 37 or
Thinking Skills 37

Extended

Exercises All

Supplements
Challenges 37
Thinking Skills 37

Other Resources:
Math in Stride, p. 42
Mathematics Their Way, pp.
246, 332-333
*Problem Solving Experiences
In Mathematics*, pp. 27, 43,
46, 57
Workjobs, pp. 224-227
Mathematics Book A, pp.
29-30

4-9

Practice

Problem Solving　　4-9

Name

Guess and Check

Read each story.
Write the coins in each circle.

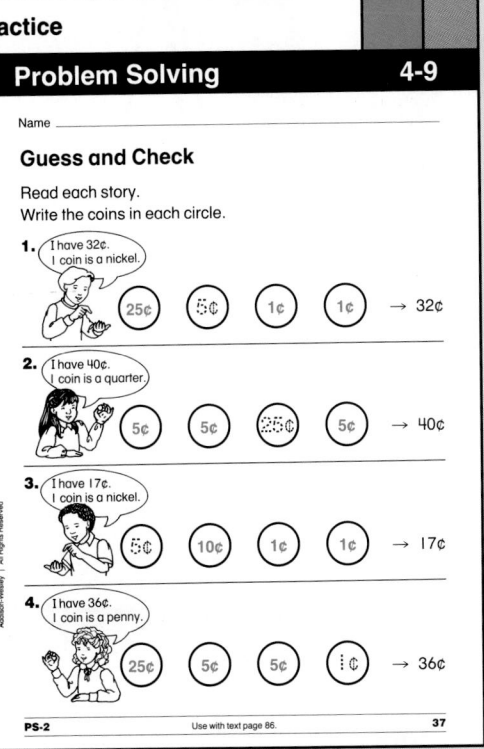

Building Thinking Skills

Data Analysis　　4-9

Name

Work Wheel

Use the work wheel
to answer the questions.

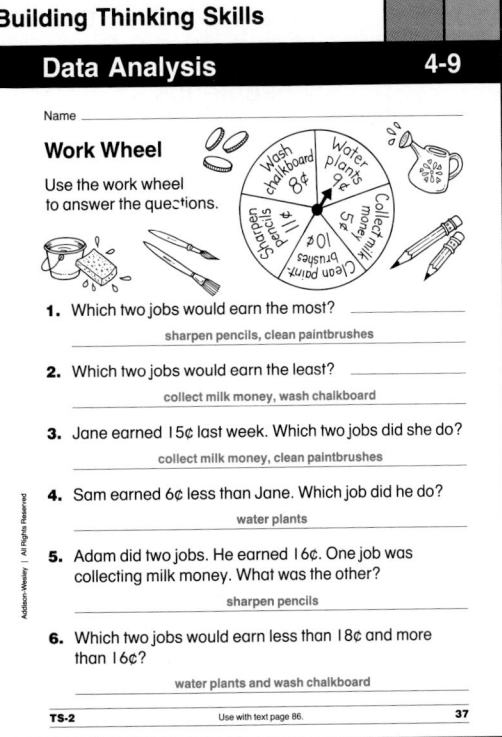

1. Which two jobs would earn the most? _____
   sharpen pencils, clean paintbrushes

2. Which two jobs would earn the least? _____
   collect milk money, wash chalkboard

3. Jane earned 15¢ last week. Which two jobs did she do? _____
   collect milk money, clean paintbrushes

4. Sam earned 6¢ less than Jane. Which job did he do? _____
   water plants

5. Adam did two jobs. He earned 16¢. One job was
   collecting milk money. What was the other? _____
   sharpen pencils

6. Which two jobs would earn less than 18¢ and more
   than 16¢? _____
   water plants and wash chalkboard

TS-2　Use with text page 86.　37

PS-2　Use with text page 86.　37

Reteaching

Problem Solving　　4-9

Name

Showing the Data

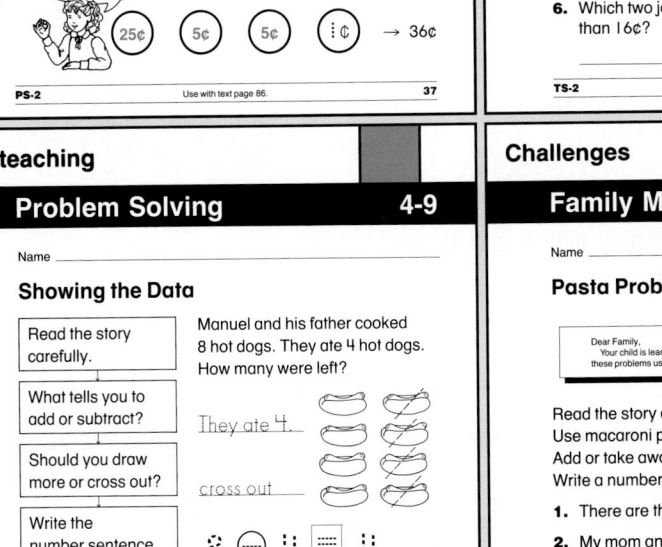

Read the story carefully.	Manuel and his father cooked 8 hot dogs. They ate 4 hot dogs. How many were left?
What tells you to add or subtract?	They ate 4.
Should you draw more or cross out?	cross out
Write the number sentence.	

Draw more or cross out to match the story.
Finish the number sentence.

1. Kevin had 3 bags of
   popcorn at the game.
   Ned had 2 bags of
   popcorn. How many bags
   did they have in all?
   3 ⊕ 2 = 5

2. Anna and her mom made
   10 cookies. Anna ate
   3 cookies. How many
   were left?
   10 ⊖ 3 = 7

RS-2　Use with text page 85.　37

Challenges

Family Math　　4-9

Name

Pasta Problems

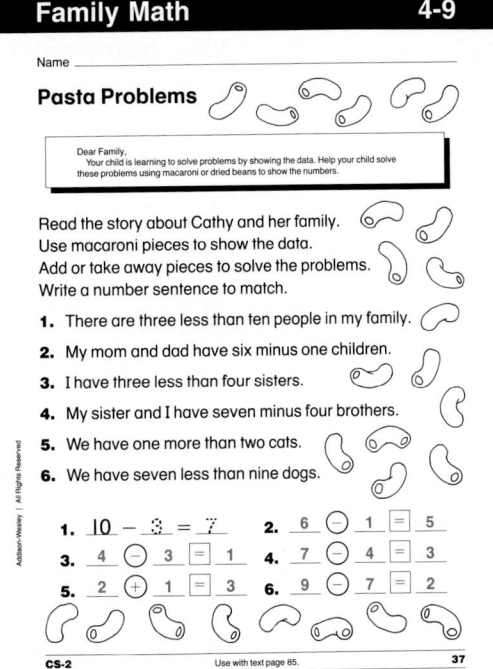

Dear Family,
　Your child is learning to solve problems by showing the data. Help your child solve
these problems using macaroni or dried beans to show the numbers.

Read the story about Cathy and her family.
Use macaroni pieces to show the data.
Add or take away pieces to solve the problems.
Write a number sentence to match.

1. There are three less than ten people in my family.
2. My mom and dad have six minus one children.
3. I have three less than four sisters.
4. My sister and I have seven minus four brothers.
5. We have one more than two cats.
6. We have seven less than nine dogs.

1. 10 − 3 = 7　　2. 6 ⊖ 1 = □
3. 4 ⊖ 3 = 1　　4. 7 ⊖ 4 = 3
5. 2 ⊕ 1 = □　　6. 9 ⊖ 7 = □

CS-2　Use with text page 85.　37

LESSON PLAN 4-9

OBJECTIVE 4-9
To solve problems by showing the data; to solve problems using the strategy Guess and Check

Materials: coin punchouts

1. MOTIVATE AND TEACH

BEFORE ▶ **Look at the first exercise. What data does the picture show?** (4 falling stars)

▶ **What must you do before you change the pictures shown for each problem?** (Possible answer: You must find the data in the story and decide how it should be shown in the picture.)

▶ **When will you draw more?** (when the story is a put-together, or addition story)

DURING ▶ **How will you plan whether to draw more or cross out to show the rest of the data?** (Read the story and decide whether to add or subtract. Draw more to add; cross out to subtract.)

AFTER ▶ **Tell how you can see if your answer is reasonable.** (Possible answer: Reread the problem to see if the picture shows the data correctly and the number sentence matches the problem.)

2. CHECK UNDERSTANDING

ERROR ALERT **Page 85** Showing data that does not match the number sentence.

Page 86 Forgetting how to count groups of coins.

Name _____

Problem Solving
Showing the Data

Draw more or cross out to match the story. Finish the number sentence.

1. Bruce saw 4 falling stars last week. Patrick saw 5 falling stars. How many did they see in all?

   __9__ stars

   $4 \oplus 5 \boxed{\cdots} 9$

2. 9 scouts looked for moon craters. 3 scouts saw a crater. How many scouts did not see any moon craters?

   __6__ scouts

   $9 \ominus 3 \boxed{=} 6$

3. Judy looked at the moon 3 times. Maya looked 2 times. Al looked 6 times. How many times did they look in all?

   __11__ times

   $3 \oplus 2 \oplus 6 \boxed{=} 11$

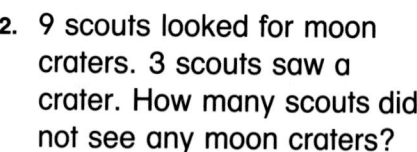

Chapter 4   More Practice, page 413, set B   (eighty-five)

TEACHING OPTIONS

RETEACHING TIPS Have students use coin punchouts to solve guess and check problems. For example: Use 6 coins–2 dimes, 2 nickels, 2 pennies. Ted's 3 coins are worth 12¢. 1 is a penny. Ann's 3 coins are worth 20¢. What coins does each have? Use Reteaching Supplement 37 for help in showing

ENRICHMENT **Family Math**
Ask a family member to collect several pennies, nickels, and dimes, and hide a number of coins. Tell the student how many coins are hidden, their total worth, and the value of one of the coins. The student determines which coins are hidden.

roblem Solving Strategy
uess and Check

sten to the story.
se coin punchouts
help. Write the coin
mount in each circle.

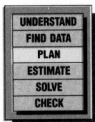

Maria

 I had 11¢. I coin was a nickel.

(5¢) (5¢) (1¢) ⟶ 11¢

James

I had 16¢.

(10¢) (5¢) (1¢) ⟶ 16¢

Carl

I had 15¢.

(5¢) (5¢) (5¢) ⟶ 15¢

(eighty-six)   Chapter 4

UNDERSTAND / FIND DATA / PLAN / ESTIMATE / SOLVE / CHECK

3. PRACTICE AND APPLY

Basic	All
Average	All
Extended	All

Read the following story to students:
*Maria, James, and Carl played a game.
They each put 3 coins into a dish. When
they looked into the dish, they saw 1
dime, 6 nickels, and 2 pennies. When the
game was over, the children wanted their
money back. Maria remembered she had
11¢ and that one coin was a nickel. All
James remembered was that he had 16¢.
Carl remembered having 15¢.*
Have students punchout coins to find
which coins belong to each child.
▶ **What clues can you use to find out
what coins Maria has?** (Possible
answer: One of her coins is a nickel; she
has 11¢ in all; the remaining 2 coins
equal 11 − 5, or 6¢.)
▶ **What strategy can you use to solve
these problems with coin punchouts?**
(Possible answer: Show all the coins. Try
different combinations of a nickel and 2
other coins to find a total of 11¢.
Remove them. Work with the 6 coins
left to find ones that total 16¢. Remove
them to find Carl's coins.)

4-9

LOSE AND ASSESS

HOW WHAT YOU KNOW

'rite 7 + 2 and 9 − 2 on the
alkboard. Ask students to draw
ctures to match the number
ntences, solve them, and tell a story
go with their pictures. Have
udents solve this problem: Dan and
e each have 3 coins. Dan has 16¢;
e has 12¢. What coins do they
ve? (Dan: dime, nickel, penny; Joe:
me, 2 pennies)

QUICK QUIZ

Draw a picture and solve.
Vera caught 8 crabs. She put 5 back
into the ocean. How many does she
have now? (3)

CHAPTER 4

WRAP UP

INTRODUCTION The Wrap Up provides activities emphasizing math language and thinking skills for the chapter.

USING PAGE 87

Math Words ▶ **How will the answers for Exercises 1 and 2 be similar?** (Possible answers: They will each show only 2 different numbers in the number sentences because 1 number will be shown twice; they are doubles facts.)
▶ **What is a subtraction word that means *what is left*?** (*difference*)

Math Reasoning ▶ **Explain how you can use the picture to help you find the answers to Exercise 7.** (Possible answer: You could use counters in two colors—one for the ducks and one for the chickens—to model the questions. You could draw the chickens that you cannot see in the coop.)

Name _____

WRAP UP

MATH WORDS

Write a subtraction fact. Answers may vary. Sample answer is show

1. This is a subtraction double.   8 (−) 4 [=] 4

2. This is an add-to-check fact for 4 − 2 = 2.   2 (+) 2 [=] 4

3. This is the related subtraction fact for 7 − 5 = 2.   7 (−) 2 [=] 5

4. This fact gives the difference between 11 and 9.   11 (−) 9 [=] 2

MATH REASONING

5. A farmer has 10 ducks and chickens in all. All the ducks are in the yard. Some chickens are hiding in the coop.

   How many ducks are there in all?   ___3___ ducks

   How many chickens are there in all?   ___7___ chicker

   How many chickens are in the coop?   ___3___ chicker

TEACHING OPTIONS

ENRICHMENT Ask students to draw a barnyard scene that shows farm animals and a barn. Have them draw some of the animals out in the open and then write questions like those on this page for a partner to answer. Have them write number sentences to show how they found the answers.

Continue this activity by having students make up stories about their animals. Have them include questions such as *The farmer sold 2 sheep; how many sheep are left?* and *5 cows wandered out to the field; how many cows are still in the barn?* Partners use counters or drawings to show the answers.

Name _____

CHAPTER REVIEW/TEST

Subtract.

8	5	11	4	7	6
−2	−0	−9	−4	−5	−1
6	5	2	0	2	5

9	9	10	10	9	10
−0	−2	−5	−7	−6	−8
9	7	5	3	3	2

Subtract. Write the add-to-check fact.

8	4		12	6		16	8
−4	+4		−6	+6		−8	+8
4	8		6	12		8	16

Finish the fact family. Add or subtract.

$3 + 5 = \underline{8}$ $8 - \underline{5} = \underline{3}$

$5 + \underline{3} = \underline{8}$ $8 - \underline{3} = \underline{5}$

Draw more or cross out to match the story.
Finish the number sentence.

Ben had 8 rocks. He threw 5 rocks in the pond. How many rocks did he still have?

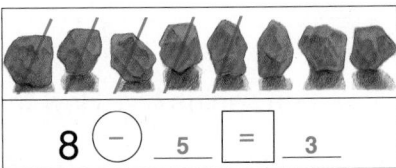

$8 \ominus \underline{5} \boxed{=} \underline{3}$

CHAPTER REVIEW/TEST

INTRODUCTION The Review/Test is provided to review and evaluate the skills and concepts presented in Chapter 4.

USING PAGE 88
If you prefer to use this page for review, you may want to use the **Multiple-Choice Posttest** (pages 15-16) or the **Free Response Posttest** (pages 15-16) to evaluate mastery of chapter objectives.

ITEM ANALYSIS The table below correlates the Chapter Review/Test items with the lesson objectives for the chapter.

Items	Objectives
1	4-1, 4-2, 4-6
2	4-3, 4-6
3	4-5, 4-6
4	4-2, 4-5
5	4-7, 4-8
6	4-5, 4-9

INFORMAL ASSESSMENT

Using Manipulatives Have small groups draw pictures on the chalkboard or use objects on the flannelboard to show how they find answers to exercises that include counting back, doubles, subtracting from 9 and 10, counting up, add-to-check, and fact families. Work with students who need further assistance.

Communication *How can you tell whether 3 numbers are members of a fact family?* (Possible answer: Add the 2 smaller numbers to see if the sum is equal to the other number.)

Critical Thinking ▶ **Describe at least three ways to check the answer to 10 − 2 = 8.** (Possible answer: You could add 2 + 8 to check, use a 10-frame and model the problem with counters, or you could count back on a number line by showing 2 jumps from 10 to 8.)

CHAPTER 4

ENRICHMENT

INTRODUCTION By identifying all the possible color combinations available, students are learning to predict and to search for patterns.

USING PAGE 89

This Enrichment page is provided for all students. You may wish to use it after they have completed the Chapter Review/Test on page 88.

▶ **What kind of pattern might you look for as you color the clothes?**
(Possible answer: There are 3 rows and 3 different colors of shorts. Follow a pattern of making the shorts in each row 1 color and show a different color shirt with each pair of shorts.)

▶ **How can you find the total number of ways Carlos can combine his shirts and shorts?** (Possible answer: You can count each combination of colors or you can add 4 + 4 + 4 to show the number of combinations in each of the 3 rows.)

EXTENSION Discuss jobs in which people might use a chart to show different combinations of things. For example: a cook making menus, businesses where employees must wear uniforms, and a park director planning games. Ask students to pretend they work in an office. They have 2 different-colored shirts and 3 different-colored pants or skirts to choose from. They cannot wear the same combination 2 days in a row. Have each student make a chart labeled Monday through Saturday. Then have them show the colors of their shirts and pants or skirts. Have them fill in their charts to show what combination they plan to wear each day. Discuss how they kept track of the combinations they had left to use.

Name _____

ENRICHMENT
Finding All Combinations

Carlos has these shirts.

He has these shorts.

Color to show all the ways Carlos can wear his shirts and shorts.

Order of answers may vary.

	b	g	y
	r	r	r
	b	g	y
	b	b	b
	b	g	y
	g	g	g

How many shirts?

__4__ shirts

How many shorts?

__3__ shorts

How many ways

__12__ ways

Chapter 4   Enrichment: Finding All Combinations

(eighty-nine)

Name _____

UMULATIVE REVIEW

d.

$\begin{array}{r} 5 \\ +0 \\ \hline \end{array}$ ○ 0 ○ 3 ● 5

$\begin{array}{r} 9 \\ +9 \\ \hline \end{array}$ ○ 16 ● 18 ○ 19

$\begin{array}{r} 4¢ \\ +6¢ \\ \hline \end{array}$ ○ 2¢ ● 10¢ ○ 12¢

$\begin{array}{r} 8 \\ +5 \\ \hline \end{array}$ ○ 12 ● 13 ○ 14

5. What number is next in the pattern?

2, 4, 6, ___

○ 7
● 8
○ 9

6. How many ?

卌 Ⅲ   ⅢⅠ

● 8
○ 4
○ 12

7. What cube is next in the pattern?

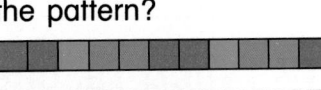

● ■
○ ■
○ ■

How many children like yellow best?

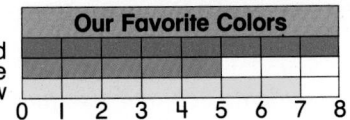

Our Favorite Colors
red
blue
yellow
0 1 2 3 4 5 6 7 8

○ 6 children
● 7 children
○ 5 children

Dave caught 6 fish. Kim caught 7 fish. How many fish did they catch in all?

○ 11 fish
● 13 fish
○ 15 fish

(ninety)

Chapter 4   Cumulative Review

CUMULATIVE REVIEW

INTRODUCTION The purpose of this Cumulative Review is to maintain previously taught skills and concepts. The emphasis in this Cumulative Review is on addition facts, Chapter 2; and on patterns and graphs, Chapter 3.

ITEM ANALYSIS The table below correlates the Cumulative Review items with the lesson objectives.

Items	Objectives
1	2-1
2	2-2
3	2-6
4	2-8
5	3-1
6, 8	3-5
7	3-3
9	2-5

CHAPTER 5 MORE SUBTRACTION FACTS

Chapter Management

OVERVIEW

Lesson	Pages	Objectives	Subject Integration	Strand Integration
Subtracting 9	91-92	5-1 To use the mental math technique of subtracting 9	language arts: *Talk About It*	patterns
Using Addition to Subtract 4, 5, and 6	93-94	5-2 To use related addition facts to find differences	social studies: fireman	logic
Fact Practice	95-96	5-3 To practice mental math to find differences	language arts: letter code	critical thinking
Problem Solving: Understanding the Operations/Mental Math	97-98	5-4 To subtract by taking away or comparing; to use mental math	language arts: reading	computation, logic
Using Addition to Subtract 7 and 8	99-100	5-5 To use related addition facts to find differences	social studies: police officer	patterns
Fact Practice	101-102	5-6 To practice mental math to find differences	social studies: consumer cost	graphing
Fact Families	103-104	5-7 To model and finish fact families	social studies: partner skills	patterns
Problem Solving: Writing a Story/Problem Solving Strategy: Draw a Picture	105-108	5-8 To write a story; to use the strategy Draw a Picture	language arts: writing	computation, patterns

MATHEMATICAL BACKGROUND

Subtraction

In Chapter 5, students continue to practice using 2 methods of subtraction. The *take away* method involves taking objects away from a group. The number left over is the answer or difference. The *comparison* method involves 2 groups of objects placed in 1-to-1 correspondence to determine how many more are in 1 group than in the other.

Mental Math

In this chapter, students use several mental math techniques to help them recall the subtraction facts. Subtracting 9 and related addition facts are two of these techniques. These and other fact strategies were reviewed in Chapter 4. At this point, students are still using counters and blocks to help them with these fact strategies. The final goal is for students to use these strategies as mental math techniques.

Problem Solving

In this chapter, students solve problems using the *take away* and *comparison* methods of subtraction, by writing a story, and by using the strategy *Draw a Picture*.

TIPS FROM TEACHERS

Help students see and use patterns to find answers when subtracting 9 from a teen *number. Write the following subtraction exercises on a poster titled* Subtracting 9:

$$11 - 9 = 2 \qquad 15 - 9 = 6$$
$$12 - 9 = 3 \qquad 16 - 9 = 7$$
$$13 - 9 = 4 \qquad 17 - 9 = 8$$
$$14 - 9 = 5 \qquad 18 - 9 = 9$$

Have students examine the poster and discuss the pattern. (The answer is always 1 more than the ones digit of the teen *number.)*

Robyn Silbey
Rosemont Elementary School
Gaithersburg, MD

> ## Subtracting 9
> $$11 - 9 = 2$$
> $$12 - 9 = 3$$
> $$13 - 9 = 4$$

Pretest — Chapter 5, page 1

Multiple-Choice Format

Name _____

1. Subtract. Think of your 10-frame to help.

$\begin{array}{r} 17 \\ -\ 9 \\ \hline \end{array}$
- Ⓐ 10
- Ⓑ 8
- C 7

2. Subtract. Choose the add-to-check fact.

$\begin{array}{r} 13 \\ -\ 5 \\ \hline \end{array}$ (5 + ■ = 13)

- A 5 + 3 = 8
- Ⓑ 5 + 8 = 13
- C 5 + 10 = 15

3. Subtract.

14 − 6 = ?
- A 10
- B 9
- Ⓒ 8

4. Subtract.

13 − 9 = ?
- Ⓐ 4
- B 5
- C 6

5. Ms. Kwan bought 11 rolls. Ms. Jones bought 5 rolls. How many more rolls did Ms. Kwan buy than Ms. Jones?
- A 5 more rolls
- Ⓑ 6 more rolls
- C 8 more rolls

6. What is the number?
It is more than 5 + 5.
It is less than 12.
- A 10
- Ⓑ 11
- C 12

MCT 2   17

Pretest — Chapter 5, page 2

Multiple-Choice Format

Name _____

7. Subtract. Choose the add-to-check fact.

$\begin{array}{r} 11 \\ -\ 7 \\ \hline \end{array}$ (7 + ■ = 11)

- A 7 + 3 = 10
- Ⓑ 7 + 4 = 11
- C 3 + 4 = 7

8. Subtract.

$\begin{array}{r} 17 \\ -\ 8 \\ \hline \end{array}$
- A 6
- B 8
- Ⓒ 9

9. Subtract.

$\begin{array}{r} 12 \\ -\ 6 \\ \hline \end{array}$
- A 5
- Ⓑ 6
- C 7

10. Which fact completes this family?

$\begin{array}{cc} 6 & 5 \\ +5 & +6 \\ \hline 11 & 11 \end{array}$
$\begin{array}{c} 11 \\ -\ 5 \\ \hline 6 \end{array}$

- A $\begin{array}{r} 6 \\ -5 \\ \hline 1 \end{array}$
- Ⓑ $\begin{array}{r} 11 \\ -\ 6 \\ \hline 5 \end{array}$

11. Draw a picture to help. Use **X** for books.
Michele put books on 5 shelves. She put 1 book on the first shelf, 2 books on the second shelf, and 3 books on the third shelf. She continued this pattern. How many books did she put on the fifth shelf?
- A 4 books
- Ⓑ 5 books
- C 6 books

18   MCT 2

Posttest — Chapter 5, page 1

Multiple-Choice Format

Name _____

1. Subtract. Think of your 10-frame to help.

$\begin{array}{r} 14 \\ -\ 9 \\ \hline \end{array}$
- A 10
- B 9
- Ⓒ 5

2. Subtract. Choose the add-to-check fact.

$\begin{array}{r} 13 \\ -\ 4 \\ \hline \end{array}$ (4 + ■ = 13)

- A 4 + 13 = 17
- B 4 + 8 = 12
- Ⓒ 4 + 9 = 13

3. Subtract.

15 − 6 = ?
- A 10
- Ⓑ 9
- C 8

4. Subtract.

18 − 9 = ?
- Ⓐ 9
- B 8
- C 7

5. Ms. Ho bought 11 rolls. Ms. Allman bought 3 rolls. How many more rolls did Ms. Ho buy than Ms. Allman?
- A 5 more rolls
- B 6 more rolls
- Ⓒ 8 more rolls

6. What is the number?
It is less than 5 + 5.
It is more than 8.
- Ⓐ 9
- B 10
- C 11

MCT 2   19

Posttest — Chapter 5, page 2

Multiple-Choice Format

Name _____

7. Subtract. Choose the add-to-check fact.

$\begin{array}{r} 13 \\ -\ 7 \\ \hline \end{array}$ (7 + ■ = 13)

- Ⓐ 7 + 6 = 13
- B 7 + 5 = 12
- C 3 + 4 = 7

8. Subtract.

$\begin{array}{r} 16 \\ -\ 8 \\ \hline \end{array}$
- A 6
- Ⓑ 8
- C 9

9. Subtract.

$\begin{array}{r} 14 \\ -\ 7 \\ \hline \end{array}$
- A 5
- B 6
- Ⓒ 7

10. Which fact completes this family?

$\begin{array}{cc} 7 & 9 \\ +9 & +7 \\ \hline 16 & 16 \end{array}$
$\begin{array}{c} 16 \\ -\ 7 \\ \hline 9 \end{array}$

- Ⓐ $\begin{array}{r} 16 \\ -\ 9 \\ \hline 7 \end{array}$
- B $\begin{array}{r} 9 \\ -7 \\ \hline 2 \end{array}$

11. Draw a picture to help. Use **X** for books.
Michele put books on 6 shelves. She put 1 book on the first shelf, 2 books on the second shelf, and 3 books on the third shelf. She continued this pattern. How many books did she put on the sixth shelf?
- A 4 books
- B 5 books
- Ⓒ 6 books

20   MCT 2

ITEM ANALYSIS

Items	Objectives
1	5-1
2	5-2
3, 4	5-3
5, 6	5-4
7	5-5
8, 9	5-6
10	5-7
11	5-8

Note: The item analysis is the same for all pretests and posttests for this chapter.

ALSO AVAILABLE

▶ **Free Response Tests**
▶ **Alternative Tests**
▶ **Thinking Strategies**
▶ **Concrete Materials**

CHAPTER 5 MORE SUBTRACTION FACTS

Optional Chapter Activities

PROJECT AND BULLETIN BOARD

Make skyscrapers on the bulletin board. Cut out 3-in. squares for each floor. Have students work in groups to design, attach, and decorate the squares to make their own skyscrapers with up to 18 floors. Arrange the finished buildings on the bulletin board to create a city scene. Compare the number of floors in 2 of the skyscrapers. Have students tell which is the taller building and then estimate how many stories taller it is. Have them count the floors in each and write a subtraction sentence to find the difference. Then ask them to check the subtraction by adding and counting on. Place the shorter building on top of the taller building. Say the number of floors in the shorter building and count on to find out how many more floors the taller building has. During sessions that follow, compare the number of floors on other skyscrapers in the same way.

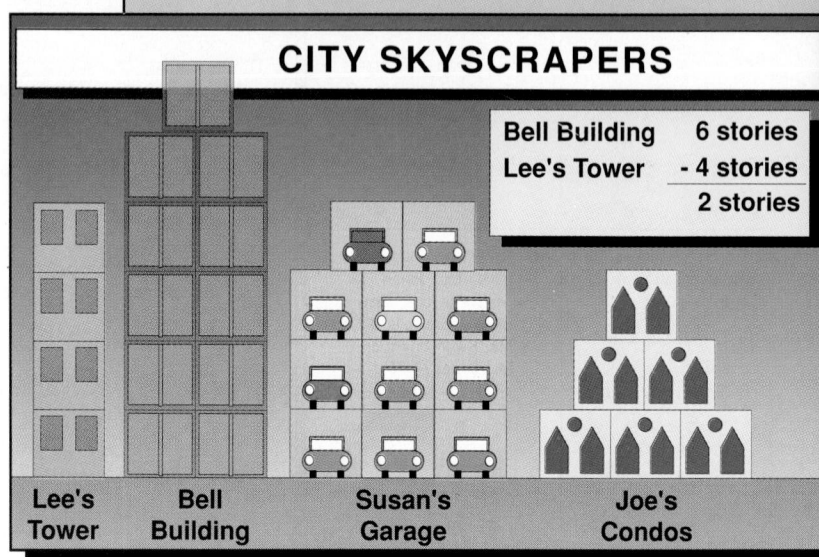

CITY SKYSCRAPERS

Bell Building	6 stories
Lee's Tower	- 4 stories
	2 stories

Lee's Tower   Bell Building   Susan's Garage   Joe's Condos

COOPERATIVE LEARNING

Divide the class into 4 teams. Identify the group skill: providing constructive feedback. Tell each team that they will participate in a Kangaroo Relay and then write subtraction facts about it. Mark 2 lines 12 ft apart on the floor. Have teams line up behind 1 line.

6 5 4 3 2 1 ⟵ 12 feet ⟶ 1

6−1=5, 6−2=4, 6−3=3, 6−4=2, 6−5=1, 6−6=0

The first team members in line hold a ball between their knees and hop from the start line to the finish line. They then roll the ball to the second team members, who repeat the activity. The relay continues until all students on the team cross the finish line. Then have 2 or 3 team members make a model of the relay using yarn for start and finish lines and a counter for each team member. Instruct them to count counters at the start line, move 1 to the finish line, and recount to show how the number of team members was subtracted during the relay. Have 2 team members write subtraction sentences to show what happened each time a teammate crossed the finish line. For example: 8 − 1 = 7, 8 − 2 = 6, and so on. Have 2 others check the subtraction using related addition facts. You will find grouping suggestions and cooperative learning activities in most lessons throughout this chapter.

LITERATURE

Viorst, Judith. *Alexander, Who Used to Be Rich Last Sunday.* New York: Aladdin Books, 1978.

Students will identify with Alexander. Money just slips through his fingers.
Have students write subtraction sentences as they follow Alexander's spending spree, page by page.

Hawkins, Colin. *Take Away Monsters.* New York: Putnam's, 1984.

Mathews, Louise. *The Great Take-Away.* New York: Dodd, Mead, 1980.

91C   Chapter 5 Optional Chapter Activities

ENGLISH AS A SECOND LANGUAGE

Group ESL children with native speakers for the creative and cooperative story-writing activity. Circulate among the groups to provide feedback. Then ask students to tell their stories, write them down and illustrate them, and perhaps tape record and save them for future review of subtraction. A tape file is exciting for students, and provides an excellent record of an ESL student's speaking progress throughout the year.

Review the positional vocabulary—*last, ahead of,* and *first*—and the synonymous expressions signaling subtraction—*left* and *keep*. Give number examples to illustrate the mental math: *the sum of my digits . . .*

Since the language of ordering may be new, draw the correspondence between *1* and *first* in activities that require only comprehension. For example, when students are in a line, ask *Who is first?* Extend the activity to speaking and deal with pronunciation difficulties by modeling the correct pronunciation and having students repeat.

GIFTED

Mathematically talented students may already know their subtraction facts to 18. Challenge these students by showing them how to complete and then create their own subtraction paths. Write a subtraction path such as the following on the chalkboard. Have students find the difference between the first 2 numbers to fill in the third space. This number becomes the first number in the next subtraction exercise.

$$18 \rightarrow - 9 \rightarrow (9) \rightarrow - 1 \rightarrow (8) \rightarrow - 3 \rightarrow (5)$$

After students understand the concept, challenge them to make their own number paths by connecting exercises in their book. To vary the activity, show students how to make paths in which they must find the number that is subtracted from the number in the first space. For example,

$$16 \rightarrow (- 3) \rightarrow 13 \rightarrow (- 4) \rightarrow 9 \rightarrow (- 7) \rightarrow 2$$

Students who are gifted in writing may wish to write their own step-by-step directions for solving subtraction paths and use their directions to teach another student.

STUDENTS AT RISK

At this level there are 2 important subtraction concepts for all students to learn, *take away* and *comparison. Take away* here refers to a single set that has members removed from it. For example: 6 birds are on a fence. 2 fly away. How many are left? $(6 - 2 = 4)$ *Comparison* requires analyzing the relationship between two different sets. For example: 6 birds are in a tree, and 2 birds are on the fence. How many more are in the tree? $(6 - 2 = 4)$ While number facts and sentences representing these concepts are identical, it is important for students to understand the difference as they begin to solve word problems with subtraction. This understanding can be encouraged by modeling the reading of number sentences with language for both situations: *six take away two* and *six is how much more than two?*

These concepts may also be illustrated with counters.
Taking away: x x x x (x x) →
To compare, display sets of 6 and 2 counters. Align the sets and then cover the ones that match up. Count the ones that are left.
Comparing: x x| x x x x
             x x|
You may also use the Reteaching Supplements and the specific Reteaching Tips from each lesson in this chapter.

Storybook

PICTURE

These pictures and accompanying stories and poems are available as storybooks.

You may want to read and discuss this story with your students before starting the chapter. The first lesson in this chapter includes a question about the story. Lessons 1, 2, 5 and 8 in this chapter have questions in the informal Assessment that refer to the story.

Mom's Special Dish

Today is the day of the big town picnic. Each year, everyone in town meets in the grove of trees down by the fire station to chatter, play, and nibble on nuts and berries, and to eat a very, very special dish.

Squeaky had been waiting and waiting and waiting for this day to arrive. Each year he got to help his mother make the very special dish. It was a big honor for someone as small and young as he. Squeaky rushed into the kitchen. "Mom, Mom, Mom! Are you ready? Can we go now?" he called.

"Slow down, Squeaky. First you need to fill your pail with nuts," said Mom, smiling at her son.

Squeaky grabbed the pail and headed for the storage room where they kept their supply of nuts. Last year he could only carry 11 nuts, but he had grown a lot this year. He could hold 15 nuts now. Pretty soon he would be able to hold 18 nuts! He dumped 15 nuts into the pail. "OK, Mom. I'm all ready!" called.

Squeaky took the pail of nuts and Mom carried an extra pail, and they scampered off. They passed Mr. George, the librarian, Ms. Lee, the mechanic, Mrs. Tuft, the mail carrier, and Squeaky's teacher, Mr. Helms. Finally they arrived at Officer Seymour's house, where the BIG MACHINE was. Squeaky didn't know where the machine came from or how long it had been in Officer Seymour's house. It took up almost an entire room. When it was on, the machine made a terrifying loud noise, and his mom insisted that Squeaky be very, very careful around it.

"OK, Squeaky, put the empty pail I carried under the spout," instructed his mother. "Now hand me some nuts from your pail when I ask for them."

Squeaky's mom turned the machine on. "Whrrrrrrrrrrr...whrrrrrrrrr...whrrrrrrrrrr."

"Now hand me some nuts from your pail," she shouted over the whir of the machine. Squeaky counted out 9 nuts and gave them to her. She put them into the mouth of the machine.

"Grrrrrind...crrrack...grrrind...crrrack... smooosch," went the machine. Squeaky ran to the spout and watched the makings of the special treat ooze out into the pail.

"Hurray! Hurray! It's working!" exclaimed Squeaky.

"Of course it is, dear. Come back and help me so that we can get done," called his mom. Squeaky and his mom finished feeding all the nuts into the machine. After they were through, Squeaky's mom turned the machine off and started to clean it. She seemed to take forever!

"Hurry, Mom! Let's go home," begged Squeaky.

"OK, Squeaky. I'm all done. We can go now," she said with a smile.

Squeaky and his mom walked carefully home, trying not to spill any of the special dish. When they arrived, his mother emptied the pail into a serving dish. Squeaky eyed the pail eagerly.

"OK, Squeaky, you've worked hard. Here," said his mom, and she handed him the almost emptied pail. Squeaky took the pail and a spoon and ran out under the oak tree. There he sat and scraped the pail, trying to eat every trace of Mom's special dish.

"Yummm!" sighed Squeaky as he leaned back, the sparkling clean pail resting next to him. "Nothing tastes as good as Mom's peanut butter!"

Subtracting 9

OBJECTIVE 5-1 To use the mental math technique of subtracting 9 to find differences

PREBOOK ACTIVITIES

QUICK REVIEW

Write + or − in each box.

7 □ 6 = 13 (+)	8 □ 2 = 6 (−)	10 □ 1 = 9 (−)
3 □ 4 = 7 (+)	7 □ 7 = 14 (+)	5 □ 3 = 2 (−)
6 □ 3 = 9 (+)	9 □ 2 = 7 (−)	6 □ 1 = 7 (+)
8 □ 9 = 17 (+)	2 □ 1 = 3 (+)	7 □ 2 = 5 (−)
5 □ 4 = 9 (+)	8 □ 5 = 3 (−)	10 □ 2 = 8 (−)

PRIOR KNOWLEDGE

Think about the people who work in your neighborhood. Why might they need to know how to subtract to do their jobs? (Possible answers: Storekeepers might subtract to make change or to find how much of an item they have sold; bakers might subtract to find how much flour or eggs to order.) *When do you use subtraction?* (Possible answers: to find how much money is left after making a purchase; to find how many more people are needed to make up a team)

COMMUNICATION

Listening and Discussing Math Ask students to raise their hands each time they hear a word that is associated with the operation of subtraction. Say the following words: *difference, sum, take away, addend, put together.*
What is the first thing that comes to your mind when you think of the number 9? (Possible answers: 9 fingers, 9 people on a baseball team, 1 less than 10, I am not 9 yet)

EXPLORE AND CONNECT

Materials: subtraction flashcards for differences of 9, counters, punchout 10-frames
Grouping Suggestions: small groups
Place the flashcards along the chalkledge. Write the answers for these facts at random above the cards, omitting 1 answer, for example, leave out 8 as the difference for 17 − 9. Have students work in small groups to determine which fact does r have an answer. Encourage them to use counters and 10-fran or to draw pictures to help them find the missing answer. As them not to volunteer their response until they are ready to prove that their answer is correct. Then have them explain th methods they used. (Possible answer: taking 9 counters away from the 10-frame and counting how many are left)

CONNECTIONS Use these anytime.

Problem of the Day

Show the Data Draw more or cross out to match the story. Finish the number sentence.
Leah threw 14 balls at the target.
Only 9 balls hit the target.
How many balls did not hit the target?
14 (−) 9 = (5)
o o o o o o o o o o o o o o

Subject Integration

Language Arts In your Math Journals, write a story about a person who has a special treasure but loses 9 pieces of it. Include how many pieces of the treasure there were to start and how many there are left. When you are finished, write a number sentence to match your story.

Mental Math

Number Sense Solve each riddle.
If you take 9 away from me, you get an even number between 3 and 5. I am 2 less than 15. What number am I? (13)
If you take 9 away from me, you get an odd number that is less than 3. I am also the sum of 5 + 5. What number am I? (10)

CLASSWORK AND HOMEWORK SUPPLEMENTS

Practice

Skills Maintenance   5-1

Name _____

Subtracting 9

Subtract.

1. $\begin{array}{r} 18 \\ -9 \\ \hline 9 \end{array}$ $\begin{array}{r} 10 \\ -9 \\ \hline 1 \end{array}$ $\begin{array}{r} 11 \\ -9 \\ \hline 2 \end{array}$ $\begin{array}{r} 12 \\ -9 \\ \hline 3 \end{array}$ $\begin{array}{r} 13 \\ -9 \\ \hline 4 \end{array}$

2. $\begin{array}{r} 14 \\ -9 \\ \hline 5 \end{array}$ $\begin{array}{r} 17 \\ -9 \\ \hline 8 \end{array}$ $\begin{array}{r} 15 \\ -9 \\ \hline 6 \end{array}$ $\begin{array}{r} 16 \\ -9 \\ \hline 7 \end{array}$ $\begin{array}{r} 18 \\ -9 \\ \hline 9 \end{array}$

3. $\begin{array}{r} 11 \\ -9 \\ \hline 2 \end{array}$ $\begin{array}{r} 13 \\ -9 \\ \hline 4 \end{array}$ $\begin{array}{r} 10 \\ -9 \\ \hline 1 \end{array}$ $\begin{array}{r} 18 \\ -9 \\ \hline 9 \end{array}$ $\begin{array}{r} 12 \\ -9 \\ \hline 3 \end{array}$

4. $\begin{array}{r} 16 \\ -9 \\ \hline 7 \end{array}$ $\begin{array}{r} 15 \\ -9 \\ \hline 6 \end{array}$ $\begin{array}{r} 17 \\ -9 \\ \hline 8 \end{array}$ $\begin{array}{r} 14 \\ -9 \\ \hline 5 \end{array}$ $\begin{array}{r} 11 \\ -9 \\ \hline 2 \end{array}$

5. $\begin{array}{r} 10 \\ -9 \\ \hline 1 \end{array}$ $\begin{array}{r} 12 \\ -9 \\ \hline 3 \end{array}$ $\begin{array}{r} 13 \\ -9 \\ \hline 4 \end{array}$ $\begin{array}{r} 18 \\ -9 \\ \hline 9 \end{array}$ $\begin{array}{r} 16 \\ -9 \\ \hline 7 \end{array}$

38   Use with text pages 91 – 92.   PS-2

Addison-Wesley | All Rights Reserved

Building Thinking Skills

Patterns   5-1

Name _____

What Is Next?

Subtract.

$\begin{array}{r} 9 \\ -9 \\ \hline 0 \end{array}$ $\begin{array}{r} 9 \\ -8 \\ \hline 1 \end{array}$ $\begin{array}{r} 11 \\ -9 \\ \hline 2 \end{array}$ $\begin{array}{r} 11 \\ -8 \\ \hline 3 \end{array}$ $\begin{array}{r} 13 \\ -9 \\ \hline 4 \end{array}$ $\begin{array}{r} 13 \\ -8 \\ \hline 5 \end{array}$

What patterns do you see?

answers are in order from 0 to 5; answers get larger;

subtracting 9, 8, 9, 8, 9, 8; top numbers: 2 nines, 2 elevens, 2 thirteens

Subtract. Write the next two number facts in the pattern.

$\begin{array}{r} 14 \\ -7 \\ \hline 7 \end{array}$ $\begin{array}{r} 14 \\ -8 \\ \hline 6 \end{array}$ $\begin{array}{r} 14 \\ -9 \\ \hline 5 \end{array}$ $\begin{array}{r} 11 \\ -7 \\ \hline 4 \end{array}$ $\begin{array}{r} 11 \\ -8 \\ \hline 3 \end{array}$ $\begin{array}{r} 11 \\ -9 \\ \hline 2 \end{array}$

What patterns do you see?

answers are in order from 7 to 2; answers get smaller;

subtracting 7, 8, 9, 7, 8, 9; top numbers: 3 fourteens, 3 elevens

Fill in numbers to make up your own pattern.

Answers will vary.

$\underline{} -9$ $\underline{} -9$ $\underline{} -9$ $\underline{} -9$ $\underline{} -9$ $\underline{} -9$

38   Use with text pages 91 – 92.   TS-2

Addison-Wesley | All Rights Reserved

Reteaching

Skills Review   5-1

Name _____

Subtracting 9

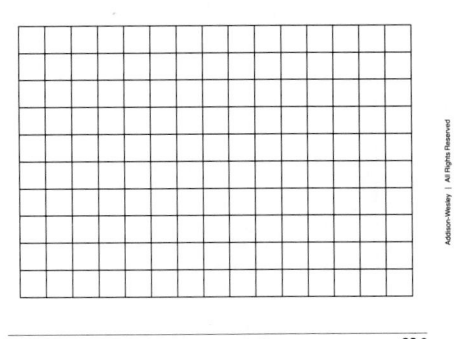

Cross out 9 clowns. $12 - 9 = 3$

Cross out 9 clowns. $15 - 9 = 6$

Subtract.

1. $18 - 9 = 9$ $14 - 9 = 5$ $9 - 9 = 0$

2. $15 - 9 = 6$ $12 - 9 = 3$ $13 - 9 = 4$

3. $11 - 9 = 2$ $10 - 9 = 1$ $16 - 9 = 7$

4. $13 - 9 = 4$ $17 - 9 = 8$ $18 - 9 = 9$

5. $9 - 9 = 0$ $16 - 9 = 7$ $11 - 9 = 2$

38   Use with text pages 91 – 92.   RS-2

Addison-Wesley | All Rights Reserved

Challenges

Cooperative Activities   5-1

Name _____

Spin Art

You need: a friend, a spinner with numbers 11 to 18, and two different-colored crayons.

Rules: Each player chooses a color.
Take turns to spin.
Subtract 9 from the number on the spinner.
Color the same number of squares as the difference.
Color squares anywhere on the board.
Work together to color a design.

38   Use with text pages 91 – 92.   CS-2

Addison-Wesley | All Rights Reserved

OPTIONS FOR INDIVIDUAL NEEDS

Basic

Exercises All

Supplements
Reteaching 38 or
Practice 38

Average

Exercises All

Supplements
Practice 38
Challenges 38 or
Thinking Skills 38

Extended

Exercises All

Supplements
Challenges 38
Thinking Skills 38

Other Resources:
Mathematics Their Way, pp. 180-194, 249
Explorations, pp. 50-59, 63-66, 69, 71, 131, 144, 190-192, 194, 205
Workjobs, pp. 210-211
Workjobs II, pp. 112-115
Developing Number Concepts With Unifix Cubes, pp. 94-96

5-1

OBJECTIVE 5-1

To use the mental math technique of subtracting 9 to find differences

> **Materials:** counters, flannelboard, felt objects, subtraction flashcards with differences of 9

1. MOTIVATE AND TEACH

LEARN ABOUT IT

Read the chapter story to the class. Have students use counters and 10-frames to act out the following problem. *How many nuts were in Squeaky's pail to start?* (15) *How many did Squeaky give his mom?* (9) *How many nuts does Squeaky have left?* (6) Direct students' attention to the tall building on page 91. Give similar subtracting 9 problems for them to solve using counters and the building's windows as a 10-frame.

▶ **How could you model 13 - 9?** (Possible answer: Fill the 10-frame with counters and show 3 more to equal 13. Take away 9 and count how many counters are left.) As students solve the problems, write the facts on the board.

▶ **Look at the top number and at the difference in each subtracting 9 fact. What pattern do you notice?** (Possible answer: The difference in each fact is always 1 more than the ones digit in the top number.)

▶ **Can you suggest a way to get the answer quickly for these subtracting 9 facts?** (Possible answers: Memorize the facts; notice the pattern in the difference and the number you are subtracting from; use addition.)

▶ **Explain how you might use addition to find subtraction answers that you do not know.** (Possible answers: Think of what number added to 9 gives the top number in the subtraction problem. Think about the other number sentences in the fact family.)

2. CHECK UNDERSTANDING

ERROR ALERT Forgetting to add the 1 counter in the 10-frame to the extra counters to find the subtraction answer.

5
More Subtraction Facts

TEACHING OPTIONS

RETEACHING TIPS Have students use a flannelboard to subtract 9. Show 10 objects in a 10-frame and place the extra objects next to it. Ask them to take 9 objects off the 10-frame and count how many are left. Have them write a number sentence to match. Assign Reteaching Supplement 38.

ENRICHMENT Have students use counters and a 10-frame to find the number they are subtracting from.

(13)	(10)	(16)	(14)
− 9	− 9	− 9	− 9
4	1	7	5

ne _____

ubtracting 9

Write a number from
0 to 18 in the box.
se your 10-frame
d counters to
btract. Then write
e differences.

Take away 9.
How many are left?
1 in the 10-frame
and 5 extra.

| 15 |
| − 9 |
| 6 |

☐
− 9

☐
− 9

Answers may vary. Check students' work.

☐
− 9

☐
− 9

☐
− 9

☐
− 9

☐
− 9

☐
− 9

btract. Think of your 10-frame to help.

13	18	14	11	17	16
− 9	− 9	− 9	− 8	− 9	− 9
4	9	5	3	8	7

9 − 9 = 0   16 − 9 = 7   10 − 7 = 3

LK ABOUT IT

Will said, "I started with 13 counters.
First I took away 4 counters. Then I took
away 5 counters. That is the same as
taking away 9." Tell why. **See teaching notes.**

---

3. PRACTICE AND APPLY

Basic	All
Average	All
Extended	All

PRACTICE

*How will you solve the problems in
Exercises 1 and 2?* (Write a number
between 10 and 18 in each box and then
use the 10-frame and counters to help
you find the differences.)

APPLY

TALK ABOUT IT ▶ **Describe the
action that takes place in this story
problem.** (Possible answer: Will is
taking away 2 groups of counters from
the total amount.)
▶ **What might you use to model the
action in this story?** (Possible answer:
Draw a picture and cross out the amounts
Will takes away; use a 10-frame and
counters.)
▶ **Why is taking away 4 and 5 the
same as taking away 9?** (Possible
answer: because 4 + 5 = 9)

5-1

LOSE AND ASSESS

AY WHAT YOU THINK Place
btraction flashcards with differences
9 in a bowl and have each student
oose one. Have students decide
ich method they will use to show
e answer for their facts. Suggest that
ey use counters and a 10-frame, a
oss-out drawing, or tell about the
mber pattern that occurs when 9 is
ing subtracted. Then have them use
e flashcards to quiz each other on
btracting-9 facts.

QUICK QUIZ

Subtract.

17	14	10	15	12
− 9	− 9	− 9	− 9	− 9
(8)	(5)	(1)	(6)	(3)

Using Addition to Subtract 4, 5, and 6

OBJECTIVE 5-2   To use the mental math technique of thinking of related addition facts to find differences

PREBOOK ACTIVITIES

QUICK REVIEW

As I say the addition fact, hold up the number card that shows the sum.

3 + 4	2 + 5	6 + 4	1 + 6	3 + 5	4 + 5
(7)	(7)	(10)	(7)	(8)	(9)

PRIOR KNOWLEDGE

Help students recall how to use addition to check subtraction.
6 firefighters saved a home.
4 firefighters arrived at the home first.
How many more came after them to help? (2)
What addition sentence can you use to check the answer?
(4 + 2 = 6)

COMMUNICATION

Reading and Discussing Math   Write **add to check** on the chalkboard. Read the phrase to students, then have them read it together. Next, write 5 − 1 on the board and ask a volunteer to write the answer. *What addition sentence can we use to check the answer to this subtraction fact?* (1 + 4 = 5) Explain that this is the **add-to-check** fact for 5 − 1 = 4. *How are these facts related? Why is 1 + 4 = 5 called the add-to-check fact?* (Possible answer: Both facts are part of a fact family: 1 + 4 = 5 is the addition fact that matches 5 − 1 = 4.)

EXPLORE AND CONNECT

Materials: Cube-A-Links; addition flashcards for 6 + 4 = 1 8 + 2 = 10, 7 + 3 = 10
Alternative Materials: counters, addition facts on index car
Grouping Suggestion: pairs
Provide each pair of students with 10 linked cubes and addition flashcards. Tell one student to snap the cubes apart show 10 − 3 = 7. *What addition fact checks the subtraction sentence 10 − 3 = 7?* Then tell the partner to hold up the **add-to-check** fact that matches the subtraction sentence sho by the cubes. (7 + 3 = 10) Have students repeat the activity show 10 − 4 = 6 and 10 − 2 = 8 and the matching add-to-check facts. (6 + 4 = 10; 8 + 2 = 10)

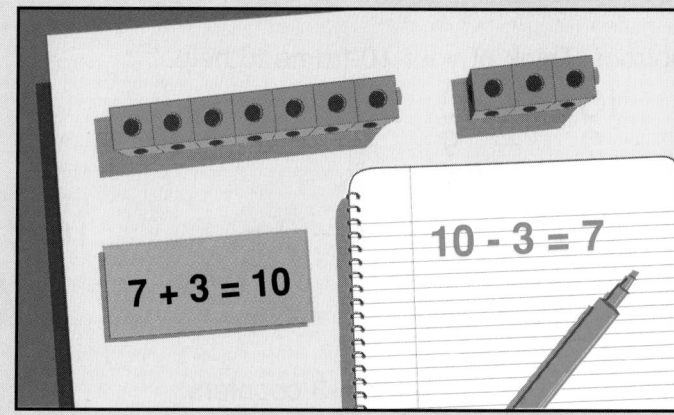

CONNECTIONS   Use these anytime.

Problem of the Day

Life Skills   Michael bought an eraser for 7¢. He gave the clerk a coin. He got 3¢ change. What coin did he give the clerk? (a dime)
Use punchout coins to show what Michael did.

Math Connection

Measurement   Cut 2 pieces of yarn the length of your math book. Then cut one of them into 2 pieces. Place both short pieces beside the whole piece of yarn to compare lengths. Are they the same? (yes) Why? (The 2 parts equal the whole.)

Minute Math

Subtraction   Write only the answers to these subtraction facts. Can you do all of them before one minute passes?

6	9	8	10	5
−2	−7	−6	−2	−5
(4)	(2)	(2)	(8)	(0)
4	10	9	7	9
−2	−1	−0	−3	−8
(2)	(9)	(9)	(4)	(1)

CLASSWORK AND HOMEWORK SUPPLEMENTS

Practice

Skills Maintenance   5-2

Name _____

Using Addition to Subtract 4, 5, and 6

Subtract. Match and add the add-to-check fact.

1.
| $\begin{array}{r} 11 \\ -4 \\ \hline 7 \end{array}$ | $\begin{array}{r} 14 \\ -6 \\ \hline 8 \end{array}$ | $\begin{array}{r} 14 \\ -5 \\ \hline 9 \end{array}$ | $\begin{array}{r} 15 \\ -6 \\ \hline 9 \end{array}$ | $\begin{array}{r} 12 \\ -5 \\ \hline 7 \end{array}$ | $\begin{array}{r} 13 \\ -4 \\ \hline 9 \end{array}$ |

2.
| $\begin{array}{r} 5 \\ +9 \\ \hline 14 \end{array}$ | $\begin{array}{r} 4 \\ +7 \\ \hline 11 \end{array}$ | $\begin{array}{r} 6 \\ +8 \\ \hline 14 \end{array}$ | $\begin{array}{r} 4 \\ +9 \\ \hline 13 \end{array}$ | $\begin{array}{r} 6 \\ +9 \\ \hline 15 \end{array}$ | $\begin{array}{r} 5 \\ +7 \\ \hline 12 \end{array}$ |

3.
| $\begin{array}{r} 13 \\ -6 \\ \hline 7 \end{array}$ | $\begin{array}{r} 15 \\ -6 \\ \hline 9 \end{array}$ | $\begin{array}{r} 14 \\ -5 \\ \hline 9 \end{array}$ | $\begin{array}{r} 12 \\ -4 \\ \hline 8 \end{array}$ | $\begin{array}{r} 11 \\ -5 \\ \hline 6 \end{array}$ | $\begin{array}{r} 13 \\ -5 \\ \hline 8 \end{array}$ |

4.
| $\begin{array}{r} 5 \\ +6 \\ \hline 11 \end{array}$ | $\begin{array}{r} 6 \\ +9 \\ \hline 15 \end{array}$ | $\begin{array}{r} 4 \\ +8 \\ \hline 12 \end{array}$ | $\begin{array}{r} 6 \\ +7 \\ \hline 13 \end{array}$ | $\begin{array}{r} 5 \\ +9 \\ \hline 14 \end{array}$ | $\begin{array}{r} 5 \\ +8 \\ \hline 13 \end{array}$ |

PS-2   Use with text pages 93–94.   39

Building Thinking Skills

Life Skills   5-2

Name _____

How Much More?

Look at the coins in each hand.
How much more money do you need to buy each toy?
Choose the coins you need from the ones pictured below.

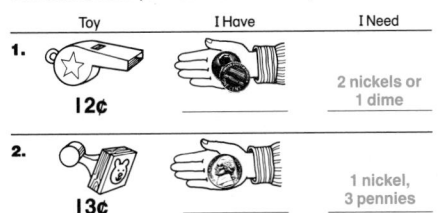

Toy	I Have	I Need
1. 12¢		2 nickels or 1 dime
2. 13¢		1 nickel, 3 pennies
3. 15¢		1 dime or 2 nickels, 1 penny

TS-2   Use with text pages 93–94.   39

Reteaching

Skills Review   5-2

Name _____

Using Addition to Subtract 4, 5, and 6

(whole) 14   Add-to-Check Fact

$\begin{array}{r} 5 \\ +9 \\ \hline 14 \end{array}$

(part) 5 $\begin{array}{r} 14 \\ -5 \\ \hline 9 \end{array}$ (part) 9

Add. Then use these facts below.

1. $4+8 = \underline{12}$ $5+7 = \underline{12}$ $6+9 = \underline{15}$
2. $4+7 = \underline{11}$ $5+6 = \underline{11}$ $6+8 = \underline{14}$
3. $4+9 = \underline{13}$ $5+8 = \underline{13}$ $6+7 = \underline{13}$

Subtract. Finish the add-to-check fact.

Ring the subtraction answer in the add-to-check fact.

4.
| $\begin{array}{r} 12 \\ -5 \\ \hline 7 \end{array}$ | $\begin{array}{r} 5 \\ +7 \\ \hline 12 \end{array}$ | $\begin{array}{r} 11 \\ -4 \\ \hline 7 \end{array}$ | $\begin{array}{r} 4 \\ +7 \\ \hline 11 \end{array}$ | $\begin{array}{r} 13 \\ -6 \\ \hline 7 \end{array}$ | $\begin{array}{r} 6 \\ +7 \\ \hline 13 \end{array}$ |

5.
| $\begin{array}{r} 15 \\ -6 \\ \hline 9 \end{array}$ | $\begin{array}{r} 6 \\ +9 \\ \hline 15 \end{array}$ | $\begin{array}{r} 13 \\ -5 \\ \hline 8 \end{array}$ | $\begin{array}{r} 5 \\ +8 \\ \hline 13 \end{array}$ | $\begin{array}{r} 13 \\ -4 \\ \hline 9 \end{array}$ | $\begin{array}{r} 4 \\ +9 \\ \hline 13 \end{array}$ |

6.
| $\begin{array}{r} 12 \\ -4 \\ \hline 8 \end{array}$ | $\begin{array}{r} 4 \\ +8 \\ \hline 12 \end{array}$ | $\begin{array}{r} 11 \\ -5 \\ \hline 6 \end{array}$ | $\begin{array}{r} 5 \\ +6 \\ \hline 11 \end{array}$ | $\begin{array}{r} 14 \\ -6 \\ \hline 8 \end{array}$ | $\begin{array}{r} 6 \\ +8 \\ \hline 14 \end{array}$ |

RS-2   Use with text pages 93–94.   39

Challenges

Cooperative Activity   5-2

Name _____

Spin, Bubble, and Roll

You need: a friend, a spinner with the numbers 4–6, a number cube with the numbers 10–15, and a marker for each player.

Rules: Let your friend go first.
Roll the number cube and spin the spinner.
Subtract ⊗ from ☐.
Move that number of spaces on the game board.
The first player to reach the bottle of bubbles wins.

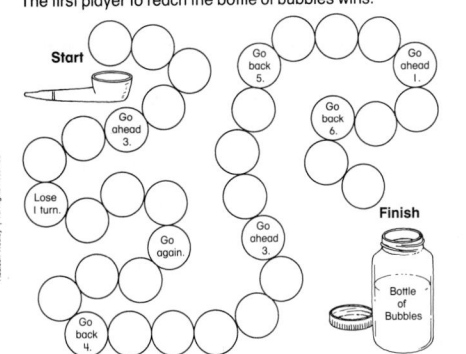

CS-2   Use with text pages 93–94.   39

OPTIONS FOR INDIVIDUAL NEEDS

Basic

Exercises All

Supplements
Reteaching 39 or
Practice 39
Challenges 39

Average

Exercises All

Supplements
Practice 39
Challenges 39 or
Thinking Skills 39

Extended

Exercises All

Supplements
Challenges 39
Thinking Skills 39

Other Resources:
Math in Stride, pp. 12-20, 29
Mathematics Their Way, pp. 180-194, 221-224, 249
Explorations, p. 190
Developing Number Concepts With Unifix Cubes, pp. 94-96, 105-108
Mathematics Book A, p. 28

5-2

LESSON PLAN 5-2

OBJECTIVE 5-2
To use the mental math technique of thinking of related addition facts to find differences

Materials: Cube-A-Links addition fact flashcards, flipover punchouts for subtracting 4, 5, and 6

Grouping Suggestions: individual work, pairs

1. MOTIVATE AND TEACH

LEARN ABOUT IT

Have students use cubes of two colors to model the subtraction fact 11 − 7 = 4. Write the fact on the chalkboard; then have students use their cubes to model an addition fact they could use to check the subtraction. (7 + 4 = 11)
Have students look at the sample exercise at the top of page 93.
▶ **Where does the subtraction answer appear in the add-to-check fact?** (in the middle; as one of the parts of the addition fact)
▶ **Why can addition be used to check subtraction?** (Possible answer: Addition joins the parts that make up the whole, or sum. The sum is the whole in the subtraction sentence.)
▶ **How can add-to-check facts help you find answers to subtraction facts?** (by matching the wholes and parts; the missing part is the answer)
▶ **How is a subtraction fact related to its add-to-check fact?** (It is part of the same fact family.)

2. CHECK UNDERSTANDING

ERROR ALERT Not seeing the relationship between a subtraction fact and its add-to-check fact.

Name _____

Using Addition to Subtract 4, 5, and 6

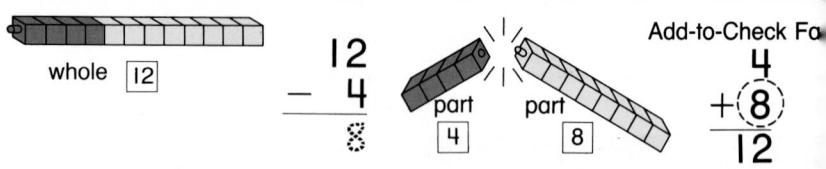

whole [12] $\begin{array}{r} 12 \\ -\ 4 \\ \hline 8 \end{array}$ part [4] part [8]   Add-to-Check Fact $\begin{array}{r} 4 \\ +8 \\ \hline 12 \end{array}$

Find the sums for these add-to-check facts.

1. $4 + 7 = \underline{11}$ $5 + 6 = \underline{11}$ $6 + 7 = \underline{13}$

2. $4 + 9 = \underline{13}$ $5 + 9 = \underline{14}$ $6 + 9 = \underline{15}$

3. $5 + 8 = \underline{13}$ $5 + 7 = \underline{12}$ $6 + 8 = \underline{14}$

Subtract. Finish the add-to-check fact.

4. $\begin{array}{r} 13 \\ -\ 4 \\ \hline 9 \end{array}$ $\begin{array}{r} 4 \\ +9 \\ \hline 13 \end{array}$ $\begin{array}{r} 12 \\ -\ 5 \\ \hline 7 \end{array}$ $\begin{array}{r} 5 \\ +7 \\ \hline 12 \end{array}$ $\begin{array}{r} 15 \\ -\ 6 \\ \hline 9 \end{array}$ $\begin{array}{r} 6 \\ +9 \\ \hline 15 \end{array}$

5. $\begin{array}{r} 14 \\ -\ 6 \\ \hline 8 \end{array}$ $\begin{array}{r} 6 \\ +8 \\ \hline 14 \end{array}$ $\begin{array}{r} 11 \\ -\ 4 \\ \hline 7 \end{array}$ $\begin{array}{r} 4 \\ +7 \\ \hline 11 \end{array}$ $\begin{array}{r} 13 \\ -\ 5 \\ \hline 8 \end{array}$ $\begin{array}{r} 5 \\ +8 \\ \hline 13 \end{array}$

6. $\begin{array}{r} 14 \\ -\ 5 \\ \hline 9 \end{array}$ $\begin{array}{r} 5 \\ +9 \\ \hline 14 \end{array}$ $\begin{array}{r} 13 \\ -\ 6 \\ \hline 7 \end{array}$ $\begin{array}{r} 6 \\ +7 \\ \hline 13 \end{array}$ $\begin{array}{r} 11 \\ -\ 5 \\ \hline 6 \end{array}$ $\begin{array}{r} 5 \\ +6 \\ \hline 11 \end{array}$

TEACHING OPTIONS

RETEACHING TIPS Write addition facts such as 8 + 4, and 9 + 5. Have students use cubes to model the facts and write matching sentences. Have them identify the whole and parts, then snap cubes apart to show, then write, the related subtraction fact. Use Reteaching Supplement 39.

ENRICHMENT **Family Math** Have students work with a family member to write a subtraction problem about something they do at home. They may draw pictures to illustrate the problem and its add-to-check fact, then dictate a sentence to describe it for a family member to write.

ubtract. Match and
d the add-to-check fact.

11	12	14	12	15
− 6	− 5	− 6	− 4	− 6
5	7	8	8	9

5	4	6	6	6
+ 7	+ 8	+ 5	+ 8	+ 9
12	12	11	14	15

13	11	13	11	14
− 6	− 4	− 4	− 5	− 5
7	7	9	6	9

4	6	5	5	4
+ 7	+ 7	+ 9	+ 6	+ 9
11	13	14	11	13

HOW WITH CUBES

ubtract. Write the add-to-check fact.
se cubes to check.

11		6
− 6	+	5
5		11

4.
13		5
− 5	+	8
8		13

5.
12		4
− 4	+	8
8		12

3. PRACTICE AND APPLY

Basic	All
Average	All
Extended	All

PRACTICE

What do you notice about the exercises in rows 1 and 2 on page 94? (Row 1 contains subtraction facts; row 2 has the matching add-to-check facts.)

APPLY

SHOW WITH CUBES ▶ **How can you use cubes to show the subtraction fact?** (You can start with 11 cubes and snap apart to subtract.)
▶ **How can the same cubes show the add-to-check fact?** (You can combine the snapped-apart cubes to find the whole.)
▶ **What can you conclude about each subtraction and add-to-check fact pair?** (They always have the same three numbers.)

5-2

LOSE AND ASSESS

HOW WHAT YOU KNOW
mind students about the chapter
ry, *Mom's Special Dish.* Last year
ueaky could carry 11 nuts. Suppose
gave his mom 4 nuts from his pail.
w many nuts would be left? (7)
ve small groups use cubes to
plore subtraction problems similar
this one.

> **QUICK QUIZ**
>
> Subtract. Then write the add-to-check fact.
>
> 12 − 4   (8; 4 + 8 = 12)
> 15 − 6   (9; 6 + 9 = 15)
> 11 − 5   (6; 5 + 6 = 11)

Fact Practice

OBJECTIVE 5-3   To practice the mental math techniques learned to find differences

PREBOOK ACTIVITIES

QUICK REVIEW

As I write a number on the chalkboard, (5), give a subtraction sentence that has this number as its difference. I will make a list on the chalkboard. (Possible answers: $9 - 4 = 5$; $8 - 3 = 5$; $10 - 5 = 5$; $11 - 6 = 5$)

PRIOR KNOWLEDGE

Assign number values 1-14 to the letters A-N and write the letters and numbers on the chalkboard. Use the letters as a code to write the following subtraction facts on the board: $N - E = \underline{(I)}$, $K - F = \underline{(E)}$, $M - H = \underline{(E)}$, $J - D = \underline{(F)}$, $L - E = \underline{(G)}$. Ask students to use the code to translate the facts and write the differences. Have volunteers write the answers. ($14 - 5 = 9$, $11 - 6 = 5$, $13 - 8 = 5$, $10 - 4 = 6$, $12 - 5 = 7$)

COMMUNICATION

Listening and Discussing Math   Read the following sentences to students. Ask them to show thumbs up if the sentence is true and thumbs down if the sentence is false.
1. The answer to a subtraction problem is the biggest number. (false)
2. When you take something away, you subtract.   (true)
3. All subtraction facts have add-to-check facts.   (true)
4. You can change the place of the numbers in a subtraction fact and still get the same answer.   (false)

EXPLORE AND CONNECT

Materials: 2-color counters, flipover punchouts for subtractin 4, 5, and 6, punchout number cards 5-9
Grouping Suggestion: cooperative learning groups of 3
Provide each group with materials. Have the first student display one of the flipover punchouts for subtracting 4, 5, or Tell the second student to hold up the punchout number card that shows the difference. Have the third student use the 2-color counters to model the matching add-to-check fact. Ha students exchange roles and encourage them to provide constructive feedback to their groupmates when appropriate.

CONNECTIONS   Use these anytime.

Problem of the Day

Logic   A store clerk put 15 new toys on the shelf on Saturday morning. By noon that day, there were only 6 left. Were more or less than 10 toys sold that morning? (less)

Math Connection

Counting Patterns   Find the differences.

13	13	13	13	13	13
-4	-5	-6	-7	-8	-9
(9)	(8)	(7)	?	?	?

Do you see a pattern? What differences will come next? (yes; 6, 5, 4)

Subject Integration

Social Studies   What are some jobs in your neighborhood? Make a list. Count how many you have in all. Now put a check by the jobs you would not like. Count your checks. Subtract the number from the total number of jobs. How many jobs would you like to have? (Answers will vary.)

CLASSWORK AND HOMEWORK SUPPLEMENTS

Practice

| Skills Maintenance | 5-3 |

Name _____

Fact Practice

Subtract.

1. $\begin{array}{r}12\\-9\\\hline 3\end{array}$ $\begin{array}{r}14\\-5\\\hline 9\end{array}$ $\begin{array}{r}11\\-9\\\hline 2\end{array}$ $\begin{array}{r}13\\-8\\\hline 5\end{array}$ $\begin{array}{r}15\\-6\\\hline 9\end{array}$

2. $\begin{array}{r}11\\-3\\\hline 8\end{array}$ $\begin{array}{r}13\\-4\\\hline 9\end{array}$ $\begin{array}{r}14\\-6\\\hline 8\end{array}$ $\begin{array}{r}12\\-8\\\hline 4\end{array}$ $\begin{array}{r}11\\-2\\\hline 9\end{array}$

3. $\begin{array}{r}18\\-9\\\hline 9\end{array}$ $\begin{array}{r}10\\-3\\\hline 7\end{array}$ $\begin{array}{r}13\\-5\\\hline 8\end{array}$ $\begin{array}{r}11\\-8\\\hline 3\end{array}$ $\begin{array}{r}16\\-9\\\hline 7\end{array}$

4. $\begin{array}{r}14\\-8\\\hline 6\end{array}$ $\begin{array}{r}12\\-6\\\hline 6\end{array}$ $\begin{array}{r}11\\-7\\\hline 4\end{array}$ $\begin{array}{r}17\\-8\\\hline 9\end{array}$ $\begin{array}{r}12\\-5\\\hline 7\end{array}$

5. $\begin{array}{r}13\\-6\\\hline 7\end{array}$ $\begin{array}{r}14\\-5\\\hline 9\end{array}$ $\begin{array}{r}17\\-9\\\hline 8\end{array}$ $\begin{array}{r}16\\-7\\\hline 9\end{array}$ $\begin{array}{r}14\\-9\\\hline 5\end{array}$

6. $\begin{array}{r}11\\-6\\\hline 5\end{array}$ $\begin{array}{r}13\\-7\\\hline 6\end{array}$ $\begin{array}{r}14\\-7\\\hline 7\end{array}$ $\begin{array}{r}12\\-4\\\hline 8\end{array}$ $\begin{array}{r}15\\-9\\\hline 6\end{array}$

40   Use with text pages 95–96.   PS-2

Building Thinking Skills

| Reading Math | 5-3 |

Name _____

Party Facts

Read the stories. Write the missing number on the line.
Complete the number sentences at the right of each story.
Match the story with its number sentence.

1. Jeff wrote sixteen party invitations. He mailed eight of them. Jeff has __8__ left to mail.

   $16 - 8 = \underline{8}$
   $16 - 0 = \underline{16}$
   $8 - 8 = \underline{0}$

2. Cassie drew twelve witches. She cut out five of them. Cassie has __7__ left to cut out.

   $12 - 7 = \underline{5}$
   $12 - 5 = \underline{7}$
   $7 - 5 = \underline{2}$

3. Nancy has eleven pumpkins. She carved seven of them. Nancy has __4__ more pumpkins to carve.

   $11 - 7 = \underline{4}$
   $11 - 4 = \underline{7}$
   $7 - 4 = \underline{3}$

4. Steve put fourteen apples in the tub. His friends bobbed for nine of them. Now __5__ apples are left.

   $14 - 5 = \underline{9}$
   $9 - 5 = \underline{4}$
   $14 - 9 = \underline{5}$

5. What kind of party is it? __Halloween party__

40   Use with text pages 95–96.   TS-2

Reteaching

| Skills Review | 5-3 |

Name _____

Fact Practice

Subtract.

1. ⑬ ⑧ ⑤ $13 - 8 = 5$ $13 - 5 = 8$

2. ⑯ ⑦ ⑨ $16 - 7 = 9$ $16 - 9 = 7$

3. ⑭ ⑨ ⑤ $14 - 9 = 5$ $14 - 5 = 9$

4. ⑮ ⑦ ⑧ $15 - 7 = 8$ $15 - 8 = 7$

5. ⑪ ⑨ ② $11 - 9 = 2$ $11 - 2 = 9$

6. ⑫ ⑦ ⑤ $12 - 7 = 5$ $12 - 5 = 7$

Subtract.

7. $\begin{array}{r}13\\-7\\\hline 6\end{array}$ $\begin{array}{r}14\\-7\\\hline 7\end{array}$ $\begin{array}{r}11\\-8\\\hline 3\end{array}$ $\begin{array}{r}15\\-6\\\hline 9\end{array}$ $\begin{array}{r}16\\-8\\\hline 8\end{array}$

8. $\begin{array}{r}14\\-6\\\hline 8\end{array}$ $\begin{array}{r}13\\-4\\\hline 9\end{array}$ $\begin{array}{r}12\\-3\\\hline 9\end{array}$ $\begin{array}{r}12\\-6\\\hline 6\end{array}$ $\begin{array}{r}11\\-6\\\hline 5\end{array}$

40   Use with text pages 95–96.   RS-2

Challenges

| Number Sense | 5-3 |

Name _____

Find the Facts

Find three numbers in a row that make a subtraction fact.
Look across or down in the direction shown by the arrows.
Ring each fact. Can you find 20?

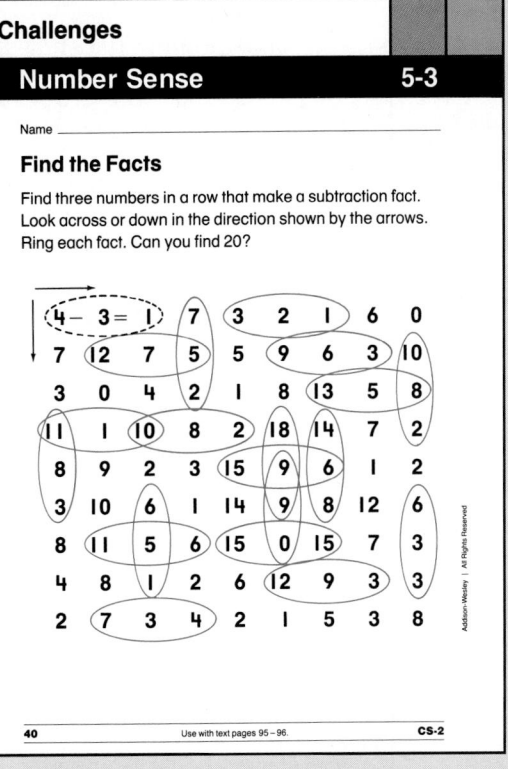

40   Use with text pages 95–96.   CS-2

Basic

Exercises All

Supplements
Reteaching 40 or
Practice 40
Thinking Skills 40

Average

Exercises All

Supplements
Practice 40
Challenges 40 or
Thinking Skills 40

Extended

Exercises All

Supplements
Challenges 40
Thinking Skills 40

Other Resources:
Mathematics Their Way, pp. 205, 248, 318
Explorations, pp. 135-136, 138, 144
Problem Solving Experiences In Mathematics, pp. 28, 29, 64, 65, 77, 112
Mathematics Book A, p. 28
The Mad Minute, pp. 96-100, 126-130

5-3

OBJECTIVE 5-3
To practice the mental math techniques learned to find differences

Materials: subtraction fact flashcards, index cards

Grouping Suggestions: individual work, small groups

1. MOTIVATE AND TEACH

LEARN ABOUT IT

Practice subtraction facts by having each student write a 4, 5, or 6 on an index card. When you call out a number between 7 and 13, students say a subtraction fact using your number and the number on their card. For example, if you call 11, a student holding a 4 says, "11 − 4 = 7."

Direct students' attention to the top of page 95. *What is the difference for the first exercise?* (1) *What code letter belongs in the number 1 box of the riddle's answer?* (U)

▶ **How could you write different subtraction facts to use in solving this riddle?** (The facts would have to have the same differences in order to match the correct letter.)

▶ **How can knowing different subtraction facts for the same difference help you solve the riddle?** (You can quickly find the letter that stands for that difference.)

2. CHECK UNDERSTANDING

ERROR ALERT Adding instead of subtracting.

Name _____

Fact Practice

Subtract. Then write the code letter that matches the number in the box below.

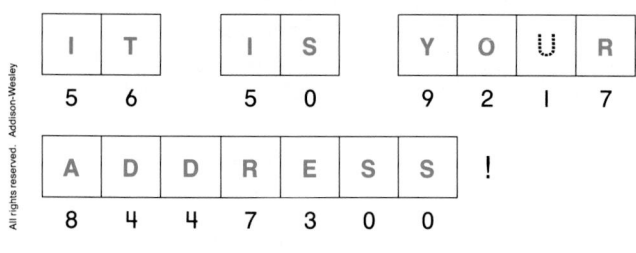

What kind of dr do you have bu never wear?

U	4 − 3 = 1

A	13 − 5 = 8	I	8 − 3 = 5

R	11 − 4 = 7	O	10 − 8 = 2	Y	15 − 6 = 9

Y	13 − 4 = 9	Y	14 − 5 = 9	T	15 − 9 = 6

O	8 − 6 = 2	T	11 − 5 = 6	D	12 − 8 = 4

S	1 − 1 = 0	D	13 − 9 = 4	I	11 − 6 = 5

A	14 − 6 = 8	R	12 − 5 = 7	E	9 − 6 = 3

I	T		I	S		Y	O	U	R
5	6		5	0		9	2	1	7

A	D	D	R	E	S	S	!
8	4	4	7	3	0	0	

Chapter 5   (ninety-five)

TEACHING OPTIONS

RETEACHING TIPS Have students solve subtraction facts, such as 13 − 4 = 9, using counters to show the whole and removing some to subtract the part. Explain that the remaining counters show the difference and have them write the subtraction sentence. Assign Reteaching Supplement 40.

ENRICHMENT **Family Math** Have students work with a family member to make up a riddle with a short answer and write a subtraction fact for each letter in the answer. Have them match answers to facts with a letter from the riddle's answer. Have students exchange and solve each other's riddles.

ubtract.

10 − 7 ___ 3	12 − 4 ___ 8	14 − 9 ___ 5	13 − 6 ___ 7	11 − 5 ___ 6

17 − 9 ___ 8	10 − 5 ___ 5	12 − 5 ___ 7	12 − 9 ___ 3	8 −4 ___ 4	11 − 9 ___ 2

11 − 4 ___ 7	16 − 8 ___ 8	14 − 6 ___ 8	18 − 9 ___ 9	13 − 4 ___ 9	12 − 6 ___ 6

15 − 9 = __6__   11 − 8 = __3__   13 − 5 = __8__

16 − 9 = __7__   14 − 7 = __7__   15 − 6 = __9__

14 − 5 = __9__   11 − 6 = __5__   6 − 3 = __3__

SE CRITICAL THINKING

Roger was last in line. Randi was ahead of Charlie.
Who was first in line? Write each name below.

	Randi	Charlie	Roger

3. PRACTICE AND APPLY

Basic	All
Average	All
Extended	All

PRACTICE

Direct students' attention to the vertical and horizontal formats of the exercises on page 96. *Can subtraction exercises written "up and down" and "sideways" be solved in the same way?* (yes)

APPLY

USE CRITICAL THINKING
▶ **What do you need to find to solve this problem?** (the animals' positions in line)
▶ **How many animals are in line?** (3)
▶ **What do you already know?** (Roger is last in line.)
▶ **What strategies might you use to find out where Randi and Charlie are standing?** (Possible answers: Draw a picture; use objects to show the animals.)
▶ **How can you check to see if your answer is correct?** (Reread the clues; see if your answer makes the clues true.)

5-3

CLOSE AND ASSESS

SAY WHAT YOU KNOW
Provide each small group with subtraction flash cards. Have each student draw a card, read it aloud, and give an answer. If the answer is correct, the student keeps the card. If the answer is incorrect, the card goes to the bottom of the pile. Encourage students to provide constructive feedback when they can.

QUICK QUIZ

Subtract.
13 − 4 = __(9)__   15 − 6 = __(9)__

17 − 8 ___ (9)	15 − 6 ___ (9)	14 − 5 ___ (9)	12 − 4 ___ (8)	11 − 5 ___ (6)

OBJECTIVE 5-4   To understand the operation of subtraction by taking away or by comparing; to use mental

PREBOOK ACTIVITIES

QUICK REVIEW

Subtract.

5	7	8	9	11	13	14	12	14
-3	-6	-1	-4	-5	-8	-6	-4	-8
(2)	(1)	(7)	(5)	(6)	(5)	(8)	(8)	(6)

PRIOR KNOWLEDGE

Ask students to imagine that they have some counters. Present each of the following situations. Have students decide whether each situation calls for comparing the counters or taking them away.
2 counters fall off your desk. (take away)
You have 7 counters. Your neighbor has 3. (compare)
You give 4 of your counters to your friend. (take away)

COMMUNICATION

Writing and Discussing Math   Write the words **take away** and **compare** on the chalkboard. *What do you know about these words?* (Possible answer: *Take away* and *compare* are two different kinds of stories that you solve by subtraction.) *Which kind of problem usually asks how many are left?* (take away) *What does a compare story usually ask?* (how many more)
Have students work in groups. Provide each group with a subtraction sentence. Have half of the groups write a *take-away* story and model it with counters. Have the other half write and model a *compare* story. Have groups share their stories with the class.

EXPLORE AND CONNECT

COOPERATIVE ACTIVITY

Grouping Suggestions: small groups
Finish the number sentence.
10 children were drinking grape juice.
6 children were drinking orange juice.
How many more children were drinking grape juice?
  (10) $-$ (6) $=$ (4)

TEACHING ACTIONS

 ▶ **How many children were drinking grape juice?** (10) **How many were drinking orange juice?** (6)
▶ **What do we want to find out?** (how many more children were drinking grape juice)
▶ **What action words help you to know that this is a compare story?** (*How many more . . . were drinking*)

 ▶ **How can you use counters to help you sol** the problem? (Show 10 counters of one color a 6 counters of another. Match up the counters of the two colors; and count how many more of the larger amoun
▶ **What should you do next?** (Finish the number sentence with the matching data: $10 - 6 = 4$.)

AFTER ▶ **What does the answer tell you?** (4 more children were drinking grape juice than orange juice.)
▶ **How do you know the answer makes sense?** (Possible answer: 4 is the difference between 10 and 6.) Have students work in small groups to make up a take-away problem and us counters to solve it.

CONNECTIONS   Use these anytime.

Problem of the Day
Understanding the Operations
Write a number sentence and solve the problem.
Sue has 8 pennies.
José has 3 pennies.
How many fewer pennies does José have?
$(8 - 3 = 5)$

Number Sense
Mental Math   Use mental math to find the sums. Write only the answers. Think of count ups, doubles, and 10 sums to help.
1. $3 + 3 + 2$ (8)   **2.** $9 + 4 + 1$ (14)
3. $6 + 3 + 6$ (15)   **4.** $2 + 0 + 8$ (10)
5. $1 + 8 + 8$ (17)   **6.** $3 + 4 + 6$ (13)
7. $2 + 9 + 3$ (14)   **8.** $7 + 3 + 7$ (17)

Subject Integration
Language Arts   Choose a picture book that you like. Find a picture that has a number of one kind of thing. Make up a subtraction story about the set of things becoming smaller. Tell your story to the class.

...th to solve number riddles

CLASSWORK AND HOMEWORK SUPPLEMENTS

Practice

Problem Solving   5-4

Name _____

Understanding the Operations

Read each story.
Finish the number sentence to answer the question.

Take Away Stories	Compare Stories
1. Joshua went for a walk in the park. He found 7 sticks. He gave 4 sticks to his sister. How many sticks did he have left?	**2.** Monique saw 12 red leaves in the park. She saw 6 orange leaves, too. How many more red leaves did she see than orange leaves?
$7 - 4 = 3$	$12 - 6 = 6$
He had _3_ sticks left.	She saw _6_ more red leaves.
3. Carlos saw 9 squirrels looking for nuts in the park. 4 of the squirrels ran away when they saw him. How many squirrels were left to look at?	**4.** Eva was walking in the park and found 11 rocks. 5 of the rocks had black specks on them. How many rocks did not have black specks on them?
$9 - 4 = 5$	$11 - 5 = 6$
There were _5_ squirrels left.	_6_ rocks did not have black specks.

Addison-Wesley | All Rights Reserved

PS-2   Use with text page 97.   41

Building Thinking Skills

Family Math   5-4

Name _____

Mental Math

> Dear Family,
>   Your child is learning to use mental math to solve problems. Help your child use the clues below to find the pearls.

12   4   9   27   18

1. A big pearl is in the oyster that is the sum of a double. It is more than 8 + 9.

The sum of its digits is _9_.

The big pearl is in oyster _18_.

2. A middle-sized pearl is in the oyster that is less than 15 − 2. It is a 1-digit number.

It is more than double 4 and less than double 5.   *Answers will vary.*

The middle-sized pearl is in oyster _9_.

3. A small pearl is in the oyster that is more than 7 + 3. The sum of the digits is less than 14 − 5.

One digit is _1 or 2_.

The small pearl is in oyster _12_.

Addison-Wesley | All Rights Reserved

TS-2   Use with text page 98.   41

Reteaching

Number Sense   5-4

Name _____

Mental Math

> Read the clues.
> Think carefully.
> What is the number?

1. I am more than 5 + 5.
I am less than 7 + 7.
I am an even number.

My number is _12_.

2. I am less than a dozen.
I am more than 5 + 5.
I am an odd number.

My number is _11_.

3. I am more than the number of fingers you have.
I am less than 8 + 8.
I am a number some people think is unlucky.

My number is _13_.

4. I am more than the number of toes you have.
I am less than 9 + 9.
I am the same as a ___, and a ___.

My number is _16_.

5. I am between 10 − 6 and 18 − 9. I am between 12 − 6 and 16 − 8.

My number is _7_.

6. I am more than a ___.
I am less than a ___.
I am a sum of a double.
I am not 6.

My number is _8_.

Addison-Wesley | All Rights Reserved

RS-2   Use with text page 98.   41

Challenges

Patterns   5-4

Name _____

Library Stories

Read the stories.
Draw an X on the **take away** stories.
Draw an O on the **compare** stories.
Write the number sentences.

1. There were 12 books in the store window. 6 were sold. How many were left?	**2.** The library has 5 record players and 7 tape players. How many are there in all?	**3.** Our class has 11 records. Ali's class has 6. How many more records do we have?
$12 - 6 = 6$	$5 + 7 = 12$	$11 - 6 = 5$
4. Al has 16 books. Sam borrowed 9. How many does Al have left?	**5.** Ben read 3 books. Then he read 8. How many did he read in all?	**6.** 13 people have library cards. 9 do not. How many more have library cards?
$16 - 9 = 7$	$3 + 8 = 11$	$13 - 9 = 4$

Addison-Wesley | All Rights Reserved

CS-2   Use with text page 97.   41

OPTIONS FOR INDIVIDUAL NEEDS

Basic

Exercises All

Supplements
Reteaching 41 or
Practice 41

Average

Exercises All

Supplements
Practice 41
Challenges 41 or
Thinking Skills 41

Extended

Exercises All

Supplements
Challenges 41
Thinking Skills 41

Other Resources:
Math in Stride, p. 77
Mathematics Their Way, pp. 205, 208
Explorations, pp. 191-192
Problem Solving Experiences In Mathematics, pp. 33, 39, 45, 57, 63, 69, 75, 99
Mathematics Book A, pp. 28-30

5-4

OBJECTIVE 5-4
To understand the operation of subtraction by taking away or by comparing; to use mental math to solve number riddles

Materials: counters, punchout number cards 1-20

1. MOTIVATE AND TEACH

LEARN ABOUT IT

 **BEFORE** ▶ **Look at Exercises 1 and 2. Describe how they are alike and different.**
(Possible answer: The data are the same and both use subtraction, but one is a take-away story and the other is a compare story.)

 **DURING** ▶ **How can you use counters to help you plan a solution for each kind of problem?** (For the take-away story, model the first number and then remove the number being taken away. For the compare story, model both numbers and line up the counters to see how many more of one group there are.)

 **AFTER** ▶ **Suggest a way that you can check your number sentence and solution.**
(Possible answers: Draw a picture; use other objects; add to check.)

2. CHECK UNDERSTANDING

ERROR ALERT **Page 97** Adding instead of subtracting to compare.
Page 98 Forgetting values of pennies, nickels, and dimes.

Name _____

Problem Solving
Understanding the Operations

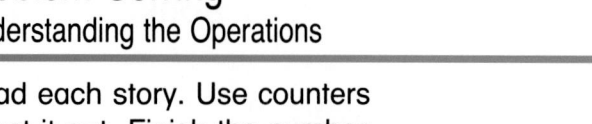

Read each story. Use counters to act it out. Finish the number sentence. Answer the question.

Take Away Stories	Compare Stories
1. Mr. Reyes baked 14 rolls. He sold 6 rolls in the morning. How many rolls did he have left? $\underline{14} - \underline{6} = \underline{8}$ He had __8__ rolls left.	2. Mr. Reyes baked 14 rolls. Mrs. Hall baked 6 rolls. How many more rolls did Mr. Reyes bake than Mrs. Hall? $\underline{14} - \underline{6} = \underline{8}$ He baked __8__ more rolls.
3. There were 12 loaves of bread in the oven. Mr. Reyes took out 5 loaves. How many loaves of bread were still in the oven? $\underline{12} - \underline{5} = \underline{7}$ __7__ loaves of bread were still in the oven.	4. There were 5 loaves of wheat bread. There were 12 loaves of rye bread. How many more loaves of rye bread were there than wheat bread? $\underline{12} - \underline{5} = \underline{7}$ There were __7__ more loaves of rye bread.

Chapter 5 (ninety-seven)

TEACHING OPTIONS

RETEACHING TIPS Place 2 different-colored objects on the flannelboard. Tell a compare story. Have students model the problem with a 1-to-1 correspondence, tell how many are left, and write a subtraction sentence to match. For help with mental math, use Reteaching Supplement 41.

COMPUTER **Fish Scales, DLM-Developmental © 1985** Practice in comparing numbers for all levels. In *Fishing Derby*, two students compete to guess how far fish are from the dock. After each guess, they are told if they are too close or too far away. The lesson requires 5-10 minutes.

ental Math

ead the clues. Find the mber. Use your number rd punchouts to help.

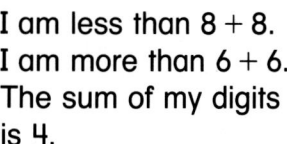

> Turn over cards you do not want.

I am less than 8 + 8.
I am more than 6 + 6.
The sum of my digits is 4.

My number is __13__.

2. I am less than 9 + 9.
I am more than 7 + 8.
I am the sum of a double.

My number is __16__.

I am between 10 − 6 and 11 − 3. I am between 11 − 5 and 15 − 6.

My number is __7__.

4. I am between 9 − 5 and 13 − 6. I am between 9 − 7 and 8 − 2.

My number is __5__.

I am less than one dozen.
I am more than 4 + 4.
One of my digits is 0.

My number is __10__.

> 12 is the same as one dozen.

(ninety-eight)

Chapter 5

3. PRACTICE AND APPLY

Basic	All
Average	All
Extended	All

Have students look at page 98.

▶ **Explain what a digit is.** (Possible answer: It is any number from 0 to 9.)
What digits are used in 17? (1 and 7)

▶ **What does it mean to use mental math to solve a problem?** (Possible answer: You do not write the problem or use objects; you solve it in your head.)

▶ **How can you organize the number cards to help you solve the problem? Explain.** (Possible answer: Put the number cards in order. As you read each clue, turn over the cards for the numbers that cannot be right.)

▶ **Why can many clues describe one number?** (Possible answer: A number and its value can be described in different ways.)

5-4

LOSE AND ASSESS

RITE WHAT YOU KNOW Ask
dents in small groups to write a
e away story, a compare story, and
iddle that describes a number.
dents should give each other
sitive feedback as they listen to
ch other's suggestions. Have groups
are their stories and use counters to
del the actions.

QUICK QUIZ

Guess Andy's age. His age is between 13 − 6 and 5 + 5. It is not the sum of a double. (9)

Using Addition to Subtract 7 and 8

OBJECTIVE 5-5   To use the mental math technique of thinking of related addition facts to find differences

PREBOOK ACTIVITIES

QUICK REVIEW

As I call out subtraction facts, hold up the punchout number card that shows the answer.

2 + 8	7 + 3	4 + 8	7 + 2	3 + 8	1 + 8
(10)	(10)	(12)	(9)	(11)	(9)

PRIOR KNOWLEDGE

Help students recall using addition to check subtraction.
  12 special Police Parking spaces are marked.
  8 police cars are parked.
  How many empty spaces are there? (4)
What addition sentence can you use to check the answer?
(8 + 4 = 12)

COMMUNICATION

Writing in Math   Have students copy and complete each sentence in their Math Journals, using one of the words below.
addition   subtraction   together
1. (Subtraction) shows taking away.
2. Addition joins (together) again.
3. (Addition) checks the subtraction answer.

EXPLORE AND CONNECT

Materials: Cube-A-Links, addition flashcards for 8 + 7 = 1.
9 + 7 = 16, 5 + 7 = 12
Alternative Materials: counters
Grouping Suggestion: pairs
Provide each pair of students with 16 cubes and addition fact flashcards. Tell one student to join 15 cubes and then snap them apart to show 15 − 8 = 7. Have the partner hold up th add-to-check fact that matches the subtraction sentence show by the cubes. *What addition fact checks the subtraction sentence 15 − 8 = 7?* (8 + 7 = 15) Have students repeat th activity using these facts: 16 − 7 = 9 and 12 − 7 = 5. (add-to-check facts: 9 + 7 = 16, 5 + 7 = 12) Encourage students to offer helpful advice to each other when necessary

7 + 8 = 15   15 - 8 = 7

CONNECTIONS   Use these anytime.

Problem of the Day

Change   Angie bought a pencil for 7¢ and an eraser for 4¢. She gave the store clerk one dime and one nickel. How much change did she receive? (4¢)

Life Skills

Reading a Map   Imagine that you are walking toward the police station from your home, which is 7 blocks from the police station. You are 3 blocks away from the station. How many blocks are you from home? (4) Draw a map or use a number line to help you.

Minute Math

Subtract   Write only the answers. Can you do all in less than a minute?

12	9	7	13	12
−8	−6	−4	−6	−7
(4)	(3)	(3)	(7)	(5)

14	13	12	10	11
−6	−7	−6	−5	−2
(8)	(6)	(6)	(5)	(9)

CLASSWORK AND HOMEWORK SUPPLEMENTS

OPTIONS FOR INDIVIDUAL NEEDS

Basic

Exercises All

Supplements
Reteaching 42 or
Practice 42

Average

Exercises All

Supplements
Practice 42
Challenges 42 or
Thinking Skills 42

Extended

Exercises All

Supplements
Challenges 42
Thinking Skills 42

Other Resources:
Math in Stride, pp. 12-20
Mathematics Their Way, pp. 180-194, 221-224, 249
Explorations, pp. 190, 193
The Mad Minute, pp. 96-100, 126-130

Practice

Skills Maintenance   5-5

Name _____

Using Addition to Subtract 7 and 8

Subtract.
Match and complete the add-to-check fact.

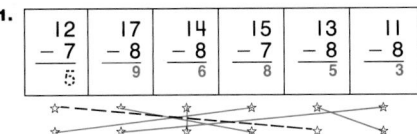

1.

| $12 - 7 = 5$ | $17 - 8 = 9$ | $14 - 8 = 6$ | $15 - 7 = 8$ | $13 - 8 = 5$ | $11 - 8 = 3$ |

2.

| $7 + 8 = 15$ | $8 + 3 = 11$ | $8 + 6 = 14$ | $8 + 9 = 17$ | $7 + 5 = 12$ | $8 + 5 = 13$ |

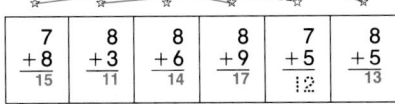

3.

| $13 - 7 = 6$ | $11 - 7 = 4$ | $12 - 8 = 4$ | $16 - 7 = 9$ | $15 - 8 = 7$ | $14 - 8 = 6$ |

4.

| $8 + 4 = 12$ | $8 + 7 = 15$ | $8 + 6 = 14$ | $7 + 6 = 13$ | $7 + 9 = 16$ | $7 + 4 = 11$ |

42   Use with text pages 99 – 100.   PS-2

Building Thinking Skills

Mental Math   5-5

Name _____

Mystery Numbers

16
$- 7$
9 ($16 - 7 = 9$)

Write the missing numbers.

1.

| $13 - 9 = 4$ | $16 - 7 = 9$ | $12 - 6 = 6$ | $15 - 9 = 6$ | $13 - 7 = 6$ |

2.

| $13 - 5 = 8$ | $15 - 8 = 7$ | $12 - 8 = 4$ | $18 - 9 = 9$ | $11 - 8 = 3$ |

3.

| $11 - 4 = 7$ | $17 - 8 = 9$ | $13 - 8 = 5$ | $14 - 6 = 8$ | $15 - 6 = 9$ |

4.

| $15 - 7 = 8$ | $13 - 6 = 7$ | $16 - 9 = 7$ | $12 - 7 = 5$ | $17 - 9 = 8$ |

42   Use with text pages 99 – 100.   TS-2

Reteaching

Skills Review   5-5

Name _____

Using Addition to Subtract 7 and 8

How many are there in each part?
Subtract.

1.

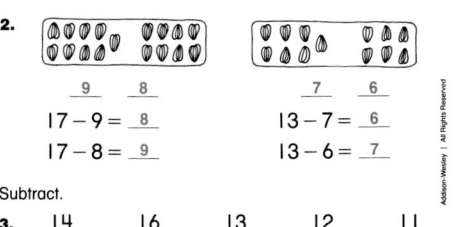

$15 - 8 = 7$
$15 - 7 = 8$

$16 - 9 = 7$
$16 - 7 = 9$

2.

$9 \quad 8$
$17 - 9 = 8$
$17 - 8 = 9$

$7 \quad 6$
$13 - 7 = 6$
$13 - 6 = 7$

Subtract.

3.

| $14 - 8 = 6$ | $16 - 8 = 8$ | $13 - 8 = 5$ | $12 - 7 = 5$ | $11 - 7 = 4$ |

42   Use with text pages 99 – 100.   RS-2

Challenges

Calculators   5-5

Name _____

Calculator Challenge

1. [6] [7] [9] [+] [−] [=]

Use each of these keys only once. Use no other keys.
Make your calculator read ⟶ [1 0]
Write the keys in the correct order.

$7 + 9 - 6 =$ or $7 - 6 + 9 =$

2. Now use these keys.

[8] [4] [9] [+] [−] [=]

Make your calculator read ⟶ [1 3]
Write what you did.

$9 - 4 + 8 =$ or $9 + 8 - 4 =$

3. Here is one more.

[8] [7] [8] [+] [−] [=]

Make your calculator read ⟶ [9]
Write how you did it.

$8 - 7 + 8 =$ or $8 + 8 - 7 =$

4. Make up your own puzzle.

42   Use with text pages 99 – 100.   CS-2

5-5

Addison-Wesley | All Rights Reserved

LESSON PLAN 5-5

OBJECTIVE 5-5
To use the mental math technique of thinking of related addition facts to find differences

Materials: subtraction fact flashcards with differences 4-8, matching add-to-check cards, TA 3 (Graph Paper), flipover punchouts for subtracting 7 and 8

Grouping Suggestions: individual work, pairs

1. MOTIVATE AND TEACH

LEARN ABOUT IT

Place the subtraction flashcards with differences 4–6 along one side of the chalkledge. Place all but one of the matching add-to-check facts randomly along the other side. Have students work together to find out which add-to-check fact is missing. Encourage them to provide helpful advice as they look for a solution.

▶ **How does the add-to-check fact show the subtraction answer?** (The missing part of the subtraction fact appears as one of the parts of the add-to-check fact.)

▶ **How can you use cubes to complete the subtraction and add-to-check facts?** (Snap the cubes apart to show subtraction; snap them together again to show addition.)

▶ **What do you notice about the numbers in each pair of subtraction and add-to-check facts?** (They are the same three numbers.)

2. CHECK UNDERSTANDING

ERROR ALERT Adding the known addend to itself instead of to the difference from the subtraction fact.

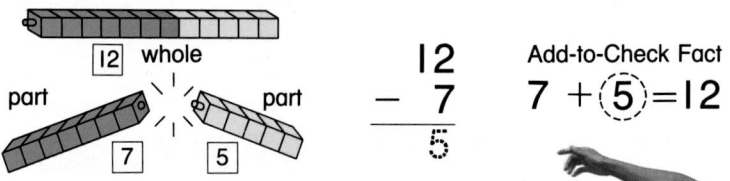

Name _____

Using Addition to Subtract 7 and 8

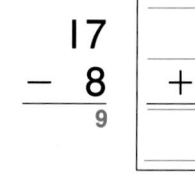

$$12$$
$$-\ 7$$
$$\overline{5}$$

Add-to-Check Fact
$$7 + ⑤ = 12$$

Find the sums for the add-to-check facts.

1. $7 + 5 = \underline{12}$ $7 + 6 = \underline{13}$ $8 + 5 = \underline{13}$

2. $7 + 8 = \underline{15}$ $7 + 9 = \underline{16}$ $8 + 9 = \underline{17}$

3. $7 + 4 = \underline{11}$ $8 + 6 = \underline{14}$ $8 + 4 = \underline{12}$

Subtract. Write the add-to-check fact.

4.
$$13$$ $$7$$ $$12$$ $$8$$ $$11$$ $$7$$
$$-\ 7$$ $$+6$$ $$-\ 8$$ $$+4$$ $$-\ 7$$ $$+\ $$
$$\overline{6}$$ $$\overline{13}$$ $$\overline{4}$$ $$\overline{12}$$ $$\overline{4}$$ $$\overline{1}$$

5.
$$13$$ $$8$$ $$15$$ $$7$$ $$17$$ $$8$$
$$-\ 8$$ $$+5$$ $$-\ 7$$ $$+8$$ $$-\ 8$$ $$+9$$
$$\overline{5}$$ $$\overline{13}$$ $$\overline{8}$$ $$\overline{15}$$ $$\overline{9}$$ $$\overline{1}$$

6.
$$14$$ $$8$$ $$12$$ $$7$$ $$16$$ $$7$$
$$-\ 8$$ $$+6$$ $$-\ 7$$ $$+5$$ $$-\ 7$$ $$+9$$
$$\overline{6}$$ $$\overline{14}$$ $$\overline{5}$$ $$\overline{12}$$ $$\overline{9}$$ $$\overline{1}$$

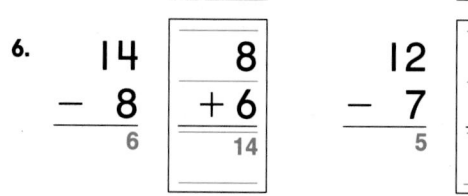

Chapter 5

(ninety-nine)

TEACHING OPTIONS

RETEACHING TIPS Write 15 − 8 on the board. On graph paper, have students color 15 squares and mark a black *X* inside 8 to show they are being subtracted. They count the unmarked squares to find how many are left. (7) Have them write the add-to-check fact. Use Reteaching Supplement 42.

ENRICHMENT Have students choose a subtraction fact and use it to write a story problem. When they have completed the problem, have them read it aloud for their classmates to solve and check.

ubtract. Match the add-to-check fact.
d it.

$12 - 8 = \underline{4}$ •   • $7 + 4 = \underline{11}$

$11 - 7 = \underline{4}$ •   • $7 + 8 = \underline{15}$

$13 - 8 = \underline{5}$ •   • $8 + 4 = \underline{12}$

$15 - 7 = \underline{8}$ •   • $8 + 5 = \underline{13}$

$11 - 6 = \underline{5}$ •   • $6 + 5 = \underline{11}$

$12 - 7 = \underline{5}$ •   • $7 + 9 = \underline{16}$

$14 - 8 = \underline{6}$ •   • $7 + 5 = \underline{12}$

$16 - 7 = \underline{9}$ •   • $8 + 6 = \underline{14}$

MIDCHAPTER REVIEW/QUIZ

ubtract. Finish the add-to-check fact.

$$\begin{array}{r} 14 \\ -\ 5 \\ \hline 9 \end{array} \qquad \begin{array}{r} 5 \\ +\ 9 \\ \hline 14 \end{array}$$

$$\begin{array}{r} 15 \\ -\ 9 \\ \hline 6 \end{array} \qquad \begin{array}{r} 9 \\ +\ 6 \\ \hline 15 \end{array}$$

$$\begin{array}{r} 12 \\ -\ 4 \\ \hline 8 \end{array} \qquad \begin{array}{r} 4 \\ +\ 8 \\ \hline 12 \end{array}$$

ubtract.

$13 - 6 = \underline{7}$ $17 - 8 = \underline{9}$ $16 - 7 = \underline{9}$

             Chapter 5

LOSE AND ASSESS

HOW WHAT YOU KNOW

emind students of Squeaky the
uirrel. *Suppose Squeaky gave his
om 7 nuts instead of 9. How many
ts would be left in the pail?* (8)
uppose Squeaky gave his mom 8
ts? How many nuts would be left in
e pail?* (7) Have students use
unters to model problems similar to
ese.

---

3. PRACTICE AND APPLY

Basic	All; Midchapter Review/Quiz
Average	All; Midchapter Review/Quiz
Extended	All; Midchapter Review/Quiz

PRACTICE

On page 100, point out the dashed line
between $12 - 8 = 4$ and $8 + 4 = 12$.
Why are these two facts connected?
(They are related: The subtraction fact
matches the add-to-check fact.)

APPLY

▶ **What is another method you can
use to check subtraction?** (Subtract the
difference from the top number.)
▶ **Which method of checking
subtraction do you like best? Why?**
(Possible answer: add to check, because
addition is easier)

MIDCHAPTER REVIEW/QUIZ

ITEM ANALYSIS The following
table correlates the Midchapter
Review/Quiz items with lesson
objectives.

Items	Objectives
1	5-1, 5-2
2	5-2, 5-5

5-5

QUICK QUIZ

Subtract. Then write the add-to-check
fact and solve.
$14 - 8$ $(6; 8 + 6 = 14)$
$15 - 7$ $(8; 7 + 8 = 15)$
$17 - 8$ $(9; 8 + 9 = 17)$

Fact Practice

OBJECTIVE 5-6   To practice the mental math techniques learned to find differences

PREBOOK ACTIVITIES

QUICK REVIEW

Subtract.

12 − 4 = _(8)_	12 − 5 = _(7)_	12 − 6 = _(6)_
13 − 4 = _(9)_	13 − 5 = _(8)_	13 − 6 = _(7)_
14 − 7 = _(7)_	14 − 8 = _(6)_	14 − 9 = _(5)_
15 − 9 = _(6)_	15 − 8 = _(7)_	15 − 7 = _(8)_

PRIOR KNOWLEDGE

Invite students to discuss some of the everyday uses of subtraction, using examples of situations in the classroom. These might include finding out how many more books, supplies, or snacks are needed so that there are enough for each student; comparing numbers of students absent on different days, and finding how many days of school are left in a week or month.

COMMUNICATION

Reading and Discussing Math   Write the following words on the chalkboard: **tally, data, bar graph.** Have students read the words aloud. Then write *red, blue, yellow,* and *green* and tell students that you want to find out which color is their favorite. *How should I collect the data?* (Vote and tally.) Have students vote and record the responses with tally marks. Ask volunteers to count the totals and record the numbers. *How can we show the data in another way?* (Make a bar graph.) Draw a graph and have students fill in the correct number of boxes. Ask questions that can be answered by reading the graph. *How many students like yellow? How many more like red than green?*

EXPLORE AND CONNECT

Materials: 12 subtraction fact flashcards with differences 4, 5, and 6; 20 counters for each group
Grouping Suggestion: cooperative learning groups of 3
Place the flashcards on the chalkboard ledge and have students in each group work together to find the answers to each fact, using counters to check when they are not sure or when answers are not agreed on. Remind students that when they disagree with an answer they should help their partners by using counters to show how the exercise should be done. Have one student keep a tally of the number of times the difference is 4, another keep a tally for the difference of 5, and another keep a tally for 6. When all groups are finished, discuss how you might collect and show their tallies on a bar graph. Use their ideas to draw a bar graph on the chalkboard and have volunteers from different groups record their data.

CONNECTIONS   Use these anytime.

Problem of the Day

Too Little Information   What information is missing?
Tony is making vegetable soup. The recipe calls for 8 carrots. He sliced some of them. How many more carrots does Tony need to slice? (how many carrots he has already sliced)

Counting Patterns

Subtraction   Finish each pattern.
1. 18, 15, 12, 9, _(6)_
2. 16, 12, 8, 4, _(0)_
3. 17, 16, 14, 13, 11, 10, _(8)_ , _(7)_
4. 18, 9, 16, 8, 14, 7, _(12)_ , _(6)_

Math Connection

Money   Use punchout coins to solve. Jerry has 1 dime, 2 nickels, and 4 pennies. Laura has 5 nickels and 3 pennies. Who has more money? Use your coins to find out how much more. (Laura has more. She has 28¢ and Jerry has 24¢. Laura has 4¢ more than Jerry.)

CLASSWORK AND HOMEWORK SUPPLEMENTS

Practice

Skills Maintenance 5-6

Name _____

Fact Practice

Subtract.

1. $\begin{array}{r} 11 \\ -7 \\ \hline 4 \end{array}$ $\begin{array}{r} 15 \\ -7 \\ \hline 8 \end{array}$ $\begin{array}{r} 14 \\ -6 \\ \hline 8 \end{array}$ $\begin{array}{r} 15 \\ -9 \\ \hline 6 \end{array}$ $\begin{array}{r} 13 \\ -6 \\ \hline 7 \end{array}$

2. $\begin{array}{r} 17 \\ -9 \\ \hline 8 \end{array}$ $\begin{array}{r} 14 \\ -9 \\ \hline 5 \end{array}$ $\begin{array}{r} 13 \\ -8 \\ \hline 5 \end{array}$ $\begin{array}{r} 15 \\ -6 \\ \hline 9 \end{array}$ $\begin{array}{r} 14 \\ -5 \\ \hline 9 \end{array}$

3. $\begin{array}{r} 11 \\ -8 \\ \hline 3 \end{array}$ $\begin{array}{r} 16 \\ -7 \\ \hline 9 \end{array}$ $\begin{array}{r} 15 \\ -8 \\ \hline 7 \end{array}$ $\begin{array}{r} 13 \\ -9 \\ \hline 4 \end{array}$ $\begin{array}{r} 14 \\ -8 \\ \hline 6 \end{array}$

4. $\begin{array}{r} 12 \\ -4 \\ \hline 8 \end{array}$ $\begin{array}{r} 11 \\ -9 \\ \hline 2 \end{array}$ $\begin{array}{r} 13 \\ -4 \\ \hline 9 \end{array}$ $\begin{array}{r} 11 \\ -5 \\ \hline 6 \end{array}$ $\begin{array}{r} 10 \\ -8 \\ \hline 2 \end{array}$

5. Subtract 7	
11	4
14	7
16	9
13	6
12	5

6. Subtract 8	
14	6
17	9
13	5
16	8
15	7

7. Subtract 9	
16	7
18	9
11	2
17	8
14	5

PS-2   Use with text pages 101 – 102.   43

Building Thinking Skills

Mental Math 5-6

Name _____

Math Machine

Here is how the Math Machine works:

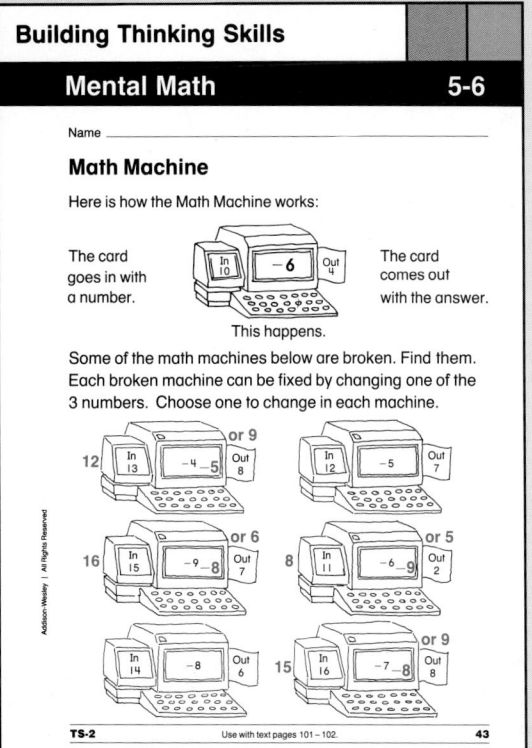

The card goes in with a number. This happens. The card comes out with the answer.

Some of the math machines below are broken. Find them. Each broken machine can be fixed by changing one of the 3 numbers. Choose one to change in each machine.

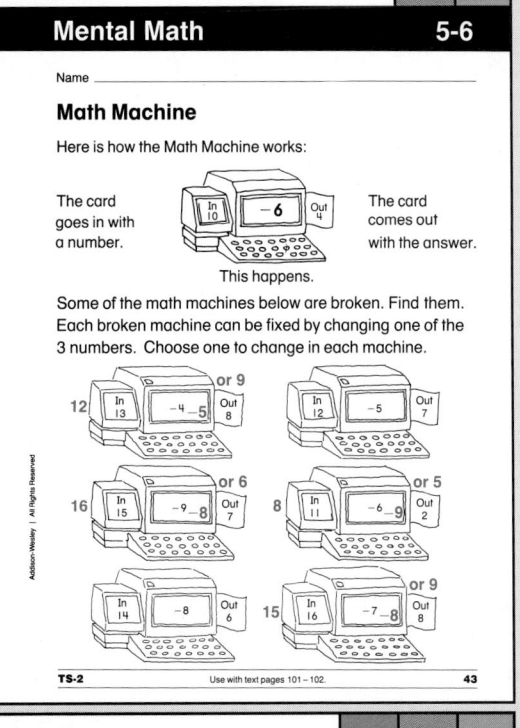

TS-2   Use with text pages 101 – 102.   43

Reteaching

Skills Review 5-6

Name _____

Fact Practice

Write the subtraction facts.

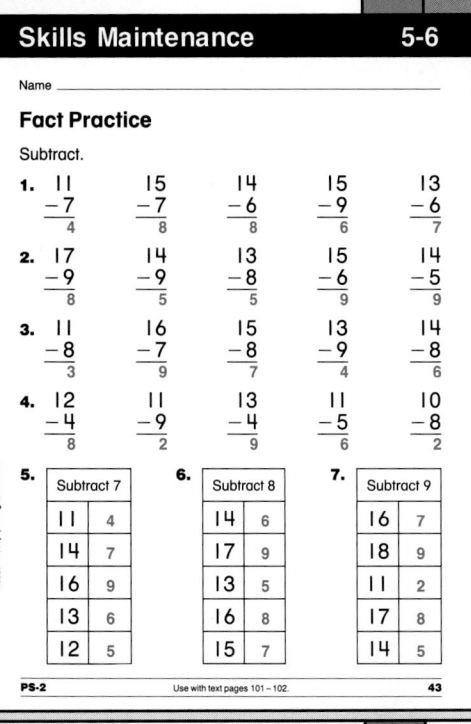

1. [14 in all]
$14 - 8 = 6$ and $14 - 6 = 8$

2. [15 in all]
$15 - 9 = \underline{6}$ and $15 - \underline{6} = \underline{9}$

3. [16 in all]
$16 - 7 = \underline{9}$ and $16 - \underline{9} = \underline{7}$

4. [17 in all]
$17 - 8 = \underline{9}$ and $17 - \underline{9} = \underline{8}$

Subtract.

5. $\begin{array}{r} 15 \\ -6 \\ \hline 9 \end{array}$ $\begin{array}{r} 15 \\ -9 \\ \hline 6 \end{array}$ $\begin{array}{r} 14 \\ -8 \\ \hline 6 \end{array}$ $\begin{array}{r} 14 \\ -6 \\ \hline 8 \end{array}$ $\begin{array}{r} 16 \\ -9 \\ \hline 7 \end{array}$ $\begin{array}{r} 16 \\ -7 \\ \hline 9 \end{array}$

6. $\begin{array}{r} 17 \\ -9 \\ \hline 8 \end{array}$ $\begin{array}{r} 17 \\ -8 \\ \hline 9 \end{array}$ $\begin{array}{r} 15 \\ -8 \\ \hline 7 \end{array}$ $\begin{array}{r} 15 \\ -7 \\ \hline 8 \end{array}$ $\begin{array}{r} 14 \\ -9 \\ \hline 5 \end{array}$ $\begin{array}{r} 14 \\ -5 \\ \hline 9 \end{array}$

RS-2   Use with text pages 101 – 102.   43

Challenges

Mental Math 5-6

Name _____

Is It True?

Write **true** if the statement is true.
Write **false** if the statement is not true.

1. $10 - 5 = 11 - 6$ true

2. $16 - 7 = 18 - 9$ true

3. $14 - 6 = 12 - 5$ false

4. $13 - 7 = 12 - 6$ true

5. $17 - 8 = 16 - 9$ false

6. $12 - 8 = 11 - 7$ true

Change each false statement to make it true.

Answers will vary. Possible answers are given.

7. $14 - 6 = 12 - 4$; $14 - 6 = 13 - 5$

8. $17 - 8 = 16 - 7$; $17 - 8 = 18 - 9$

CS-2   Use with text pages 101 – 102.   43

OPTIONS FOR INDIVIDUAL NEEDS

Basic

Exercises All
More Practice, p. 413, set C

Supplements
Reteaching 43 or
Practice 43
Challenges 43

Average

Exercises All
More Practice, p. 413, set C

Supplements
Practice 43
Challenges 43 or
Thinking Skills 43

Extended

Exercises All

Supplements
Challenges 43
Thinking Skills 43

Other Resources:
Math in Stride, p. 27
Mathematics Their Way, pp. 225, 317
Workjobs, pp. 224-227
Workjobs For Parents, pp. 106-109
The Mad Minute, pp. 96-100, 126-130
Explorations, pp. 67-68, 182-183

5-6

LESSON PLAN 5-6

OBJECTIVE 5-6
To practice the mental math techniques learned to find differences

> **Materials:** subtraction fact flashcards, counters
>
> **Grouping Suggestions:** individual work, pairs

1. MOTIVATE AND TEACH

LEARN ABOUT IT

Write subtraction facts such as 13-8, 14-9, and 15-7 on the chalkboard. Have students use counters to show the subtraction and find the difference. Ask volunteers to write their answers on the board.

Direct students' attention to page 101.

▶ **What are some subtraction strategies you can use to help you?** (Possible answers: addition with 4, 5, and 6; subtraction doubles; subtraction from 10)

▶ **How many tally marks would you write to show the differences in Rows 1–3 that are not 6, 7, or 8?** (ꟼꟼ ꟼꟼ ꟼ)

▶ **If you were adding to the data on the graph, how many boxes would you fill in to show the number of facts that had the difference of 9?** (2)

2. CHECK UNDERSTANDING

ERROR ALERT Counting back instead of using addition to help them subtract.

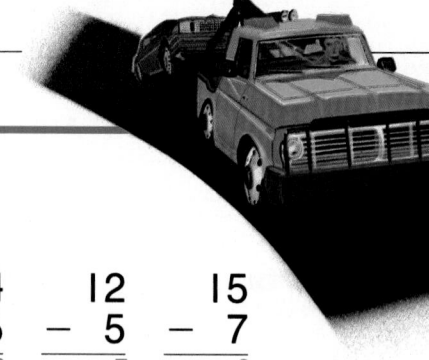

Name _____

Fact Practice

Write the differences.

1.
$$10 - 6 = 4 \qquad 13 - 7 = 6 \qquad 14 - 6 = 8 \qquad 12 - 5 = 7 \qquad 15 - 7 = 8$$

2.
$$11 - 7 = 4 \qquad 13 - 4 = 9 \qquad 14 - 8 = 6 \qquad 12 - 8 = 4 \qquad 16 - 7 = 9 \qquad 13 - 5 = 8$$

3.
$$12 - 4 = 8 \qquad 15 - 8 = 7 \qquad 12 - 7 = 5 \qquad 11 - 5 = 6 \qquad 13 - 8 = 5 \qquad 16 - 8 = 8$$

4. Tally facts above that have a difference of 6, 7, or 8.

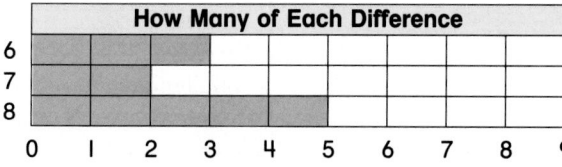

6 _____ III _____   7 _____ II _____   8 _____ ꟼꟼ _____

5. Color the graph to show the data.

How Many of Each Difference									
6	▓	▓							
7	▓	▓							
8	▓	▓	▓	▓	▓				

0 1 2 3 4 5 6 7 8 9

6. How many more differences of 8 are there than of 7?   __3__ more

Chapter 5   (one hundred one) 1(

TEACHING OPTIONS

RETEACHING TIPS Have students use counters to model addition facts with sums 11–17. Then give students related subtraction fact flashcards and have them match them to the counters for the appropriate addition facts. Assign Reteaching Supplement 43.

ENRICHMENT Draw and label two overlapping circles. Write *I have a sister* in one, *I have a brother* in the other, and *I have both* in the shared portion. Ask students with brothers and/or sisters to write their own names in the appropriate section, tally the numbers, and make up stories about the data.

rite the differences.

$$\begin{array}{r} 9 \\ -7 \\ \hline 2 \end{array} \quad \begin{array}{r} 11 \\ -5 \\ \hline 6 \end{array} \quad \begin{array}{r} 15 \\ -7 \\ \hline 8 \end{array} \quad \begin{array}{r} 10 \\ -3 \\ \hline 7 \end{array}$$

$$\begin{array}{r} 11 \\ -7 \\ \hline 4 \end{array} \quad \begin{array}{r} 9 \\ -6 \\ \hline 3 \end{array} \quad \begin{array}{r} 12 \\ -5 \\ \hline 7 \end{array} \quad \begin{array}{r} 15 \\ -9 \\ \hline 6 \end{array}$$

$$\begin{array}{r} 14 \\ -6 \\ \hline 8 \end{array} \quad \begin{array}{r} 13 \\ -4 \\ \hline 9 \end{array} \quad \begin{array}{r} 16 \\ -7 \\ \hline 9 \end{array} \quad \begin{array}{r} 13 \\ -5 \\ \hline 8 \end{array} \quad \begin{array}{r} 12 \\ -4 \\ \hline 8 \end{array} \quad \begin{array}{r} 13 \\ -6 \\ \hline 7 \end{array}$$

$11 - 6 = \underline{5}$ $8 - 6 = \underline{2}$ $12 - 7 = \underline{5}$

$13 - 9 = \underline{4}$ $12 - 8 = \underline{4}$ $13 - 8 = \underline{5}$

$14 - 8 = \underline{6}$ $14 - 9 = \underline{5}$ $15 - 6 = \underline{9}$

$10 - 7 = \underline{3}$ $13 - 7 = \underline{6}$ $11 - 8 = \underline{3}$

ROBLEM SOLVING

Al bought 1 ⊳▭▭▭▭ and 1 ⊳▭▭ .
How much more money did he pay
for the ⊳▭▭▭▭ than the ⊳▭▭?
Write the number sentence.
Answer the question.

Screws	
⊳▭▭▭▭	15¢ each
⊳▭▭	9¢ each

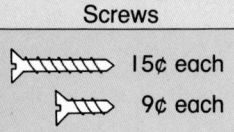 $\underline{15}$ ¢ $- \underline{9}$ ¢ $= \underline{6}$ ¢ Al paid $\underline{6}$ ¢ more.

LOSE AND ASSESS

AY WHAT YOU KNOW Ask
irs of students to make two piles of
rds, one pile containing numbers 10
rough 18, and the other pile
ntaining 7, 8, and 9. Have students
ke turns drawing a card from each
le to make subtraction facts and
swer them. Remind them to give
lpful advice when pointing out
rong answers.

QUICK QUIZ

Complete the subtraction box.

12	14	17	15	(14)	13
−5	−(8)	−9	−(7)	−7	−(6)
(7)	6	(8)	8	7	7

---

3. PRACTICE AND APPLY

Basic	All
Average	All
Extended	All

PRACTICE

*How can you check the exercises on
page 102?* (Possible answer: Use
add-to-check facts; add the difference to
the bottom number in the exercise to get
the sum, or top number.)

APPLY

PROBLEM SOLVING ▶ **Which
words in the problem tell you which
operation to use?** (*How much more*
means you subtract.)
▶ **Use punchout coins to find how
much more two little screws would
cost than one big one?** (3¢)
▶ **If Al had a quarter, how many big
screws could he buy? Explain your
answer.** (1; he would only have 10¢
left, not enough for another big screw.)

5-6

Fact Families

OBJECTIVE 5-7 To model and finish fact families

PREBOOK ACTIVITIES

QUICK REVIEW

Subtract. Write the add-to-check fact.

$11 - 4 =$ _(7)_	_(4 + 7 = 11)_
$11 - 6 =$ _(5)_	_(6 + 5 = 11)_
$12 - 8 =$ _(4)_	_(8 + 4 = 12)_
$14 - 9 =$ _(5)_	_(9 + 5 = 14)_
$13 - 5 =$ _(8)_	_(5 + 8 = 13)_

PRIOR KNOWLEDGE

Have students tell what a fact family is. Then ask them to illustrate this with an example in the classroom. *There are 6 windows in this room. 2 are open. How many are closed?* (4) *How could you write that as a number sentence?* ($6 - 2 = 4$) Have students complete the fact family, first using each fact in a number story and then writing it. ($6 - 4 = 2$, $4 + 2 = 6$, $2 + 4 = 6$)

COMMUNICATION

Reading and Writing in Math Write the following on the chalkboard. In their Math Journals, have students write the word that best completes each sentence, then read the sentences.

subtraction part family add numbers

1. When I subtract, I take away one part from the whole to get the other _(part)_.
2. When I _(add)_, I join two parts to make the whole.
3. These number sentences make up a fact _(family)_ : $5 + 3 = 8$, $3 + 5 = 8$, $8 - 5 = 3$, $8 - 3 = 5$.
4. All the _(numbers)_ in each fact of a family are the same.
5. Most fact families have two addition sentences and two _(subtraction)_ sentences.

EXPLORE AND CONNECT

Materials: 9 Cube-A-Links of 1 color for each student
Grouping Suggestion: pairs

Pair students and give each partner 9 cubes of a different color. Remind students of their earlier explorations with fact families. Have each pair make cube trains to determine how many fact families have the sum you give them (12, 14, 16, or 18). Have one partner make a train to show one part and the other partner complete the train to make the sum. Have students write the addition sentences in the fact family, then snap apart their trains and write the subtraction sentences. Encourage students to give each other constructive feedback. If they think an answer is incorrect, they should help their partner figure out how to get the right answer. Have students share their results with the class. *Are all fact families made up of four facts—two addition and two subtraction?* (No, doubles facts only have two facts in their family.)

CONNECTIONS   Use these anytime.

Problem of the Day

Circus Animals There are 7 elephants and 9 horses in the Big Circle Circus. How many animals are there altogether? (16) Write all the facts in this fact family. ($7 + 9 = 16$, $9 + 7 = 16$, $16 - 7 = 9$, $16 - 9 = 7$)

Math Connection

Money I have 1 nickel and 7 pennies. How much money do I have in all? (12¢) Write all the facts in this fact family. ($5 + 7 = 12$, $7 + 5 = 12$, $12 - 5 = 7$, $12 - 7 = 5$)

Creative Thinking

Fact Families Use what you know about fact families to solve this riddle. I am a number less than $7 + 5$ or $5 + 7$. I am more than the difference of one of the subtraction facts in the family, but less than the difference of the other. (6)

CLASSWORK AND HOMEWORK SUPPLEMENTS

Practice

Skills Maintenance　　5-7

Name _____

Fact Families

Subtract to finish the wheels.

$12 - 7 = 5$

44　　Use with text pages 103–104.　　PS-2

Building Thinking Skills

Number Sense　　5-7

Name _____

In The Family

Think of the fact family.
Cross out the number that does not belong.

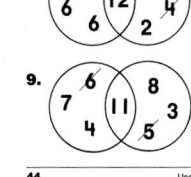

1. 7　6 / 13　5
2. 5　15 / 14　9
3. 6　15 / 9　13
4. 8　13 / 5　14
5. 6　4 / 7　11
6. 9　6 / 10　4

Cross out the two numbers that do not belong.

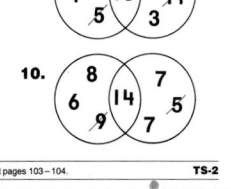

7. 7　10 / 6　12　4 / 6　2
8. 9　10 / 4　13　11 / 5　3
9. 6　8 / 7　11　3 / 4　5
10. 8　7 / 6　14　5 / 9　2

44　　Use with text pages 103–104.　　TS-2

Reteaching

Skills Review　　5-7

Name _____

Fact Families

Subtract and add to make a fact family.

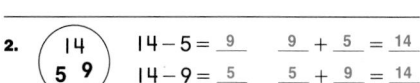

1.
13　8 5
$13 - 8 = 5$　　$5 + 8 = 13$
$13 - 5 = 8$　　$8 + 5 = 13$

2.
14　5 9
$14 - 5 = \underline{9}$　　$9 + 5 = 14$
$14 - 9 = \underline{5}$　　$5 + 9 = 14$

3.
15　9 6
$15 - 9 = \underline{6}$　　$6 + 9 = 15$
$15 - 6 = \underline{9}$　　$9 + 6 = 15$

4.
16　7 9
$16 - 7 = \underline{9}$　　$9 + 7 = 16$
$16 - 9 = \underline{7}$　　$7 + 9 = 16$

5.
17　9 8
$17 - 9 = \underline{8}$　　$8 + 9 = 17$
$17 - 8 = \underline{9}$　　$9 + 8 = 17$

44　　Use with text pages 103–104.　　RS-2

Challenges

Reading Math　　5-7

Name _____

Falling Leaves

Write a number sentence for each story.

1. Amy had 7 leaves. She found 5 more on her way home from school. How many does she have in all?

   $7 + 5 = 12$

2. Amy put all her leaves in a pile. Just then a big wind came along. 5 leaves blew away! How many leaves does Amy have now?

   $12 - 5 = 7$

3. Amy went to look for leaves in the park. She wanted to have as many leaves in all as she had before. How many leaves does Amy need to find?

   $12 - 7 = 5$

4. Look at the number sentences you wrote. What fact is missing from the fact family?

   $5 + 7 = 12$

5. Finish the story about Amy and her leaves. Write a problem to match the last number sentence.

   Answers will vary.

44　　Use with text pages 103–104.　　CS-2

OBJECTIVE 5-7
To model and finish fact families

> **Materials:** 9 Cube-A-Links of one color for each student, fact family flashcards
>
> **Grouping Suggestions:** pairs, individual work

1. MOTIVATE AND TEACH

LEARN ABOUT IT

On the chalkboard, write the sums of 13, 15, and 17. Have pairs of students make cube trains to show the addition facts for these sums and write the matching sentences. Then have them snap apart the cubes to find and write the subtraction facts in the family. Ask volunteers to write each fact in the family on the board.

Have students complete Exercise 1 on page 103.

▶ **Explain how you know how to fill in all the missing parts of each fact family.** (Once you know one fact in the family, you know them all.)

▶ **What is the fact family for the addition double 8 + 8?** (8 + 8 = 16, 16 − 8 = 8)

▶ **Why are there only two facts in a doubles family?** (The parts, or addends, are the same, so one addition fact and one subtraction fact are enough to show the whole family.)

2. CHECK UNDERSTANDING

ERROR ALERT Not understanding how to find all the facts in a family when they know only one.

Name _____

Fact Families

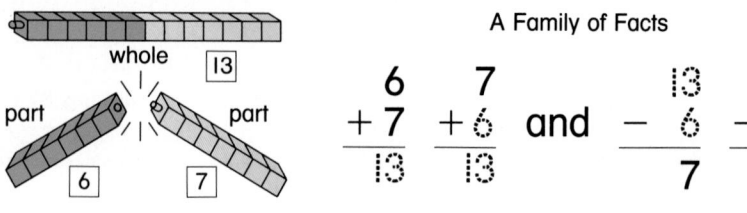

A Family of Facts

$$\begin{array}{cc} 6 & 7 \\ +7 & +6 \end{array} \text{ and } \begin{array}{c} 13 \\ -6 \\ \hline 7 \end{array}$$

Work with a partner. Finish the fact family.
Add or subtract. Use cubes to check.

> When you know one in the family, you know all.

1. $$\begin{array}{cc} 8 & 5 \\ +5 & +8 \\ \hline 13 & 13 \end{array} \text{ and } \begin{array}{c} 13 \\ -8 \\ \hline 5 \end{array}$$

2. $$\begin{array}{cc} 6 & 5 \\ +5 & +6 \\ \hline 11 & 11 \end{array} \text{ and } \begin{array}{c} 11 \\ -6 \\ \hline 5 \end{array}$$

3. $$\begin{array}{cc} 5 & 9 \\ +9 & +5 \\ \hline 14 & 14 \end{array} \text{ and } \begin{array}{c} 14 \\ -5 \\ \hline 9 \end{array}$$

4. $$\begin{array}{cc} 7 & 5 \\ +5 & +7 \\ \hline 12 & 12 \end{array} \text{ and } \begin{array}{c} 12 \\ -7 \\ \hline 5 \end{array}$$

Chapter 5

(one hundred three)

TEACHING OPTIONS

RETEACHING TIPS Have students use red and blue cubes to find a pair of addends that add to 9, then show that when they begin with either part and add the other, they get a sum of 9. When they begin with 9 and subtract either part, they get the other part. Assign Reteaching Supplement 44.

COMPUTER **Arithmetic Critters** **MECC © 1986** For use with all levels. In *Foul Play,* students count how many birds fly away from their nests. They practice by subtracting 1-9 from 10-18. The game requires 15 minutes to complete.

ld or subtract.
ng facts to make a
mily in each row.

| $\begin{array}{r}6\\+9\\\hline 15\end{array}$ | $\begin{array}{r}9\\+6\\\hline 15\end{array}$ | $\begin{array}{r}15\\-7\\\hline 8\end{array}$ | $\begin{array}{r}15\\-9\\\hline 6\end{array}$ | $\begin{array}{r}15\\-6\\\hline 9\end{array}$ | $\begin{array}{r}7\\+8\\\hline 15\end{array}$ |

| $\begin{array}{r}4\\+5\\\hline 9\end{array}$ | $\begin{array}{r}4\\+6\\\hline 10\end{array}$ | $\begin{array}{r}5\\+4\\\hline 9\end{array}$ | $\begin{array}{r}9\\-4\\\hline 5\end{array}$ | $\begin{array}{r}10\\-4\\\hline 6\end{array}$ | $\begin{array}{r}9\\-5\\\hline 4\end{array}$ |

| $\begin{array}{r}7\\+7\\\hline 14\end{array}$ | $\begin{array}{r}8\\+8\\\hline 16\end{array}$ | $\begin{array}{r}13\\-7\\\hline 6\end{array}$ | $\begin{array}{r}14\\-7\\\hline 7\end{array}$ | $\begin{array}{r}15\\-8\\\hline 7\end{array}$ | $\begin{array}{r}14\\-8\\\hline 6\end{array}$ |

| $\begin{array}{r}6\\+7\\\hline 13\end{array}$ | $\begin{array}{r}6\\+6\\\hline 12\end{array}$ | $\begin{array}{r}7\\+6\\\hline 13\end{array}$ | $\begin{array}{r}13\\-6\\\hline 7\end{array}$ | $\begin{array}{r}13\\-5\\\hline 8\end{array}$ | $\begin{array}{r}13\\-7\\\hline 6\end{array}$ |

MIXED REVIEW

ld or subtract.

$3 - 0 = \underline{3}$ $16 - 7 = \underline{9}$ $5 + 3 = \underline{8}$

$15 - 9 = \underline{6}$ $6 + 7 = \underline{13}$ $12 - 5 = \underline{7}$

$9 + 8 = \underline{17}$ $14 - 7 = \underline{7}$ $10 - 2 = \underline{8}$

(one hundred four)   Chapter 5

3. PRACTICE AND APPLY

Basic	All, Mixed Review
Average	All, Mixed Review
Extended	All, Mixed Review

PRACTICE

How will you complete Exercises 1-4 on page 104? (Add or subtract, then ring the facts that make a fact family.)

APPLY

▶ **If the largest number in a family is 11 and the smallest number is 5, what is the other number in the family?** (6)
▶ **How did you get that answer?**
(Possible response: If 11 is the largest number, you have to subtract 5 from 11 to find the third number.)

MIXED REVIEW   *What will you do in these exercises?* (Add or subtract.)

5-7

LOSE AND ASSESS

AY WHAT YOU THINK   Hold
a flashcard and read it aloud. Call
3 volunteers, each of whom will
1, in turn, one other fact in the
ne fact family. Write each fact on
e chalkboard as it is said so that
dents can see which facts have
eady been given. Continue with
er flashcards until each student has
d a turn.

QUICK QUIZ

Write the fact families for these groups of numbers.

| 12
5 7 | 15
6 9 | 12
6 6 | 13
8 5 |

Problem Solving: Writing a Story

OBJECTIVE 5-8   To solve problems by writing a story

PREBOOK ACTIVITIES

QUICK REVIEW

Write the word for each ordinal number.
1st   2nd   3rd   4th   5th
(First, second, third, fourth, fifth)

PRIOR KNOWLEDGE

Ask students to imagine that they have read a story problem about apples. Have them tell whether each question you read is an addition question or a subtraction question or whether the question could be for either addition or subtraction, depending on the story. *How many apples are there in all?* (addition) *How many more green apples are there than red apples?* (subtraction) *How many apples were left?* (subtraction) *How many apples are there now?* (addition or subtraction) *How much did the apples cost altogether?* (addition) *How many apples were eaten?* (addition or subtraction)

COMMUNICATION

Discussing Math   Use Cube-A-Links or other small objects to create and display a 1/3/5 growing pattern. Ask students to describe the pattern using the words *first, second,* and *third.* For example: The second group has 3 cubes, which is 2 more cubes than the first; the third group has 5 cubes, which is 2 more cubes than the second. *How many cubes will you need for the fourth arrangement?* (7)

EXPLORE AND CONNECT

COOPERATIVE ACTIVITY

Grouping Suggestion: small groups
Finish the story. Use the number sentence to help you.
9 – _____ = _____   Michael had 9 peaches.

TEACHING ACTIONS

BEFORE
▶ **Tell what you know about the story.** (Possible answer: Michael had 9 peaches.)
▶ **How do you know there will be fewer peaches at the end of the story?** (Possible answer: because the number sentence shows subtraction)
▶ **Tell how you will choose data to complete the story. Explain your answer.** (Possible answer: The number taken away must be 9 or less because the difference cannot be less than zero.)

DURING
▶ **How can you plan to write the subtraction story?** (Possible answer: Write a sentence telling what happened to some of the peaches; ask a question such as *How many are left?*)
▶ **Describe your plan for writing and solving the problem** (Possible answer: Write a subtraction story and a matching number sentence. Then solve.)

AFTER
▶ **How would you check your answer?** (Possible answers: Read the problem. See if the number sentence matches it. Use objects to check)
Have students work in small groups to write the subtraction story and the matching number sentence.

CONNECTIONS   Use these anytime.

Problem of the Day

Logic   Draw a picture to help you solve the problem. Joe, Judy, and Jamal are in line at the store. Joe is not first. Jamal is in front of Judy. Judy is not third. What is the order of the students in line? (Jamal, Judy, Joe)

Subject Integration

Language Arts   Read the beginning of the story. Complete the story with a question. Then write a number sentence that matches your question and solve it. "I worked 7 hours this week," said Renée. "I worked 5 hours this week," said Jorgé. The store owner thought, "Hmm. _____?" (Answers may vary.)

Counting Patterns

Copy each pattern and model it with blocks. Then tell the next three numbers in the pattern.
1, 2, 3, 4, (5), (6), (7)
2, 4, 6, 8, (10), (12), (14)
1, 4, 7, 10, (13), (16), (19)
1, 2, 4, 7, (11), (16), (22)

roblem Solving: Draw a Picture

solve problems using the strategy Draw a Picture

CLASSWORK AND HOMEWORK SUPPLEMENTS

Practice

Creative Thinking   5-8

Name _____

Problem Solving Strategy: Draw a Picture

Read the story.
Draw a picture to help solve it.
Use Xs for books.

1. Sasha put books on 5 shelves.
She put 3 books on the first shelf,
4 books on the second shelf, and
5 books on the third shelf.
She continued this pattern for all the shelves.
How many books did Sasha put on the fifth shelf?

           __7__ books

1st shelf	X X X
2nd shelf	X X X X
3rd shelf	X X X X X
4th shelf	X X X X X X
5th shelf	X X X X X X X

2. Todd put books on 5 other shelves.
He put 4 books on the first shelf,
5 books on the second shelf, and
6 books on the third shelf.
He continued this pattern for all the shelves.
How many books did Todd put on all 5 shelves?

           __30__ books

1st shelf	X X X X
2nd shelf	X X X X X
3rd shelf	X X X X X X
4th shelf	X X X X X X X
5th shelf	X X X X X X X X

PS-2   Use with text page 106.   45

Building Thinking Skills

Life Skills   5-8

Name _____

Grocery Shopping

Read the story. Draw a picture to help solve it. Make an X
for each item. Then answer the questions below.

Rob and Rebecca went to the market. They each took a
cart. Rob got 3 loaves of bread, 1 jar of peanut butter,
6 bananas, 2 boxes of cereal, 4 packages of cheese,
2 cartons of milk, and 3 bottles of juice. Rebecca put
4 packages of napkins, 3 packs of paper plates, and
2 boxes of spoons in her cart.

1. How many items did Rob put in his cart? __21__

2. How many items did Rebecca put in her cart? __9__

3. How many items should Rob put in Rebecca's cart
so they can both use the express lane? __6__

TS-2   Use with text page 106.   45

Reteaching

Writing Math   5-8

Name _____

Problem Solving: Writing a Story

Finish writing the bicycle story for $12 - 5 =$ __7__ .
Ask a subtraction question in your story.
Use words in the Word Bank to help.
Then answer the question.

Word Bank			
went away	tires	training wheels	lost	horns
children	in all	handle bars	were left
baskets	went riding	how many	kick stands

The Bicycle Story

_____

RS-2   Use with text page 105.   45

Challenges

Cooperative Activities   5-8

Name _____

A Game of More or Less

You need: a friend, a number cube with the numbers 1 to 6,
50 paper clips in a bowl, 2 counters.

Rules: Take turns. Toss the number cube.
Move the counter that number of spaces on the game board.
Read the words on the space. If they tell about addition,
take that many clips. If the words tell about subtraction,
put that many clips back in the bowl. When you reach **Finish**,
add your clips to your friend's. What is the total?

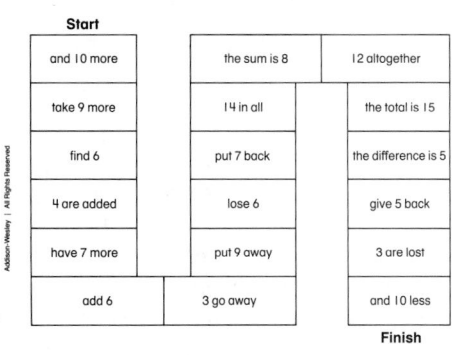

Start

and 10 more	the sum is 8	12 altogether
take 9 more	14 in all	the total is 15
find 6	put 7 back	the difference is 5
4 are added	lose 6	give 5 back
have 7 more	put 9 away	3 are lost
add 6	3 go away	and 10 less

Finish

CS-2   Use with text page 105.   45

OPTIONS FOR INDIVIDUAL NEEDS

Basic

Exercises All
Computer Bank, p. 407
More Practice, p. 414, set A

Supplements
Reteaching 45 or
Practice 45

Average

Exercises All
Computer Bank, p. 407
More Practice, p. 414, set A

Supplements
Practice 45
Challenges 45 or
Thinking Skills 45

Extended

Exercises All
Computer Bank, p. 407

Supplements
Challenges 45
Thinking Skills 45

Other Resources:
Math in Stride, p. 77
Explorations, pp. 67, 191-192
*Problem Solving Experiences
In Mathematics*, pp. 39, 45,
57, 75
*Developing Number Concepts
With Unifix Cubes*, pp. 80-82,
87-88, 111
Mathematics Book A, pp.
18-20, 29-30, 191, 194

5-8

OBJECTIVE 5-8
To solve problems by writing a story; to solve problems using the strategy Draw a Picture

1. MOTIVATE AND TEACH

LEARN ABOUT IT

 **BEFORE** ▶ **Look at the Word Bank. Which words might be useful in completing the carrot story?** (Possible answers: *gave away; lost, ate, fed; how many; were left*)

 **DURING** ▶ **What can you plan about your story before you actually write it?** (Possible answer: what happens to the carrots)

▶ **What must you understand before you can finish writing the carrot story?** (Possible answer: what questions can be asked for a subtraction sentence)

 **AFTER** ▶ **Suggest a way that you can check your story problem.** (Possible answer: Reread the problem and make sure it matches the number sentence.)

2. CHECK UNDERSTANDING

ERROR ALERT **Page 105** Using an addition sentence to ask a subtraction question.

Page 106 Failing to continue a pattern correctly.

Name _____

Problem Solving
Writing a Story

| UNDERSTAND |
| FIND DATA |
| PLAN |
| ESTIMATE |
| SOLVE |
| CHECK |

Finish writing the story for
$8 - 2 =$ ____ .
Use the Word Bank to help.

Ask a subtraction question.
Finish the number sentence.
Then answer the question.
Stories may vary. $8 - 2 = 6$

Word Bank	
gave away	did
had	did not
ate	bought
lost	how many
found	were left
fed	in all

The Carrot Story

I bought 8 carrots.

Chapter 5   More Practice, page 414, set A   (one hundred five)

TEACHING OPTIONS

RETEACHING TIPS Place rows of 1, 2, 3, and 4 red circles on a flannelboard. *What shape is the pattern making?* (a triangle) Ask students to place the next row of circles and trace the pattern with their fingers. For help in writing stories to solve problems, use Reteaching Supplement 45.

ENRICHMENT **Patterns** Provide pairs with a collection of objects, such as paper clips, toothpicks, and crayons. Ask one student to make a growing pattern with some of the objects. Have the other continue the pattern. Then have them switch roles and make another pattern.

roblem Solving Strategy

aw a Picture

UNDERSTAND
FIND DATA
PLAN
ESTIMATE
SOLVE
CHECK

olve. Draw a picture
help. Use X for cans.

Carla put cans on 5 shelves.
She put I can on the first shelf,
2 cans on the second, and
3 cans on the third. She continued
this pattern. How many cans did
Carla put on the fifth shelf?

__5__ cans

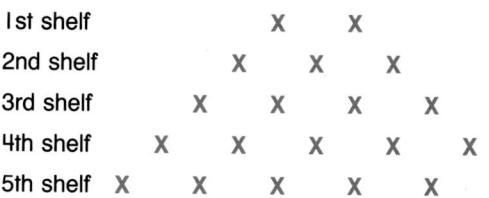

1st shelf   X
2nd shelf   X   X
3rd shelf   X   X   X
4th shelf   X   X   X   X
5th shelf X   X   X   X   X

Carla put cans on 5 other shelves.
She put 2 cans on the first shelf,
3 cans on the second, and
4 cans on the third. She continued
this pattern. How many cans did
Carla put on all 5 shelves?   __20__ cans

1st shelf   X   X
2nd shelf   X   X   X
3rd shelf   X   X   X   X
4th shelf   X   X   X   X   X
5th shelf X   X   X   X   X   X

3. PRACTICE AND APPLY

Basic	All
Average	All
Extended	All

PRACTICE

On page 106, how will you show the cans on each shelf? (Read the data, and draw an X for each can on that shelf.) *What is the pattern for each exercise?* (Add one more for each shelf.) *What must you find before you can find the total in Exercise 2?* (Find the number of cans on the fourth and fifth shelves.)

► **Explain what it means to continue a pattern.** (Possible answer: to make a design and repeat it, change it in the same way each time you repeat it)

► **What is the purpose of the patterns in this market?** (Possible answer: They make the display look attractive; it is easier to see what you are buying.)

► **How can a picture help to solve a problem?** (Possible answer: A picture will make it easier to see what the pattern is; if you can identify the pattern, you can predict what comes next.)

► **How can you check to see if your answer is correct?** (Possible answer: Use objects to build the pattern; write the matching number pattern and see if your answer matches it.)

5-8

LOSE AND ASSESS

RITE WHAT YOU KNOW

view with students the chapter
ry, *Mom's Special Dish*. Have
dents write a story about Squeaky
ing the number sentence 9 − 3. The
ry might begin *Squeaky found 9
ts*. Then have students write a
oblem about Squeaky in which they
st draw a picture to find the
swer.

QUICK QUIZ

How many circles will the fifth row
have? (2)
Row 1 ○○○○○○○○○○
Row 2   ○○○○○○○○
Row 3   ○○○○○○

CHAPTER 5

WRAP UP

INTRODUCTION The Wrap Up provides activities emphasizing math language and thinking skills for the chapter.

USING PAGE 107

Math Words ▶ **Explain how the phrases *in all* and *are left* are used in math.** (Possible answer: *In all* is used to signal the addition of numbers; *are left* is used to signal the subtraction of numbers.)

▶ **How are the problems in Exercises 1 and 4 alike?** (Possible answer: Looking at them tells you they could be both add-to-check-facts and part of a fact family. You need to read the question to see how the problem is used in each sentence.)

Math Reasoning ▶ **Tell what you might use to help you solve Exercise 6.** (Possible answer: Use counters or make a drawing to show how many shells each child has.)

Name _____

WRAP UP

MATH WORDS

Use one of these phrases to finish each sentence.

are left	add-to-check fact
in all	fact family
difference	

1. $4 + 5 = 9$ is the ___add-to-check fact___ for $9 - 4 =$

2. You subtract to find how many ___are left___

3. You also subtract to find the ___difference___

4. $13 - 7 = 6$ and $6 + 7 = 13$ belong in the same ___fact family___

5. You add to find how many ___in all___

MATH REASONING

6. Write the answers.
Maria has 14 shells.
Tim has 5 fewer than Maria.
Maria has 4 more than Lynn.

How many shells does Tim have? ___9___ she

How many shells does Lynn have? ___10___ shel

Chapter 5 Wrap Up   (one hundred seven)

TEACHING OPTIONS

ENRICHMENT Have small groups use counters to answer questions about Exercise 6, such as: *Tim gives Lynn 2 shells. Now how many does Tim have? How many does Lynn have?* (7; 12) These questions build on the answer previously given and require students to decide which operation to use. Have students draw a beach scene with different numbers of birds, shells, pails, and boats. Have them display their pictures and ask subtraction questions. For example: *3 birds fly away. How many birds are left?* Students look at the picture to find the answer.

Name _____

CHAPTER REVIEW/TEST

Subtract. Finish the add-to-check fact.

13	4	12	4	13	5
− 4	+ 9	− 4	+ 8	− 5	+ 8
9	13	8	12	8	13

11	6	16	7	15	8
− 6	+ 5	− 7	+ 9	− 8	+ 7
5	11	9	16	7	15

Subtract.

$17 - 9 = \underline{8}$ $15 - 6 = \underline{9}$ $16 - 9 = \underline{7}$

18	11	13	14	12	15
− 9	− 9	− 6	− 5	− 8	− 7
9	2	7	9	4	8

Add or subtract. Ring facts to make a family.

(8 +6)	(6 +8)	14 −7	(14 −8)	(14 −6)	14 −9
14	14	7	6	8	5

Josh pulled out 12 carrots. Ben pulled out 7. How many more carrots did Josh pull out?

$12 - 7 = 5$

$\underline{5}$ more

INFORMAL ASSESSMENT

Using Manipulatives On the chalkboard, write several subtraction exercises of the types covered in this chapter. Include subtracting 9, add-to-check, and fact families. Have pairs of students take turns using counters to model the subtraction, then write the number sentence.

Communication *Write a sentence that tells why drawing a picture can help you plan how to solve a story problem.* (Possible answer: When you draw a picture, you can see what action has happened in the story problem.)

Critical Thinking ▶ Explain how addition can help you find a subtraction answer. (Possible answer: When you subtract, you start with the sum of 2 numbers and take away 1 of them. The answer is the other number. You can add the 2 numbers or parts to find the sum, or the number you started with.)

CHAPTER 5

CHAPTER REVIEW/TEST

INTRODUCTION The Review/Test is provided to review and evaluate the skills and concepts presented in Chapter 5.

USING PAGE 108
If you prefer to use this page for review, you may want to use the **Multiple-Choice Posttest** (pages 19-20) or the **Free-Response Posttest** (pages 19–20) to evaluate mastery of chapter objectives.

ITEM ANALYSIS The table below correlates the Chapter Review/Test items with the lesson objectives for the chapter.

Items	Objectives
1	5-2
2	5-5
3, 4	5-1, 5-3, 5-6
5	5-7
6	5-4

CHAPTER 5

ENRICHMENT

INTRODUCTION Working with Roman numerals will help students become familiar with a historical set of number symbols that we still see today.

USING PAGE 109
This Enrichment page is provided for all students. You may wish to use it after they have completed the Chapter Review/Test on page 108.
Explain to students that the symbols used in the code were actual numbers used by the ancient Romans. Both the Roman numeral and its corresponding number represent the same amount.
▶ **Look at the symbols in the code. What kind of a pattern do you notice?** (Possible answer: The first 8 numbers are represented by *I*s and *V*s. The pattern begins to repeat from 11 through 18.)

EXTENSION Have students work in small groups to make up subtraction exercises like the ones in Chapter 5, using Roman numerals instead of numbers. Encourage students to use the code on this page to help them write the exercises. Then have groups trade papers and solve the exercises. Discuss whether Roman numerals are harder or easier to use than our own numbers in writing a number sentence. Ask some students to research the subject and show the class the Roman numerals for numbers from 2 to 50.

Name _____

ENRICHMENT
Roman Numerals

What is hiding in the grass? Connect the dots to find out. Use the code to help. The code uses **roman numerals.**

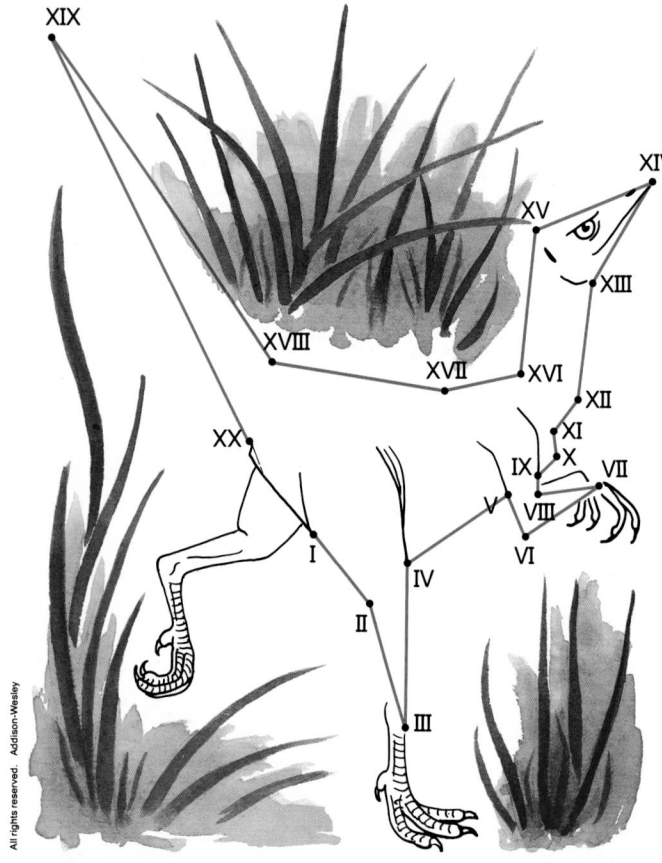

Code	
1	I
2	II
3	III
4	IV
5	V
6	VI
7	VII
8	VIII
9	IX
10	X
11	XI
12	XII
13	XIII
14	XIV
15	XV
16	XVI
17	XVII
18	XVIII
19	XIX
20	XX

Chapter 5 Enrichment: Roman Numerals

(one hundred nine) 10

Name _____

CUMULATIVE REVIEW

What comes next?

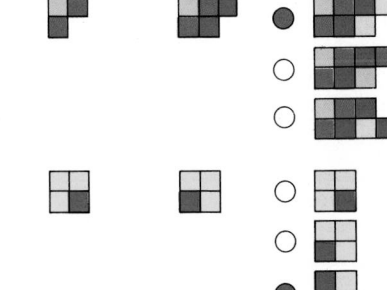

How many children walk to school?

How We Get to School	
bus	🏠 🏠 🏠 🏠 🏠 🏠
car	🏠 🏠
walk	🏠 🏠 🏠

- ● 6 children
- ○ 3 children
- ○ 12 children

Each 🏠 means 2 children.

Finish the fact family.

$8 + 3 = 11$ ● $11 - 8 = 3$
$3 + 8 = 11$ ○ $6 + 5 = 11$
$11 - 3 = 8$ ○ $8 + 4 = 12$

Subtract.

5.
$$\begin{array}{r} 9 \\ -0 \\ \hline \end{array}$$
○ 0
● 9
○ 6

6.
$$\begin{array}{r} 16 \\ -8 \\ \hline \end{array}$$
● 8
○ 6
○ 9

7.
$$\begin{array}{r} 10 \\ -7 \\ \hline \end{array}$$
● 3
○ 10
○ 17

8.
$$\begin{array}{r} 11 \\ -9 \\ \hline \end{array}$$
○ 8
○ 3
● 2

Dad made 8 pancakes. Pam ate 3. How many were left?

- ● 11 pancakes
- ○ 5 pancakes
- ○ 6 pancakes

0 (one hundred ten)

Chapter 5 Cumulative Review

CUMULATIVE REVIEW

INTRODUCTION The purpose of this Cumulative Review is to maintain previously taught skills and concepts. The emphasis in this Cumulative Review is on subtraction, Chapters 4 and 5; and on patterns and graphs, Chapter 3.

ITEM ANALYSIS The table below correlates the Cumulative Review items with the lesson objectives.

Items	Objectives
1, 2	3-2
3	3-7
4	4-8
5	4-1
6	4-2
7	4-3
8	5-1
9	4-4

CHAPTER 6 MEASUREMENT

Chapter Management

OVERVIEW

Lesson	Pages	Objectives	Subject Integration	Strand Integration
Estimating and Measuring Length: Nonstandard Units	111-112	6-1 To estimate and measure length using nonstandard units	social studies: partner skills	critical thinking
Estimating and Measuring Length: Nearest Inch	113-114	6-2 To estimate and measure to the nearest inch	science: body measurement	number sense, estimation
Measurement and Graphs	115-116	6-3 To measure to the nearest inch; to make and read bar graphs	health and fitness: dental care	estimation
Problem Solving: Understanding the Operations/Estimating Curve Lengths	117-118	6-4 To add to explore perimeter; to estimate curve lengths	social studies: map skills	computation, estimation
Estimating and Measuring Length: Feet and Yards	119-120	6-5 To estimate and measure using feet and yards	social studies: partner skills	number sense, estimation
Estimating and Measuring Capacity: Nonstandard Units/Cups, Pints, and Quarts	121-122	6-6 To measure capacity with nonstandard units, cups, pints, and quarts	social studies: group skills	number sense, consumer skills
Estimating and Measuring Weight: Nonstandard Units/Pounds	123-124	6-7 To measure weight with nonstandard units and pounds	social studies: partner skills	critical thinking, estimation
My Centimeter Book	125-126	6-8 To estimate and measure to the nearest centimeter	science: body measurement	estimation
Estimation and Measuring Length: Decimeters and Meters	127-128	6-9 To estimate and measure using decimeters and meters	social studies: group skills	computation, estimation
Estimating and Measuring Capacity: Liters/Estimating and Measuring Weight: Kilograms	129-130	6-10 To measure capacity with liters, and mass with kilograms	social studies: group skills	problem solving
Problem Solving: Determining Reasonable Answers/Problem Solving Strategy: Use Logical Reasoning	131-132	6-11 To determine if answers are reasonable; to use the strategy Use Logical Reasoning	health and fitness: softball	estimation, geometry: area

MATHEMATICAL BACKGROUND

Measurement

Measurement is a basic skill in elementary mathematics curriculum, and involves identifying an attribute of the object to be measured; choosing a unit of measurement; counting the number of times the unit is contained in the object to be measured; and developing mental images of the units of measurement. Teaching measurement concepts and skills falls into three major categories: activities that teach the meaning of measurement concepts such as length, time, area, capacity, and weight; measurement of objects with nonstandard units; introduction of standard units of measurement. Students are given a substantial amount of practice in estimating with standard units and then measuring to check the estimate.

Problems Solving

In this chapter, students solve problems using the strategy *Use Logical Reasoning* and use estimation to determine whether answers are reasonable.

TIPS FROM TEACHERS

Give each student a piece of string one meter long. Have them measure each other, their desks, the classroom, the hallway, and so on. Students can work in groups to measure the playground. Use longer lengths of string to demonstrate greater distances.

Bill Davis
Lakewood Elementary School
Dallas, TX

ASSESSMENT

Pretest — Chapter 6, page 1
Multiple-Choice Format

Name _____

1. Use ⬭ as units. Measure.
- (A) 2 ⬭
- B 3 ⬭
- C 5 ⬭

2. Estimate the length of the line to the nearest inch. _____
- (A) 1 inch
- B 3 inches
- C 10 inches

3. Measure to the nearest inch.
inches 1 2
- (A) 2 inches
- B 1 inch
- C 3 inches

4. Find the total length of the path on the map.
I + I + I + I = ?
- A 2 inches
- B 1 inch
- (C) 4 inches

5. Choose the best estimate for your height.
- (A) more than 1 foot
- B 1 foot
- C less than 1 foot

6. Choose the better estimate.
- A more than 1 quart
- (B) less than 1 quart

MCT 2   21

Pretest — Chapter 6, page 2
Multiple-Choice Format

Name _____

7. Estimate how much one crayon weighs.
- A 1 pound
- B more than 1 pound
- (C) less than 1 pound

8. Measure to the nearest centimeter.
centimeters 1 2 3 4 5
- A 3 cm
- (B) 4 cm
- C 5 cm

9. Choose the best estimate for the height of a door.
- A 1 meter
- (B) more than 1 meter
- C less than 1 meter

10. Estimate how many small cups would fill a liter.
- (A) more than 2
- B 2
- C less than 2

11. Choose the best estimate for your weight.
- A 1 kilogram
- B less than 1 kilogram
- (C) more than 1 kilogram

12. Does the answer make sense?
How many ☐ will cover ▭?
Answer: 4
- A Yes, it makes sense.
- (B) No, it doesn't.

22   MCT 2

Posttest — Chapter 6, page 1
Multiple-Choice Format

Name _____

1. Use ⬭ as units. Measure.
- A 4 ⬭
- (B) 1 ⬭
- C 2 ⬭

2. Estimate the length of the line to the nearest inch. _____
- (A) 2 inches
- B 6 inches
- C 10 inches

3. Measure to the nearest inch.
inches 1 2
- A 3 inches
- B 2 inches
- (C) 1 inch

4. Find the total length of the path on the map.
I + I + I = ?
- A 1 inch
- (B) 3 inches
- C 6 inches

5. Choose the best estimate for the length of your finger.
- A 1 foot
- B more than 1 foot
- (C) less than 1 foot

6. Choose the better estimate.
- (A) more than 1 pint
- B less than 1 pint

MCT 2   23

Posttest — Chapter 6, page 2
Multiple-Choice Format

Name _____

7. Estimate how much one desk weighs.
- A 1 pound
- (B) more than 1 pound
- C less than 1 pound

8. Measure to the nearest centimeter.
centimeters 1 2 3 4 5
- A 2 cm
- B 4 cm
- (C) 1 cm

9. Choose the best estimate for your teacher's height.
- A 1 meter
- (B) more than 1 meter
- C less than 1 meter

10. Estimate how many large cups would fill a liter.
- (A) more than 1
- B 1
- C less than 1

11. Choose the best estimate for your pencil's weight.
- A 1 kilogram
- (B) less than 1 kilogram
- C more than 1 kilogram

12. Does the answer make sense?
How many ☐ will cover ☐?
Answer: 4
- (A) Yes, it makes sense.
- B No, it doesn't.

24   MCT 2

ITEM ANALYSIS

Items	Objectives
1	6-1
2	6-2
3	6-3
4	6-4
5	6-5
6	6-6
7	6-7
8	6-8
9	6-9
10, 11	6-10
12	6-11

Note: The item analysis is the same for all pretests and posttests for this chapter.

ALSO AVAILABLE
- ▶ Free Response Tests
- ▶ Alternative Tests
- ▶ Thinking Strategies
- ▶ Concrete Materials

CHAPTER 6 MEASUREMENT

Optional Chapter Activities

PROJECT AND BULLETIN BOARD

Have students work in small groups and copy the names of the following dinosaurs on index cards: *Tyrannosaurus Rex, Brachiosaurus, Trachodon, Triceratops, Brontosaurus, Stegosaurus.* Have students estimate the dinosaurs' lengths in meters and write the estimates on the backs of the cards. Direct them to find the actual length of each dinosaur by looking in encyclopedias or other reference books. Tell them to write the length on the back of the card. (They may find a range is given.) Then, go outdoors to an open space, such as a playground or city sidewalk. Use a meter stick to show the length of each dinosaur. Back in the classroom, have students write a short paragraph about their assigned dinosaur. Ask them to draw pictures showing the size of the dinosaur compared to the other dinosaurs. Display their work on the bulletin board.

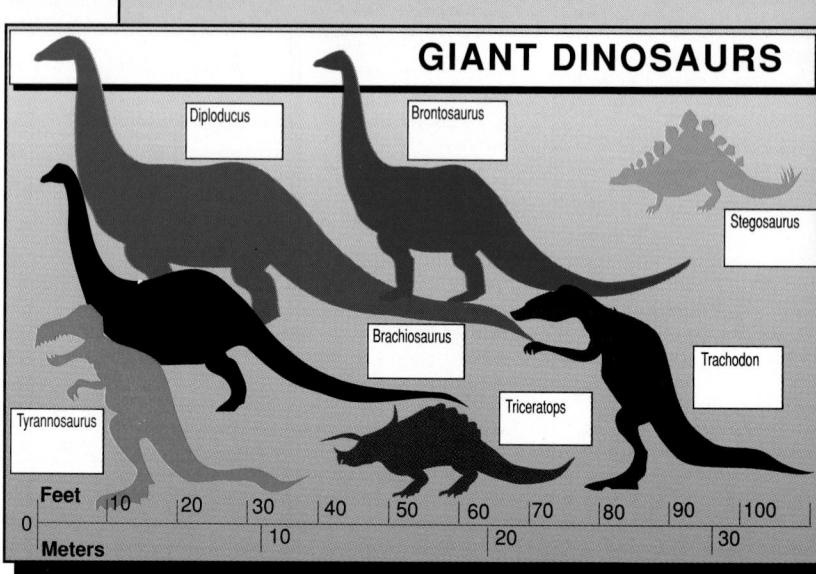

GIANT DINOSAURS

Diploducus · Brontosaurus · Stegosaurus · Brachiosaurus · Trachodon · Triceratops · Tyrannosaurus

Feet: 0, 10, 20, 30, 40, 50, 60, 70, 80, 90, 100
Meters: 10, 20, 30

COOPERATIVE LEARNING

Divide the class into 4 groups. Identify the group skill: disagreeing constructively. Tell students that they are going to compare the height of bean sprouts grown in sunlight with sprouts grown in darkness. Provide each group with 2 styrofoam cups, soil, and beans. Have students plant the beans in the cups and mark the cups with the words *dark* and *light*. Each day, have one group member place the cups in areas of the classroom with the kind of lighting marked on the cup. A second group member will water the plants daily, a third will measure the growth of the plants each day, and a fourth will record the measurement on a chart such as the one shown. After 5 days, discuss the results and have students tell why they think the sprouts grew at different rates. If they disagree, remind them to give their reasons.

You will find grouping suggestions and cooperative learning activities in most lessons throughout this chapter.

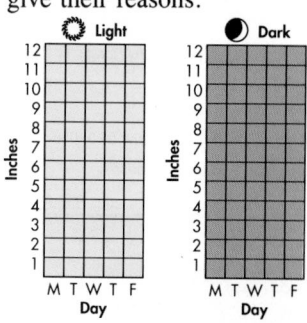

LITERATURE

Anno, Mitsumara. *The King's Flower.* Cleveland, Ohio: William Collins Publishers, 1979.

The king in this story wants everything he has to be the biggest. One day, however, he orders the royal gardener to grow the biggest flower, and finds out that nature does not cater to kings.
This story lends itself to discussion of the different sizes of things and the different methods of measuring them. Have students measure their heights in feet and inches and record the information on a class chart.

Olney, Ross & Patricia. *How Long? To Go, To Grow, To Know.* New York: William Morrow & Co., 1984.

Thurber, James. *The Thirteen Clocks.* New York: Simon and Schuster, 1950.

ENGLISH AS A SECOND LANGUAGE

Use the problem solving activity to create a cooperative, atmosphere in which ESL students can write, tape record, and share stories with each other and the class. In addition, have students create a picture file for the 4 kinds of measurements: height, weight, length, and capacity. The problem solving exercises are linguistically complex, using different forms of the same word and possessives in deleted comparisons. For example, *Teri can reach* (verb) *higher than Jan. Jill's reach* (noun) *is lower than Jan's.* Paraphrase these problems by using the same word forms and by expanding on deleted forms such as . . . *than Jan's reach.*

Make sure students understand the elements of the graph. Give students the language necessary to express estimation: *I think it is about . . .* Establish clear connections between different words used to express the same reality: long and length, tall and height. Practice the pronunciations.

GIFTED

Mathematically talented students may already understand units of measure and be able to work with them readily. They will nevertheless likely be interested in many of the activities presented in this chapter. After they have completed their book work, challenge these students to create and describe an imaginary animal. Have them begin by drawing and naming the animal. Then explain that they will describe their animal by measuring its height, weight, and the amount of food it eats. Help students choose between standard and metric measures, and be sure they remain consistent as they use different units of measurement. For example, after the lessons on estimating and measuring length, students may list and measure their animal's features (head, body, legs, paws) in centimeters and meters, or in inches and feet. As students complete lessons on weight, they will describe their animal's weight, and the amount of food it eats each day. Finally, they will describe how much their animal drinks, using units of standard or metric capacity. Students may create a table showing all of their information, and display it along with their animal picture on a classroom bulletin board.

STUDENTS AT RISK

Throughout this chapter, provide plenty of hands-on experience with measuring instruments, both standard and nonstandard. After students have become familiar with each measuring tool, have them make guesses about the length, weight, or capacity of various objects and then check to confirm their predictions. Provide them with opportunities for comparing the length, weight or capacity of different objects, as well. Give students the opportunity to observe directly different measurement quantities, such as feeling water that is 32° F, holding a 1-pound book, drinking $\frac{1}{2}$ cup of juice, eating 1 ounce of cheese, running 50 yards.

After the different kinds of measurement have been introduced, ask students questions about choosing the most appropriate measure. For example, when measurement concepts are new, you might ask, *Would you **weigh** an elephant in yards, pounds, or cups?* After students have had more experience, focus on the unit of measure: *Would you measure the length of a football field in miles, yards, or inches?* Ask students to explain their choice. A picture file can be used for this purpose and students may initiate special projects during these discussions. You may also use the Reteaching Supplements and the specific Reteaching Tips from each lesson in this chapter.

Chapter 6 Optional Chapter Activities

PICTURE

These pictures and accompanying stories and poems are available as storybooks.

You may want to read and discuss this story with your students before starting the chapter. The first lesson in this chapter includes a question about the story. Lessons 1, 2, 5, 8, and 11 in this chapter have questions in the informal Assessment that refer to the story.

Ceci Grows Up

Ceci, a young female chimpanzee, peeked out from behind a huge tree. Her mother spotted her and told her sharply, "You're too young to wander off by yourself, so stop playing hide-and-seek with me!"

Ceci was tired of being treated like a baby. She threw a tantrum as young chimpanzees sometimes do when they do not get their way. Her mother knew that Ceci was getting to be old enough to start doing things by herself. But she worried that Ceci might fall from a tree or get lost. Finally she came up with a plan.

"I know how much you want to play in the jungle without me," she said, "but I think you need to wait until your arms are a little longer and you can easily swing from branch to branch. When your arms are 10 units long, you can play in the jungle with the older children. Does that seem fair?"

Ceci knew that she was growing quickly. She thought that perhaps her arms were already 10 units long, so she agreed. She begged her mother to measure her arms right away. She lay down on the ground and stretched out her arm as far as she could. Mother looked around. "Let's see, what shall I use for a measuring unit? I guess the leaves from this vine will do." She picked the leaves and carefully laid them end-to-end along Ceci's arm. "That's 1, 2, 3, 4, 5, 6, 7 units," she said.

"Oh, no!" Ceci moaned. "I'll never get to play vine swing tag in the jungle with my friends. My arms have to grow three more units."

A month passed and Ceci asked her mother to measure her arms again. Again she lay on the ground and s-t-r-e-t-c-h-e-d with all her might. This time, Mother decided to use bananas for the measuring unit. As she lay the bananas down to measure Ceci's arm, she counted, "1, 2, 3, 4 units."

Ceci was very upset. Her arms were only four units long now. Were her arms growing shorter?

The next month, Ceci asked for another measurement. This time Ceci asked if she could choose the measuring unit, and her mother agreed. "Here, Mother, use the petals from this flower," Ceci said.

Mother laid the small petals end-to-end along Ceci's arm and counted the units, "1, 2, 3, 4, 5, 6, 7, 8, 9, 10, 11, 12, 13...." On and on she counted.

My arm is 20 units long!" Ceci exclaimed.

Mother knew that she had been outsmarted. But she decided that a bargain was a bargain. Ceci should be allowed to play in the jungle. Besides, her daughter must be pretty smart to figure out a trick like that.

LESSON OPTIONS 6-1

Estimating and Measuring Length: Nonstandard Units

OBJECTIVE 6-1   To estimate and measure length using nonstandard units

PREBOOK ACTIVITIES

QUICK REVIEW

Write 4 number sentences to make a fact family for each group.
2, 5, 7 $(2 + 5 = 7, 5 + 2 = 7, 7 - 2 = 5, 7 - 5 = 2)$
17, 8, 9 $(8 + 9 = 17, 9 + 8 = 17, 17 - 9 = 8, 17 - 8 = 9)$
6, 10, 4 $(6 + 4 = 10, 4 + 6 = 10, 10 - 6 = 4, 10 - 4 = 6)$
7, 8, 15 $(7 + 8 = 15, 8 + 7 = 15, 15 - 7 = 8, 15 - 8 = 7)$
6, 0, 6 $(6 + 0 = 6, 0 + 6 = 6, 6 - 0 = 6, 6 - 6 = 0)$

PRIOR KNOWLEDGE

Imagine that you are stranded on a desert island and you do not have a ruler. What method might you use to measure your height? (Possible answer: Lie down in the sand to get an imprint of your body, and then use your hand or a palm branch to measure the length from head to toe.) *What problem might you have using this system?* (Possible answer: No one but you would understand it; you may not be able to find the same size palm branch the next time you measure.)

COMMUNICATION

Reading Discussing Math   Write the words *nonstandard units* on the chalkboard and read them aloud with students. Explain that if a unit of measure is nonstandard, it is not used by everyone in a group of people. *What are some things you could use to measure length?* (Possible answers: paper clips, pencils, hands, rulers) *When might you need to estimate the length of something?* (Possible answer: when you do not have a tool to measure with; when buying material to make a dress; when cutting paper or ribbon to wrap a package) *How can estimating length save you time?* (Possible answer: Estimating helps you make a decision without having to measure exactly.)

EXPLORE AND CONNECT

Grouping Suggestions: small groups
Demonstrate how you might use your hand to measure the length of an object in the room. Show students how to position their hands at the point where the measurement ended each time their hand is moved. Have students form small groups and ask them to estimate the length of objects in the room and then measure the objects using their handspans, their thumbs, and their pencils. Ask a student to record in a chart students' names, names of the objects, the estimates, and the measurements for each nonstandard unit used. *Were your estimates close to the measurements?* (Answers will vary.) *What might cause your measurement to be different from your classmates'?* (Possible answer: The different lengths of our hands, thumbs, and pencils make the measurements different.)

CONNECTIONS   Use these anytime.

Problem of the Day

Writing a Story   Choose from the words below to finish writing a banana story for $5 + 2 = $ _____. Ask an addition question in your story and complete the number sentence.
picked   found   monkey   tree
in all   ate   how many   had
(Stories will vary. $5 + 2 = 7$)

Life Skills

Jobs   Read the names of the workers. Write the name of something for which each might estimate length.
firefighter (height to raise a ladder)
dressmaker (length of material)
grocer (length of space on shelves)
swimmer (length of a pool)
carpenter (length of a board)

Subject Integration

Physical Education   On a playground or in the gym, estimate the length of several distances using nonstandard units, such as baby steps or giant steps. Then walk the distance using these steps. How did your measurements compare to your estimates? How else might you use your body to measure this distance?

CLASSWORK AND HOMEWORK SUPPLEMENTS

Basic

Exercises All

Supplements
Reteaching 46 or
Practice 46

Average

Exercises All

Supplements
Practice 46
Challenges 46 or
Thinking Skills 46

Extended

Exercises All

Supplements
Challenges 46
Thinking Skills 46

6-1

Practice

Estimation 6-1

Name _____

**Estimating and Measuring Length:
Nonstandard Units**

Use cubes and paper clips.
Estimate the length for each unit.
Then measure. Write the number of units.   Answers may vary.

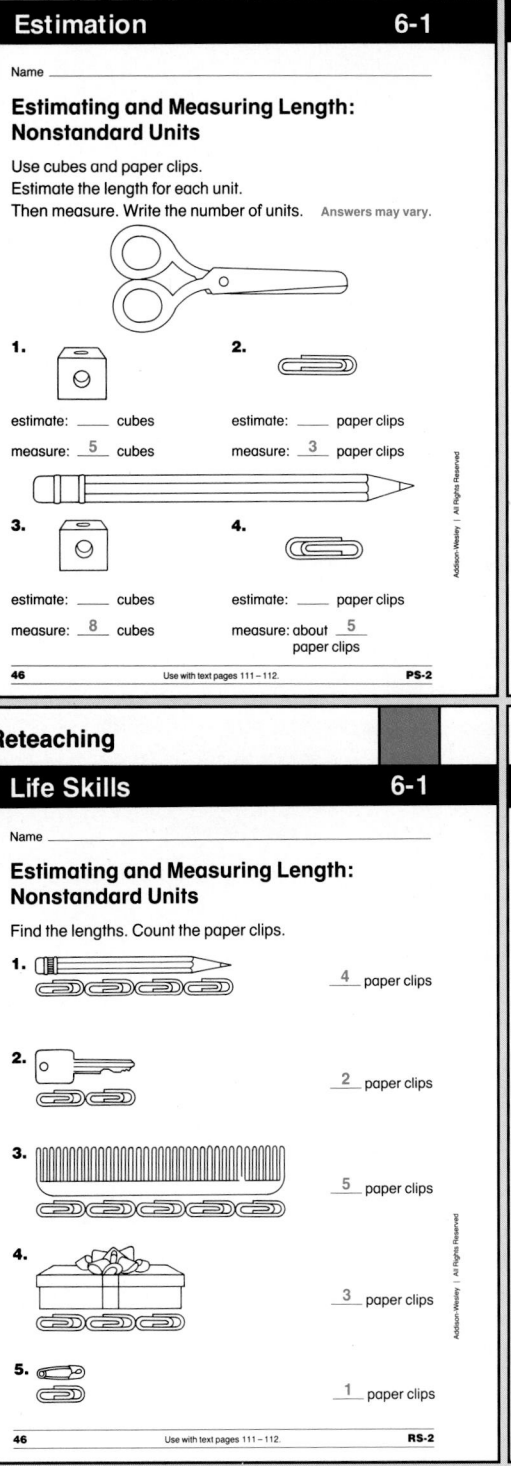

1.

estimate: _____ cubes

measure: __5__ cubes

2.

estimate: _____ paper clips

measure: __3__ paper clips

3.

estimate: _____ cubes

measure: __8__ cubes

4.

estimate: _____ paper clips

measure: about __5__ paper clips

46   Use with text pages 111–112.   **PS-2**

Building Thinking Skills

Critical Thinking 6-1

Name _____

Ways to Measure

Think about measuring each object.
Ring the better unit of measure to use.

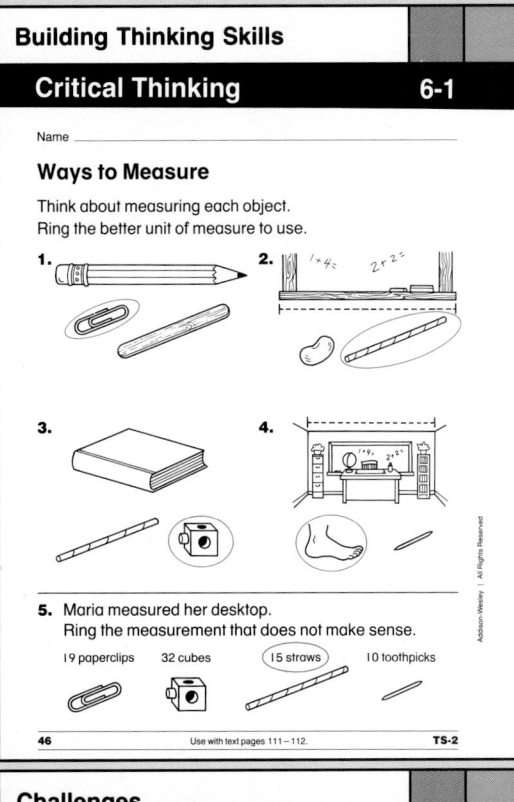

1.   2.

3.   4.

5. Maria measured her desktop.
Ring the measurement that does not make sense.

19 paperclips   32 cubes   (15 straws)   10 toothpicks

46   Use with text pages 111–112.   **TS-2**

Reteaching

Life Skills 6-1

Name _____

**Estimating and Measuring Length:
Nonstandard Units**

Find the lengths. Count the paper clips.

1.   __4__ paper clips

2.   __2__ paper clips

3.   __5__ paper clips

4.   __3__ paper clips

5.   __1__ paper clips

46   Use with text pages 111–112.   **RS-2**

Challenges

Manipulatives 6-1

Name _____

Guess and Measure

Find things to measure.
Pick a unit to use.
First estimate, then measure.
Fill in the chart.
Try measuring the same thing
using different units of measure.

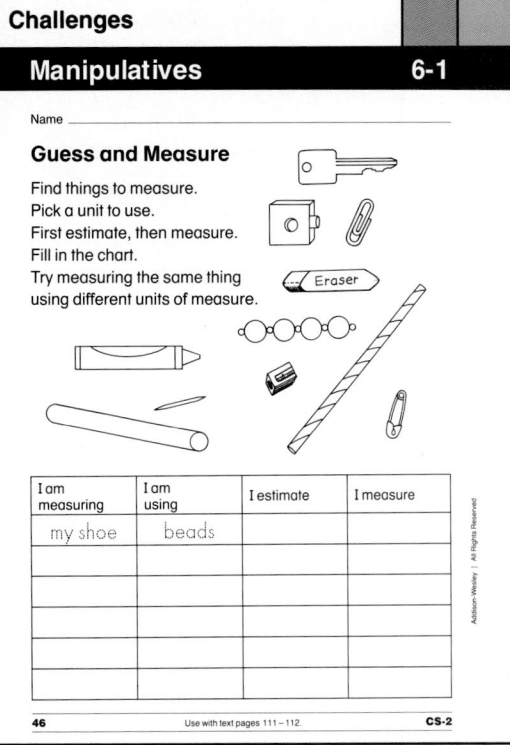

I am measuring	I am using	I estimate	I measure
my shoe	beads		

46   Use with text pages 111–112.   **CS-2**

Other Resources:
Math in Stride, pp. 114-120
Mathematics Their Way, pp. 135, 307
Explorations, pp. 158-159, 161-162, 168, 331
Problem-Solving Experiences In Mathematics, p. 65
Workjobs, pp. 218-219
Mathematics Book A, p. 11
Developing Number Concepts with Unifix Cubes, pp. 155-160

OBJECTIVE 6-1
To estimate and measure length using nonstandard units

> **Materials:** nonstandard units of measure, such as paper clips, toothpicks, scissors, crayons
>
> **Grouping Suggestions:** cooperative learning groups of 3, pairs

1. MOTIVATE AND TEACH

LEARN ABOUT IT

Read the chapter story to the class. *Do you think that Ceci's arms got shorter? What do you think happened?* (Possible answer: No; the bananas were longer than the leaves, so it took fewer units to measure Ceci's arms.) *How did Ceci outsmart her mother?* (She used a smaller unit to measure, so her arm seemed longer.) Divide students into groups of 3 and ask them to choose things they can use to measure the hand on page 111 from the edge of the glove to the end of the longest finger. The first student estimates, the second measures, and the third records the results.

▶ **Why are the measurements different for every unit?** (Possible answer: The units are not the same size, so it takes more small units to measure the length.)

▶ **Describe how your estimates are different from your measurements.** (Answers will vary.)

▶ **Why might a stick make a better unit of measure than a pencil or a crayon?** (Possible answer: A pencil or a crayon will get smaller as it is used, so the measurement would change.)

▶ **What conclusion can you draw about measuring objects from doing this page?** (Possible answer: It is important to use a unit of measure that will not change size and that everyone can use and understand.)

2. CHECK UNDERSTANDING

ERROR ALERT Forgetting to line up the units end to end in order to get an accurate measurement.

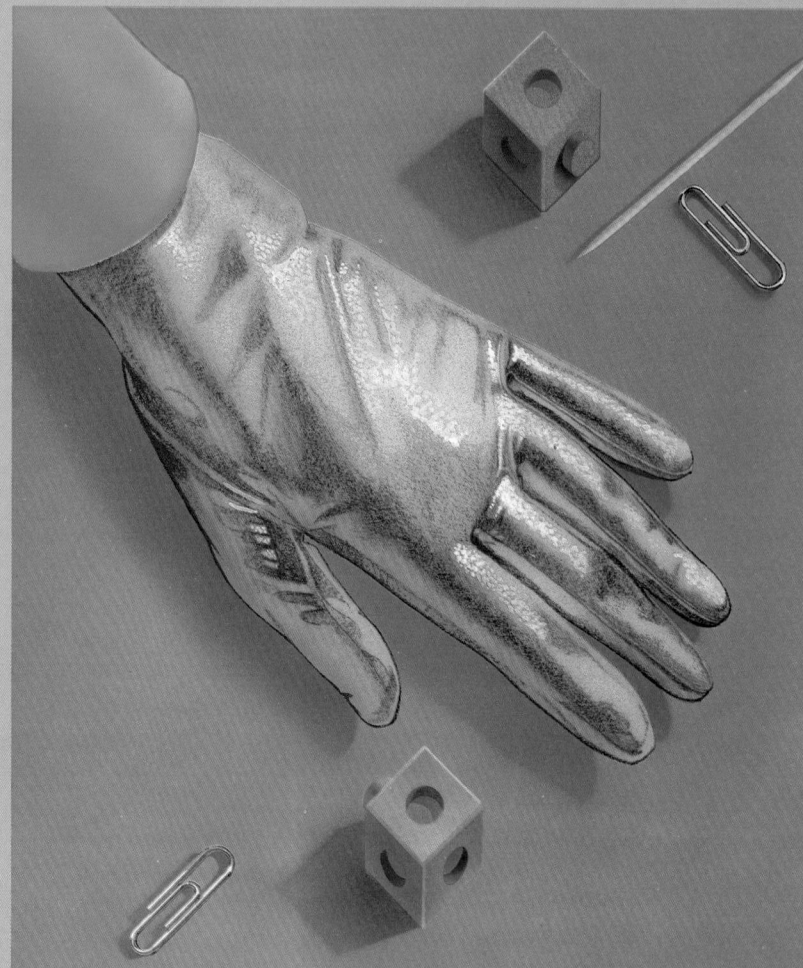

$\dfrac{6}{}$

Measurement

TEACHING OPTIONS

RETEACHING TIPS Have students draw a line on paper, place a paper clip at the end of the line, and mark the line where the paper clip ends. Move the paper clip along the line, marking each length, until they reach the end. Then count the marks. Assign Reteaching Supplement 46.

ENRICHMENT Have students choose a nonstandard unit of measure. Make a 3-column chart listing names of objects, number of units used to measure each length, and number of units it might take to measure 2 of the same object. Have them show their work.

ne _____

stimating and Measuring Length
nstandard Units

ork with a partner. Use cubes and
per clips as units. Estimate the
ngth of your hand. Then measure.
rite the number of units.
swers may vary. Check students' work.

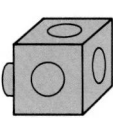

estimate: ____ cubes

measure: ____ cubes

2. estimate: ____ paper clips

measure: ____ paper clips

timate the length of the
pper. Then measure.
rite the number of units.

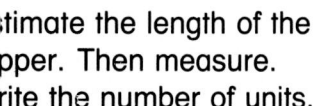

estimate: ____ cubes

measure: ____ cubes

4. estimate: ____ paper clips

measure: ____ paper clips

Answers may vary. Check students' work.

LK ABOUT IT

Did you use more cube units or more paper
clip units to measure each length? Tell why. See teaching notes.

2 (one hundred twelve)

Chapter 6

LOSE AND ASSESS

OW WHAT YOU KNOW

k students to pretend that they are
ilders. Have them draw a plan of a
droom they would like to have.
en have them use a nonstandard
it of measure to estimate and
asure each side of the room. Ask
m to record the measurements on
ir picture. Discuss what would
ppen if everyone involved in
ilding the room did not use the
ne unit of measurement.

QUICK QUIZ

Trace around your shoe. Estimate its
length using cubes. Measure the
drawing using cubes and record your
results.

3. PRACTICE AND APPLY

Basic	All
Average	All
Extended	All

PRACTICE

*What are you to do with the objects
pictured in Exercises 1 and 2?* (Estimate
how many of each object it will take to
measure your hand. Then use the objects
to measure.) *What will you measure in
Exercises 3 and 4?* (the golden slipper)

APPLY

TALK ABOUT IT ▶ **Describe your
estimates in Exercises 1–4. Were they
close to the measurements?** (Answers
will vary.)
▶ **Tell whether you think it would
take more paper clips or more cubes
to measure each length on this page
and explain why.** (Possible answer: It
would take more cubes, because they are
smaller than paper clips.)

6-1

Chapter 6 Lesson 1   **112**

Estimating and Measuring Length: Nearest Inch

OBJECTIVE 6-2   To estimate and measure to the nearest inch

PREBOOK ACTIVITIES

QUICK REVIEW

		About . . .	or About . . .
1.	crayon	3 paper clips	8 paper clips
2.	pencil	5 paper clips	15 paper clips
3.	your longest finger	6 cubes	2 cubes
4.	your math book	4 cubes	12 cubes

Tell the better estimate of length.

PRIOR KNOWLEDGE

Discuss measuring with cubes and paper clips and ask what students think might be difficult about using these things to measure. (Possible responses: It would take a long time to measure big things; it would be hard to measure round things; different-sized clips and cubes would give different measurements for the same thing.) Discuss familiar linear measurements, such as people's heights, and ask students if they know how they are measured. (in feet and inches)

COMMUNICATION

Reading and Discussing Math   Hold up an inch ruler. Tell students that instead of using a paper clip or a cube to measure, this ruler uses a unit called an **inch.** Write the words **inch** and **ruler** on the chalkboard. *What is the distance between each pair of numbers on the ruler?* (one inch) Point to various numbers on the ruler and ask students to read the number of inches.

Extend the discussion to include the words **length** and **long, width** and **wide,** and **height** and **tall.** Demonstrate how to measure a book. *If we find out how many inches long the book is, what measurement do we know?* (the length of the book)

EXPLORE AND CONNECT

Materials: punchout inch ruler for each student
Grouping Suggestion: pairs

Pair students and distribute a **ruler** to each student. Show students the length of 1 **inch** on their rulers and ask them to use their rulers to find a place on their hands that is about an inch wide or an inch long. *What objects can you think of that are about 1 inch long?* (a cube, a paper clip, a postage stamp, a large button) Have partners estimate and record, then measure and record, various classroom objects, such as a pencil, a crayon, an eraser, and a notebook. *How close were your estimates? Do measurements always come out to an exact number of inches?* (Answers will vary.) Have partners determine whether the end of the object is at an inch mark or between two marks. Ask them to decide which two inch marks it falls between. *Which inch mark is closer? How long is it to the nearest inch?*

CONNECTIONS   Use these anytime.

Problem of the Day

Add or Subtract   Tom measured his foot, then his father's foot. Tom's foot is about 6 inches long, and his father's is about 11 inches long. Compare the lengths of their feet. Do you add or subtract? Write the number sentence and tell what it shows. $(11 - 6 = 5;$ Tom's foot is 5 inches shorter than his father's.)

Math Connection

Estimating with Straws   Make a list of 5 things you estimate are shorter than a straw, and 5 things you estimate are longer than a straw. Then check your estimates by using the straw to measure the objects. How close were you? (Possible answers: shorter—a crayon, a pencil, a leaf; longer—a book, a necklace, a belt)

Creative Thinking

How to Measure   You need to measure the length of the teacher's desk. You have a broken ruler that shows only 9 inches and a ball of string. How can you use them both to measure? (Stretch the string from one end of the desk to the other and mark the length. Then find out how many rulers long the string is and add all the 9s.)

CLASSWORK AND HOMEWORK SUPPLEMENTS

Practice

Life Skills — 6-2

Name

Estimating and Measuring Length: Nearest Inch

Estimate each length.
Then measure to the nearest inch. **Estimates will vary.**

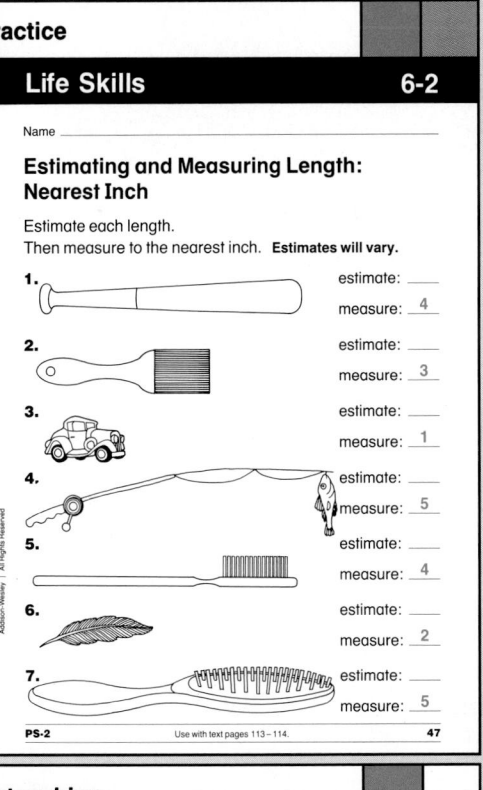

1. estimate: ___ measure: 4
2. estimate: ___ measure: 3
3. estimate: ___ measure: 1
4. estimate: ___ measure: 5
5. estimate: ___ measure: 4
6. estimate: ___ measure: 2
7. estimate: ___ measure: 5

PS-2 — Use with text pages 113–114. — 47

Building Thinking Skills

Math Reasoning — 6-2

Name

Measure, Think, and Write

Use your inch ruler.
Find the length to the nearest $\frac{1}{2}$ inch.

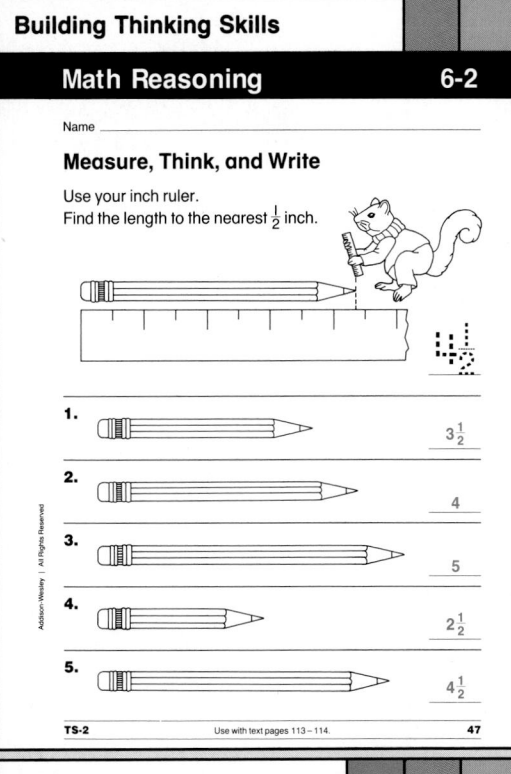

1. $3\frac{1}{2}$
2. 4
3. 5
4. $2\frac{1}{2}$
5. $4\frac{1}{2}$

TS-2 — Use with text pages 113–114. — 47

Reteaching

Skills Review — 6-2

Name

Estimating and Measuring Length: Nearest Inch

close to 5 inches

Estimate each length. **Estimates will vary.**
Then measure to the nearest inch.

1. estimate: ___ measure: 3
2. estimate: ___ measure: 4
3. estimate: ___ measure: 5

RS-2 — Use with text pages 113–114. — 47

Challenges

Estimation — 6-2

Name

Sea Stars

Connect the stars in order from letters A to H.
Then draw a line between H and D.

Describe your picture. **a sailboat**

Estimate the length from A to D. estimate: ___ inches

Measure the length from A to D. measure: 2 nearest inch

Estimate which lines are almost as long as A to D.

A to B, C to B, G to F

Estimate which line is nearest to 1 inch. C to D

Now measure the lines to the nearest inch to check.

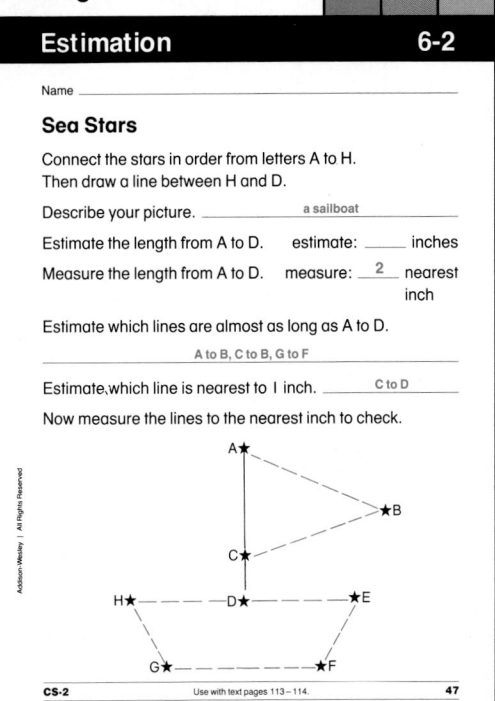

CS-2 — Use with text pages 113–114. — 47

LESSON PLAN 6-2

To estimate and measure to the nearest inch

> **Materials:** punchout inch ruler for each student, classroom and other objects up to 9 inches long
>
> **Grouping Suggestion:** pairs

1. MOTIVATE AND TEACH

LEARN ABOUT IT

On the chalkboard, list classroom objects such as a paperclip, an eraser, a pencil, and a book. Have students estimate the lengths in inches and record the estimate. Then have them use their rulers to measure the objects. *Which of your estimates were closest to the actual measurements?* (Answers will vary.) Do the sample exercise at the top of page 113 as a class.

▶ **Why do you think that we line up the left edge of the ruler with the left edge of the object we want to measure?** (Possible answer: because the left edge is 0, the beginning of the measurement)

▶ **Was 6 inches a reasonable estimate for the length of the carrot? Explain.** (Yes, because the actual length was between 5 and 6 inches, so an estimate of 6 inches is reasonable.)

▶ **Why do we estimate measurements of things before we actually measure them?** (Possible answers: to give us an idea of how long they are without having to measure; because in real life we often compare sizes of things without actually measuring them)

▶ **If an object is between two inch marks on the ruler, how do we decide which is the <u>nearest</u> inch?** (We choose the inch mark it is nearest, or closest, to.)

2. CHECK UNDERSTANDING

ERROR ALERT Not lining up the end of the object with the edge of the ruler. Difficulty identifying which of two numbers on the ruler is the nearest inch.

Name _____

Estimating and Measuring Length
Nearest Inch

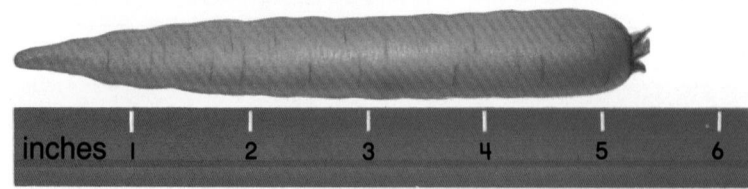

■━━━━━ **I inch** (in.)   estimate: __5__ inches

measure: between __5__ and __6__ inches   nearest inch: __5

Work with a partner. Estimate each length. Then measure. Write the number of inches. Answers may vary. Check students' wor

	length of	estimate	measure	nearest inch
1.	your shoe	_____ inches	between _____ and _____ inches	_____
2.	your lower arm	_____ inches	between _____ and _____ inches	_____

3. **Ring the best answer.** Answers may vary. Check students' work.

My shoe is   longer than / shorter than / about the same length as   my lower arr

Chapter 6   (one hundred thirteen)

TEACHING OPTIONS

RETEACHING TIPS Set up 2 rulers to measure the same objects. Place identical chalk pieces at the 1-in. mark on one ruler and at the left edge of the other ruler. Have students tell which piece is lined up correctly and give the length. Repeat with other objects. Assign Reteaching Supplement 47.

COMPUTER **Fish Scales, DLM** © **1985** For use with all levels. In *Todays Catch,* students measure the length of various fish using a ruler. In *Look and Hook,* they hook a fish by guessing the right depth for the hook. The recommended lesson takes 5-10 minutes.

Work with a partner. Estimate each height. Then measure to the nearest inch. Write the number of inches.

Answers may vary.
Check students' work.

1. your knee height

estimate:

____ inches

measure:

____ inches

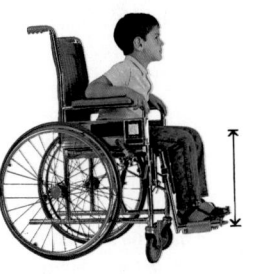

2. your chair seat height

estimate:

____ inches

measure:

____ inches

3. your back height

estimate:

____ inches

measure:

____ inches

4. your chair back height

estimate:

____ inches

measure:

____ inches

FIND THE DATA

Data Hunt Find two objects that each measure 6 inches long to the nearest inch. Write them here. Answers may vary.

_____   _____

- - - - - - - - - -   - - - - - - - - - -

114 (one hundred fourteen)   More Practice, page 414, set B   Chapter 6

---

3. PRACTICE AND APPLY

Basic	All
Average	All
Extended	All

PRACTICE

For Exercise 4, tell students that if their chair fits, their knee height should be 2 to 3 inches more than the chair seat height and their back height should be about the same or 2 to 3 inches more than the chair back height.

APPLY

FIND THE DATA
▶ **How will you decide which objects to measure?** (Possible answers: by estimating; by using ideas of how long things are)
▶ **What numbers on the ruler will you have to look at to decide if objects are 6 inches long to the nearest inch?** (5 or 7)

6-2

CLOSE AND ASSESS

SHOW WHAT YOU KNOW
Remind students of the story about Ceci the chimpanzee, and ask why it is helpful to have a standard unit of measurement. Have students work in pairs or small groups to act out situations like the ones in the chapter story to show how inches would make a better measurement than bananas or leaves.

QUICK QUIZ

Measure the following to the nearest inch: your middle finger, your thumb, the palm of your hand, your pencil, and the paper you are writing on. Write the measurement for each.

Measurement and Graphs

OBJECTIVE 6-3   To measure to the nearest inch; to make and read bar graphs

PREBOOK ACTIVITIES

QUICK REVIEW

Use your hand span to measure the following: the length of a book, desk, arm, and shoe and the height of a chair. Then order the measurements from least to greatest. (Possible answer: book, shoe, arm, desk, chair)

PRIOR KNOWLEDGE

Present the following situation: *If you were going to snap enough cubes together to make a train as long as yourself, how many cubes do you think you would need?* (Answers will vary.) *How can you be sure how many cubes you will need to measure your height?* (Possible answer: Snap enough cubes together to equal your height and count them.)

COMMUNICATION

Discussing Math   Display an inch ruler. Write the word **inch** on the chalkboard and point to the space between two of the inch marks. *How many of your fingers do you think will fit in 1 inch?* (Possible answer: 2) *How many inches long do you think your pencil is? How can you check your estimate?* (Possible answer: Measure with a ruler.) *If we measure several objects, how can we show all the measurements from shortest to longest?* (Possible answer: on a bar graph)

EXPLORE AND CONNECT

Materials: string, punchout inch rulers, small cards
Grouping Suggestions: small groups
Have students work in small groups to measure their wrists b placing string around the wrist and cutting or marking it. Hav them compare string lengths in their groups. *Who has the shortest piece of string? Who has the longest piece?* (Answer: will vary.) Ask students to put their string pieces in order fro shortest to longest. *Why do you think your strings are differer lengths?* (Possible answer: We have different wrist sizes.) Assist students in using the string pieces to make bar graphs. Place an inch ruler horizontally. Write students' names on cards and arrange them vertically. Have students place their strings beside their names and compare the lengths. *What is th difference in inches between the longest and the shortest piece of string?* (Answers will vary.)

CONNECTIONS   Use these anytime.

Problem of the Day

Logic   Sean is 4 ft 6 in. tall. Shane is 3 in. taller than Sean. Sherika is 1 in shorter than Shane. How tall is Sherika? (4 ft 8 in.)

Math Connection

Numbers and Numeration   Find an object that is less than 12 in. long. Estimate and then measure the object with a ruler or a tape measure. How long is it? Write a subtraction sentence to show the difference between your estimation and the actual length of the object. (Subtraction sentences will vary.)

Minute Math

Measure and Compare   Use a piece of string or yarn to find out the distance around your head. Do the same to find the distance around your knee. How many more inches is it around your head then around your knee? (Answers will vary.)

CLASSWORK AND HOMEWORK SUPPLEMENTS

Practice

Skills Maintenance   6-3

Name _____

Measurement and Graphs

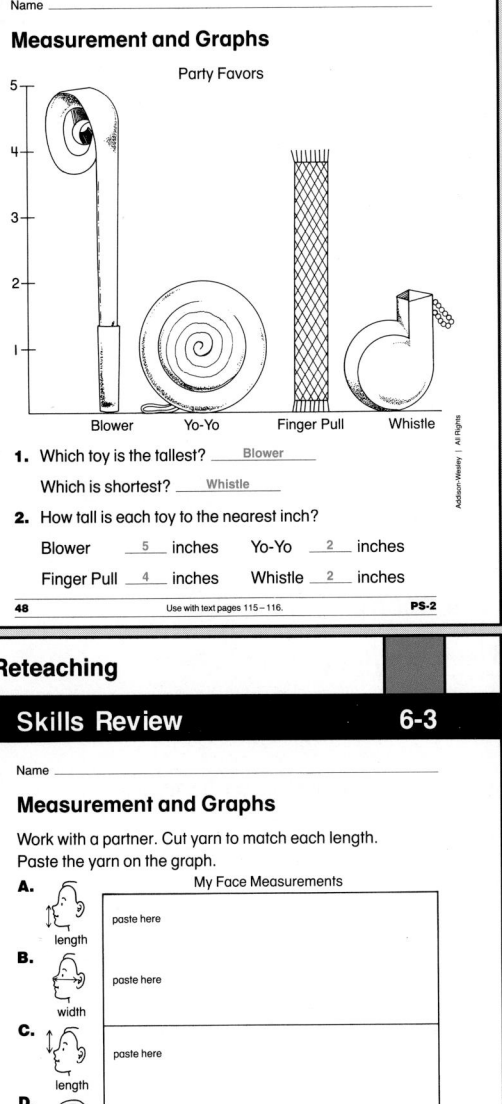

Party Favors

1. Which toy is the tallest? _Blower_

   Which is shortest? _Whistle_

2. How tall is each toy to the nearest inch?

   Blower _5_ inches   Yo-Yo _2_ inches

   Finger Pull _4_ inches   Whistle _2_ inches

48   Use with text pages 115–116.   **PS-2**

Building Thinking Skills

Data Analysis   6-3

Name _____

Wearing Out Graph

Ted measured his pencils and crayons.

black pencil = 8 inches	purple crayon = 3 inches
blue pencil = 6 inches	brown crayon = 4 inches
red pencil = 7 inches	

Imagine that Ted uses his pencils and crayons for a while.
Now each pencil is 2 inches shorter.
Each crayon is 1 inch shorter.
Draw each pencil and crayon on the graph
to show the length it is now.
Use the colors on Ted's list.

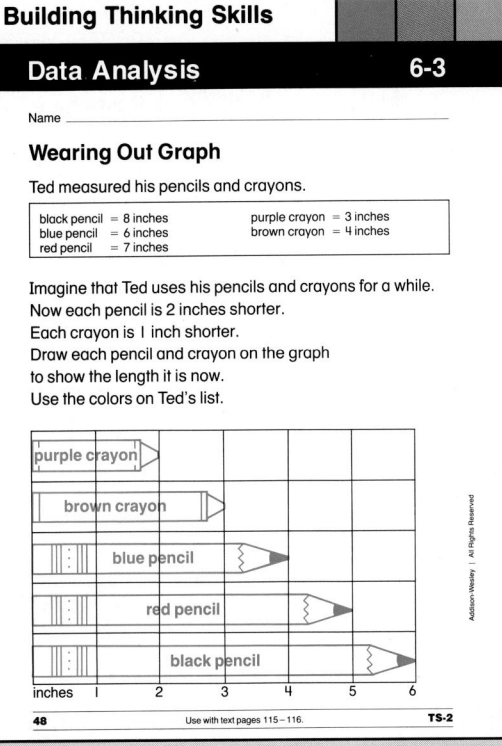

48   Use with text pages 115–116.   **TS-2**

Reteaching

Skills Review   6-3

Name _____

Measurement and Graphs

Work with a partner. Cut yarn to match each length.
Paste the yarn on the graph.

My Face Measurements

A. length — paste here

B. width — paste here

C. length — paste here

D. width — paste here

inches   1   2   3   4   5

Use your graph.

1. Write each measurement to the nearest inch.

   A. ___ inches   C. ___ inches

   B. ___ inches   D. ___ inches

2. Which length is longer? _Answers will vary._

3. Which width is wider? _Answers will vary._

48   Use with text pages 115–116.   **RS-2**

Challenges

Family Math   6-3

Name _____

Measuring at Home

> Dear Family,
> Your child is learning about measuring in inches and making graphs. Provide an inch ruler and help your child find three items around your home that are less than 12 inches long.

Work with a family member. Find three things to measure.
Measure each item to the nearest inch.
Fill in the chart. Ask your family member to write the
names of the items.

Item	Nearest Inch

Make a graph to show the data. Write the name of the item
on the side of the graph. Color one box for each inch.

_____

_____

_____

Talk about what the graph tells you.
Which item is longest? Which is the shortest?

48   Use with text pages 115–116.   **CS-2**

OPTIONS FOR INDIVIDUAL NEEDS

Basic

Exercises All

Supplements
Reteaching 48 or
Practice 48
Thinking Skills 48

Average

Exercises All

Supplements
Practice 48
Challenges 48 or
Thinking Skills 48

Extended

Exercises All

Supplements
Challenges 48
Thinking Skills 48

Other Resources:
Math in Stride, pp. 121-122
Explorations, pp. 159, 168
Workjobs, pp. 220-223

6-3

OBJECTIVE 6-3
To measure to the nearest inch; to make and read bar graphs

Materials: rulers, string, strips of paper, classroom objects 1-12 in. long

Grouping Suggestion: small groups

---

1. MOTIVATE AND TEACH

LEARN ABOUT IT

Have students help each other use string to measure the length of their hands, then have them compare their string lengths.

▶ **How can you find out whose hand is longest?** (Possible answers: Compare string lengths; measure strings with a ruler.)

How long is your hand to the nearest inch? (Answers will vary.)

▶ **How can you write an addition sentence showing your combined hand span and wrist lengths?** (Use each measure as an addend and find the sum.)

▶ **When do you think it might be easier to measure with a ruler than with a piece of string?** (Possible answer: when you are measuring a straight line or something flat)

▶ **When is a piece of string easier to use?** (Possible answer: when you are measuring something round or bumpy)

▶ **Why should you cut the string for a bracelet a little longer than your wrist measure?** (Possible answer: so you can get it over your hand)

2. CHECK UNDERSTANDING

ERROR ALERT Lining up the end of the object with the 1-in. mark instead of with the left edge of the ruler.

Name _____

Measurement and Graphs

1. Work with a partner. Cut string to match each length. Paste on the graph.

My Hand Measurements

A	palm	Paste here.
B	wrist	Paste here.
C	longest finger	Paste here.
D	span	Paste here.

inches   1   2   3   4   5

Use the graph to help you.

2. Write each length to the nearest inch. **Answers may vary. Check students' work.**

   A ____ inches   B ____ inches

   C ____ inches   D ____ inches

3. Use letters. Put in order from shortest to longest.
   Answers may vary.

   ____ ____ ____ ____

Chapter 6   (one hundred fifteen)

TEACHING OPTIONS

RETEACHING TIPS Use objects 1-12 in. in length. Show how to measure with the ruler, aligning the end of the object and the left edge of the ruler. *How would the measurement differ if you lined up the object with the 1-in. mark?* (It would be 1 in. too long.) Assign Reteaching Supplement 48.

ENRICHMENT Have students draw a picture to solve this problem: Samantha is taller than Sharon. Nima is taller than Sharon but shorter than Samantha. Who is the tallest? (Samantha) Who is the shortest? (Sharon)

3. PRACTICE AND APPLY

Basic	All
Average	All
Extended	All

PRACTICE

How can you find out how tall each puppet is? (Possible answer: Line up the top of each puppet with the nearest inch on the left side of the graph.)

APPLY

Can you name the puppets in order from the shortest to the tallest? (yes; Floss, Tooth, Toothpaste, Toothbrush)

► **What pattern can you see in the length of the puppets?** (Possible answer: Each puppet is about 1 in. taller than the one before.)

► **Are Toothpaste and Floss together longer or shorter than Toothbrush? How do you know?** (Possible answer: Longer, because Toothpaste and Floss total 6 in; Toothbrush is 5 in. long.)

► **Name the pairs of puppets that are closest in length.** (Floss and Tooth, Toothbrush and Toothpaste)

6-3

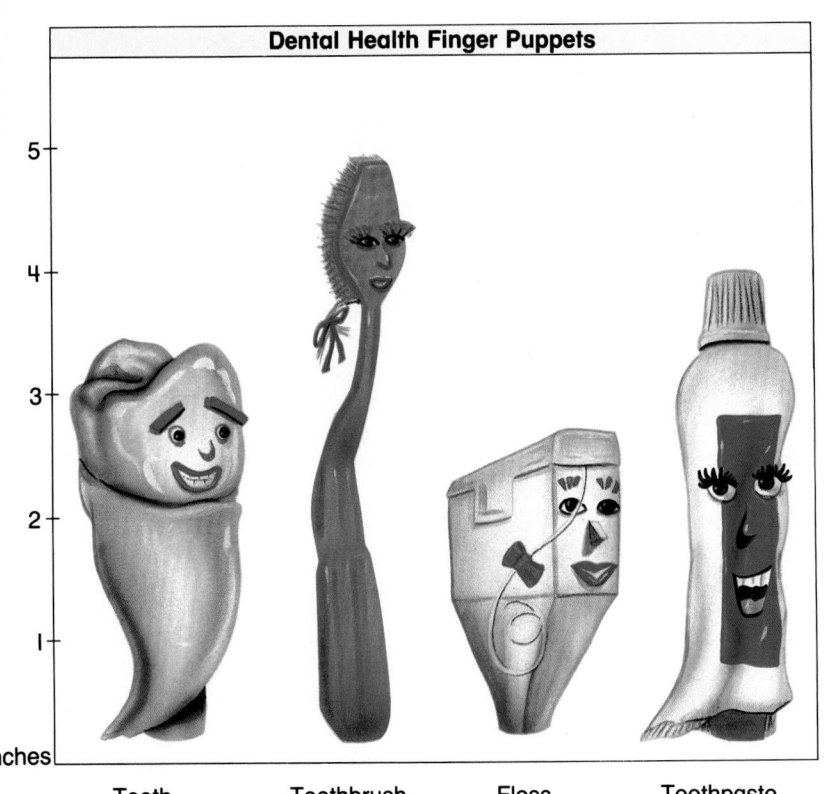

Dental Health Finger Puppets

Tooth Toothbrush Floss Toothpaste

. Which puppet is tallest? ___Toothbrush___

. Which puppet is shortest? ___Floss___

. How tall is each puppet to the nearest inch?

Tooth __3__ inches   Toothbrush __5__ inches

Floss __2__ inches   Toothpaste __4__ inches

CLOSE AND ASSESS

SHOW WHAT YOU KNOW

Provide small groups with 4 strips of paper of different lengths. Ask students to measure the strips and use them to make a bar graph. Have each student make up a question about their graph. Ask groups to present their graphs to the class and have other students read the graphs to answer the questions.

QUICK QUIZ

Measure the length of these objects to the nearest inch: a crayon, a pencil, your shortest finger, your longest finger. (Answers will vary.)

LESSON OPTIONS 6-4

Problem Solving: Understanding the Operations

OBJECTIVE 6-4   To understand the operation of addition by putting together; to explore perimeter

PREBOOK ACTIVITIES

PRIOR KNOWLEDGE

Help students recall that they have added 3 numbers to find a sum. *What do you know about the order of addends when you add 3 numbers together?* (Possible answer: The order does not change the sum.) *What strategies do you use for adding 3 or more numbers together?* (Possible answers: Look for sums of 10; add doubles or doubles plus one.)

COMMUNICATION

Reading and Discussing Math   Write the word **perimeter** on the chalkboard. Read the word aloud and have the class read it together. Explain that the perimeter is the distance around an area. *Suppose you wanted to find the perimeter of this classroom. How might you plan to get this information?* (Measure each side and add to find the total.) Have students walk around the classroom, counting their steps along each side. As students complete each side, write the number of steps on the chalkboard to make an addition sentence. Write *The perimeter of our classroom is* _____ *steps*. With students, add the number of steps and complete the sentence.

EXPLORE AND CONNECT

COOPERATIVE ACTIVITY

Grouping Suggestion: small groups
Draw a triangle 6 in. by 6 in. by 2 in. on the chalkboard. Label *home, library,* and *school,* one at each corner. *Marc walked from his home to school.* (6 in.) *He ran from school to the library.* (6 in.) *He skipped home from the library* (2 in.) *How many inches on the map did Marc travel in all?*
___ + ___ + ___ = ___ in. (6 + 6 + 2 = 14)

TEACHING ACTIONS

 **BEFORE**
► **Explain what is happening in the story.** (Possible answer: Marc is traveling from home to school to the library and home again.)
► **Which data is important in the story? Which data is not important?** (Possible answers: The distances traveled are important. The ways Marc traveled—walked, ran, skipped—are not important.)

 **DURING**
► **What steps must you plan to use to solve the problem?** (Possible answer: First, measure each distance. Then, add the distances to find the total distance traveled.)
► **What measuring tool will you need to find the solution?** (an inch ruler to measure the distances)

AFTER
► **Describe how you would check your answer.** (Possible answers: Measure each side again; add the distances in a different order to check addition; compare the answer with the data in the problem to make sure it makes sense.)
Have students work in small groups to solve the problem.

CONNECTIONS   Use these anytime.

Problem of the Day

Understanding the Operations
Draw a picture to help you solve the problem.
Carrie ran 3 blocks north and 4 blocks east. Then she ran back to her starting point along the same paths. How many blocks did she run in all? (14)

Math Connection

Measurement   Cut a piece of string and measure it on your inch ruler. Now curve the string and trace the curve on a piece of paper. Challenge a classmate to estimate and then find the length of the curve. Check the answers against the actual measurement. Take turns making curves to measure.

Minute Math

Addition   Write only the answers. How many can you solve in 1 min.?
5 + 5 + 2 = __(12)__
4 + 6 + 8 = __(18)__
5 + 3 + 6 = __(14)__
8 + 3 + 2 = __(13)__
8 + 1 + 2 = __(11)__
7 + 3 + 7 = __(17)__
2 + 2 + 7 = __(11)__

Estimating Curve Lengths

o estimate curve lengths

CLASSWORK AND HOMEWORK SUPPLEMENTS

Practice

Estimation   6-4

Name

Estimating Curve Lengths

Look at the paths.

1. Which path is longest? Which is shortest? Ring your guesses.   Answers will vary.

Longest   A   B   C   D

Shortest   A   B   C   D

2. Place string along each path. Measure the string to the nearest inch. Write the number of inches.

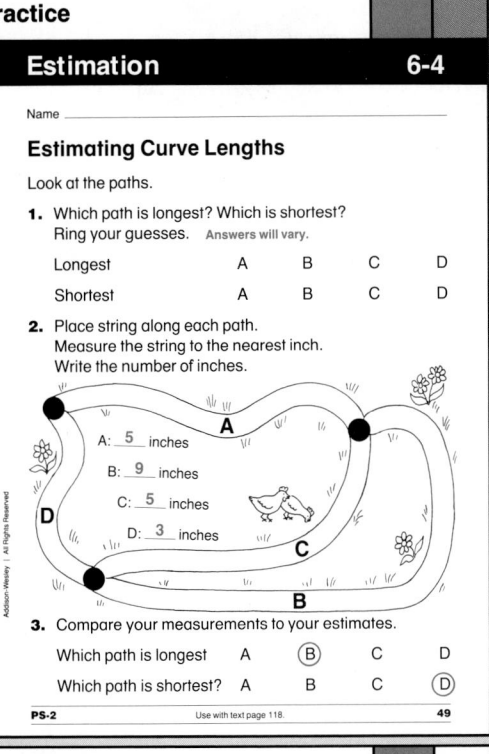

A: __5__ inches

B: __9__ inches

C: __5__ inches

D: __3__ inches

3. Compare your measurements to your estimates.

Which path is longest   A   (B)   C   D

Which path is shortest?   A   B   C   (D)

PS-2   Use with text page 118.   49

Building Thinking Skills

Creative Thinking   6-4

Name

String Curves

You will need a piece of string, a ruler, and a curved object to measure, such as a ball or a vase.

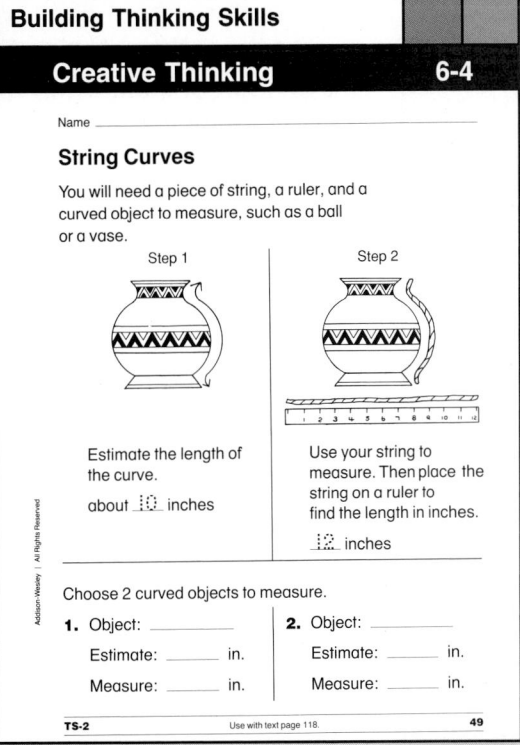

Step 1

Step 2

Estimate the length of the curve.

about __10__ inches

Use your string to measure. Then place the string on a ruler to find the length in inches.

__12__ inches

Choose 2 curved objects to measure.

1. Object: _____

Estimate: _____ in.

Measure: _____ in.

2. Object: _____

Estimate: _____ in.

Measure: _____ in.

TS-2   Use with text page 118.   49

Reteaching

Problem Solving   6-4

Name

Understanding the Operations

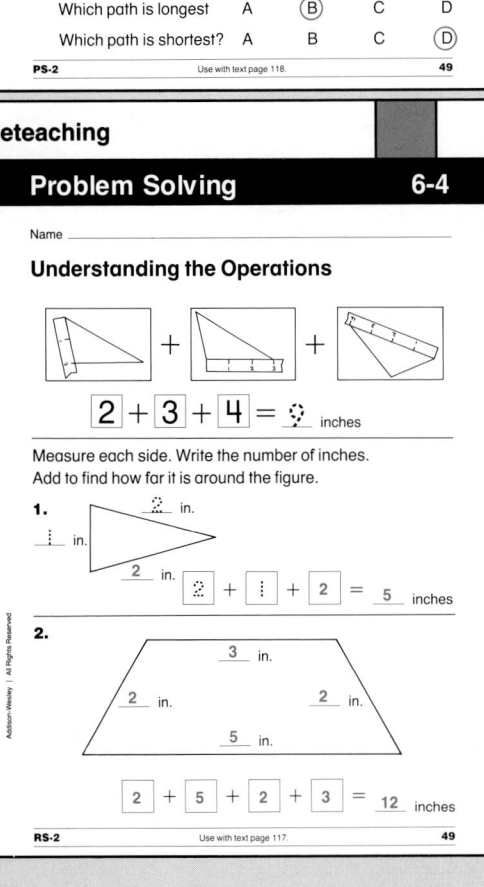

$2 + 3 + 4 = 9$ inches

Measure each side. Write the number of inches. Add to find how far it is around the figure.

1.

__2__ in.

__1__ in.

__2__ in.

$2 + 1 + 2 = 5$ inches

2.

__3__ in.

__2__ in.   __2__ in.

__5__ in.

$2 + 5 + 2 + 3 = 12$ inches

RS-2   Use with text page 117.   49

Challenges

Problem Solving   6-4

Name

A Long Walk

Alvin Ant can walk 1 inch each hour. How many hours will it take him to walk around the figure? Hint: Use mental math. Count on to add as you measure each side.

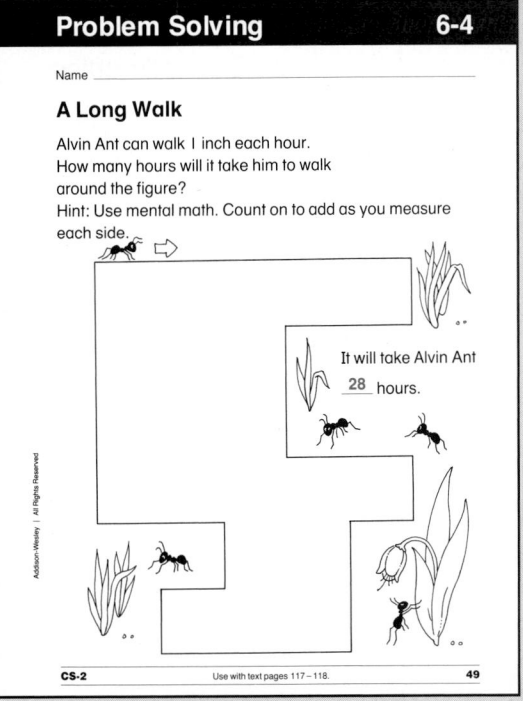

It will take Alvin Ant __28__ hours.

CS-2   Use with text pages 117 – 118.   49

OPTIONS FOR INDIVIDUAL NEEDS

Basic

Exercises All
Computer Bank, p. 405

Supplements
Reteaching 49 or
Practice 49

Average

Exercises All
Computer Bank, p. 405

Supplements
Practice 49
Challenges 49 or
Thinking Skills 49

Extended

Exercises All
Computer Bank, p. 405

Supplements
Challenges 49
Thinking Skills 49

Other Resources:
Explorations, pp. 164-167, 169, 172
Mathematics Book A, pp. 11, 49
Math in Stride, p. 120
Developing Number Concepts with Unifix Cubes, pp. 155-156

6-4

OBJECTIVE 6-4

To understand the operation of addition by putting together; to explore perimeter; to estimate curve lengths

Materials: inch ruler; string or yarn

Grouping Suggestions: pairs, small groups

1. MOTIVATE AND TEACH

LEARN ABOUT IT

 **BEFORE** ► **Look at the exercises. What plan will you make to find the total distance of each adventure walk?** (Possible answer: Measure each part of the walk, add the parts to find the total distance.)
► **What must you plan before you begin to measure? Explain.** (Possible answer: the order that the lines will be measured so the same line will not be measured twice)

 **DURING** ► **Explain what you will do if a distance is between two units of measure?** (Measure to the nearest inch.)

AFTER ► **Develop a plan to check your answer.** (Possible answer: Measure again to check; combine numbers in a different order to check addition.)

2. CHECK UNDERSTANDING

ERROR ALERT **Page 117** Not adding all the sides to find the perimeter. **Page 118** Misreading the ruler to the nearest inch.

Name _____

Problem Solving
Understanding the Operations

UNDERSTAND
FIND DATA
PLAN
ESTIMATE
SOLVE
CHECK

Work with a partner. Tell a story about each walk. Measure each length to the nearest inch. Then find the total length.

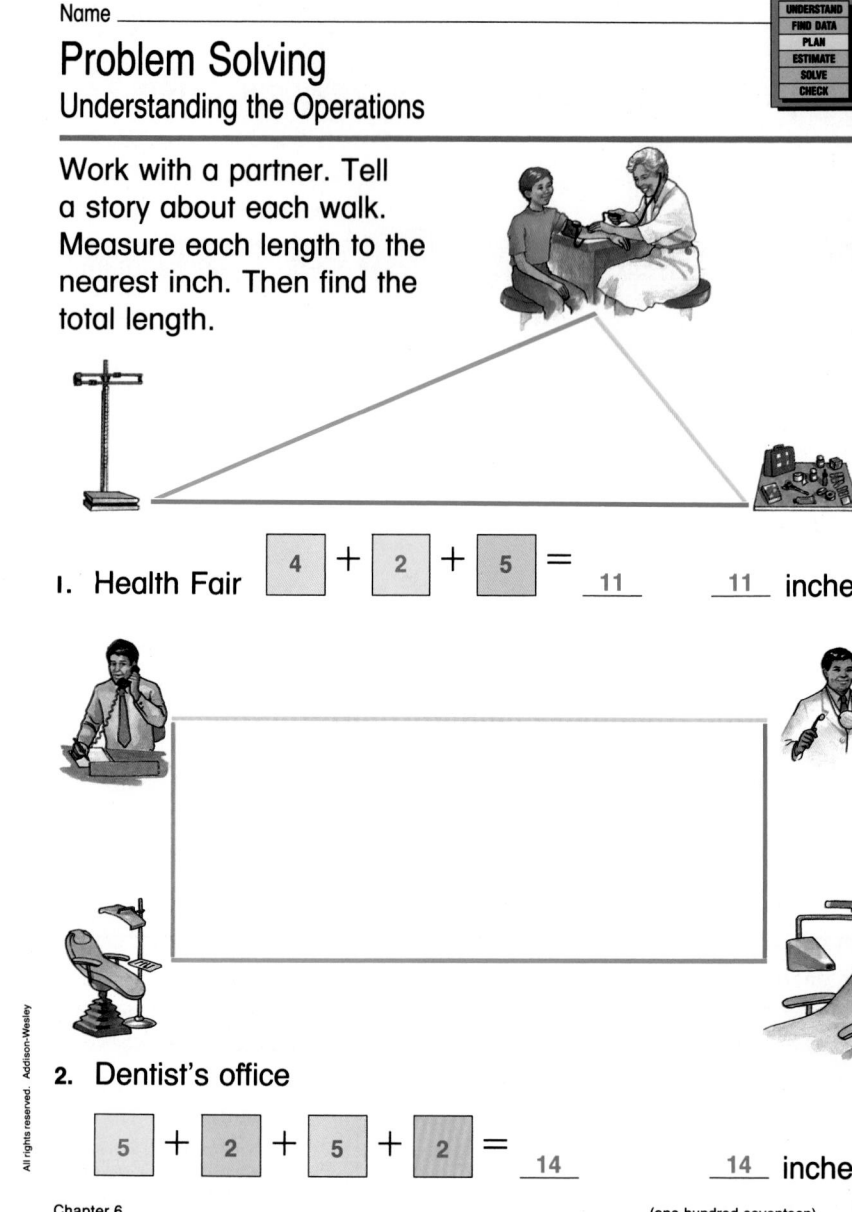

1. Health Fair ☐4☐ + ☐2☐ + ☐5☐ = __11__ __11__ inches

2. Dentist's office

☐5☐ + ☐2☐ + ☐5☐ + ☐2☐ = __14__ __14__ inches

Chapter 6 (one hundred seventeen)

TEACHING OPTIONS

RETEACHING TIPS Place lengths of string, crayons, pencils, and a ruler on a table. Have students estimate the length of an object, then line up one end of it with the ruler's edge. Help them identify the inch mark closest to the end of the object. For help with perimeter, assign Reteaching Supplement 49.

ENRICHMENT Ask students to create illustrated maps, using 2 straight sides and 1 curved side. After they have estimated and measured their own maps, have them exchange maps with a partner. Partners estimate and measure; then compare answers. Have them recheck answers if they disagree.

stimating Curve Lengths

ok at each curve. Estimate the length
inches. Then place a string along the
rve. Measure the string to the nearest
ch. Write the number of inches.
timates may vary. Check students' work.

estimate: __4__ inches   measure: __5__ inches

estimate: ____ inches   measure: __7__ inches

estimate: ____ inches   measure: __6__ inches

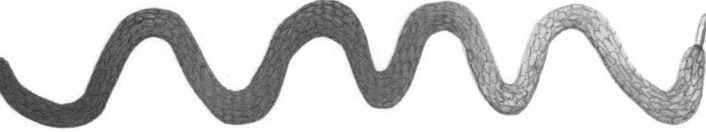

estimate: ____ inches   measure: __11__ inches

3. PRACTICE AND APPLY

Basic	All
Average	All
Extended	All

*How will you prepare to solve the
problems on page 118?* (Possible answer:
Collect the materials needed before
beginning.) *How can you decide if your
answer is sensible?* (Possible answer:
Compare the actual answer with the
estimate.)

▶ **Explain what a curve is.** (Possible
answers: a line that is not straight; a
wavy line)

▶ **Describe a plan for measuring the
length of a curve.** (Possible answer:
Place a string along the curve and cut;
straighten the string and measure with a
ruler.)

▶ **Why should you estimate the
length before you measure?** (Possible
answer: An estimate will help you decide
if your actual measurement is
reasonable.)

▶ **How can you check to see if your
answers make sense?** (Possible
answers: Compare the actual
measurement with your estimate;
compare answers with a classmate;
measure again.)

6-4

LOSE AND ASSESS

HOW WHAT YOU KNOW Ask
all groups of students to design and
aw a 4-sided path. At least one side
the path should be curved. Students
n estimate the length of each side.
ve one student lay a piece of string
the path and then measure it with a
er to find the total length in inches.

QUICK QUIZ

Measure each side to the nearest inch.
Then find the total length.

1 in. | 2 in. | 2¼ in. | ⅞ in.   (about 6 inches)

Estimating and Measuring Length: Feet and Yards

OBJECTIVE 6-5   To estimate and measure using feet and yards

PREBOOK ACTIVITIES

Add or subtract.

3 + 7 = __(10)__	14 = 7 = __(7)__	8 + 7 = __(15)__
9 + 6 = __(15)__	9 − 3 = __(6)__	4 + 6 = __(10)__
12 − 6 = __(6)__	13 − 7 = __(6)__	7 + 7 = __(14)__
16 − 7 = __(9)__	7 − 0 = __(7)__	7 + 9 = __(16)__

PRIOR KNOWLEDGE

Have students describe the different routes they could take from their classroom to an exit from school. *Which route do you think is the shortest? the longest?* (Answers will vary.) *How can we find out exactly how long each route is?* (Measure.) *Would it be easier to measure with a short unit, such as an inch, or with a longer unit?* (a longer unit)

COMMUNICATION

Discussing Math   *What unit would you use to measure your pencil?* (Possible answers: inch, paper clip) Write the words **foot** and **yard** on the chalkboard. Display a foot ruler and a yardstick or tape measure and compare the lengths of a foot and a yard. *Which unit would you use to measure your height? the door?* (Possible answers: foot, yard) *Name something that is about 1 ft long. about 1 yard long.* (Answers will vary.) *Why do you think it is better to measure a long object in feet or yards instead of in inches?* (Possible answer: The measurement will be a smaller number and easier to use; it takes less time to measure with larger units.)

Materials: foot rulers
Grouping Suggestions: pairs
Have students suggest 6 objects to measure in the classroom. List the suggestions on the chalkboard. Have students in each pair take turns estimating the length of the item in inches. Th have them check their estiamtes by measuring. Display a rule and have students count the inches in a foot. *Did you measur anything that was about 1 ft long?* (Answers will vary.) *What would happen if you estimated and measured in feet instead of in inches?* (Possible answer: We would come up with a much smaller number of feet than inches.) *Is it appropriate to measure everything in inches? Why or wh not?* (Possible answer: No, because it is harder to use inches measure larger items.)

CONNECTIONS   Use these anytime.

Problem of the Day

Estimation   Trace your left foot on construction paper. Cut it out. Estimate how many of your feet equal your height. Get a friend to help you check your estimate by measuring your height with your foot cut out. How many of your feet did it take? (Answers will vary.)

Creative Thinking

Fold a paper into 2 equal parts. Draw a small school on the top half and draw a post office on the bottom half. Estimate the distance between the school and the post office in paper clips. Measure with paper clips. How close was your estimate? (Answers will vary.)

Math Connection

Measurement   Pick an object, such as a toothpick, pen, or pencil, to be your unit of length. Find 3 objects that are longer than your unit and 3 objects that are shorter than your unit. Estimate and measure lengths. Draw a picture or make a chart to show what you found.

CLASSWORK AND HOMEWORK SUPPLEMENTS

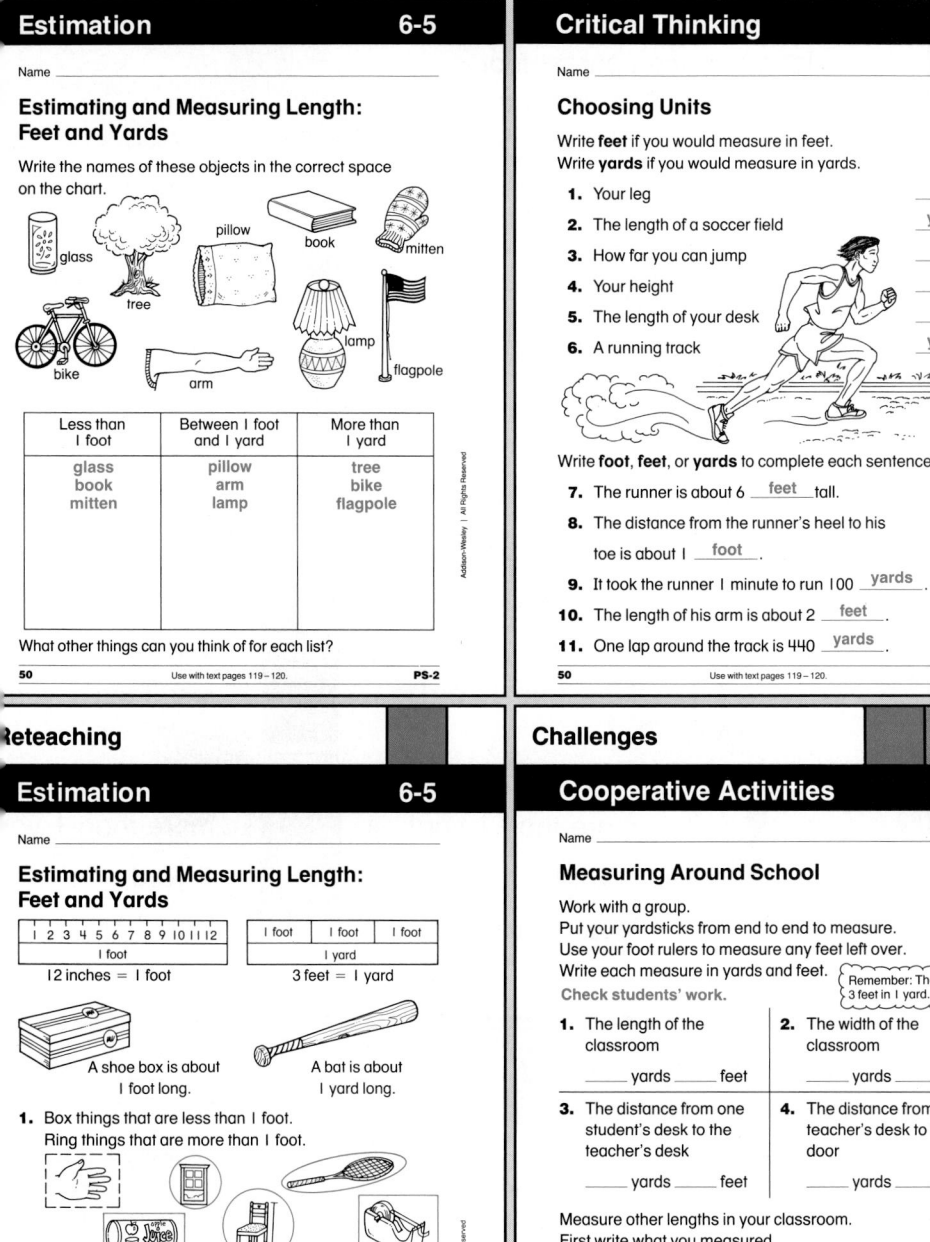

Practice

Estimation   6-5

Name _____

Estimating and Measuring Length: Feet and Yards

Write the names of these objects in the correct space on the chart.

glass · tree · pillow · book · mitten · bike · arm · lamp · flagpole

Less than 1 foot	Between 1 foot and 1 yard	More than 1 yard
glass	pillow	tree
book	arm	bike
mitten	lamp	flagpole

What other things can you think of for each list?

50   Use with text pages 119 – 120.   PS-2

Building Thinking Skills

Critical Thinking   6-5

Name _____

Choosing Units

Write **feet** if you would measure in feet.
Write **yards** if you would measure in yards.

1. Your leg   feet
2. The length of a soccer field   yards
3. How far you can jump   feet
4. Your height   feet
5. The length of your desk   feet
6. A running track   yards

Write **foot**, **feet**, or **yards** to complete each sentence.

7. The runner is about 6 __feet__ tall.
8. The distance from the runner's heel to his toe is about 1 __foot__.
9. It took the runner 1 minute to run 100 __yards__.
10. The length of his arm is about 2 __feet__.
11. One lap around the track is 440 __yards__.

50   Use with text pages 119 – 120.   TS-2

Reteaching

Estimation   6-5

Name _____

Estimating and Measuring Length: Feet and Yards

| 1 2 3 4 5 6 7 8 9 10 11 12 | | 1 foot | 1 foot | 1 foot |
| 1 foot | | 1 yard |

12 inches = 1 foot   3 feet = 1 yard

A shoe box is about 1 foot long.   A bat is about 1 yard long.

1. Box things that are less than 1 foot.
   Ring things that are more than 1 foot.

2. Box things that are less than 1 yard.
   Ring things that are more than 1 yard.

50   Use with text pages 119 – 120.   RS-2

Challenges

Cooperative Activities   6-5

Name _____

Measuring Around School

Work with a group.
Put your yardsticks from end to end to measure.
Use your foot rulers to measure any feet left over.
Write each measure in yards and feet.
Check students' work.

Remember: There are 3 feet in 1 yard.

1. The length of the classroom
   _____ yards _____ feet

2. The width of the classroom
   _____ yards _____ feet

3. The distance from one student's desk to the teacher's desk
   _____ yards _____ feet

4. The distance from the teacher's desk to the door
   _____ yards _____ feet

Measure other lengths in your classroom.
First write what you measured.
Then write the length in yards and feet.

5. _____
   _____ yards _____ foot _____ feet

6. _____
   _____ yards _____ foot _____ feet

50   Use with text pages 119 – 120.   CS-2

OPTIONS FOR INDIVIDUAL NEEDS

Basic

Exercises All

Supplements
Reteaching 50 or
Practice 50
Challenges 50

Average

Exercises All

Supplements
Practice 50
Challenges 50 or
Thinking Skills 50

Extended

Exercises All

Supplements
Challenges 50
Thinking Skills 50

Other Resources:
Explorations, pp. 163, 168
Workjobs, pp. 218-219
Mathematics Book A, pp. 11, 49

6-5

LESSON PLAN 6-5

OBJECTIVE 6-5
To estimate and measure using feet and yards

Materials: four 1-ft strips of paper per pair, Cube-A-Links, rulers, yardsticks

Alternative materials: counters

Grouping Suggestions: pairs, individual work, cooperative groups of 3

---

1. MOTIVATE AND TEACH

LEARN ABOUT IT

Have students make 1-ft and 1-yd units with the paper strips. **How can you be sure your yard units are *exactly* 3 ft long?** (Measure them with a foot ruler.) Direct students' attention to page 119. Have them record their estimates on the page before they measure.

▶ **How can you decide whether an object is more or less than 1 ft long?** (Possible answer: Think of an object you know is 1 ft long, such as a 12-in. ruler. Compare that length to the length of the object you are estimating.)

▶ **What do you notice when you compare Exercises 1-4 to Exercises 5-8?** (Possible answer: In Exercises 5-8, we are estimating and measuring objects that are longer than the objects in Exercises 1-4.)

▶ **How do your estimates compare to the actual measurements? Which of your estimates were very close to the actual measure?** (Answers will vary.)

2. CHECK UNDERSTANDING

ERROR ALERT Being unable to tell whether the length of an object measures exactly 1 ft or 1 yd or more or less than those lengths.

Estimating and Measuring Length
Feet and Yards

I foot = 12 inches · I yard = 3 feet

Work with a partner. Cut some 1-**foot** (ft) units from paper strips. Tape 3 together to make a 1-**yard** (yd) unit. Estimate the length to the nearest foot. Measure. Then ring the best measure. Answers may vary. Check students' work.

1. more than 1 foot / 1 foot / less than 1 foot

2. more than 1 foot / 1 foot / less than 1 foot

3.  more than 1 foot / 1 foot / less than 1 foot

4. more than 1 foot / 1 foot / less than 1 foot

Estimate the length to the nearest yard. Measure. Then ring the best measure. Answers may vary. Check students' work.

5.  more than 1 yard / 1 yard / less than 1 yard

6. more than 1 yard / 1 yard / less than 1 yard

7.  more than 1 yard / 1 yard / less than 1 yard

8.  more than 1 yard / 1 yard / less than 1 yard

Chapter 6

(one hundred nineteen)

TEACHING OPTIONS

RETEACHING TIPS Have students estimate lengths or widths of several objects. Then have them use their foot and yard units to measure. Ask them to record the measurements in a table. Assign Reteaching Supplement 50.

ENRICHMENT **Family Math** Have students' family members estimate their heights in feet. Each person stands in a doorway while another family member uses pencil or tape to mark the height. Measure the heights with a foot ruler or tape measure. Whose estimate was closest to their actual height?

timate to the nearest foot. Measure.
en write the number of feet. **Answers may vary.**
Check students' work.

your height

2. your reach

estimate:

estimate:

___ feet

___ feet

measure:

measure:

___ feet

___ feet

timate to the nearest yard. Measure. **Answers may vary.**
en write the number of yards. **Check students' work.**

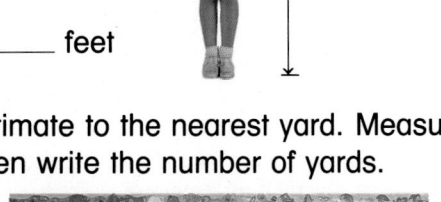

estimate: ___ yards

measure: ___ yards

estimate: ___ yards

measure: ___ yards

RITE ABOUT IT

A <u>yard</u> is longer than a <u>foot</u>

A <u>foot</u> is shorter than a <u>yard</u>

A <u>yard</u> is 3 feet long. yard foot

Chapter 6

3. PRACTICE AND APPLY

Basic	All
Average	All
Extended	All

PRACTICE

Why do you think you are asked to use a foot ruler for Exercises 1-2 and a yardstick for Exercises 3-4 on page 120?
(Possible answer: Items in Exercises 3 and 4 are larger than those in Exercises 1 and 2.)

APPLY

WRITE ABOUT IT ▶ **How would you compare a yard to a foot?**
(Possible answer: A yard is three times longer than a foot.)
▶ **How would you decide whether to use a foot ruler or a yardstick?**
(Possible answer: Think about the distance to be measured. Choose larger units for greater distances.)

6-5

LOSE AND ASSESS

IOW WHAT YOU KNOW

view with students the chapter
ry, *Ceci Grows Up*. Have students
rk with a partner. Have them
etch out their arms and measure the
gth from finger tip to finger tip.
out how many feet is this distance?
iswers will vary.)

QUICK QUIZ

Estimate and measure each of the following objects: length of your desktop; height of your desk; width of your classroom; width of your classroom door. (Answers may vary.)

Chapter 6 Lesson 5 **120**

Estimating and Measuring Capacity: Nonstandard Units

OBJECTIVE 6-6   To estimate and measure capacity using nonstandard units

---

Complete the following addition subtraction sentences.

9 + 4 = <u>(13)</u>	15 − 9 = <u>(6)</u>	8 + <u>(8)</u> = 16
12 − 5 = <u>(7)</u>	14 − 7 = <u>(7)</u>	18 − <u>(9)</u> = 9
9 + 3 = <u>(12)</u>	<u>(8)</u> + 7 = 15	13 − <u>(7)</u> = 6
9 + 8 = <u>(17)</u>	8 + 6 = <u>(14)</u>	12 − <u>(6)</u> = 6

PRIOR KNOWLEDGE

Which do you think holds more water—a bathtub or a sink? Why? (bathtub; a bathtub is larger than a sink.) *Is the milk carton you get with your lunch at school the same size as the one you have at home? Which one holds more milk?* (Possible answer: no; the one at home) Describe the sizes of milk or juice containers you have seen. (Possible answers: $\frac{1}{2}$ pints, pints, $\frac{1}{2}$ gallons, gallons, quarts)

COMMUNICATION

Discussing Math   *Which do you think holds more water—a glass or a pitcher?* (pitcher) *How can you be sure?* (Students may suggest filling the glass and pouring it into a pitcher.) Label a measuring cup, a pint container, and a quart container and show them to students. *Cup, pint, and quart tell the capacity of each container. The capacity is how much a container can hold. Which container do you think holds the least?* (cup) *Which container do you think holds the most?* (quart) Have a student put the containers in order from smallest to largest. Write *cup, pint,* and *quart* on the chalkboard. *How can we be sure we have ordered the containers correctly?* (Possible answer: Fill each container and pour it into another.)

Materials: 5 containers of different shapes and sizes (1 qt th‚ largest), small plastic cups

Grouping Suggestion: small groups

Display a set of 5 containers. *Which one do you think will ho‚ the most water? the least water?* (Answers will vary.) Have each group show how much they think each container holds ‚ ordering them from smallest to largest. *How can you check to see if the order is correct?* (Possible answer: by filling the containers) Hold up a small plastic cup. *How many of these cups do you think it will take to fill each container?* (Answer‚ will vary.) Have each group record its estimates. *How can yo‚ check your estimates?* (Possible answer: Fill each container using the plastic cup.) *How can you keep track of the number of times you use the plastic cup?* (Possible answer: Use tally marks or numbers.)

CONNECTIONS   Use these anytime.

Problem of the Day

Logic   At a tea party, Alice had 4 more cups of tea than Thomas. Together, they had 10 cups of tea. How many cups did each have?

Draw a picture to answer the question.

(Alice had 7; Thomas had 3.)

Life Skills

Capacity   Cut, from magazines or newspapers pictures of items that are measured in cups, pints, and quarts. Use your pictures to make a chart showing the number of cups in a pint, pints in a quart, and cups in a quart. (2 c = 1 pt, 2 pt = 1 qt, 4 c = 1 qt)

Subject Integration

Science   Fill a wide-mouth plastic container about half full with water. Mark the water level with a crayon. Carefully drop a small rock into the container. What happens to the water level? (It rises.) Take out the rock and put in a larger object or add another small rock. What happens this time? (The water level rises higher.)

Estimating and Measuring Capacity: Cups, Pints, and Quarts

estimate and measure capacity using cups, pints, and quarts

CLASSWORK AND HOMEWORK SUPPLEMENTS

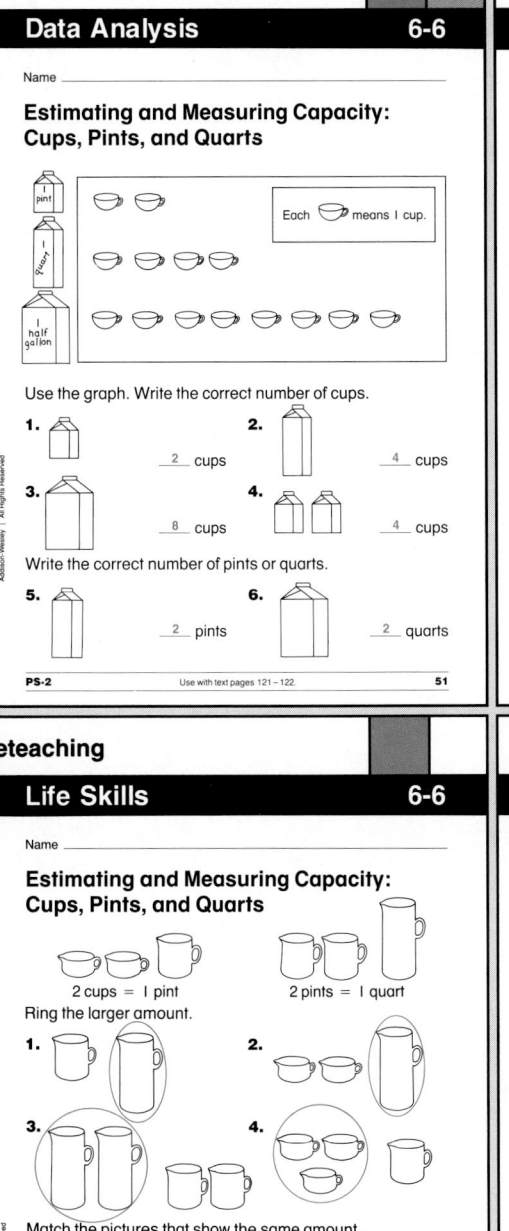

Practice

Data Analysis 6-6

Name _____

Estimating and Measuring Capacity: Cups, Pints, and Quarts

Each 🥤 means 1 cup.

Use the graph. Write the correct number of cups.

1. ___2___ cups
2. ___4___ cups
3. ___8___ cups
4. ___4___ cups

Write the correct number of pints or quarts.

5. ___2___ pints
6. ___2___ quarts

PS-2   Use with text pages 121–122.   51

Building Thinking Skills

Mental Math 6-6

Name _____

Are You Sure?

The Peters family is not too sure about measuring.

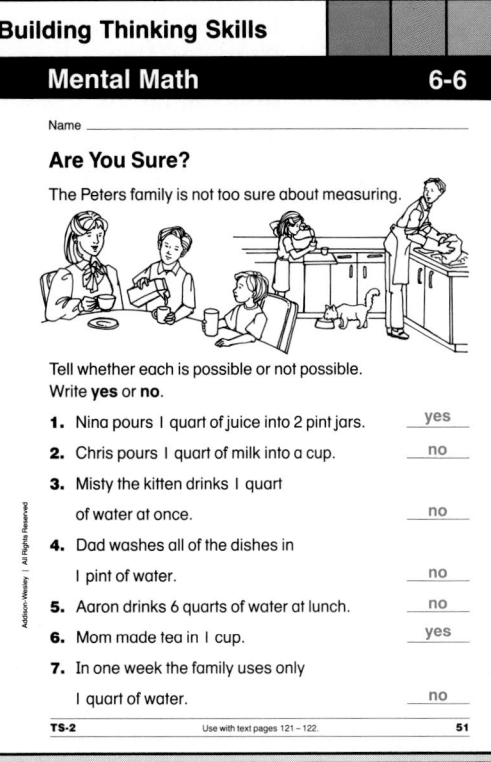

Tell whether each is possible or not possible.
Write **yes** or **no**.

1. Nina pours 1 quart of juice into 2 pint jars.   yes
2. Chris pours 1 quart of milk into a cup.   no
3. Misty the kitten drinks 1 quart of water at once.   no
4. Dad washes all of the dishes in 1 pint of water.   no
5. Aaron drinks 6 quarts of water at lunch.   no
6. Mom made tea in 1 cup.   yes
7. In one week the family uses only 1 quart of water.   no

TS-2   Use with text pages 121–122.   51

Reteaching

Life Skills 6-6

Name _____

Estimating and Measuring Capacity: Cups, Pints, and Quarts

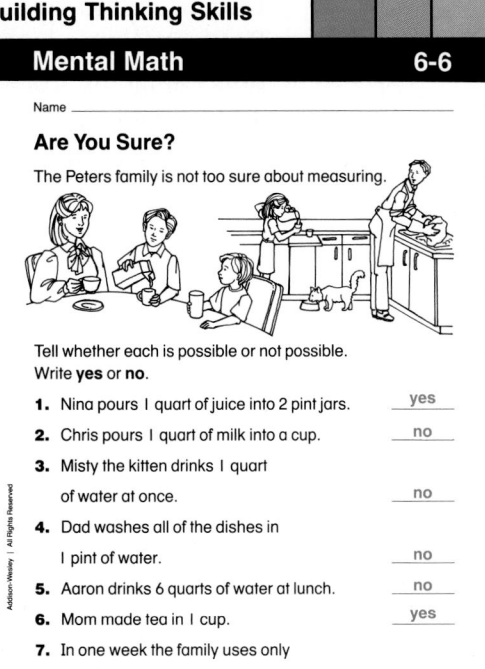

2 cups = 1 pint   2 pints = 1 quart

Ring the larger amount.

1.
2.
3.
4.

Match the pictures that show the same amount.

5.
6.

RS-2   Use with text pages 121–122.   51

Challenges

Critical Thinking 6-6

Name _____

Measuring for a Party

Emma wants to make party punch.
She uses this recipe.
She has only a 1-cup measure.

Party Punch	cups
3 pints pineapple juice	6
1 quart orange juice	8
2 pints lime juice	4
1 pint ice cream	2

Can you help her?
Change all of the measures to cups.

REMEMBER: 2 cups = 1 pint   2 pints = 1 quart

Now use the recipe to answer the questions.

1. How many pints are there in the recipe? ___8___
2. How many cups of lime juice would you need to make one half of the recipe? ___2___
3. Will this recipe make enough punch for 15 people to have 1 cup each? ___yes___

CS-2   Use with text pages 121–122.   51

OPTIONS FOR INDIVIDUAL NEEDS

Basic

Exercises All
More Practice, p. 415, set A

Supplements
Reteaching 51
Practice 51
Thinking Skills 51

Average

Exercises All
More Practice, p. 415, set A

Supplements
Practice 51
Challenges 51 or
Thinking Skills 51

Extended

Exercises All

Supplements
Challenges 51
Thinking Skills 51

Other Resources:
Mathematics Their Way, pp. 136, 232-233, 245
Explorations, pp. 308-315, 330, 334
Problem-Solving Experiences In Mathematics, p. 111
Workjobs, pp. 22-23, 232-233
Workjobs for Parents, pp. 22-23

6-6

OBJECTIVE 6-6

To estimate and measure capacity using nonstandard units

Materials: drinking glasses, cake pans, small paper cups, tin cans

Grouping Suggestion: small groups

---

1. MOTIVATE AND TEACH

LEARN ABOUT IT

Display a drinking glass, a small paper cup, and a tin can. *Do you think the glass will hold more cups or cans of water?* (Answers will vary.) *How could you find out?* (Possible answer: See how many cups it takes to fill the glass. Then do the same with the can. Compare.)

▶ **Look at the large containers in Exercises 1, 2, and 3. Which container do you think will be filled the fastest? Why?** (Possible answer: the drinking glass; it is the smallest.)

▶ **Look at the container in Exercise 3. Do you think it will hold more than the container in Exercise 1? Why?** (Possible answer: Yes; it is wider.)

▶ **Look at the container that holds the least. Do you think it holds half as much as the container that holds the most? How could you find out?** (Empty each container into the cups or cans and count them.)

▶ **How close were your estimates to the actual measures?** (Answers will vary.)

2. CHECK UNDERSTANDING

ERROR ALERT Being confused by the height and width of the container when estimating.

3. PRACTICE AND APPLY

Basic	All
Average	All
Extended	All

Name _____

Estimating and Measuring Capacity
Nonstandard Units

I estimate 5 cups.

I estimate 2 cans.

Work in a group.
Use cups and tin cans.
Estimate how many of each unit will fill the object.
Then measure. Use tally marks to count the units.
Write the number.

Answers may vary. Check students' work.

	🥤 cup unit	🥫 tin can unit
1. 	estimate: _____ cups tally: _____ cups measure: _____ cups	estimate: _____ cans tally: _____ cans measure: _____ cans
2.	estimate: _____ cups tally: _____ cups measure: _____ cups	estimate: _____ cans tally: _____ cans measure: _____ cans
3. 	estimate: _____ cups tally: _____ cups measure: _____ cups	estimate: _____ cans tally: _____ cans measure: _____ cans

Chapter 6   (one hundred twenty-one)

TEACHING OPTIONS

RETEACHING TIPS Have students in small groups fill a 1-qt container with water and empty it into pints. *How many pints does it take to fill 1 qt?* (2) Have students empty one of the pint containers into cups. *How many cups does it take to fill 1 pt?* (2) Assign Reteaching Supplement 51.

ENRICHMENT Label 5 containers A, B, C, D, E. Have groups of students choose 1 container, fill it with water, then choose another and decide whether the new one holds more, less, or the same as the first one. Repeat. Then arrange all 5 in order from smallest to largest.

stimating and Measuring Capacity
ups, Pints, and Quarts

Answers may vary depending on size of containers.

Work in a group. Estimate how many cups will fill the jar. Then measure. Write the number. Color to match.

A **pint** (pt) fills 2 cups.
A **cup** (c) is less than a pint.

I pint   I cup

A **quart** (qt) fills 2 pints.
A quart holds more than a pint.

I quart   I pint

estimate: ＿ cups

measure: ＿ cups

Estimate how many pints will fill the bowl. Then measure. Write the number. Color to match.

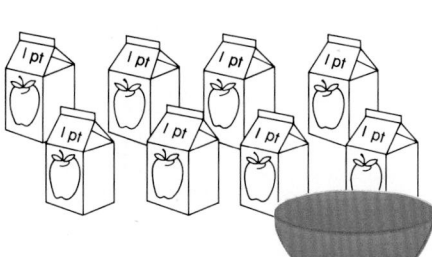

estimate: ＿ pints   measure: ＿ pints

Estimate how many quarts will fill the largest carton. Then measure. Write the number. Color to match.

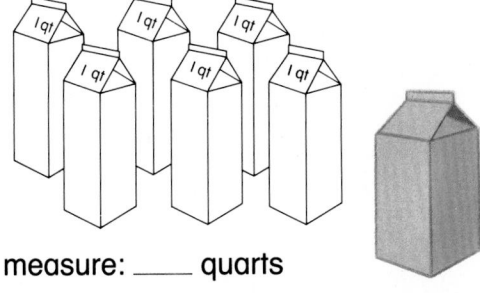

estimate: ＿ quarts   measure: ＿ quarts

OBJECTIVE 6-6
To estimate and measure capacity using cups, pints, and quarts

Materials: measuring containers

1. MOTIVATE AND TEACH

LEARN ABOUT IT

Have students in small groups estimate and then check how many cups 1 pt will fill and how many pints 1 qt will fill.
▶ **How many cup measures do you think 1 qt will fill? Why?** (4 c; if 1 pt fills 2 c and 1 qt fills 2 pt, then 1 qt must fill 4 c.)

2. CHECK UNDERSTANDING

ERROR ALERT Forgetting relationships between cups, pints, and quarts.

3. PRACTICE AND APPLY

Basic	All
Average	All
Extended	All

6-6

LOSE AND ASSESS

HOW WHAT YOU KNOW

rovide small groups of students with plastic gallon jug and cup, pint, and uart measures. Have them estimate nd then measure how many of each nit fills the jug. Then ask each group o choose its own nonstandard unit nd repeat the activity, comparing the esults.

QUICK QUIZ

Fill in the blank.
2 c = 1 _(pt)_
1 q = _(2)_ pt
4 c = 1 _(qt)_
2 pt = 1 _(qt)_

Estimating and Measuring Weight: Nonstandard Units

OBJECTIVE 6-7   To estimate and measure weight using nonstandard units

PREBOOK ACTIVITIES

QUICK REVIEW

Write the number in each pair that is greater.

15 and 28 (28)	7 and 12 (12)	9 and 17 (17)
23 and 30 (30)	13 and 5 (13)	24 and 12 (24)
12 and 15 (15)	29 and 47 (47)	

PRIOR KNOWLEDGE

Ask students to name foods from the grocery store that are weighed before they are sold, such as meat, fruits, and vegetables. *Why do you think the clerk has to know the exact weight?* (Possible answer: so he or she knows how much to charge you) *When you eat an apple, do you know exactly how much it weighs?* (no) Have students help you make lists of things that are weighed exactly and things whose weight is estimated. Record the lists on chart paper or on the chalkboard.

COMMUNICATION

Reading and Discussing Math   List the following measurement words on the chalkboard and have students copy them in their Math Journals: **pound, scale, weight.** Read the words aloud with students. *What do you know about these words?* (Possible answers: **Pounds** tell how much something weighs; a **scale** is used to measure how heavy something is; **weight** is the lightness or heaviness of something.) Have students write a definition for each word in their journals.

EXPLORE AND CONNECT

Materials: small classroom objects
Grouping Suggestion: small groups
Provide each group with 4 classroom objects, such as a chalkboard eraser, a book, a pair of scissors, and an envelope. Have students hold the objects and arrange them in order from lightest to heaviest. Encourage students to work cooperatively and come to agreement as a group. Have groups compare the findings.

CONNECTIONS   Use these anytime.

Problem of the Day

Logic   Susan wants to buy a pound each of apples, grapes, and oranges. Which fruit will Susan be able to weigh so that it comes close to exactly 1 pound? Why? (the grapes; they are smaller, so they can be measured closer to an exact amount)

Number Sense

Estimation   Choose some objects in your desk that you think might weigh 5 pounds in all. Weigh the objects. How close was your estimate? Choose different objects and try again. Is your second estimate closer? Why? (Answers will vary.)

Creative Thinking

Music   Imagine that music made by instruments has weight. The sound of a triangle would be light, and the sound of a drum would be heavy. Draw pictures of 4 musical instruments, ordering their sounds from lightest to heaviest. Use your imagination to help you!

stimating and Measuring Weight: Pounds

estimate and measure weight using pounds

CLASSWORK AND HOMEWORK SUPPLEMENTS

Practice

Estimation   6-7

Name _____

Estimating and Measuring Weight: Pounds

Ring the better estimate.

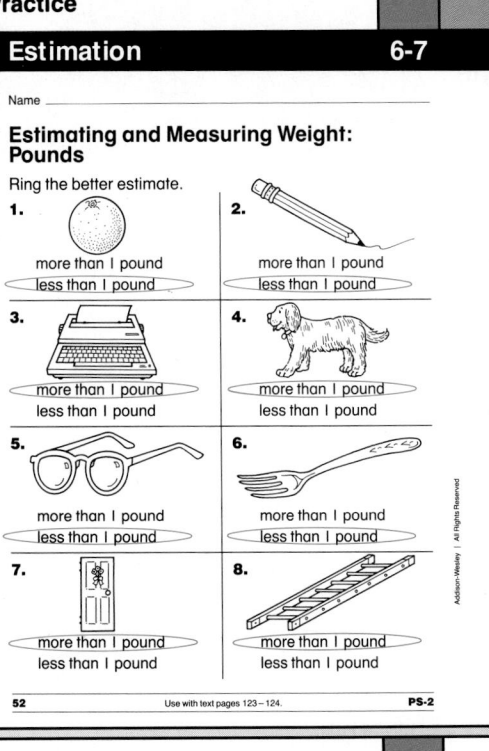

1. more than I pound / less than I pound
2. more than I pound / less than I pound
3. more than I pound / less than I pound
4. more than I pound / less than I pound
5. more than I pound / less than I pound
6. more than I pound / less than I pound
7. more than I pound / less than I pound
8. more than I pound / less than I pound

52   Use with text pages 123–124.   PS-2

Building Thinking Skills

Data Analysis   6-7

Name _____

Weighing Zoo Friends

It is weigh-in time at the Children's Zoo.
The results are on graph.

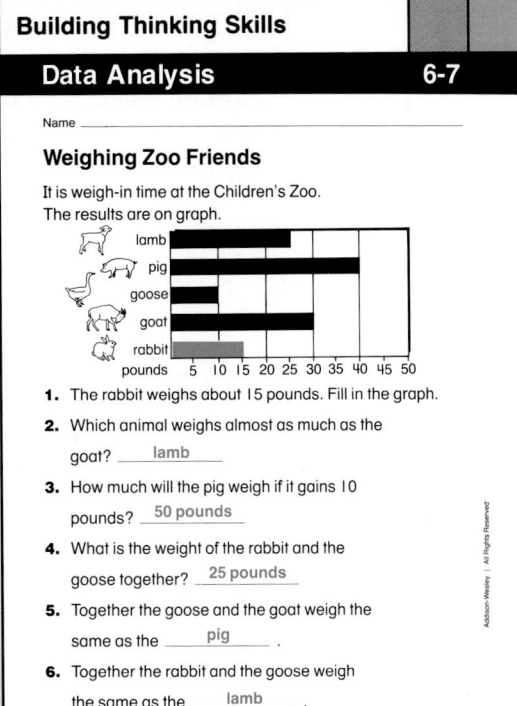

1. The rabbit weighs about 15 pounds. Fill in the graph.
2. Which animal weighs almost as much as the goat? __lamb__
3. How much will the pig weigh if it gains 10 pounds? __50 pounds__
4. What is the weight of the rabbit and the goose together? __25 pounds__
5. Together the goose and the goat weigh the same as the ___pig___ .
6. Together the rabbit and the goose weigh the same as the ___lamb___ .

52   Use with text pages 123–124.   TS-2

Reteaching

Estimation   6-7

Name _____

Estimating and Measuring Weight: Pounds

Each scale shows I pound.

 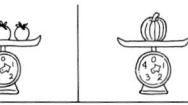

1. Ring the objects that weigh less than I pound.

2. Ring the objects that weigh more than I pound.

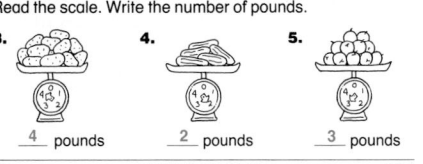

Read the scale. Write the number of pounds.

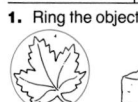 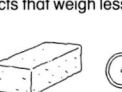 

3. __4__ pounds   4. __2__ pounds   5. __3__ pounds

52   Use with text pages 123–124.   RS-2

Challenges

Life Skills   6-7

Name _____

Estimate and Weigh

Estimate what will happen to your weight.
Then use a scale to measure. **Answers will vary.**

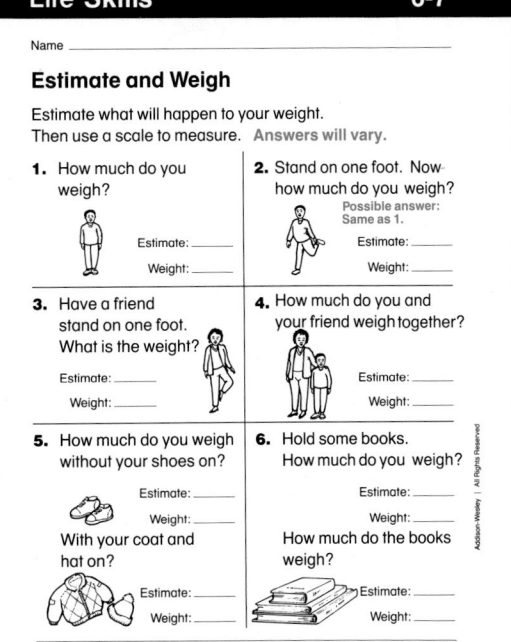

1. How much do you weigh?
   Estimate: _____
   Weight: _____

2. Stand on one foot. Now how much do you weigh?
   Possible answer: Same as 1.
   Estimate: _____
   Weight: _____

3. Have a friend stand on one foot. What is the weight?
   Estimate: _____
   Weight: _____

4. How much do you and your friend weigh together?
   Estimate: _____
   Weight: _____

5. How much do you weigh without your shoes on?
   Estimate: _____
   Weight: _____
   With your coat and hat on?

6. Hold some books. How much do you weigh?
   Estimate: _____
   Weight: _____
   How much do the books weigh?

52   Use with text pages 123–124.   CS-2

OPTIONS FOR INDIVIDUAL NEEDS

Basic

Exercises All, Midchapter Review/Quiz

Supplements
Reteaching 52 or
Practice 52
Challenges 52

Average

Exercises All, Midchapter Review/Quiz

Supplements
Practice 52
Challenges 52 or
Thinking Skills 52

Extended

Exercises All, Midchapter Review/Quiz

Supplements
Challenges 52
Thinking Skills 52

Other Resources:
Math in Stride, pp. 101-102
Explorations, pp. 316-319, 330-331, 334
Workjobs, pp. 22-23
Workjobs For Parents, pp. 22-23, 28-29
Mathematics Their Way, pp. 232-233

6-7

OBJECTIVE 6-7
To estimate and measure weight using nonstandard units

Materials balance scale, pound weights, bolts, counters, paper clips, paper cup, 1-lb loaf of bread, belt, classroom objects

Grouping Suggestions: individual work, cooperative groups of 3

---

1. MOTIVATE AND TEACH

LEARN ABOUT IT

Practice weighing objects using nonstandard units by holding up two classroom objects and asking students how they could find out which weighs more. (Use a scale to weigh them.)

▶ **How many cubes do you think it would take to balance each of the objects on a scale?** (Answers will vary.) Allow time for students to actually balance the objects on the scale, using cubes or counters.

▶ **Why were your estimates different for the cubes and the counters?** (They are different weights.)

▶ **In Exercise 4, why do you need more of one unit than another?** (The less a unit weighs, the more units you need.)

2. CHECK UNDERSTANDING

ERROR ALERT Having difficulty balancing the scale.

3. PRACTICE AND APPLY

Basic	All
Average	All
Extended	All

How will you know when both sides of the scale have the same weight? (The scale will be balanced.)

Name _____

Estimating and Measuring Weight
Nonstandard Units

Work with a partner.
Use cubes and counters.
Estimate how many of each unit will balance the object. Then measure.
Write the number.
Answers may vary.
Check students' work.

 cube unit    counter unit

1.
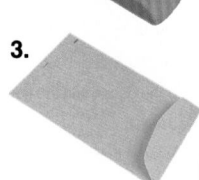

estimate: ____ cubes	estimate: ____ counters
measure: ____ cubes	measure: ____ counters

2.

estimate: ____ cubes	estimate: ____ counters
measure: ____ cubes	measure: ____ counter

3.

estimate: ____ cubes	estimate: ____ counters
measure: ____ cubes	measure: ____ counters

4. Suppose you weighed your pencil.

Would you need more  units or more

 units to balance it? Ring one.   Answers may vary. Check students' wor

more 🎲 units   more ⬭ units

Chapter 6   (one hundred twenty-three) 12

TEACHING OPTIONS

RETEACHING TIPS Use bolts, pound weights, and a balance scale. Have students place a 1-lb weight on one side of the balance, then place one bolt at a time on the other side until the scale balances. Have them tell what happened. (scale balances when weights match) Assign Reteaching Supplement 52.

COMPUTER **How to Weigh an Elephant, Learning Technologies** © **1985** For use with all levels of students. In *How to Weigh an Elephant*, students judge weight by determining which of 3 animals in a boat is heaviest by telling which boat rides lowest. The lesson takes 5-15 minutes.

stimating and Measuring Weight
ounds

ck up each object. Estimate its weight
pounds. Then weigh and match.

**Estimates may vary.
Check students' work.**

| ghter than I pound | I pound (lb) | heavier than I pound |

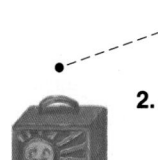 **2.**  **3.** 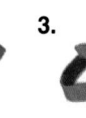 **4.**  **5.**

MIDCHAPTER REVIEW/QUIZ   Estimates may vary.

stimate each length. Then measure to the nearest inch.

estimate: ___ inches   measure: _5_ inches

estimate: ___ inches   measure: _7_ inches

Ring the better estimate.   (more than I pint)

    less than I pint

---

OBJECTIVE 6-7
To estimate and measure weight using pounds

Materials: balance scale, classroom objects

1. MOTIVATE AND TEACH

▶ **How will estimating and measuring pounds help you measure other units?** (Use the weight of one pound to compare.)

2. CHECK UNDERSTANDING

ERROR ALERT   Having difficulty balancing the scale.

3. PRACTICE AND APPLY

Basic	All, Midchapter Review/Quiz
Average	All, Midchapter Review/Quiz
Extended	All, Midchapter Review/Quiz

▶ **How can you estimate whether an object weighs more or less than one pound?** (Possible answer: Hold object in one hand and pound weight in the other.)

MIDCHAPTER REVIEW/QUIZ

Items	Objectives
1-2	6-2
3	6-6

6-7

CLOSE AND ASSESS

HOW WHAT YOU KNOW
ovide small groups of students with
balance scale, a pound weight, and
veral nonstandard units used to
easure weight. Have each student
oose a unit, then write an estimate
how many units it would take to
alance a shoe. Have them weigh the
oe and compare the measure with
eir estimate.

QUICK QUIZ

Estimate the weight: less than 1 lb,
about 1 lb, or greater than 1 lb.
television (>)   flower (<)
feather   (<)   desk   (>)
baby   (>)   tomato (<)

My Centimeter Book

OBJECTIVE 6-8   To estimate and measure to the nearest centimeter

PREBOOK ACTIVITIES

QUICK REVIEW

Name two things around you that are about as long as your little finger. (Possible answers: rubber eraser, chalk, belt buckle)

PRIOR KNOWLEDGE

Name things that you estimate are less than 1 inch long. (Possible answers: an earring, a pea, an ant, a seed) *Name things that you estimate are more than 1 inch long.* (Possible answers: their leg, a dog, a shoe, a loaf of bread) *What words could you use to describe something that is less than 1 inch in length?* (Possible answers: *tiny, small, little*)

COMMUNICATION

Reading and Discussing Math   Write the word **centimeter** on the chalkboard. Read the word and explain that a **centimeter** is another unit that is used to measure objects. Show students how long a centimeter is on a centimeter ruler and ask them what words could describe something that is 1 centimeter long. (Possible answers: little, tiny, small) *What can you measure with a centimeter ruler?* (Possible answers: height, width, length)

EXPLORE AND CONNECT

Materials: string, centimeter ruler for pairs of students
Grouping Suggestion: pairs
Have students use their centimeter rulers to measure something on their hands that is about 1 centimeter long. (Possible responses: fingernail, fingertip) Have students work in pairs to estimate and measure the length, width, or distance around small objects in the room. Pairs should choose an object and estimate its length. One student should use string to measure the object. The second student should cut the string and tape to paper under the estimate. *How can you use the string to find the exact measurement?* (Possible answer: Use a centimeter ruler to measure the string.) Repeat with several objects. *How close were your estimates?* (Answers will vary.) Remind students to work together to find answers they can agree on.

CONNECTIONS   Use these anytime.

Problem of the Day

Traveling   Write a question you can answer using this data. Then answer it.

Days	Miles traveled
Monday	6
Tuesday	8

(Possible answer: How many miles were traveled in all? 14)

Number Sense

Estimation   Put a check (√) next to the objects that you think measure more than 1 centimeter.
the width of a hair
the length of your foot (√)
the height of your math book (√)
the sharpened tip of a pencil

Counting Patterns

Finish the patterns.
25, 30, 35, 40, _____ (45)
100, 90, 80, _____ (70)
60, 55, 50, _____ (45)
2, 7, 12, _____ (17)

CLASSWORK AND HOMEWORK SUPPLEMENTS

Practice

Estimation   6-8

Name _____

Centimeters

First estimate each length.
Then measure with your centimeter ruler.

Estimates will vary.

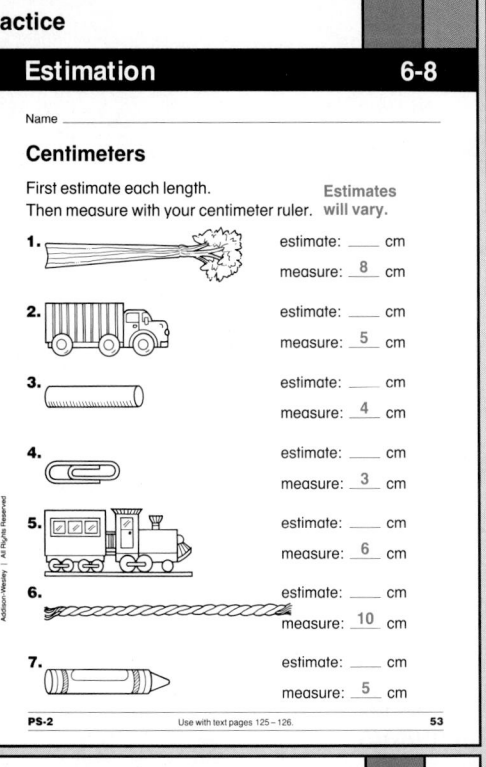

1. estimate: _____ cm
   measure: _8_ cm

2. estimate: _____ cm
   measure: _5_ cm

3. estimate: _____ cm
   measure: _4_ cm

4. estimate: _____ cm
   measure: _3_ cm

5. estimate: _____ cm
   measure: _6_ cm

6. estimate: _____ cm
   measure: _10_ cm

7. estimate: _____ cm
   measure: _5_ cm

PS-2   Use with text pages 125–126.   53

Building Thinking Skills

Creative Thinking   6-8

Name _____

A Mouse Walk

The mice must stay on a line.
They can go right or down.
Each one goes 16 centimeters in all.
How many different paths can you find?
Two paths are shown. **Students will draw several different 16-cm paths.**

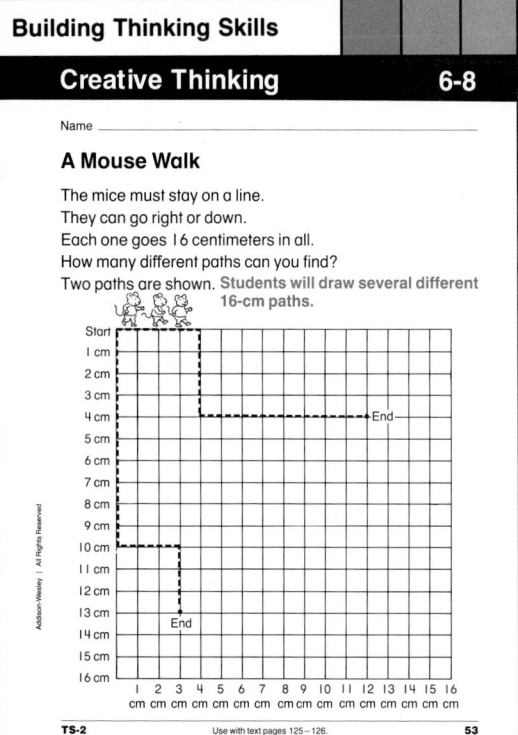

TS-2   Use with text pages 125–126.   53

Reteaching

Life Skills   6-8

Name _____

Centimeters

How long?
Write the length to the nearest centimeter.

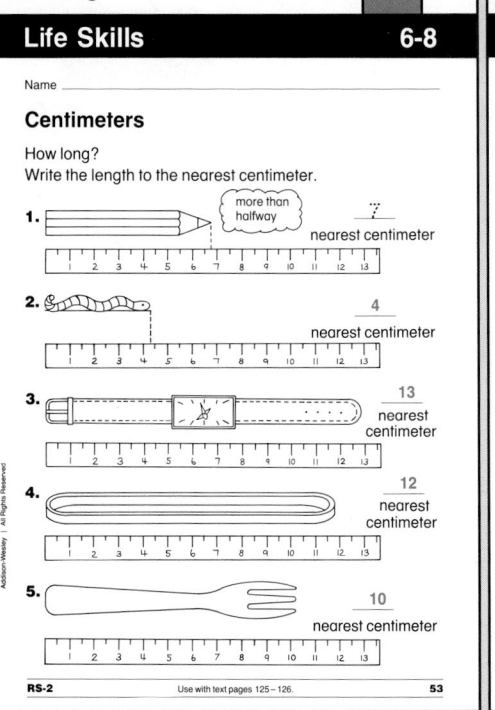

1. more than halfway   _7_ nearest centimeter

2. _4_ nearest centimeter

3. _13_ nearest centimeter

4. _12_ nearest centimeter

5. _10_ nearest centimeter

RS-2   Use with text pages 125–126.   53

Challenges

Estimation   6-8

Name _____

Estimating Lengths

About how long is it?
Answers will vary.

A centimeter is this long. ⊢—⊣

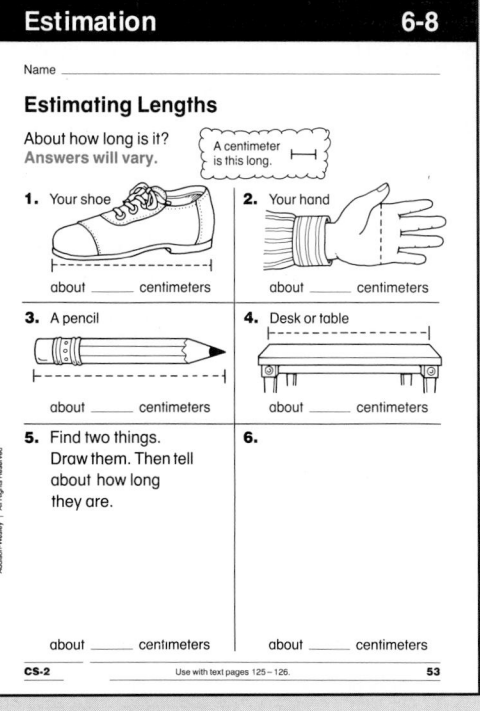

1. Your shoe   about _____ centimeters

2. Your hand   about _____ centimeters

3. A pencil   about _____ centimeters

4. Desk or table   about _____ centimeters

5. Find two things.
   Draw them. Then tell
   about how long
   they are.

6.

about _____ centimeters   about _____ centimeters

CS-2   Use with text pages 125–126.   53

OPTIONS FOR INDIVIDUAL NEEDS

Basic

Exercises All
More Practice, p. 415, set B

Supplements
Reteaching 53 or
Practice 53
Thinking Skills 53

Average

Exercises All
More Practice, p. 415, set B

Supplements
Practice 53
Challenges 53 or
Thinking Skills 53

Extended

Exercises All

Supplements
Challenges 53
Thinking Skills 53

Other Resources:

Mathematics Their Way, pp. 119-121, 136
Explorations, pp. 164-167, 169, 172, 331
Mathematics Book A, p. 49

6-8

Chapter 6 Lesson 8   **125B**

LESSON PLAN 6-8

OBJECTIVE 6-8
To estimate and measure to the nearest centimeter

Materials: centimeter rulers, small objects

Grouping Suggestions: pairs, cooperative groups of 3

1. MOTIVATE AND TEACH

LEARN ABOUT IT

Display a centimeter ruler and show students the length of 1 centimeter. Display a variety of small objects, such as paper clips, staples, pencils, and chalk.

▶ **How could you estimate how many centimeters long each of these objects is?** (Possible answer: Visualize a centimeter length and guess how many would fit next to the object.)

▶ **How can the boy on page 125 use the string to measure parts of his body?** (Possible answer: Wrap it around the body part, mark the length on the string, then measure the string with the centimeter ruler.)

▶ **Describe how a partner can help you measure the different parts of your body.** (Possible answer: The partner can mark the string for you in the right place so you can measure, cut, and paste it on the page.)

Before partners begin measuring, have them cut out the pages of the centimeter book. When they have finished estimating, measuring, and pasting, have them staple their books together.

2. CHECK UNDERSTANDING

ERROR ALERT Lining up the string on the centimeter ruler incorrectly.

Name _____

My Centimeter Book

I used string to help measure parts of my body to the nearest centimeter.

Dear Famil Ask your ch to read this book to you

This is a **centimeter** (cm) unit: ■■ I cm.

Estimate the length around your ankle to the nearest centimeter. Then measure. Write the number of centimeters.
Answers may vary. Check students' work.

estimate: ____ centimeters

measure: ____ centimeters

Paste your string here.

Estimate the width of your mouth to the nearest centimeter. Then measure. Write the number of centimeters.
Answers may vary. Check students' work.

estimate: ____ centimeters

measure: ____ centimeters

Paste your string here.

Chapter 6

(one hundred twenty-five) I.

TEACHING OPTIONS

RETEACHING TIPS Ask students to place a crayon at 3 different starting places on their centimeter rulers. Discuss the measurements they get. *Why is it important to line up objects with 0?* (to get a correct measurement) Assign Reteaching Supplement 53.

ENRICHMENT Have students use a cm ruler and graph paper to create straight line designs for a partner to draw by following directions. Draw the design first, then write directions such as: Draw a 3-cm line; turn right and draw a 5-cm line; and so on. Display the designs side-by-side.

stimate the length around your neck
the nearest centimeter. Then measure.
rite the number of centimeters.
swers may vary. Check students' work.

timate: _____ centimeters

easure: _____ centimeters

Paste your string here.

timate the length around your arm
uscle to the nearest centimeter.
en measure. Write the number
centimeters.
swers may vary.
eck students' work.

timate: _____ centimeters

easure: _____ centimeters

Paste your string here.

oose a part of your body to measure.
timate. Then measure.
rite the number of centimeters.
swers may vary. Check students' work.

timate: _____ centimeters

easure: _____ centimeters

Paste your string here.

3. PRACTICE AND APPLY

Basic	All
Average	All
Extended	All

PRACTICE

How can you estimate the distance around your neck or arm without actually measuring it? (Possible answer: Think of the length of a centimeter and try to visualize how many centimeter units will go around your neck or arm.)

APPLY

▶ **What can you conclude about the parts of your body you are to measure by looking at the size of the string boxes on each page?** (Possible answer: None of the measurements will be longer than 18 cm.)

▶ **Explain why it is important to estimate first.** (Possible answer: It tells you if the answer you get by measuring is reasonable.)

6-8

LOSE AND ASSESS

HOW WHAT YOU KNOW
mind students about the units of
easure that Ceci used in the chapter
ry. *Do you think the bananas or
leaves were a greater number of
ntimeters long?* Have students tell
at they think and then cut out their
n bananas and leaves from
nstruction paper and measure them.

QUICK QUIZ

Draw lines that have the following
lengths:
6 centimeters
2 centimeters
10 centimeters

Estimating and Measuring Length: Decimeters and Meters

OBJECTIVE 6-9 To estimate and measure using decimeters and meters

PREBOOK ACTIVITIES

QUICK REVIEW

Estimate the length of each object in centimeters.
your thumb   (about 4 cm)
your hand   (about 8 cm)
your foot   (about 15 cm)

PRIOR KNOWLEDGE

How would you describe a centimeter? (Possible answer: It is a small unit of measure.) *Would it be easy to measure the length of an elephant in centimeters? Why or why not?* (Possible answer: No, because an elephant is very large.) *What types of things are easy to measure using centimeters?* (Possible answer: small things such as a crayon, a toothbrush, and a comb)

COMMUNICATION

Reading and Discussing Math   Draw on the chalkboard a line that measures 1 decimeter in length and write **decimeter** next to it. Read the word to students and ask them to look around the room for objects to use to complete this sentence: _____ measures about 1 decimeter. Repeat this activity for **meter.** *Which of these measurements is longer?* (meter) *How do a decimeter and a meter compare to a centimeter?* (Possible answer: Both of them are larger units of measure than a centimeter.) *When might you want to use a decimeter or a meter instead of a centimeter to measure something?* (Possible answer: when the object's length, height, or width is very long)

EXPLORE AND CONNECT

Materials: objects of different lengths, widths, and heights; centimeter ruler
Display three objects—one about 1 decimeter long, one about 5 centimeters long, and one about 15 centimeters long. *Which of these objects has a length of about 10 centimeters?* Show centimeters on a centimeter ruler and explain that another name for 10 centimeters is 1 decimeter. Then display 3 more objects of which only one is about 1 decimeter long, wide, or tall. *Which of these objects measures about 1 decimeter? Which do you think measures more than 1 decimeter? Which object measures less than 1 decimeter?* Record the estimates, then have students measure the items and compare their estimates. Repeat this activity for **meter** with 3 objects, only one of which measures about 1 meter. *Which of these objects measures about 10 decimeters?* Explain that another name for 10 decimeters is 1 meter.

CONNECTIONS   Use these anytime.

Problem of the Day

Tell whether you would use centimeters or meters to measure the length or width of these objects.
   spool of thread (cm)
   key (cm)
   car (m)
   book (cm)
   chalkboard (m)
   slide (m)

Subject Integration

Physical Education   Show what kind of steps you would take to show these measurements: centimeter, decimeter, meter.

Math Connection

Measurement   Use one of your shoes to measure 3 items in your classroom. Record your findings. Compare your measurements to others. Were the measurements the same? Why or why not? (No, because the shoes were different in size.)

CLASSWORK AND HOMEWORK SUPPLEMENTS

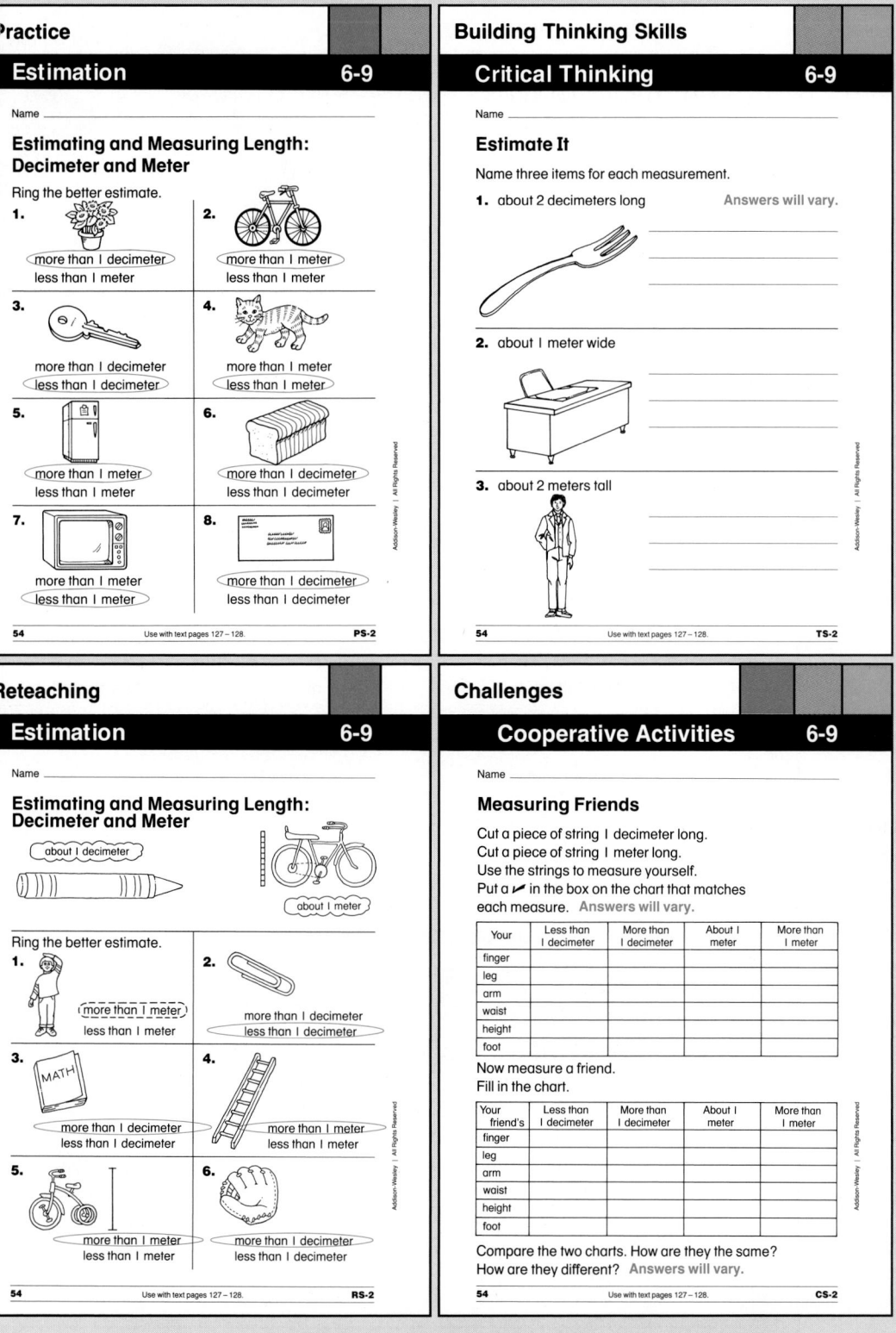

Basic

Exercises All, Mixed Review
Computer Bank, p. 406

Supplements
Reteaching 54 or
Practice 54
Challenges 54

Average

Exercises All, Mixed Review
Computer Bank, p. 406

Supplements
Practice 54
Challenges 54 or
Thinking Skills 54

Extended

Exercises All, Mixed Review
Computer Bank, p. 406

Supplements
Challenges 54
Thinking Skills 54

Other Resources:
Explorations, pp. 163-164
Mathematics Their Way, pp. 232-233

6-9

LESSON PLAN 6-9

OBJECTIVE 6-9
To estimate and measure using decimeters and meters

> **Materials:** white and red paper strips cut in 1-decimeter units, magazines, poster paper
>
> **Grouping Suggestions:** small groups

1. MOTIVATE AND TEACH

LEARN ABOUT IT

Draw three lengths on the chalkboard: 1 cm, 1 dm, and 1 m. Label each line and ask students to estimate the length with their hands as you point to the lines. Show students how the measurements are related by marking off 10 cm on the decimeter line and 10 dm on the meter line. Have students look at the picture on page 127.

▶ **How many red and white decimeter strips will you need if you alternate the colors to make 1 meter? Why?** (Possible answer: There are 10 dm in 1 m, so you would need 5 red strips and 5 white strips.)

▶ **How can you describe an object that does not measure exactly 1 decimeter or 1 meter but is close to that measurement in length?** (Possible answer: The object is *about 1* dm or *about 1* m long.)

▶ **What sentences can you write to show how centimeters, decimeters, and meters are related?** (10 cm = 1 dm; 10 dm = 1 m)

▶ **How does the relationship between centimeters, decimeters, and meters make the metric system easy to use?** (Possible answer: Everything is related by tens; tens are easy to use.)

2. CHECK UNDERSTANDING

ERROR ALERT Not being able to visualize the distance measured by a decimeter or a meter; difficulty accepting that an estimate and the actual measurement do not match.

Name _____

Estimating and Measuring Length
Decimeters and Meters | I decimeter

cm | 1   2   3   4   5   6   7   8   9   10

Work in a group. Cut 1-**decimeter** (dm) units from paper strips. Tape 10 decimeter units together to make a 1-**meter** (m) unit.

I m equals 10 dm.

I dm equals 10 cm.

1. Find some objects you estimate are 1 decimeter long, wide, or tall. Measure. Write what you found.
   Answers may vary. Check students' work.

more than 1 dm	1 dm	less than 1 dm

2. Find some objects you estimate are 1 meter long, wide, or tall. Measure. Write what you found. Answers may vary. Check students' work.

more than 1 m	1 m	less than 1 m

Chapter 6   (one hundred twenty-seven) 1.

TEACHING OPTIONS

RETEACHING TIPS Mark 1 dm on the floor with tape. Have students take a small step to show that distance. Explain that 10 of these steps will equal a meter. Let them try jumping 1 m, then mark off 1 m on the floor to measure their jumps. Assign Reteaching Supplement 54.

ENRICHMENT **Family Math** Have students work with a family member to make a map of one of the rooms in their home. Use meters to measure the perimeter of the room and decimeters or centimeters to mark smaller distances or measurements of objects.

timate to the nearest decimeter. Then
asure. Write the number of decimeters.
swers may vary. Check students' work.

your height

estimate:

_____ decimeters

measure:

_____ decimeters

**2. The width
of a window
in your
classroom**

estimate: _____ decimeters

measure: _____ decimeters

timate to the
arest meter.
en measure.
rite the number
meters.

the width of your classroom

estimate: _____ meters   measure: _____ meters

Mixed Review

d or subtract.

$10 - 9 = \underline{1}$ $8 + 0 = \underline{8}$ $6 + 6 = \underline{12}$

$13 - 7 = \underline{6}$ $15 - 6 = \underline{9}$ $11 - 2 = \underline{9}$

$8 - 4 = \underline{4}$ $2 + 8 = \underline{10}$ $5 - 5 = \underline{0}$

(one hundred twenty-eight)   Chapter 6

3. Practice and Apply

Basic	All
Average	All
Extended	All

PRACTICE

*Why do you think we use decimeters
instead of meters to measure our
heights?* (Possible answer: They are
smaller units; they give a better idea of
how tall we are.)

APPLY

▶ **How can a partner help you
measure objects accurately?** (Possible
answer: One person can mark the place
where the strip ends so the other can
move it and continue measuring.)
▶ **Would you measure the height of a
tree using cm, dm, or m? Explain.**
(Possible answer: meters, because a tree
is very tall; it would take too long with
small units of measure)

MIXED REVIEW *Why must you look
carefully at the signs in these exercises?*
(so you will know whether to add or
subtract)

6-9

LOSE AND ASSESS

HOW WHAT YOU KNOW Ask
all groups of students to cut out of
gazines 10 pictures of objects that
be measured in decimeters and
ters. Have them label two posters:
asure in Decimeters; Measure in
ters. Then students sort the pictures
paste them on the appropriate
ster.

QUICK QUIZ

Circle the better estimate of length.

swingset	4 decimeters	<u>4 meters</u>
pocket comb	<u>1 decimeter</u>	1 meter
bicycle	2 decimeters	<u>2 meters</u>
flashlight	<u>2 decimeters</u>	2 meters

Estimating and Measuring: Capacity–Liters

OBJECTIVE 6-10   To estimate and measure capacity using liters

PREBOOK ACTIVITIES

QUICK REVIEW

Write the length, weight, or capacity to show what each unit measures.

centimeter (length)	feet (length)	yard (length)
pint (capacity)	meter (length)	cup (capacity)
pound (weight)	quart (capacity)	inch (length)

PRIOR KNOWLEDGE

If you wanted to weigh your dog, what type of measurement would you use? (pounds) *If you are baking bran muffins and need to add water, what type of measurement might you use?* (cup) *Why is it important to know different types of measurements?* (Possible answers: Certain kinds of measurements, such as pounds, would not help you when you are measuring a liquid; measurements need to make sense with what you are measuring.)

COMMUNICATION

Listening and Writing in Math   Write **liter** and **kilogram** in 2 columns on the chalkboard. Display a liter of water. *What does a liter measure?* (capacity) Display 2 math books and place them on a balance scale. *What does a kilogram measure?* (weight) *Raise your left hand if I name something that might be measured by a liter. Raise your right hand if I name something that might be measured by a kilogram.* Examples include orange juice (L), can of green beans (kg), meat (kg), milk (L), and lemonade (L). Write *capacity* above *liter* and *weight* above *kilogram,* and have students name other types of measurement for capacity or weight. (cup, pint, quart, pound)

EXPLORE AND CONNECT

Materials: 1-L containers, containers of varying capacities
Grouping Suggestion: small groups
Display a 1-L container filled with water and several other containers, including shallow pans and tall vases. *How much the water in this 1-L container do you estimate will fit in eac of these other containers?* Let students estimate. Note their answers on the chalkboard. have small groups of students explore by pouring water from a 1-L container into the other containers to see if their estimates were correct. Be sure each member of a group has a chance to pour. Discuss their findin when they have finished. *Were you surprised by the amount each of the containers held?* (Answers will vary). Compare t list on the chalkboard to the students' actual findings.

CONNECTIONS   Use these anytime.

Problem of the Day

Measurement   Use the information to fill in the blanks. Together, the _____ and the _____ weigh 11 kg. (dog, cat)

dog—9 kg	bird—1 kg
cat—2 kg	duck—3 kg

Life Skills

Using Liters   Name a way that you or your family might encounter or use liters in everyday life. (putting gas in the car, buying 2-L containers of juice or milk, reading labels on bottles)

Subject Integration

Social Studies   List workers who might measure with kilograms when doing their jobs. (grocers, scientists, doctors, vets, postal workers)

Estimating and Measuring Weight: Kilograms

To estimate and measure mass using kilograms

CLASSWORK AND HOMEWORK SUPPLEMENTS

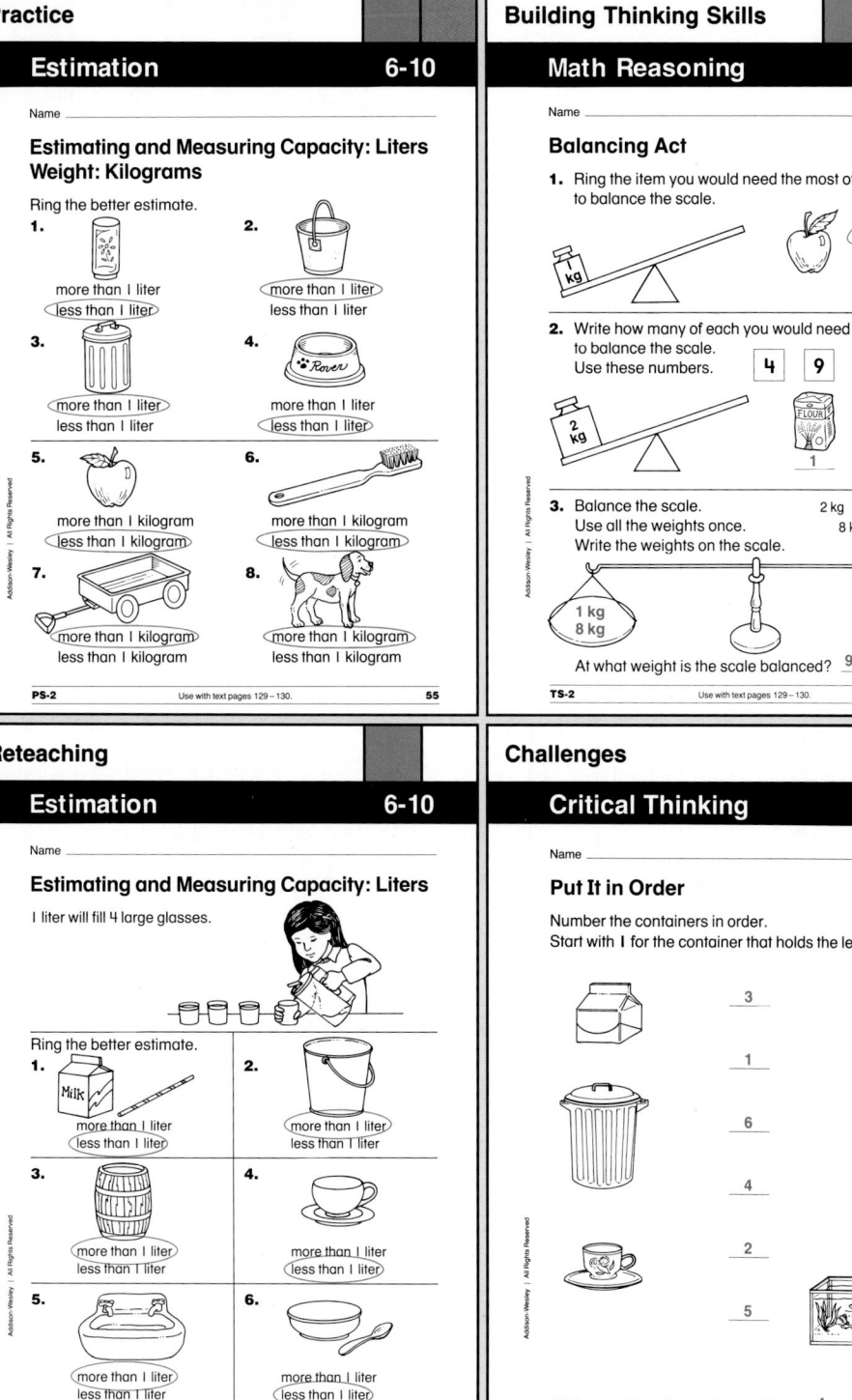

Practice

Estimation 6-10

Name _____

Estimating and Measuring Capacity: Liters
Weight: Kilograms

Ring the better estimate.

1.   more than I liter
     (less than I liter)

2.   (more than I liter)
     less than I liter

3.   (more than I liter)
     less than I liter

4.   more than I liter
     (less than I liter)

5.   more than I kilogram
     (less than I kilogram)

6.   more than I kilogram
     (less than I kilogram)

7.   (more than I kilogram)
     less than I kilogram

8.   (more than I kilogram)
     less than I kilogram

PS-2   Use with text pages 129–130.   55

Building Thinking Skills

Math Reasoning 6-10

Name _____

Balancing Act

1. Ring the item you would need the most of to balance the scale.

2. Write how many of each you would need to balance the scale. Use these numbers.

   4   9   1

   1   9   4

3. Balance the scale.
   Use all the weights once.
   Write the weights on the scale.

   2 kg   I kg   3 kg
   8 kg   4 kg

   1 kg   2 kg 3 kg
   8 kg   4 kg

   At what weight is the scale balanced? __9 kg__

TS-2   Use with text pages 129–130.   55

Reteaching

Estimation 6-10

Name _____

Estimating and Measuring Capacity: Liters

I liter will fill 4 large glasses.

Ring the better estimate.

1.   more than I liter
     (less than I liter)

2.   (more than I liter)
     less than I liter

3.   (more than I liter)
     less than I liter

4.   more than I liter
     (less than I liter)

5.   (more than I liter)
     less than I liter

6.   more than I liter
     (less than I liter)

RS-2   Use with text pages 129–130.   55

Challenges

Critical Thinking 6-10

Name _____

Put It in Order

Number the containers in order.
Start with I for the container that holds the least.

3

1

6

4

2

5

Which container holds about a liter? __4__

CS-2   Use with text pages 129–130.   55

OPTIONS FOR INDIVIDUAL NEEDS

Basic

Exercises All

Supplements
Reteaching 55 or
Practice 55
Thinking Skills 55

Average

Exercises All

Supplements
Practice 55
Challenges 55 or
Thinking Skills 55

Extended

Exercises All

Supplements
Challenges 55
Thinking Skills 55

Other Resources:
Mathematics Their Way, 8-9,
131-132, 245
Explorations, pp. 314-315,
320, 330, 334

6-10

OBJECTIVE 6-10
To estimate and measure capacity using liters

Materials: 1-L container, small and large containers

Grouping Suggestions: pairs, small groups

1. MOTIVATE AND TEACH

LEARN ABOUT IT

Point out the label on a 2-L bottle. Invite two students to pour water from two 1-L containers into the bottle to see if it really holds 2 L. *Name things you would measure in liters.* (liquids)

▶ **Look at the containers on page 129. Do you think a 1-L container will fill a greater number of large containers or small containers?** (Possible answer: small; they hold less liquid so more will be filled)

▶ **Why might results vary from group to group?** (Possible answers: Some groups might not start with exactly 1 L; some groups may spill.)

2. CHECK UNDERSTANDING

ERROR ALERT Not checking to make sure the 1-L container is full before measuring.

3. PRACTICE AND APPLY

Basic	All
Average	All
Extended	All

PRACTICE

Explain what you are to do first for each exercise. (Estimate how many containers 1-L will fill.) *How will you show the answers on page 129?* (Write the estimate, color the containers to show how many were filled, and then write the amount you measured.)

Name _____

Estimating and Measuring Capacity
Liters   **Answers may vary depending on actual container sizes.**

Work in a group. Estimate.
Then measure. Color to match.

1. I estimate I **liter** (L) will fill

____ large glasses.

I measured ____ large glasses.

2. I estimate I liter will fill ____ small cups.

I measured ____ small cups.

3. I estimate I liter will fill ____ cans.

I measured ____ cans.

Chapter 6   (one hundred twenty-nine) I

TEACHING OPTIONS

RETEACHING TIPS Have students close their eyes and concentrate on a 1-kg weight in one hand. Place an object in their other hand while they guess if it weighs about the same, more, or less than 1 kg. Use a balance scale to check. For liter measurement, use Reteaching Supplement 55.

ENRICHMENT Have students bring empty containers from home. Have pairs make a chart with headings *Less Than 1 L, About 1 L, More Than 1 L*. Have them use a 1-L container to fill their containers and record their estimates and measurements.

stimating and Measuring Weight
ograms

ork with a partner. Pick up each object.
stimate its weight in **kilograms** (kg).
hen weigh. Ring the best measure.
swers may vary. Check students' work.

more than I kilogram

I kilogram

less than I kilogram

2.

more than I kilogram

I kilogram

less than I kilogram

more than I kilogram

I kilogram

less than I kilogram

4.

more than I kilogram

I kilogram

less than I kilogram

ROBLEM SOLVING

Mike placed three items on a scale. Together they
weighed 12 kg. Ring the items Mike weighed.

2 kg   5 kg   8 kg   4 kg   3 kg

OBJECTIVE 6-10   To estimate and
measure mass using kilograms

Materials: 1-kg weight, balance scale
---

1. MOTIVATE AND TEACH

► **Look at the objects on page 130.
Describe how you can estimate their
weight.** (Possible answer: Hold a 1-kg
weight in one hand and compare it to the
object to be weighed in the other hand.)

2. CHECK UNDERSTANDING

ERROR ALERT   Experiencing
difficulty using a balance scale.

3. PRACTICE AND APPLY

Basic	All
Average	All
Extended	All

PROBLEM SOLVING   ► **Explain
one way you could find the 3 items
Mike weighed.** (Possible answer: Write
the weight of each of the 5 items on slips
of paper. Combine 3 at a time to find the
3 items that add to 12.)

6-10

LOSE AND ASSESS

AY WHAT YOU KNOW   Write
e headings *liter* and *kilogram* on the
oard. Ask students to name items
at would be measured in liters or in
lograms and write the names under
e appropriate heading. Encourage
udents to give helpful comments
hen they disagree with the placement
f an item.

QUICK QUIZ

Circle the appropriate unit of measure.
water   <u>liters</u>   kilograms
bricks   liters   <u>kilograms</u>
grape juice   <u>liters</u>   kilograms

Problem Solving: Determining Reasonable Answers

OBJECTIVE 6-11   To determine by estimation whether answers to problems are reasonable

PREBOOK ACTIVITIES

QUICK REVIEW

Draw lines on your paper that are the following lengths:
3 in.   5 in.   7 in.   8 in.   2 in.

PRIOR KNOWLEDGE

Help students recall what they know about estimating and measuring length using nonstandard units, such as paper clips, and using inches and centimeters, *What is the first thing you must do before you find the length of an object?* (Possible answers: Read the problem to find out what measuring tool you are to use; estimate the length.) *Explain why it is helpful to estimate the* **length** *before you measure.* (Possible answer: An estimate helps you determine whether or not your answer makes sense.)

COMMUNICATION

Discussing Math   Provide students with a collection of paper clips and an unsharpened pencil. *Would you estimate the length of this pencil to be closer to 1 clip, 10 clips, or 90 clips? Explain your answer.* (10 clips; 1 clip is too short; 90 clips are too long.) *How might you get an even closer estimate?* (Possible answer: Place a clip at one end of the pencil and estimate how many more clips it would take to get to the other end.) *How could you check to see if your estimate is reasonable?* (Possible answer: Place clips end-to-end along the pencil and count the number.)

EXPLORE AND CONNECT

COOPERATIVE ACTIVITY

Grouping Suggestion: small groups
How many index cards do you think you would need to cover desktop?

TEACHING ACTIONS

▶ **What is the question asking you to do?** (Think about how many index cards would cover desktop, then make an estimate.)
▶ **What data do you have so far?** (Possible answer: The unit of measurement is an index card.)

▶ **How will you make a plan to solve the problem?** (Possible answer: First estimate the number of cards needed to cover the desktop; the check by measuring.)

▶ **Why do you need to estimate before actually measuring?** (The estimate helps you determine if the measurement is sensible.)

▶ **What will you do if your measured amount does not match the estimate?** (Possible answers: Remeasure using another arrangement to cover the desk; ask another student to remeasure and compare answers.)

Have groups of students use cards to estimate and measure their desktops. Then have them use other units, such as block to estimate and measure the desktop.

CONNECTIONS   Use these anytime.

Problem of the Day

Logic   Judy is 52 in. tall. Mary is 4 in. shorter than Belinda. Belinda is 1 in. taller than Judy. How tall are Mary and Belinda? (Mary is 49 in. tall, Belinda is 53 in. tall.)

Math Connection

Estimation   Estimate the number of index cards it would take to cover your math book. Then estimate the number of Cube-A-Links it would take. Which estimate is a larger number? Why? (It would take more cubes than cards because cubes are smaller.) Now cover your math book first with index cards, then with cubes, to check your estimates.

Number Sense

Patterns   Rearrange each set of numbers to make a pattern. Tell what the pattern is. (Answers may vary.)
1. 1, 1, 2, 3, 3, 2
2. 5, 6, 4, 6, 5, 4, 5, 6, 6
3. 12, 8, 2, 4, 6, 10
4. 6, 3, 9, 0, 15, 12

Problem Solving Strategy: Use Logical Reasoning

solve problems using the strategy use Logical Reasoning

CLASSWORK AND HOMEWORK

Basic

Practice

Problem Solving   6-11

Name _____

Determining Reasonable Answers

How many squares will cover each shape?
Does the estimate make sense? Ring **yes** or **no**.
Use the grid at the bottom of the page to check.
Trace each figure. Place the tracing on the grid.
Then count the squares.

[ ] I square

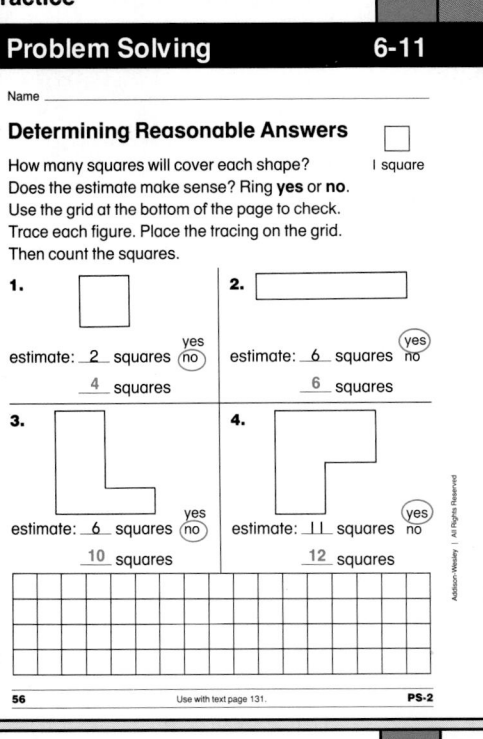

1. estimate: __2__ squares (yes / no̅)
    __4__ squares

2. estimate: __6__ squares (y̅e̅s̅) no
    __6__ squares

3. estimate: __6__ squares (yes / no̅)
    __10__ squares

4. estimate: __11__ squares (y̅e̅s̅) no
    __12__ squares

56   Use with text page 131.   PS-2

Building Thinking Skills

Math Reasoning   6-11

Name _____

Zegs and Zogs

1. These are zegs.   These are not zegs.

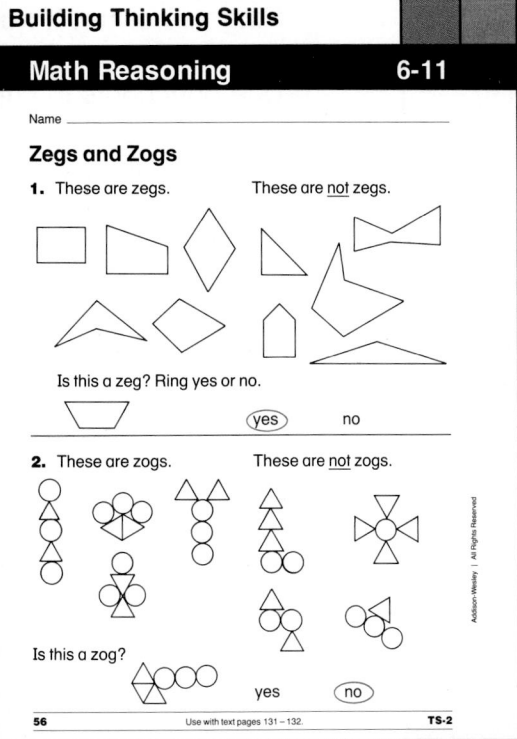

Is this a zeg? Ring yes or no.

(yes)   no

2. These are zogs.   These are not zogs.

Is this a zog?

yes   (no̅)

56   Use with text pages 131–132.   TS-2

Average

Reteaching

Problem Solving   6-11

Name _____

Use Logical Reasoning

Read the clues.
Match each cat with its name tag.

Clue 1: Sam is the smallest.
Clue 2: Frisky does not have stripes.

56   Use with text pages 131–132.   RS-2

Challenges

Estimation   6-11

Name _____

How Many Squares?

Use straight lines to draw a shape on your
paper. Count the number of squares it covers.
Exchange papers with a partner.
Estimate how many squares each other's
shape covers. Then count.

__9__ squares

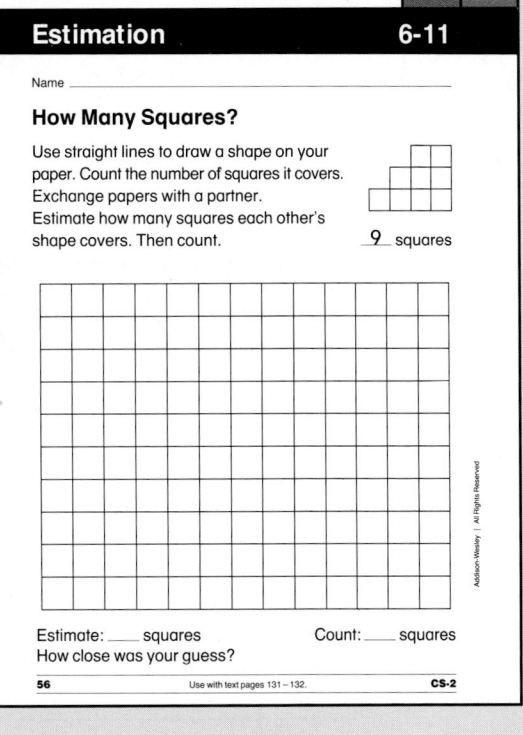

Estimate: ____ squares   Count: ____ squares
How close was your guess?

56   Use with text pages 131–132.   CS-2

Extended

Other Resources:
Math in Stride, pp. 115-119
Mathematics Their Way, pp. 131-132
Explorations, pp. 308-309, 311-313, 316-319, 322, 331, 334
Problem-Solving Experiences In Mathematics, pp. 64-65, 70, 76-77, 94, 161
Developing Number Concepts With Unifix Cubes, p. 159

6-11

OBJECTIVE 6-11
To determine by estimation whether answers to problems are reasonable; to solve problems using the strategy Use Logical Reasoning

Materials: punchout colored squares, rug squares, stickers, index cards

1. MOTIVATE AND TEACH

| LEARN ABOUT IT |

 **BEFORE** ▶ **Look at Exercise 1. Do you think the answer makes sense? Explain.**
(No, it looks as if more than 3 squares are needed to cover the bulletin board.)

 **DURING** ▶ **Suggest a way that you could estimate the number of squares needed for Exercise 1.** (Possible answer: Try to picture how many squares would be needed to cover the top half of the bulletin board; add the same number for the bottom half.)

 **AFTER** ▶ **How can you check your estimate?** (Use punchouts to cover the area; count how many you used.)
▶ **Why might it be more difficult to make an estimate for Exercise 3 than for Exercises 1 and 2?** (Possible answer: The shape is not a rectangle; the shape is not the same at the top and bottom.)

2. CHECK UNDERSTANDING

ERROR ALERT **Page 131**
Incorrectly estimating the area of a shape.
Page 132 Not finding the given clues in a logical reasoning problem.

Name _____

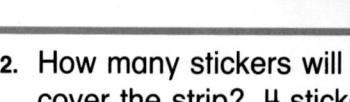

Problem Solving
Determining Reasonable Answers

Does the answer make sense? Ring **yes** or **no**. If **no**, make an estimate that does make sense. Use punchouts to check.
Estimates may vary.

1. How many squares will cover the bulletin board? 3 squares

yes

(no)

I estimate __6__ squares.

3. How many rug squares will cover the floor?
6 rug squares

yes (no)

I estimate __8__ rug squares.

2. How many stickers will cover the strip? 4 sticke[r]

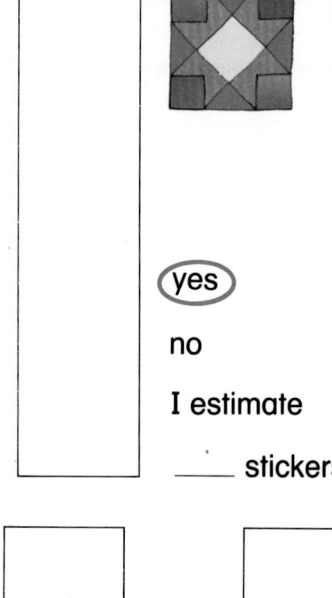

(yes)

no

I estimate

____ stickers

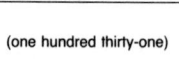

Chapter 6   More Practice, page 415, set C   (one hundred thirty-one) 1

| TEACHING OPTIONS |

RETEACHING TIPS Give students an index card and 50 square tiles. Ask them to guess the lowest and highest number of tiles needed to cover the card. Then have them measure and compare the answer with their estimate. For help in logical reasoning, use Reteaching Supplement 56.

ENRICHMENT **Family Math**
Have students and a family member choose a square or rectangular table to use in estimating area. Use notecards or square pieces of paper as a unit of measure. Estimate the number of notecards needed to cover the table, then check by measuring.

roblem Solving Strategy
se Logical Reasoning

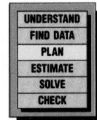

UNDERSTAND
FIND DATA
PLAN
ESTIMATE
SOLVE
CHECK

sten to the story.
nswer the questions below.

Jan   Jill   Teri

Teri can reach higher than Jan.
Jill's reach is lower than Jan's.
Write the girls' names above.

Jill can throw the ball farther than Teri.
Jill cannot throw the ball as far as Jan.
Ring the name of the girl above who can
throw the farthest.

2   (one hundred thirty-two)   Chapter 6

---

3. PRACTICE AND APPLY

Basic	All
Average	All
Extended	All

Read the following story to the class:
*Jan, Jill, and Terri learned how to play
softball in school. Now it is time to join
the spring softball league. Each girl
shows the coach how well she throws
and reaches. Then the coach assigns
each position on the team and gives each
a team cap to wear.*

▶ **Why is it important for the coach to
have data on throwing and
reaching?** (Possible answer: to decide
which position each girl should play)

▶ **What plan will you use to solve the
problem?** (Possible answer: Read each
clue; use the clues to draw a picture and
find the picture that matches all the
clues.)

▶ **How can you check your answer to
see if it matches the clues?** (Possible
answers: Make a checkmark after you
have used each clue; work backward.)

6-11

LOSE AND ASSESS

HOW WHAT YOU KNOW

eview with students the chapter
ory. *Ceci can reach higher than
enny. Benny's reach is lower than
enny's. Who can reach the highest?*
Ceci) Ask students to give a
easonable answer and then draw a
icture of each animal's reach to show
hether their answer is correct.

QUICK QUIZ

Estimate the number of Cube-A-Links
you would need to cover a chalkboard
eraser. Write down your estimate,
then measure to check. How close
was your estimate?

CHAPTER 6

CHAPTER REVIEW/TEST

INTRODUCTION The Review/Test is provided to review and evaluate the skills and concepts presented in Chapter 6.

USING PAGE 133
If you prefer to use this page for review, you may want to use the **Multiple-Choice Posttest** (pages 23-24) or the **Free-Response Posttest** (pages 23-24) to evaluate mastery of chapter objectives.

ITEM ANALYSIS
The table below correlates the Chapter Review/Test Items with the lesson objectives.

Items	Objectives
1, 2	6-2
3	6-4
4	6-5
5	6-6
6	6-7
7	6-3

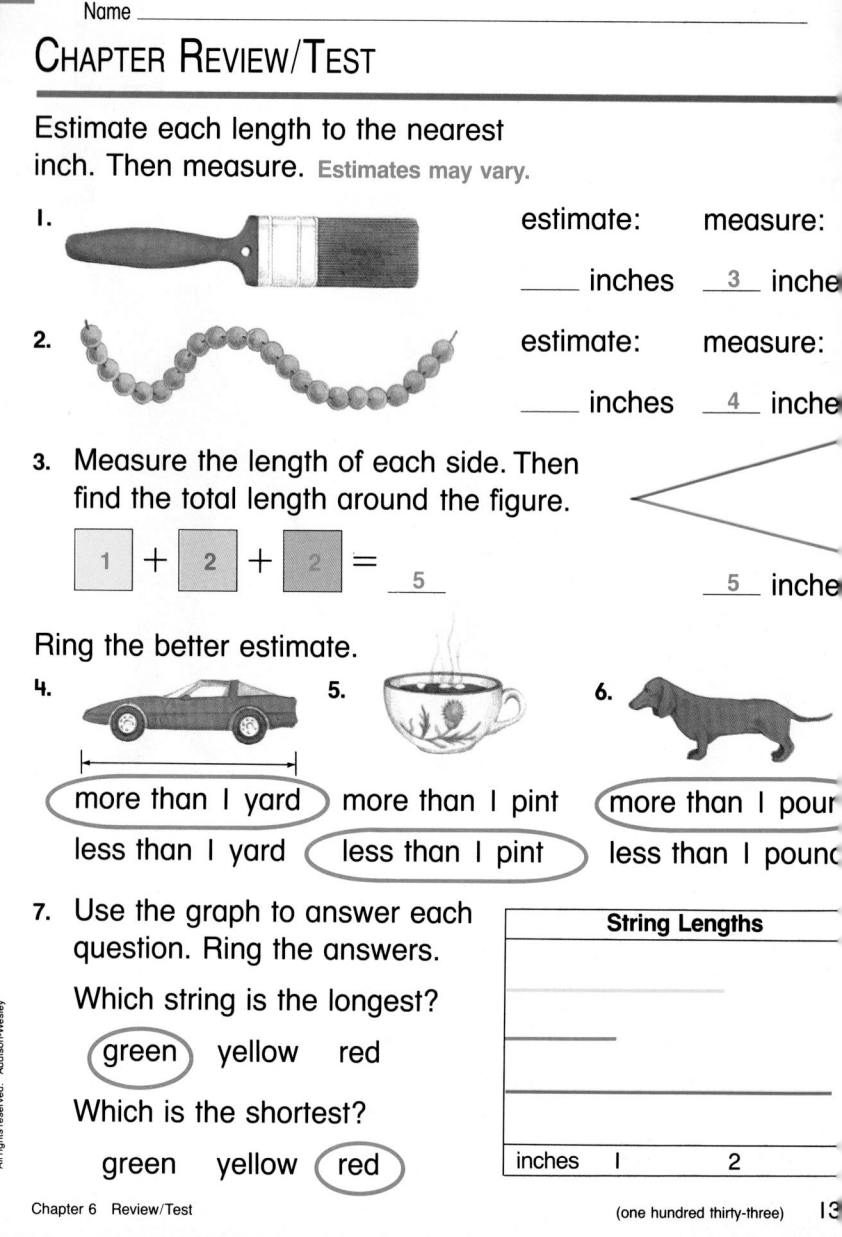

Name _____

CHAPTER REVIEW/TEST

Estimate each length to the nearest inch. Then measure. Estimates may vary.

1. estimate: ____ inches   measure: __3__ inches

2. estimate: ____ inches   measure: __4__ inches

3. Measure the length of each side. Then find the total length around the figure.

1 + 2 + 2 = __5__

__5__ inches

Ring the better estimate.

4. **more than 1 yard** / less than 1 yard

5. more than 1 pint / **less than 1 pint**

6. **more than 1 pound** / less than 1 pound

7. Use the graph to answer each question. Ring the answers.

Which string is the longest?

green   yellow   red

Which is the shortest?

green   yellow   **red**

String Lengths

| inches | 1 | 2 |

Chapter 6 Review/Test

(one hundred thirty-three) 13

INFORMAL ASSESSMENT

Using Manipulatives Give students an inch ruler and several classroom objects. Ask them to estimate the length of 1 object in inches, measure to check, and then compare the estimate to the measurement. Have students estimate and measure each of the other objects.

Communication *Why is an estimate useful before measuring an object?* (Possible answer: It helps you decide if the actual measure is reasonable.)

Critical Thinking *What do you have to decide before you can measure an object?* (Possible answers: the unit of measure to use; the kind of measurement needed—capacity, weight, length)

Name _____

HAPTER REVIEW/TEST

:timate each length to the nearest **Estimates may vary.**
ntimeter. Then measure.

1. estimate: _____ centimeters
   measure: __6__ centimeters

2. estimate: _____ centimeters
   measure: __3__ centimeters

ng the better estimate.

3.
(more than I decimeter)
less than I decimeter

4.
more than I meter
(less than I meter)

5.
more than I liter
(less than I liter)

6.
(more than I kilogram)
less than I kilogram

How many tiles will
cover the floor? 6 tiles
Does the answer make   yes
sense? Ring one.   (no)

If **no,** make an estimate
that does make sense. __4__ tiles

:4 (one hundred thirty-four)   Chapter 6   Review/Test

CHAPTER REVIEW/TEST

INTRODUCTION   The Review/Test is
provided to review and evaluate the skills
and concepts presented in Chapter 6.

USING PAGE 134
If you prefer to use this page for review,
you may want to use the
Multiple-Choice Posttest (pages 23-24)
or the **Free-Response Posttest** (pages
23-24) to evaluate mastery of chapter
objectives.

ITEM ANALYSIS   The table below
correlates the Chapter Review/Test Items
with the lesson objectives.

Items	Objectives
1 2,	6-8
3, 4	6-9
5, 6	6-10
6	6-11

.ing Manipulatives Give student
·rs a centimeter ruler. Help them
ke a chart labeled *All About Me* in
·ich measurements of fingers, toes,
·nds, feet, heads, and ears are
·orded. Students will measure and
·ord for their partners. Students can
·n illustrate their own charts.

·mmunication *Describe how you
·uld measure an object using a
·ntimeter ruler.* (Possible answer:
·ne up 1 edge of the object with the

0 end of the ruler. Look for the
number on the ruler that is closest to
the other edge of the object.)

Critical Thinking *How can you
decide when to measure an object
using centimeters and when to
measure using meters?* (Possible
answer: Measure shorter objects with
a centimeter ruler, since the unit of
measure is smaller. A meter is useful
for measuring longer objects.)

CHAPTER 6

ENRICHMENT

INTRODUCTION Identifying and continuing patterns helps students develop understanding of numbers and number sense.

USING PAGE 135

This Enrichment page is provided for all students. You may wish to use it after they have completed the Chapter Review/Tests on pages 133 and 134. Help students appreciate the various formats in which patterns are present. Point out that patterns may appear in measurement and geometry as well as in number sequences.

▶ **How can you tell what number comes next in a pattern?** (Possible answer: Continue counting in the same way; add on; say the next number in the pattern.)

▶ **How can you find the next number in a pattern if the numbers get smaller?** (Count backward; subtract.)

EXTENSION Provide pairs of students with a collection of pattern blocks and number lines. The first student creates a pattern with blocks similar to those shown in Exercises 3 and 4 on page 135. The second student shows the numbers in the pattern on the number line and provides the number that would come next. Students reverse roles and repeat the activity.

Name _____

ENRICHMENT
Finding Patterns

1. Peg measured the height of her plant each month. The first month it was 2 inches tall, the second month, 4 inches tall, and the third, 6 inches tall. Suppose this pattern continued. How tall would it be the fourth month?

__8__ inches

2. The Lees' bag of fruit weighed 17 pounds on Monday, 15 pounds on Tuesday, and 13 pounds on Wednesday. Suppose this pattern continued. How much would it weigh on Thursday?

__11__ poun

3. How many blocks would you need in all to continue this pattern two more times? Use blocks to help.

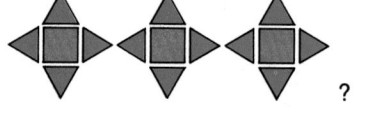

__25__ blocks

5, 10, 15, __20__ , 2

4. How many blocks would you need in all to continue this pattern two more times? Use blocks to help.

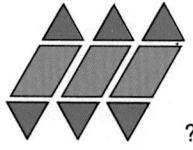

__15__ blocks

3, 6, 9, __12__ , 1

Chapter 6 Enrichment: Finding Patterns

(one hundred thirty-five)

Name _____

UMULATIVE REVIEW

btract.

$6 - 1 =$
- ○ 9
- ● 5
- ○ 7

$10 - 7 =$
- ● 3
- ○ 2
- ○ 7

Which is the related subtraction fact for $9 - 6 = 3$?
- ○ $9 - 4 = 5$
- ● $9 - 3 = 6$
- ○ $9 - 5 = 4$

Finish the fact family.

$7 + 4 = 11$
$4 + 7 = 11$
$11 - 7 = 4$
- ○ $4 + 4 = 8$
- ○ $7 - 3 = 4$
- ● $11 - 4 = 7$

5.
$\begin{array}{r} 11 \\ -\ 8 \\ \hline \end{array}$
- ○ 4
- ● 3
- ○ 2

6.
$\begin{array}{r} 17 \\ -\ 9 \\ \hline \end{array}$
- ● 8
- ○ 6
- ○ 9

7.
$\begin{array}{r} 12 \\ -\ 5 \\ \hline \end{array}$
- ○ 8
- ○ 3
- ● 7

8.
$\begin{array}{r} 14 \\ -\ 6 \\ \hline \end{array}$
- ○ 4
- ● 8
- ○ 5

Mrs. Bell bought 5 dresses.
Mrs. Chin bought 3 dresses.
How many more dresses did
Mrs. Bell buy than Mrs. Chin?
- ○ 8 more dresses
- ● 2 more dresses
- ○ 3 more dresses

CUMULATIVE REVIEW

INTRODUCTION   The purpose of this Cumulative Review is to maintain previously taught skills and concepts. The emphasis in this Cumulative Review is on subtraction facts, Chapter 4 and Chapter 5.

ITEM ANALYSIS   The table below correlates the Cumulative Review items with the lesson objectives.

Items	Objectives
1	4-1
2	4-3
3	4-7
4	4-8
5	5-5
6	5-1
7, 8	5-2
9	5-4

CHAPTER 7 PLACE VALUE: NUMBERS TO 100

Chapter Management

OVERVIEW

Lesson	Pages	Objectives	Subject Integration	Strand Integration
Recording Tens and Ones	137-138	7-1 To group and write the number of tens and ones	language arts: writing	number
Modeling Tens and Ones	139-140	7-2 To model tens and ones	fine arts: cut & paste	number
Modeling and Writing Decade Numbers	141-142	7-3 To model and write decade numbers	language arts: writing	number
Modeling and Writing 2-Digit Numbers	143-144	7-4 To model and write 2-digit numbers	social studies: bakery	consumer math
Problem Solving: Understanding the Operations/Using Critical Thinking	145-146	7-5 To subtract by comparing; to draw conclusions	social studies: city jobs	computation, critical thinking
Dimes and Pennies	147-148	7-6 To count dimes and pennies	social studies: toy products	problem solving
Reading and Writing Number Names	149-150	7-7 To read and write word names for 2-digit numbers	social studies: mailing letters	number
Understanding 100	151-152	7-8 To write numbers around 100	social studies: bakery	patterns
Problem Solving: Using Data from a Pictograph/Problem Solving Strategy: Use Objects	153-154	7-9 To use data from a pictograph; to use the strategy Use Objects	language arts: newspaper sales	data analysis

MATHEMATICAL BACKGROUND

Place Value

A solid understanding of place value is essential to almost all computational work done in elementary grades. Many computational errors found in adding, subtracting, multiplying, and dividing whole numbers can be traced to a poor foundation in the concept of place value. The instructional approach used in this chapter begins with concrete models (place value cubes), connecting language (number names), and symbols (numbers). Understanding of place value can only be achieved when students have many opportunities to translate a physical situation (models) into symbols. This chapter emphasizes experiences in which the student is given groups of tens and ones (using concrete objects and pictures of objects), is asked to identify how many tens and ones are shown, and then is directed to write the number in standard form.

Money

Dimes and pennies are used in this chapter to reinforce place value concepts. Lesson 7-6 uses coin punchouts as models: dimes represent tens, pennies represent ones. Money is a familiar model to most children.

Problem Solving

In this chapter, students solve problems using data from a pictograph and by using the strategy *Use Objects*.

TIPS FROM TEACHERS

Have each student glue 10 beans to a tongue depressor. Explain that the tongue depressor can be used as 1 ten, and it can be traded for 10 loose beans. have students show the number 100 using ten of the 1-ten tongue depressors.

Jean Worsh
South River School
Marshfield, MA

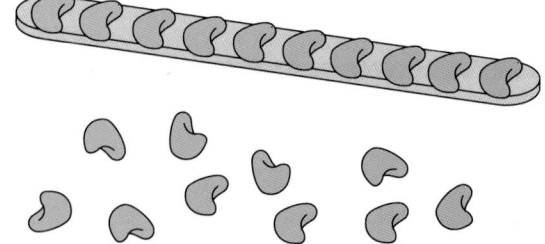

ASSESSMENT

ITEM ANALYSIS

Items	Objectives
1	7-1
2	7-2
3	7-3
4, 5	7-4
6	7-5
7	7-6
8, 9	7-7
10	7-8
11	7-9

Note: The item analysis is the same for all pretests and posttests for this chapter.

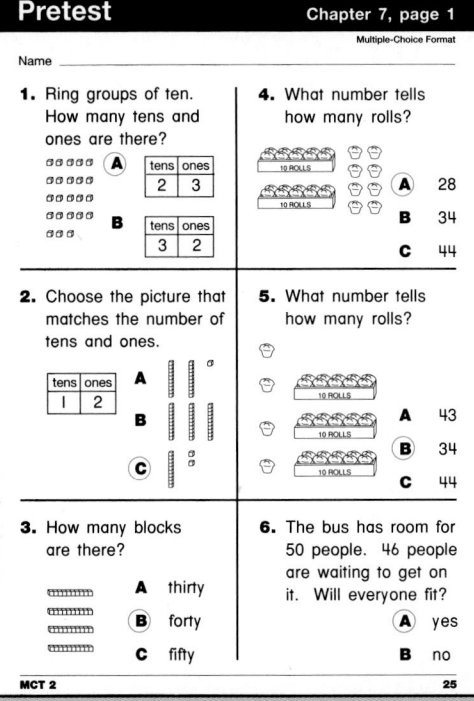

Pretest — Chapter 7, page 1

Multiple-Choice Format

Name _____

1. Ring groups of ten. How many tens and ones are there?

A tens | ones = 2 | 3
B tens | ones = 3 | 2

2. Choose the picture that matches the number of tens and ones.

tens | ones = 1 | 2

A, B, **C**

3. How many blocks are there?

A thirty
B forty
C fifty

4. What number tells how many rolls?

A 28
B 34
C 44

5. What number tells how many rolls?

A 43
B 34
C 44

6. The bus has room for 50 people. 46 people are waiting to get on it. Will everyone fit?

A yes
B no

MCT 2   25

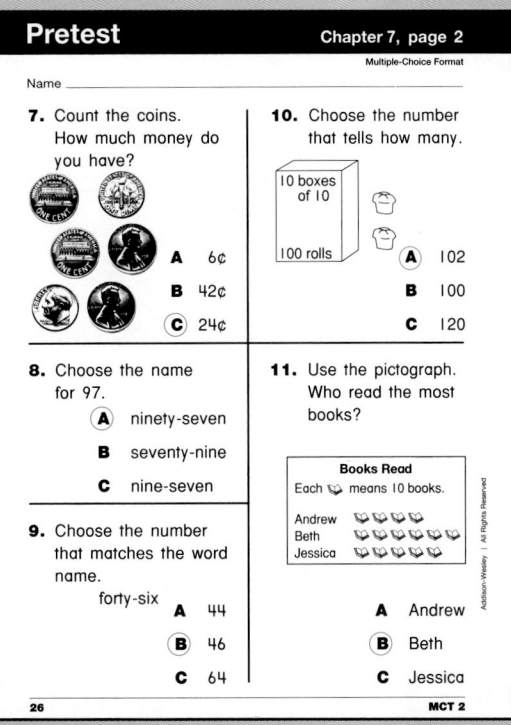

Pretest — Chapter 7, page 2

Multiple-Choice Format

Name _____

7. Count the coins. How much money do you have?

A 6¢
B 42¢
C 24¢

8. Choose the name for 97.

A ninety-seven
B seventy-nine
C nine-seven

9. Choose the number that matches the word name.

forty-six
A 44
B 46
C 64

10. Choose the number that tells how many.

10 boxes of 10
100 rolls

A 102
B 100
C 120

11. Use the pictograph. Who read the most books?

Books Read
Each 📖 means 10 books.

Andrew 📖📖📖📖📖
Beth 📖📖📖📖
Jessica 📖📖📖📖📖

A Andrew
B Beth
C Jessica

26   MCT 2

Posttest — Chapter 7, page 1

Multiple-Choice Format

Name _____

1. Ring groups of ten. How many tens and ones are there?

A tens | ones = 2 | 6
B tens | ones = 6 | 2

2. Choose the picture that matches the number of tens and ones.

tens | ones = 1 | 5

A, **B**, C

3. How many blocks are there?

A twenty
B sixty
C forty

4. What number tells how many rolls?

A 29
B 23
C 32

5. What number tells how many rolls?

A 54
B 45
C 55

6. The bus has room for 35 people. 42 people are waiting to get on it. Will everyone fit?

A yes
B no

MCT 2   27

Posttest — Chapter 7, page 2

Multiple-Choice Format

Name _____

7. Count the coins. How much money do you have?

A 5¢
B 23¢
C 32¢

8. Choose the name for 79.

A ninety-seven
B seventy-nine
C seven-nine

9. Choose the number that matches the word name.

sixty-eight
A 86
B 88
C 68

10. Choose the number that tell how many.

10 boxes of 10
100 rolls

A 101
B 100
C 110

11. Use the pictograph. Who read the most books?

Books Read
Each 📖 means 10 books.

Tomika 📖📖📖📖
Polly 📖📖📖📖
Leander 📖📖📖📖📖

A Tomika
B Polly
C Leander

28   MCT 2

ALSO AVAILABLE

► **Free Response Tests**
► **Alternative Tests**
► **Thinking Strategies**
► **Concrete Materials**

CHAPTER 7 PLACE VALUE: NUMBERS TO 100

Optional Chapter Activities

PROJECT AND BULLETIN BOARD

Draw and cut out of tagboard a school bus similiar to the one shown. Draw lines to separate the bus into puzzle pieces. Write a number on one side of each line and the corresponding word name directly opposite it. Cut the pieces apart and post them on the bulletin board. Have students put the puzzle together. Explain that each puzzle piece will have either a number or a word name on it. The adjoining piece must have the number or word that matches. At another time, have students draw and cut out pictures of other kinds of transportation, such as bicycles, cars, trucks, and trains, and make 2-piece puzzles with a number on one side and the matching word name on the other. Have volunteers piece the objects together, read the numbers and word names, and tack the pictures to the bulletin board. Periodically the puzzles can be taken apart and reassembled by individual students.

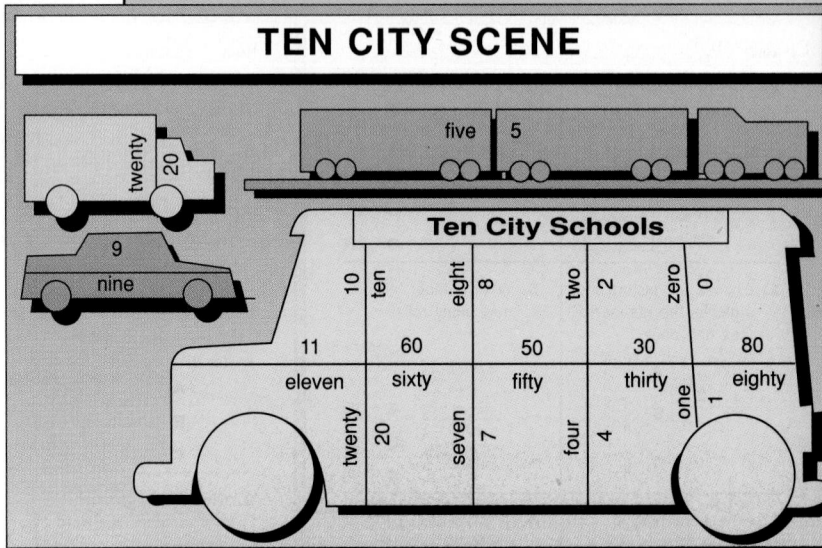

TEN CITY SCENE

COOPERATIVE LEARNING

Divide the class into groups of 6. Identify the group skill: encouraging each other to participate. Display tens and ones gameboards similar to those shown. Explain to students that they will use the gameboards to practice place value. Have group members divide the following tasks: draw the gameboards on the floor with masking tape; measure and draw a line 6 feet from the *0* ends of the gameboards; 2 students stand behind the lines and toss beanbags onto the ones and tens boards; use counters to model the number; identify and write the 2-digit number. Have groups try the activity 5 more times, so each member of the group has a chance to do each task. Then, have each group display its list of 2-digit numbers. Did any other group toss the same numbers?

You will find grouping suggestions and cooperative learning activities in most lessons throughout this chapter.

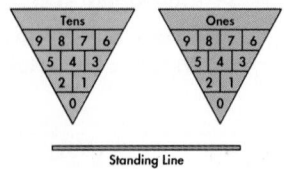

LITERATURE

Shannon, George. *Beanboy.* New York: Greenwillow Books, William Morrow & Co., 1984.

Beanboy is all alone in the world with only a cup of beans to sustain him. He goes in search of a job and has many kinds of experiences. Have students group piles of beans in tens and ones. Then have them make their own bean books, drawing different combinations of tens and ones and writing the numbers to match.

Cretan, Gladys T. *Ten Brothers With Camels.* New York: Western Publishing Co., 1975.

Galdone, Paul. *The House that Jack Built.* New York: McGraw Hill, 1961

ENGLISH AS A SECOND LANGUAGE

It is important for ESL students to understand the meaning and function of new verb forms used in this chapter. Expand the use of the future with *will*, by asking yes and no questions, using a calender, and playing circle games. Students should practice the short responses *will* and *won't*. For *should*, begin the problem solving activity by talking about sharing and being fair. Divide an apple unequally. Have students discuss what is fair, and what is unfair, and what should be done, so that they can get a sense, even implicitly, of what *should* means. Also, since the actual problems are rather long, do the first one with the class, breaking it into separate questions.

When reading and writing the word names for numbers, encourage students to speak aloud while others hold up the corresponding number card. In this way, you can detect any pronunciation or stress problems ESL students might have and correct them in a cooperative way.

GIFTED

Mathematically talented students may already understand place value for 2-digit numbers. They will nevertheless likely be interested in many of the strategies presented in this chapter. You may wish to challenge these students, after they have completed their student book work, by having them make 2-part place value puzzles. For example, after Lesson 4 on writing and modeling 2-digit numbers, write 4 tens 3 ones + 5 ones on the chalkboard, and ask students to tell the number of tens and ones (4 tens 8 ones). Ask if they know another way to say and write the number. (48; forty-eight) Use place value models to demonstrate, if necessary. Vary the puzzles by showing students the following:
4 tens 6 ones − 4 ones (42); 4 tens 6 ones + 3 tens (76); 4 tens 6 ones − 1 ten (36). Then challenge students to write 2-part place value puzzles for other numbers from their book. For the artistically talented, provide a hundred chart (TA6) in which students may design a picture. Then have them describe each square using a 2-part place value puzzle. For example, if 23 is red, they might write *6 tens 3 ones − 4 tens: red*. Students exchange puzzles and complete each other's designs.

STUDENTS AT RISK

Have each student make 2 sets of number cards marked 0-9. As you say a number from 1 to 99, have students display the 2 cards that make that number. Provide immediate correction for students who show the numbers in the wrong place. Repeat the activity by having them write the numbers on the chalkboard. Some learning disabled students have difficulty with the *-teen* numbers because these contradict the rule that what is *said* first is in the tens place. Use a Hundred Chart (TA6) and spinners to play a Travel Game to practice mental arithmetic and help students discover the visual patterns and rules which govern adding numbers with sums greater than 20. This game has a Go Ahead version, beginning at 1 on the chart and a Go Back version, beginning at 100. Students spin and move a counter forward (or backward) the number of spaces shown by the spinner.

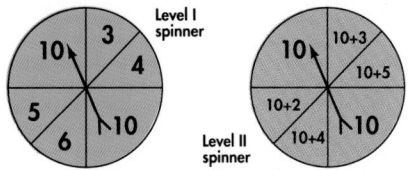

You may also use the Reteaching Supplements and the specific Reteaching Tips from each lesson in this chapter.

Storybook

PICTURE

These pictures and accompanying stories and poems are available as storybooks.

You may want to read and discuss this story with your students before starting the chapter. The first lesson in this chapter includes a question about the story. Lessons 1, 2, 3, 4, and 6 in this chapter have questions in the informal Assessment that refer to the story.

The Surprise

The sun was shining in Kerry Kitten's eyes as she woke up. She looked at the clock. It was already 10 o'clock! "My goodness! I've overslept again, and there is so much to do today!" she cried. Today was her friend Kevin's birthday, and she was planning his surprise party. She needed to get the food and the hats and the BIG cake!

There would be 24 animals in all for the party. Kerry needed to get enough food for everyone. She grabbed her list and headed out to Ten Town.

"First stop, the market," said Kerry as she looked at her list. At the market, she stopped in front of the fish counter. All the fish were laid out in rows of ten. Kerry counted 53 pieces of fish. "Oh, good! There are enough for my party," cried Kerry, happily. She bought all 53 pieces because she wanted to be sure there was plenty of food for everyone.

"Next stop, the bakery," thought Kerry, crossing out "fish" on her list. At the baker's, she saw rolls grouped in tens on trays. She counted 38 rolls in all. "Great! There are enough rolls for my party!" exclaimed Kerry. She bought all 38 rolls because she wanted to be sure there was plenty of food for everyone. She crossed off "rolls" from her list.

Then she strolled to the toy store. "I need colorful party hats for everyone to wear," thought

Kerry. Inside she found the hats stacked in groups of 10. She counted 20 hats. "Oh my!" she exclaimed. "There are not enough hats for everyone. What am I to do?" Then she saw the bright red balloons with "Happy Birthday" written on them. "Why, I'll buy some balloons," she said. "Some animals can hold balloons instead." The balloons were in bags of 10. "I'll get 10 balloons, too." She paid 54¢ for the hats and balloons.

Finally, there was only one thing left on her list, the BIG cake. "What would a birthday party be without cake and candles?" wondered Kerry. She went inside the pastry shop to ask for the cake she had ordered. It was to have "Happy Birthday, Kevin" written on it with pink icing. "Annie, is my cake for Kevin ready?" asked Kerry.

Annie looked puzzled, "Kerry, I thought you wanted it tomorrow, on Friday."

"Isn't today Friday?" questioned Kerry with a sinking feeling.

"No, I'm afraid it is only Thursday," said Annie regretfully.

"What a surprise party," giggled Kerry. "The surprise is on me. I guess everything will keep for one day. Now I can sleep in tomorrow since I've done all my shopping today!"

Recording Tens and Ones

OBJECTIVE 7-1   To group and write the number of tens and ones

PREBOOK ACTIVITIES

QUICK REVIEW

Add or subtract.

6 + 4 = (10)	10 − 5 = (5)	10 − 2 = (8)
4 + 6 = (10)	3 + 7 = (10)	10 − 1 = (9)
5 + 5 = (10)	10 − 8 = (2)	10 + 0 = (10)
10 − 9 = (1)	10 − 7 = (3)	10 − 6 = (4)

PRIOR KNOWLEDGE

Pretend that you have a piggy bank full of pennies. You want to count them, but you keep getting interrupted. Each time you have to start over again. How might you group the pennies so that you do not keep losing your place? (Possible answer: Put them in groups of 5 or 10. Then you can quickly skip count to see how many you have.)

COMMUNICATION

Reading and Discussing Math   Write **tens** and **ones** on the chalkboard. Explain that 10 like items can be placed in a group of ten. Extra items that cannot be grouped in tens are called ones. Have students read the words and hold 10 fingers to show tens and one finger to show ones.

Describe a business in your town that might group items in tens before it sells them. (Possible answers: A bakery might display goods in rows of 10; a flower shop might sell flowers in bunches of 10.)

EXPLORE AND CONNECT

Materials: counters, TA5 (Place Value Chart)
Grouping Suggestions: small groups
Provide each group with counters and a place value chart. Model counting objects by taking a handful and counting out groups of ten. Explain that the extra objects are called **ones.** Write the number of **tens** and ones in a place value chart on the chalkboard. Have students take turns counting groups of t and recording the amount of tens and ones on their own place value chart. Increase and decrease the number of objects students count so the number is different each time. *What would you call a group of 10 objects?* (1 ten) *What would you call 2 groups of 10 objects?* (2 tens)
Introduce Ten City by explaining that the people who live the use this rule: *Whenever 10 things are alike, make a group of 10.*

CONNECTIONS   Use these anytime.

Problem of the Day

Understanding the Operation
Read the story. Use counters to act it out. Then answer the question.
Brett colored 10 pictures. He gave 4 of them to his teacher. How many pictures did he have left?
 (10) − (4) = (6)
He had (6) pictures left.

Subject Integration

Fine Arts   On a large piece of paper, draw groups of 10 objects that are alike. Make a class Tens Mural by combining your drawing with others. When the mural is finished, discuss how the groups look the same and different and count the number of tens on the mural.

Life Skills

Occupations   Read the name of each worker. Name something each might group in tens to make his or her job easier.
mail carrier   (letters)
librarian (books, magazines)
waitress (orders, empty plates)
florist (flowers)
builder (nails, boards, bricks)

CLASSWORK AND HOMEWORK SUPPLEMENTS

OPTIONS FOR INDIVIDUAL NEEDS

Basic

Exercises All
More Practice, p. 416, set A

Supplements
Reteaching 57 or
Practice 57

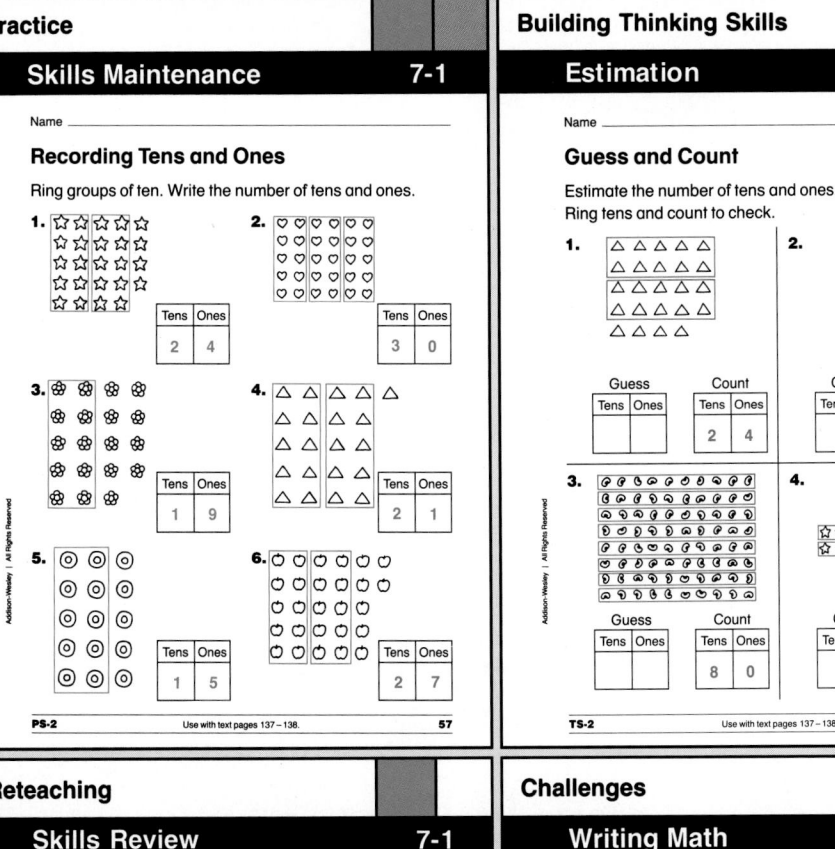

Practice

Skills Maintenance — 7-1

Name _____

Recording Tens and Ones

Ring groups of ten. Write the number of tens and ones.

1. | Tens | Ones |
   |------|------|
   | 2 | 4 |

2. | Tens | Ones |
   |------|------|
   | 3 | 0 |

3. | Tens | Ones |
   |------|------|
   | 1 | 9 |

4. | Tens | Ones |
   |------|------|
   | 2 | 1 |

5. | Tens | Ones |
   |------|------|
   | 1 | 5 |

6. | Tens | Ones |
   |------|------|
   | 2 | 7 |

PS-2   Use with text pages 137–138.   57

Building Thinking Skills

Estimation — 7-1

Name _____

Guess and Count

Estimate the number of tens and ones.
Ring tens and count to check.   Estimates will vary.

1. | Guess | | Count | |
   |-------|---|-------|---|
   | Tens | Ones | Tens | Ones |
   | | | 2 | 4 |

2. | Guess | | Count | |
   |-------|---|-------|---|
   | Tens | Ones | Tens | Ones |
   | | | 4 | 6 |

3. | Guess | | Count | |
   |-------|---|-------|---|
   | Tens | Ones | Tens | Ones |
   | | | 8 | 0 |

4. | Guess | | Count | |
   |-------|---|-------|---|
   | Tens | Ones | Tens | Ones |
   | | | 4 | 4 |

TS-2   Use with text pages 137–138.   57

Average

Exercises All
More Practice, p. 416, set A

Supplements
Practice 57
Challenges 57 or
Thinking Skills 57

Reteaching

Skills Review — 7-1

Name _____

Recording Tens and Ones

23 ones   2 tens   3 ones

23 ones   or   2 tens 3 ones

Ring tens. Write the number of tens and ones.   0 ones

1. 2 tens 5 ones
2. 2 tens 0 ones
3. 2 tens 6 ones
4. 3 tens 2 ones
5. 2 tens 1 ones
6. 1 tens 8 ones

RS-2   Use with text pages 137–138.   57

Challenges

Writing Math — 7-1

Name _____

How Many?

Count the cubes.
Complete a sentence to tell how many tens and ones.

1. There are ___2 tens___ and ___3 ones___.
2. There are ___5 tens___ and ___5 ones___.
3. There are ___4 tens___ and ___8 ones___.
4. There are ___6 tens___ and ___3 ones___.
5. There are ___8 tens___ and ___0 ones___.

CS-2   Use with text pages 137–138.   57

Extended

Exercises All

Supplements
Challenges 57
Thinking Skills 57

Other Resources:
Math in Stride, p. 71
Mathematics Their Way, pp. 276-315
Explorations, pp. 98-99, 105-116 120, 122-123, 126-127, 130
Workjobs II, pp. 116-117
Developing Number Concepts With Unifix Cubes, pp. 135-145, 148-154, 160

7-1

OBJECTIVE 7-1

To group and write the number of tens and ones

Materials: Cube-A-Links, index cards, TA3 (Graph Paper), TA5 (Place Value Chart)

Grouping Suggestion: pairs

---

1. MOTIVATE AND TEACH

LEARN ABOUT IT

Read the chapter story. Have students count out 24 cubes to show how many animals were going to be at the party. Then have them show how many tens and ones there are. (24; 2 tens, 4 ones) Have students describe what they see on page 137. (Possible answer: a park with people, animals, and trees)

▶ **How could you use cubes to find the number of people in this picture of Ten City?** (Possible answer: Place a cube on each person. Then remove the cubes and group them in tens. Record the number of tens and ones to see how many people there are.)

Have students find the number of dogs and trees in the same way. Record the number of tens and ones in a place value chart on the chalkboard.

▶ **How could you tell whether there are more dogs than people?** (Possible answer: See which has more groups of ten.)

▶ **How can grouping things in tens help you count large numbers of objects?** (Possible answers: It makes it easier to count accurately; you can count more quickly.)

2. CHECK UNDERSTANDING

ERROR ALERT Reversing the position of tens and ones when recording values in a place value chart.

7
Place Value
Numbers to 100

TEACHING OPTIONS

RETEACHING TIPS Draw 32 *X*s on the chalkboard. Have students count the *X*s and circle groups of 10. Directly under the picture, draw a place value chart. Ask students to count the number of tens and write it in the chart. Then have them write the number of ones. Assign Reteaching Supplement 57.

ENRICHMENT Have students make a set of 6 cards with a 2-digit number on each. Have them make a second set of 6 by cutting, coloring, and pasting graph paper tens strips and unit squares to show each number. Shuffle the cards, each take 6, and match pairs of cards by asking for numbers of tens and ones.

...ecording Tens and Ones

...me _____

...ork with a partner. Take
...andfuls of cubes from a bag.
...ake as many tens as you can.
...rite the number of tens and ones.
...nswers may vary. Check students' work.

Tens	Ones
1	3

...2 handfuls

Tens	Ones

2. 3 handfuls

Tens	Ones

3. 4 handfuls

Tens	Ones

...ing groups of ten. Write the number of tens and ones.

Tens	Ones
2	2

5.

Tens	Ones
3	1

Tens	Ones
1	8

7.

Tens	Ones
2	9

...RITE ABOUT IT

Ralph counted his cubes. He had

Ralph's Cubes

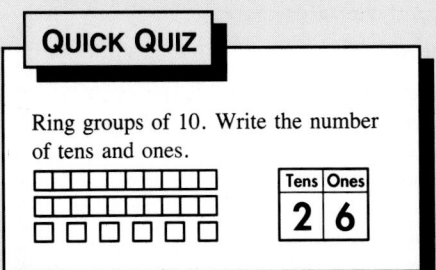

_____ _____ .

3 ___tens___ and 4 ___ones___ .

---

3. PRACTICE AND APPLY

Basic	All
Average	All
Extended	All

PRACTICE

Will everyone's answers be the same for Exercises 1-3? (No, because everyone will be using a different number of cubes.) *How do you record the numbers of tens and ones in Exercises 4-7?* (Count groups of 10 and write that number under tens. Repeat for ones.)

APPLY

▶ **Will the number of tens get smaller or larger as you do Exercises 1-3? Why?** (Possible answer: larger, because you will be counting a larger number of cubes in each exercise)

▶ **What is the largest number you can have in the ones column? Why?** (Possible answer: 9, because the next number would be 10, and you would record it as 1 ten in the tens column)

WRITE ABOUT IT ▶ **Explain what you will write on the lines in Exercise 8.** (Possible answer: words that describe how the cubes in the picture are grouped)

7-1

...LOSE AND ASSESS

...HOW WHAT YOU KNOW

...ave pairs of students draw pictures ...f a number of like objects or ...nimals. Then have them exchange ...apers and place a cube on each item ...s they count it. Ask students to group ...e cubes in tens and ones and record ...e number on a place value chart. If ...ere is not enough room for cubes on ...e picture, have students draw circles ...round groups of 10.

QUICK QUIZ

Ring groups of 10. Write the number of tens and ones.

Tens	Ones
2	6

Modeling Tens and Ones

OBJECTIVE 7-2   To model tens and ones

PREBOOK ACTIVITIES

Draw the following on the chalkboard. Have students tell how many tens and how many ones are in each picture.

1. ▯▯▯▯▯▯▯ ▯▯▯▯▯▯▯ ▯ ▯ ▯ ▯ ▯ (2 tens, 5 ones)
2. ▯▯▯▯▯▯▯ ▯▯▯▯▯▯▯ ▯▯▯▯▯▯▯
   ▯▯▯▯▯▯▯ ▯ ▯ ▯ ▯ ▯ ▯ ▯ (4 tens, 7 ones)
3. ▯▯▯▯▯▯▯ ▯▯▯▯▯▯▯ ▯▯▯▯▯▯▯ ▯ (3 tens, 1 one)

PRIOR KNOWLEDGE

Display in a container a large quantity of small objects, such as cubes, counters, or paper clips. *What are some of the ways you could group these?* (Possible answers: by twos, fives, or tens) *If you wanted to count all the objects, what do you think would be the best way to group them? Why?* (Possible answer: Group by tens, because then it would be easier to count how many tens and extras you have.) *What are some things you might want to group by tens?* (Possible answers: baseball cards, marbles, pennies)

COMMUNICATION

Reading in Math   Write the words **ten, tens,** and **ones** and the following sentences on the chalkboard. Have students copy them in their Math Journals, write the word (or words) that completes each sentence and read the sentence aloud.

1. You can make a ten with (ten) ones.
2. You can show 7 (ones) with 7 cubes.
3. If you have 9 cubes, you cannot make any (tens) .
4. Ten (ones) is the same as one (ten) .
5. You can group 23 beads as 2 (tens) and 3 (ones) .

Materials: a large number of counters; scooping utensils, suc as plastic cups; TA 5 (Place Value Chart)
Alternative Materials: beans, large beads
Grouping Suggestion: cooperative learning groups of 3
Provide each group with a box or bag of up to 90 objects, a scooping utensil, and a place value chart. Have students take turns at these tasks: scooping 1, 2, or 3 scoopfuls of objects; grouping the objects in tens and ones; and recording the number of tens and ones on the chart. Tell students that all group members should check the grouping and recording and give their ideas. After students have completed several rounds show on the chalkboard a tens and ones chart with an amount such as 3 tens and 6 ones. Ask the groups to show that amount, grouping their objects by tens and ones. Have student check the number by counting.

CONNECTIONS   Use these anytime.

Problem of the Day

Using a Picture   Katie baked these muffins:

🧁🧁🧁🧁🧁🧁🧁🧁 🧁🧁
🧁🧁🧁🧁🧁🧁🧁🧁 🧁🧁

How many muffins would Katie have left if she gave away 1 group of ten? Write the amount of tens and ones. (1 ten and 4 ones)

Math Connection

Measurement   Make a chain of 10 paper clips. Use your chain and extra single clips to measure the length of a desk or table in the classroom. How many tens? How many ones? How many altogether?

Creative Thinking

Design   Enter the Ten City Art Show. Use beads, beans, pasta, buttons, and other small objects. Make groups of tens and ones. Glue them on a large piece of paper. Display your collage on a wall in the classroom.

CLASSWORK AND HOMEWORK SUPPLEMENTS

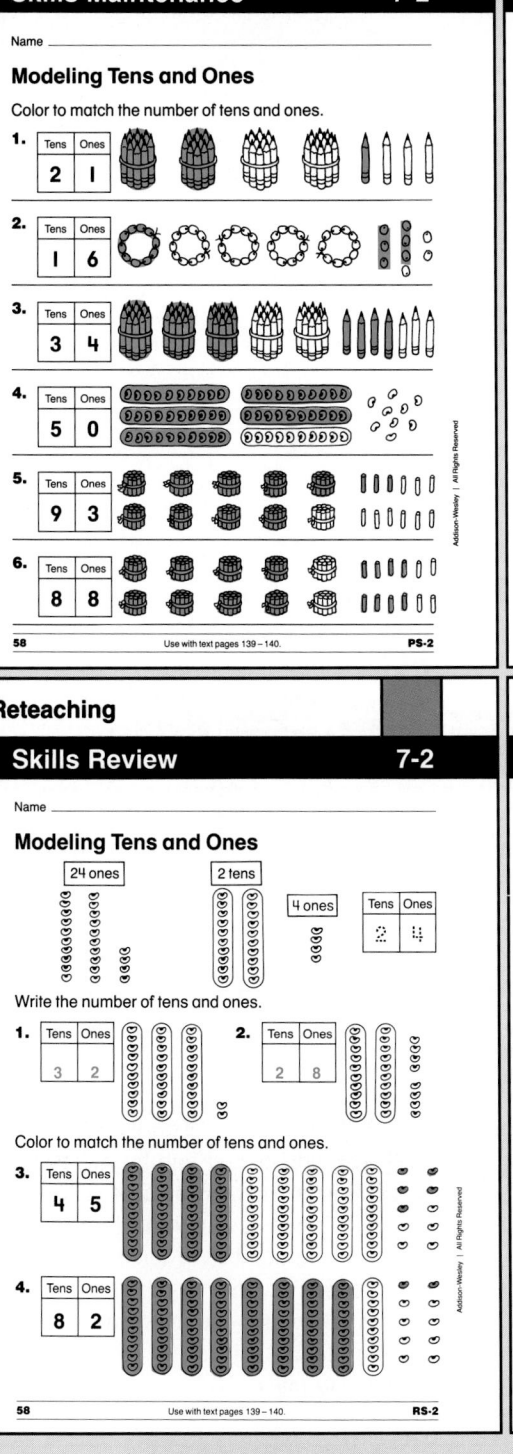

Practice

Skills Maintenance   7-2

Name _____

Modeling Tens and Ones

Color to match the number of tens and ones.

1. Tens 2 Ones 1
2. Tens 1 Ones 6
3. Tens 3 Ones 4
4. Tens 5 Ones 0
5. Tens 9 Ones 3
6. Tens 8 Ones 8

58   Use with text pages 139–140.   PS-2

Reteaching

Skills Review   7-2

Name _____

Modeling Tens and Ones

24 ones   2 tens   4 ones   Tens Ones

Write the number of tens and ones.

1. Tens 3 Ones 2   2. Tens 2 Ones 8

Color to match the number of tens and ones.

3. Tens 4 Ones 5
4. Tens 8 Ones 2

58   Use with text pages 139–140.   RS-2

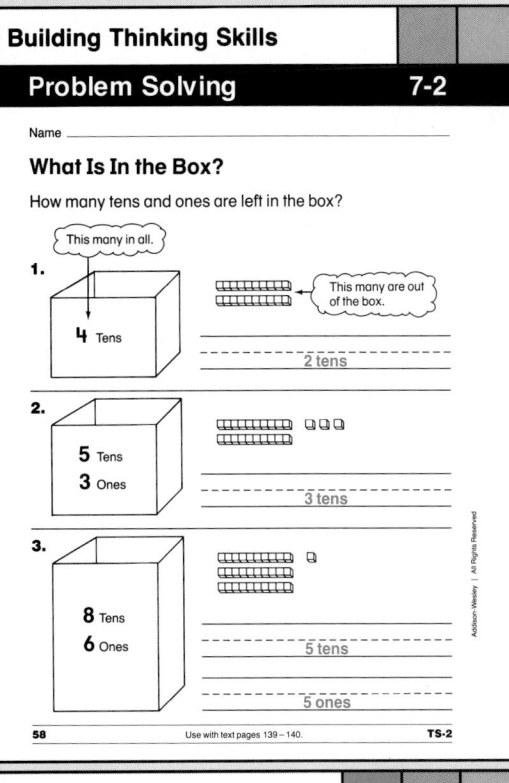

Building Thinking Skills

Problem Solving   7-2

Name _____

What Is In the Box?

How many tens and ones are left in the box?

This many in all.

1. 4 Tens   This many are out of the box.
_____ 2 tens

2. 5 Tens 3 Ones
_____ 3 tens

3. 8 Tens 6 Ones
_____ 5 tens
_____ 5 ones

58   Use with text pages 139–140.   TS-2

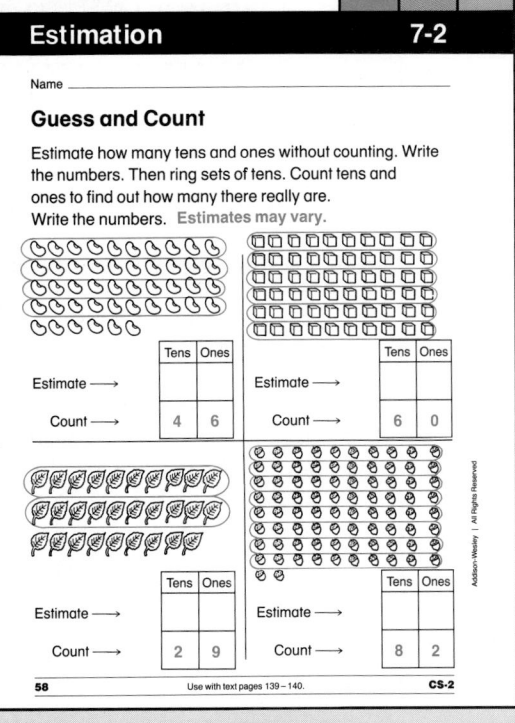

Challenges

Estimation   7-2

Name _____

Guess and Count

Estimate how many tens and ones without counting. Write the numbers. Then ring sets of tens. Count tens and ones to find out how many there really are.
Write the numbers. **Estimates may vary.**

Estimate ⟶   Count ⟶ Tens 4 Ones 6

Estimate ⟶   Count ⟶ Tens 6 Ones 0

Estimate ⟶   Count ⟶ Tens 2 Ones 9

Estimate ⟶   Count ⟶ Tens 8 Ones 2

58   Use with text pages 139–140.   CS-2

OPTIONS FOR INDIVIDUAL NEEDS

Basic

Exercises All

Supplements
Reteaching 58 or
Practice 58
Challenges 58

Average

Exercises All

Supplements
Practice 58
Challenges 58 or
Thinking Skills 58

Extended

Exercises All

Supplements
Challenges 58
Thinking Skills 58

Other Resources:
Math in Stride, pp. 71-76
Mathematics Their Way, pp. 276-308
Explorations, pp. 105-116, 120, 122-123, 126-127, 130
Workjobs II, pp. 116-117
Developing Number Concepts With Unifix Cubes, pp. 135, 145, 148-154, 160

7-2

Chapter 7 Lesson 2   **139B**

OBJECTIVE 7-2
To model tens and ones

> **Materials:** TA 5 (Place Value Chart)
> 1-in. by 10-in. paper strips and strips of
> tagboard; base-ten blocks
>
> **Grouping Suggestions:** individual
> work, pairs

1. MOTIVATE AND TEACH

LEARN ABOUT IT

Discuss the model at the top of page
139.
▶ **How will you know which groups
of tens and ones to paste next to the
place value chart?** (Match the picture
of the tens to the tens digit; match the
picture of the ones to the ones digit.)
▶ **What is the least number of ones
you can have in the ones box of your
place value chart?** (0)
▶ **What is the greatest number of
ones you can have in the ones box?
Why?** (9; if you have more than 9 ones,
you would have a ten.)
▶ **What is the least number of tens
you can have in the tens box?** (0)
▶ **Predict what you think will be the
greatest number of tens you can
have in the tens box.** (9)
▶ **Why do you think we group and
count numbers by tens?** (Possible
answer: because tens are easy to use;
because people probably started counting
with their 10 fingers)

2. CHECK UNDERSTANDING

ERROR ALERT Not understanding
the concept of 10 ones being joined to
make 1 ten.

Name _____

Modeling Tens and Ones

Look at the tens and ones
numbers in the boxes.
Cut and paste to match.

1.

Tens	Ones
1	8

Paste here.
1 ten / 8 ones

2.

Tens	Ones
6	0

Paste here.
6 tens / 0 ones

3.

Tens	One
4	7

Paste here.
4 tens / 7 one

4.

Tens	Ones
3	4

Paste here.
3 tens / 4 ones

5.

Tens	Ones
5	2

Paste here.
5 tens / 2 ones

6.

Tens	Ones
2	6

Paste here.
2 tens / 6 ones

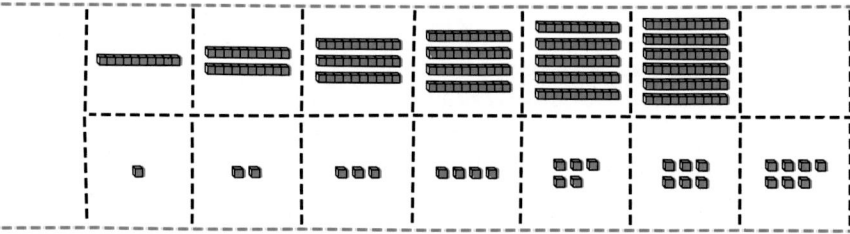

Chapter 7   (one hundred thirty-nine)

TEACHING OPTIONS

RETEACHING TIPS Cut paper
strips into individual squares and
have students paste 10 of them onto
strips of tagboard to make 1 ten.
Then have them match the ten-strips
and leftover squares to numbers
similar to those on page 139. Assign
Reteaching Supplement 58.

ENRICHMENT **Family Math**
Have students and family members
fill a jar with small objects. They
count by tens as they fill the jar and
record the number of tens. When no
more tens fit, they count as they add
ones. Bring the jars to school and
have the class guess the number of
tens and ones.

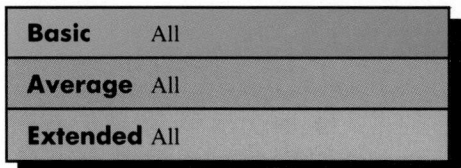

...lor to match the number of tens and ones.

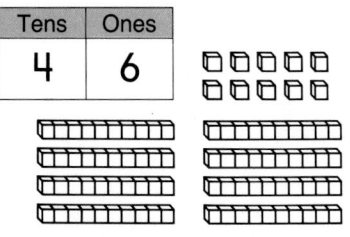

2.

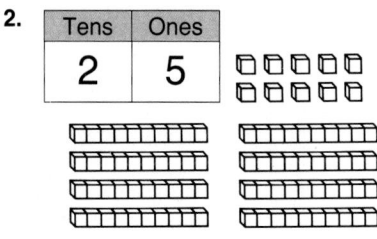

Color 4 tens and 6 ones.

Color 2 tens and 5 ones.

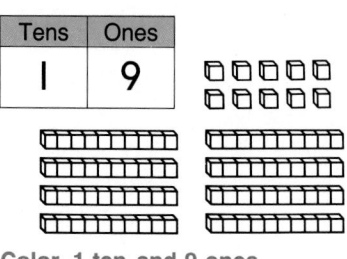

4.

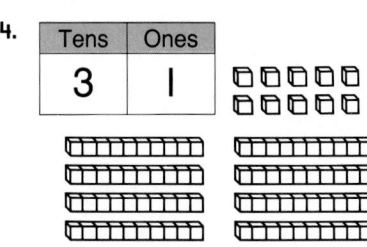

Color 1 ten and 9 ones.

Color 3 tens and 1 one.

Tens	Ones
	8

6.

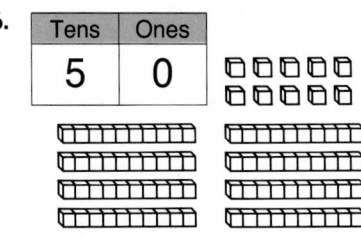

Color 8 ones.

Color 5 tens.

3. PRACTICE AND APPLY

Basic	All
Average	All
Extended	All

PRACTICE

How will you show the tens and ones in Exercise 1 on page 140? (Color 4 tens and 6 ones to match the number of tens and ones in the box.)

APPLY

▶ **What would happen in Ten City if a family already had 4 dogs and one of the dogs had 8 puppies? How would you group the new amount of dogs in tens and ones? Draw a picture.** (1 ten, 2 ones; 12 dogs)

▶ **Put these amounts in order, from least to greatest: 3 tens 4 ones, 7 tens 2 ones, 5 tens 1 one.** (3 tens 4 ones, 5 tens 1 one, 7 tens 2 ones)

7-2

...LOSE AND ASSESS

...HOW WHAT YOU KNOW

...view with students the chapter
...ry, *The Surprise*. Ask students to
...k at the story picture and then use
...s and ones blocks to show how
...any fish Kerry bought. (53) *Suppose
...rry only bought 37 fish. How would
...u show that number with your
...cks?*

QUICK QUIZ

Show the following with circles.
1. 3 tens 3 ones   **2.** 2 tens 8 ones
3. 0 tens 1 one   **4.** 1 ten 6 ones
5. 4 tens 9 ones   **6.** 2 tens 0 ones

LESSON OPTIONS 7-3

Modeling and Writing Decade Numbers

OBJECTIVE 7-3   To model and write decade numbers

PREBOOK ACTIVITIES

PRIOR KNOWLEDGE

Ask students to count to 90 in as many different ways as they know how. (by 1s, 2s, 5s, 10s) *Which way took the longest? Which was fastest? Which was hardest? Which was easiest? Which was the most fun?*

Have students count off around the room by 10s, starting again with 10 after reaching 90. After several rounds, randomly call out a decade number and have students say the next decade number in the count.

COMMUNICATION

Reading and Discussing Math   Write the decade numbers 10–90 in a column on the chalkboard. Next to each number, write the decade name. Point to each name and have students read it aloud with you. Ask volunteers to use each name in a sentence, starting with **ten.** Continue in this order through **ninety.** Then extend the activity to a cumulative story. Begin by saying, *I went to the beach and took ten beachballs.* Have a student repeat your sentence and add a phrase with **twenty,** such as *I went to the beach and took ten beachballs and twenty umbrellas.* Students continue until they reach ninety.

EXPLORE AND CONNECT

Materials: 3 base-ten blocks and 20 unit blocks for each student
Grouping Suggestion: small groups
Have each student make a row of 10 unit blocks and have group members check each other's work. Ask them to compare their rows of unit blocks with 1 base-ten block. *What do you notice?* (The 10 unit blocks and the base-ten block are the same length.) *How many ones does the ten-block stand for?* (10) Have them make a second row with 10 more unit blocks and compare the 2 rows to 2 base-ten blocks. *How many ones do 2 tens stand for?* (20) Repeat for 30. *Can you tell, without using rows of unit blocks, how many ones 4 tens stand for?* (40) Continue through 90, and have groups check with base-ten blocks.

Encourage students to ask for each other's help and ideas.

CONNECTIONS   Use these anytime.

Problem of the Day

How Old Is She?   David's grandmother is having a birthday. She asks David to guess her age and gives him these clues: My age is a tens number. It is more than 50 and less than 70. How old is David's grandmother? (60)

Counting Patterns

Counting by Tens   Fill in the missing numbers:
1. 10, 20, _(30)_, 40, 50, 60, _(70)_
2. 20, 40, 60, _(80)_
3. 90, 80, _(70)_, 60, _(50)_, 40
4. 90, 70, _(50)_, 30, _(10)_

Creative Thinking

Stretch Your Mind   If 4 + 4 = 8, how much do you think 40 + 40 equals? How much do you think 40 + 50 equals? (80; 90)

CLASSWORK AND HOMEWORK SUPPLEMENTS

Basic

Exercises All

Supplements
Reteaching 59 or
Practice 59
Thinking Skills 59

Average

Exercises All

Supplements
Practice 59
Challenges 59 or
Thinking Skills 59

Extended

Exercises All

Supplements
Challenges 59
Thinking Skills 59

Practice

Reading Math   7-3

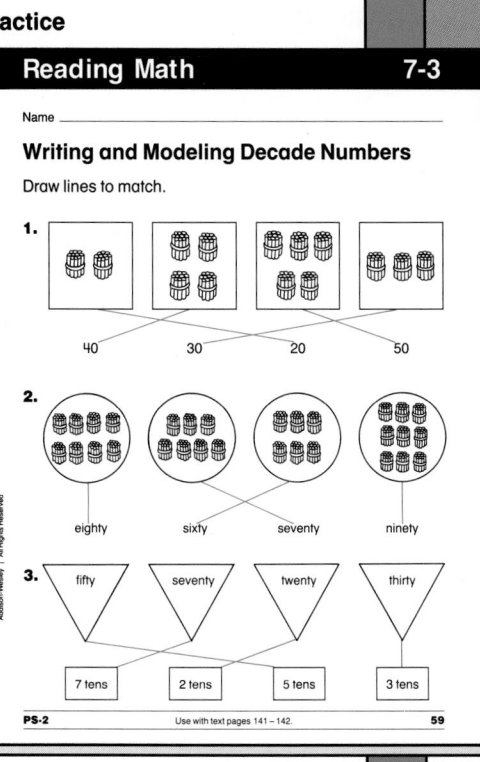

Name _____

Writing and Modeling Decade Numbers
Draw lines to match.

1.
40   30   20   50

2.
eighty   sixty   seventy   ninety

3.
fifty   seventy   twenty   thirty

7 tens   2 tens   5 tens   3 tens

PS-2   Use with text pages 141–142.   59

Building Thinking Skills

Number Sense   7-3

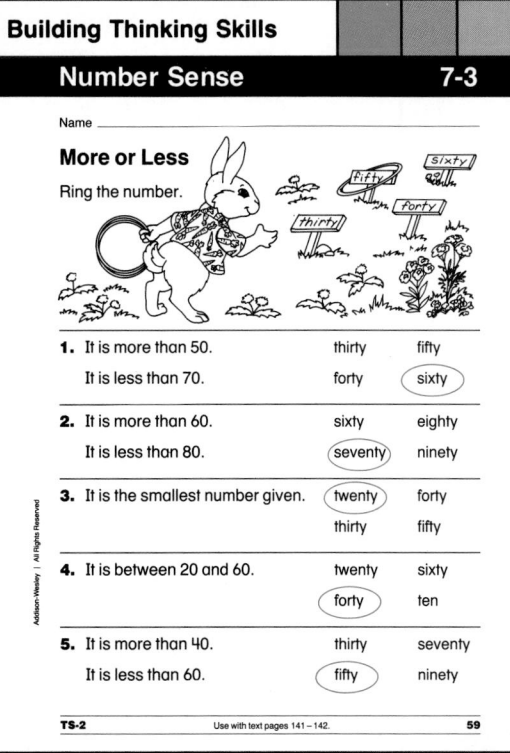

Name _____

More or Less
Ring the number.

1. It is more than 50.   thirty   fifty
   It is less than 70.   forty   (sixty)

2. It is more than 60.   sixty   eighty
   It is less than 80.   (seventy) ninety

3. It is the smallest number given.   (twenty)   forty
                                       thirty   fifty

4. It is between 20 and 60.   twenty   sixty
                               (forty)   ten

5. It is more than 40.   thirty   seventy
   It is less than 60.   (fifty)   ninety

TS-2   Use with text pages 141–142.   59

Reteaching

Writing Math   7-3

Name _____

Modeling and Writing Decade Numbers

2 tens = 20
twenty

Write how many tens. Then write the number.

1. 3 tens
    30
    thirty

2. 4 tens
    40
    forty

3. 5 tens
    50
    fifty

4. 8 tens
    80
    eighty

5. Write the missing numbers.
   Then say all the numbers.

20	**30**	40	**50**	60	70	**80**	90
twenty	thirty	forty	fifty	sixty	seventy	eighty	ninety

RS-2   Use with text pages 141–142.   59

Challenges

Data Analysis   7-3

Name _____

On Target
Each ★ shows where a dart hit.
Write the score.
Then write the word name.

1. 20
    twenty

2. 30
    thirty

3. 10
    ten

4. 40
    forty

Make ★s to show the score.

5. 7 asterisks
    70

6. 6 asterisks
    60

CS-2   Use with text pages 141–142.   59

Other Resources:
Math in Stride, pp. 71-76
Mathematics Their Way, pp. 305-306, 321
Explorations, pp. 105-116, 120, 122-123, 126-127, 130
Workjobs II, pp. 116-117
Developing Number Concepts With Unifix Cubes, pp. 153, 176-177
Mathematics Book A, pp. 5-6

7-3

LESSON PLAN 7-3

OBJECTIVE 7-3
To model and write decade numbers

Materials: 10 base-ten blocks for each group, 10-sticks, spinners labeled 0-3 and 3-6

Grouping Suggestions: small groups, pairs

1. MOTIVATE AND TEACH

LEARN ABOUT IT

On the chalkboard, write 10, 20, and 30. Have students count unit blocks to match each number. Then have them match the groups of unit blocks to the appropriate number of tens blocks. *How many unit blocks are the same as two tens blocks?* (20) *as 3 tens blocks?* (30) Have groups of students divide the tasks for page 141.

▶ **How are all the decade numbers alike?** (They all have zero in the ones place.)

▶ **If you place all the number cards in order, what do you notice about the tens digits?** (Possible answer: Each is 1 greater than the one before it.)

▶ **If the trucking company delivered 2 tens in the morning and 4 tens in the afternoon, how many did it deliver in all? Say the number.** (6 tens; sixty)

▶ **What is the greatest number of blocks the truck can deliver? the least?** (90; 10)

▶ **What would you do if you were in charge of the trucking company and received shipments that had leftover blocks?** (Possible answer: Save them in a pile and ship them when there are 10.)

2. CHECK UNDERSTANDING

ERROR ALERT Not understanding that each of the decade numbers stands for a certain number of tens.

Name _____

Modeling and Writing Decade Numbers

Work in a group. Cut out the number cards. Put a card on the truck. Show the number with blocks on the loading dock. Write the number in the box.

Check students' work.

1. `20`   2. ☐   3. ☐

4. ☐   5. ☐   6. ☐

7. ☐   8. ☐   9. ☐

2 tens
0 ones
20

twenty
20

Loading Dock

All rights reserved. Addison-Wesley

10. Mix up the cards. Place the colored side up. Take turns reading the numbers. Check by turning the cards over.

ten	twenty	thirty	forty	fifty	sixty	seventy	eighty
10	20	30	40	50	60	70	80

Chapter 7   (one hundred forty-one)

TEACHING OPTIONS

RETEACHING TIPS Have each student count the units on a 10-stick. Identify this number as 1 *ten*. Repeat with 2 sticks identified as 2 tens and ask what number we call that amount. (*twenty*) Continue counting 10s to 90. Assign Reteaching Supplement 59.

ENRICHMENT Use two spinners, one labeled 0-3 and the other 3-6, each number standing for groups of 10. Pairs of students spin to find the number of tens to add. They record the number of tens on each spinner, add them, and write the word name for the total.

ıt number cards on the trucks. Show
ow many blocks Sid will load onto each
ıck. Check by counting. Then paste.

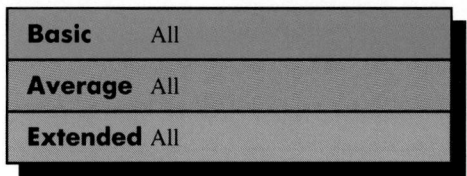

2.

4.

6.

rite the word name.

40 _____ forty _____

8. 70 _____ seventy _____

80	70	60	50	40	30	20	10

(one hundred forty-two)   Chapter 7

---

3. PRACTICE AND APPLY

Basic	All
Average	All
Extended	All

PRACTICE

What is a quick way to count how many blocks Sid will load on the truck? (Count by 10s.)

APPLY

▶ **Write the word names of 2 numbers that are larger than 50.**
(Possible answers: any of these numbers: sixty, seventy, eighty, ninety)

▶ **How are those word names like the number of tens they stand for?**
(They begin with the words *six, seven, eight,* and *nine.*)

▶ **How are the word names for 20, 30, 40, and 50 different from the number of tens they stand for?**
(Possible answer: *Twenty, thirty, forty,* and *fifty* do not use the exact number name at the beginning of the word even though some sound almost the same.)

7-3

LOSE AND ASSESS

RITE WHAT YOU KNOW Ask
dents to think about some of the
ngs Kerry bought in the chapter
ry. *Use your blocks to show how
ny party hats Kerry bought. Then
ite that number.* (20) *Use your
ocks to show how many balloons
rry bought. Then write that
mber.* (10)

QUICK QUIZ

Complete.
eighty = (8) tens   (thirty) = 3 tens
fifty = (5) tens   (ninety) = 9 tens
forty = (4) tens   ten = (1) ten

Modeling and Writing 2-Digit Numbers

OBJECTIVE 7-4   To model and write 2-digit numbers

PREBOOK ACTIVITIES

QUICK REVIEW

How many tens and ones are there?

(2 tens, 5 ones) (4 tens, 1 one) (3 tens, 6 ones) (5 tens, 5 ones)

PRIOR KNOWLEDGE

Ask students to find examples of 2-digit numbers in the classroom—for example, calendar dates, clock numbers, thermometer numbers, and page numbers. Then model a 2-digit number with classroom objects. For example, gather 23 books and write the number on the chalkboard. Display the books as 2 stacks of ten and 3 single books. Ask students how many tens and ones there are and write *2 tens* and *3 ones* on the board. Have students check that the number of tens matches the first digit in the number on the board and that the number of ones matches the second digit.

COMMUNICATION

Listening in Math   Read the following story. Have students raise their hands whenever they hear a decade number.
On March 10, our class held a turtle race. Twenty turtles entered. The class sold 40 tickets ahead of time, and 30 other people bought tickets at the door. But we had only 60 chairs, so we had to find 10 more. Finally, all 70 people were seated. The turtle race began—and turtle number 20 won!

EXPLORE AND CONNECT

Materials: base-ten blocks, TA 5 (Place Value Charts)
Grouping Suggestion: small groups
Have group members take turns placing 1-9 tens blocks on the **Tens** side of a place value chart and 1-9 unit blocks on the **Ones** side. Have them count the blocks on each side and record the number of tens and ones on a separate sheet of paper. Then ask students to write the 2-digit number. Provide model on the chalkboard:

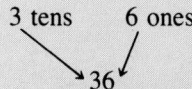

3 tens   6 ones
36

To help students read the 2-digit numbers they model, sugges this strategy: Count the tens out loud: *ten, twenty, thirty*. The count the ones: *one, two, three, four, five, six. The number i thirty-six.*

CONNECTIONS   Use these anytime.

Problem of the Day

What is the Question?   Tom was making fruit salad. He had 22 pieces of apple, 11 orange sections, and 32 grapes. What math questions might you ask about what Tom is doing? (Possible answers: How many pieces of fruit did Tom have altogether? Which fruit did Tom have most of? least of? How many more grapes than orange sections were there?)

Number Sense

Mental Math   Work with a partner and a pack of number cards 1–9. Each choose a card. Use the two cards to make the greatest 2-digit number you can. Then make the least 2-digit number. For example, if you picked 2 and 4, what is the greatest number you can make? (42) the least number? (24) Explain why. (4 tens are more than 2 tens.)

Counting Patterns

Using a Calculator   Count on from a number as you press keys on a calculator. For example, to count on from 20 by 1s press the following:

Try counting by 2s. Press the following:

CLASSWORK AND HOMEWORK SUPPLEMENTS

Practice

Manipulatives 7-4

Name

Writing and Modeling 2-Digit Numbers

Show the same number in a different way.
Make as many tens as you can.
Use place-value blocks to help.

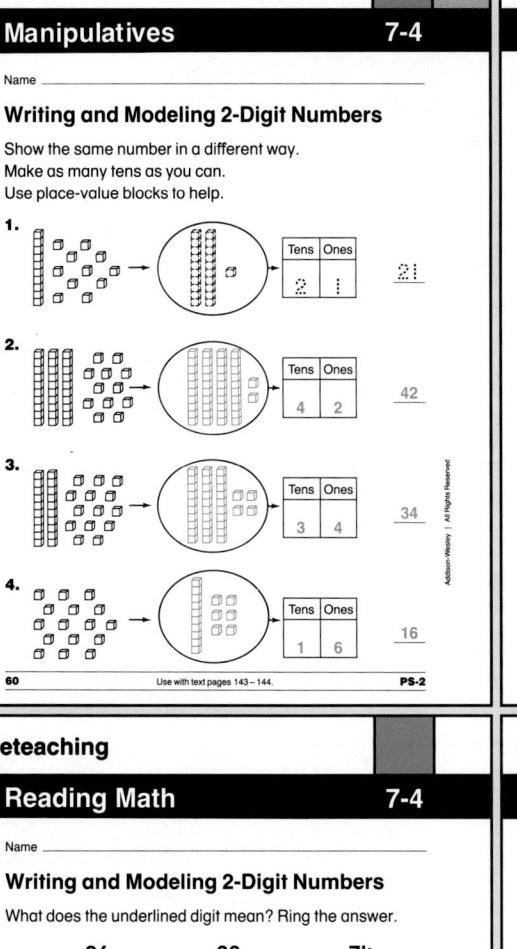

1. | Tens | Ones |
   | 2 | 1 | → 21

2. | Tens | Ones |
   | 4 | 2 | 42

3. | Tens | Ones |
   | 3 | 4 | 34

4. | Tens | Ones |
   | 1 | 6 | 16

60   Use with text pages 143–144.   PS-2

Building Thinking Skills

Number Sense 7-4

Name

Make a New Number

1. How many 2-digit numbers can you make with these cards?
   Do not use doubles (22, 55, 44).

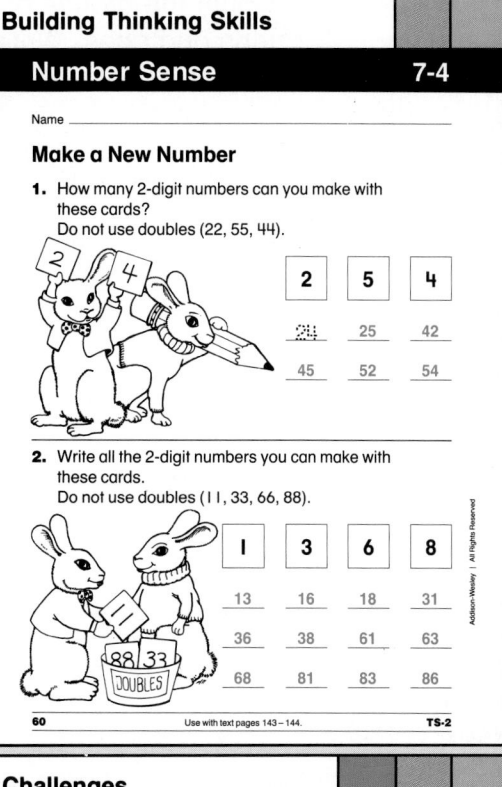

| 2 | 5 | 4 |

24   25   42
45   52   54

2. Write all the 2-digit numbers you can make with these cards.
   Do not use doubles (11, 33, 66, 88).

| 1 | 3 | 6 | 8 |

13   16   18   31
36   38   61   63
68   81   83   86

60   Use with text pages 143–144.   TS-2

Reteaching

Reading Math 7-4

Name

Writing and Modeling 2-Digit Numbers

What does the underlined digit mean? Ring the answer.

1. **2**6   **3**8   **7**4
   (2 tens) 2 ones (3 tens) 3 ones   4 tens (4 ones)

2. 8**9**   **4**7   6**1**
   9 tens (9 ones) (4 tens) 4 ones   1 ten (1 one)

How many are there?

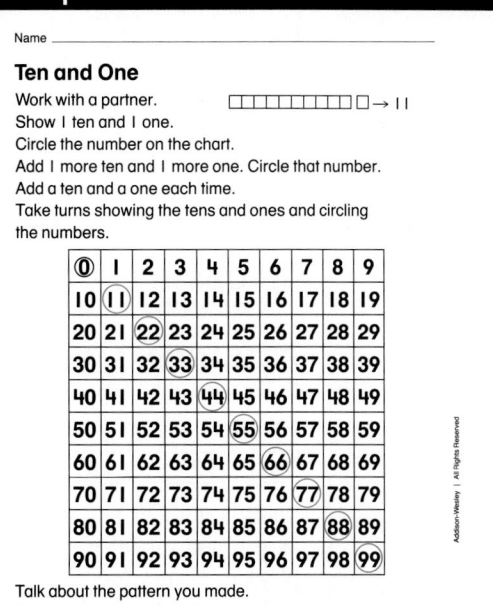

3. ___ tens   ___ ones   ___ in all   (3 tens, 6 ones, 36 in all)

4. 2 tens   4 ones   24 in all

5. 1 tens   8 ones   18 in all

6. 2 tens   5 ones   25 in all

60   Use with text pages 143–144.   RS-2

Challenges

Cooperative Activities 7-4

Name

Ten and One

Work with a partner.   ⬚⬚⬚⬚⬚⬚⬚⬚⬚⬚⬚ → 11

Show 1 ten and 1 one.
Circle the number on the chart.
Add 1 more ten and 1 more one. Circle that number.
Add a ten and a one each time.
Take turns showing the tens and ones and circling the numbers.

⓪	1	2	3	4	5	6	7	8	9
10	⑪	12	13	14	15	16	17	18	19
20	21	㉒	23	24	25	26	27	28	29
30	31	32	㉝	34	35	36	37	38	39
40	41	42	43	㊹	45	46	47	48	49
50	51	52	53	54	㊺	56	57	58	59
60	61	62	63	64	65	㊏	67	68	69
70	71	72	73	74	75	76	㊆	78	79
80	81	82	83	84	85	86	87	㊚	89
90	91	92	93	94	95	96	97	98	㊾

Talk about the pattern you made.
Play again. Start with a different number.

60   Use with text pages 143–144.   CS-2

OPTIONS FOR INDIVIDUAL NEEDS

Basic

Exercises All

Supplements
Reteaching 60 or
Practice 60
Challenges 60

Average

Exercises All

Supplements
Practice 60
Challenges 60 or
Thinking Skills 60

Extended

Exercises All

Supplements
Challenges 60
Thinking Skills 60

Other Resources:
Math in Stride, pp. 71-76, 140
Mathematics Their Way, pp. 305-306
Explorations, pp. 105-116, 120, 122-123, 126-127, 130
Workjobs II, pp. 116-117
Developing Number Concepts With Unifix Cubes, pp. 162-163, 176-177

7-4

OBJECTIVE 7-4
To model and write 2-digit numbers

Materials: base-ten blocks, blank cards, TA 6 (Numbered Hundred Chart)

1. MOTIVATE AND TEACH

LEARN ABOUT IT

Have students use base-ten blocks to model 3 tens and 2 ones, then have them say the number aloud. Direct students' attention to Exercise 1. *How many rolls are there?* (32). *How can you tell which rolls are tens and which are ones?* (Tens are in boxes and ones are single rolls.)

▶ **Does it matter on which side of the picture the boxes of ten rolls and the single rolls are on? Why?** (No; you can tell from the picture which are groups of ten and which are ones.)

▶ **When you write the number of rolls as a 2-digit number, does it matter where you write the number of tens and the number of ones? Explain your answer.** (Possible answer: Yes; in a 2-digit number, the left place is always for tens and the right place is for ones; if you write the tens and ones in the wrong places, you will write a different number.)

2. CHECK UNDERSTANDING

ERROR ALERT Counting the rolls individually instead of in groups of ten and ones. In Exercises 4 and 5, reversing the tens and ones digits.

Name _____

Modeling and Writing 2-Digit Numbers

Look at the rolls people bought at the bakery. Count the groups of tens and ones. Write how many.

1. `32`

2. `46`

3. `67`

4. `26`

5. `19`

6. `60`

Chapter 7

(one hundred forty-three)

TEACHING OPTIONS

RETEACHING TIPS Make 2-digit number cards alternating red and black for the 2 digits.

`7 3`   `24`   `5 8`   `36`   `1 9`

Show a number and have students read it and model it with base-ten blocks. Assign Reteaching Supplement 60.

COMPUTER Arithmetic Critters, MECC © 1986 For use with all levels of students. In *Egg Plant*, students practice writing numbers 1-99 by counting the number of eggs that come out of the factory on trucks in groups of tens. The recommended lesson takes 15 minutes.

he numbers tell how many rolls
ome people ordered from the
akery. Color tens and ones
show each number.

24

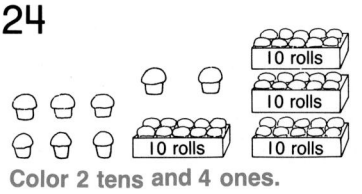

Color 2 tens and 4 ones.

2. 16

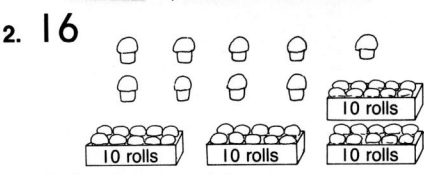

Color 1 ten and 6 ones.

30

Color 3 tens.

4. 45

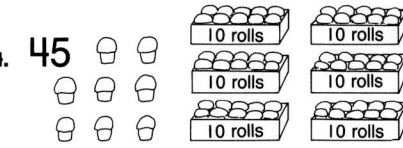

Color 4 tens and 5 ones.

MIDCHAPTER REVIEW/QUIZ

Vrite the number of tens and ones.

Tens	Ones
2	3

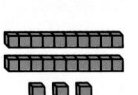

2.

Tens	Ones
4	6

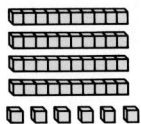

Match.

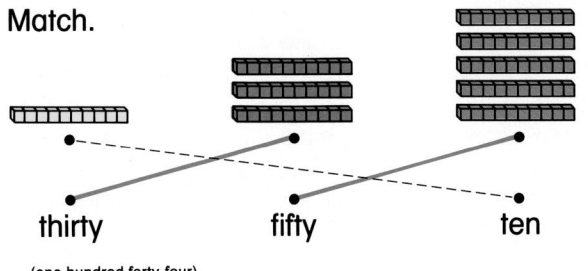

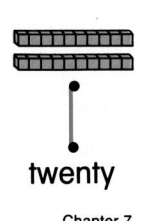

thirty   fifty   ten   twenty

---

3. PRACTICE AND APPLY

Basic	All, Midchapter Review/Quiz
Average	All, Midchapter Review/Quiz
Extended	All, Midchapter Review/Quiz

PRACTICE

How will you do Exercises 1-4 on page 144? (Read the number, then color tens and ones to match the number.) Students may use blocks to model the number before they color the corresponding number of rolls.

APPLY

▶ **Suppose you had to write 24, 16, 30, and 45 in order from least to greatest, but you could only look at one digit in each number. Which digit should you look at?** (the tens digit)

MIDCHAPTER REVIEW/QUIZ

ITEM ANALYSIS The table correlates the Midchapter Review/Quiz with lesson objectives.

Items	Objectives
1, 2	7-1
3	7-3

7-4

CLOSE AND ASSESS

WRITE WHAT YOU KNOW

eview with students the chapter
ory, *The Surprise*. Have students
ork in small groups and use base-ten
ocks to model how many rolls Kerry
ught. Then have them write the
digit number. (38) Have students act
t selling different numbers of rolls
d model and write these numbers.

QUICK QUIZ

Write these 2-digit numbers:
7 tens 1 one (71)   4 tens 5 ones (45)
8 tens 3 ones (83)   1 ten 8 ones (18)
6 tens 0 ones (60)
2 tens 9 ones (29)

Problem Solving: Understanding the Operation

OBJECTIVE 7-5 To understand the operation of subtraction by comparing

PREBOOK ACTIVITIES

QUICK REVIEW

Circle the number that is greater in each number pair below.

30	(40)	17	(37)	(51)	15
12	(21)	26	(29)	47	(74)
(35)	24	18	(21)	(10)	3
(83)	38	(77)	66	40	(60)
18	(81)	24	(25)	(59)	49

PRIOR KNOWLEDGE

Help students recall what they know about comparing. *I have 3 crayons. You have 10 crayons. How many more crayons do you have? What are you comparing when you ask that question?* (Possible answer: amounts of something; crayons; 10 and 3)

COMMUNICATION

Discussing and Writing Math *Look around the room and name 2 things that we can compare.* (Possible answers: the sizes of 2 students, the number of books on 2 shelves, the number of boys and girls) *What are we doing when we compare 2 things?* (Possible answer: looking at them to see how they are the same or different; seeing which is larger or smaller)

Write **how many more** on the chalkboard and have students read the phrase. Explain that this phrase is often used in story problems to compare 2 numbers in the story. Ask students to write a question about something in the classroom that begins with *How many more . . .* (Possible answer: How many more students are there than teachers?)

EXPLORE AND CONNECT

COOPERATIVE ACTIVITY

Grouping Suggestion: small groups
8 people are cutting lawns. 2 people are trimming trees. How many more people are cutting lawns? _____ more people

TEACHING ACTIONS

 **BEFORE**

▶ **Describe what is going on in the story.** (Possible answer: There are more people cutting lawns than trimming trees.)

▶ **How do the words in the question help you know how to use the data in the story?** (Possible answer: The phrase *how many more* tells me to compare the numbers representing the 2 groups of people.)

 **DURING**

▶ **How do you plan to compare the data in the story?** (Possible answer: To find how many more people are cutting lawns than trimming trees subtract the smaller from the larger number.)

What can you use to solve this problem? (Possible answer: I can show 8 counters of 1 color and 2 counters of another color. To find out how many more, I can match counters from the 2 groups and count how many more of 1 color there are.)

AFTER

▶ **How can you use a model to write a number sentence?** (Possible answer: The number sentence will match the model—8 − 2 = 6.) The answer can be checked by counting the counters that are left. Have students work in small groups using counters to compare the numbers and writing number sentences for stories like the one on this page.

CONNECTIONS Use these anytime.

Problem of the Day

Understanding the Operation
Write a number sentence to tell how many more. Use counters or cubes if you need to.
9 people are in the school library.
4 people are in the principal's office.
How many more people are in the library?
 (9 − 4 = 5) 5 more people

Math Connection

Comparing Compare the number of people in your family to each item below. Would there be enough room for everyone in your family to use each item?
a 5-person tent
a 3-seated bicycle
an 8-person van
a 2-person couch

Minute Math

Number Riddle Read the clues. Answer the riddle.
I am an even nunber.
When you add 2 to me, my sum is between 9 and 11.
How many more than 4 am I? (4)

sing Critical Thinking Skills

• use critical thinking to draw conclusions of quantities

CLASSWORK AND HOMEWORK SUPPLEMENTS

Practice

Problem Solving 7-5

Name _____

Using Critical Thinking

Compare the numbers. Use blocks to help.
Ring **yes** or **no** to answer the question.

1. The parking lot has room for 50 cars. 35 cars are waiting to get in. Will they all fit?

(yes)   no

2. The classroom has 30 chairs. 23 children come in. Will they all have a seat?

(yes)   no

3. The box will hold 30 books. There are 43 books. Will they all fit in the box?

yes   (no)

4. Pam's book holds 50 stickers. Pam has 64 stickers. Will they all fit?

yes   (no)

5. 27 children want juice. There are 30 cups. Are there enough cups?

(yes)   no

6. Craig has 50¢. He wants a toy that costs 72¢. Does he have enough?

yes   (no)

7. Use mental math to solve.
The park has 6 swings. 10 children are waiting to get on. How many will have to wait another turn?

__4__ children

PS-2   Use with text page 146.   61

Building Thinking Skills

Critical Thinking 7-5

Name _____

Packing Up

Mike has sorted his books.
Now he has to pack them up.
Which box should he put each group of books in?
Draw lines to match.   Answers may vary.

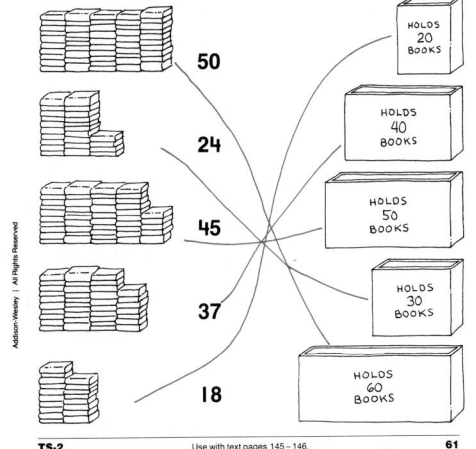

50   24   45   37   18

HOLDS 20 BOOKS
HOLDS 40 BOOKS
HOLDS 50 BOOKS
HOLDS 30 BOOKS
HOLDS 60 BOOKS

TS-2   Use with text pages 145 – 146.   61

Reteaching

Problem Solving 7-5

Name _____

Understanding the Operations

Subtract to find out how may more.

There were 6 black dogs.
There were 2 white dogs.
How many more black dogs were there?

$6 - 2 = 4$

black dogs | white dogs | more black dogs

__4__ more black dogs

Use two colors of cubes. Show the number of dogs.
Write a number sentence to tell how many more.
Then write the answer.

1. 7 dogs are running. 5 dogs are resting. How many more dogs are running?

$7 - 5 = 2$

__2__ more dogs

2. 11 dogs are in the yard. 5 dogs are in the house. How many more dogs are in the yard?

$11 - 5 = 6$

__6__ more dogs

3. 3 dogs won blue ribbons. 12 dogs won red ribbons. How many more dogs won red ribbons?

$12 - 3 = 9$

__9__ more dogs

4. 8 dogs are playing with balls. 12 dogs are playing with sticks. How many more dogs are playing with sticks?

$12 - 8 = 4$

__4__ more dogs

RS-2   Use with text page 145.   61

Challenges

Problem Solving 7-5

Name _____

Write the Data

Read each story.
Fill in the missing data so the story is true.   Answers will vary.
Write the matching subtraction sentence to check.

1. Brian ran ____ miles.

Fran ran ____ miles.
Brian ran 5 more miles than Fran.

_____

2. Lisa jumped ____ feet.

Kevin jumped ____ feet.
Lisa jumped 3 more feet than Kevin.

_____

3. Tom ran ____ laps.

Roz ran ____ laps.
Roz ran 7 more laps than Tom.

_____

4. There were ____ swimming races. There were ____ running races. There were 4 more running races.

_____

5. Our team won ____ blue ribbons and ____ red ribbons. We won 2 more blue ribbons.

_____

6. This year there were ____ events. Next year there will be ____ events. There will be 1 more event next year.

_____

CS-2   Use with text pages 145 – 146.   61

OPTIONS FOR INDIVIDUAL NEEDS

Basic

Exercises All

Supplements
Reteaching 61 or
Practice 61

Average

Exercises All

Supplements
Practice 61
Challenges 61 or
Thinking Skills 61

Extended

Exercises All

Supplements
Challenges 61
Thinking Skills 61

Other Resources:
Math in Stride, pp. 77–78
Mathematics Their Way, pp. 205, 207–208, 307
Explorations, pp. 124–130
Problem-Solving Experiences In Mathematics, pp. 33, 45, 51, 57, 63, 69, 75, 92, 98, 99, 111, 128

7-5

LESSON PLAN 7-5

OBJECTIVE 7-5

To understand the operation of subtraction by comparing; to use critical thinking to draw conclusions based on comparison of quantities

Materials: Cube-A-Links in 2 colors, base-ten blocks

1. MOTIVATE AND TEACH

LEARN ABOUT IT

BEFORE ▶ **How can you determine what you are to do in Exercise 1?** (Possible answer: Read the story and see what the question asks about the data in the story.)

DURING ▶ **How can you show that this problem involves subtraction?** (Possible answer: Show each number in the story with cubes of a different color. Match the cubes in each group one to one. The cubes left over will tell the difference.)

AFTER ▶ **How can you check the answer in Exercise 1?** (Possible answer: First, see if the answer makes sense. Then add to check.)

2. CHECK UNDERSTANDING

ERROR ALERT   Page 145 Not being able to write a number sentence to show how many more.
Page 146 Not being able to visualize whether one number or group is less than another.

Name _____

Problem Solving
Understanding the Operations

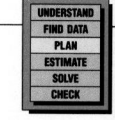

Use two colors of cubes. Show the number of people. Write a number sentence to tell how many more.

1. 8 people are fighting a fire. 3 people are helping traffic move. How many more people are fighting a fire?

   $8 - 3 = 5$ ___ ___5___ more people

2. 7 people are building a road. 12 people are building a school. How many more people are building a school?

   $12 - 7 = 5$ ___ ___5___ more people

3. 14 people are cleaning the street. 5 people are cutting grass. How many more people are cleaning the street?

   $14 - 5 = 9$ ___ ___9___ more people

4. 11 people are driving buses. 3 people are working on the train. How many more people are driving buses?

   $11 - 3 = 8$ ___ ___8___ more people

5. 6 people are sorting letters. 13 people are delivering mail. How many more people are delivering mail?

   $13 - 6 = 7$ ___ ___7___ more people

Chapter 7   (one hundred forty-five)

TEACHING OPTIONS

RETEACHING TIPS Have students count the number of chairs in a row. Ask whether a certain number of students could each take a chair. Then have them sit in the chairs 1 by 1, counting as each sits down. Repeat. For help with how many more, use Reteaching Supplement 61.

COMPUTER   Galaxy Math Facts Game, Random House © 1985 For use with all levels of students. In *Place Value*, students must fill their rockets with fuel, load torpedoes, and energize their space bomb for a journey. Students may set the level of difficulty. The lesson takes 25 minutes to complete.

sing Critical Thinking

se blocks to compare the numbers.
ill everyone fit on the bus?
ng **yes** or **no**.

The bus has room for 50 people. 37 people are waiting to get on it. Will they all fit?   (yes)   no

The bus has room for 50 people. 62 people are waiting to get on it. Will they all fit?   yes   (no)

The bus has room for 40 people. 28 people are waiting to get on it. Will they all fit?   (yes)   no

The bus has room for 50 people. 72 people are waiting to get on it. Will they all fit?   yes   (no)

The bus has room for 40 people. 40 people are waiting to get on it. Will they all fit?   (yes)   no

The bus has room for 50 people. 47 people are waiting to get on it. Will they all fit?   (yes)   no

The bus has room for only 8 people. 10 people are waiting to get on it. How many will have to wait for the next bus? Use mental math.   __2__ people

6   (one hundred forty-six)   Chapter 7

3. PRACTICE AND APPLY

Basic	All
Average	All
Extended	All

How will you show your answer on page 146? (Ring either *yes* or *no*.) *Read Exercise 7. How is it like the problems on page 145?* (It is a *how many more* question when you use subtraction to find the answer.)

▶ **Read Exercise 1. When you compare the 2 numbers, what will you look at first?** (Possible answer: First, look at the tens. Is 5 tens greater than 3 tens? If so, then you know the people will fit on the bus.)

▶ **What will you do if the tens in each number are the same?** (Possible answer: Compare the digits in the ones place of each number to see which number is greater.)

▶ **How might you model these problems?** (Possible answer: Use base-ten blocks to represent the number of people in each situation.)

7-5

LOSE AND ASSESS

RITE WHAT YOU KNOW Tell
e class a *How many more?* story
oblem. Have students draw pictures
show the number sentence for the
oblem. Then ask small groups to
rite critical thinking problems like
e ones on page 146 to match the
eme of your story problem. Solve
e problems as a class.

QUICK QUIZ

Will everyone fit in the room? Ring
yes or *no*.
A room holds 70 people. 49 people
are waiting to get in. Will they all fit?
(yes)   no

Dimes and Pennies

OBJECTIVE 7-6   To count dimes and pennies

PREBOOK ACTIVITIES

QUICK REVIEW

Count the groups of tens and ones. Write how many.

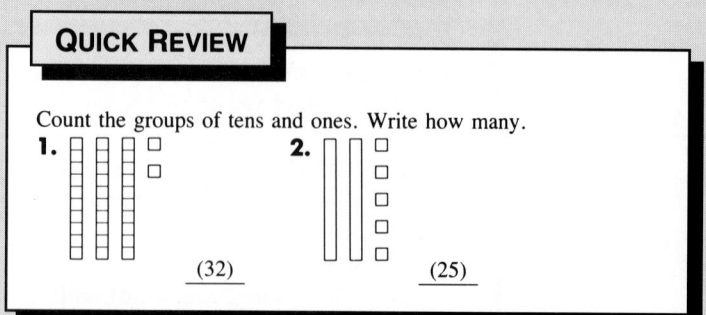

1. ___(32)___   2. ___(25)___

PRIOR KNOWLEDGE

To help students recall grouping tens and ones, draw groups of 10 to 50 dots on the chalkboard. For each set, ask students to estimate the number, then count the dots. Ask volunteers to draw circles around sets of 10 to make counting easier.

COMMUNICATION

Reading and Discussing Math List the following money words on the chalkboard: **dime** and **penny.** Read the words aloud with students. Next, write the amounts 1¢ and 10¢. Ask students to draw lines to match the money amounts to the words.

Encourage students to describe what they know about the words *dime* and *penny.* (Possible answers: The words name kinds of money; a dime is worth 10¢ and a penny is worth 1¢; 10 pennies is the same amount as 1 dime.)

EXPLORE AND CONNECT

Materials: dime and penny punchouts
Grouping Suggestion: pairs
How many ones make 1 ten? (10) *With your penny punchouts show how many pennies equal 1 dime.* Allow students time to group 10 pennies. Then tell students that **dimes** and **pennies** are like tens and ones. *Would a dime stand for tens or ones? Why?* (Possible answer: Tens, because a dime stands for a group of 10 pennies.) Write the amount 12¢ on the chalkboard. *How many tens and ones make up 12¢?* (1 ten, 2 ones) Ask students to model this amount using 1 dime and 2 pennies. Repeat this activity with the amount 37¢. Have partners take turns writing and modeling the amounts with their dime and penny punchouts. Ask the pairs to discuss with the rest of the class any amounts they had trouble showing.

CONNECTIONS   Use these anytime.

Problem of the Day

Logic Use punchout pennies.
   A ride ticket costs 11¢.
   Mike has 6¢.
   Sue has 6¢.
Together, do they have enough money for 1 ticket? Explain. (Yes; They have 12¢, and the ticket costs 11¢.)

Life Skills

Careers You are a florist. You need to plant 33 flowers. Each pot holds 10 flowers. Draw a picture to show how many pots you can fill with flowers. Do you have any flowers left over? (3 pots, 3 flowers left over)

Mental Math

Jumping Tens As I say a number, listen for the number in the tens place. Then jump in place that many times.
   54   (jump 5 times)
   17   (jump 1 time)
   21   (jump 2 times)
   37   (jump 3 times)
   40   (jump 4 times)
   11   (jump 1 time)

CLASSWORK AND HOMEWORK SUPPLEMENTS

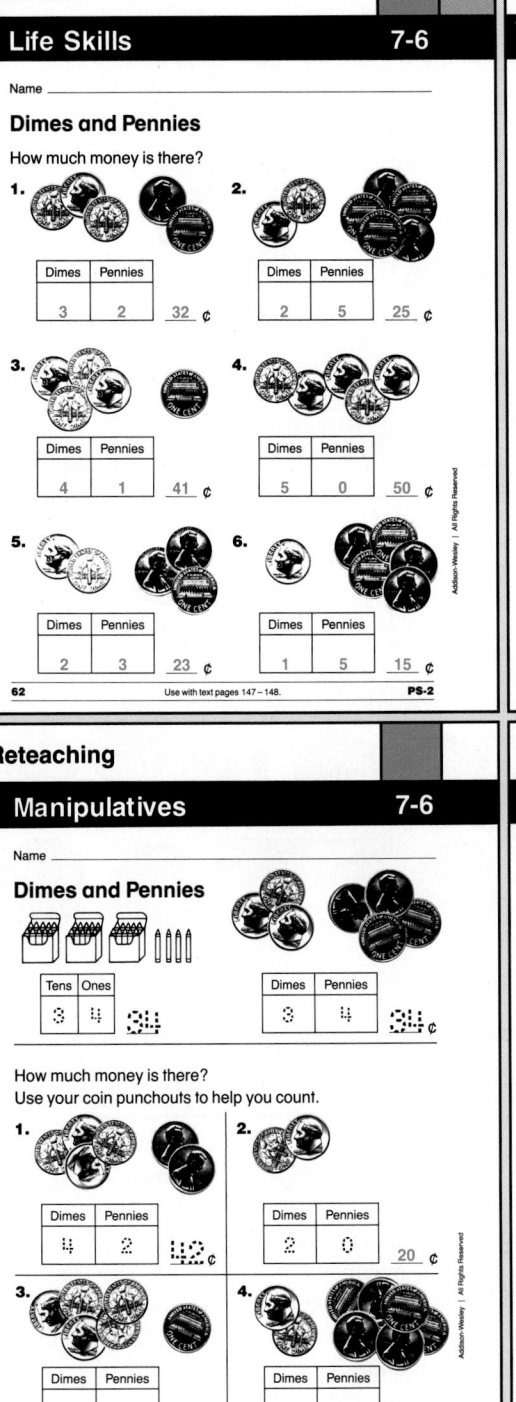

Practice

Life Skills   7-6

Name _____

Dimes and Pennies

How much money is there?

1.

Dimes	Pennies
3	2

32 ¢

2.

Dimes	Pennies
2	5

25 ¢

3.

Dimes	Pennies
4	1

41 ¢

4.

Dimes	Pennies
5	0

50 ¢

5.

Dimes	Pennies
2	3

23 ¢

6.

Dimes	Pennies
1	5

15 ¢

62   Use with text pages 147–148.   PS-2

Reteaching

Manipulatives   7-6

Name _____

Dimes and Pennies

Tens	Ones
3	4

34

Dimes	Pennies
3	4

34 ¢

How much money is there?
Use your coin punchouts to help you count.

1.

Dimes	Pennies
4	2

42 ¢

2.

Dimes	Pennies
2	0

20 ¢

3.

Dimes	Pennies
5	1

51 ¢

4.

Dimes	Pennies
2	6

26 ¢

62   Use with text pages 147–148.   RS-2

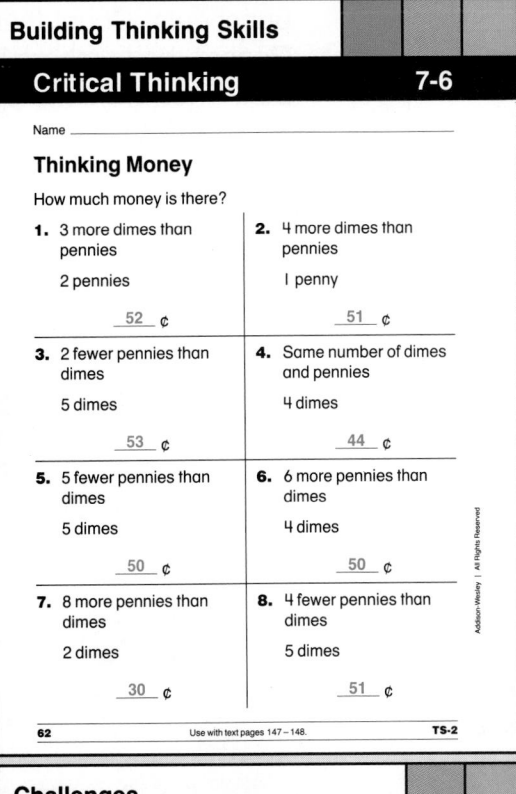

Building Thinking Skills

Critical Thinking   7-6

Name _____

Thinking Money

How much money is there?

1. 3 more dimes than pennies

   2 pennies

   ___52___ ¢

2. 4 more dimes than pennies

   1 penny

   ___51___ ¢

3. 2 fewer pennies than dimes

   5 dimes

   ___53___ ¢

4. Same number of dimes and pennies

   4 dimes

   ___44___ ¢

5. 5 fewer pennies than dimes

   5 dimes

   ___50___ ¢

6. 6 more pennies than dimes

   4 dimes

   ___50___ ¢

7. 8 more pennies than dimes

   2 dimes

   ___30___ ¢

8. 4 fewer pennies than dimes

   5 dimes

   ___51___ ¢

62   Use with text pages 147–148.   TS-2

Challenges

Problem Solving   7-6

Name _____

Do Not Spend It All

What coins are left?

These are the coins you have.	This is what you buy.	What coins do you have left?
1.	22¢	__1__ dimes __2__ pennies
2.	12¢	__2__ dimes __2__ pennies
3.	34¢	__1__ dimes __0__ pennies
4.	33¢	__2__ dimes __3__ pennies
5.	56¢	__1__ dimes __2__ pennies

62   Use with text pages 147–148.   CS-2

OPTIONS FOR INDIVIDUAL NEEDS

Basic

Exercises All
More Practice, p. 416, set B

Supplements
Reteaching 62 or
Practice 62
Thinking Skills 62

Average

Exercises All
More Practice, p. 416, set B

Supplements
Practice 62
Challenges 62 or
Thinking Skills 62

Extended

Exercises All

Supplements
Challenges 62
Thinking Skills 62

Other Resources:
Mathematics Their Way, pp. 332-333
Explorations, pp. 109, 113, 120, 124-125, 129
Workjobs, pp. 224-227
Mathematics Book A, pp. 5-6

7-6

LESSON PLAN 7-6

OBJECTIVE 7-6
To count dimes and pennies

Materials: punchout dimes and pennies, magazines, tagboard

Grouping Suggestions: individual work, pairs

1. MOTIVATE AND TEACH

LEARN ABOUT IT

Write on the chalkboard: 1 ten 5 ones. *How can you use your punchout pennies and dimes to show this?* (Possible answers: 1 dime 5 pennies; 10 pennies grouped and 5 single pennies) *How are dimes and pennies like tens and ones?* (Possible answer: One dime is the same as 1 ten; 1 penny is the same as 1 one.) Have students look at the picture on page 147 and explain that the Ten City Toy Store accepts only dimes and pennies.
▶ **Can you just count the number of coins shown to find the price of the object? Explain.** (Possible answer: No, a dime is worth more than a penny.)
▶ **How can your punchout coins help you find the answer?** (Possible answer: You can put your dimes and pennies in separate groups to count.)
▶ **Explain how recording the number of dimes and pennies in the box will help you know the price of the item.** (Possible answer: It helps you put the dimes in the tens place and the pennies in the ones place.)

2. CHECK UNDERSTANDING

ERROR ALERT Not understanding that the dimes stand for tens and pennies stand for ones.

Name _____

Dimes and Pennies

Cover the coins with your coin punchouts. Take off the punchouts. Count them. Record the numbers in the box. Then write the price.

Dimes and pennies are like tens and ones.

1.

Dimes	Pennies
2	5

2.

Dimes	Pennies
3	2

3.

Dimes	Pennies
1	5

4.

Dimes	Pennies
4	2

Chapter 7

(one hundred forty-seven)

TEACHING OPTIONS

RETEACHING TIPS
Draw the chart on the board. Write 24¢. Have students model the amount with punchout pennies and dimes and then fill in the chart. Assign Reteaching Supplement 62.

Dimes Tens	Pennies Ones
2	4

ENRICHMENT Family Math
Have students take turns playing store owner and customer with a member of their family. The store owner shows the price of an item less than 99¢, and the customer use dimes and pennies to show the amount.

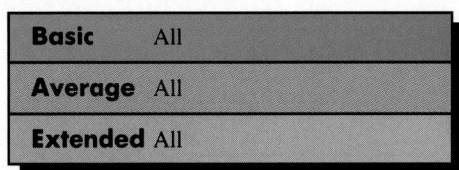

lor the coins you need.

se ◖▭▷ for dimes.

se ◖▭▷ for pennies.

24¢ is
2 dimes and
4 pennies.

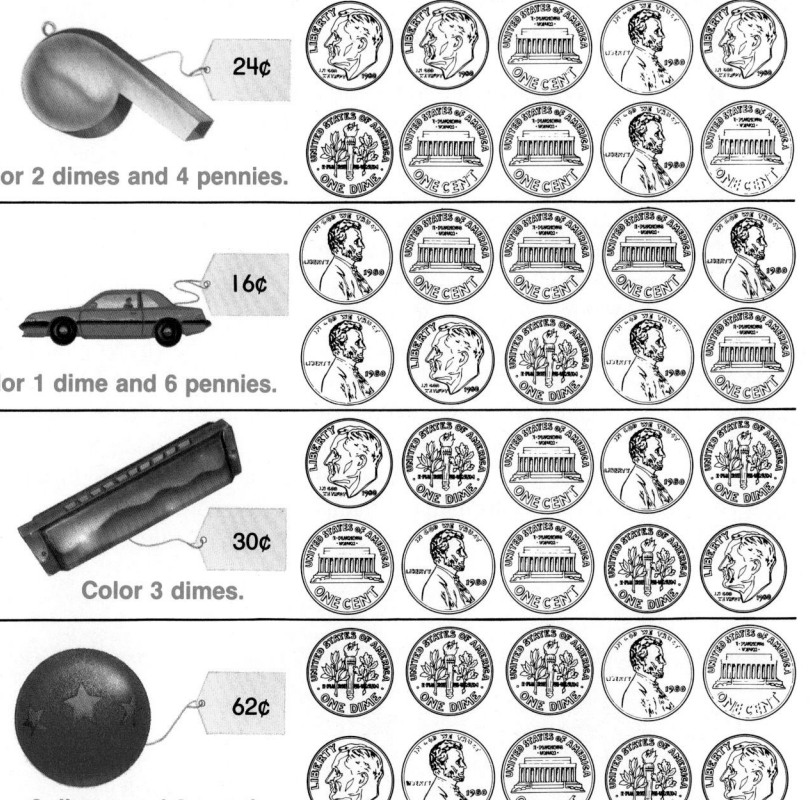

lor 2 dimes and 4 pennies.   24¢

lor 1 dime and 6 pennies.   16¢

Color 3 dimes.   30¢

lor 6 dimes and 2 pennies.   62¢

ROBLEM SOLVING

Brad has 8 pennies. LaDawn has 12 pennies.
How many more pennies does LaDawn have?   __4__ more

3. PRACTICE AND APPLY

Basic	All
Average	All
Extended	All

PRACTICE

Why are some of the coins shaded in Exercise 1? (to show the coins needed to buy the toy) *Which coins will you color in each exercise?* (the ones that show the price) *What colors will you use?* (red for dimes; blue for pennies)

APPLY

PROBLEM SOLVING ▶ **What can you use to compare how many more pennies LaDawn has than Brad?** (Possible answers: Show the two amounts using punchout pennies; draw pictures of the pennies that each person has.)
▶ **Will you add or subtract to find the answer? Explain.** (Subtract, because you want to find out how many more pennies LaDawn has.)

7-6

LOSE AND ASSESS

HOW WHAT YOU KNOW Ask
dents to tell about the errands
rry Kitten went on in preparation
her party. *How much money did
rry spend on the hats and the
lloons?* (54¢) Let students use
nchout coins to model the amount.
mpare the different combinations
y might have used to get the total.

QUICK QUIZ

Use punchout pennies and dimes to
show these amounts:
47¢   13¢   39¢   26¢   11¢

Reading and Writing Number Names

OBJECTIVE 7-7   To read and write word names for 2-digit numbers

PREBOOK ACTIVITIES

QUICK REVIEW

Read each amount. Write how much money there is in all.

4 dimes 1 penny	(41¢)	5 dimes 7 pennies	(57¢)
1 dime 6 pennies	(16¢)	3 dimes 4 pennies	(34¢)
2 dimes 0 pennies	(20¢)	4 dimes 9 pennies	(49¢)

PRIOR KNOWLEDGE

Where are some places you see numbers every day? (Possible answers: on houses, mailboxes, buildings, books, newspapers, telephones) *Are numbers always written the same way?* (No, they can be plain, fancy, written as numerals, or written as words.)

COMMUNICATION

Reading and Writing in Math   Write **29** and **twenty-nine** on the chalkboard. Ask students to read the two items to themselves. *How are these items alike?* (They are both ways of writing 29.) Write **32, 15, thirty-two,** and **fifteen** on the board. Point to a number and ask a volunteer to draw a line to its word name and read it aloud. Explain that 2-digit numbers between 21 and 99 have a hyphen in their word names. Ask volunteers to circle the hyphens in the word names on the board.

Ask each student to write a sentence that has a number name in it. Invite them to share their sentences.

EXPLORE AND CONNECT

Materials: base-ten blocks, flashcards, blank cards
Grouping Suggestion: groups of 3
Use the blocks to display 2 tens and 4 ones. *What are two ways I can write the number that these blocks show?* Write *24* and *twenty-four* as students name them. Ask students to read the number and the word name aloud with you. Give cooperative groups of three 10 blank cards and 10 flashcards with number words on them. One student selects a card and reads the word name; the second uses the blocks to model the number. The third student writes the numeral on a blank card. Have students change roles after each number. When students have used all the flashcards, have the groups place their cards facedown and play Concentration. Students alternate turning up 2 cards to try to match a number to its word name. Remind students to encourage one another to participate.

CONNECTIONS   Use these anytime.

Problem of the Day

Number Names   Write the word name for the sum.
Nine puppies were sold on Tuesday.
Six more puppies were sold on Wednesday.
How many puppies were sold altogether?
(fifteen puppies)

Number Sense

Estimation   Estimate the ages of the people you live with. Write a sentence about their ages, using the word name for the number in the sentence.

Subject Integration

Physical Education   Read each sentence. Do what it says.
Hop up and down thirteen times.
Take twenty-eight little steps.
Nod your head thirty-one times.
Blink your eyes seventeen times.
Take forty-five steps backward.

CLASSWORK AND HOMEWORK SUPPLEMENTS

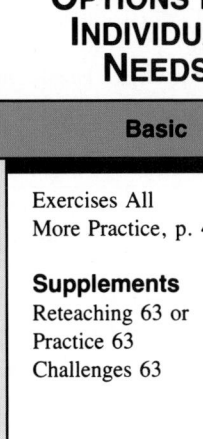

Basic

Exercises All
More Practice, p. 416, set C

Supplements
Reteaching 63 or
Practice 63
Challenges 63

Average

Exercises All
More Practice, p.416, set C

Supplements
Practice 63
Challenges 63 or
Thinking Skills 63

Extended

Exercises All

Supplements
Challenges 63
Thinking Skills 63

Other Resources:
Mathematics their Way, pp. 300, 305-306
Explorations, pp. 130-131
Developing Number Concepts with Unifix Cubes, pp. 145, 170

Practice

Reading Math 7-7

Name _____

Reading and Writing Number Names

Write the number.

1. forty-seven _47_   twenty-two _22_   sixty-five _65_

2. thirty-six _36_   fifteen _15_   eighty-one _81_

3. fifty-four _54_   seventy-two _72_   nineteen _19_

4. ninety-five _95_   seventeen _17_   fifty-eight _58_

5. twelve _12_   forty-three _43_   ninety-two _92_

6. twenty-nine _29_   seventy-nine _79_   sixty-seven _67_

7. eighty-six _86_   thirty-one _31_   thirteen _13_

8. forty-four _44_   eleven _11_   ninety-nine _99_

9. sixty-one _61_   fifty-two _52_   twenty-five _25_

PS-2   Use with text pages 149–150.   63

Building Thinking Skills

Number Sense 7-7

Name _____

Riddles

Read the number riddle.
Match the riddle to the number.

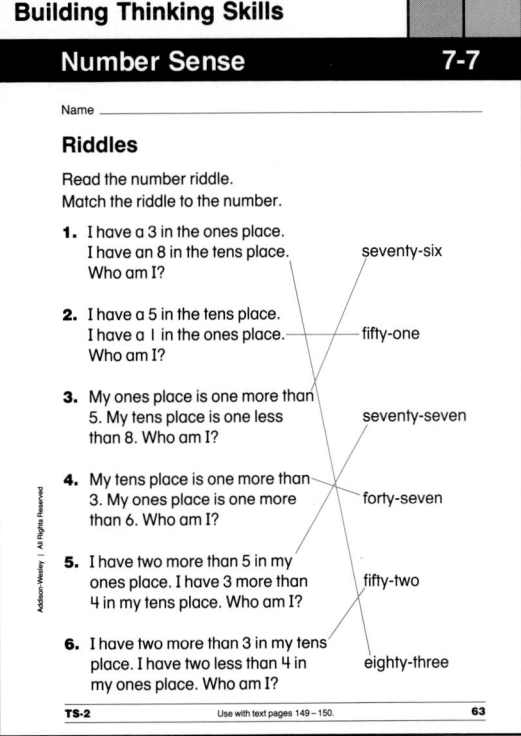

1. I have a 3 in the ones place.
   I have an 8 in the tens place.
   Who am I?

2. I have a 5 in the tens place.
   I have a 1 in the ones place.
   Who am I?

3. My ones place is one more than 5. My tens place is one less than 8. Who am I?

4. My tens place is one more than 3. My ones place is one more than 6. Who am I?

5. I have two more than 5 in my ones place. I have 3 more than 4 in my tens place. Who am I?

6. I have two more than 3 in my tens place. I have two less than 4 in my ones place. Who am I?

seventy-six

fifty-one

seventy-seven

forty-seven

fifty-two

eighty-three

TS-2   Use with text pages 149–150.   63

Reteaching

Reading Math 7-7

Name _____

Reading and Writing Number Names

Draw lines to match.

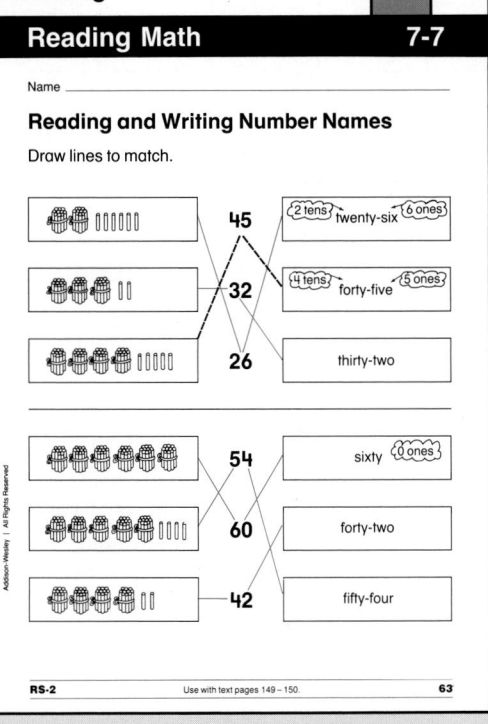

RS-2   Use with text pages 149–150.   63

Challenges

Family Math 7-7

Name _____

Crossnumber Puzzle

Dear Family,
In our math book we just studied the reading and writing of 2-digit numbers. Have your child read the number names aloud before writing the numbers in the puzzle. Then work together to write the clues for the second puzzle. Help with spelling as needed.

Read the clues. Write the numbers.

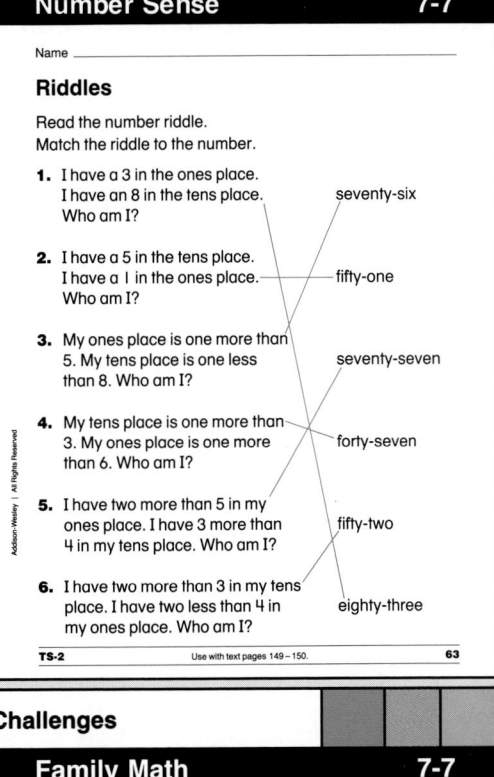

Across
A. forty-four
C. twenty-three
E. twenty-nine
G. sixty-seven
I. sixteen
J. eighty-three

Down
B. forty-two
D. thirty-one
F. ninety-six
H. seventy-eight
I. thirteen
K. thirty-nine

Write the clues for the puzzle. Use extra paper.

CS-2   Use with text pages 149–150.   63

7-7

OBJECTIVE 7-7
To read and write word names for 2-digit numbers

Materials: base-ten blocks, blank flash cards

Grouping Suggestion: pairs

1. MOTIVATE AND TEACH

LEARN ABOUT IT

Write *42* and *forty-two* on the chalkboard. Ask students to read both ways of writing the number. Then call on students to write the numbers and the word names that come before and after 42 as you say them.

▶ **Examine the words at the bottom of page 149. Why are there two rows of number cards?** (Possible answer: The first row names ones; the second row names tens; you need to use a word from each row.)

▶ **Explain how you will know what number cards to put in the flag of the mailbox at the top of page 149?** (Possible answer: After you count the tens and ones blocks, you find the number cards to match the amount.)

▶ **What is the greatest number you could write? The least?** (99, 21)

▶ **What numbers could you write that have the same tens and ones digits?** (22, 33, 44, 55, 66, 77, 88, 99)

2. CHECK UNDERSTANDING

ERROR ALERT Reversing the tens and ones digits in the word names for the 2-digit numbers.

Name _____

Reading and Writing Number Names

Work with a partner. Cut out the number cards. Have your partner put some blocks in the mailbox. Put number cards in the flag to match. Say and write the number. Then write its word name.

Answers may vary. Check students' work. Numerals and word names should match.

1. _____ _____

2. _____ _____

3. _____ _____

-one	-two	-three	-four	-five	-six	-seven	-eight
	twenty	thirty	forty	fifty	sixty	seventy	eighty

Chapter 7   (one hundred forty-nine)

TEACHING OPTIONS

RETEACHING TIPS Ask partners to place the tens cards in one pile and the ones cards in another. Have them select one card from each pile. Have one partner use base-ten blocks to model the number while the other reads and writes it. For further help, use Reteaching Supplement 63.

ENRICHMENT Have students cut out 2-digit numbers from the newspaper. Have them paste the numbers on a large piece of paper and then write the word name below each number. Ask them to use a calculator to total the numbers and write this amount as both a number and a word.

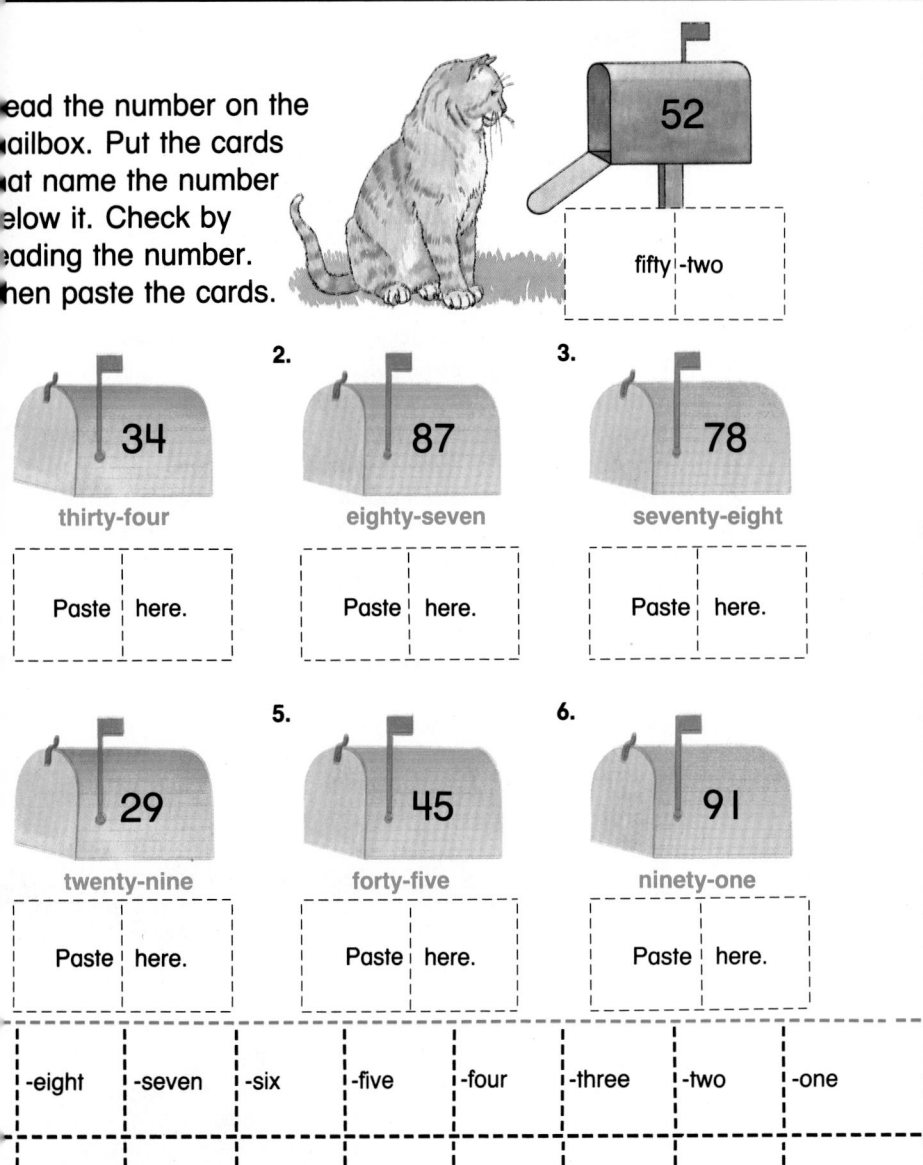

ead the number on the
ailbox. Put the cards
at name the number
elow it. Check by
eading the number.
hen paste the cards.

52

fifty -two

2.
34

thirty-four

Paste here.

87

eighty-seven

Paste here.

3.
78

seventy-eight

Paste here.

5.
29

twenty-nine

Paste here.

45

forty-five

Paste here.

6.
91

ninety-one

Paste here.

-eight	-seven	-six	-five	-four	-three	-two	-one
eighty	seventy	sixty	fifty	forty	thirty	twenty	

0 (one hundred fifty)   More Practice, page 416, set C   Chapter 7

3. PRACTICE AND APPLY

Basic	All
Average	All
Extended	All

PRACTICE

What goes in the boxes below the mailboxes? (the word names for the numbers on the mailbox) *How can you check the word name?* (Read it aloud to see if it matches the number.)

APPLY

▶ **How can you use models to show one of the numbers on page 150?** (Use base-ten blocks to show the tens and the ones.)
▶ **Compare the tens word names. How are they alike?** (Possible answer: They all end with the letter *y;* the beginning is like the ones name.)

7-7

LOSE AND ASSESS

HOW WHAT YOU KNOW
ave partners make 10 flashcards for
-digit numbers and 10 flashcards for
e corresponding word names.
ncourage partners to assist each other
reading and writing the numbers.
ix up the cards and place them
cedown. Have students alternate
rning up 2 cards to try to match the
ord name with its number.

QUICK QUIZ

Match the number to its word name.

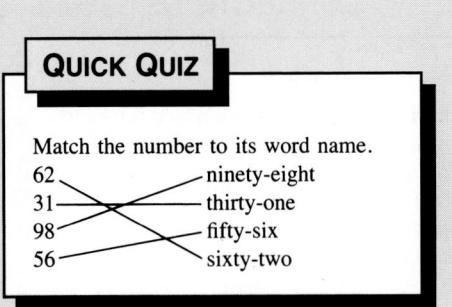

62 — ninety-eight
31 — thirty-one
98 — fifty-six
56 — sixty-two

Chapter 7 Lesson 7   **150**

Understanding 100

OBJECTIVE 7-8   To write numbers around 100

PREBOOK ACTIVITIES

QUICK REVIEW

Write the numbers in each row from least to greatest.
69 72 53 41 17   (17, 41, 53, 69, 72)
12 95 60 28 15   (12, 15, 28, 60, 95)
88 86 78 67 76   (67, 76, 78, 86, 88)
29 19 49 99 39   (19, 29, 39, 49, 99)

PRIOR KNOWLEDGE

Help students recall 2-digit place-value concepts by asking them to name some 2-digit numbers. Write their suggestions on the chalkboard and ask volunteers to circle the numbers in the tens place. Repeat with different 2-digit numbers and have students underline the numbers in the ones place.

COMMUNICATION

Reading and Discussing Math   Write the words **ones, tens,** and **hundreds** on the chalkboard. Read the words with the students. *Which words will help you talk about a 2-digit number such as 28?* (ones, tens) *Which words will help you talk about a 3-digit number such as 105?* (ones, tens, hundreds) Write 67 and the following sentence on the board and ask students to complete them in their Math Journals: 7 is in the (ones) place. 6 is in the (tens) place. Write 102 and have students repeat the activity using these sentences: 2 is in the (ones) place. 0 is in the (tens) place. 1 is in the (hundreds) place. *Do you own **one hundred** of anything?* (Possible answers: pennies, hairs, baseball cards)

EXPLORE AND CONNECT

Materials: base-ten blocks, a 100 flat for each pair
Grouping suggestion: pairs
Write the number 98 on the chalkboard and have students model the number with base-ten blocks. *How can you use blocks to show the number after 98?* (Add one unit block.) *What happens when you add one block to 99? Try it.* (You have 10 ones blocks.) *What can you trade 10 ones blocks for* (1 ten) Have students make the trade and then place the 10 te on top of a 100 flat. *How many equal 100?* (10) *How could you model the number 101?* (Use a 100 flat and a ones block. Have pairs practice using the 100 flat by modeling and writin numbers from 100 to 105.
Draw on the chalkboard a place-value chart that includes the words **hundreds, tens,** and **ones.** Model both 2-digit and 3-digit numbers. Ask students to fill in the chart with the appropriate numbers.

CONNECTIONS   Use these anytime.

Problem of the Day
Use your base-ten blocks to find the answer to this problem.
   Kim baked 30 cookies.
   She sold 10 cookies.
   How many did she have left? (20)
Make up a word problem. Ask a partner to solve it using base-ten blocks.

Number Sense

Estimation   How long would it take to jump rope 100 times? How far on the playground would 100 heel-to-toe steps take you? How wide is 100 inches? (Have students estimate and then actually check their answers.)

Mental Math

10 More or Less   Say the numbers that are 10 more and 10 less than the following:
20   (30, 10)
60   (70, 50)
90   (100, 80)
10   (20, 0)
40   (50, 30)

CLASSWORK AND HOMEWORK SUPPLEMENTS

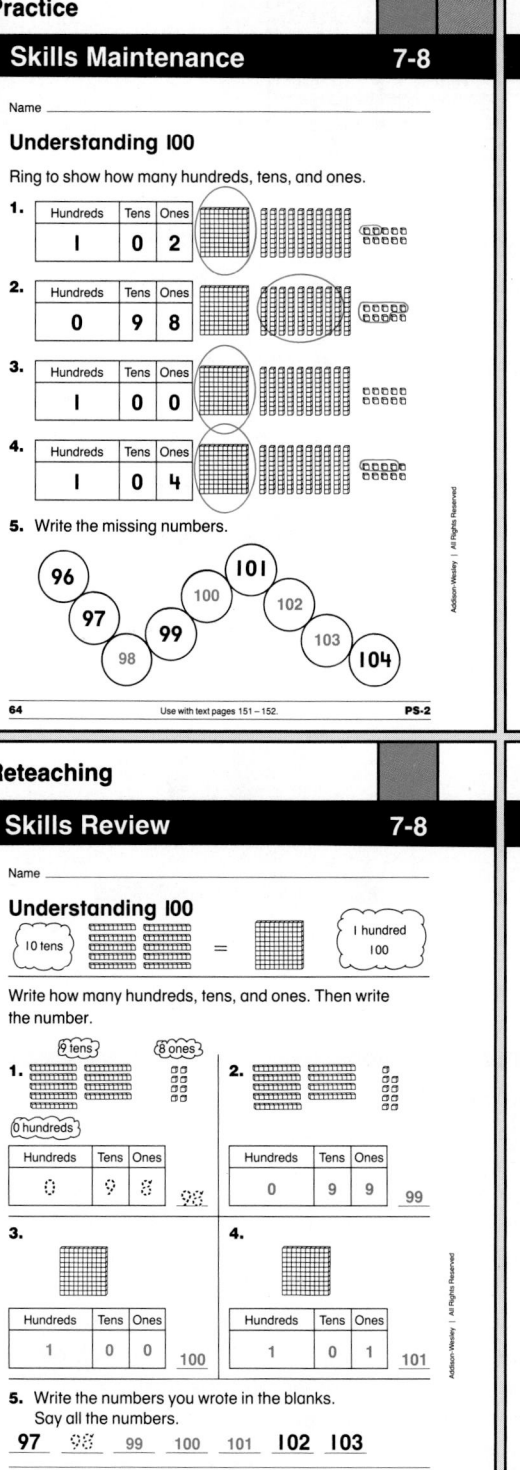

Practice

Skills Maintenance 7-8

Name _____

Understanding 100

Ring to show how many hundreds, tens, and ones.

1.

Hundreds	Tens	Ones
1	0	2

2.

Hundreds	Tens	Ones
0	9	8

3.

Hundreds	Tens	Ones
1	0	0

4.

Hundreds	Tens	Ones
1	0	4

5. Write the missing numbers.

96, 97, 98, 99, 100, 101, 102, 103, 104

64   Use with text pages 151 – 152.   PS-2

Reteaching

Skills Review 7-8

Name _____

Understanding 100

(10 tens) ▦▦▦ = ▦ (1 hundred 100)

Write how many hundreds, tens, and ones. Then write the number.

1. (9 tens) (8 ones) (0 hundreds)

Hundreds	Tens	Ones
0	9	8

98

2.

Hundreds	Tens	Ones
0	9	9

99

3.

Hundreds	Tens	Ones
1	0	0

100

4.

Hundreds	Tens	Ones
1	0	1

101

5. Write the numbers you wrote in the blanks.
Say all the numbers.

97, 98, 99, 100, 101, **102**, **103**

64   Use with text pages 151 – 152.   RS-2

Building Thinking Skills

Creative Thinking 7-8

Name _____

Beans, Beans, Beans

How many beans are there?
Here is an easy way to find out.
▶ Put a ring around 10 beans. ▶ Put a box around 10 rings.

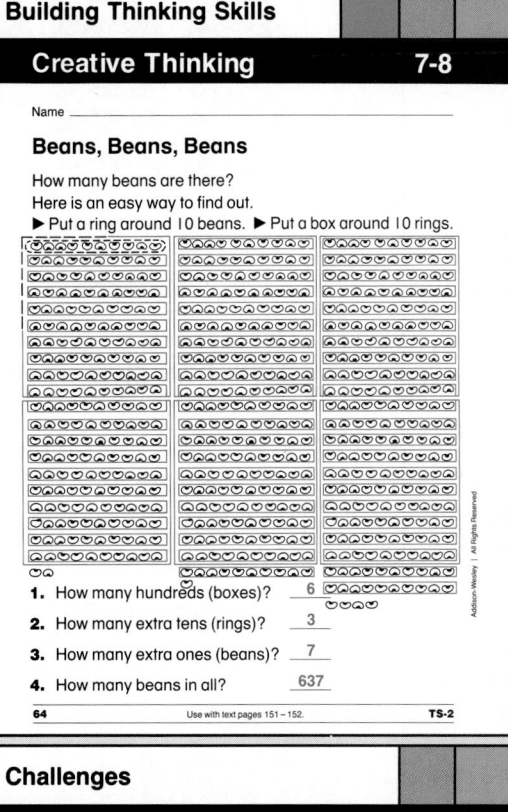

1. How many hundreds (boxes)?   6
2. How many extra tens (rings)?   3
3. How many extra ones (beans)?   7
4. How many beans in all?   637

64   Use with text pages 151 – 152.   TS-2

Challenges

Calculators 7-8

Name _____

Press and Write

Use your ▦. Press the keys in order.
Write the numbers you see.

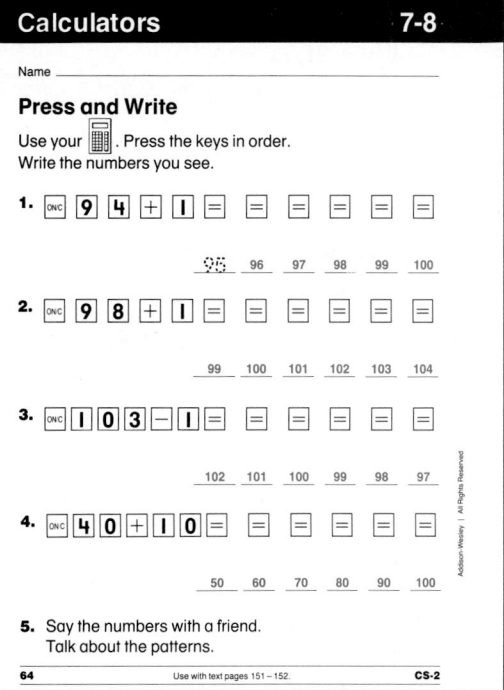

1. [ON/C] [9] [4] [+] [1] [=] [=] [=] [=] [=] [=]

95 96 97 98 99 100

2. [ON/C] [9] [8] [+] [1] [=] [=] [=] [=] [=] [=]

99 100 101 102 103 104

3. [ON/C] [1] [0] [3] [−] [1] [=] [=] [=] [=] [=] [=]

102 101 100 99 98 97

4. [ON/C] [4] [0] [+] [1] [0] [=] [=] [=] [=] [=] [=]

50 60 70 80 90 100

5. Say the numbers with a friend.
Talk about the patterns.

64   Use with text pages 151 – 152.   CS-2

OPTIONS FOR INDIVIDUAL NEEDS

Basic

Exercises All
Calculator Bank, p. 401
More Practice, p. 417, set A

Supplements
Reteaching 64 or
Practice 64
Thinking Skills 64

Average

Exercises All
Calculator Bank, p. 401
More Practice, p. 417, set A

Supplements
Practice 64
Challenges 64 or
Thinking Skills 64

Extended

Exercises All
Calculator Bank, p. 401

Supplements
Challenges 64
Thinking Skills 64

Other Resources:
Math in Stride, pp. 118-119, 142-143
Mathematics Their Way, pp. 309-312
Explorations, pp. 244, 246-251
Workjobs II, pp. 30-31

7-8

LESSON PLAN 7-8

OBJECTIVE 7-8
To write numbers around 100

Materials: base-ten blocks, 100 flats

Grouping Suggestions: individual work, pairs

1. MOTIVATE AND TEACH

LEARN ABOUT IT

Model the number 99 with base-ten blocks. Ask a student to add one more cube to make 100. *How many tens equal 1 hundred?* (10) Count the tens together and then hold up a 100 flat and count the rows of tens to show that the amounts match. *What blocks would you use to show the number 104?* (1 hundred, 4 ones) Ask a student to model the amount and read the number. Have students look at the picture at the top of page 151. *How do the Ten City bakers group their rolls?* (Possible answer: They put 10 rolls in a box: when there are 10 boxes of 10 they group them in a hundreds box.)

▶ **Describe what you see in Exercise 1.** (Possible answer: 1 box of 100 and 3 single rolls: no boxes of 10)

▶ **How could you write a number that has a hundreds digit and a ones digit but no tens digit?** (Possible answer: Put a 0 in the tens place.)

▶ **How does the place-value chart help you?** (Possible answers: You can count and write the number of ones, tens, and hundreds in the chart; it makes the number easier to read.)

▶ **Why would you put a zero in the place-value chart?** (Possible answers: to show that you looked for ones, tens, or hundreds, but there were none; to hold the place)

2. CHECK UNDERSTANDING

ERROR ALERT Not understanding how a zero is used to show place value in a 3-digit number without a hundreds, tens, or ones digit.

Name _____

Understanding 100

10 boxes of 10 = 1 box of 100
10 tens = 1 hundred

Write how many hundreds, tens, and ones.
Then write the number.

1.

100 rolls

Hundreds	Tens	Ones
1	0	3

103

2.

10 rolls (multiple boxes)

Hundreds	Tens	Ones
0	9	7

97

3.

100 rolls

Hundreds	Tens	Ones
1	0	2

102

4.

100 rolls

Hundreds	Tens	Ones
1	0	4

104

Chapter 7

(one hundred fifty-one)

TEACHING OPTIONS

RETEACHING TIPS Write on the board: ___ hundreds ___ tens ___ ones. Have students model 101 with base-ten blocks. Count hundreds, tens, and ones and write 1, 0, and 1 in the blanks. *What does the zero in the tens place mean?* (no tens) Model other 3-digit numbers. Assign Reteaching Supplement 64.

ENRICHMENT Have students cut small squares of different-colored construction paper. Count out 100 squares. Have them make a mosaic picture by pasting the squares close together but not touching each other. Display the *100 Art* in the classroom.

Write how many hundreds, tens, and ones.
Then write the number.

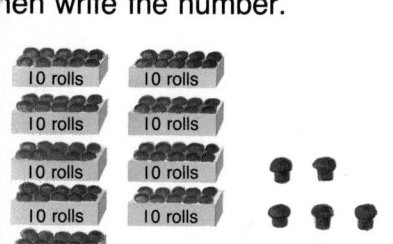

2.

Hundreds	Tens	Ones
0	9	8

98

Hundreds	Tens	Ones
0	9	9

99

100 rolls

4.
100 rolls

Hundreds	Tens	Ones
1	0	0

100

Hundreds	Tens	Ones
1	0	1

101

MIXED REVIEW

Continue the pattern.

6, 8, 10, _12_, _14_, _16_

15, 13, 11, _9_, _7_, _5_

Estimate the length. Then measure to the nearest inch.
Estimates may vary.

estimate: ____ inches

measure: _3_ inches

2   (one hundred fifty-two)   More Practice, page 417, set A   Chapter 7

Basic	All; Mixed Review
Average	All; Mixed Review
Extended	All; Mixed Review

PRACTICE

What do you learn by counting the rolls in Exercises 1-4? (how many hundreds, tens, and ones there are) *What is the last number you will write in Exercise 5?* (104)

APPLY

▶ **Which is easier to count—10 boxes of 100 rolls or 1 box of 100? Why?** (Possible answer: 1 box; you know it equals 10 tens without counting.)
▶ **What would happen if you did not use a zero to hold the tens place in a 3-digit number that has no tens?** (Possible answer: You would write the wrong number; if the number is 101, it would be read as 11 if the zero is not there to hold the tens place.)

MIXED REVIEW *What unit of measure will you use to estimate the length of the yarn in Exercise 3?* (inches)

7-8

CLOSE AND ASSESS

SHOW WHAT YOU KNOW

Have one student in a pair be a baker and the other a customer at the Ten City bakery. The baker counts base-ten blocks to represent the customer's order and then writes the number. The customer checks the order by counting the blocks and reading the number.

QUICK QUIZ

Complete the chart.

	Hundreds	Tens	Ones
105	(1)	(0)	(5)
92	(0)	(9)	(2)
100	(1)	(0)	(0)

Problem Solving: Using Data From a Pictograph

OBJECTIVE 7-9   To solve problems using data from a pictograph

PREBOOK ACTIVITIES

QUICK REVIEW

Write the number that each picture represents.

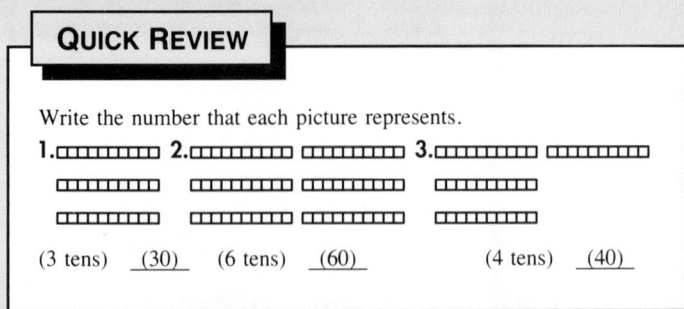

(3 tens) __(30)__   (6 tens) __(60)__   (4 tens) __(40)__

PRIOR KNOWLEDGE

Help students recall what they know about graphs. Ask the following questions: *What are graphs?* (Possible answer: pictures with numbers and labels used to organize information) *Why do we use graphs?* (Possible answers: They are easy to read; they help you find information quickly.) *Suppose that our class just had a bake sale. What information about it might we put in a graph?* (Possible answers: how many of each item was sold; how much money was made each day)

COMMUNICATION

Discussing Math   Write *pictograph* on the chalkboard and read it aloud. *How does a pictograph show data?* (Possible answer: It uses pictures to show numbers of things.) *Why is a pictograph easy to read?* (Possible answer: You can tell what it is about by looking at the pictures.) *How do you share something with someone?* (Possible answer: You give them part of what you have.) *How would you know if you shared something equally with a friend?* (Possible answer: Count your items and then your friend's items to see if you both have the same amount.)

EXPLORE AND CONNECT

COOPERATIVE ACTIVITY

Grouping Suggestions: small groups
The class made a pictograph to show how many paper flowers they made to decorate the room for Parents' Day.

Paper Flowers

Monday		Each ✿
Tuesday		means
Wednesday		10 flowers.

TEACHING ACTIONS

BEFORE ▶ **Name the parts of the pictograph that help you understand what it shows.** (Possible answer: the title of the graph; the key that tells how many flowers each picture represents)

▶ **How could you change the meaning of the picture on this pictograph?** (Possible answer: You could have 1 flower represent a different number of paper flowers.)

DURING ▶ **How can you use the data in the graph to answer questions about it?** (Possible answer: Count by 10s to find a total number of flowers for each day.)

▶ **Why does a pictograph not show a picture for every flower made?** (Possible answer: There would not be enough room on the graph and it could not be read as quickly.)

AFTER ▶ **How can you check to be sure you have counted correctly?** (Possible answer: Draw 10 tally marks by each picture and count them to see if the totals match.) Have students in small groups make up a question about the pictograph for other students to answer.

CONNECTIONS   Use these anytime.

Problem of the Day

Logic   Ali and Amy had a party. Ali bought a cake for $9. Amy spent $3 on juice. They decided to share the cost. How much did Amy need to pay Ali so that they each spent the same amount?
($3)

Math Connection

Use Objects   Compare the 2 numbers. Tell what you need to do to the large number to get a difference equal to the small number. Use counters if necessary.

9, 4	(Subtract 5 from 9.)
6, 3	(Subtract 3 from 6.)
10, 4	(Subtract 6 from 10.)
18, 9	(Subtract 9 from 18.)
12, 8	(Subtract 4 from 12.)

Life Skills

Reading a Calendar   Work with a partner. Write the months on strips of paper. Place the cards in order, beginning with January, in a column on a desk or table. One of you should close your eyes while the other turns over a few cards. Have the partner determine the missing months. Take turns.

Problem Solving Strategy: Use Objects

• solve problems using the strategy Use Objects

CLASSWORK AND HOMEWORK SUPPLEMENTS

OPTIONS FOR INDIVIDUAL NEEDS

Basic

Exercises All

Supplements
Reteaching 65 or
Practice 65

Average

Exercises All

Supplements
Practice 65
Challenges 65 or
Thinking Skills 65

Extended

Exercises All

Supplements
Challenges 65
Thinking Skills 65

Other Resources:
Math in Stride, pp. 75-76
Mathematices Their Way, pp. 311-312
Explorations, pp. 110-131, 196-200, 263

Practice

Problem Solving 7-9

Name _____

Use Objects

Read the problem. Decide how each pair of children can have the same number.
Use cubes to find the answer. Finish the sentence.

1. Nan has 7 apples. Amy has 11 apples.

__Amy__ should give _2_ apples to __Nan__.

2. Sal has 14 baseball cards. Li has 10 basketball cards.

__Sal__ should give _2_ cards to __Li__.

3. Paco has 12 crayons. Pam has 18 crayons.

__Pam__ should give _3_ crayons to __Paco__.

4. Jo has 17 shells. Kim has 9 shells.

__Jo__ should give _4_ shells to __Kim__.

5. Ben has 15 cars. Bob has 21 cars.

__Bob__ should give _3_ cars to __Ben__.

PS-2 Use with text page 154. 65

Building Thinking Skills

Data Analysis 7-9

Name _____

Lemonade Sales

Peter sold lemonade for 10¢ a glass.
On Monday he sold 4 glasses. On Tuesday he sold 2 fewer glasses. On Wednesday he sold 5 glasses. On Thursday he sold the same number of glasses as he did on Monday.
On Friday Peter sold 2 more glasses than on Wednesday.
Color the graph to match the data.
Color 1 🌎 for each 10¢ Peter earned.

Ring the answer.

1. On which day did Peter earn the most money?
Wednesday (Friday) Monday

2. On which day did he earn the least?
Monday (Tuesday) Thursday

3. How much did Peter earn in the first 2 days?
40¢ (60¢) 90¢

TS-2 Use with text pages 153–154. 65

Reteaching

Problem Solving 7-9

Name _____

Using Data from a Pictograph

The pictograph shows how many tickets the class sold for the play.
Each 🎟 means 10 tickets.

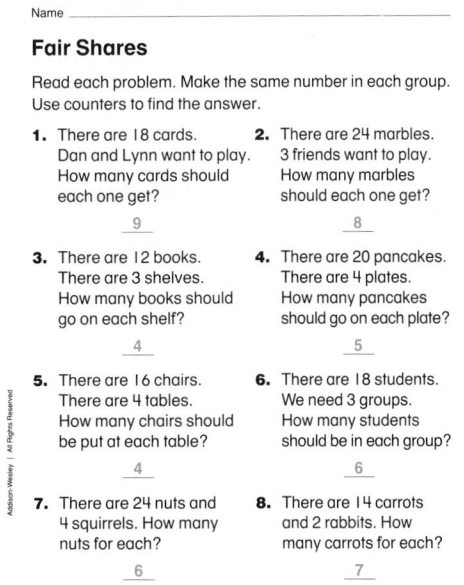

1. How many tickets were sold
on Monday? 20 (2 tens = 20) on Tuesday? _10_
on Wednesday? _40_ on Thursday? _30_
on Friday? _50_

2. On which day were the most tickets sold?
Ring the answer.
Monday Wednesday (Friday)

3. On which day were the fewest tickets sold?
Ring the answer.
Monday (Tuesday) Thursday

RS-2 Use with text page 153. 65

Challenges

Problem Solving 7-9

Name _____

Fair Shares

Read each problem. Make the same number in each group.
Use counters to find the answer.

1. There are 18 cards. Dan and Lynn want to play. How many cards should each one get? _9_

2. There are 24 marbles. 3 friends want to play. How many marbles should each one get? _8_

3. There are 12 books. There are 3 shelves. How many books should go on each shelf? _4_

4. There are 20 pancakes. There are 4 plates. How many pancakes should go on each plate? _5_

5. There are 16 chairs. There are 4 tables. How many chairs should be put at each table? _4_

6. There are 18 students. We need 3 groups. How many students should be in each group? _6_

7. There are 24 nuts and 4 squirrels. How many nuts for each? _6_

8. There are 14 carrots and 2 rabbits. How many carrots for each? _7_

CS-2 Use with text pages 153–154. 65

LESSON PLAN 7-9

OBJECTIVE 7-9

To solve problems using data from a pictograph; to solve problems using the strategy Use Objects

Materials: cubes, counters

Grouping Suggestion: pairs

1. MOTIVATE AND TEACH

BEFORE ▶ **Explain how Andrew organized the information in the pictograph.** (Possible answer: He used a picture to show every 10 newspapers that he sold during 1 week.)

DURING ▶ **How will Exercise 1 help you find the answers in Exercises 2 and 3?** (Possible answer: You can look at the totals for each day and compare the information.)

▶ **How can you tell, by looking at the pictograph, which days were good sales days and which days were slow sales days?** (The days with many pictures indicate that Andrew sold many newspapers. The days with few pictures indicate slower days.)

AFTER ▶ **How can you use the information in the pictograph to draw conclusions about Exercise 4?** (Possible answer: Since Andrew sells newspapers outside, rain would most likely reduce his sales. The rainy day was probably Thursday.)

2. CHECK UNDERSTANDING

ERROR ALERT   Page 153

Difficulty comparing data from a pictograph.

Page 154   Taking too many or too few from the larger set, making the two sets unequal.

Name _____

Problem Solving
Using Data from a Pictograph

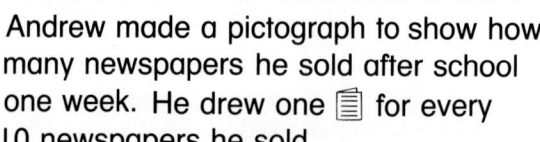

Andrew made a pictograph to show how many newspapers he sold after school one week. He drew one 📰 for every 10 newspapers he sold.

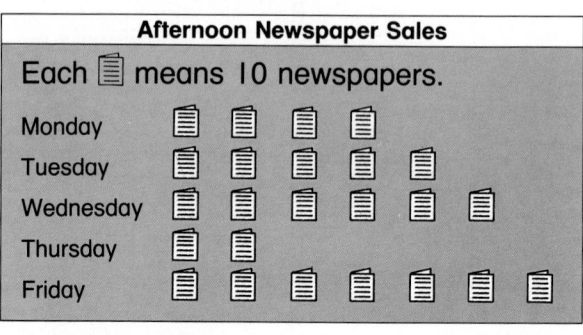

1. How many newspapers did Andrew sell each day?

   Monday __40__   Tuesday __50__

   Wednesday __60__   Thursday __20__   Friday __70__

2. Did he sell more on Tuesday or on Wednesday?   **Wednesday**

3. On which day did Andrew sell the most newspapers?   **Friday**

4. It rained one of the days. Which day do you think it was? Tell why. **See teaching notes.**

Chapter 7   (one hundred fifty-three)

TEACHING OPTIONS

RETEACHING TIPS   Ask pairs of students to pretend that they are delivering letters at school. To begin, give each partner a different number of blank cards to use as letters. Have the student with more letters give some to the partner to make their numbers equal. Assign Reteaching Supplement 65.

ENRICHMENT   Have students pretend they own a store and make a pictograph that shows the number of items they sold each day for 1 wk. Each picture should stand for 10 items. Display the pictographs. Have students think of questions that can be answered by reading the data on the graphs.

153   Chapter 7 Lesson 9

Problem Solving Strategy
Use Objects

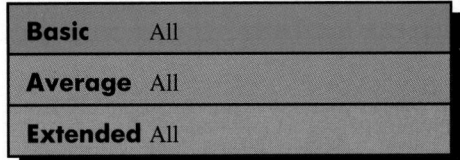

Each pair of students wants to share newspapers so that both students deliver the same number. Use cubes to find the answer.

Taro has 4 more. If he gives Lupe 2, then they will both have the same number.

Lupe has 7 newspapers to deliver. 🔲🔲🔲🔲🔲🔲🔲
Taro has 11 newspapers to deliver. 🔲🔲🔲🔲🔲🔲🔲🔲🔲🔲🔲

 **Taro** should give **2** newspapers to **Lupe**.

Jan has 16 newspapers. Bev has 12 newspapers.

_____ **Jan** should give **2** newspapers to _____ **Bev**.

Lin has 11 newspapers. Ann has 19 newspapers.

_____ **Ann** should give **4** newspapers to _____ **Lin**.

Sol has 14 newspapers. Al has 20 newspapers.

_____ **Al** should give **3** newspapers to _____ **Sol**.

3. PRACTICE AND APPLY

Basic	All
Average	All
Extended	All

▶ **Explain what Taro and Lupe are doing in Exercise 1.** (Possible answer: They want to deliver the same number of newspapers; Taro has to give some to Lupe to make both amounts equal.)

▶ **How can you use cubes to model the data in Exercise 1? What action do you show?** (Possible answer: You show a set of 11 cubes and a set of 7 cubes. You take away 1 cube at a time from the larger set and give it to the smaller set until both sets are equal.)

▶ **How might working with a partner help you check your answers?** (Possible answer: Each partner could use cubes to model one set in a problem and then both could count carefully to be sure the amounts are the same.)

7-9

CLOSE AND ASSESS

SHOW WHAT YOU KNOW
Give each student in a small group a different even number of counters. Then ask the group to make a pictograph that shows how many counters each one has. Next, have two students in each group use their counters to demonstrate how they could make their amounts equal.

QUICK QUIZ

Write what has to be done so that both students have the same number.
Jill has 14 pennies.
Phil has 10 pennies.
(Jill) should give (2) pennies to (Phil).

Chapter 7 Lesson 9   **154**

CHAPTER 7

WRAP UP

INTRODUCTION The Wrap Up provides activities emphasizing math language and thinking skills for the chapter.

USING PAGE 155

Number Names ▶ When reading the number name, what is a clue that will help you know what number to write? (Possible answer: The first part you read will be the decade name and will stand for the number in the tens place. The next part of the name will be the number that will fall in the ones position. If there is only the decade name to read, then the number in the ones place is 0.)

Math Reasoning ▶ In Exercise 3, what pattern might you use to be sure you have used all the number combinations without repeating any numbers? (Possible answer: Start with the number in the first box. Pair it with the number in the other two boxes, always keeping the number in the starting box in the tens position. Then go to the middle box and end box and repeat this process. This way, you know that you have used each number in the tens position and the ones position.)

Name _____

WRAP UP

MATH WORDS

1. Write the number next to each number name. Then write each number as hundreds, tens, and ones.

	Number	✔	Hundreds	Tens	Ones
twenty-five	25	✔	0	2	5
thirty	30	✔	0	3	0
ninety-two	92	✔	0	9	2
fifty	50	✔	0	5	0
one hundred	100		1	0	0

2. Look at the numbers you wrote. Put a ✔ next to each 2-digit number.

MATH REASONING

3. Make six different 2-digit numbers with these cards. Do not use the same card twice in a number you write.

4	7	9
47	49	74
79	94	97

(one hundred fifty-five) 15

TEACHING OPTIONS

ENRICHMENT Have students explore 2-digit numbers further by having small groups choose 4 cards from number cards 0-9. Ask students to make as many different 2-digit numbers as they can with these cards, without using the same card twice in a number. Discuss how many combinations were possible and what happened when 0 was involved. *Could you make as many 2-digit numbers? Why or why not?* (No; 0 could be used in only the ones place.)

Name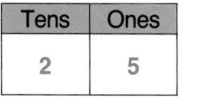

CHAPTER REVIEW/TEST

Write how many tens and ones.
Then write the number.

Tens	Ones
2	5

25

2.

Hundreds	Tens	Ones
1	0	5

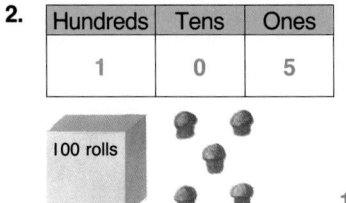

100 rolls

105

Match.

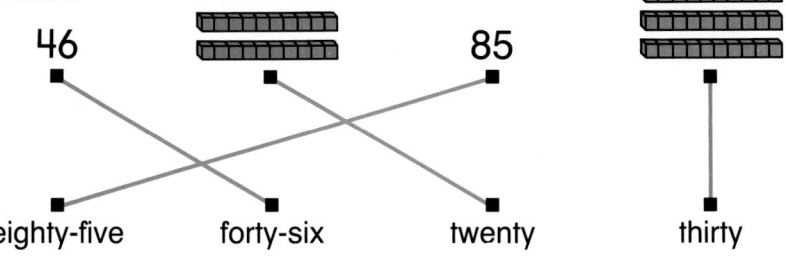

46   85

eighty-five   forty-six   twenty   thirty

Write how much.

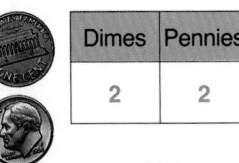

Dimes	Pennies
2	2

22¢

5. Write how many.

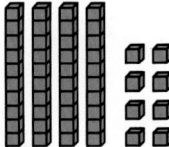

48

12 houses are white.
4 houses are brown.
How many more white
houses are there?

$12 - 4 = 8$

__8__ more white houses

CHAPTER REVIEW/TEST

INTRODUCTION The Review/Test is provided to review and evaluate the skills and concepts presented in Chapter 7.

USING PAGE 156
If you prefer to use this page for review, you may want to use the **Multiple Choice Posttest** (pages 27-28) or the **Free Response Posttest** (pages 27-28) to evaluate mastery of chapter objectives.

ITEM ANALYSIS The table below correlates the Chapter Review/Test items with the lesson objectives for the chapter.

Items	Objectives
1	7-1
2	7-8
3	7-2
4	7-3, 7-7
5	7-4
6	7-6
7	7-5

FORMAL ASSESSMENT

Using Manipulatives Have students use base-ten blocks to model 2- and 3-digit numbers that you write on the chalkboard and read aloud. Observe the models to see if they have shown the correct place value. Then have students use punchout dimes and pennies to show 2-digit amounts.

Communication *Why is it important that the place value of a number be correct when you write it?* (Possible answer: If the place value is wrong,

the number you think you are writing will be read as a different number.)

Critical Thinking ► Explain why the number 0 plays an important part in the place value of 2- and 3-digit numbers. (Possible answer: If there are no ones in a 2-digit number or no tens or ones in a 3-digit number, 0 must be written to show this. Otherwise, a 3-digit number would have only 2 digits and a 2-digit number would have only 1 digit.)

Chapter 7 Chapter Review/Test   **156**

ENRICHMENT

INTRODUCTION Knowing how to read 2-digit numbers will help students understand the meanings of degree markings on a thermometer.

USING PAGE 157

This Enrichment page is provided for all students. You may wish to use it after they have completed the Chapter Review/Test on page 156.

▶ **What do you notice about the numbers on the thermometer at the top of the page?** (Possible answer: The numbers increase by ten; the higher the number, the warmer the temperature.)

▶ **How do you read a thermometer?** (Possible answer: Look at the colored part at the bottom of the thermometer. Find the number it lines up with where the colored part meets the white part. That number is the temperature.)

EXTENSIONS Display a map of the United States and Canada. Have students consult newspapers to see how the temperatures in certain cities on the map compare to each other. Record this information for several days and look for any great temperature changes in any of these cities. Discuss what might cause these changes and talk about the type of clothing people might wear to be comfortable at that temperature. If possible, find cities with temperatures of only 1 digit and note their location to see what they might have in common. Discuss what temperature range students would most like to live in and then talk about how the temperature changes with the seasons.

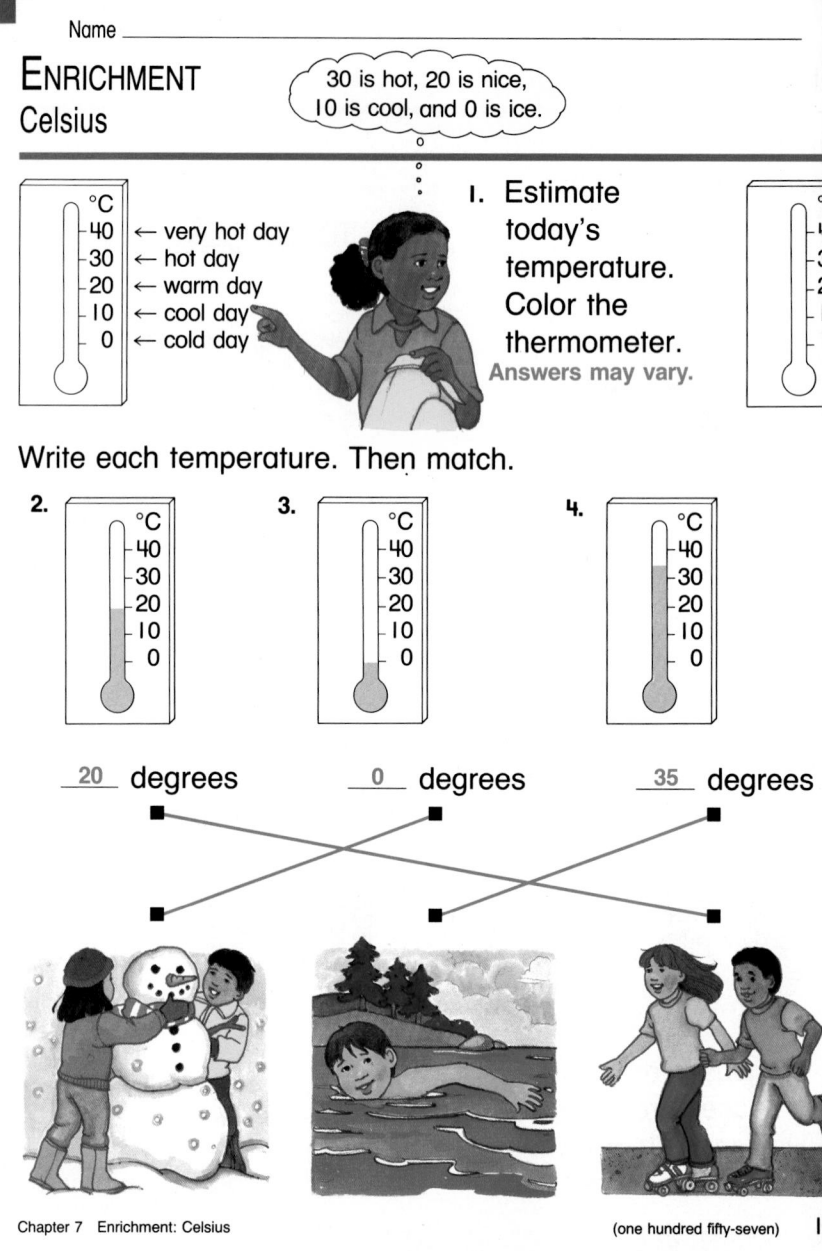

Name _____

ENRICHMENT
Celsius

30 is hot, 20 is nice, 10 is cool, and 0 is ice.

°C
- 40 ← very hot day
- 30 ← hot day
- 20 ← warm day
- 10 ← cool day
- 0 ← cold day

1. Estimate today's temperature. Color the thermometer.
Answers may vary.

Write each temperature. Then match.

2. °C 40 30 20 10 0

3. °C 40 30 20 10 0

4. °C 40 30 20 10 0

__20__ degrees   __0__ degrees   __35__ degrees

Chapter 7 Enrichment: Celsius   (one hundred fifty-seven)

Name _____

CUMULATIVE REVIEW

Subtract.

$$\begin{array}{r} 16 \\ -\ 9 \\ \hline \end{array}$$
- ○ 6
- ● 7
- ○ 8

$$\begin{array}{r} 13 \\ -\ 4 \\ \hline \end{array}$$
- ● 9
- ○ 6
- ○ 8

$$\begin{array}{r} 11 \\ -\ 5 \\ \hline \end{array}$$
- ○ 7
- ○ 5
- ● 6

$$\begin{array}{r} 15 \\ -\ 7 \\ \hline \end{array}$$
- ○ 7
- ○ 10
- ● 8

$$\begin{array}{r} 17 \\ -\ 8 \\ \hline \end{array}$$
- ● 9
- ○ 5
- ○ 6

6. How many centimeters long is the crayon?

- ○ 2 centimeters
- ● 5 centimeters
- ○ 7 centimeters

Which is the best estimate?

7.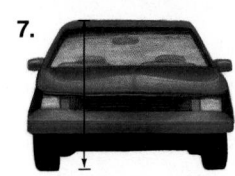
- ● more than 1 foot
- ○ 1 foot
- ○ less than 1 foot

8.
- ● more than 1 liter
- ○ 1 liter
- ○ less than 1 liter

Ann put 2 books on the first shelf, 4 books on the second, and 6 books on the third. She continued this pattern. How many books did she put on the fourth shelf?

- ○ 12 books
- ● 8 books
- ○ 10 books

CUMULATIVE REVIEW

INTRODUCTION   The purpose of this Cumulative Review is to maintain previously taught skills and concepts. The emphasis in this Cumulative Review is on subtraction, Chapter 5; and on measurement, Chapter 6.

ITEM ANALYSIS   The table below correlates the Cumulative Review items with the lessons objectives.

Items	Objectives
1	5-1
2	5-2
3	5-5
4	6-8
5	6-4
6	6-5
7, 8	6-10
9	5-8

CHAPTER 8 NUMBER RELATIONSHIPS AND COUNTING

Chapter Management

OVERVIEW

Lesson	Pages	Objectives	Subject Integration	Strand Integration
Modeling and Writing Numbers Before, After, and Between	159-160	8-1 To write numbers before, after, and between	language arts: book pages	critical thinking
Counting On and Back by 1s	161-162	8-2 To count on and back by 1s	social studies: partner skills	problem solving
Counting On and Back by 10s	163-164	8-3 To count on and back by 10s	social studies: partner skills	graphing
Comparing Numbers	165-166	8-4 To compare numbers using > and <	language arts: book pages	patterns
Problem Solving: Understanding the Operations/Informal Algebra: Finishing Number Sentences	167-168	8-5 To use addition and subtraction; to use > or <	language arts: reading	computation
Counting Patterns for 2s, 3s, and 4s	169-170	8-6 To count by 2s, 3s, and 4s	social studies: partner skills	calculators
Counting Patterns for 5s and 25s	171-172	8-7 To count by 5s and 25s	social studies: group skills	computation, patterns
Ordinal Numbers	173-174	8-8 To count ordinal numbers 1st through 31st	fine arts: cut & paste	patterns
Problem Solving: Finding Extra Data/Problem Solving Strategy: Act It Out	175-176	8-9 To find extra data; to use the strategy Act It Out	language arts: books	consumer math

MATHEMATICAL BACKGROUND

Number Relationships

Lesson 8-1 introduces number relationships using models (book pages and blocks). Activities are provided to reinforce students' understanding of the concepts *before*, *after*, and *between*.

Counting Patterns

As with place value, a strong foundation in counting skills influences students' success with subsequent skills taught in the elementary school curriculum. This chapter develops a student's counting skills from 1 to 100, beginning with counting on and back by 1s and then by 10s. Number charts and place value blocks help students develop the concept of counting patterns. In Lesson 8-8, students learn to count ordinal numbers 1st through 31st. Skip counting helps students gain a greater understanding of numbers and their sequence and provides an important foundation for learning multiplication facts. Knowing the oral sequence for multiples of 2s, 3s, 4s, 5s, and 10s helps students evaluate their thinking when learning multiplication facts. Also, skip counting by 2s prepares students for understanding even and odd numbers.

Problem Solving

In this chapter, students solve problems by eliminating extra data and by using the strategy Act It Out.

TIPS FROM TEACHERS

Have students make patterns using colored toothpicks. Prepare index cards, using watercolor markers to draw patterns of colored lines to represent toothpicks. Have students continue each pattern using real toothpicks. Students also enjoy making their own pattern cards.

Marilyn Majer
Kings Highway School
Clearwater, FL

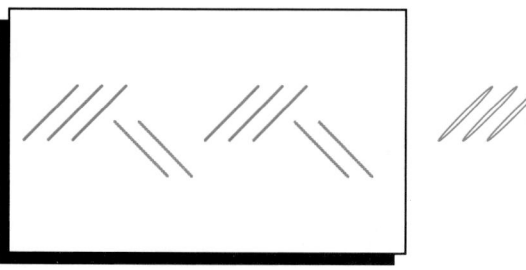

ASSESSMENT

Pretest — Chapter 8, page 1

Multiple-Choice Format

Name _____

1. Choose the number that comes **between**.

46, _?_, 48

- A 45
- **B** 47
- C 49

2. Choose the number that comes **after**.

23, 24, _?_

- A 21
- **B** 25
- C 26

3. Count on. Choose the correct number.

12, 13, _?_

- A 11
- B 15
- **C** 14

4. Count back. Choose the correct number.

21, 20, _?_

- **A** 19
- B 22

5. Count back by 10's. Choose the correct number.

_?_, 63, 73

- **A** 53
- B 43
- C 62

6. Choose > or < for the ○.

36 ○ 63

- **A** <
- B >

7. Choose the number sentence that matches the story.

Amy has 7 stamps. Dan has 9 stamps. How many stamps do they have in all?

- **A** 7 + 9 = 16
- B 9 − 7 = 2
- C 9 − 2 = 7

MCT 2   29

Pretest — Chapter 8, page 2

Multiple-Choice Format

Name _____

8. Count by 2's. Choose the number that comes next.

4, 6, 8, _?_

- A 9
- **B** 10

9. Count by 4's. Choose the number that comes next.

4, 8, _?_

- A 9
- **B** 12

10. Count by 5's. Choose the number that comes next.

40, 45, _?_

- **A** 50
- B 46

11. Count by 25's. Choose the number that comes next.

25, 50, _?_

- A 51
- **B** 75

12. Choose the place in line of the black car.

- A second
- **B** third
- C fourth

13. Choose the answer for the story. Betty has 10 red trucks. Andy has 6 red trucks. Andy has 7 blue trucks. How many more red trucks does Betty have than Andy?

- **A** 4 red trucks
- B 2 red trucks
- C 3 red trucks

30   MCT 2

Posttest — Chapter 8, page 1

Multiple-Choice Format

Name _____

1. Choose the number that comes **between**.

33, _?_, 35

- A 36
- **B** 34
- C 32

2. Choose the number that comes **after**.

44, 45, _?_

- A 43
- **B** 46
- C 50

3. Count on. Choose the correct number.

25, 26, _?_

- A 30
- B 24
- **C** 27

4. Count back. Choose the correct number.

50, 49, _?_

- **A** 48
- B 50

5. Count back by 10's. Choose the correct number.

_?_, 38, 48

- A 28
- **B** 30
- C 58

6. Choose > or < for the ○.

94 ○ 49

- A <
- **B** >

7. Choose the number sentence that matches the story.

Lindy has 3 stickers. Marcus has 8 stickers. How many stickers do they have in all?

- A 8 + 0 = 8
- **B** 3 + 8 = 11
- C 8 − 3 = 5

MCT 2   31

Posttest — Chapter 8, page 2

Multiple-Choice Format

Name _____

8. Count by 2's. Choose the number that comes next.

10, 12, 14, _?_

- **A** 16
- B 8

9. Count by 4's. Choose the number that comes next.

8, 12, _?_

- **A** 16
- B 10

10. Count by 5's. Choose the number that comes next.

65, 70, _?_

- A 71
- **B** 75

11. Count by 25's. Choose the number that comes next.

50, 75, _?_

- **A** 100
- B 80

12. Choose the place in line of the black car.

- A third
- **B** fifth
- C first

13. Choose the answer for the story. Al has 5 blue blocks. Tom has 8 red blocks. Tom has 6 blue blocks. How many more blue blocks does Tom have than Al?

- **A** 1 blue block
- B 11 blue blocks
- C 14 blue blocks

32   MCT 2

ITEM ANALYSIS

Items	Objectives
1, 2	8-1
3, 4	8-2
5	8-3
6	8-4
7	8-5
8, 9	8-6
10, 11	8-7
12	8-8
13	8-9

Note: The item analysis is the same for all pretests and posttests for this chapter.

ALSO AVAILABLE

► **Free Response Tests**
► **Alternative Tests**
► **Thinking Strategies**
► **Concrete Materials**

Optional Chapter Activities

PROJECT AND BULLETIN BOARD

Practice counting by 3s with this bulletin board project. Use number cards 1-100 to make a hundred chart. During session 1, have students skip count by 3s. As they count, ask them to turn over the cards *not* used when counting by 3s and look for a pattern. During session 2, have a volunteer choose any 2 numbers showing on the 3s chart. Add the numbers to discover if the sum is also a multiple of 3. Experiment by having every student choose and add 2 numbers from the chart to find out if the sum is always a multiple of 3. During session 3, copy the dot-to-dot pattern on the board. Have students connect the dots for skip counting by 3s.

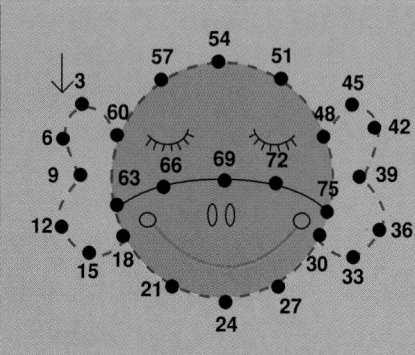

SKIP COUNTING

1	2	3	4	5	6	7	8	9	10
11	12	13	14	15	16	17	18	19	20
21	22	23	24	25	26	27	28	29	30
31	32	33	34	35	36	37	28	29	40
41	42	43	44	45	46	47	48	49	50
51	52	53	54	55	56	57	58	59	60
61	62	63	64	65	66	67	68	69	70
71	72	73	74	75	76	77	78	79	80
81	82	83	84	85	86	87	88	89	90
91	92	93	94	95	96	97	98	99	100

COOPERATIVE LEARNING

Identify the group skill: avoiding destructive criticism. Have students illustrate the song *The Mulberry Bush*. Assign a verse to each of 6 groups. Have students draw a picture to show the action and label it as *first verse, second verse,* and so on. Display the pictures in order. Have students stand in a circle. As they sing the chorus, they skip to the right. During each verse, they stand in place and pantomime the actions. Encourage those students who skip well to hold hands with and skip beside those who are having difficulty. Remind them to avoid unnecessary criticism and provide help instead.

Chorus: Here we go round the mulberry bush.
The mulberry bush, the mulberry bush,
Here we go round the mulberry bush,
So early in the morning.

Verses: **1.** This is the way we wash our clothes
2. This is the way we iron our clothes
3. This is the way we tie our shoes
4. This is the way we sweep the floor
5. This is the way we pour our milk
6. This is the way we eat our toast

You will find grouping suggestions and cooperative learning activities in most lessons throughout this chapter.

LITERATURE

Anno, Mitsumasa. *Anno's Counting Book.* New York: Harper & Row, 1977.

This book shows the changing of the seasons and how the land is altered by the people and animals who live there.

Have students count the number of objects in the pictures. Then have them look for, count, and write the patterns of objects and people in 2s, 3s, and 4s.

Bang, Molly. *Ten, Nine, Eight.* New York: Penguin, 1985

Mayer, Mercer. *Just For You.* New York: Golden Press, 1975.

ENGLISH AS A SECOND LANGUAGE

This chapter involves ordering using the terms *before, after,* and *between.* Use flashcards with pictures of logical, obvious sequences of events and ask students to order them, talking out loud as they complete the task. Then have students form a line and assign a number to each student. Ask questions such as, *Who is before number 7? Will the person between numbers 5 and 7 please hop on 1 foot?*

When discussing the kinds of books that can be found in the library, remind students of books about hobbies. Have them describe their hobbies as a series of steps.

Ordinal numbers are difficult to pronounce. Ask native speakers to make audiotapes of stories using ordinal numbers. Have ESL students listen to these tapes, transcribe the numbers they hear, then record themselves. If necessary, ask native speakers to physically show ESL students how to make the sounds correctly. Keep these tapes in the tape file suggested in Chapter 5.

GIFTED

Mathematically talented students may already understand counting patterns and skip count by a variety of numbers. You may wish to challenge these students, after they have completed their Student Edition work, by having them create their own follow-the-dot pictures. Have them place tracing paper over a picture of a simple object or shape and make a series of dots on the outline. They then number the dots, skip counting by 2s, 3s, 4s, 5s, or 10s in the order in which the dots should be connected. Remind them to include the starting and ending points. Have students exchange papers and complete each other's drawings. If this appeals to your students, you may wish to use the following variations as you do this chapter: Have students start from the highest number and skip count backward to zero; have students skip count by a different number, such as 6, 7, or 9, and challenge a partner to determine the counting pattern made by the picture.

STUDENTS AT RISK

It is helpful to many learning-disabled students to see patterns as they count orally. One method is to have them color the numbers in the pattern (5, 10, 15, for example) on a Hundred Chart (TA6). To help them recognize the pattern created when 10 is added to a number, have them begin with a number between 1 and 10, color it, count 10 more squares and color, and so on. With practice of this sort, they will begin to see the pattern of adding tens and will eventually be able to do the operation mentally.

As students line up to leave the classroom, ask them to identify their ordinal place in line. As another activity, perform a series of tasks with students and then have them recall the sequence. Ask them to include such words as *first, second,* and *third* when they describe the activity.

Think of a number between 1 and 20. As students guess, say *higher* or *lower* to give clues. Remind them to pay attention to the clues and see how few guesses they need. The student who guesses correctly may think of the next number. Continue this game with larger numbers and use the hundred chart as an organizer of information.

You may also use the Reteaching Supplements and the specific Reteaching Tips from each lesson in this chapter.

Chapter 8 Optional Chapter Activities

These pictures and accompanying stories and poems are available as storybooks.

You may want to read and discuss this poem with your students before starting the chapter. The first lesson in this chapter includes a question about the poem. Lessons 1, 2, 3, 4 and 8 in this chapter have questions in the informal Assessment that refer to the poem.

Check It Out

"Places to go! Things to see!
Welcome to our school library!"
Thus exclaims our parrot, Pierre,
As he flies smartly through the air.

Pierre helps us find books we need.
We tell him what we want to read.
He then shows us where to look,
Be it magazine, record, map, or book.

Book number 53 has your information.
Books numbered 50 to 60 are in this
    location.
Ah, yes, I see it there. Just between
Books 52 and 54 it can be seen.

Now that you finally have your book
The table of contents is the place to look.
Pages 25 through 27 have what you need.
How many pages will you read?

When all the kids have gone away
The library closes for the day.
"It's safe to come out!" Pierre announces.
Out from the bookdrop his first friend
    bounces.

A knight in armor, a child on the prairie,
An elephant king, a beautiful fairy,
A bear that loves honey and a spider that
    writes
Are all returned after action-filled nights.

"How was your trip? Was it a good
    lend?"
Pierre questions each returning friend.
The spider replies, "My story was great.
We talked by flashlight till very late."

Each friend takes a turn and tells his story,
Returned to the library with tales of glory.
Pierre enjoys each and every tale.
He travels places without setting sail.

Soon it's time for the kids to return,
And Pierre is ready to help them learn.
"Places to go! Things to see!
Welcome to our school library!"

Modeling and Writing Numbers Before, After, and Between

OBJECTIVE 8-1   To model and write numbers before, after, or between

PREBOOK ACTIVITIES

QUICK REVIEW

Say the number that comes before and the number that comes after each number.

3	(2, 4)	9	(8, 10)	7	(6, 8)
11	(10, 12)	18	(17, 19)	15	(14, 16)

PRIOR KNOWLEDGE

Pose questions such as the following to discuss students' daily schedules. Use the words *before, after,* and *between.*
What did we do before our math lesson? What do we usually do after lunch? What do you do between the time you get up in the morning and the time you leave for school? What do you like to do after school? What do you do between dinnertime and bedtime?

COMMUNICATION

Reading and Discussing Math   On the chalkboard, write, the words **before, after,** and **between** and read them aloud. Display a hundreds chart on the overhead projector. Point to a number, such as 34, and have students say the number aloud. Have students use the hundreds chart to answer such questions as: *What number comes after 34?* (35) *What number comes before 34?* (33) *What numbers come between 33 and 36?* (34 and 35) Point to each number as it is identified. Repeat for other numbers. Extend this activity by giving students clues and having them guess the number on the hundreds chart. For example: *I am thinking of the number before 66.* (65) *I am thinking of the number between 40 and 42.* (41)

EXPLORE AND CONNECT

Materials: base-ten blocks, punchout number cards 0-9
Grouping Suggestions: pairs
Provide each pair with tens sticks and ones cubes and 3 sets of number cards. Have each student choose 1 number card to form a 2-digit number, then work together to model the number with base-ten blocks. Next, ask a student to add 1 ones cube to the model. The other student makes the number **after** with number cards and places it beside the original number. Students read the 2 numbers aloud. Students repeat this process several times. Change the activity by asking students to build a 2-digit number and take 1 ones cube away. The partner makes the number **before** with number cards and places it in front of the original number. Again, students read the 2 numbers, but this time they read the original number first, then the number before. Encourage students to avoid destructive criticism by helping each other when necessary and working as a team.

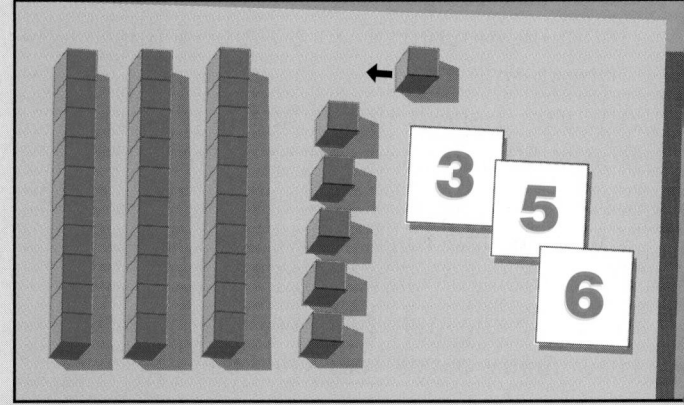

CONNECTIONS   Use these anytime.

Problem of the Day

Use Objects   Use punchout coins to solve this problem.
Alice has 3 dimes and 4 pennies. She finds 1 more penny. How much money does Alice have now? (35¢) How much will she have if she spends 2¢? (33¢)

Subject Integration

Language Arts   Look through your reading book. Write the page numbers on which your favorite story begins and ends. Then write the numbers that come between without looking. Use your reading book to check your answers.

Counting Patterns

Calculator   Enter a 2-digit number on your calculator. Think of the number that comes after. Add 1 to your number and write it. Is it the number you guessed? Add 1 five more times and write the pattern. Now subtract 1 from the number on your calculator until you reach your original number. Say the pattern backward.

CLASSWORK AND HOMEWORK SUPPLEMENTS

Practice

Number Sense 8-1

Name _____

Modeling and Writing Numbers Before, After, and Between

1. Write the number that comes **before**.   **2.** Write the number that comes **after**.   **3.** Write the number that comes **between**.

before	after	between
_29_, 30	46, _47_	55, _56_, 57
_60_, 61	59, _60_	82, _83_, 84
_73_, 74	27, _28_	79, _80_, 81
_92_, 93	68, _69_	16, _17_, 18
_49_, 50	79, _80_	28, _29_, 30
_28_, 29	14, _15_	39, _40_, 41
_86_, 87	32, _33_	64, _65_, 66
_65_, 66	19, _20_	91, _92_, 93

66   Use with text pages 159–160.   PS-2

Building Thinking Skills

Number Sense 8-1

Name _____

Pathmaker

Play with a partner. Each needs a game sheet.
You also need 2 number cubes: 1 – 6 and 4 – 9.
Take turns. Roll both cubes.
Choose your number. If you roll , choose 64 or 46.
Write the number on one of the stones.
Every time you roll a number, write it in order
(before or after) on the path. If there is no empty stone
before or after, you lose your turn.
The player who fills up the path first is the winner.

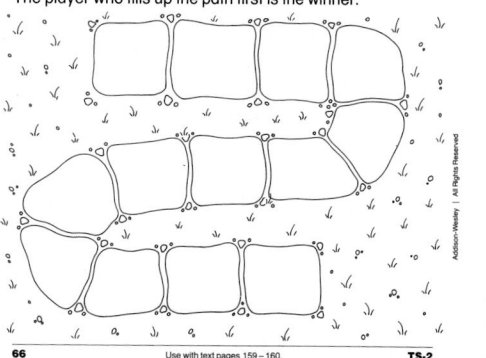

66   Use with text pages 159 – 160.   TS-2

Reteaching

Number Sense 8-1

Name _____

Modeling and Writing Numbers Before, After, and Between

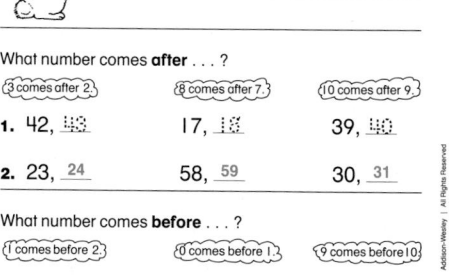

I see a pattern!

1	2	3	4	5	6	7	8	9	10
11	12	13	14	15	16	17	18	19	20
21	22	23	24	25	26	27	28	29	30
31	32	33	34	35	36	37	38	39	40

What number comes **after** . . . ?

(3 comes after 2.)   (8 comes after 7.)   (10 comes after 9.)

1. 42, _43_   17, _18_   39, _40_

2. 23, _24_   58, _59_   30, _31_

What number comes **before** . . . ?

(1 comes before 2.)   (0 comes before 1.)   (9 comes before 10.)

3. _31_, 32   _40_, 41   _49_, 50

4. _57_, 58   _19_, 20   _60_, 61

66   Use with text pages 159 – 160.   RS-2

Challenges

Cooperative Activities 8-1

Name _____

Hidden Numbers

Play with a partner. Player 1 takes 5 counters and covers
5 numbers.
Player 2 tells what numbers are hidden.
Player 1 writes the numbers on a piece of paper.
Both players check by taking off the counters.
Now Player 2 covers 5 numbers.

1	2	3	4	5	6	7	8	9	10
11	12	13	14	15	16	17	18	19	20
21	22	23	24	25	26	27	28	29	30
31	32	33	34	35	36	37	38	39	40
41	42	43	44	45	46	47	48	49	50
51	52	53	54	55	56	57	58	59	60
61	62	63	64	65	66	67	68	69	70
71	72	73	74	75	76	77	78	79	80
81	82	83	84	85	86	87	88	89	90
91	92	93	94	95	96	97	98	99	100

66   Use with text pages 159 – 160.   CS-2

OPTIONS FOR INDIVIDUAL NEEDS

Basic

Exercises All
More Practice, p. 417, set B

Supplements
Reteaching 66 or
Practice 66

Average

Exercises All
More Practice, p. 417, set B

Supplements
Practice 66
Challenges 66 or
Thinking Skills 66

Extended

Exercises All

Supplements
Challenges 66
Thinking Skills 66

Other Resources:
Math in Stride, pp. 75-76
Explorations, pp. 6, 30, 123, 136-137, 263
Problem-Solving Experiences In Mathematics, pp. 125, 143
Workjobs, pp. 134-137, 140-145, 182-191
Workjobs For Parents, pp. 78-91, 100-103

8-1

OBJECTIVE 8-1

To model and write numbers before, after, or between

Materials: punchout number cards 0-9, base-ten blocks, number cubes, TA6 (Hundred Chart)

Grouping Suggestions: individual work, cooperative learning groups of 3

---

1. MOTIVATE AND TEACH

LEARN ABOUT IT

Read the chapter poem to the class. Have students use blocks to show the number 25. *What number comes after 25? Add a block to show this number.* (26) Have students make the number 38 with punchout number cards and place the cards on the line on the yellow page on page 159. Then have them place blocks above the number on the yellow page to model 38.

▶ **What can you predict about the number on the blue page?** (It will be 1 more because it is the next page.)

▶ **How can you find the number that is after 38?** (Possible answers: Say the next number by counting; add 1 more ones cube and name the new number that is modeled.)

▶ **How can you find the number that is before 38?** (Possible answers: Subtract 1; count back 1; take 1 ones cube away and count.)

▶ **Suppose the yellow page is numbered 58 but the blue page is not numbered. You turn the page and you see the next page is 60. How can you find the missing number between the 2 numbers?** (Possible answers: Count up from the first number or count back from the last number.)

2. CHECK UNDERSTANDING

ERROR ALERT Supplying the number after when asked for the number before.

8
Number Relationships and Counting Patterns

TEACHING OPTIONS

RETEACHING TIPS Have students hold consecutive number cards and line up in order. They identify the number before or after by looking at each other's numbers; then one hides a card. Students tell the missing number (between). Use Reteaching Supplement 66.

ENRICHMENT Have students take a hundred chart and cut along the lines to make a jigsaw puzzle. Each piece should have at least 3 numbers. Have students piece together their own puzzles or trade pieces with a partner to complete.

Name _____

odeling and Writing Numbers
efore, After, and Between

se blocks to show each page number.

Show and write the number that comes **after.**

Show and write the number that comes **before.**

Show and write the numbers that come **between.**

rite the numbers that come after, before,
r between. Use blocks to check.

(after) 72, _73_   47, _48_   39, _40_   80, _81_

(before) _55_, 56   _17_, 18   _59_, 60   _99_, 100

(between) 41, _42_, _43_, 44   59, _60_, _61_, _62_, 63

SE CRITICAL THINKING

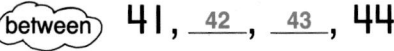

Ring the numbers that are closer to 60 than to 50.

53   (58)   52   (56)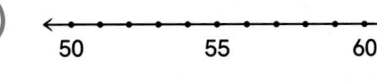

50   55   60

3. PRACTICE AND APPLY

Basic	All
Average	All
Extended	All

PRACTICE

How is finding the number that comes after different when the digit in the ones place is 9? (You must go to the next ten and put a zero in the ones place, because 9 is the highest number that can go in the ones place.)

APPLY

USE CRITICAL THINKING ▶ **How can the number line help you find the numbers that are closer to 60?** (Possible answer: You can count the marks to find the number and see whether it is closer to 50 or 60.)
▶ **What methods can you use to check your work?** (Possible answers: Look at the numbers on a hundred chart; model the numbers and compare how many times you have to add ones or take away ones to get to 50 or 60.)
▶ **What other numbers on the number line are closer to 60 than to 50?** (57, 59)

8-1

LOSE AND ASSESS

HOW WHAT YOU KNOW

ovide groups with hundred charts, 2 mber cubes, and several ones ocks. One student rolls 2 cubes, ys a 2-digit number, and places a ock over that number on the chart. ithout looking, another student tells e number that comes after, and a ird tells the one that comes before. peat, rolling number cubes and ling the numbers that come tween.

> ## QUICK QUIZ
>
> Write the numbers after, before, or between.
> After   13, (14)   85, (86)   59, (60)
> Before   (36), 37   (20), 21   (39) 40
> Between   46, (47), (48) (49), 50

Counting On and Back by 1s

OBJECTIVE 8-2   To count on and back by 1s

PREBOOK ACTIVITIES

QUICK REVIEW

I will write on the chalkboard a number between 1 and 19. Then I will say *more* or *less*. If I say *more*, hold up the number card that shows what number comes after. If I say *less*, hold up the number card that shows what number comes before.

3, less (2)   7, more (8)   15, more (16)   12, less (11)
10, more (11)   9, less (8)   13, more (14)

PRIOR KNOWLEDGE

Read these stories to help students recall counting on and counting back.

Samantha put 17 pennies in her piggy bank.
She added 1 more penny.
How many pennies does she have now?   (18)
Samantha had 18 pennies in her piggy bank.
She took 1 penny out.
How many pennies does she have now?   (17)

What happens to the number when you add 1 penny? (The answer is the number that comes next.) *What happens to the number when you take 1 penny away?* (The answer is the number that comes before.)

COMMUNICATION

Writing in Math   In their Math Journals, have students copy and complete each sentence using one of the following words:

adding   on   subtract   back

1. To find the number that comes next, count   (on) .
2. Counting on is the same as   (adding) .
3. To find the number that comes before, count   (back) .
4. You can count back to   (subtract) .

EXPLORE AND CONNECT

Materials: base-ten blocks, TA 6 (Hundred Chart)
Grouping Suggestion: pairs

Provide each pair with tens and ones blocks and a hundred chart. Give a starting number, such as 38. Have one student model the number with base-ten blocks. Have the second student add cubes and make appropriate trades to count on 1, 2, or 3. *What number do you have?* (39, 40, or 41) Students may use the hundred chart to check their answers. Repeat, having students remove cubes from the original number to count back. (37, 36, or 35) *What happened to the digit in the ones place when you counted on 2?* (It became zero.) *What happened to the digit in the tens place?* (It changed from 3 to 4.) Have students change tasks and repeat with other 2-digit numbers, asking questions about how the digits change as a decade number is crossed. Encourage students to help each other without criticizing each other's work.

CONNECTIONS   Use these anytime.

Problem of the Day

Logic   Imagine a number line beginning at 60 and ending at 70. From which number can you count on and back the same amount to arrive at either end? (65)

Math Connection

Money   Which coin would you use for counting on and counting back by ones? Why? (pennies, because they are worth one cent)

Counting

Patterns   Suppose you are counting on by 1s from 54 ten times. What would be your new number? (64) What other ways could you count on to find the answer? (Count by 2s five times, count by 5s two times, count by 10s one time.)

CLASSWORK AND HOMEWORK SUPPLEMENTS

Practice

Skills Maintenance   8-2

Name _____

Counting On and Back by 1s

Count on.

1. 72 _73_ _74_ _75_   49 _50_ _51_ _52_

2. 60 _61_ _62_ _63_   83 _84_ _85_ _86_

3. 91 _92_ _93_ _94_   67 _68_ _69_ _70_

4. 46 _47_ _48_ _49_   59 _60_ _61_ _62_

5. 19 _20_ _21_ _22_   97 _98_ _99_ _100_

Count back.

6. 54 _53_ _52_ _51_   27 _26_ _25_ _24_

7. 31 _30_ _29_ _28_   75 _74_ _73_ _72_

8. 12 _11_ _10_ _9_   44 _43_ _42_ _41_

9. 66 _65_ _64_ _63_   96 _95_ _94_ _93_

10. 87 _86_ _85_ _84_   19 _18_ _17_ _16_

PS-2   Use with text pages 161–162.   67

Building Thinking Skills

Reading Math   8-2

Name _____

Puzzle Pages

Amy, Bob, Cal, and Dina have the same puzzle book.

1. Amy is on page 44.
Bob is on the next page.

What page is Bob on? _45_

Did you count on or count back? _count on_

2. Dina is doing a puzzle on page 32.
Cal is on the page before.

What page is Cal on? _31_

Did you count on or count back? _count back_

3. Amy colored the picture on page 57.
Dina gave her the crayons she had used
on the page before.

On which page did Dina use crayons? _56_

Did you count on or count back? _count back_

4. Bob wants to cut out page 83 to make an airplane.
So he did the next page first.

What page did Bob do first? _84_

Did you count on or count back? _count on_

TS-2   Use with text pages 161–162.   67

Reteaching

Skills Review   8-2

Name _____

Counting On and Back by 1s

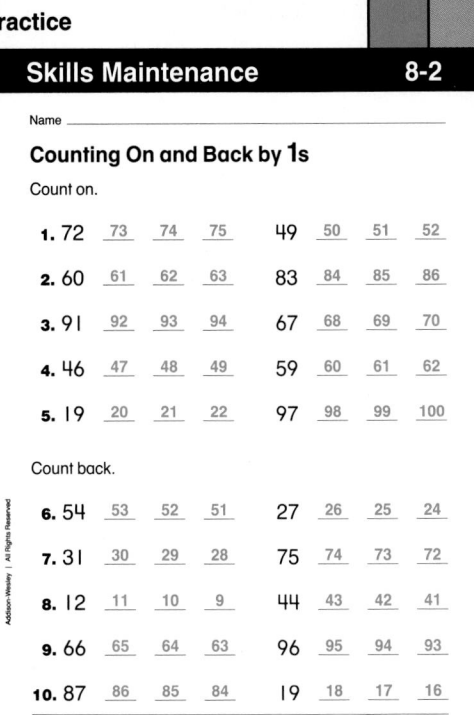

	One Less	One More
	26	**27** 28
	34	**35** 36
	42	**43**
	50	**51**
	31	**32**

1. ← Count back. | Tens | Ones | Count on. →
11 12 13 | **1** | **4** | 15 16 17

2. ← Count back. | Tens | Ones | Count on. →
22 23 24 | **2** | **5** | 26 27 28

3. ← Count back. | Tens | Ones | Count on. →
33 34 35 | **3** | **6** | 37 38 39

4. ← Count back. | Tens | Ones | Count on. →
44 45 46 | **4** | **7** | 48 49 50

RS-2   Use with text pages 161–162.   67

Challenges

Mental Math   8-2

Name _____

Find Rusty's Bone

Start at number 34. Color the number that
comes next. You can go left, right, up, or down.

34	35	53	77	47	97	39	18	85	60	17	69	46	29	94	55
43	36	31	43	49	34	54	26	96	52	16	80	71	98	83	28
67	37	52	41	42	43	44	47	61	15	79	45	12	54	99	27
48	38	39	40	51	25	45	54	97	40	70	95	82	93	26	57
28	62	76	61	92	48	46	64	76	51	13	86	30	53	56	38
86	41	63	60	15	51	47	74	14	81	44	78	43	25	93	72
62	34	60	40	50	49	48	60	69	55	40	26	36	46	56	49
78	85	48	15	51	84	26	49	42	47	78	62	63	64	65	66
84	22	98	25	52	56	72	84	37	85	72	61	36	32	85	67
35	80	90	35	53	54	55	56	57	58	59	60	29	67	86	68
62	91	49	59	38	44	43	65	75	68	63	46	44	38	96	69
79	21	91	33	58	66	50	48	65	54	47	74	73	72	71	70
69	89	82	90	19	68	57	53	72	31	57	75	37	27	67	92
36	66	20	90	73	24	81	87	77	76	57	92	75	56	93
63	83	64	87	45	67	74	52	46	71	84	77	85	28	38	38
64	43	32	44	68	23	88	32	41	40	68	78	79	80	81	82
37	65	88	51	67	89	76	42	70	75	27	19	97	64	37	83

CS-2   Use with text pages 161–162.   67

8-2

LESSON PLAN 8-2

OBJECTIVE 8-2
To count on and back by 1s

Materials: spinners, TA 6 (Hundred Chart), Cube-A-Links or counters

Grouping Suggestions: pairs, individual work

---

1. MOTIVATE AND TEACH

LEARN ABOUT IT

Display a large hundred chart. Write a starting number on the chalkboard, such as 28, and ask students to model the number and count on 1, 2, and 3 with cubes. As volunteers call out the new numbers (29, 30, 31), write them on the board. Repeat the activity for counting back.

▶ **What happens to the digits in the tens and ones places when you count past 30?** (Possible answer: The tens digit gets bigger by 1; you begin counting the ones from 0 again.) Direct students' attention to Exercise 1 on page 161.

▶ **How is counting on like adding?** (You add 1 each time.)

▶ **How is counting back like subtracting?** (You subtract 1 each time.)

▶ **What happens to the ones digits as you count on from 64?** (They get bigger by 1 each time.) **What happens to the tens digits as you count on from 64?** (It stays the same until you reach 70.)

▶ **What will happen to the tens digit if you count back 2 from 61?** (Possible answers: It will change to 5; it will be 1 less.)

▶ **What happens to the ones digit when you count back 2 from 61?** (Possible answers: It changes to 9; you have to start counting back from 9.)

2. CHECK UNDERSTANDING

ERROR ALERT Difficulty completing a counting sequence where counting on or back across a decade is necessary.

Name _____

Counting On and Back by 1s

Work in a group. Use your spinner. Spin a tens number. Spin a ones number. Write the numbers in the box. Count on and back.
Answers may vary.
Check students' work.

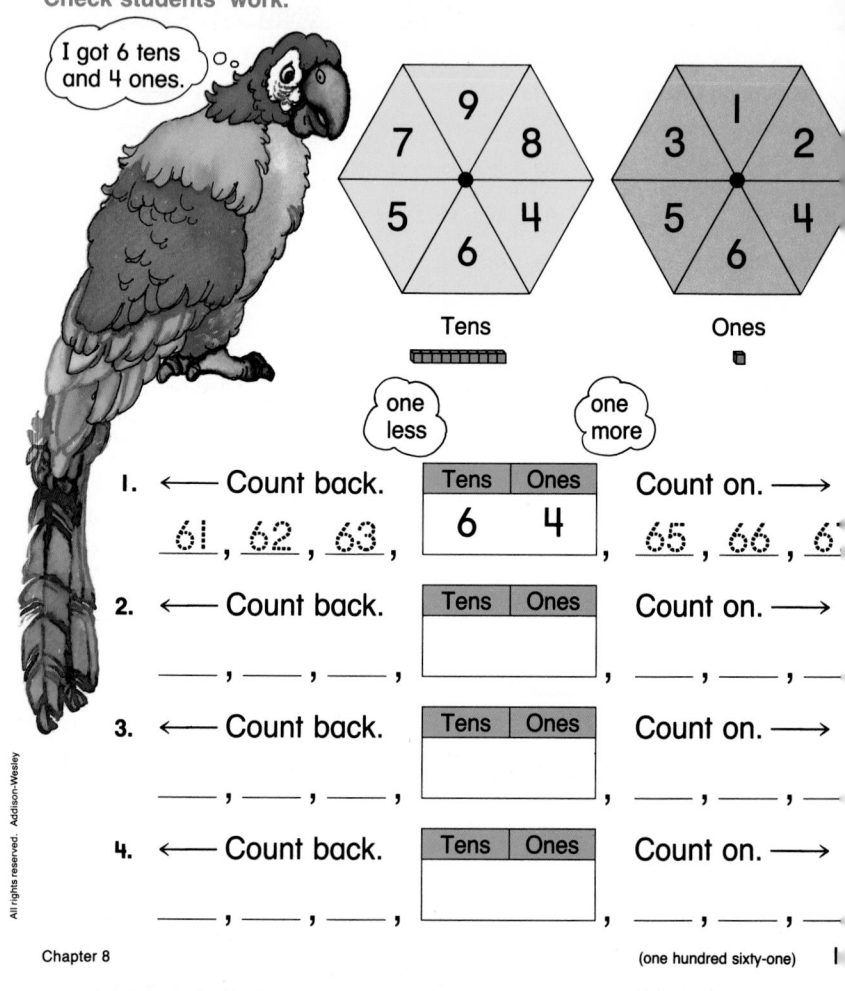

I got 6 tens and 4 ones.

Tens   Ones

one less   one more

1. ⟵ Count back.

Tens	Ones
6	4

61, 62, 63,   , 65, 66, 6[]

Count on. ⟶

2. ⟵ Count back.

Tens	Ones

____ , ____ , ____ ,   , ____ , ____ ,

Count on. ⟶

3. ⟵ Count back.

Tens	Ones

____ , ____ , ____ ,   , ____ , ____ ,

Count on. ⟶

4. ⟵ Count back.

Tens	Ones

____ , ____ , ____ ,   , ____ , ____ ,

Count on. ⟶

Chapter 8

(one hundred sixty-one)

TEACHING OPTIONS

RETEACHING TIPS Have students model 28 by joining 2 groups of 10 and 1 of 8 cubes. Count on 3 by adding 3 more cubes. *How many now?* (31) *Can you make another 10?* (yes) Then count back 2 by taking away 2 cubes. *How many now?* (29) Use Reteaching Supplement 67.

ENRICHMENT **Family Math** Have students bring the following number pairs home: 45 - 42, 73 - 77, 59 - 62, 91 - 87. Have an adult say the number pairs aloud. The student tells how to count on or back to get from one number to the other. For example, for 45 - 42, they say, "Count back 3."

ount on and back.

← Count back. | Count on. →

__64__, __65__, __66__, __67__, **68**, __69__, __70__, __71__, __72__

__88__, __89__, __90__, __91__, **92**, __93__, __94__, __95__, __96__

__13__, __14__, __15__, __16__, **I7**, __18__, __19__, __20__, __21__

Count on and back to finish the chart.

1	2	3	4	5	6	7	8	9	10
11	12	13	14	15	16	17	18	19	20
21	22	23	24	25	26	27	28	29	30
31	32	33	34	35	36	37	38	39	40
41	42	43	44	45	46	47	48	49	50
51	52	53	54	55	56	57	58	59	60
61	62	63	64	65	66	67	68	69	70
71	72	73	74	75	76	77	78	79	80
81	82	83	84	85	86	87	88	89	90
91	92	93	94	95	96	97	98	99	100

ROBLEM SOLVING

BASEBALL

The library had 19 sports books.
Lamar checked out 3 sports books.
How many sports books are left? __16__ books

2 (one hundred sixty-two)   Chapter 8

3. PRACTICE AND APPLY

Basic	All
Average	All
Extended	All

PRACTICE

In Exercise 4 on page 162, how do the dashed numbers help you fill in the chart? (They help you see what numbers come before or go after them.)

APPLY

PROBLEM SOLVING ▶ **Which operation will you use to solve the problem?** (subtraction, counting back)
▶ **Explain how you knew to subtract or count back.** (Possible answers: You need to find out how many books are left; you are taking away books.)
▶ **Is it easier to subtract 3 or count back 3? Why?** (Answers will vary. Students may say that it is easier to count back 3 because they can do it mentally.)

8-2

CLOSE AND ASSESS

SHOW WHAT YOU KNOW
eview with students the chapter
oem, *Check It Out,* and ask them to
ok at the picture. *Book number 53
as your information.* Have students
ork in small groups to count on from
3 to 60 and back from 53 to 45.
emind them to help each other
lentify the number that comes next.

QUICK QUIZ

Copy and complete the pattern. Count on and back.
__(86)__, __(87)__, __(88)__, 89,
__(90)__, __(91)__, __(92)__

Counting On and Back by 10s

OBJECTIVE 8-3   To count on and back by 10s

PREBOOK ACTIVITIES

QUICK REVIEW

Write the next three numbers in each pattern. 2, 4, 6, (8, 10, 12)
5, 10, 15, 20, (25, 30, 35)
10, 20, 30, (40, 50, 60)

PRIOR KNOWLEDGE

Ask students to tell stories about how they use counting on or
counting back by 10 in their own lives. Help them brainstorm
by offering topics such as adding or subtracting dimes, keeping
score, and using things that come in tens. Have students listen
to each other's stories and offer positive comments when
appropriate.

COMMUNICATION

Discussing Math   Write the following number pattern
vertically on the chalkboard: *12, 22, 32, 42, 52.* Read the
pattern aloud with students. *What pattern do you see?* (Possible
answer: The numbers are counted by tens.) *What pattern do
you see in the tens place?* (The numbers increase by one each
time.) *What happens in the ones place?* (The number stays the
same.) *What do you think will come next in this number
pattern?* (62) *Explain how you got your answer.* (added 1 to
the tens place; counted by tens)

EXPLORE AND CONNECT

Materials: number cubes, base-ten blocks, TA 6 (Numbered
Hundred Chart)
Grouping suggestion: cooperative learning groups of 3
Have one student roll 2 number cubes until a 2-digit number
over 30 can be made. A second student uses base-ten blocks ▪
model the number; a third says the original number and adds
more tens block at a time to make the next three numbers,
counting on by tens. Group members check their work by
reading the sequence aloud or by using the hundred chart. Th▪
have them count back by tens from the original number,
removing 1 tens block at a time, until 3 tens have been
removed. Help students avoid destructive criticism by
suggesting that they count on and back together. *What happer▪
to the ones digit when you count on and back by 10s?* (It stay
the same.) What happens to the tens digit? (It changes by 1
each time.)

CONNECTIONS   Use these anytime.

Problem of the Day

Wayne has 35¢ in his bank. He adds a
dime every day. Will he have more or
less than a dollar after 10 days? (more)
How did you find your answer? (counted
on by tens)

Counting Patterns

Imagine that the book you are reading
has 53 pages. You want to show the
number with your fingers. How would
you do it? (Show all 10 fingers 5 times,
then show 3 fingers.) Why? (By showing
10 fingers 5 times, you are counting by
10s to 50. Then you show 3 more fingers
to show 3 more, or 53.)

Number Sense

How do the numbers in a hundred chart
make counting on and back by tens easy?
(The numbers can be counted by reading
up or down the chart.) Why? (Each row
is ten more or ten less.)

CLASSWORK AND HOMEWORK SUPPLEMENTS

Practice

Skills Maintenance   8-3

Name

Counting On and Back by 10s

Count on by 10s.

1. 23, _33_ , _43_ , _53_   2. 38, _48_ , _58_ , _68_

3. 4, _14_ , _24_ , _34_   4. 46, _56_ , _66_ , _76_

Count back by 10s.

5. _66_ , _76_ , _86_ , 96   6. _40_ , _50_ , _60_ , 70

7. _5_ , _15_ , _25_ , 35   8. _17_ , _27_ , _37_ , 47

Count on and back by 10s.

9. _29_ , _39_ , 49, _59_ , _69_ , _79_ , _89_ , _99_

10. _7_ , _17_ , _27_ , _37_ , _47_ , _57_ , 67, _77_

Count on and back by 10s.
Write the number of each apartment on its shutter.

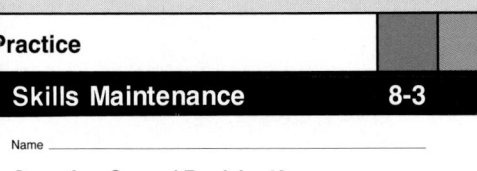

	76
	66
	56
	46
	36
	26
	16

68   Use with text pages 163–164.   PS-2

Building Thinking Skills

Life Skills   8-3

Name

Reading a Bus Schedule

The buses leave every 10 minutes.
Count on or count back by 10s to finish the chart.

After School Bus Schedule		
Red Bus To: Scouts	Blue Bus To: Art Class	Orange Bus To: Dance Center
3:05	3: _18_	3: _21_
3: _15_	3:28	3: _31_
3: _25_	3: _38_	3: _41_
3: _35_	3: _48_	3:51

Use the schedule to answer the questions.

1. What time is the first bus to the art class? 3: _18_

2. What time is the first bus to the Dance Center? 3: _21_

3. What time is the last bus to Scouts? 3: _35_

4. Wendy goes to dance class after school.
   Her school day ends at 3:25.
   What time is the first bus she can take? 3: _31_

5. Eddie goes to Scouts today.
   He leaves school at 3:20.
   Which bus will get him to Scouts the soonest? 3: _25_

68   Use with text pages 163–164.   TS-2

Average

Exercises All
Calculator Bank, p. 401

Supplements
Practice 68
Challenges 68 or
Thinking Skills 68

Exercises All
Calculator Bank, p. 401

Supplements
Reteaching 68 or
Practice 68
Thinking Skills 68

Reteaching

Skills Review   8-3

Name

Counting On and Back by 10s

1. Count on by 10s.

33	12	18	24	47
43	22	28	34	57
53	32	38	44	67
63	42	48	54	77

2. Count back by 10s.

14	26	33	42	51
24	36	43	52	61
34	46	53	62	71
44	56	63	72	81

68   Use with text pages 163–164.   RS-2

Challenges

Calculators   8-3

Name

An Amazing Trip

Help the kangaroo hop through the maze.
Use your calculator to fill in all the blanks. Then color the path
of addition sentences that lead to the food.

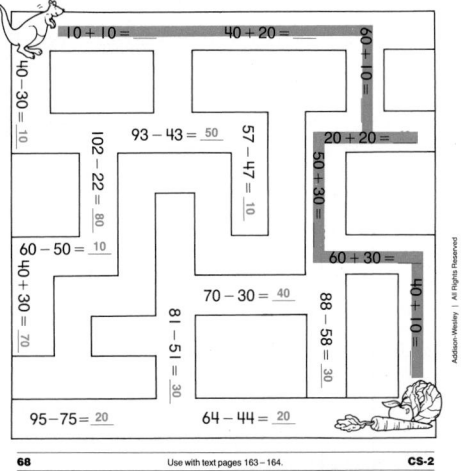

| 10 + 10 = | 40 + 20 = | 60 + 10 = |

40 − 30 = _10_

102 − 22 = _80_

93 − 43 = _50_

57 − 47 = _10_

20 + 20 =

50 + 30 =

60 − 50 = _10_

40 + 30 = _70_

70 − 30 = _40_

60 + 30 =

81 − 51 = _30_

88 − 58 = _30_

40 + 10 =

95 − 75 = _20_

64 − 44 = _20_

68   Use with text pages 163–164.   CS-2

Extended

Exercises All
Calculator Bank, p. 401

Supplements
Challenges 68
Thinking Skills 68

8-3

Other Resources:
Math in Stride, p. 71
Explorations, pp. 100-116,
124-131, 173, 204, 235,
243-244
*Developing Number Concepts
With Unifix Cubes*, pp. 43-46
Mathematics Book A, p. 17

LESSON PLAN 8-3

OBJECTIVE 8-3
To count on and back by 10s

Materials: TA 6 (Numbered Hundred Chart), base-ten blocks

Grouping Suggestion: pairs

1. MOTIVATE AND TEACH

LEARN ABOUT IT

Say a number, such as 56, and have students use base-ten blocks to show it. Ask them to add 1 tens block to the number. *What is the new number?* (66) Repeat 3 more times so that students have models up to 96. Explain that this is counting on by tens. Repeat the activity for counting back from 56 to 16. Have students look at the example at the top of page 163.

▶ **How are the numbers in the first example similar? How are they different?** (They all have the same number of ones; the numbers in the tens place grows by 1.)

▶ **Why does the number in the ones place stay the same?** (You are adding tens but not adding any ones.)

▶ **What do you notice about the number patterns in Exercises 1 and 2?** (They all grow by ten if read from top to bottom.)

2. CHECK UNDERSTANDING

ERROR ALERT In Exercise 2, reversing the order of the numbers by counting on instead of counting back.

Name _____

Counting On and Back by 10s

(thought bubble) 43, . . . 53, 63, 73

Work with a partner.
Use blocks to show the number.
Put down 3 more tens.
Count on for each ten.
Write the numbers.

1.

35	52	8	66	70	21
45	62	18	76	80	31
55	72	28	86	90	41
65	82	38	96	100	51

(thought bubble) 43, . . . 33, 23, 13

Use blocks to show the number. Pick up 3 tens. Count back for each ten. Write the numbers.

2.

37	5	44	61	20	59
47	15	54	71	30	69
57	25	64	81	40	79
67	35	74	91	50	89

3. Tell what happens to the ones place when you count on or back by 10s. The ones place does not change.

Chapter 8   (one hundred sixty-three)

TEACHING OPTIONS

RETEACHING TIPS Cover 3 numbers above and below 47 on a hundred chart. Have students model 47, then add or remove tens blocks to count on or back by 10s three times, saying the numbers as they count. Uncover numbers on the chart as they say them. Assign Reteaching Supplement 68.

ENRICHMENT Have students create dot-to-dot pictures by making a simple line drawing. Place 9 dots at points on the outline. Write a number pattern for counting on or back by 10s. Write the numbers in order by the dots. Erase the outline. Exchange pictures with a classmate and complete.

ount on by 10s.

. 18, __28__, __38__, __48__   2. 6, __16__, __26__, __36__

. 37, __47__, __57__, __67__   4. 65, __75__, __85__, __95__

ount back by 10s.

. __28__, __38__, __48__, 58   6. __4__, __14__, __24__, 34

. __49__, __59__, __69__, 79   8. __70__, __80__, __90__, 100

ount on and back by 10s.

. __10__, __20__, __30__, 40, __50__, __60__, __70__, __80__, __90__

. __1__, __11__, __21__, __31__, __41__, __51__, 61, __71__, __81__

ND THE DATA

se data from the graph.

. Write how many books
were checked out.

morning __50__ books

afternoon __40__ books

night __60__ books

Number of Books Checked Out

Each 📖 means ten books.

Morning 📖 📖 📖 📖 📖

Afternoon 📖 📖 📖 📖

Night 📖 📖 📖 📖 📖 📖

Data Hunt Find something you can count by 10s.
Count and write how many. Answers may vary.

What I counted.	Number I counted.

(one hundred sixty-four)   Chapter 8

3. PRACTICE AND APPLY

Basic	All
Average	All
Extended	All

PRACTICE

How can you check your answers? (Read
from left to right, making sure that each
number is 10 more than the number
before it.)

APPLY

FIND THE DATA ▸ **Why is 1 book
used to show 10 books?** (Possible
answer: It would take too much space to
show the actual number on the graph.)
▸ **How can you count the number of
books?** (Since each book stands for 10
books, count on by 10s to find the
totals.)
▸ **When is it easier to count things by
10?** (when there are large amounts of
things; when things come in groups of
ten)

8-3

LOSE AND ASSESS

AY WHAT YOU KNOW Reread
e chapter poem about Pierre Parrot
d the library and repeat the line,
*ooks numbered 50 to 60 are in this
cation. When you count by 10s,*
at 3 numbers follow the number
? (70, 80, 90) Have students count
10s, using base-10 blocks if
cessary.

QUICK QUIZ

Copy and complete the pattern. Count
on and back by 10s.
__(26)__ __(36)__ __(46)__ 56 __(66)__ __(76)__
__(86)__

Comparing Numbers

OBJECTIVE 8-4   To compare numbers using > and <

PREBOOK ACTIVITIES

Does the group have more or less than 10?
the number of people in this room   (more)
the number of books in your desk   (less)
the number of teachers in the school   (more)
the number of windows in your classroom   (probably less)
the number of pages in your math book   (more)

PRIOR KNOWLEDGE

Remind students that they have learned how to count on and back by 1s and 10s. *What happens when you count on by 1s or 10s?* (The numbers get larger.) *What happens when you count back by 1s or 10s?* (The numbers get smaller.) *How can you tell on a hundred chart which number is larger or smaller?* (The number closer to 1 is smaller; the number closer to 100 is larger.)

COMMUNICATION

Reading and Discussing Math   On the chalkboard, write **greater than** and **less than.** Read the phrases aloud with students. Next, write the numbers 15 and 68 on the chalkboard. Ask students to read the numbers and tell how many tens and ones each number has. *Which number is bigger? Why?* (68; it has more tens.) Encourage students to tell what they know about the words *greater than* and *less than*. (Possible answers: If something is bigger than something else, it is greater. If something is smaller, it is less.) *How can you use the phrase greater than to compare 15 and 68?* (68 is greater than 15.) *How can you use the phrase less than to compare 15 and 68?* (15 is less than 68.)

EXPLORE AND CONNECT

Materials: spinner, base-ten blocks, punchout Booky Bookworm
Grouping Suggestions: pairs
Have each student spin the spinner two times to form a 2-digit number and then model the number with the base-ten blocks. Partners then compare their numbers (for example, 63 and 47) using the phrases **greater than,** and **less than.** *What will you do first to compare the numbers?* (Possible answer: Compare tens.) *Which number is greater?* (63; the number with the mo[re] tens) *How can you compare two numbers that have the same ten digits?* (Possible answer: Compare the ones.)
Write the symbols > and < and have students punch out Booky Bookworm. Explain that Booky's mouth is always open to a greater number. Have students place Booky next to their numbers. *How do you know which number is greater?* (Compare the tens, then compare the ones.)

CONNECTIONS   Use these anytime.

Problem of the Day

Logic   We are 2 numbers that are greater than 50 and less than 70. We both have the same number of ones as tens. Which numbers are we? (55 and 66)

Number Sense

Estimation   Renee tossed 2 number cubes and got 26 on her first turn. She tossed 31 on her second turn. Was her total score more than or less than 50? (more)

Minute Math

Add and Subtract   Write only the answers. Can you do them all in a minute?

14	17	25	32
+ 3	− 1	+ 2	+ 1
(17)	(16)	(27)	(33)

46	86	54	95
− 3	− 1	+ 2	− 2
(43)	(85)	(56)	(93)

CLASSWORK AND HOMEWORK SUPPLEMENTS

Practice

Skills Maintenance | 8-4

Name _____

Comparing Numbers

Write > or < in each ◯ .

1. 5 ⓛ 9   60 ⓖ 40   71 ⓖ 17
   is less than   is greater than   is greater than

2. 30 ⓛ 50   70 ◯ 60   20 ⓛ 40

3. 25 ⓛ 35   57 ◯ 47   88 ⓛ 98

4. 4 ⓛ 8   3 ◯ 1   6 ◯ 2

5. 64 ⓛ 73   19 ◯ 16   22 ◯ 18

Fill the blanks. Use the numbers in the ring.

6. (68, 72, 81)   7. (43, 29, 35)

   _68_   _72_ _81_   _29_   _35_ _43_
   least   greatest   least   greatest

8. (26, 18, 55)   9. (92, 83, 75)

   _18_   _26_ _55_   _75_   _83_ _92_
   least   greatest   least   greatest

PS-2   Use with text pages 165–166.   69

Building Thinking Skills

Math Reasoning | 8-4

Name _____

Least Number, Greatest Number

Write the least number.
Write the greatest number.

1. Use these number cards.

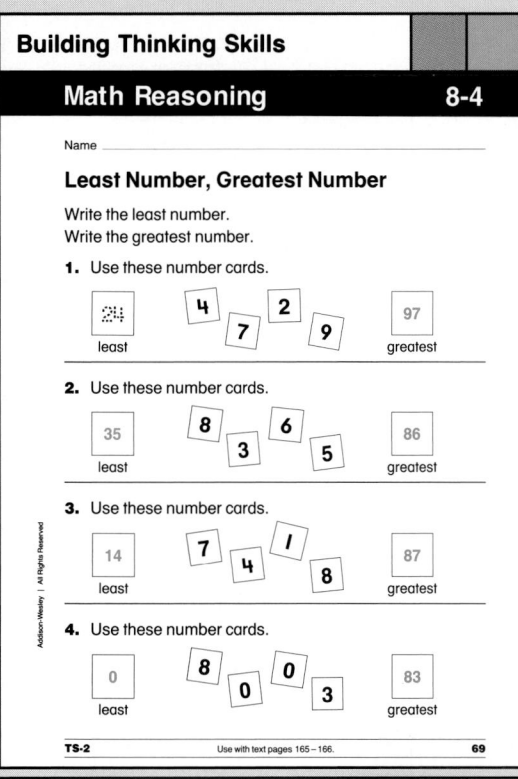

least   4 7 2 9   97 greatest

2. Use these number cards.

35   8 3 6 5   86
least   greatest

3. Use these number cards.

14   7 4 1 8   87
least   greatest

4. Use these number cards.

0   8 0 3   83
least   greatest

TS-2   Use with text pages 165–166.   69

Reteaching

Skills Review | 8-4

Name _____

Comparing Numbers

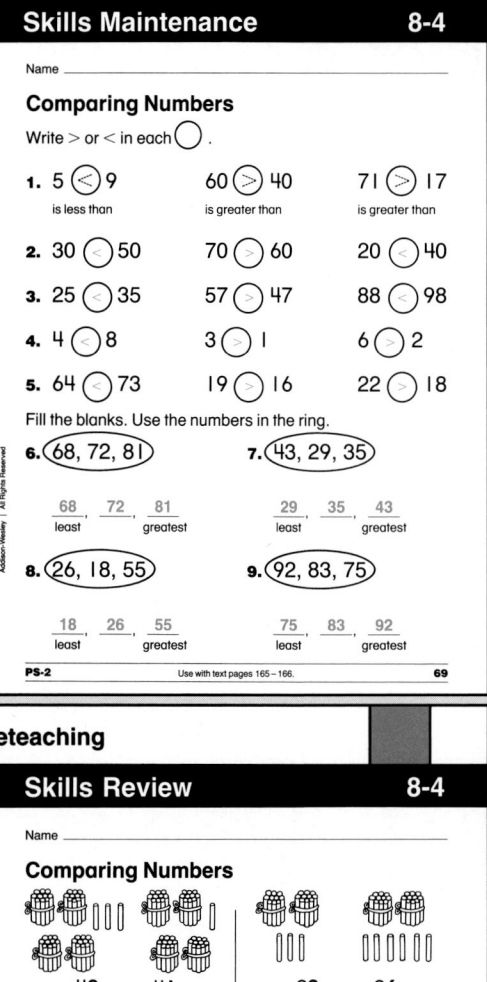

   43   41   23   26
(3 is greater than 1.)   (3 is less than 6.)
43 is greater than 41.   23 is less than 26.

   43 > 41   23 < 26

Write > or < in each ◯ .

1. 35 ⓖ 33   40 ⓛ 50   59 ⓛ 60
   (5 > 3)   (4 < 5)   (5 < 6)

2. 21 ◯ 20   18 ◯ 15   48 ◯ 49

3. 32 ⓛ 38   45 ◯ 32   70 ◯ 59

4. 60 ◯ 40   21 ⓛ 25   40 ⓛ 41

5. 53 ◯ 48   22 ⓛ 30   85 ⓛ 90

RS-2   Use with text pages 165–166.   69

Challenges

Creative Thinking | 8-4

Name _____

Which Bookworm?

In each pair of numbers, which number is greater?
Find that number on the chart and color it red.

17, 10   44, 34   75, 65
16, 26   23, 53   86, 68
33, 35   64, 46   79, 97

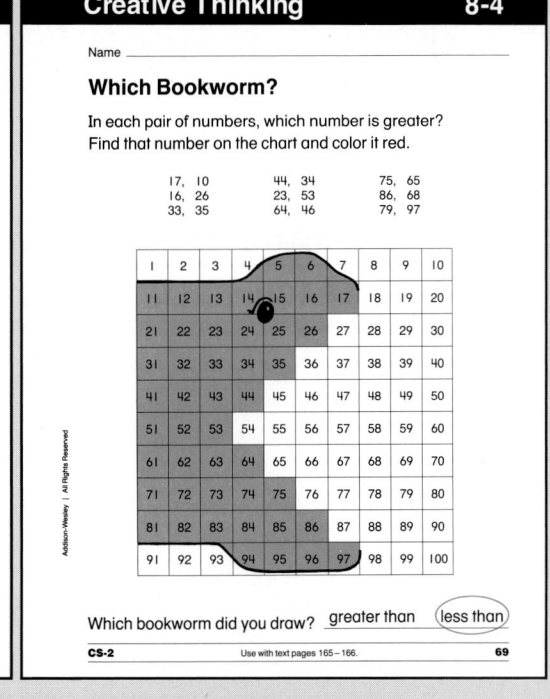

Which bookworm did you draw? greater than (less than)

CS-2   Use with text pages 165–166.   69

OPTIONS FOR INDIVIDUAL NEEDS

Basic

Exercises All
More Practice, p. 417, set C

Supplements
Reteaching 69 or
Practice 69
Challenges 69

Average

Exercises All
More Practice, p. 417, set C

Supplements
Practice 69
Challenges 69 or
Thinking Skills 69

Extended

Exercises All

Supplements
Challenges 69
Thinking Skills 69

Other Resources:
Mathematics Their Way, pp. 116-137, 320
Explorations, pp. 123-131, 138-139, 144, 204, 302
Problem-Solving Experiences In Mathematics, pp. 71, 132, 144
Workjobs, pp. 148-149
Workjobs For Parents, pp. 102-103

8-4

LESSON PLAN 8-4

OBJECTIVE 8-4
To compare numbers using > and <

Materials: base-ten blocks, punchout Booky Bookworm, number cards 0-9, counters labeled L and G

Grouping Suggestions: individual work, small groups

1. MOTIVATE AND TEACH

LEARN ABOUT IT

Write the numbers 26 and 43 on the chalkboard. Have students use base-ten blocks to model the numbers. Then have them compare to see which number is greater. (43; it has more tens.) *What do you do when you compare numbers?* (Compare the tens first; then compare the ones.) Introduce the > and < symbols and Booky Bookworm. Have a student pretend to be Booky Bookworm and stand at the chalkboard between 26 and 43, using a hand to show the greater number. Do the sample exercises at the top of page 165 with students to be sure they know that Booky's mouth is always open to the greater number.
▶ **In Exercise 1, why is 52 greater than 25?** (It has more tens.)
▶ **What do you notice about the numbers in Exercise 2?** (They have the same number of ones.)
▶ **How can you compare the numbers in Exercise 2?** (Look at the tens place.)
▶ **Can you compare the tens in Exercise 3 to find the greater number? Why?** (No; both numbers have the same number of tens, so you have to compare the number of ones.)
▶ **How can you check your answers for these exercises?** (Use base-ten blocks to compare the number of tens and/or ones.)

2. CHECK UNDERSTANDING

ERROR ALERT Difficulty remembering the direction and meaning of the signs > and <.

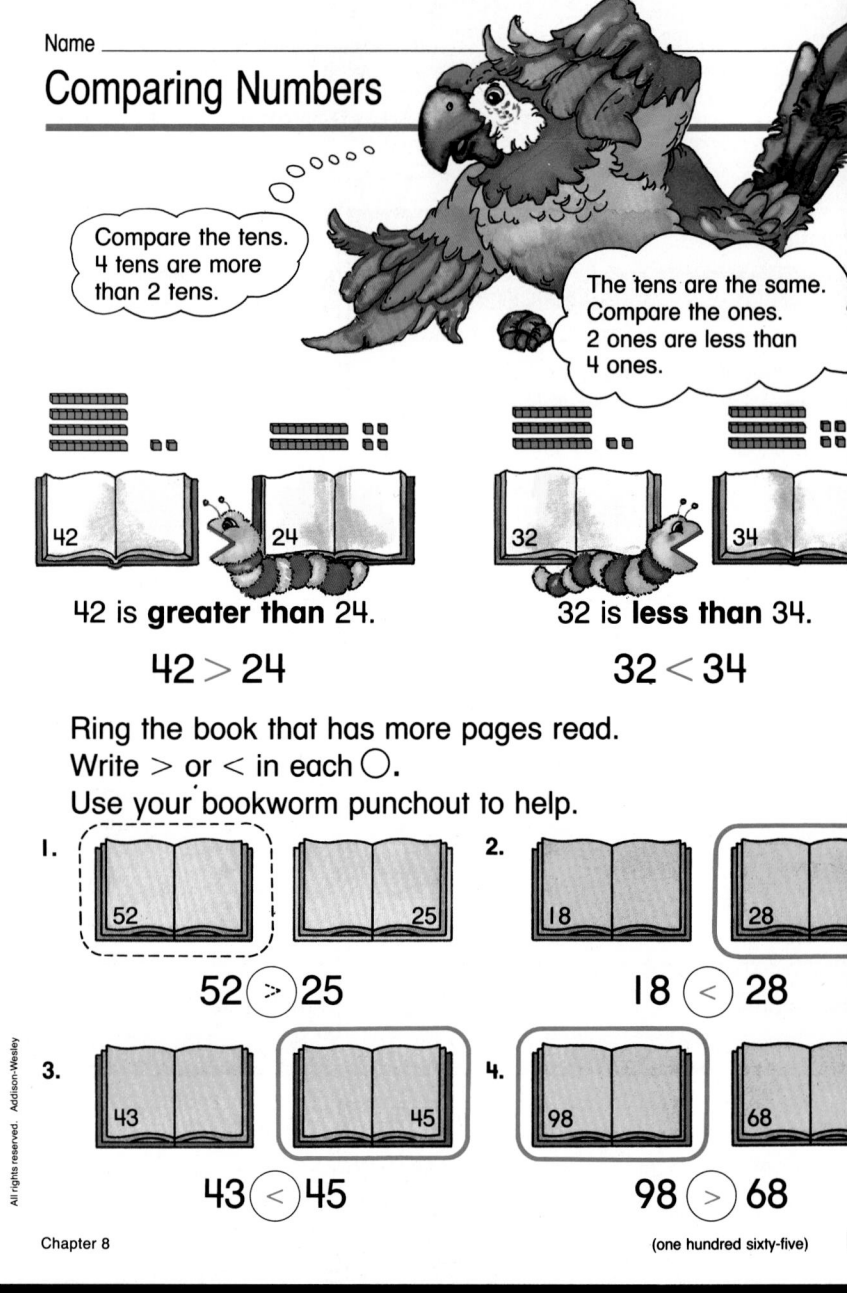

Name _____

Comparing Numbers

Compare the tens. 4 tens are more than 2 tens.

The tens are the same. Compare the ones. 2 ones are less than 4 ones.

42 is **greater than** 24.

42 > 24

32 is **less than** 34.

32 < 34

Ring the book that has more pages read.
Write > or < in each ◯.
Use your bookworm punchout to help.

1. 52   25
52 ⬗> 25

2. 18   28
18 ◯< 28

3. 43   45
43 ◯< 45

4. 98   68
98 ◯> 68

Chapter 8

(one hundred sixty-five)

TEACHING OPTIONS

RETEACHING TIPS Write number pairs on the board: 8, 14; 91, 75; 32, 23; 86, 88. Have students use base-ten blocks to compare numbers. Have them say which number in each pair is greater or less, using their hands to show the signs > and <. Use Reteaching Supplement 69.

ENRICHMENT Have pairs use 2 sets of cards 0–9 and a counter labeled *L* and *G*. Place the cards face down and toss the counter. Take turns. Draw 2 cards. Make the least or greatest number according to whether *L* or *G* was tossed. Compare. The one whose number is greater or less keeps the cards.

rite > or < in each ◯.

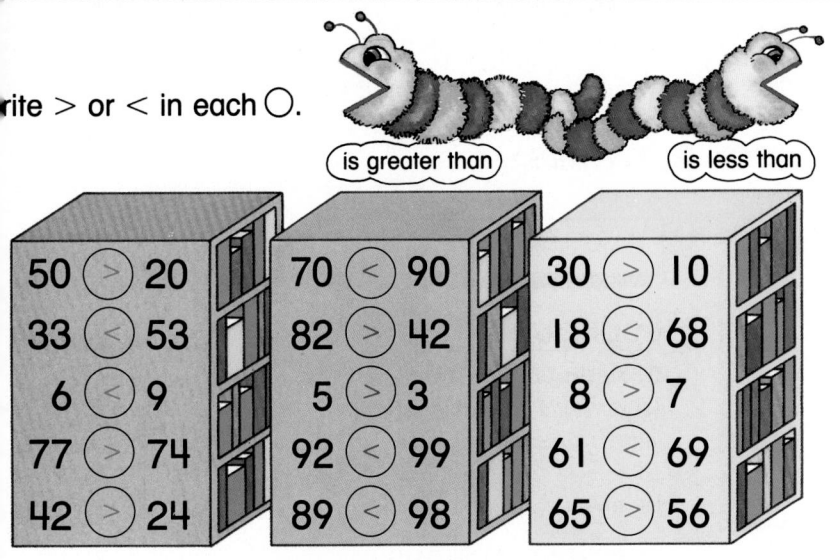

is greater than   is less than

50 > 20	70 < 90	30 > 10
33 < 53	82 > 42	18 < 68
6 < 9	5 > 3	8 > 7
77 > 74	92 < 99	61 < 69
42 > 24	89 < 98	65 > 56

Ring the greatest number in each box.

(56) 51 53 | 36 63 (90)

Ring the least number in each box.

67 62 (60) | 88 (58) 85

MIDCHAPTER REVIEW/QUIZ

Write the number that comes after. 27, __28__

Write the numbers that come between. 38, __39__, __40__, 41

Write the number that comes before. __49__, 50

Count on and back by 1s. __80__, 81, __82__

Count on and back by 10s.

__4__, __14__, __24__, __34__, __44__, 54, __64__, __74__, __84__

(one hundred sixty-six)   More Practice, page 417, set C   Chapter 8

LOSE AND ASSESS

HOW WHAT YOU KNOW
view with students the chapter
em, *Check It Out. Pierre sees a
cial book for you between books 52
d 54. Which number is greater, 52
54?* Have pairs of students work
gether to use blocks to model each
mber. Then have them explain
ich number is greater using their
del.

QUICK QUIZ
Write > or < in each ◯.
35 ◯ 46 (<)   89 ◯ 56 (>)
42 ◯ 29 (>)   27 ◯ 25 (>)
21 ◯ 60 (<)   66 ◯ 68 (<)

3. PRACTICE AND APPLY

Basic	All; Midchapter Review/Quiz
Average	All; Midchapter Review/Quiz
Extended	All; Midchapter Review/Quiz

PRACTICE

On page 166, students use their bookworms to help them write the signs showing which number is greater than or less than the other. *To which number does the open mouth always face?* (the greater number)

APPLY

▶ **When might you compare numbers in everyday life?** (Possible answers: prices, distances, heights, scores)
▶ **How can you use comparing two numbers to help you compare three numbers?** (Compare two numbers, then compare each number to the third.)

MIDCHAPTER REVIEW/QUIZ

ITEM ANALYSIS The following table correlates the Midchapter Review/Quiz items with lesson objectives.

Items	Objectives
1-3	8-1
4	8-2
5	8-3

8-4

Chapter 8 Lesson 4   **166**

Problem Solving: Understanding the Operations

OBJECTIVE 8-5   To understand the operation of addition and subtraction by putting together or by comparing

PREBOOK ACTIVITIES

QUICK REVIEW

Circle the smaller number in each number pair.

71	<u>17</u>	53	<u>35</u>	<u>16</u>	18
22	33	84	<u>48</u>	<u>13</u>	31
79	<u>76</u>	<u>68</u>	86	14	<u>11</u>
77	<u>67</u>	98	<u>89</u>	<u>38</u>	39
<u>40</u>	50	<u>19</u>	21	49	<u>46</u>

PRIOR KNOWLEDGE

Pretend that you own a bookstore and must keep track of the total number of books you have. Would you add or subtract from your total in each of the following situations?
1. You receive a shipment of 20 new books. (add)
2. 14 books are ruined by water. (subtract)
3. You sell 11 books on Monday. (subtract)
4. A customer returns a book. (add)

COMMUNICATION

Listening and Writing Math   Remind students that the actions in story problems can help them decide whether to add or subtract. Ask students to listen as you read these questions. Have them raise their left hand if the action means addition and their right hand if the action means subtraction. *How many went away?* (subtraction) *What is the action?* (going away) *How many joined them?* (addition) *What is the action?* (putting together)
Write *44 is less than 46* and *71 is greater than 65* on the chalkboard. Ask students to read each sentence. Then rewrite the sentences using the symbols < and > in place of the words.

EXPLORE AND CONNECT

COOPERATIVE ACTIVITY

Grouping Suggestions: small groups
Weston had 16 stamps. He gave 9 stamps to his mother. How many stamps did he have left?
16 + 9 = _____   16 − 9 = _____
He had _____ stamps left.

TEACHING ACTIONS

▶ **Describe the action in the story.** (Possible answer: There is a take-away action because Weston takes stamps from his total and gives them away.)
▶ **Explain what data, both numbers and actions, are important to the story.** (Possible answer: The total number stamps is 16 and he *gave away* 9.)

▶ **How can you use this data to decide which number sentence matches the story?** (Possible answer: Put the action and data together and then decide whether it makes more sense to add or subtract.)
▶ **How can you use counters to eliminate a number sentence that does not belong?** (Possible answer: Use counters to model each number sentence. If the action in the sentence does not match the action in the story, then it does not belong.)

AFTER ▶ **How can you be sure your number senten is correct?** (Possible answer: Look at the answer to both sentences and decide which one makes sense.) Have groups of students use counters to model the action in similar addition and subtraction stories.

CONNECTIONS   Use these anytime.

Problem of the Day

Circle the number sentence that matches the story. Then write the answer.
12 cars were in front of the store.
4 cars moved away.
How many cars were left?
<u>12 − 4</u> = _____
12 + 4 = _____
 <u>(8)</u> cars were left.

Number Sense

Comparing Numbers   Write the smallest and the largest 2-digit numbers that you can make from each set of 4 digits.
5 8 3 8   (35, 88)
1 9 4 2   (12, 94)
5 0 4 7   (40, 75)
6 2 9 5   (25, 96)
7 0 5 8   (50, 87)

Subject Integration

Language Arts   With a partner, choose 3 numbers that will form related facts, such as 5 + 4 = 9 and 9 − 5 = 4. Write a number sentence to show each related fact. Then write a story for each of the number sentences. Share your stories with another pair of students and have them find the answer to each number sentence.

Informal Algebra: Finishing Number Sentences

• use informal algebra to finish number sentences with > or <

CLASSWORK AND HOMEWORK SUPPLEMENTS

Practice

Algebra 8-5

Name _____

Finishing Number Sentences

Write a number from the box to finish
each number sentence.
Cross out each number you use.
Read each number sentence to check.

Numbers
47 38 79
15 63 22

Answers may vary. Check students' work.

1. (I walked 24 blocks.) (I walked fewer blocks.)   2. (I picked 30 plums.) (I picked a greater number of plums.)

24 blocks > ____ blocks
is greater than

30 plums < ____ plums
is less than

3. (I have 55 books.) (I have fewer books.)   4. (I found 43 leaves.) (I found a greater number of leaves.)

55 books > ____ books

43 leaves < ____ leaves

70   Use with text page 168.   PS-2

Reteaching

Problem Solving 8-5

Name _____

Understanding the Operations

Read the story.
Finish the number sentence that matches.
Cross out the other number sentence.
Complete the answer.

1. Donna painted 8 pictures last month.
This month she painted 5.
How many did she paint altogether?

   (Add to find the total.)
   $8 + 5 = 13$
   $8 - 5 =$

   She painted __13__ pictures.

2. Cindy picked 9 tomatoes.
6 of them were red.
How many were not red?

   (Subtract to compare.)
   $9 + 6 =$
   $9 - 6 = \underline{3}$

   __3__ were not red.

3. There were 10 chicks in the yard.
3 ran away.
How many were still in the yard?

   (Subtract to take away.)
   $10 + 3 =$
   $10 - 3 = \underline{7}$

   __7__ were still in the yard.

70   Use with text page 167.   RS-2

Building Thinking Skills

Life Skills 8-5

Name _____

Fruity Problems

Use the data on the sign.
Add or subtract in your head. Write the answer.

apples 13¢ each   oranges 8¢ each   cherries 4¢ each   plums 7¢ each   bananas 11¢ each

1. Ann bought 1 orange and 1 cherry. How much did she spend?

   12¢

2. Ray had 10¢. He bought a plum. How much does he have left?

   3¢

3. Tara gave 15¢ for an apple. How much change should she get?

   2¢

4. Hank bought 2 oranges. How much did he spend?

   16¢

5. How much more for a banana than an orange?

   3¢

6. How much more for an apple than a plum?

   6¢

7. How much for 3 cherries?

   12¢

8. How much more for 2 oranges than 1 apple?

   3¢

70   Use with text pages 167 – 168.   TS-2

Challenges

Number Sense 8-5

Name _____

Sign Sense

Follow the sentence.
Write > or < in each ○.

1. 95 (>) 63 (>) 54 (<) 82 (<) 99
2. 33 (<) 25 (<) 76 (>) 66 (<) 87
3. 91 (>) 72 (>) 60 (>) 46 (>) 25
4. 44 (>) 21 (>) 15 (<) 76 (>) 59

Follow the signs. Write a 2-digit number in each □.
Answers will vary.

5. 86 (>) □ (>) □ (<) □
6. 45 (<) □ (<) □ (<) □
7. 99 (>) □ (>) □ (<) □ (>) □
8. 16 (<) □ (>) □ (<) □ (>) □

70   Use with text pages 167 – 168.   CS-2

OPTIONS FOR INDIVIDUAL NEEDS

Basic

Exercises All

Supplements
Reteaching 70 or
Practice 70

Average

Exercises All

Supplements
Practice 70
Challenges 70 or
Thinking Skills 70

Extended

Exercises All

Supplements
Challenges 70
Thinking Skills 70

8-5

Other Resources:
Math in Stride, pp. 77-78
Explorations, pp. 50-59, 130, 136-139, 144, 191
Problem-Solving Experiences In Mathematics, pp. 33, 39, 45, 57, 63, 69, 71, 75, 81, 87, 99, 111, 132, 144
Developing Number Concepts With Unifix Cubes, pp. 64-75, 160-161

OBJECTIVE 8-5

To understand the operation of addition and subtraction by putting together or by comparing; to use informal algebra to finish number sentences with > or <

Materials: counters in 2 colors, punchout Booky Bookworm

 **BEFORE** ▶ **What should you look for to help you understand each story?**

(Possible answer: Read carefully to find out what action is taking place. Are things being put together or taken away?)

 **DURING** ▶ **Look at Exercise 1. How can you prove that the action shows subtraction?**

(Possible answer: Use counters in 2 colors to show how many books each person read. Match the counters one to one. Then take away counters from the larger set to see how many more books that person read.)

 **AFTER** ▶ **How might the question be changed in Exercise 1 to make it an addition problem?** (Possible answer: *How many books did they read all together?*) *What should you do to show that one number sentence does not fit in each exercise?* (Cross it out.) *What plan will help you solve the problems?* (Read what the question asks about the problem. Check the data to see how they should be arranged to show the action of the story.)

What should you do after you answer each problem? (Check it to see if it makes sense for the data in the problem.)

2. CHECK UNDERSTANDING

ERROR ALERT **Page 167** Not being able to identify the action in the story.
Page 168 Reversing the meanings of the less than and greater than symbols.

Name _____

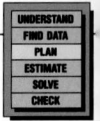

Problem Solving
Understanding the Operations

Ring and finish the number sentence that shows the story. Write the answer.

1. Jason read 5 books in one week. Belinda read 7 books. How many more books did Belinda read?

   $7 + 5 =$ ___ $(7 - 5 = \underline{2})$

   She read __2__ more books.

2. Austin read 9 books. Paula read 11 books. How many more books did Paula read?

   $11 + 9 =$ ___ $(11 - 9 = \underline{2})$

   She read __2__ more books.

3. Erica read 7 books in one week. Lance read 8 books. How many books did they read?

   $(8 + 7 = \underline{15})$ $8 - 7 =$ ___ They read __15__ books.

4. Chris read 9 books in 2 weeks. Alice read 8 books. How many books did they read?

   $(9 + 8 = \underline{17})$ $9 - 8 =$ ___ They read __17__ books.

5. Erin read 7 books. Luke read 5 books. How many books did they read?

   $(7 + 5 = \underline{12})$ $7 - 5 =$ ___ They read __12__ books.

Chapter 8   (one hundred sixty-seven) 167

TEACHING OPTIONS

RETEACHING TIPS Have pairs of students use the punchout bookworm to complete number sentences comparing 2 numbers, such as 35 ◯ 21. Remind them that the bookworm's mouth is always open toward the greater number. Assign Reteaching Supplement 70.

ENRICHMENT Make 2 sets of cards labeled 0-9. Have each student in a pair choose 2 cards and have them make the smallest and the largest 2-digit numbers they can from their combination of 4 cards. Then have them compare the numbers in a sentence, using the greater than or the less than symbol.

formal Algebra
nishing Number Sentences

nish the number sentence.
ross out each number you use.
ead each sentence to check.

24	33	76
30	80	92
15	61	27

swers may vary. Check students' work.

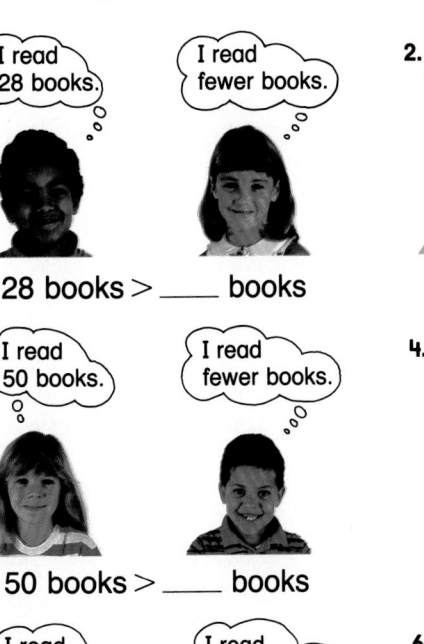

28 books > _____ books

2. 16 books < _____ books

50 books > _____ books

4. 42 books < _____ books

34 books > _____ books

6. 74 books < _____ books

8   (one hundred sixty-eight)   Chapter 8

---

3. PRACTICE AND APPLY

Basic	All
Average	All
Extended	All

▶ **How can the thought clouds above each picture help you solve each exercise?** (Possible answer: They use the words *fewer* or *greater* to tell what size number to choose.)

▶ **Will everyone's answers be the same on this page? Why or why not?** (Possible answer: No; several numbers will work for each number sentence, so there is more than one possible answer.)

▶ **Describe a good way to check your answer.** (Possible answer: After you write an answer in the sentence, read it to yourself to be sure it makes sense.) *What does the symbol > mean? (greater than) What does the symbol < mean? (less than) If you think of the symbol as Booky Bookworm, which number is the mouth always open to? (the greater number) What should you do after you use each number in the box? (Cross it out.)*

CLOSE AND ASSESS

WRITE WHAT YOU THINK

ead addition and subtraction story
roblems aloud to students. At the end
f each problem, read 2 number
ntences about the story. Ask
udents to write the number sentence
at matches the story. Then have
em use 2 numbers from the story to
ake up a number sentence that uses
> or < sign.

QUICK QUIZ

Write the number that completes each
number sentence.
      69   43
58 boxes > _(43)_ boxes
45 boxes < _(69)_ boxes

Counting Patterns for 2s, 3s, and 4s

OBJECTIVE 8-6   To count by 2s, 3s, and 4s

PREBOOK ACTIVITIES

Write the number that comes before and after each number.

_____, 7, _____   (6, 8)
_____, 19, _____   (18, 20)
_____, 24, _____   (23, 25)
_____, 9, _____   (8, 10)
_____, 41, _____   (40, 42)

PRIOR KNOWLEDGE

Ask students to show you their hands, feet, ears, and eyes. *What number makes these things alike? Explain.* (Possible answer: 2; they are things we have 2 of.) *What are some things that come in 3s? What things can you name that come in groups of 4?* (Answers will vary.)

COMMUNICATION

Discussing Math   Scoop a handful of pennies from a bag and have students estimate how many pennies they think you have. After they make a few guesses, have students count them together. *How close was your guess to the actual number?* (Answers may vary.) *When you counted, how many pennies did you count at a time?* (Possible answer: 1) Write **skip counting** on the chalkboard and read the words aloud. *What do you think* **skip counting** *means?* (Possible answer: skipping some numbers as you count) *How might you have skip counted the pennies?* (Possible answer: by 2s, 3s, or 4s) Help students skip count the pennies by 2s. *Why do you think we learn to skip count?* (Possible answer: It can be a faster way to count objects.)

EXPLORE AND CONNECT

Materials: punchout red triangles
Ask: *How many eyes do 7 people have?* (Answers may vary.) Have 7 students come to the front of the class. *How many eyes does 1 student have?* (2) *2 students?* (4) *3 students?* (6) Continue until 7 students' eyes have been counted. Write the numbers on the chalkboard as students respond. *What pattern do you see in the number of eyes you counted?* (Possible answer: **skip counting** by 2s) Display 5 triangles. *How many sides does 1 triangle have?* (3) *2 triangles?* (6) *3 triangles?* (9) Have students count sides for 4 and 5 punchout triangles. Write the numbers of sides on the board. *What pattern do you see this time?* (Possible answer: skip counting by 3s) Put out 5 chairs. *How many legs do you see on 1 chair?* (4) *2 chairs?* (8) *3 chairs?* (12) Have students count the legs for 4 and 5 chairs. Write each number on the board. *How is the pattern different this time?* (Possible answer: We are skip counting by 4s.)

CONNECTIONS   Use these anytime.

Problem of the Day

Logic   Use the clues to find the magic number. You say the number when you count by 2s. You say the number when you count by 3s. You say the number when you count by 4s. The number is more than 20 and less than 30. (24)

Math Connection

Geometry   Estimate the number of sides on 8 triangles. Now check your estimate by drawing 8 triangles on paper and counting the sides. What pattern did you observe? (counting by 3s)

Minute Math

Who Am I?   I am less than 10. You say my name when you count by 2s. You say my name when you count by 3s. What number am I? (6)

CLASSWORK AND HOMEWORK SUPPLEMENTS

Practice

Skills Maintenance 8-6

Name _____

Counting Patterns for 2s, 3s, and 4s

1. Skip count by 3s. Color the boxes.

1	2	3	4	5	6	7	8	9	10
11	12	13	14	15	16	17	18	19	20
21	22	23	24	25	26	27	28	29	30
31	32	33	34	35	36	37	38	39	40

Connect the dots.

2. Skip count by 2s.   **3.** Skip count by 4s.

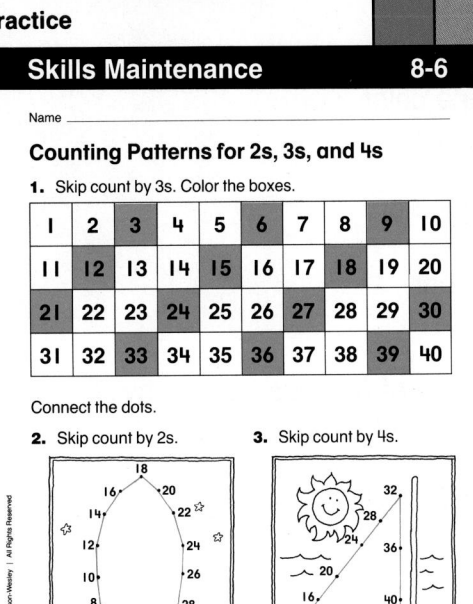

PS-2   Use with text pages 169 – 170.   71

Reteaching

Skills Review 8-6

Name _____

Counting Patterns for 2s, 3s, and 4s

1. Skip count by 2s. Draw the jumps. Write the numbers.

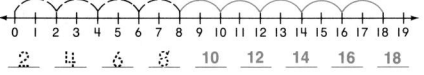

2 4 6 8 10 12 14 16 18

2. Skip count by 3s. Draw the jumps. Write the numbers.

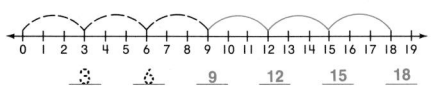

3 6 9 12 15 18

3. Skip count by 4s. Draw the jumps. Write the numbers.

4 8 12 16

4. Connect the dots. Skip count by 2s.

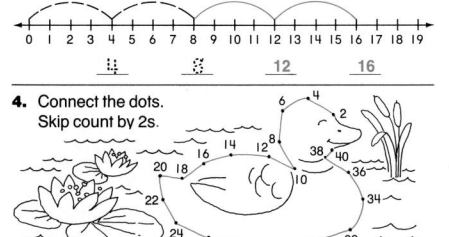

RS-2   Use with text pages 169 – 170.   71

Building Thinking Skills

Family Math 8-6

Name _____

Skip Counting

Dear Family,
We have just learned to skip count by 2s, 3s, and 4s. Help your child practice by playing this game. You will need a dime and pencil and paper to write the counting patterns.

Turn this page upside down. Take turns.
Put the dime on the Name line.
Flick it with your finger so it lands on the game board.
If your dime lands on a number in the counting pattern
▷ for 2s = 1 point   ▷ for 3s = 1 point
▷ for 2s and 4s = 2 points   ▷ for 2s and 3s = 3 points
▷ for 2s, 3s, and 4s = 4 points
The first player to get 25 points wins.

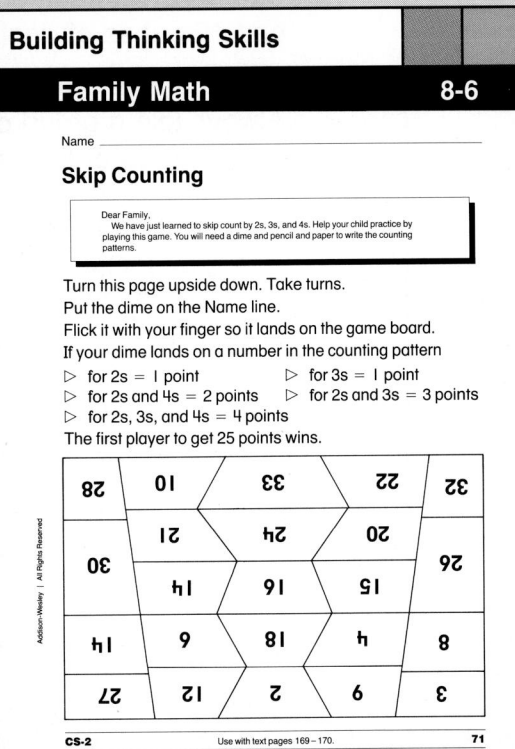
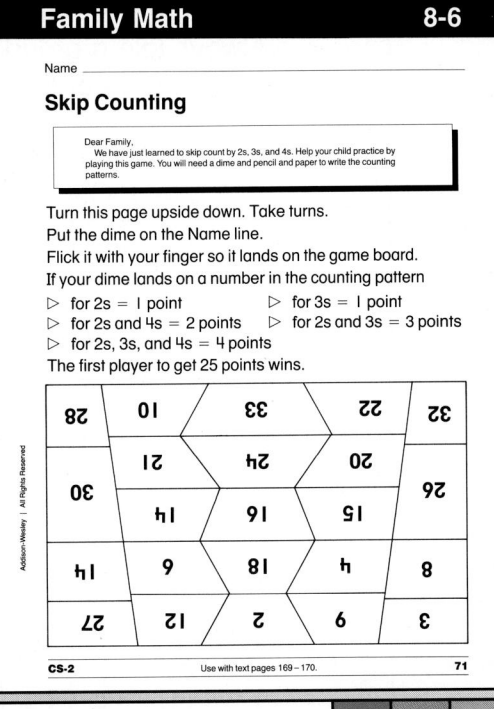
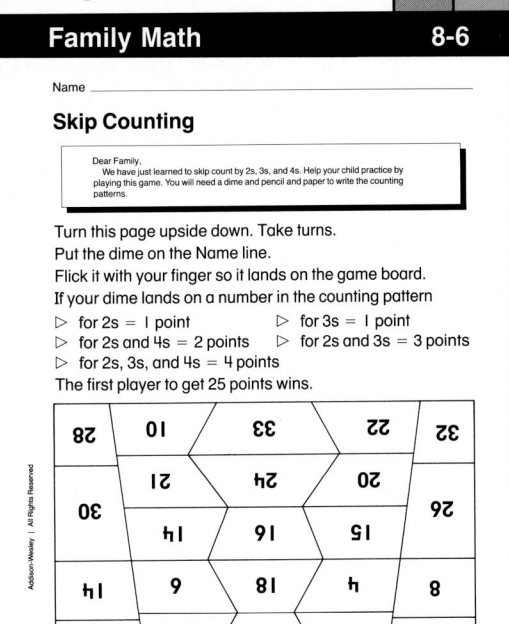

CS-2   Use with text pages 169 – 170.   71

Challenges

Number Sense 8-6

Name _____

Mystery Numbers

Can you find the mystery numbers?

1. I am between 4 and 8. You say me when you skip count by 2s.
Who am I?
6

2. I am more than 15. I am less than 21. You say me when you skip count by 3s.
Who am I?
18

3. I am less than 40. I am more than 32. You say me when you skip count by 4s.
Who am I?
36

4. I am between 28 and 32. You say me when you skip count by 2s.
Who am I?
30

5. I am less than 48. I am more than 40. You say me when you skip count by 4s.
Who am I?
44

6. I am between 24 and 30. You say me when you skip count by 3s.
Who am I?
27

Now make a mystery number riddle of your own!
Answers will vary. _____ Who am I?

TS-2   Use with text pages 169 – 170.   71

OPTIONS FOR INDIVIDUAL NEEDS

Basic

Exercises All
Calculator Bank, p. 401
More Practice, p. 418, set A

Supplements
Reteaching 71 or
Practice 71
Challenges 71

Average

Exercises All
Calculator Bank, p. 401
More Practice, p. 418, set A

Supplements
Practice 71
Challenges 71 or
Thinking Skills 71

Extended

Exercises All
Calculator Bank, p. 401

Supplements
Challenges 71
Thinking Skills 71

Other Resources:
Math in Stride, pp. 44-45, 58-59
Mathematics Their Way, pp. 267-271, 321-322, 328-332, 334-337, 350, 353, 358-359
Explorations, pp. 100, 112-116, 133, 204, 235, 243, 244

8-6

LESSON PLAN 8-6

OBJECTIVE 8-6
To skip count by 2s, 3s, and 4s

Materials: 12 Cube-A-Links in each of 2 colors per pair, colored chalk, calculators

Grouping Suggestions: pairs, cooperative learning groups of 3

1. MOTIVATE AND TEACH

LEARN ABOUT IT

Have students build trains of 10 cubes, joining 2 cubes of one color to 2 of a second color. Then ask them to count by 2s aloud as you write the numbers they say on the chalkboard. Direct their attention to page 169.

▶ **What pattern do you see when you skip count by 2s and color the numbers?** (Every other box and every other column is colored.)

▶ **How can you tell if any of the numbers on the chart are part of the counting pattern for both 2 and 3?** (Find the boxes that are yellow with a red ring.)

▶ **Why do the blue Xs fall into yellow boxes?** (Possible answer: because patterns of 4s fall into the counting pattern for 2s)

▶ **Why are some boxes left uncolored?** (They have numbers that are not a part of the counting patterns for 2s, 3s, and 4s.)

▶ **How are 12 and 24 alike?** (They are the only numbers on the chart that are in the counting patterns for 2s, 3s, *and* 4s.)

2. CHECK UNDERSTANDING

ERROR ALERT Not understanding how to skip count by 2s, 3s, or 4s.

Name _____

Counting Patterns for 2s, 3s, and 4s

2, 4, 6, 8

Work with a partner.
Share 12 cubes of one color and 12 cubes of another color.

Use cubes to make trains. Always join a group of one color with a group of the other color.

1. Make a train. Use groups of 2 cubes. Count by 2s. Color each number you say.

2. Make a train. Use groups of 3 cubes. Count by 3s. Ring each number you say.

3. Make a train. Use groups of 4 cubes. Count by 4s. Mark a X on each number you say.

	y	r	y		y		y	r	y			y
1	2	3	4	5	6	7	8	9	10	11	12
			b		r		b				b r

	y	r	y		y		y	r	y			y
13	14	15	16	17	18	19	20	21	22	23	24
			b		r		b				b r

4. Look at your chart. Talk about the patterns you made. See teaching notes.

5. Tell how 12 and 24 are alike. See teaching notes.

Chapter 8   (one hundred sixty-nine) 1

TEACHING OPTIONS

RETEACHING TIPS On the chalkboard, draw 3 number lines. Have students use different-colored chalk to draw the jumps when they count by 2s, 3s, or 4s on the number line. Then have them retrace the jumps with their fingers, counting aloud as they do so. Assign Reteaching Supplement 70.

COMPUTER Number Munchers, MECC © 1986 For use with all levels. In *Multiples,* students move the Number Muncher around the grid to eat multiples of the target number before Toggle Monster eats Number Muncher. Skip games if necessary. The game requires 10-15 minutes.

Count by 2s. Write the missing numbers.

2, _4_ , _6_ , _8_ , _10_ , _12_ , _14_ , _16_ , _18_ ,

_20_ , _22_ , _24_ , _26_ , _28_ , _30_ , _32_ , _34_ , _36_ ,

_38_ , _40_ , _42_ , _44_ , _46_ , _48_ , _50_ , _52_ , _54_

Count by 3s. Write the missing numbers.

3, _6_ , _9_ , _12_ , _15_ , _18_ , _21_ , _24_ , _27_ ,

_30_ , _33_ , _36_ , _39_ , _42_ , _45_ , _48_ , _51_ , _54_ ,

_57_ , _60_ , _63_ , _66_ , _69_ , _72_ , _75_ , _78_ , _81_

Count by 4s. Write the missing numbers.

4, _8_ , _12_ , _16_ , _20_ , _24_ , _28_ , _32_ ,

_36_ , _40_ , _44_ , _48_ , _52_ , _56_ , _60_ , _64_ , _68_

RY A CALCULATOR

ress |ON/C| |2| |+| |=| to count

y 2s starting from 0.

eep pressing |=| until you see | 100 |.

Ring the numbers that do not
appear on your calculator. Tell why.

18 (27) (31) 44   See teaching notes.

(65) 72 86 (99)

0 (one hundred seventy)   More Practice, page 418, set A   Chapter 8

---

3. PRACTICE AND APPLY

Basic	All
Average	All
Extended	All

PRACTICE

*What is the first number that is the same
when you skip count by both 2s and 3s?*
(6) *What is the first number that is the
same when you count by 2s, 3s, and 4s?*
(12)

APPLY

TRY A CALCULATOR *What did the
calculator do each time you pressed* ⊟*?*
(added 2 to the number before)

▶ **Compare the numbers you circled
with the other numbers. Explain how
they are different.** (Numbers that are
counted by 2s are even numbers. The
circled numbers are odd numbers.)

▶ **Which of these numbers do you
think will appear on your calculator if
you skip count by 4s? Check and see.**
(44)

8-6

LOSE AND ASSESS

HOW WHAT YOU KNOW

rganize students in groups of 3.
ave one student use a calculator to
ip count by 2s from 0 to 100 and
cord the numbers on a strip of
per. Have the second and third
udents count by 3s and 4s and
cord their numbers in the same
anner. Have students compare their
ts and ring the numbers that appear
all three lists.

Counting Patterns for 5s and 25s

OBJECTIVE 8-7   To count by 5s and 25s

PREBOOK ACTIVITIES

QUICK REVIEW

Copy the numbers. Then write the next two numbers in the pattern.

2, 4, 6, _____, _____   (8, 10)
3, 6, 9, _____, _____   (12, 15)
4, 8, 12, _____, _____   (16, 20)
21, 24, 27, _____, _____   (30, 33)
76, 80, 84, _____, _____   (88, 92)

PRIOR KNOWLEDGE

What kinds of things come in 5s? (Answers will vary.) *What kind of money equals 5¢?* (Possible answer: a nickel) *If you save a nickel each day, how much will you have in 2 days?* (10¢) *in 3 days?* (15¢) *How much are you adding each time to find out how much money you have?* (5¢) *How much will you have in 6 days?* (30¢)

COMMUNICATION

Discussing Math   Have students estimate how many fingers 10 children have all together. Have each of 10 students stand in turn and hold out his or her hands. Count the number of fingers in one hand, stopping after each hand. Make a chart to record the number of fingers by 5s. After recording 15, have students predict. *What do you think comes next in the pattern? Why do you think that?* (20; the pattern is counting by 5s) Complete counting and recording fingers as students continue to predict what the next number will be. *What other part of our bodies can we use to count by fives?* (toes) *Why do we learn to count by 5s?* (Possible answer: It is a faster way of counting.)

EXPLORE AND CONNECT

Materials: 25 Cube-A-Links per group
Alternative Materials: 25 counters per group
Grouping Suggestions: small groups
Have students group the cubes in 5s. *How many groups are there?* (5) *How many cubes are in 1 group?* (5) *2 groups?* (1(*3 groups?* (15) Write 5, 10, 15, 20 on the chalkboard. *What (you think will come next?* (25) *What number pattern do you see?* (counting by 5s) *If we kept counting by 5s, what number would come next?* (30) *next?* (35) Have students continue the pattern to 100. Record the pattern on the chalkboard.
What is an easy way to find out how many cubes the whole class has? (count by 25s). Have students *count by 25s.* Circle 25, 50, 75, 100. *How many groups of 25 cubes are there in 100?* (4)

CONNECTIONS   Use these anytime.

Problem of the Day

Logic Riddle   You say me when you count by 5s.
You say me when you count by 25s.
I am more than 50.
I am less than 100.
What number am I?   (75)

Math Connection

Money   If you return a book late, the library charges a fine of 5¢ for each day the book is overdue. Draw a table and complete it to show the fine you would pay if your book were 5 days late.

Days	1	2	3	4	5
Fine	5¢	10¢	15¢	(20¢)	(25¢)

Minute Math

Logic   What is the number? It is greater than 50. It is less than 70. It is an even number. You say it when you count by 5s. (60)

CLASSWORK AND HOMEWORK SUPPLEMENTS

Practice

Patterns 8-7

Name _____

Counting Patterns for 5s and 25s

Finish the counting patterns.

1. Count by 5s.

10 , 15 , 20 , 25 , 30 , 35 , 40 , 45 , 50

55 , 60 , 65 , 70 , 75 , 80 , 85 , 90 , 95

2. Count by 25s.

25 , 50 , 75 , 100

3. Count by 5s. Write the numbers you counted in red.

4. Count by 25s. Ring the numbers you counted in blue.

I		5		10
11		15		20
21		(25)		30
31		35		40
41		45		(50)
51		55		60
61		65		70
71		(75)		80
81		85		90
91		95		(100)

Addison-Wesley | All Rights Reserved

72   Use with text pages 171 – 172.   PS-2

Building Thinking Skills

Calculators 8-7

Name _____

Fast Fives

Use your 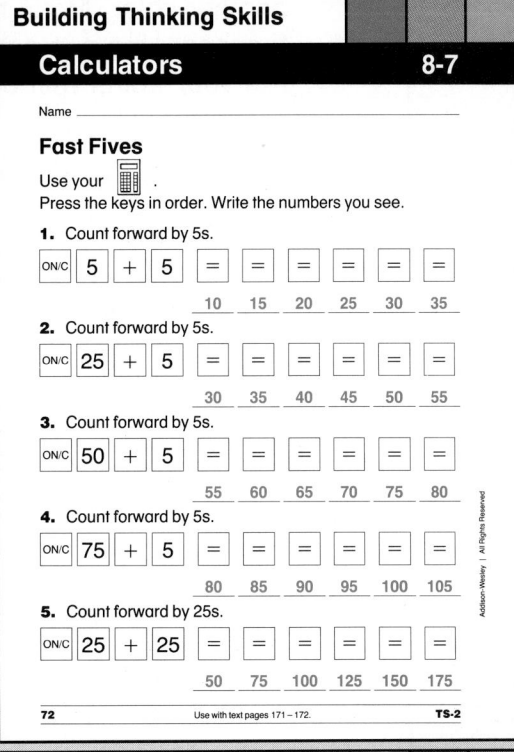 .
Press the keys in order. Write the numbers you see.

1. Count forward by 5s.

ON/C	5	+	5	=	=	=	=	=	=

10   15   20   25   30   35

2. Count forward by 5s.

ON/C	25	+	5	=	=	=	=	=	=

30   35   40   45   50   55

3. Count forward by 5s.

ON/C	50	+	5	=	=	=	=	=	=

55   60   65   70   75   80

4. Count forward by 5s.

ON/C	75	+	5	=	=	=	=	=	=

80   85   90   95   100   105

5. Count forward by 25s.

ON/C	25	+	25	=	=	=	=	=	=

50   75   100   125   150   175

Addison-Wesley | All Rights Reserved

72   Use with text pages 171 – 172.   TS-2

Reteaching

Skills Review 8-7

Name _____

Counting Patterns for 5s and 25s

Counting by 5s means you add groups of 5.

5 10 15 20 25 30 35 40 45

Counting by 25s means you add groups of 25.

25
50
75
100

1. Count by 5s.

5	10	15	20	25	30
35	40	45	50	55	60
65	70	75	80	85	90
95	100				

2. Count by 25s.

25   50   75   100

Addison-Wesley | All Rights Reserved

72   Use with text pages 171 – 172.   RS-2

Challenges

Cooperative Activities 8-7

Name _____

Quarterback

Count by 5s to connect the dots.

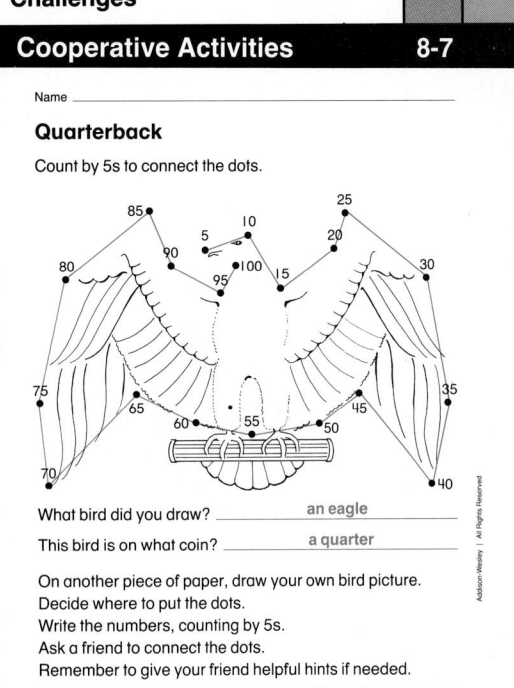

What bird did you draw? ___ an eagle

This bird is on what coin? ___ a quarter

On another piece of paper, draw your own bird picture.
Decide where to put the dots.
Write the numbers, counting by 5s.
Ask a friend to connect the dots.
Remember to give your friend helpful hints if needed.

72   Use with text pages 171 – 172.   CS-2

8-7

OBJECTIVE 8-7
To count by 5s and 25s

> **Materials:** Cube-A-Links, counters
>
> **Grouping Suggestion:** small groups

1. MOTIVATE AND TEACH

LEARN ABOUT IT

Have students make trains of 5 cubes. Write 5, 10, 15, 20, 25, and 30 on the chalkboard. Have students show each number by joining trains of fives. **What number pattern do you see?** (counting by fives) **How many groups of 5 did you make to show 20?** (4 groups) **25?** (5 groups)
Look at the chart on page 171.
▶ **What do you notice about the numbers you have colored?** (All the numbers have a 5 or a 0 in the ones place.)
▶ **Why is the number 61 left out when you are counting by 5s?** (because it does not have a 5 or a 0 in the ones place)
▶ **Why are the numbers with a red ring in 2 different columns?** [because two end in a five (25, 75) and two end in a zero (50, 100)]
▶ **What coin might you use to count money by 5s?** (a nickel)
▶ **What coin could help you count by 25s?** (a quarter)

2. CHECK UNDERSTANDING

ERROR ALERT Not mastering the concept of number positions necessary to understand skip counting by 5s and 25s.

Name _____

Counting Patterns for 5s and 25s

Work in a group. Use 25 cubes of one color and 25 cubes of another color. Make trains of 5 cubes. Use one color for each. Put your trains with another group's.

1. Count by 5s.
   Color 🖍 each number you say.

2. Put 5 short trains together to make long trains of 25 cubes. Count by 25s.
   Ring 🖍 each number you say.

3. Look at the patterns you made on your chart. Tell how 25, 50, 75, and 100 are alike.

   See teaching notes.

1	2	3	4	5	6	7	8	9	10
11	12	13	14	15	16	17	18	19	20
21	22	23	24	25	26	27	28	29	30
31	32	33	34	35	36	37	38	39	40
41	42	43	44	45	46	47	48	49	50
51	52	53	54	55	56	57	58	59	60
61	62	63	64	65	66	67	68	69	70
71	72	73	74	75	76	77	78	79	80
81	82	83	84	85	86	87	88	89	90
91	92	93	94	95	96	97	98	99	100

Chapter 8

(one hundred seventy-one)

TEACHING OPTIONS

RETEACHING TIPS Make a number line showing 0-100. Have students count aloud by 1s. When they say 5 or a multiple, put a counter above that number. Then have them count to 100 by 5s only. Repeat, counting by 25s. Assign Reteaching Supplement 72.

ENRICHMENT Have students complete the table. Marita and Don start their books on the same day. Marita reads 3 pages a day and Don reads 5. What page will Don be on when Marita is on page 18? (page 30)

Day	1	2	3	4	5	6
Mar.	3	6	9	12	15	18
Don	5	10	(15)	(20)	(25)	(30)

nish the counting
tterns.

Count by 5s.

5, 10, 15, 20, 25, 30, 35, 40, 45,

50, 55, 60, 65, 70, 75, 80, 85, 90

Count by 25s.

25, 50, 75, 100

ount on by 5s.

25, 30, 35, 40, 45, 50, 55, 60, 65

50, 55, 60, 65, 70, 75, 80, 85, 90

75, 80, 85, 90, 95, 100

MIXED REVIEW

Estimate to the nearest centimeter.
Then measure. Write the number of centimeters.

estimate: ___ centimeters   measure: 10 centimeters
Estimates may vary.

btract.

13 − 7 = 6   14 − 5 = 9   17 − 9 = 8

14 − 9 = 5   11 − 4 = 7   15 − 8 = 7

3. PRACTICE AND APPLY

Basic	All, Mixed Review
Average	All, Mixed Review
Extended	All, Mixed Review

PRACTICE

When you count by 5s on page 172, how many numbers do you count before you get to 25? (4) How many 25s are there in 100? (4)

APPLY

► **What do you notice about the first numbers in Exercises 3, 4, and 5?** (They form a pattern of skip counting by 25s.)

► **Why are there fewer numbers in Exercise 2?** (because you are counting by 25s)

MIXED REVIEW   *In Exercise 6 is the pencil longer or shorter than 10 centimeters?* (longer)

► **How can you check your answers in Exercises 7 and 8?** (Use the add-to-check fact.)

8-7

LOSE AND ASSESS

HOW WHAT YOU KNOW

ave students in small groups practice
awing five-pointed stars (★). Ask
em to count the points on one star
d record the number. Then have
em make stars in an increasing
ttern and record the total number of
ints in each design. *How many
ints are in one star?* (5) 2 stars? (10)

QUICK QUIZ

Finish the skip counting.
  5, 10, 15, ____, ____   (20, 25)
  25, 30, 35, ____, ____   (40, 45)
  25, 50, ____, ____   (75, 100)
  60, 65, 70, ____, ____   (75, 80)

Ordinal Numbers

OBJECTIVE 8-8   To count ordinal numbers 1st through 31st

PREBOOK ACTIVITIES

QUICK REVIEW

Write the numbers in the order from smallest to largest.

9, 2, 7	(2, 7, 9)	53, 24, 9	(9, 24, 53)
11, 9, 37	(9, 11, 37)	12, 22, 32	(12, 22, 32)
14, 0, 17	(0, 14, 17)	67, 42, 28	(28, 42, 67)

PRIOR KNOWLEDGE

Present the following situation: *Have you ever been to a place such as a doctor's office or a bakery that has a take-a-number machine?* (Possible answer: yes) *Why did you have to take a number?* (Possible number: to wait for a turn) *Do you think people should have to take numbers in the emergency room of a hospital? Why? Can you think of other places where people should take a number?* (Answers may vary.)

COMMUNICATION

Discussing Math   Write the word **order** on the chalkboard. To help students understand sequencing, ask: *How do you make a peanut butter sandwich?* Write students' suggestions on the board. Have students review the sequence. *What do you have to do first? then second? then third? Is there anything out of order on the list?* (Answers may vary.) After the list is in the correct order, write the ordinal number word **first** and the ordinal number **1st** beside the first step. *How many ways can you write* **first**? (2 ways—first, 1st) Repeat this procedure for the second step, the third step, and so on.

EXPLORE AND CONNECT

Materials: ordinal number cards 1st-31st

Have all students stand in a line. *Suppose all of you are lined up to buy a ticket to a movie. Who will buy the ticket first? second? third? fourth? fifth?* (students' names) Hand tickets to the first two students and have them sit down. *Now, who is first in line? second? third?* (students' names)

Why did the third student's position change? (Two students sat down. The student who was third in line is now first.)

Have a student correctly place ordinal number cards in order on the floor beside the students in line. *Who is the last student in line?* (student's name) *If we had 31 students in the class, how many students would be in front of the last student?* (30 students)

CONNECTIONS   Use these anytime.

Problem of the Day

Logic   Draw a picture to help you solve this problem: In a race, Sue was 6 m behind Chris. Lynn was 7 m ahead of Dave. Dave was 2 m ahead of Chris. How did the race turn out? Who finished 1st, 2nd, 3rd, 4th? (Lynn, Dave, Chris, Sue)

Minute Math

Write 1st-9th to show the order of steps in mailing a letter. (Answers may vary. Sample given.)

Seal envelope	(1)	Insert Letter in mailbox	(6)
Write address on envelope	(2)	Put postage on envelope	(3)
Stop at mailbox	(4)	Open mailbox	(5)

Subject Integration

Science   In your Math Journal, make a list telling how to plant a flower. Write down every step you can think of. Now put your list in order. Write 1st, 2nd, 3rd, in front of each step to show the order. How many things did you have to do to plant a flower? (Answers may vary.)

CLASSWORK AND HOMEWORK SUPPLEMENTS

Practice

Skills Maintenance 8-8

Name _____

Ordinal Numbers

Randy is first on the list. Who is

1. fourth?	Bill	Randy
2. seventh?	Tammy	Mary
3. tenth?	Carl	Debbie
4. second?	Mary	Bill
5. fifth?	Jason	Jason
6. ninth?	Cindy	Liz
7. eighth?	Sandy	Tammy
		Sandy
		Cindy
		Carl

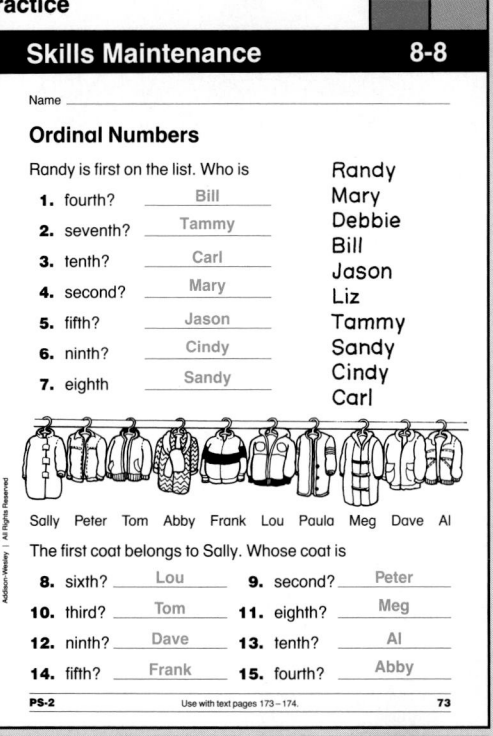

Sally Peter Tom Abby Frank Lou Paula Meg Dave Al

The first coat belongs to Sally. Whose coat is

8. sixth?	Lou	**9.** second?	Peter
10. third?	Tom	**11.** eighth?	Meg
12. ninth?	Dave	**13.** tenth?	Al
14. fifth?	Frank	**15.** fourth?	Abby

PS-2   Use with text pages 173 – 174.   73

Building Thinking Skills

Critical Thinking 8-8

Name _____

Who's on First?

Read the clues to find the batting order.
1st is on the card of the player who is up first.
Write 2nd, 3rd, 4th, 5th, 6th, 7th, 8th, 9th, 10th, and
11th on the other cards.

Clues: The first player on the bench bats third.
The second player bats seventh.
The fourth girl bats eighth.
The second girl bats fifth.
The last player on the bench bats fourth.
The fifth boy bats second.
The second boy bats ninth.
The sixth player bats eleventh.
The third girl bats tenth.
The next to last player bats sixth.

| 3rd | 7th | 9th | 5th | 1st | 11th | 2nd | 10th | 8th | 6th | 4th |

TS-2   Use with text pages 173 – 174.   73

Reteaching

Skills Review 8-8

Name _____

Ordinal Numbers

first 1st second 2nd third 3rd fourth 4th fifth 5th sixth 6th seventh 7th eighth 8th ninth 9th tenth 10th

1. Ring the third bike.
2. Put an X on the fifth bike.
3. Color the second bike red.
4. Write **1st** under the first bike.
5. Draw a box around the seventh bike.
6. Write **10th** under the tenth bike.
7. Color the eighth bike green.
8. Draw a triangle around the fourth bike.
9. Write **6th** under the sixth bike.
10. Draw a horn on the ninth bike.
11. Write **7th** under the seventh bike.
12. Draw a basket on the second bike.

RS-2   Use with text pages 173 – 174.   73

Challenges

Family Math 8-8

Name _____

Hop, Skip, and Jump

Dear Family,
Your child is learning the order of numbers, first through tenth. Follow the directions to finish the game board together, then play the game. You will need a number cube to tell how many spaces to move, and a marker for each player.

1. Write **go back 1** on the 4th, 7th, and 12th spaces.
2. Write **go ahead 2** on the 8th, 17th, and 21st spaces.
3. Write **lose 1 turn** on the 11th and 24th spaces.

Roll the number cube and move that many spaces.
Follow the directions in the space.
The first player to land on FINISH wins.

CS-2   Use with text pages 173 – 174.   73

OPTIONS FOR INDIVIDUAL NEEDS

Basic

Exercises All
More Practice, p. 418, set B

Supplements
Reteaching 73 or
Practice 73
Challenges 73

Average

Exercises All
More Practice, p. 418, set B

Supplements
Practice 73
Challenges 73 or
Thinking Skills 73

Extended

Exercises All

Supplements
Challenges 73
Thinking Skills 73

Other Resources:
Mathematics Their Way, pp. 205, 207
Explorations, pp. 42, 99-100, 135-136
Problem-Solving Experiences in Mathematics, pp. 52-53, 58, 89, 107, 112, 113

8-8

OBJECTIVE 8-8
To count ordinal numbers 1st through 31st

> **Materials:** number cards 1st-10th, small objects such as counters, cubes, and paper clips
>
> **Grouping Suggestions:** individual work, pairs

1. MOTIVATE AND TEACH

LEARN ABOUT IT

Have students stand in a line and imagine that they are in line at the water fountain. Have one student at a time pretend to get a drink of water and sit down. As each student sits down, discuss the new positions in line. *Who is first in line now?* (Answers will vary.) *Is the same person still last in line?* (yes) *What do you notice about the number of puppets and students on page 173?* (They are the same.) *Which puppet is between the second and fourth puppet?* (third)

▶ **If only seven puppets were in line, which would be last?** (seventh) **Which two puppets are in the middle of the line?** (fifth and sixth)

▶ **How did you decide which puppets were in the middle?** (Possible answer: Match the first four to the last four; the fifth and sixth are left in the middle.)

▶ **If the seventh puppet left the show, which one would become the new seventh puppet?** (the eighth)

2. CHECK UNDERSTANDING

ERROR ALERT Confusion in associating ordinal number words (first) with the appropriate ordinal number (1st).

Name _____

Ordinal Numbers

1st 2nd 3rd 4th 5th 6th 7th 8th 9th 10th

Cut out the puppets. Put them in order from first to tenth. Check by counting. Then paste.

Paste here. fifth

Paste here. sixth

Paste here. fourth

Paste here. seventh

Paste here. third

Paste here. eighth

Paste here. second

Paste here. ninth

Paste here. first

Paste here. tenth

Chapter 8

(one hundred seventy-three)

TEACHING OPTIONS

RETEACHING TIPS Make number cards labeled first through tenth. Write the numbers 1 through 10 on the chalkboard. Have students place number cards on the chalk ledge under the matching number. Repeat this procedure several times. For additional help, use Reteaching Supplement 73.

ENRICHMENT Display the current month's calendar. Have students write ordinal numbers to show the date of the first Monday, the fourth Wednesday, the second Tuesday, the third Sunday, the first day of month, and the last day of month.

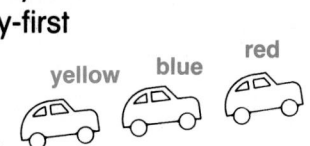

Count and color the cars in line.

1. Color 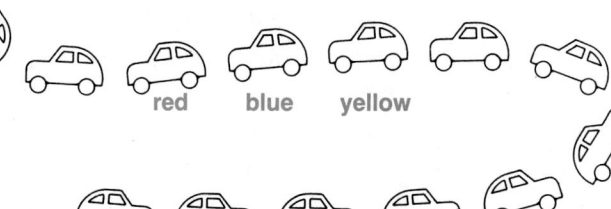.

first	twenty-first
sixth	twenty-sixth
eleventh	thirty-first
sixteenth	

2. Color 🖍.

2nd   7th   12th   17th   22nd   27th

3. Color 🖍.

third	eighteenth
eighth	twenty-third
thirteenth	twenty-eighth

4. Talk about the color patterns you made.   See teaching notes.

Basic	All
Average	All
Extended	All

PRACTICE

On page 174: *How many cars are waiting to park?* (31) *What would be a good way of counting all the cars?* (by 5s) *What would be a good way of counting the colored cars?* (by 3s)

APPLY

What color pattern do you observe? (red, blue, yellow, no color, no color)

► **What would you color the next car that drives in? Why?** (blue, to follow the pattern)

► **At least how many people will see the puppet show? Why?** (31; there is at least 1 person in each car.)

► **Why do we use ordinal numbers?** (to show the place or order of things)

8-8

LOSE AND ASSESS

HOW WHAT YOU KNOW

splay the picture for the chapter
em and have students describe
rre's friends. *Pierre's friends came
ck in this order: knight, child,
phant, king, fairy, spider, bear.
o came third?* (elephant) Have
dents line up and act out each
aracter, stepping forward when their
aracter's order in line is called.

QUICK QUIZ

Write the position of the letters in *MATHEMATICS*.

M _____ , _____   (1st, 6th)
H _____ (4th)   S _____ (11th)
C _____ (10th)

Chapter 8 Lesson 8   **174**

Problem Solving: Finding Extra Data

OBJECTIVE 8-9   To solve problems by finding extra data

PREBOOK ACTIVITIES

QUICK REVIEW

Write the numbers that come after, before, or between.
1. 49, _(50)_   68, _(69)_   93, _(94)_   30, _(31)_
2. _(24)_ , 25   _(87)_ , 88   _(42)_ , 43   _(38)_ , 39
3. 61, _(62)_ , _(63)_ 64   79, _(80)_ , _(81)_ , 82
4. 91, _(92)_   _(14)_ , 15   28, _(29)_ , _(30)_ , 31

PRIOR KNOWLEDGE

Read the following instructions for making a peanut butter sandwich. Ask students to say *yes* if the information is important to the instructions and *no* if it is not important.
1. Buy peanut butter that is on sale. (no)
2. Spread peanut butter on 1 piece of bread. (yes)
3. Put this piece on top of another piece of bread. (yes)
4. Peanut butter jars come in 3 sizes. (no)
5. Slice the sandwich before you eat it. (yes)

COMMUNICATION

Discussing and Reading Math   Explain that some of the instructions for making the sandwich were **extra data**. *What would be considered extra data in a story problem?* (Possible answer: Information that does not help solve the problem.) Write **Act It Out** on the chalkboard and ask students to read the phrase. Explain that this is a way to solve problems. *Give an example of a story problem that you could act out.* (Possible answer: Dean has 13 books. He gave 8 to Joanne. How many books does he have left?)

EXPLORE AND CONNECT

COOPERATIVE ACTIVITY

Grouping Suggestions: small groups
Kim has 11 kittens. They are 5 weeks old. 7 kittens have stripes. How many kittens do not have stripes?
_(11 − 7 = 4)_   _(4)_ do not have stripes.

TEACHING ACTIONS

BEFORE ▶ **Explain what this problem tells you.** (Possible answer: The problem tells how many kittens Kim has, how old they are, and how many of them have stripes. It asks how many do not have stripes.)
▶ **Identify the data in this problem.** (Possible answer: 11 kittens are 5 weeks old and 7 of them have stripes.)

DURING ▶ **How will you use this data to help you plan a solution? What data will you not use?** (Possible answer: Take away the number of kittens with stripes from the total number to see how many do not have stripes. The fact that they are 5 weeks old is **extra data** and not needed to solve the problem.)
▶ **Describe how you will organize the useful data to carry out your plan.** (Possible answer: Write a number sentence that shows the operation.)

AFTER ▶ **Tell how you can be sure the extra data in the story was not needed to solve it.** (Possible answer: The number sentence and answer make sense in solving the problem. The other information does not apply.) Have students work in small groups to identify extra data and to write number sentences for other stories.

CONNECTIONS   Use these anytime.

Problem of the Day

Extra Data   Underline the extra data in the story. Then write a number sentence and answer.
There were 7 ponies at the fair.
Dean bought 6 pony-ride tickets.
His brother bought him 2 more tickets.
How many tickets did he have?
_(6 + 2 = 8)_   Dean had _(8)_ tickets.

Math Connection

Act It Out   Read the story and Act It Out with your friends.
A farmer had 3 hens. He collected 2 eggs from each hen. How many eggs did the farmer collect?
(3 students could be hens. Each holds 2 objects. A fourth student could be the farmer collecting and counting the 6 eggs.)

Life Skills

Giving Directions   Write directions for how to do something, such as how to make a bed or how to brush your teeth. Include one step that provides extra data. Give your directions to a friend and have him or her act them out. See if your friend can identify the information that is not necessary and tell you why.

roblem Solving Strategy: Act It Out

o solve problems using the strategy Act It Out

CLASSWORK AND HOMEWORK SUPPLEMENTS

Practice

Problem Solving 8-9

Name _____

Act It Out

Kim, Jim, and Tim ran a race.
What different ways can they finish the race?

Work in a group of 3.
Make name tags. Act out the problem.
Write the names as you find each way.

Order may vary.

	First Place	Second Place	Third Place
1.	Kim	Jim	Tim
2.	Kim	Tim	Jim
3.	Jim	Kim	Tim
4.	Jim	Tim	Kim
5.	Tim	Kim	Jim
6.	Tim	Jim	Kim

74   Use with text page 176.   **PS-2**

Building Thinking Skills

Writing Math 8-9

Name _____

A New Story

Read the story. Write a number sentence and complete the answer. Draw a line under the extra data.

John has 9 toy cars. Gary has 6 toy cars.
3 of Gary's cars are blue.
How many of Gary's cars are not blue?

<u>6 − 3 = 3</u>   <u>3</u> cars are not blue.

Reread the story. Think of another question you could ask.
Write the story and the question.
Leave out the data that is extra this time.   *Answers may vary.*
Write a number sentence and the answer. *Possible answer given.*

John has 9 toy cars.

Gary has 6 toy cars.

How many cars do they have in all?

9 + 6 = 15

They have 15 toy cars in all.

74   Use with text pages 175–176.   **TS-2**

Reteaching

Problem Solving 8-9

Name _____

Finding Extra Data

Ray is 9 years old.
He had 4 girls at his party.
He had 10 boys at his party.
How many children were at Ray's party?

You do not need to know how old Ray is.

$4 + 10 = 14$ 14 children were at the party.

Read the story. Finish the number sentence.
Write the answer. Draw a line under the extra data.

1. Ray got 14 presents.
He got 5 sports books
and 4 mystery books.
How many books did
Ray get?

$5 + 4 = $ <u>9</u>

Ray got <u>9</u> books.

2. Ray had a cake with
15 candles. The cake
was 12 inches long.
Ray blew out 9 candles.
How many candles
stayed lit?

$15 − 9 = $ <u>6</u>

<u>6</u> candles stayed lit.

3. Ray's mom made
16 party bags. Each
bag had 4 things. Ray
gave out 9 party bags.
How many were left?

$16 − 9 = $ <u>7</u>

<u>7</u> party bags were left.

4. Ray had $10. He spent
$7 on a dinosaur kit.
The kit had 20 pieces.
How much money did
Ray have left?

$10 − $7 = $ <u>3</u>

Ray had $<u>3</u> left.

74   Use with text page 175.   **RS-2**

Challenges

Problem Solving 8-9

Name _____

Line Up

Read the clues.
Write each name to show the order.

Anna is first in line.
David is between Anna and Ellen.
Ellen is not fourth or fifth in line.
Craig is not last.
Which students are 2nd, 3rd, 4th, and last in line?

Anna	David	Ellen	Craig	Betty
first	second	third	fourth	last

74   Use with text page 176.   **CS-2**

OPTIONS FOR INDIVIDUAL NEEDS

Basic

Exercises All
More Practice, p. 418, set C

Supplements
Reteaching 74 or
Practice 74

Average

Exercises All
More Practice, p. 418, set C

Supplements
Practice 74
Challenges 74 or
Thinking Skills 74

Extended

Exercises All

Supplements
Challenges 74
Thinking Skills 74

8-9

Other Resources:
Mathematics Their Way, pp. 204-208
Explorations, pp. 56-59, 67, 71, 144, 191, 204, 206, 330-341, 347
Problem-Solving Experiences In Mathematics, pp. 4, 5, 40, 100
Mathematics Book A, p. 17

LESSON PLAN 8-9

OBJECTIVE 8-9

To solve problems by finding extra data; to solve problems using the strategy Act It Out

1. MOTIVATE AND TEACH

LEARN ABOUT IT

▶ **What is the difference between finding important data and finding extra data?** (Possible answer: To find extra data, you look for information that will not help you solve the problem; to find important data, you look for data that will help you understand and solve the problem.)

▶ **Explain how you should treat the extra data you find.** (Possible answer: Go on solving the problem as if the extra data is not there.)

▶ **How can you check to make sure you found extra data and not data that is needed to solve the problem?** (Possible answer: Read the problem again, leaving out the extra data. Check to make sure you have enough data to solve the problem.)
What will you do after you read each story problem on this page? (Find the extra data and underline it, write a number sentence; find the answer.) *How will you know whether to add or subtract?* (First, decide what action is being shown in the problem. Then use counters or a picture to show what is being put together or taken away.) *What data will appear in each number sentence?* (only data that is important to solving the problem)

2. CHECK UNDERSTANDING

ERROR ALERT **Page 175** Being unable to distinguish between important data and extra data.
Page 176 Being unable to recognize a pattern of combinations when acting out a problem.

Name _____

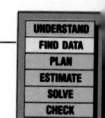

Problem Solving
Finding Extra Data

Write a number sentence and the answer for each story. Draw a line under the extra data.

1. Abbey gets 25¢ each week. She bought 1 stamp for 8¢ and 1 stamp for 7¢. How much did she spend?

   $$8¢ + 7¢ = 15¢$$

   She spent _15_ ¢.

2. Mark has 13 baseball cards in a box. <u>The box holds 50 cards.</u> He gave 4 cards to his brother. How many does he have left?

   $$13 - 4 = 9$$

   He has _9_ cards left.

3. Jill has 12 dolls. <u>Ann has 6 dolls.</u> 8 of Jill's dolls have coats. How many of Jill dolls do not have coats

   $$12 - 8 = 4$$

   _4_ do not have coats

4. <u>Jack has 20 fish.</u> He has 8 spotted catfish and 4 plain ones. How many catfish does he have?

   $$8 + 4 = 12$$

   He has _12_ catfish.

5. Bill's dog has 10 puppie They are 2 weeks old. 6 have spots. How man do not have spots?

   $$10 - 6 = 4$$

   _4_ do not have spots.

Chapter 8   More Practice, page 418, set C   (one hundred seventy-five)

TEACHING OPTIONS

RETEACHING TIPS Have 4 students act out a story about a family of 4 that owns a bicycle built for 2. Students work together to plan the combinations of people who can ride. A fifth student records all the combinations. For help in finding extra data, use Reteaching Supplement 74.

COMPUTER **Path Tactics, MECC © 1986** For use with all levels. Choose the operation to be practiced. Given three numbers, students create an equation whose solution is the number of steps the Robot needs to reach the end of the path. The recommended game requires 10 minutes.

roblem Solving Strategy

t It Out

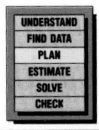

UNDERSTAND
FIND DATA
PLAN
ESTIMATE
SOLVE
CHECK

here are 4 books. There are only
bookstands. What different pairs of
ooks could you put on the 2 stands?

Order of pairs may vary.

ork in a group. Act out the problem to
lve it. Color to match each pair you find.

air 1

red	yellow

Pair 2

red	green

Pair 3

red	blue

air 4

yellow	green

Pair 5

yellow	blue

Pair 6

green	blue

6 (one hundred seventy-six)

Chapter 8

3. PRACTICE AND APPLY

Basic	All
Average	All
Extended	All

► **Explain the problem on this page.**
(Possible answer: You need to find
combinations of 4 books to fit 2 at a
time on 2 bookstands.)

► **Plan what you need to do in order
to act out this problem.** (Possible
answer: First, you might ask 4 people to
each represent 1 book and use 2 chairs to
represent the bookstands. Then you must
plan how you will record the
combinations so none is repeated.)

► **How will you know whether you
have shown all the combinations?**
(Possible answer: Students representing
the books will begin to see that they
have been paired with someone before.
You can also check to see that the color
combinations have not been repeated.)
*How can you show which book you are
representing?* (Possible answer: Hold a
piece of construction paper that has the
same color and title as the one on the
page.) *What can you do on the page as
each pair is being acted out?* (Color the
boxes to match the pair being shown.)

8-9

CLOSE AND ASSESS

ROVE WHAT YOU KNOW On
e chalkboard, write an addition or a
btraction story problem that contains
xtra data. Ask students to read it and
ink about the data that is not
eded. Ask a volunteer to find the
xtra data and write the number
ntence for the problem. Challenge
e student to prove his or her answer
y modeling the action using counters
r drawing a picture of the action in
e story.

QUICK QUIZ

Draw a line under the extra data. Mrs.
James has 18 spools of thread in a
case. The case holds 35 spools. She
loaned 9 spools to a friend. How
many spools does she have left?

Chapter 8 Lesson 9   **176**

CHAPTER 8

WRAP UP

INTRODUCTION The Wrap Up provides activities emphasizing math language and thinking skills for the chapter.

USING PAGE 177

Order Words ▶ **Why are order words important to know and understand when working with recipes and cooking?** (Possible answer: You need to be able to use step-by-step directions when cooking; you need to do things in a specific order when you are following a recipe.)

▶ **Name other areas in which order words are important.** (Possible answers: building a house; doing an art or science project; learning or playing a sport)

Math Reasoning ▶ **What operation are you using when you find the number that is before? Why?** (subtraction; because you are finding a number that is less or closer to 0; you are counting back)

▶ **How can you find the pattern in a number sequence?** (Possible answer: Count the numbers between each listed number; look on a number line or a hundred chart.)

Name _____

WRAP UP

MATH WORDS

1. Write the words to show the order. | first   second   third   fourth |

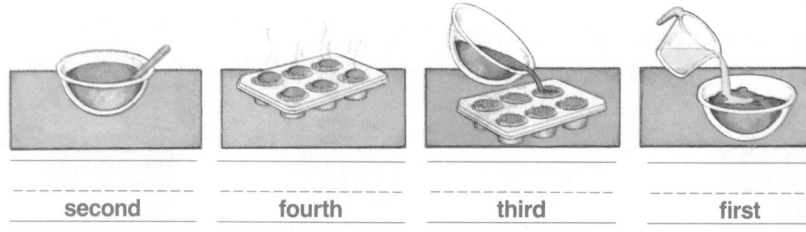

_____   _____   _____   _____
second   fourth   third   first

MATH REASONING

Choose the answer from the box.

5	2	3	10	4	60
<	>	62	before	after	

2. 5, 10, 15, 20, 25 is counting by __5__ s.

3. 2, 4, 6, 8, 10, 12 is counting by __2__ s.

4. 3, 6, 9, 12, 15, 18, 21 is counting by __3__ s.

5. 4, 8, 12, 16, 20 is counting by __4__ s.

6. 10, 20, 30, 40, 50, 60 is counting by __10__ s.

7. 45 _<_ 54

8. Count by 1s. The number after 61 is __62__ .

9. Count by 1s. 63 is ____before____ 64.

TEACHING OPTIONS

ENRICHMENT Have students in small groups pick up as many base-ten ones blocks in 2 hands as possible. Have them count the blocks by putting them in rows of 10 with some left over. Write students' names on the chalkboard and record the number of blocks each picked up; in order from least to greatest. Invite volunteers to write and say number sentences comparing their number to another's using inequality signs or the words *before* or *after*. Next, review ordinal numbers by asking students to identify specific numbers, such as the third greatest, the second to the least, and so on.

Name _____

CHAPTER REVIEW/TEST

Write the numbers.

53,  _54_    _35_ , 36   68, 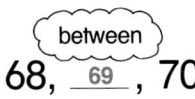 _69_ , 70

. Count on and back by 1s.   3. Count on and back by 10s.

_73_ , _74_ , 75, _76_ , _77_   _2_ , _12_ , 22, _32_ , _42_

. Write > or < in each ◯.

11 ⓒ 13   47 ⓒ 74   86 ⓞ 81

. Count by 2s.   6. Count by 3s.

2, 4, _6_ , _8_ , 10   6, 9, _12_ , _15_ , _18_

. Count by 5s.   8. Count by 25s.

25, 30, _35_ , _40_ , _45_   25, 50, _75_ , _100_

. Ring the fourth and seventh students.

. Ring and finish the number
sentence that shows the story.
Write the answer.

$14 + 9 =$ ___

Jessica had 14 toy cars. Brian had 9.
How many more did Jessica have?

$14 - 9 =$ _5_

She had _5_ more.

8 (one hundred seventy-eight)   Chapter 8 Review/Test

CHAPTER REVIEW/TEST

INTRODUCTION The Review/Test is provided to review and evaluate the skills and concepts presented in Chapter 8.

USING PAGE 178
If you prefer to use this page for review, you may want to use the **Multiple Choice Posttest** (pages 31–32) or the **Free-Response Posttest** (pages 31–32) to evaluate mastery of chapter objectives.

ITEM ANALYSIS The table below correlates the Chapter Review/Test Items with the lesson objectives.

Items	Objectives
1	8-1
2	8-2
3	8-3
4	8-4
5, 6	8-6
7, 8	8-7
9	8-8
10	8-5

IFORMAL ASSESSMENT

sing Manipulatives Make a ip-counting pocket chart by cutting ts in a large piece of cardboard and ping a strip of paper behind the slits. ake number cards from 0-99. Have dents demonstrate counting by 2s, , 4s, 5s, and 10s by inserting the propriate cards in the chart.

ommunication *How are counting 1s and counting by 10s alike? How e they different?* (Possible answer: both cases, the numbers get larger.

When you count by 1s, the digit in the ones place increases by 1; when you count by 10s, the digit in the tens place increases by 1.)

Critical Thinking *Why do you need to know addition and subtraction to find the numbers just before and just after?* (Possible answer: You need to count on or add 1 to find the number just after and count back or subtract 1 to find the number just before.)

CHAPTER 8

ENRICHMENT

INTRODUCTION Skip counting and identifying even and odd numbers will help students analyze and extend number patterns.

USING PAGE 179
This Enrichment page is provided for all students. You may wish to use it after they have completed the Chapter Review/Test on page 178.

▶ **Could any numbers be colored red and blue? Why?** (No; no numbers can be even *and* odd.)

▶ **What numbers will be colored red, green, and yellow?** (odd numbers that are found by counting by 3s and 5s—15, 45, 75)

▶ **What numbers will be colored blue, green, and yellow?** (even numbers that are found by counting by 3s and 5s—30, 60, 90)

▶ **Which students in your group color most? Why?** (Students coloring even or odd numbers; they color every other number.)

▶ **Which students color least? Why?** (Students coloring numbers counted by 5s; they color every fifth number.)

EXTENSION Have students use a completed hundred chart to make up their own coloring rules. They may choose colors for counting by 2s, 3s, 4s, 5s, or 10s or color numbers that have a 7 in the ones place or a 9 in the tens place. Have them trade charts with another student, then use their partner's rules to color.

Name _____

ENRICHMENT
Number Patterns

Work in a group.

Color [crayon] all odd numbers on your chart.	Use [crayon]. Color the number 3. Count by 3s. Color each number you counted.
Color [crayon] all even numbers on your chart.	Use [crayon]. Color the number 5. Count by 5s. Color each number you counted.

1 ʳ	2 ᵇ	3 ʳ g	4 ᵇ	5 ʳ	6 ᵇ g	7 ʳ	8 ᵇ	9 ʳ g	10 ᵇ y
11 ʳ	12 ᵇ g	13 ʳ	14 ᵇ	15 ᵇ y g	16 ᵇ	17 ʳ	18 ᵇ g	19 ʳ	20 ᵇ
21 ʳ g	22 ᵇ	23 ʳ	24 ᵇ g	25 ʳ y	26 ᵇ	27 ʳ g	28 ᵇ	29 ʳ y	30 ᵇ g
31 ʳ	32 ᵇ	33 ʳ g	34 ᵇ	35 ʳ y	36 ᵇ g	37 ʳ	38 ᵇ	39 ʳ g	40 ᵇ
41 ʳ	42 ᵇ g	43 ʳ	44 ᵇ y	45 ʳ y g	46 ᵇ	47 ʳ	48 ᵇ g	49 ʳ	50 ᵇ y
51 ʳ g	52 ᵇ	53 ʳ	54 ᵇ g	55 ʳ y	56 ᵇ	57 ʳ g	58 ᵇ	59 ʳ y	60 ᵇ g
61 ʳ	62 ᵇ	63 ʳ g	64 ᵇ	65 ʳ y	66 ᵇ g	67 ʳ	68 ᵇ	69 ʳ g	70 ᵇ y
71 ʳ	72 ᵇ g	73 ʳ	74 ᵇ y	75 ʳ y g	76 ᵇ	77 ʳ	78 ᵇ g	79 ʳ	80 ᵇ
81 ʳ g	82 ᵇ	83 ʳ	84 ᵇ g	85 ʳ y	86 ᵇ	87 ʳ g	88 ᵇ	89 ʳ y	90 ᵇ g
91 ʳ	92 ᵇ	93 ʳ g	94 ᵇ	95 ʳ y	96 ᵇ g	97 ʳ	98 ᵇ	99 ʳ g	100 ᵇ y

Compare your charts. Which numbers are colored more than once? Talk about the patterns you see. See teaching notes.

Chapter 8 Enrichment: Number Patterns   (one hundred seventy-nine) 179

Name _____

CUMULATIVE REVIEW

The pencil is about

○ 2
○ 1
○ 3

_____  units long.

Which is the best estimate?

○ 1 cup
○ 3 cups
● 8 cups

○ 1 meter
● more than 1 meter
○ less than 1 meter

The book weighs about _____.

○ 5 pounds
● 1 pound
○ 10 pounds

How many are there?

5.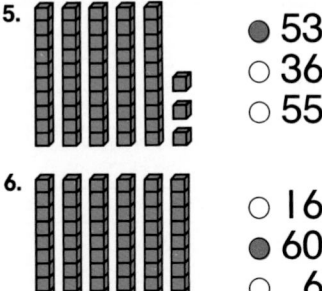

● 53
○ 36
○ 55

6.

○ 16
● 60
○ 6

7. How much money is there?

● 35¢
○ 53¢
○ 8¢

8. Which is the correct word name?

26

○ sixteen
○ twenty
● twenty-six

6 children skip.
11 children run.
How many more children run?

○ 17 more children
● 5 more children
○ 6 more children

CUMULATIVE REVIEW

INTRODUCTION The purpose of this Cumulative Review is to maintain previously taught skills and concepts. The emphasis in this Cumulative Review is on subtraction, Chapter 5; measurement, Chapter 6; and on place value, Chapter 7.

ITEM ANALYSIS The table below correlates the Cumulative Review items with the lesson objectives.

Items	Objectives
1	6-1
2	6-6
3	6-9
4	6-7
5	7-4
6	7-3
7	7-6
8	7-7
9	5-4

CHAPTER 9 TIME AND MONEY

Chapter Management

MATHEMATICAL BACKGROUND

Time

Chapter 9 begins by teaching students to tell time to 5-min intervals and then to 15-min intervals. Counting by 5s, a skill mastered by most students in Grade 1 (and reviewed in Chapter 8), provides a useful foundation for teaching time in both 5- and 15-min intervals. In this chapter, students are taught to tell time as so many minutes after the hour. Focusing on minutes after the hour allows students to use the skill of counting by 5s and helps them learn how to write time using symbols. This chapter furthers students' understanding of days, weeks, and months by focusing on the cyclic nature of these units of time.

Money

Most second graders have some foundation in concepts related to money and will probably have an understanding of the concept of value and the relation between the cost of an item and its value.

Problem Solving

In this chapter, students solve problems using data from a chart and using the strategy Make a Table.

TIPS FROM TEACHERS

Study money as part of the daily calendar activities. Have students take turns counting the number of pennies that represent the date. Later, include nickels, dimes, and quarters.

**Mary Ann Zatlukal
Clarkstown School
West Nyack, NY**

ASSESSMENT

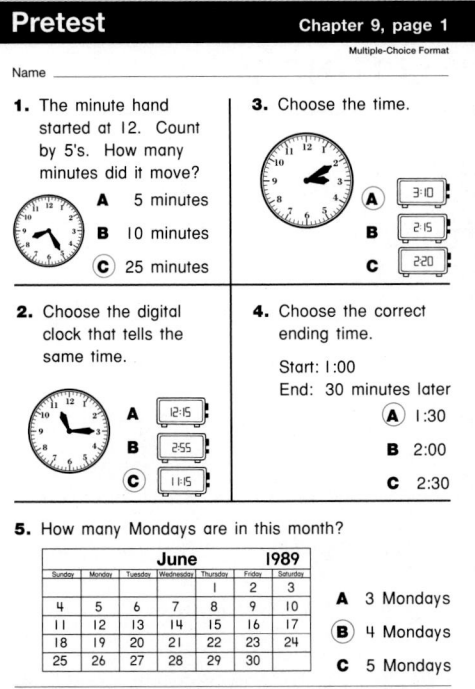

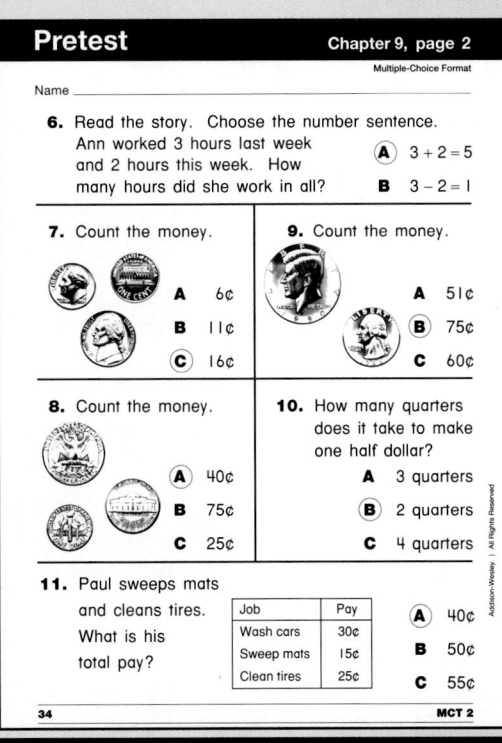

Pretest — Chapter 9, page 1
Multiple-Choice Format

Name _____

1. The minute hand started at 12. Count by 5's. How many minutes did it move?
- **A** 5 minutes
- **B** 10 minutes
- **C** 25 minutes

2. Choose the digital clock that tells the same time.
- **A** 12:15
- **B** 2:55
- **C** 1:15

3. Choose the time.
- **A** 3:10
- **B** 2:15
- **C** 2:20

4. Choose the correct ending time.
Start: 1:00
End: 30 minutes later
- **A** 1:30
- **B** 2:00
- **C** 2:30

5. How many Mondays are in this month?

June					1989	
Sunday	Monday	Tuesday	Wednesday	Thursday	Friday	Saturday
				1	2	3
4	5	6	7	8	9	10
11	12	13	14	15	16	17
18	19	20	21	22	23	24
25	26	27	28	29	30	

- **A** 3 Mondays
- **B** 4 Mondays
- **C** 5 Mondays

MCT 2 — 33

Pretest — Chapter 9, page 2
Multiple-Choice Format

Name _____

6. Read the story. Choose the number sentence. Ann worked 3 hours last week and 2 hours this week. How many hours did she work in all?
- **A** $3 + 2 = 5$
- **B** $3 - 2 = 1$

7. Count the money.
- **A** 6¢
- **B** 11¢
- **C** 16¢

8. Count the money.
- **A** 40¢
- **B** 75¢
- **C** 25¢

9. Count the money.
- **A** 51¢
- **B** 75¢
- **C** 60¢

10. How many quarters does it take to make one half dollar?
- **A** 3 quarters
- **B** 2 quarters
- **C** 4 quarters

11. Paul sweeps mats and cleans tires. What is his total pay?

Job	Pay
Wash cars	30¢
Sweep mats	15¢
Clean tires	25¢

- **A** 40¢
- **B** 50¢
- **C** 55¢

34 — MCT 2

Posttest — Chapter 9, page 1
Multiple-Choice Format

Name _____

1. The minute hand started at 12. Count by 5's. How many minutes did it move?
- **A** 10 minutes
- **B** 20 minutes
- **C** 5 minutes

2. Choose the digital clock that tells the same time.
- **A** 2:45
- **B** 2:15
- **C** 1:45

3. Choose the time.
- **A** 8:35
- **B** 8:15
- **C** 7:35

4. Choose the correct ending time.
Start: 7:00
End: 30 minutes later
- **A** 7:30
- **B** 8:00
- **C** 6:30

5. How many Fridays are in this month?

June					1989	
Sunday	Monday	Tuesday	Wednesday	Thursday	Friday	Saturday
				1	2	3
4	5	6	7	8	9	10
11	12	13	14	15	16	17
18	19	20	21	22	23	24
25	26	27	28	29	30	

- **A** 3 Fridays
- **B** 4 Fridays
- **C** 5 Fridays

MCT 2 — 35

Posttest — Chapter 9, page 2
Multiple-Choice Format

Name _____

6. Read the story. Choose the number sentence. John worked 6 hours last week and 3 hours this week. How many hours did he work in all?
- **A** $6 - 3 = 3$
- **B** $6 + 3 = 9$

7. Count the money.
- **A** 26¢
- **B** 21¢
- **C** 16¢

8. Count the money.
- **A** 31¢
- **B** 35¢
- **C** 25¢

9. Count the money.
- **A** 75¢
- **B** 80¢
- **C** 85¢

10. How many dimes does it take to make one half dollar?
- **A** 3 dimes
- **B** 5 dimes
- **C** 4 dimes

11. Paula washes cars and cleans tires. What is her total pay?

Job	Pay
Wash cars	30¢
Sweep mats	15¢
Clean tires	25¢

- **A** 40¢
- **B** 45¢
- **C** 55¢

36 — MCT 2

ITEM ANALYSIS

Items	Objectives
1	9-1
2	9-2
3	9-3
4	9-4
5	9-5
6	9-6
7	9-7
8	9-8
9	9-9
10	9-10
11	9-11

Note: The item analysis is the same for all pretests and posttests for this chapter.

ALSO AVAILABLE

- ▶ **Free Response Tests**
- ▶ **Alternative Tests**
- ▶ **Thinking Strategies**
- ▶ **Concrete Materials**

PROJECT AND BULLETIN BOARD

Draw on the bulletin board a sample television listing such as the one shown. Point out the features of each listing, including the name of the program, the time it begins and ends, and the channel on which it may be seen. During session 1, have students identify programs that appear at a specific time. During session 2, have them identify both the beginning and the ending time for specific programs. During session 3, students should identify elapsed time. As a challenge during session 4, have students use both addition and subtraction to calculate elapsed time. Suggest that the movie *Star Battles* has ten 1-min commercials. If you taped the movie and erased the commercials, how long would it take to watch the movie from beginning to end? Have students bring in television schedules and write similar questions about time.

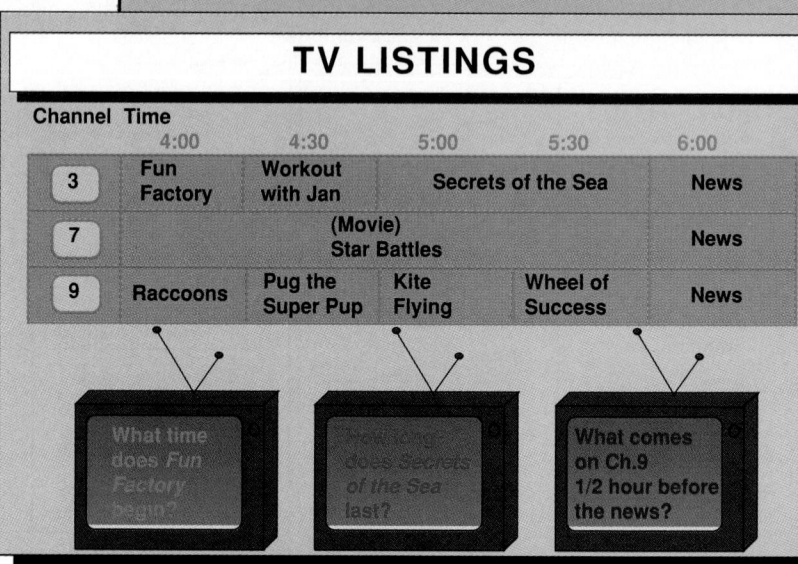

COOPERATIVE LEARNING

Divide the class into groups of 4-6. Identify the group skill: building on the strengths in each other's ideas rather than focusing on weaknesses. Copy the rental chart on the chalkboard. Have students count nickels, dimes, quarters, and half dollars to determine the rental fees for skating equipment. Individual students in each group will play the roles of skaters (tell what they want to rent and count coins for the rental fees); clerk (read prices; use calculator to add rental charges); and cashier (collect and recount coins paid by skaters). It is the cashier's responsibility to check to see that fees have been correctly calculated and the money correctly counted out. If there is an error, encourage cashiers to point out the steps where the fees were correctly counted as well as where mistakes were made. Have students change roles frequently.

You will find grouping suggestions and cooperative learning activities in most lessons through this chapter.

LITERATURE

Hutchins, Pat. *Clocks and More Clocks.* New York: Macmillan, 1970.

The man in this story keeps buying clock after clock. He checks and compares them and is satisfied only when he realizes they are all telling the time correctly. Use the story to help students understand 5- and 10-min intervals of time. Ask them to draw or make their own clocks and discuss time intervals they have chosen to depict.

Brenner, Barbara. *The Five Pennies.* New York: Knopf, 1963.

Kotzwinkle, William. *The Day the Gang Got Rich.* New York: Viking 1970.

ENGLISH AS A SECOND LANGUAGE

The activities in this chapter are visual, manipulative, and cooperative. Before putting students in pairs or groups, discuss as much language and information as possible about the subjects (clocks, calendars, money). Provide students with the language they need to carry out the tasks. For *Write About It* on page 188, minimize possible anxiety about writing by having ESL students dictate their stories to native speakers. The ESL student then reads the story aloud. Depending on the ESL student's ability and confidence in writing, this activity might be reversed.

The problem solving lesson on page 201 contains *-ing* forms. Questions are in the past tense and include irregular forms that may be unfamiliar. Break down problems by asking *yes* or *no* questions. *Did Raoul feed the fish? How much was he paid for feeding the fish?* Have students create verb flashcards with present tense, past tense and *-ing* forms.

GIFTED

Mathematically talented students may already know how to tell time. They will nevertheless likely be interested in many of the activities presented in this chapter. Challenge these students, after they have completed their Student Edition work, to demonstrate how to show elapsed time to 5-min intervals. For example, after Lesson 4 on elapsed time, write a typical daily schedule on the chalkboard. Include the time school begins, then show $1\frac{1}{2}$ h for morning work and the new time, followed by a 15-min break for recess and the new time, and so on through the school day. For each activity, show the time elapsed and the new time on analog and digital clocks. Then challenge students to make up their own daily schedule, using school as just part of their day. Encourage them to begin at their normal wake-up time and go through the day to bedtime. Artistically talented students may wish to illustrate each activity and place their work in a book titled *A Day in the Life of (student's name)*.

STUDENTS AT RISK

Prepare large copies of a clock face and cut construction-paper wedge shapes to cover 5-min increments. Draw an hour hand but no minute hand on 1 of the clock faces. Have students use the wedge shapes to cover each 5-min increment in order as they say the time aloud. Repeat for several different hours.

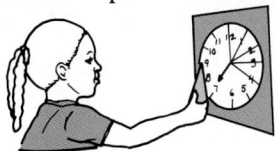

Prepare a large master grid for use as calendar pages. Have students work in small groups to make calendars. Each student should contribute at least 1 month, showing the name of the month, days of the week, and dates, as well as an illustration of a common event for that month.

Have students bring in clean, empty food containers, such as cereal boxes and egg cartons. Make up prices less than 1 dollar and have students use play money to practice making purchases with the exact amount.

You may also use the Reteaching Supplements and the specific Reteaching Tips from each lesson in this chapter.

PICTURE

These pictures and accompanying stories and poems are available as storybooks.

You may want to read and discuss this story with your students before starting the chapter. The first lesson in this chapter includes a question about the story. Lessons 1, 3, 4, 7, and 9 in this chapter have questions in the informal Assessment that refer to the story.

Alice's Present

"Alice! Alice! Wake up! Wake up! It's time for your afternoon feeding. Ted is waiting for you," urged Sara, the giraffe. Alice, the tiger, stirred ever so slightly, twitching her long tail. "Please, Alice! Wake up!" begged Sara. Alice's mouth opened in a big yawn. Her eyes flickered open once, twice, three times. She saw Sara.

"Oh, my! What time is it?" asked Alice, as she sprang up.

"Hurry, Alice. Ted is waiting. It's time for your 1 o'clock feeding," said Sara.

Alice gave herself a shake and ran off. "Thanks, Sara," she called back.

Alice was an outstanding tiger in every way. She was beautiful—long and lean—with stylish black stripes on her ruddy orange fur and a lovely bib of pure white under her chin. She was intelligent, sensitive, and kind. She was friends with all the other animals in the zoo. But the truth was, Alice was never on time. This often got her in trouble with Ted, the zookeeper. Alice's friends tried to look after her, but they often were too busy with their own schedules.

Alice finally made it to the feeding arena. There stood Ted looking very upset. "Alice, I've watched the minute hand on my watch move from the 12 to the 5 waiting for you. You are late!" exclaimed Ted. "This is the last straw. If you are late one more time, I will send you to another zoo. You had better be on time for your 6 o'clock feeding!"

Alice felt crushed. Leave her friends? Her comfortable surroundings? Why, this zoo was home to her. She never wanted to go anywhere else. Alice hung her head as she walked back to her bed.

"Alice, why do you look so sad?" asked Sara. Alice explained what had happened as she flopped down dejectedly on her bed.

"What am I to do?" asked Alice. "I just never seem to know the time." She rolled over with a big sigh.

"Don't worry. The other animals and I will think of something. We don't want you to leave either," said Sara encouragingly.

Sara and the other animals got together to talk about what they could do. Bob, the bear, suggested moving Alice's bed into the feeding arena, but everyone knew that Ted would never approve that idea. Ernie, the elephant, thought that maybe he should move in with Alice since he remembered everything. But once again, they knew Ted wouldn't approve.

"I know!" roared Larry, the lion. "Let's buy Alice a watch. Then she'll always know what time it is." The others agreed.

"OK, how much money do you have?" asked Sara. Everyone took out their money.

"I have one nickel," said Rita, the zebra.

"I have one dime," added Larry.

"I only have three pennies," said Bob unhappily.

"That's OK. I have two dimes," replied Ernie.

"With my two nickels," said Sara, "we should have enough for a watch."

The animals happily went and bought the watch and wrapped it with a big red bow. They were ready to present it to Alice.

"Alice, we have something that may solve all your problems," said Sara, as she gave the box to Alice. The animals looked on as Alice unwrapped the box.

"Oh, my! How wonderful! A watch! I'll never be late again," said Alice joyfully. She gave each of them a big hug, and then put on her watch for all to see. "Hey, it's almost 6 o'clock. I'd better be off for my evening feeding. Thank you everyone. You're the best friends a tiger could ever have!"

Understanding 5-Minute Intervals

OBJECTIVE 9-1   To count 5-minute intervals on the clock

PREBOOK ACTIVITIES

QUICK REVIEW

Count by 5s. Complete the pattern.
5, _(10)_ , _(15)_ , 20, _(25)_ , _(30)_ , _(35)_ , 40, _(45)_ , _(50)_ ,
_(55)_ , 60

PRIOR KNOWLEDGE

Display an analog clock. Remind students that they already know how to tell time to the hour and half hour. Show times such as 3:00 and 3:30, then set the clock to 5:00. *Where is the hour hand when it is 5 0'clock?* (on the 5) *Where is the minute hand?* (on the 12) *Why do you think the* o'clock *times might be called* the top of the hour? (Possible answer: The minute hand is at the top of the clock.) *Where is the minute hand when it is five-thirty?* (on the 6) *Why do you think the* thirty *times are sometimes called* half-past the hour? (Possible answer: The minute hand is halfway around the clock.)

COMMUNICATION

Discussing and Writing Math   Write the word **minute** on the chalkboard. Tell students to close their eyes and open them when they think 1 min is up. Say *Stop* when the minute is up. *Was a minute longer or shorter than you thought? Could you erase the chalkboard in 1 min? Could you walk around the room in 1 min?* Have students complete the following sentence with something they can do: I can _____ in 1 minute. Then have them illustrates their sentences.

EXPLORE AND CONNECT

Materials: demonstration clock, punchout clocks and clock hands, brads
Grouping Suggestion: pairs
Have students use brads to fasten the hands on their punchout clocks. Review the hour and minute hands. *The short word (hour) goes with the short hand; the long word (minute) goes with the long hand.* Have students write these words on the hands of their punchout clocks. Have pairs of students set their clocks to 12 o'clock. The first student moves the minute hand dot by dot and counts by 1s around the clock to 60; the second student counts by 5s as the minute hand passes each number. Have students make a tally mark for each minute they count. *How many minutes are there from 12 to 1?* (5) *from 1 to 2?* (5) *from 12 to 2?* (10) Continue around the clock until there are 12 sets of tally marks. Have students count by 5s to show there are 60 min in 1 h. Encourage them to help each other.

CONNECTIONS   Use these anytime.

Problem of the Day

Act It Out   Use a punchout clock to solve this problem.
Anthony started cleaning his room when the minute hand was at 12. When he finished, the minute hand was at 3. The hour hand had hardly moved at all. How long did it take Anthony to clean his room? (15 min)

Life Skills

Schedules   Draw the hands on blank clock faces to the nearest hour to show the times that you: 1) get up, 2) arrive at school, 3) eat lunch, 4) return home, 5) eat dinner, and 6) go to bed. Label each clock with the event of the day.

Subject Integration

Art   Cut out from magazines and newspapers pictures showing clocks and watches. Paste them on a piece of construction paper. Tell the class how the clocks and watches on your paper are alike and how they are different.

CLASSWORK AND HOMEWORK SUPPLEMENTS

ractice

Life Skills   9-1

Name _____

Understanding 5-Minute Intervals

The minute hand started at 12 cn each clock.
How many minutes did it move?
Count by 5s. Then write the number.

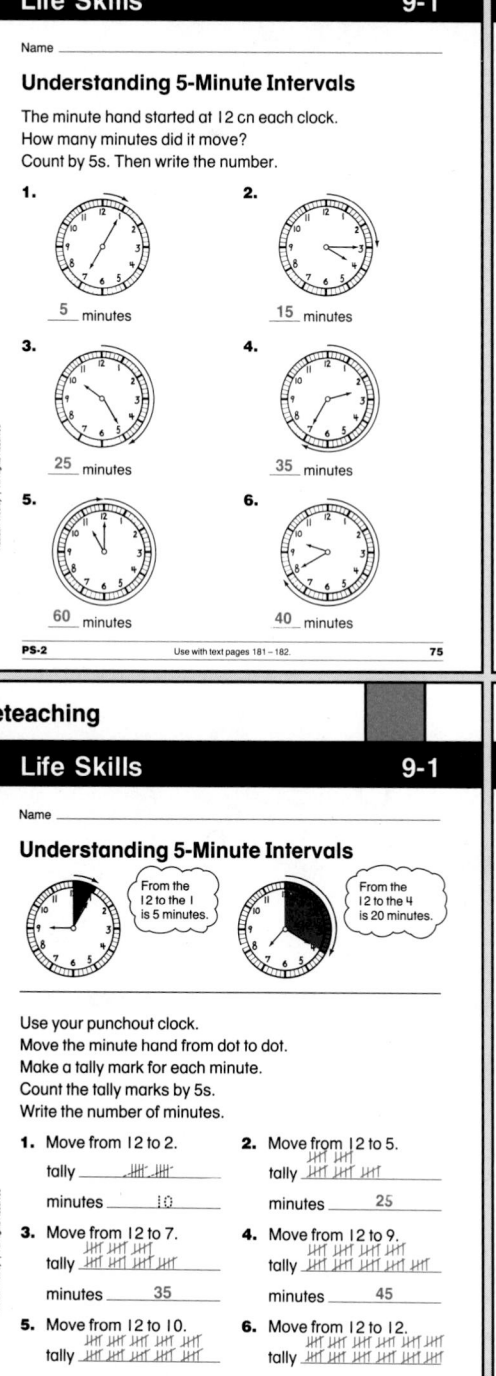

1. __5__ minutes

2. __15__ minutes

3. __25__ minutes

4. __35__ minutes

5. __60__ minutes

6. __40__ minutes

PS-2   Use with text pages 181–182.   75

Building Thinking Skills

Mental Math   9-1

Name _____

No Time to Loaf

Jo, Jan, and Jim are baking bread. They began at 3:05.
Look at the clock in each picture. How many minutes
did each step take?

1. Jan mixed the ingredients.
From: `3:05`
To: `3:25`
It took __20__ minutes.

2. They let the dough rest.
From: `3:25`
To: `3:40`
It rested __15__ minutes.

3. Jim kneaded the dough.
From: `3:40`
To: `3:45`
He kneaded __5__ minutes.

4. Jo kneaded it, too.
From: `3:45`
To: `3:50`
She kneaded __5__ minutes.

5. They let the dough rise.
From: `3:50`
To: `5:50`
That took __2__ hours.

6. They put it in the oven.
From: `5:50`
To: `6:30`
It baked __40__ minutes.

TS-2   Use with text pages 181–182.   75

eteaching

Life Skills   9-1

Name _____

Understanding 5-Minute Intervals

From the 12 to the 1 is 5 minutes.

From the 12 to the 4 is 20 minutes.

Use your punchout clock.
Move the minute hand from dot to dot.
Make a tally mark for each minute.
Count the tally marks by 5s.
Write the number of minutes.

1. Move from 12 to 2.
tally _____ JHH JHH
minutes __10__

2. Move from 12 to 5.
tally JHH JHH JHH
minutes __25__

3. Move from 12 to 7.
tally JHH JHH JHH JHH JHH
minutes __35__

4. Move from 12 to 9.
tally JHH JHH JHH JHH JHH
minutes __45__

5. Move from 12 to 10.
tally JHH JHH JHH JHH JHH JHH
minutes __50__

6. Move from 12 to 12.
tally JHH JHH JHH JHH JHH JHH
minutes __60__

RS-2   Use with text pages 181–182.   75

Challenges

Family Math   9-1

Name _____

How Long Will It Take?

> Dear Family,
> Your child is learning about time in 5-minute intervals. Help your child with this activity
> to provide practice in predicting how long a task will take.

Look at this list of jobs.

brush my teeth	eat breakfast	walk the dog
get dressed	clear my dishes	travel to school
make my bed	feed the cat	set the table
clean up my room	feed the dog	take a bath

How long do you think each one takes?
Choose one job to finish each sentence below.
Ask a family member to time you. Do the job.
Then write the number of minutes the job took.

1. In 5 MINUTES I think I can _____.
It took ___ minutes.

2. In 10 MINUTES I think I can _____.
It took ___ minutes.

3. In 15 MINUTES I think I can _____.
It took ___ minutes.

4. In 30 MINUTES I think I can _____.
It took ___ minutes.

CS-2   Use with text pages 181–182.   75

OPTIONS FOR INDIVIDUAL NEEDS

Basic

Exercises All

Supplements
Reteaching 75 or
Practice 75

Average

Exercises All

Supplements
Practice 75
Challenges 75 or
Thinking Skills 75

Extended

Exercises All

Supplements
Challenges 75
Thinking Skills 75

Other Resources:
Mathematics Their Way, pp.
95, 123-124, 155, 247
Explorations, pp. 152-155,
169, 204, 234, 266, 302
Workjobs, pp. 228-229

9-1

OBJECTIVE 9-1
To count 5-minute intervals on the clock

> **Materials:** punchout clocks, punchout clock hands, brads, demonstration clock, index cards
>
> **Grouping Suggestions:** individual work, pairs

1. MOTIVATE AND TEACH

LEARN ABOUT IT

Have students construct the clock on page 181 by attaching a set of clock hands with a brad. Read the chapter story to students. *What time was Alice's afternoon feeding? Show the time on your clock.* (1 o'clock) *How long did Ted wait for Alice? Count the dots from 12 to 5 on your clock.* (25 min)

▶ **How many tally marks, or minutes, are there from the 12 to the 1?** (5)

▶ **How many tally marks, or minutes, from the 1 to the 2?** (5)

▶ **Skip count from the 12 to the 2. How many minutes?** (10 min) **Does this match the number of tally marks? Why?** (yes; it takes 5 min for the minute hand to move from one number to another. From the 12 to the 2 is 2 numbers, so that is 10 min.) Have students continue around the clock until they have written 12 sets of tally marks.

▶ **Count by 5s. How many marks did you make to show the minutes around the clock?** (60)

▶ **What do you know about the relationship between minutes and hours?** (There are 60 min in 1 h.)

2. CHECK UNDERSTANDING

ERROR ALERT Confusing the minute and hour hands and the use of the numbers on the clock face.

9
Time and Money

TEACHING OPTIONS

RETEACHING TIPS Draw a number line with 60 marks labeled in 5s. Suggest the line be wrapped around a circle like minute marks on a clock. Move a minute hand and have students count to show 5 min between each number on the clock face. Use Reteaching Supplement 75.

ENRICHMENT **Family Math** Have students keep a record of the times it takes to do several activities at home, such as washing dishes, setting the table, and reading a story. Students record the numbers the minute hand is pointing to when the activities begin and end, then write the total number of minutes.

Name _____

Understanding 5-Minute Intervals

From the 12 to the 2 is 10 minutes.

Use your punchout clock. Move the minute hand from dot to dot. Make a tally mark for each minute. Count the tally marks by 5s. Write the number of minutes.

Ⅲ Ⅲ Ⅲ

move from 12 to 1 tally ____Ⅲ Ⅲ____ minutes ___5___

move from 12 to 3 tally __Ⅲ Ⅲ Ⅲ__ minutes ___15___

move from 12 to 4 tally _Ⅲ Ⅲ Ⅲ Ⅲ_ minutes ___20___

The minute hand started at 12 on each clock. How many minutes did it move? Count by 5s. Then write the number.

⑤ ⑩ ⑮ ⑳ ㉕

5.

6.

_25_ minutes   _40_ minutes   _60_ minutes = _1_ hour

USE CRITICAL THINKING

Tina started with the minute hand at 12. She moved it 35 minutes. What number did it point to then? ___7___

182 (one hundred eighty-two)   Chapter 9

---

3. PRACTICE AND APPLY

Basic	All
Average	All
Extended	All

PRACTICE

Why can you count by 5s to find the number of minutes from one number on the clock to another? (Because there are 5 min from one number to the next.)

APPLY

USE CRITICAL THINKING

▶ **What do you have to find out in order to answer the question?** (Possible answer: which number the minute hand points to in 35 min)

▶ **Describe a plan for answering the question.** (Possible answer: Start the minute hand at 12; move from number to number and count by 5s. See what number the minute hand is on when you say 35.)

▶ **What if Tina started at the 1 and moved the minute hand 35 min? What number would the minute hand point to then?** (8)

CLOSE AND ASSESS

SHOW WHAT YOU KNOW Give pairs 2 punchout clocks and several index cards. One student writes a number between 1 and 11 on an index card. The second moves the minute hand, starting at 12 and ending at the number on the card, and records each minute with a tally mark. When the student reaches the number, he or she counts by 5s and supplies the number of minutes that have elapsed from 12 to that number.

QUICK QUIZ

Put the minute hand of your clock at 12. How many minutes does it take to get to the 8? (40 min)

9-1

Telling and Writing Time: 15-Minute Intervals

OBJECTIVE 9-2   To tell and write time to 15-minute intervals

PREBOOK ACTIVITIES

QUICK REVIEW

Count by 5s. Fill in the missing numbers.
0, 5, 10, _(15)_ , 20, 25, _(30)_ , 35, 40, _(45)_ , 50, 55, _(60)_

PRIOR KNOWLEDGE

Discuss significant times in the students' days: what time they get up in the morning, what time they leave for school, what time school begins, and so on. Use a real or demonstration clock to show the times that students give as answers. Ask volunteers to show some of the times on the clock and emphasize the quarter and half hours as they are mentioned.

COMMUNICATION

Reading and Listening in Math   Introduce the concept of quarters by quartering an apple. *How many pieces are there?* (4) Explain to students that we can also divide a clock into quarters. Quarter a clock by placing yarn loops around the demonstration clock. Ask students to help you mark the quarter or 15-min interval times. *How many minutes are in each quarter?* (15) Have students count by 5s as you move the minute hand around the clock: o'clock, 5, 10, 15, . . . Then have them count by 15-min intervals: *o'clock, 15, 30, 45.* Have volunteers stand and show with their arms the minute-hand placement for the times in the count.

EXPLORE AND CONNECT

Materials: punchout clocks (traditional and digital)
Grouping Suggestion: pairs
Pair students and have them use their punchout clocks. Display a time such as 4 o'clock on the demonstration clock. Tell one partner to set the hands on the punchout clock. Have the other pretend to be inside a clock and use their arms to show the time on their "body clock." Then have both students set their digital clocks to match. Encourage students while they are involved in this activity to praise their partners for work done well and not to criticize wrong answers. Continue having students manipulate their clocks to show various 15-min interval times that you read. Include 3:15, 3:45, 9:15, and 9:45, as well as 6:30 and 12:00, when clock hands overlap.

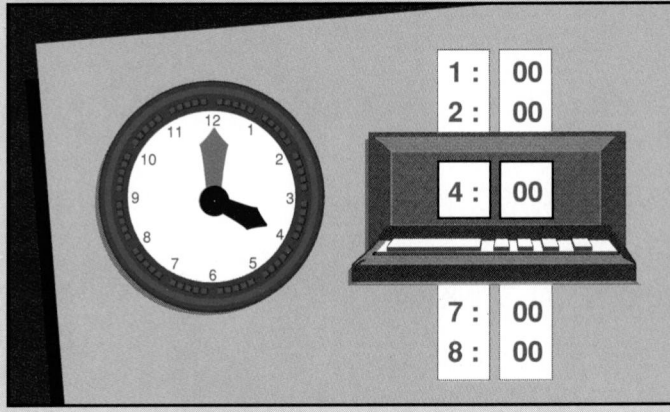

CONNECTIONS   Use these anytime.

Problem of the Day

What Time Is It?   Tamara is going to a party at 4:30. She has a half hour to get ready. What time is it now? (4 o'clock)

Life Skills

Daylight Savings Time   Last spring, when we set our clocks ahead by 1 h, Wesley's family asked him to help. They have one regular clock and one digital clock. Wesley helped to change the clocks at 9 o'clock. Draw the two clocks to show how they looked after they were changed. (🕐 10:00)

Subject Integration

Language Arts   With a partner, talk about what these sayings mean.
Time flies.
Take your time.
I have time on my hands.
Time flies when you are having fun.
A stitch in time saves nine.
Choose one saying. Print it on a poster and draw a picture to go with it.

CLASSWORK AND HOMEWORK SUPPLEMENTS

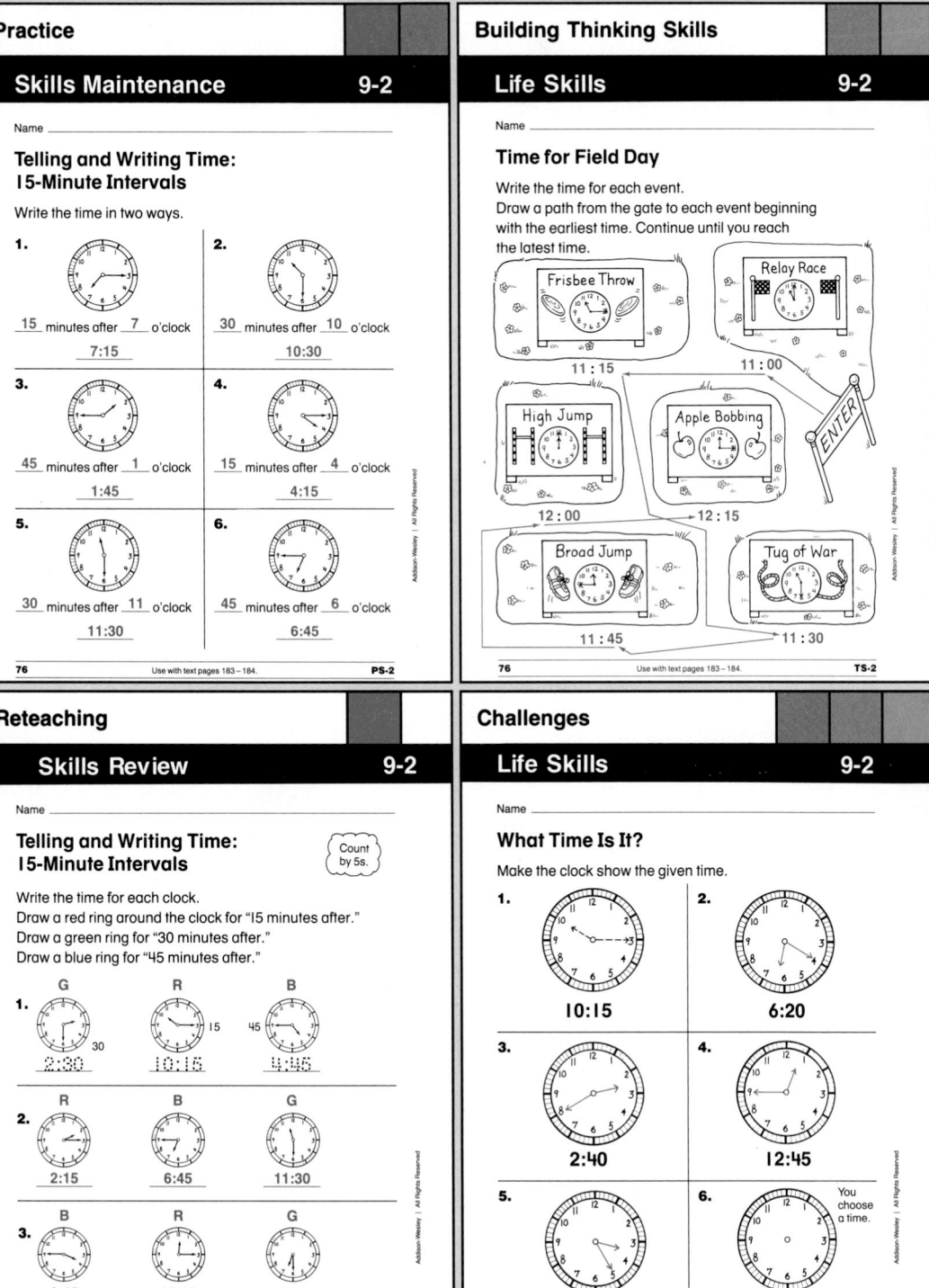

Practice

Skills Maintenance — 9-2

Name _____

Telling and Writing Time: 15-Minute Intervals

Write the time in two ways.

1. 15 minutes after 7 o'clock — 7:15
2. 30 minutes after 10 o'clock — 10:30
3. 45 minutes after 1 o'clock — 1:45
4. 15 minutes after 4 o'clock — 4:15
5. 30 minutes after 11 o'clock — 11:30
6. 45 minutes after 6 o'clock — 6:45

76   Use with text pages 183–184.   PS-2

Building Thinking Skills

Life Skills — 9-2

Name _____

Time for Field Day

Write the time for each event.
Draw a path from the gate to each event beginning with the earliest time. Continue until you reach the latest time.

- Frisbee Throw — 11:15
- Relay Race — 11:00
- High Jump — 12:00
- Apple Bobbing — 12:15
- Broad Jump — 11:45
- Tug of War — 11:30

76   Use with text pages 183–184.   TS-2

Reteaching

Skills Review — 9-2

Name _____

Telling and Writing Time: 15-Minute Intervals

Count by 5s.

Write the time for each clock.
Draw a red ring around the clock for "15 minutes after."
Draw a green ring for "30 minutes after."
Draw a blue ring for "45 minutes after."

1. G 2:30   R 10:15   B 4:45
2. R 2:15   B 6:45   G 11:30
3. B 3:45   R 12:15   G 6:30

76   Use with text pages 183–184.   RS-2

Challenges

Life Skills — 9-2

Name _____

What Time Is It?

Make the clock show the given time.

1. 10:15
2. 6:20
3. 2:40
4. 12:45
5. 3:25
6. You choose a time. Answers will vary.

76   Use with text pages 183–184.   CS-2

OPTIONS FOR INDIVIDUAL NEEDS

Basic

Exercises All
More Practice, p. 419, set A

Supplements
Reteaching 76 or
Practice 76
Challenges 76

Average

Exercises All
More Practice, p. 419, set A

Supplements
Practice 76
Challenges 76 or
Thinking Skills 76

Extended

Exercises All

Supplements
Challenges 76
Thinking Skills 76

Other Resources:
Mathematics Their Way, pp. 95, 123-124, 155, 247
Explanations, pp. 152-155, 169, 234, 266, 302
Workjobs, pp. 228-229

9-2

LESSON PLAN 9-2

OBJECTIVE 9-2
To tell and write time to 15-minute intervals

Materials: punchout clocks, TA 8 (Blank Clock Faces—15-minute intervals)

1. MOTIVATE AND TEACH

LEARN ABOUT IT

On a demonstration clock, show a time on the hour, such as 2:00. Have students show the time on their punchout clocks and read the time aloud with you. Continue with 2:15, 2:30, 2:45, 15 min after 2, 30 min after 2, and 45 min after 2. Have students read the feeding times from chart on page 183.
▶ **What number is the minute hand on when it is 15 min after the hour?** (3)
▶ **What number is the minute hand on when it is 30 min after the hour?** (6)
▶ **What number is the minute hand on when it is 45 min after the hour?** (9)
▶ **How much later than the lion is the seal fed?** (15 min)
▶ **Which animal is fed 30 min after the lion?** (the wolf)
▶ **What if the zoo fed its zebras 2 h after the wolf? What time would the zebras eat?** (4:15, or 15 min after 4)

2. CHECK UNDERSTANDING

ERROR ALERT Counting by 5-min intervals rather than 15-min intervals.

Name _____

Telling and Writing Time
15-Minute Intervals

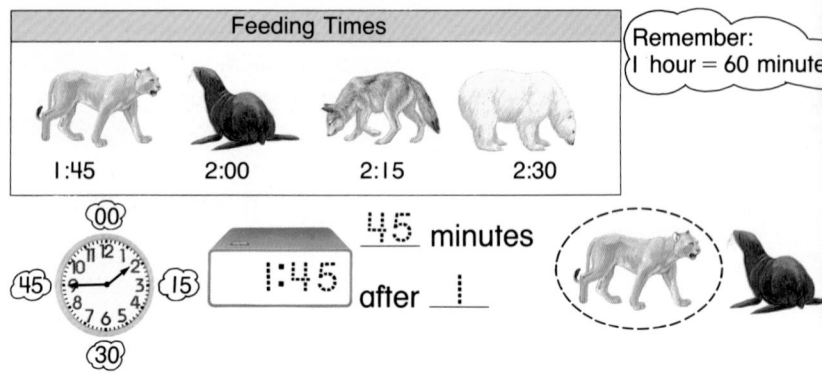

Remember: 1 hour = 60 minutes

<u>45</u> minutes
1:45 after <u>1</u>

Write each time two ways.
Ring the animal to be fed at that time.

1. feeding time for

2:00

<u>2</u> o'clock

2. feeding time for

2:15

<u>15</u> minutes after <u>2</u>

3. feeding time for

2:30

<u>30</u> minutes after <u>2</u>

Chapter 9

(one hundred eighty-three) 183

TEACHING OPTIONS

RETEACHING TIPS Give each student 4 blank clock faces. Move the minute hand on a demonstration clock and count aloud as you pass each mark; o'clock, 15, 30, 45. Have students draw the minute hand at 12, 3, 6, and 9 for each interval. Use Reteaching Supplement 76 for additional help.

ENRICHMENT **Family Math** Have a family member help students keep a record of what they are doing at 15-min intervals after they arrive home from school. Have them draw a picture of 4 activities, one for each interval: o'clock, 15, 30, and 45 minutes after an hour. Write the time below the picture.

rite the time for each animal show.

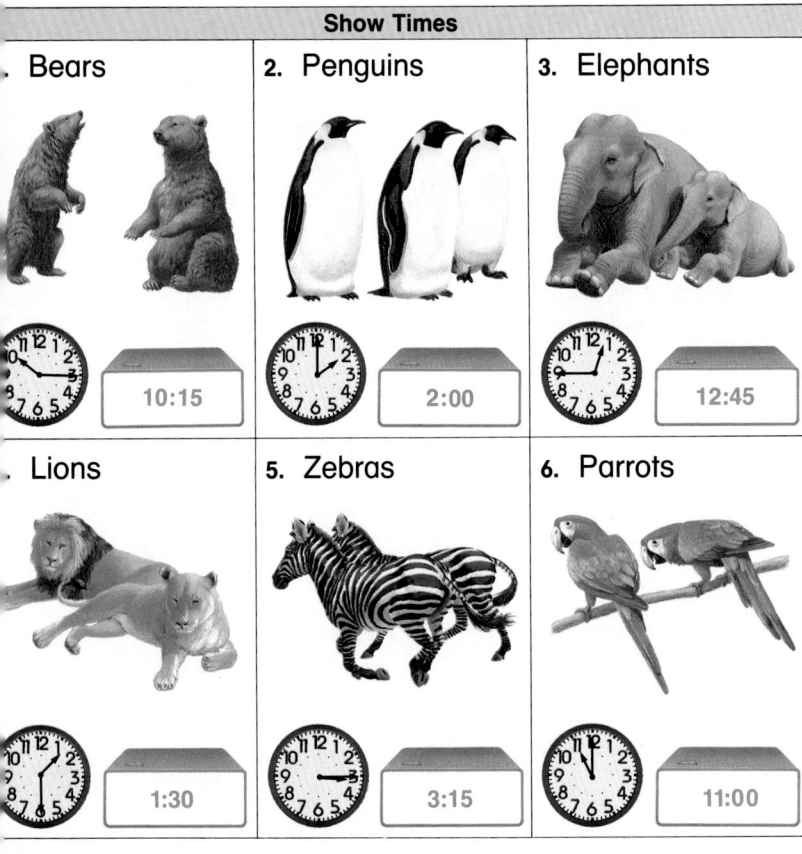

Show Times		
Bears	2. Penguins	3. Elephants
10:15	2:00	12:45
Lions	5. Zebras	6. Parrots
1:30	3:15	11:00

AKE AN ESTIMATE

Ring the closer time. Then write that time.

The time is closer to 8:00 (8:30)

It is about __8:30__ .

3. PRACTICE AND APPLY

Basic	All
Average	All
Extended	All

PRACTICE

Where will you find the information you need for Exercises 1-6 on page 184? (from the clocks)

APPLY

MAKE AN ESTIMATE   Discuss the fact that we often estimate time on a traditional clock.
▶ **To which of the 2 times in Exercise 7 would 7 minutes after 8 be closer?** (8:00)
▶ **Why do we sometimes use estimates of time rather than the exact times?** (Possible answer: We do not always need to know the exact time.)
▶ **Why do we not estimate time when we are using a digital clock?** (because it always shows the numbers for time to the minute)

LOSE AND ASSESS

HOW WHAT YOU KNOW
gin telling a story such as the
lowing: *At 10:00, the members of
e Adventure Club started out on an
-day trip. At 10:15, they climbed a
l. At 10:30, they took pictures.* Ask
dents to show the times on their
nchout clocks as you speak.
dents may continue the story with
eas of their own.

QUICK QUIZ

Write the time for each clock.

(10:15, 3:30, 1:45, 7:00)

9-2

Chapter 9 Lesson 2   **184**

Telling and Writing Time: 5-Minute Intervals

OBJECTIVE 9-3   To tell and write time to 5-minute intervals

PREBOOK ACTIVITIES

QUICK REVIEW

What time is it?

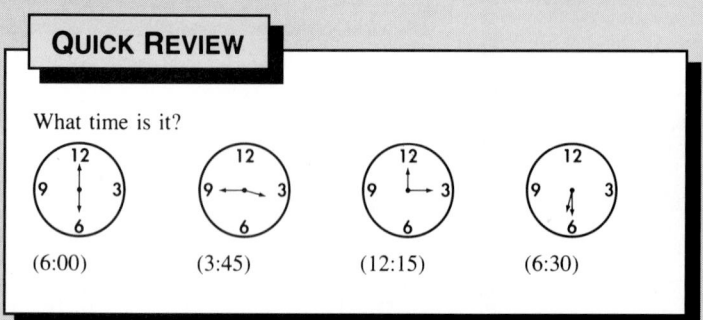

(6:00)   (3:45)   (12:15)   (6:30)

PRIOR KNOWLEDGE

Have students follow as you do exercises that involve counting by 5s or patterns of 5. For example, use an accumulation pattern such as 5 claps / 5 snaps / 5 taps on the head. Ask students to add further movements in groups of 5. Next, have students count aloud in turn to 60 by 1s, with each person who says a multiple of 5 standing up. Finally, have students count by 5s to 60. Extend this last activity to show the movement of the clock hands as each number is said.

COMMUNICATION

Discussing and Writing in Math   Have students work in small groups to discuss and list occasions when they have to know what time it is. To help them get started, ask what times they need to know first thing in the morning. (Possible answers: when to get up; when to be ready for the bus; when school starts) Have students take turns recording the group's ideas. Remind students while they are working to build on each other's good ideas rather than to make fun of ideas that may not fit in with the activity. Have the groups share their lists with the rest of the class by reading them aloud. Write several times and activities on the chalkboard.

EXPLORE AND CONNECT

Materials: punchout clocks, demonstration clock

Set a demonstration clock to 11:20. Ask students to set their punchout clocks to 11:00. Then have them count aloud by 5s as they move the minute hands on their clocks from number to number to get to 11:20. As they say each 5-minute interval, write the time on the chalkboard. (11:05, 11:10, 11:15, 11:20) Continue by setting the demonstration clock to 11:55 and have students move their clock hands and count 5-minute intervals as you record the times. *What time will it be 5 minutes after 11:55?* (12:00) *What time is it 5 minutes before 11:30?* (11:2.. *5 minutes after 11:30?* (11:35) Write times such as 1:10, 2:2.. 3:40, and 4:50 on the chalkboard, and have students set their clocks to match.

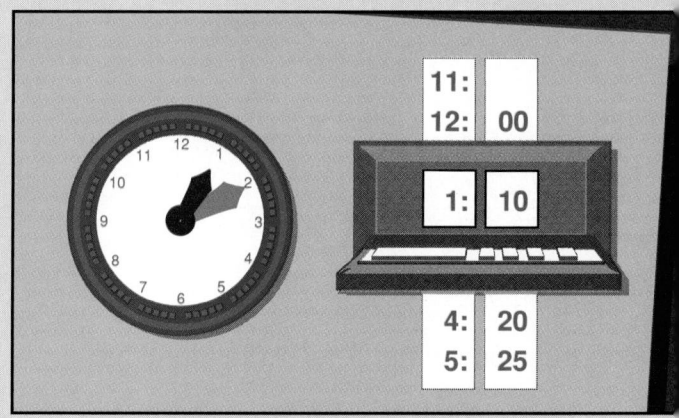

CONNECTIONS   Use these anytime.

Problem of the Day

Baking Time Suki is baking macaroni and cheese. The recipe says it should bake for 30 min. She put the dish in the oven at 4:15. When will it be ready? (4:45)

Number Sense

Estimation In which of these two situations is it all right to give an estimate of the time rather than the exact time? (2)
1. Your mother has to catch the 7:10 train to get to work.
2. Your family is going on a picnic this afternoon.

Subject Integration

Art Work with a partner to draw a clock or watch that might be used in the future. First talk about these questions: What will it look like? How will it show the time? What special features will it have? Display your drawing on a bulletin board.

CLASSWORK AND HOMEWORK SUPPLEMENTS

Basic

Exercises All
Data Bank, p. 399
More Practice, p. 419, set B

Supplements
Reteaching 77 or
Practice 77
Thinking Skills 77

Average

Exercises All
Data Bank, p. 399
More Practice, p. 419, set B

Supplements
Practice 77
Challenges 77 or
Thinking Skills 77

Extended

Exercises All
Data Bank, p. 399

Supplements
Challenges 77
Thinking Skills 77

Other Resources:
Mathematics Their Way pp. 95, 123-124, 155, 247
Explorations, pp. 234, 266, 302
Workjobs, pp. 228-229

Practice

Life Skills · 9-3

Name _____

Telling and Writing Time: 5-Minute Intervals

Write the time in two ways.

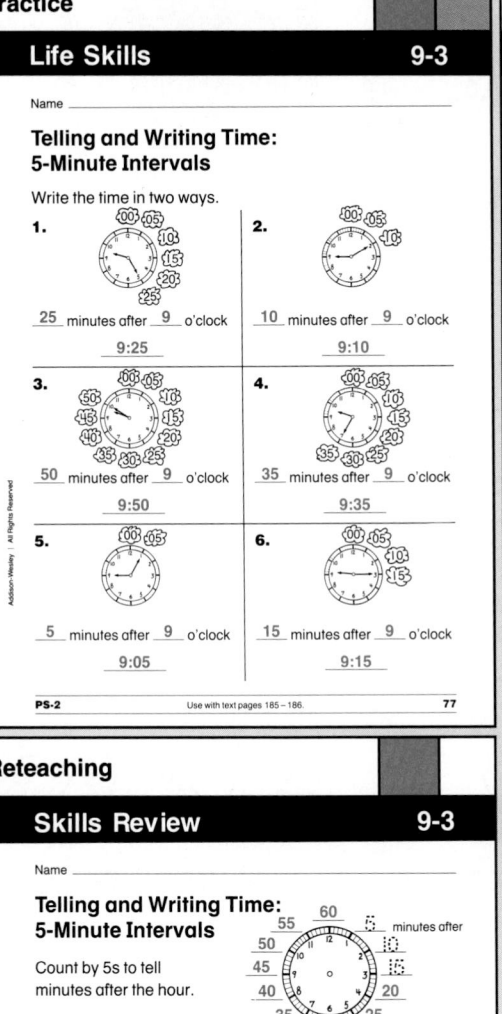

1. ___25___ minutes after ___9___ o'clock
   9:25

2. ___10___ minutes after ___9___ o'clock
   9:10

3. ___50___ minutes after ___9___ o'clock
   9:50

4. ___35___ minutes after ___9___ o'clock
   9:35

5. ___5___ minutes after ___9___ o'clock
   9:05

6. ___15___ minutes after ___9___ o'clock
   9:15

PS-2 · Use with text pages 185 – 186. · 77

Building Thinking Skills

Life Skills · 9-3

Name _____

Circus Time

Look at the clock next to each ride.
Read the sign.
Decide when the ride will open.
Write the time.
Which ride will open first?
Number the rides in order from 1 to 5.

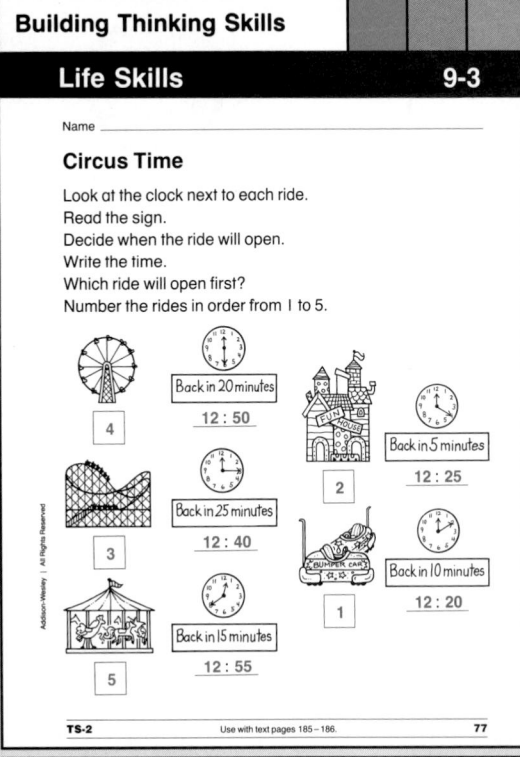

4	Back in 20 minutes · 12 : 50
2	Back in 5 minutes · 12 : 25
3	Back in 25 minutes · 12 : 40
1	Back in 10 minutes · 12 : 20
5	Back in 15 minutes · 12 : 55

TS-2 · Use with text pages 185 – 186. · 77

Reteaching

Skills Review · 9-3

Name _____

Telling and Writing Time: 5-Minute Intervals

Count by 5s to tell minutes after the hour.

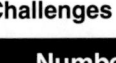

Write the times. Use the clock above to help you.

1. ___20___ minutes after ___7___ o'clock
   7:20

2. ___40___ minutes after ___2___ o'clock
   2:40

3. ___55___ minutes after ___6___ o'clock (Count by 5s.)
   6:55

4. ___30___ minutes after ___8___ o'clock (Count by 5s.)
   8:30

RS-2 · Use with text pages 185 – 186. · 77

Challenges

Number Sense · 9-3

Name _____

What Do You Think?

Think about the minute hand only.

From the 2 to the 5 is 15 minutes.

How many minutes?

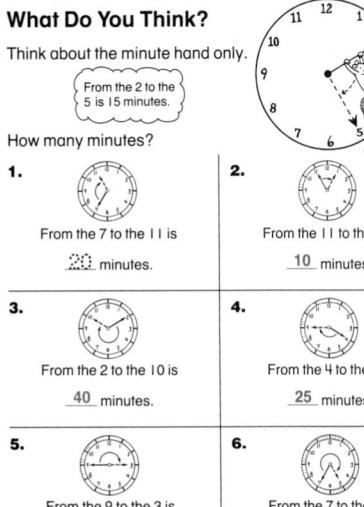

1. From the 7 to the 11 is ___20___ minutes.

2. From the 11 to the 1 is ___10___ minutes.

3. From the 2 to the 10 is ___40___ minutes.

4. From the 4 to the 9 is ___25___ minutes.

5. From the 9 to the 3 is ___30___ minutes.

6. From the 7 to the 5 is ___50___ minutes.

CS-2 · Use with text pages 185 – 186. · 77

LESSON PLAN 9-3

OBJECTIVE 9-3
To tell and write time to 5-minute intervals

Materials: punchout clocks, TA9 and TA10 (blank clock faces)

Grouping Suggestions: individual work, pairs

1. MOTIVATE AND TEACH

LEARN ABOUT IT

On a demonstration clock, show a 15-min time, such as 12:15. *What time will it be in 5 min? in 10 min?* (12:20, 12:25) Have students count by 5s from 15 to find out. Continue with other times.

Discuss the model at the top of page 185. Have students tell the time on the left (1:45), then read the time on the right (1:55) by counting by 5s. *In which exercises did you count on by one 5, or 5 min?* (Exercises 1 and 3) *In which exercise did you count on by two 5s or 10 min?* (Exercises 2 and 4)

▶ **When the minute hand points to 5, from which time on the clock will you count on by 5s? What number on the clock is this?** (Possible answer: from 15 min after the hour; 3)

▶ **How many minutes after the hour will it be then?** (25)

▶ **When the minute hand points to 7, from which time on the clock will you count on by 5s? What number on the clock is this?** (Possible answer: from 30 min after the hour; 6)

▶ **How many minutes after the hour will it be?** (35)

▶ **How many minutes after the hour will it be when the minute hand is at 1?** (5 min) **at 10?** (50 min)

2. CHECK UNDERSTANDING

ERROR ALERT Not counting on minutes to find the time because they have learned to tell time before the hour instead of after the hour.

Name _____

Telling and Writing Time
5-Minute Intervals

Draw the minute hand. Then write the times. Use counting on to help.

1.
9:15   9:20

2.
3:30   3:40

3.
6:45   6:50

4.
5:00   5:10

Chapter 9   (one hundred eighty-five)   18

TEACHING OPTIONS

RETEACHING TIPS Give each student a blank clock face (TA9). Have students write the missing minutes in the circles by counting on by 5s, then write the hours in the squares. Have them use their clocks to help read times you show on a demonstration clock. Assign Reteaching Supplement 77.

COMPUTER Clock, Hartley Courseware © 1985 For use with all levels. Using a clock face, students practice converting digital and analog time. After a tutorial, three practice activities require the student to set the clock. The game requires 5-10 minutes.

rite the times.

4:35   11:25   2:50   7:10

9:20   1:55   12:05   5:40

6:30   10:15   8:00   3:45

ND THE DATA

Who starts to work at the time shown on the clock? Ring the name.

Josh   Gillian   (Cristina)   Casey

Data Bank What time does Rex have math? (See page 399.) ___8:30___

Junior Zoo Keeper Work Times	
Name	Starts Work
Josh	2:45
Cristina	2:05
Gillian	2:30
Casey	2:20

LOSE AND ASSESS

RITE WHAT YOU KNOW
view with students the chapter
ry, *Alice's Present.* Ask students to
d the time showing on Alice's
tch in the story picture. *What time
d Alice finally show up for her 1
clock feeding?* (1:25) *Show it on
ur punchout clock and write the
e.*

QUICK QUIZ

Show these times on your punchout clock.
3:20   6:55   1:05   7:00   5:10
9:50   12:40   10:25   8:35   11:55

3. PRACTICE AND APPLY

Basic	All
Average	All
Extended	All

PRACTICE

How will you do Exercise 1-3? (Write the times the clocks show.)

APPLY

FIND THE DATA   Where will you find the data for Exercise 4? (on the chart)
► **Who begins work next after Cristina?** (Casey)
► **Who is last to begin work?** (Josh)
► **Show the starting times for each person on your punchout clock.**
Help students find the Data Bank on page 399 for Exercise 5.
► **What other subject does Rex have in the morning?** (Reading)
► **What is the last subject of the day?** (Art) **How do you know that?** (It is at 2:20, which is near the end of school.)

Elapsed Time

OBJECTIVE 9-4 To write elapsed time

PREBOOK ACTIVITIES

QUICK REVIEW

Use your punchouts. Show these times on a regular clock and a digital clock.

2 o'clock   30 min after 2
3 o'clock   30 min after 4
30 min after 7:00   8 o'clock

PRIOR KNOWLEDGE

Write the time on the chalkboard. Then lead a discussion about how long it takes students to do particular activities, such as walking, or riding to school, eating breakfast, brushing their teeth, and eating lunch. Extend the discussion to make comparisons. *Does it take longer to brush your teeth or to take a bath? to get to school or to get to your grandparents' house?* Then look at the time and ask students to estimate how long the discussion took. Write the estimates on the chalkboard, then write the time and show the amount of time that was spent on the discussion.

COMMUNICATION

Reading and Discussing Math   Read to students a book about a series of events that takes place during a few hours or a day. (Suggestion: *The Philharmonic Gets Dressed* by Karla Kuskin, Harper and Row, 1982). Follow with a discussion of how long each event or action might have taken. Write the actions on strips of tagboard and put them in scrambled order on the chalkboard ledge. Then ask students to sequence the cards to show the order in which the events took place in the story.

EXPLORE AND CONNECT

Materials: punchout clocks (traditional and digital)
Grouping Suggestion: pairs
Show a starting time (always a time on the hour) on a demonstration clock and ask students to show a time later. U» these amounts of elapsed time: 30 min, 1 h, 1 h and 30 min, h. Have one partner show the later time on the traditional clo« punchout and the other on the digital clock punchout. Talk about what happens to the movement of the hour hand as well as the minute hand as time passes. Discuss the fact that when moving the minute hand 1 h and 30 min it is helpful to break down the movement into 2 parts: move 1 h and then move 30 more min. With 2 h, move 1 h and then 1 more h. Invite students to set their clocks to a time on the hour and have the partners show the time 30 min later, 1 h later, 1 h and 30 mi» later, and 2 h later.

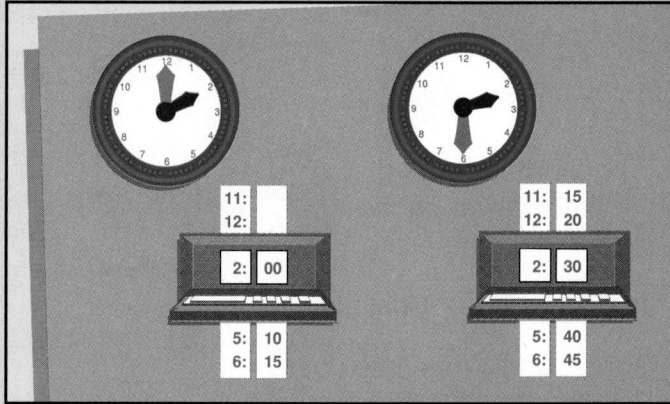

CONNECTIONS   Use these anytime.

Problem of the Day

How Many Miles?   Alan can ride his bike 2 mi in 30 min. If he keeps up this speed, how many miles will he have covered 1 h after he started out? (4 mi)

Number Sense

Estimation   Choose a book to read, look through it, and write down your estimation of how long it will take you to read it. Then write down your starting time and read the book. When you are finished, write down the time. How long did it take to read the book? Was your estimate reasonable?

Subject Integration

Physical Education   Use a kitchen timer to time yourself doing these activities.
run for 1 min
skip for 2 min
march in place for 1 min
do jumping jacks for 1 min
Make up your own 5-min workout and teach it to a friend.

CLASSWORK AND HOMEWORK SUPPLEMENTS

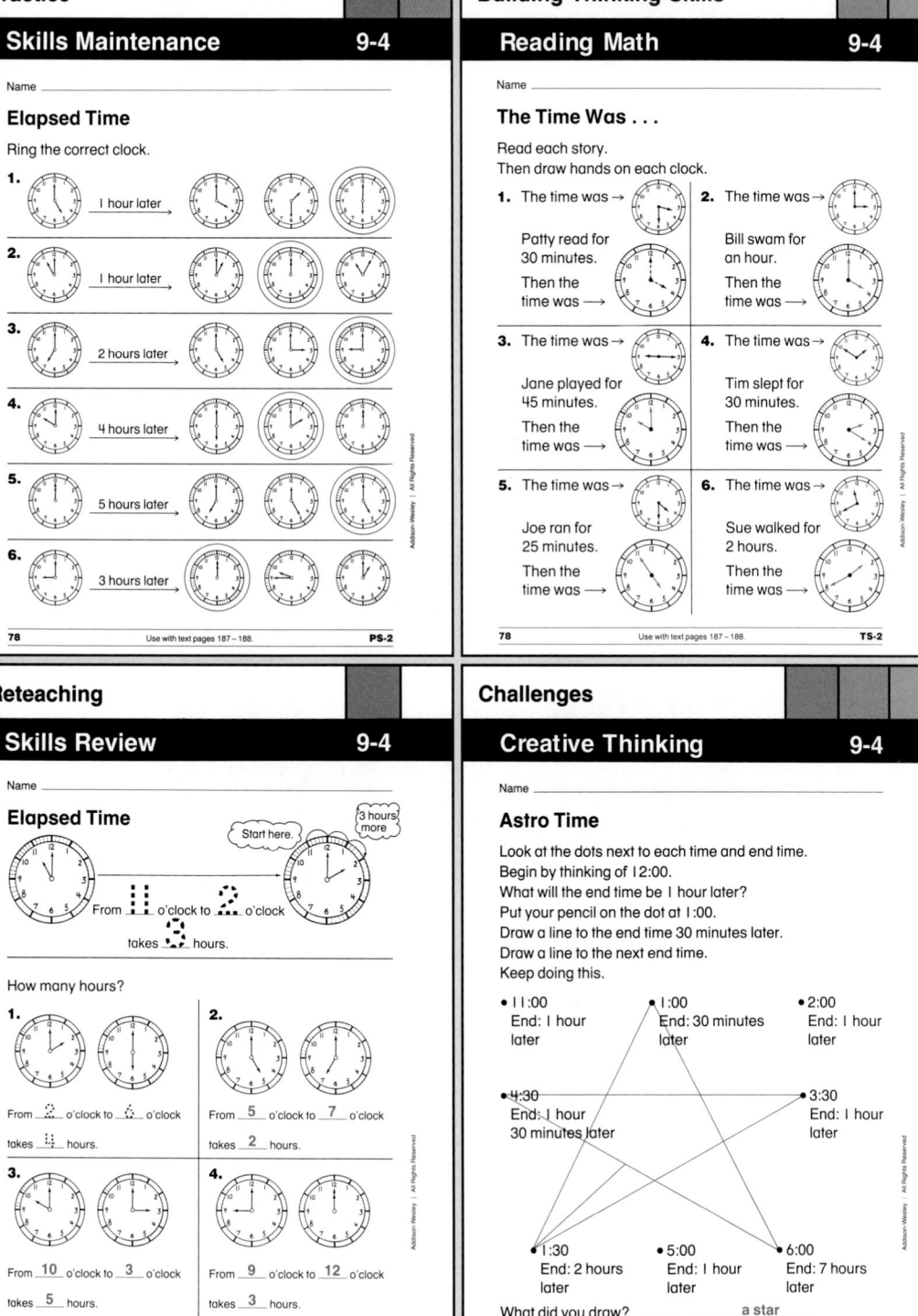

Practice

Skills Maintenance — 9-4

Name

Elapsed Time

Ring the correct clock.

1. 1 hour later
2. 1 hour later
3. 2 hours later
4. 4 hours later
5. 5 hours later
6. 3 hours later

78   Use with text pages 187-188.   PS-2

Building Thinking Skills

Reading Math — 9-4

Name

The Time Was . . .

Read each story.
Then draw hands on each clock.

1. The time was →
Patty read for 30 minutes.
Then the time was →

2. The time was →
Bill swam for an hour.
Then the time was →

3. The time was →
Jane played for 45 minutes.
Then the time was →

4. The time was →
Tim slept for 30 minutes.
Then the time was →

5. The time was →
Joe ran for 25 minutes.
Then the time was →

6. The time was →
Sue walked for 2 hours.
Then the time was →

78   Use with text pages 187-188.   TS-2

Reteaching

Skills Review — 9-4

Name

Elapsed Time

Start here.   3 hours more

From **1** o'clock to **2** o'clock takes **3** hours.

How many hours?

1. From **2** o'clock to **6** o'clock takes **4** hours.

2. From **5** o'clock to **7** o'clock takes **2** hours.

3. From **10** o'clock to **3** o'clock takes **5** hours.

4. From **9** o'clock to **12** o'clock takes **3** hours.

78   Use with text pages 187-188.   RS-2

Challenges

Creative Thinking — 9-4

Name

Astro Time

Look at the dots next to each time and end time.
Begin by thinking of 12:00.
What will the end time be 1 hour later?
Put your pencil on the dot at 1:00.
Draw a line to the end time 30 minutes later.
Draw a line to the next end time.
Keep doing this.

• 11:00   End: 1 hour later
• 1:00   End: 30 minutes later
• 2:00   End: 1 hour later
• 4:30   End: 1 hour 30 minutes later
• 3:30   End: 1 hour later
• 1:30   End: 2 hours later
• 5:00   End: 1 hour later
• 6:00   End: 7 hours later

What did you draw? _____ a star

78   Use with text pages 187-188.   CS-2

9-4

OBJECTIVE 9-4
To write elapsed time

> **Materials:** punchout clocks, TA 10
> (Clock Faces), timer, television listings
>
> **Grouping Suggestions:** individual
> work, small groups

1. MOTIVATE AND TEACH

LEARN ABOUT IT

Introduce the concept of elapsed time by showing on a demonstration clock times on the hour and elapsed times of 30 min, 1 h, 1 h and 30 min, and 2 h. Have students set their punchout clocks to match and say the times aloud with you. Discuss the pictures and clocks at the top of page 187. *How much time did it take the family to get to the zoo?* (1h 30 min)
▶ **If another group of people went on the zoo train trip at 12:00, would they come back in time to see the seals get fed?** (no)
▶ **Explain your answer.** (The zookeeper finishes feeding the seals at 1:30, and the people would not get back until 1:30.)
▶ **Would that same group come back in time to see the artist working on her picture?** (yes)
▶ **Explain your answer.** (They would be back by 1:30, and she would be working until 2:00.)
▶ **What if the family has to be home at 5:30? By what time should they leave the zoo?** (4:00)

2. CHECK UNDERSTANDING

ERROR ALERT Not understanding the concept of duration of time.

Name _____

Elapsed Time

I hour and 30 minutes later

Cut out the clocks. Find the clock that shows the later time. Paste the clock.

1.

Paste here.

2:00

2 hours later

2.

Paste here.

1:30

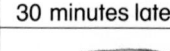 30 minutes later

3.

Paste here.

10:30

I hour and 30 minutes later

Chapter 9   (one hundred eighty-seven)

TEACHING OPTIONS

RETEACHING TIPS Set a timer for 1 min. Have students close their eyes and raise their hands when they think 1 min is up. Compare estimates with the actual time. Repeat for 2 min. Use a clock with a second hand to help them count seconds for 1 min. Assign Reteaching Supplement 78.

ENRICHMENT Distribute television listings. Have students find: 2 shows lasting 30 min; 2 shows lasting 1 h; and a movie or sports event lasting 1 h 30 min or 2 h. Ask students to list the programs and the times they begin and end.

Match the ending time.

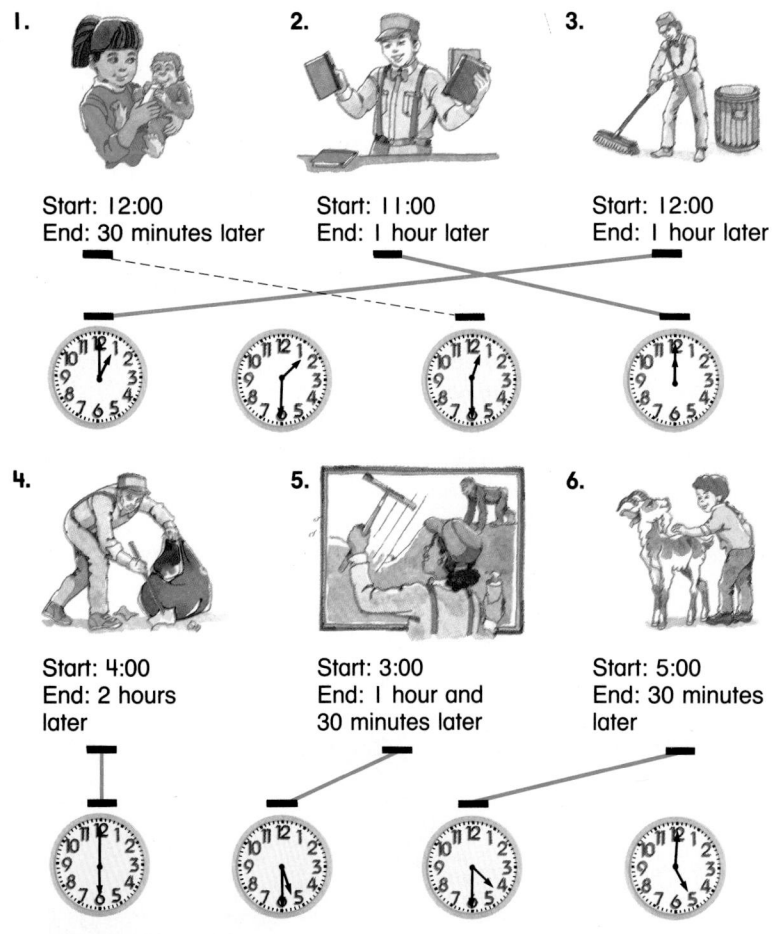

1. Start: 12:00
   End: 30 minutes later

2. Start: 11:00
   End: 1 hour later

3. Start: 12:00
   End: 1 hour later

4. Start: 4:00
   End: 2 hours later

5. Start: 3:00
   End: 1 hour and 30 minutes later

6. Start: 5:00
   End: 30 minutes later

WRITE ABOUT IT

7. Write something you can do in 1 hour.

_____

_ _

Answers may vary. Check students' work.

3. PRACTICE AND APPLY

Basic	All
Average	All
Extended	All

PRACTICE

How will you show the answers in Exercises 1-6 on page 188? (by drawing a line from the exercise to the clock that shows the correct ending time)

APPLY

WRITE ABOUT IT   Discuss some things students might be able to do in 1 h and have them write what they are. Have students share what they write with the class.

► **What are some things you can do in 30 min?**
► **What are some things you can do in 2 h?**
► **About how long would it take to wash the classroom windows? to paint the classroom walls?** (Answers will vary.)

CLOSE AND ASSESS

TELL WHAT YOU KNOW

Remind students of times during the day that were important to Alice and her keeper. *How much time is there between Alice's 1 o'clock and 6 o'clock feedings?* Have pairs of students use their punchout clocks to find how many hours elapsed between the two feedings. (5 hours)

QUICK QUIZ

Show the time 2 h later. 5:00, 12:00, 11:00   (7:00, 2:00, 1:00)
Show the time 30 min later. 1:00, 4:00, 9:00   (1:30, 4:30, 9:30)

9-4

Calendar

OBJECTIVE 9-5   To read a calendar

PREBOOK ACTIVITIES

QUICK REVIEW

Use the class calendar to help you answer these questions.
What day is it today?
What is the date?
What day was yesterday?
What day is tomorrow?
Will we be in school tomorrow? Why or why not?

EXPLORE AND CONNECT

Materials: a calendar for the current month and year for each group; crayons
Grouping Suggestion: small groups
Prepare a list of questions on the chalkboard or on a ditto. Have groups answer the questions and prepare a data sheet. Remind students to build on any good ideas others have rather than focusing on weak ideas.
Use questions such as: *What* **day** *is it today? yesterday? tomorrow? What day comes before Thursday? after Monday? How many more days of school do we have this* **week?** *What is today's date? the date a week ago? the date a week from now? the date of the first Monday in this* **month?** *the date of the last Tuesday in this month? How many Sundays are in this month? What month will it be next month? What month was it 2 mo ago? What months have the same number of days as this month? What month comes before July?*

PRIOR KNOWLEDGE

In what units do clocks measure time? (hours, minutes, seconds) *Do you know how we measure time in units greater than hours?* (Possible answer: in days) *What is the next greater amount of time we measure?* (weeks) *The next greater?* (months) *The next?* (years) *Where we can see these units of measurement?* (on a calendar)

COMMUNICATION

Reading and Discussing Math   Write the following on the chalkboard: **day, week, month, year.** *What is today's date?* Write the date on the chalkboard; for example, Thursday, January 11, 1991. *What word tells us the day of the week?* (Thursday) *What word tells us the month of the year?* (January) *What number tells us the day of the month?* (11) *the year?* (1991)
Using a class calendar, ask students how many days there are in a week. (7) Have students recite the days of the week, starting with Sunday. *How many days usually make a month?* (30 or 31) *How many months are in a year?* (12) Have students recite the months aloud for one year starting with January.

CONNECTIONS   Use these anytime.

Problem of the Day

Who Is Older?   Ben's birthday is in June. He will be 8 years old. Elena's birthday is in July, and she will be 8 years old, too. Whose birthday comes first? (Ben's) Who is older? (Ben)

Math Connection

Data Analysis   Work with 3 other students. Write your birthday month on a card. Sort the cards in order from January to December. Now combine them with the cards of another group. Keep combining with other groups until all the cards are sorted by month. Then tally the birthdays in each month and make a bar graph to show the data.

Subject Integration

Social Studies   A time capsule is a sealed container of articles that is put away. When it is opened in the future it will show people what our life was like. Work with a partner. Think of 5 items that will give people of the future a good idea of what the life of second-graders was like in the 1990s. Draw a picture of what you will put in your time capsule.

CLASSWORK AND HOMEWORK SUPPLEMENTS

Basic

Exercises All

Supplements
Reteaching 79 or
Practice 79
Thinking Skills 79

Average

Exercises All

Supplements
Practice 79
Challenges 79 or
Thinking Skills 79

Extended

Exercises All

Supplements
Challenges 79
Thinking Skills 79

Other Resources:
Problem Solving Experiences In Mathematics, p. 162
Mathematics Their Way, pp. 155-157, 247
Explorations, pp. 6, 42, 74, 100, 150, 172, 204, 234, 266, 302, 334
Workjobs, pp. 74-75

Practice

Skills Maintenance 9-5

Name

Calendar

There are 12 months in a year.

1. What month comes before

May? **April**   September? **August**

October? **September**   February? **January**

2. What month comes after

January? **February**   March? **April**

August? **September**   December? **January**

3. January is the first month of the year. What is the

third month? **March**   fourth month? **April**

fifth month? **May**   eighth month? **August**

ninth month? **September**   twelfth month? **December**

PS-2 · Use with text pages 189 – 190. · 79

Building Thinking Skills

Data Analysis 9-5

Name

Birthdays Are Fun!

Write the name of your birthday month on the calendar.
Write the numbers for the days of that month this year.

Sunday	Monday	Tuesday	Wednesday	Thursday	Friday	Saturday

Answers will vary.

1. In what month were you born? _____

2. In what month were you one month old? _____

3. In what month were you six months old? _____

4. How many months after your birthday is Halloween? ___

5. How many months after your birthday is Thanksgiving?

6. How many months before your birthday is July 4th? ___

7. What is your favorite month? Tell why. _____

TS-2 · Use with text pages 189 – 190. · 79

Reteaching

Skills Review 9-5

Name

Calendar

Use the calendar to answer the questions.

May

Sunday	Monday	Tuesday	Wednesday	Thursday	Friday	Saturday
					1	2
3	4	5	6	7	8	9
10	11	12	13	14	15	16
17	18	19	20	21	22	23
24	25	26	27	28	29	30
31						

1. How many days are in this month? **31**

2. How many

Tuesdays? **4**   Thursdays? **4**   Fridays? **5**

Saturdays? **5**   Mondays? **4**   Sundays? **5**

3. Write the day of the week for each.

May 4 **Monday**   May 30 **Saturday**

May 11 **Monday**   May 15 **Friday**

May 20 **Wednesday**   May 3 **Sunday**

RS-2 · Use with text pages 189 – 190. · 79

Challenges

Family Math 9-5

Name

Calendar Memories

Dear Family,
Your child is learning how to read and use a calendar. Use this activity to help your child become familiar with the days of the week and months of the year.

Look at a calendar with your family.
Talk about the things your family does each month.
Think about what dates are important to your family.
Write a sentence or draw a picture to explain what each month means to your family.

January	February	March	April

May	June	July	August

September	October	November	December

CS-2 · Use with text pages 189 – 190. · 79

9-5

LESSON PLAN 9-5

OBJECTIVE 9-5
To read a calendar

> **Materials:** calendars
>
> **Grouping Suggestions:** individual work, pairs

1. MOTIVATE AND TEACH

LEARN ABOUT IT

Gather students around the class calendar. Focus attention on the days of the week, the dates in a month, and the months in a year by asking questions such as those presented in Explore and Connect.

As students fill in the calendar on page 189, check to see that the numbers are properly placed.

▶ **How many weekends are in this month?**

▶ **What is the date of the day after tomorrow?**

▶ **What is the date of the day before yesterday?**

▶ **What is the date 5 d from now? (or 5 d ago if it is less than 5 d to the end of the month)**

▶ **What is the date a week from now?** (or a week ago)

▶ **What day of the week will be first next month?**

▶ **Why do you think we need a calendar?** (Possible answer: so we can plan ahead; so people will know when they have to do something or be somewhere)

2. CHECK UNDERSTANDING

ERROR ALERT Not understanding that some months begin and end on irregular days instead of beginning on Sunday and ending on Saturday.

Name _____

Calendar

Write the name and the numbers for this month.
Check students' work.

Month						
Sunday	Monday	Tuesday	Wednesday	Thursday	Friday	Saturday

Use the calendar to answer the questions. Check students' work for Exercises 3-5.

1. How many days are in a week? __7__ days

2. How many days are in 2 weeks? __14__ days

3. How many days are in this month? ____ days _____

4. What day of the week is first in this month? _____

5. How many Saturdays are in this month? ____ Saturdays

Ring the days. Use the colors shown. Check students' work.

6. ◀▥▥▶ the tenth day   7. ◀▥▥▶ the third Wednesday

Chapter 9   (one hundred eighty-nine)   189

TEACHING OPTIONS

RETEACHING TIPS   Use a month that begins on a Sunday and the month that follows. Have students point to days and dates of the first month. After the last date in the month, show how the first date of the next starts in the middle of the week. Assign Reteaching Supplement 79.

ENRICHMENT   Post a chart such as the one below.

Winter	Spring	Summer	Fall
December	March	June	September
January	April	July	October
February	May	August	November

Have small groups create a poster for one season, writing the months and illustrating the season.

here are 12 months in a year.

January					
	1	2	3	4	5
7	8	9	10	11	12
14	15	16	17	18	19
21	22	23	24	25	26
28	29	30	31		

February					
				1	2
3	4	5	6	7	8	9
10	11	12	13	14	15	16
17	18	19	20	21	22	23
24	25	26	27	28		

March					
				1	2
3	4	5	6	7	8	9
10	11	12	13	14	15	16
17	18	19	20	21	22	23
24/31	25	26	27	28	29	30

April					
	1	2	3	4	5	6
7	8	9	10	11	12	13
14	15	16	17	18	19	20
21	22	23	24	25	26	27
28	29	30			

May					
		1	2	3	4
6	7	8	9	10	11
13	14	15	16	17	18
20	21	22	23	24	25
27	28	29	30	31	

June					
					1
2	3	4	5	6	7	8
9	10	11	12	13	14	15
16	17	18	19	20	21	22
23/30	24	25	26	27	28	29

July					
	1	2	3	4	5	6
7	8	9	10	11	12	13
14	15	16	17	18	19	20
21	22	23	24	25	26	27
28	29	30	31		

August					
				1	2	3
4	5	6	7	8	9	10
11	12	13	14	15	16	17
18	19	20	21	22	23	24
25	26	27	28	29	30	31

September					
2	3	4	5	6	7
9	10	11	12	13	14
16	17	18	19	20	21
23	24	25	26	27	28
30					

October					
	1	2	3	4	5
6	7	8	9	10	11	12
13	14	15	16	17	18	19
20	21	22	23	24	25	26
27	28	29	30	31	

November					
				1	2
3	4	5	6	7	8	9
10	11	12	13	14	15	16
17	18	19	20	21	22	23
24	25	26	27	28	29	30

December					
1	2	3	4	5	6	7
8	9	10	11	12	13	14
15	16	17	18	19	20	21
22	23	24	25	26	27	28
29	30	31			

Ring 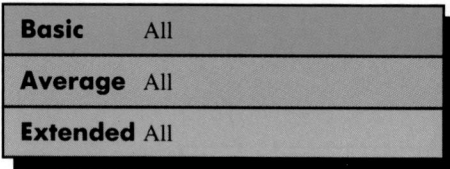 each month with exactly 30 days.
April, June, September, November

Ring 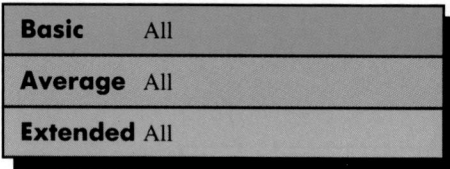 each month with 31 days.
January, March, May, July, August, October, December

Write the name of the
month you did not ring. **February**

ROBLEM SOLVING

Pia wrote 1 letter in January, 2 in
February, and 3 in March. She
continued this pattern for April and
May. How many did she write in all? __15__ letters

---

3. PRACTICE AND APPLY

Basic	All
Average	All
Extended	All

PRACTICE

*Where will you find the information you
need for Exercises 1-3 on page 190?* (in
the calendars on the page) *How will you
show the answers to Exercises 1 and 2?*
(by ringing the months in blue and red)

APPLY

PROBLEM SOLVING ▶ **What are
some of the different ways you could
solve the problem in Exercise 4?**
(Possible answers: Write the number
pattern, then add the numbers to find
how many letters in all; write the months
and list how many letters Pia wrote each
month, then add.)

▶ **How many letters would Pia write
if she continued the pattern for 2
more months?** (28)

LOSE AND ASSESS

ELL WHAT YOU KNOW Have
irs of students use a current
lendar to find information. Types of
formation might include the year,
e name of each month that begins
a Tuesday, and the two months in
row that have 31 days (July and
ugust). Have pairs quiz each other
th the information they find.

QUICK QUIZ

What is tomorrow's date? What day
of the week follows that day? What is
next Sunday's date? What is the date
a week after that? What month is
next?

9-5

Problem Solving: Understanding the Operations/Probability

OBJECTIVE 9-6 To understand the operations of addition and subtraction by putting together or by comparing;

PREBOOK ACTIVITIES

QUICK REVIEW

Draw a clock face to show each of these times.

| 1:30 | 3:15 | 4:25 | 7:40 | 1:55 |
| 5:20 | 6:45 | 10:50 | 2:10 |

PRIOR KNOWLEDGE

Why might a runner use a timer to see how fast he or she runs? (Possible answer: to compare a new time to a previous time to see if he or she is running faster) *What are other sports in which athletes or trainers might compare times to see if their speed has improved.* (Possible answers: swimming, horse racing, baseball) *Name something you do in which you might want to compare your time to see if you can do it faster.* (Possible answers: write math facts; a job around the house)

COMMUNICATION

Reading and Discussing Math Write **probability** on the chalkboard. *If I say, What is the probability that it will rain today? what do I mean?* (Possible answer: *What is the chance it will rain?*) Suggest that *probability* means the same as *chance.* Ask students to use *probability* in a sentence. *What are some of the actions you find in story problems?* (Possible answer: putting together, taking away, comparing) *What operation do you use when you compare things?* (Possible answer: subtraction, because you are finding the answer to the question *how many more . . . ?* or *how many fewer . . . ?*)

EXPLORE AND CONNECT

COOPERATIVE ACTIVITY

Materials: punchout numbers and punchout operation cards
Grouping Suggestions: small groups
Have students write a number sentence to show the answer. *A baby goat was awake 17 hours a day. A baby bear was awake 9 hours a day. How many more hours was the baby goat awake?* _____ *It was awake* _____ *more hours.*

TEACHING ACTIONS

BEFORE ▶ **What does the question in this story ask you to do?** (Possible answer: Compare the time that each animal in the story was awake.)
▶ **What data will you compare?** (17 h and 9 h)

DURING ▶ **As you plan how to solve this problem, does it matter whether you are comparing minutes or hours? Why or why not?** (Possible answer: It does not matter as long as both units are the same. If both numbers are hours or days or minutes, then you need only to think about the numbers.)
▶ **How might you model the number sentence for this story?** (Possible answer: Arrange the punchout number cards and operation cards to show $17 - 9 = 8$.)

AFTER ▶ **How can you check your answer?** (Possible answer: Use counters or make a drawing to see if the answer makes sense.)
Have groups use punchout cards to solve other problems involving put together addition or comparison subtraction.

CONNECTIONS Use these anytime.

Problem of the Day

Understanding the Operation
Write a number sentence that shows the answer. Jill spent 10 min walking the llama and 8 min walking the baby goat. How long did she walk?
  (10 + 8 = 18)
She walked (18) min.

Mental Math

Comparing Time Find the answer. Sid can ride his bike 3 blocks in 1 min. At this speed, how many blocks can he ride in 2 min? (6 blocks) Nan can read 1 book in 2 d. At this rate, how many books can she read in 6 d? (3 books)

Life Skills

Probability Give ideas for ways that might improve your chance to do well in each situation.
getting a good report card
making a friend
being on a soccer team
earning money for a gift
(Answers will vary.)

tell which event is more likely to occur

CLASSWORK AND HOMEWORK SUPPLEMENTS

OPTIONS FOR INDIVIDUAL NEEDS

Basic

Exercises All

Supplements
Reteaching 80 or
Practice 80

Average

Exercises All

Supplements
Practice 80
Challenges 80 or
Thinking Skills 80

Extended

Exercises All

Supplements
Challenges 80
Thinking Skills 80

Practice

Problem Solving   9-6

Name _____

Understanding the Operations

Read the story. Write a number sentence to answer the question. Complete the sentences.

1. Brian's family is taking a trip. On the first day, they drive 6 hours. On the second they drive 4 hours. How many more hours did they drive the first day?

$6 - 4 = 2$

They drove _2_ more hours the first day.

2. Tiffany is Brian's sister. Brian is 11. Tiffany is 9. How many years older is Brian than Tiffany?

$11 - 9 = 2$

Brian is _2_ years older than Tiffany.

3. By the third day, Tiffany and Brian had each read 2 books. Their sister Kim had read 1 book. How many books had they read in all?

$2 + 2 + 1 = 5$

They had read _5_ books in all.

4. Brian's dad drove the first 3 days of the trip. His mom drove the last 5 days. How many days did it take to drive in all?

$3 + 5 = 8$

It took _8_ days to drive in all.

80   Use with text page 191.   PS-2

Building Thinking Skills

Data Analysis   9-6

Name _____

Pet Litters

A litter is the number of baby animals born at one time. Look at the chart. Answer the questions below. Write number sentences to show your answers.

	Guinea pig	Goat	Rabbit	Hedgehog
Number in a litter	2 to 6	1 to 3	10 to 15	3 to 7

1. Which animal has the biggest difference between its smallest litter and its largest? ___rabbit___

$15 \ominus 10 = 5$

2. Which animal has the smallest difference between its smallest litter and its largest? ___goat___

$3 \ominus 1 = 2$

3. If a guinea pig, goat, and hedgehog had litters at the same time, what is the greatest number of babies they could have? $6 \oplus 3 \oplus 7 = 16$

4. What is the difference between a rabbit's largest litter and a hedgehog's largest litter? $15 \ominus 7 = 8$

80   Use with text page 191.   TS-2

Reteaching

Math Reasoning   9-6

Name _____

Probability

Play this game. Get some crayons. Make a spinner like this one. Use a paper clip and a pencil for a dial.

(Rabbit / Turtle spinner)

Rules: Spin the paper clip. If it lands on **Rabbit**, color 1 space on the Rabbit's path. If it lands on **Turtle**, color 1 space on the Turtle's path. Before you start, predict which animal will win the race.

The winner will be: _____

Race 1 Rabbit
Turtle
Race 2 Rabbit
Turtle

Was your prediction correct? _____
Which animal won the race? _____
Play again. Who won the second race? _____

80   Use with text page 192.   RS-2

Challenges

Mental Math   9-6

Name _____

Probability

You need: 2 number cubes with numbers 1 to 6, crayons.

Rules: Roll 2 number cubes. Name the sum.
If the sum is even, color a square in the Even Sum pyramid.
If the sum is odd, color a square in the Odd Sum pyramid.
If you roll doubles, color a square in the Doubles pyramid and in the Even Sum pyramid.
Keep rolling the number cubes until you have filled in one pyramid. Predict which pyramid you will fill first:

Answers will vary.

Doubles

Even Sum   Odd Sum

80   Use with text page 192.   CS-2

Other Resources:
Math in Stride, p. 77
Mathematics Their Way, pp. 205, 207-208, 225
Developing Number Concepts With Unifix Cubes, pp. 113-125
Explorations, pp. 69, 190, 194
Problem Solving Experiences In Mathematics, pp. 9, 33, 39, 45, 51, 57, 63, 69, 75, 81, 87, 93, 99, 111

LESSON PLAN 9-6

OBJECTIVE 9-6
To understand the operations of addition and subtraction by putting together or by comparing; to tell which event is more likely to occur

1. MOTIVATE AND TEACH

LEARN ABOUT IT

 ▶ **Explain how reading each story carefully will help you find important data.** (Possible answer: You will find numbers you need to answer the question in each problem.)

 ▶ **Why is it a good idea to estimate your answer before you solve the problem?** (Possible answers: If you estimate first you will have a sensible idea of what your answer should be. You will know if your answer is reasonable.)

 ▶ **Explain why it is important to write a number sentence for each problem?** (Possible answer: Writing a number sentence is one way to organize your plan for each problem. From there you can solve the problem and write the answer.)

2. CHECK UNDERSTANDING

ERROR ALERT
Page 191 Not understanding when to put together (+) or to compare (−).
Page 192 Not understanding how a larger blue area will increase chances of going to the zoo.

Name _____

UNDERSTAND
FIND DATA
PLAN
ESTIMATE
SOLVE
CHECK

Problem Solving
Understanding the Operations

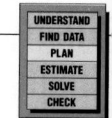

Write a number sentence for each story.
Then write the answer.

1. A tiger cub slept 15 hours a day. It was awake 9 hours a day. How many more hours was the tiger cub asleep than awake?

   $15 - 9 = 6$

   It was asleep __6__ more hours.

2. A baby goat was in the nursery 8 weeks. A lamb was in the nursery 13 weeks. How much longer was the lamb in the nursery?

   $13 - 8 = 5$ _____ It was in __5__ weeks longer.

3. Jill feeds baby animals. Last week she worked 3 hours one day, 5 hours another day, and 4 hours another day. How many hours did she work in all?

   $3 + 5 + 4 = 12$ _____ She worked __12__ hours in all.

4. It takes Jill 8 minutes to feed a tiger cub and 9 minutes to feed a bear cub. How long does it take to feed the two animals?

   $8 + 9 = 17$ _____ It takes __17__ minutes.

Chapter 9   (one hundred ninety-one)   1

TEACHING OPTIONS

RETEACHING TIPS Tell students put-together and comparison story problems involving time. Have them actually move hands on a clock or mark off days or months on a calendar to show whether time is added or taken away. For help with probability, use Reteaching Supplement 80.

ENRICHMENT Have small groups try making a game like the one on this page. Suggest changing the way the spinner is colored each time. Then have them add a third section saying *Lose 1 turn*. *Will this section increase the probability that you will spin one of the colors?*

robability

ay this game. Get your spinner,

○, 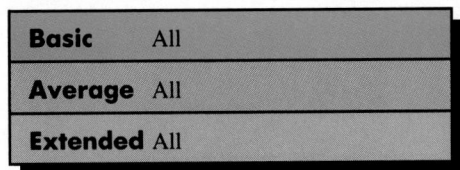.

ıles
Color 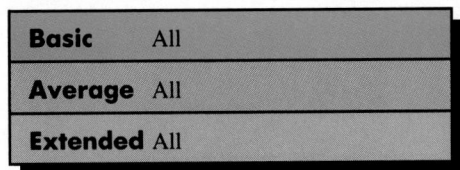 part of the spinner.
Color 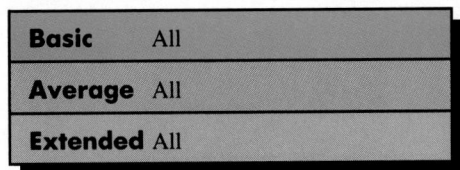 the other part.
Put a counter on START. Spin.
If you spin 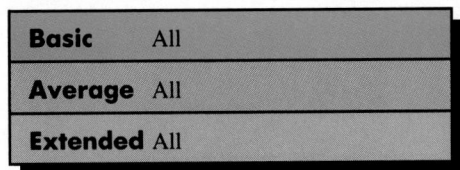, move left 1 space.
If you spin 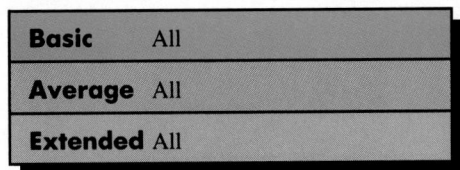, move right 1 space.
Keep playing until you reach the zoo
or the bedroom.

← blue

Go to the zoo.			START			Clean your room.

red ——————→

Ring where you stopped.   the zoo   the bedroom
Answers may vary.
How did you color the spinner? Ring one.
Answers may vary. See teaching notes.
equal parts blue and red   more blue   more red

Suppose you color it a different way.
Tell if you think you would reach the same place.
Answers may vary. See teaching notes.

3. PRACTICE AND APPLY

Basic	All
Average	All
Extended	All

What do you need to play the game on this page? (a counter, a red and blue crayon, and a spinner)

▶ **Explain how to play the game on this page.** (Possible answer: You color the spinner red and blue. Then you spin to find out in which direction to move. You will move either 1 space toward the zoo or 1 space toward the messy room.)

▶ **What do you notice about the spinner?** (Possible answer: it is not divided equally; one section is much larger than the other.)

▶ **How can you use this knowledge when you color the spinner to help you get to the zoo?** (Possible answer: You get to the zoo by moving left, which is indicated by blue. So you want to color the larger part of the spinner blue to increase your chances.)

LOSE AND ASSESS

ELL WHAT YOU KNOW Ask
udents to describe the action in a
ory problem about time and write a
umber sentence for that problem.
hen color the sides of 2 cubes with
ifferent combinations of 2 colors.
iscuss with students which color
ey will be more likely to roll for
ach cube.

QUICK QUIZ

Write the number sentence.
Doing dishes takes 15 min.
Making a bed takes 5 min.
How much longer does it take to do
dishes? ($15 - 5 = 10$; 10 min)

9-6

Counting Dimes, Nickels, and Pennies

OBJECTIVE 9-7   To count dimes, nickels, and pennies

PREBOOK ACTIVITIES

QUICK REVIEW

Count by 5s to 50 starting with each of the following numbers.
35   (35, 40, 45, 50)
20   (20, 25, 30, 35, 40, 45, 50)
40   (40, 45, 50)
10   (10, 15, 20, 25, 30, 35, 40, 45, 50)
25   (25, 30, 35, 40, 45, 50)

PRIOR KNOWLEDGE

Have students pretend they are buying items in a store. They must pay the store owner using only dimes and pennies. *If you buy something that costs 16¢, what coins will you use?* (1 dime, 6 pennies) *What coins will you use to pay for something that costs 23¢?* (2 dimes, 3 pennies) Discuss why it is easier to count out the dimes first and then the pennies.

COMMUNICATION

Reading and Discussing Math   Write these words on the chalkboard and read them to the students: **dime, nickel, penny.** *How are these words alike?* (Possible answer: They are all names of coins.) Then write these sentences on the board: A _____ is worth 10¢. A _____ is worth 5¢. A _____ is worth 1¢. In their Math Journals, have students write the sentence, filling in the correct word. Then have them read the completed sentence.
Describe a dime, a nickel, and a penny. Which is the biggest in size? (nickel) *Which is the smallest in size?* (dime) *In what way do they all look alike?* (They each have a heads side and a tails side.) *Do you save any of these coins? Why?* (Answers will vary.)

EXPLORE AND CONNECT

Materials: punchout pennies, nickels, and dimes; nickel and dime coverups; counting board
Grouping Suggestion: pairs
Tape these punchout coins on the counting board in order: 3 dimes, 1 nickel, and 4 pennies. *I want to see how much mone I have. In what order should I count these coins? Why?* (Possible answer: dimes, nickels, pennies; start with dimes so you can count by tens, then fives, and then ones) Count the coins in that order aloud and write the amount under each coi Try counting in the reverse order to show that the first way of counting is easier.
Have partners count different amounts of dimes, nickels, and pennies. Have one student use punchout money to count and find the total number of cents. Have the other student check the answer using money coverups and a counting board. Students should alternate tasks.

CONNECTIONS   Use these anytime.

Problem of the Day

Money   What do you need to know before you can find the answer?
John has 1 dime more than his brother. How much money does John have? (You need to know how much money John's brother has.)

Mental Math

Counting Money   Read these clues to find the answer.
You say it when you count by nickels. It is more than the value of 4 nickels. It is less than 26¢. You do not say it when you count by dimes. What is the number? (25¢)

Counting Patterns

Dimes, Nickels, Pennies   Fill in the blanks to complete each pattern.
20¢, 30¢, 40¢, 50¢, (60¢)
15¢, (20¢), 25¢, 30¢, 35¢
37¢, 38¢, 39¢, (40¢), 41¢
55¢, 65¢, 75¢, (85¢), 95¢

CLASSWORK AND HOMEWORK SUPPLEMENTS

Practice

Skills Maintenance   9-7

Counting Dimes, Nickels, and Pennies

Count the money. Write the price.

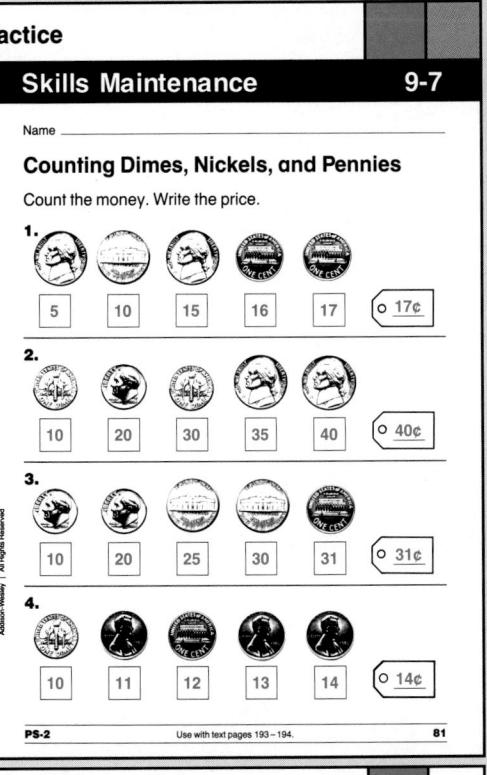

PS-2 | Use with text pages 193–194. | 81

Building Thinking Skills

Manipulatives   9-7

Buy It

How could you pay?

Use your coin punchouts to help you decide.
Use the fewest coins possible.

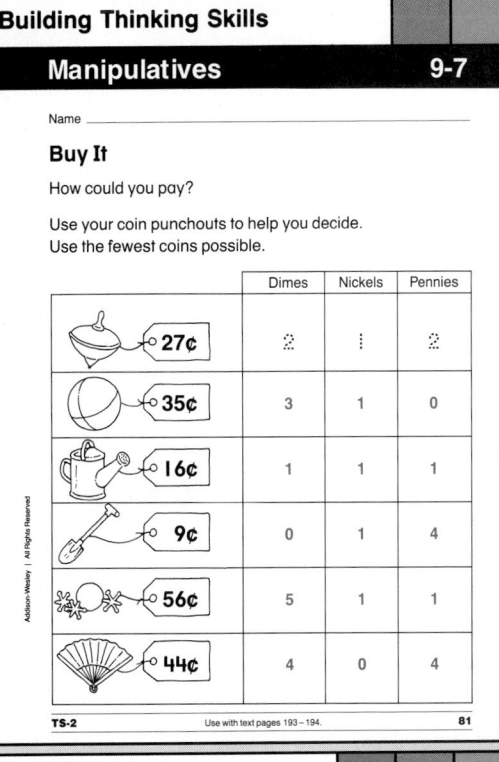

TS-2 | Use with text pages 193–194. | 81

Reteaching

Skills Review   9-7

Counting Dimes, Nickels, and Pennies

Count the money. Write the price.

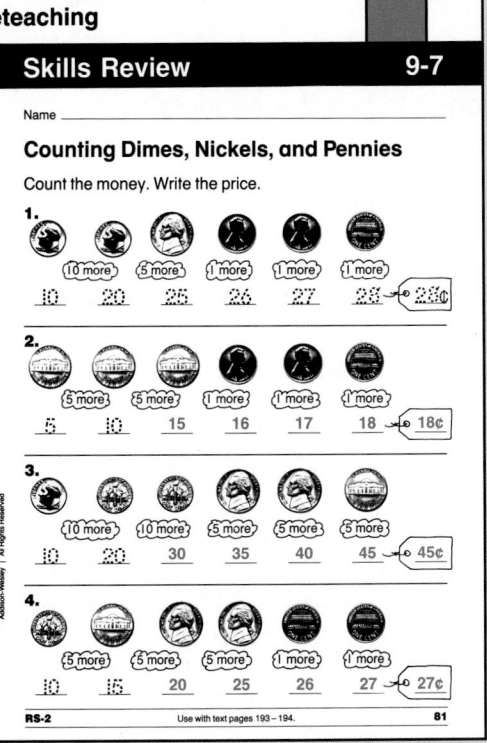

RS-2 | Use with text pages 193–194. | 81

Challenges

Mental Math   9-7

Price the Toys

How much is each toy?
Write the amount on the tag.

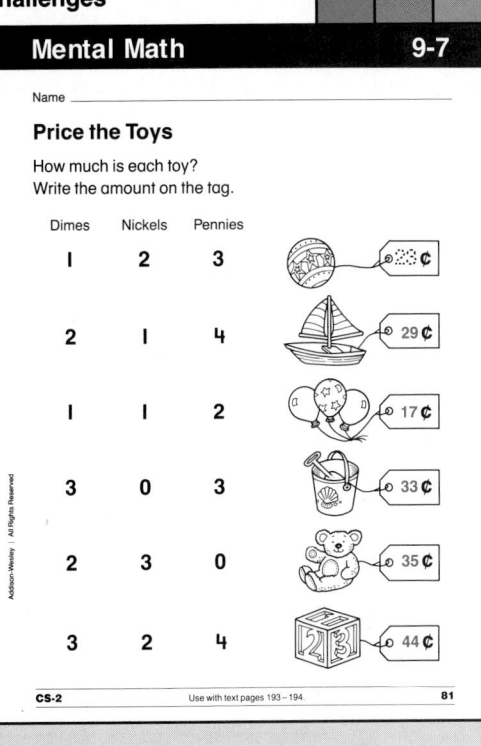

CS-2 | Use with text pages 193–194. | 81

OPTIONS FOR INDIVIDUAL NEEDS

Basic

Exercises All
Calculator Bank, p. 401

Supplements
Reteaching 81 or
Practice 81
Challenges 81

Average

Exercises All
Calculator Bank, p. 401

Supplements
Practice 81
Challenges 81 or
Thinking Skills 81

Extended

Exercises All
Calculator Bank, p. 401

Supplements
Challenges 81
Thinking Skills 81

Other Resources:
Math in Stride, p. 42
Mathematics Their Way, pp. 246, 332-333
Explorations, pp. 100, 109, 113, 115, 120, 124-125
Problem Solving Experiences In Mathematics, pp. 22-23, 59, 124, 137, 148
Workjobs, pp. 224-227
Workjobs for Parents, pp. 106-109

9-7

LESSON PLAN 9-7

OBJECTIVE 9-7
To count dimes, nickels, and pennies

> **Materials:** punchout dimes, nickels, and pennies; money coverups; counting boards; real dimes, nickels, and pennies
>
> **Grouping Suggestion:** pairs

1. MOTIVATE AND TEACH

LEARN ABOUT IT

Ask students to use their punchout dimes, nickels, and pennies to model 3 dimes, 2 nickels, and 4 pennies. Have students count the amount aloud, starting with dimes, then nickels, and finally pennies. Write the total on the chalkboard. (44¢)

▶ **Look at the money at the top of page 193. Explain why the number 40 is written under the dimes.** (Possible answer: There are 4 dimes; they add up to 40.)

▶ **What do you notice about the price of the peanuts and the total amount of money?** (There is not enough money to buy the peanuts.)

▶ **How have the coins been organized in each exercise?** (dimes, nickels, pennies)

▶ **Why do you think the coins have been placed together in groups?** (Possible answer: It is easier to count when like coins have been grouped together; it is best to start counting with coins of greater value.)

▶ **Do you write the value of each individual coin on the lines? Explain.** (No. Write the amount you get by counting on as you add the coin to the previous total.)

2. CHECK UNDERSTANDING

ERROR ALERT Having difficulty counting on with the nickels and pennies after the dimes have been counted.

Name _____

Counting Dimes, Nickels, and Pennies

> 52 is less than 60.
> There is not enoug[h]
> money for [peanuts]

60¢

40 , 45 , 50 , 51 , 52 , 52

Count the money. Write each amount.

1. Tom's Money

60 , 65 , 70 , 75 , 80 , 80

2. Mai's money

30 , 35 , 40 , 45 , 46 , 47 , 47

3. Juan's money

50 , 55 , 60 , 61 , 62 , 63 , 63

4. **Who has enough money to buy the peanuts? Ring the names.**

(Tom)   Mai   (Juan)

(one hundred ninety-three)

TEACHING OPTIONS

RETEACHING TIPS Give each student a collection of nickels and pennies. Write the value of a group of 6 dimes. (60¢) Ask students to model the following amounts as you add to the dimes. (65¢, 70¢, 71¢, 72¢, 73¢) Repeat, starting with a different amount. Assign Reteaching Supplement 81.

ENRICHMENT Have students make a chart like the one below. Ask them to make 20¢ in as many different ways as they can. Some possibilities are shown on the chart.

Dimes	Nickels	Pennies
2	0	0
1	1	5

Count dimes first, then nickels, then pennies.

...se your coin punchouts. Count ...e money as you cover each ...cture. Write the total amount.

↑ Start here.

Sal's money

62¢

Tran's money

76¢

Maria's money

81¢

Who has enough money to buy bird food? Ring the names.

Sal　(Tran)　(Maria)

Bird Food 75¢

MIDCHAPTER REVIEW/QUIZ

Write the times.

12:45　　　7:10　　　3:55

Ring the correct clock.

　2 hours later →　　　　

(one hundred ninety-four)　　　Chapter 9

3. PRACTICE AND APPLY

Basic	All, Midchapter Review/Quiz
Average	All, Midchapter Review/Quiz
Extended	All, Midchapter Review/Quiz

PRACTICE

In what order should you place your coin punchouts over each picture and count on page 194? (dimes, nickels, pennies) *In Exercise 4, to what will you compare the price of bird food?* (the amount of money each person has)

APPLY

▶ **In Exercise 2, what counting patterns could you use?** (Count by 10s, then count by 5s.)
▶ **How could you count nickels by 10s?** (Possible answer: Count 2 nickels at a time.)

MIDCHAPTER REVIEW/QUIZ

ITEM ANALYSIS The table correlates the Midchapter Review/Quiz with lesson objectives.

Items	Objectives
1	9-2, 9-3
2	9-4

...LOSE AND ASSESS

...HOW WHAT YOU THINK

...eview with students the chapter ...ory, *Alice's Present. How much ...oney did the animals collect?* (48¢) ...ave students use paper, crayons, and ...al coins to make a rubbing that ...ows what each animal contributed ...ward buying the gift. Remind ...udents to compliment each other on ...orrect answers.

QUICK QUIZ

Find the amounts.
2 dimes, 1 nickel, 3 pennies = (28¢)
7 dimes, 2 nickels, 1 penny = (81¢)
5 dimes, 0 nickels, 2 pennies = (52¢)
8 dimes, 1 nickel, 4 pennies = (89¢)

9-7

Counting On From Quarters

OBJECTIVE 9-8   To count quarters, dimes, nickels, and pennies

PREBOOK ACTIVITIES

QUICK REVIEW

Match the amount at the left with same amount in the right column.
1 dime, 1 nickel, 1 penny ——————— 45¢
2 dimes, 0 nickels, 3 pennies ———— 16¢
5 dimes, 2 nickels, 2 pennies ———— 34¢
4 dimes, 1 nickel, 0 pennies ———— 62¢
2 dimes, 2 nickels, 4 pennies ———— 23¢

PRIOR KNOWLEDGE

Ask students to count by 25s to 100. Write the numbers 25, 50, 75, and 100 as they say them. Then ask volunteers to count by 10s starting with the number 25 and going to 95. Repeat this activity having students count by 5s starting with 25 and going to 100.

COMMUNICATION

Listening and Discussing Math   Write the following on the chalkboard: **1. quarter, 2. dime, 3. nickel, 4. penny.** Read the words aloud and explain that a quarter is the name of a coin worth 25¢. As students listen to the following amounts, ask them to raise 1, 2, 3, or 4 fingers to show what coin on the board is worth that amount: **10 cents** (2), **1 cent** (4), **25 cents** (1), **5 cents** (3).
Compare a quarter to a dime. How is it different? (Possible answer: A quarter is larger; it is worth more money.) *How is it the same?* (Possible answer: A quarter and a dime are the same color; they both have a heads side and a tails side.) *How many quarters equal 100¢?* (4) *How did you find that number?* (Count by 25s to 100.)

EXPLORE AND CONNECT

Materials: punchout quarters, dimes, nickels, and pennies; money coverups, counting board
Grouping Suggestion: pairs
Write on the chalkboard: *1 quarter, 2 dimes.* Under the word draw 3 circles (1 large, 2 small) to represent these coins. Model counting by pointing to the quarter and writing *25¢* under it. Then write *35¢* and *45¢* under the dimes. *What order is easiest to use when we count money?* (Start with the coins the greatest value and end with the coins of the smallest value. Write specific numbers of coins on the board, such as 1 quarter, 1 nickel. Ask one student in each pair to use punchout money to count and tell the total amount. Have the partner check the answer using money coverups on a counting board. Students should begin with 2 coins and work up to 5 coins. Have partners take turns using the different counting methods.

CONNECTIONS   Use these anytime.

Problem of the Day

Money   Use punchout money to find the answer.
Lou has 3 dimes, 1 nickel, and 1 penny. Kay has 3 dimes, 1 nickel, and 3 pennies. Who has enough money to buy a toy that costs 37¢? (Kay)

Subject Integration

Art   Trace around quarters, dimes, nickels, and pennies to make a picture of an object. When it is complete, count the coins you used and write how much your object is worth. The object could be real or make-believe. Share it with the rest of the class.

Minute Math

Money   Say the total you get when you add the coins to each amount.
50¢ + 1 dime   (60¢)
25¢ + 1 quarter   (50¢)
35¢ + 1 nickel   (40¢)
90¢ + 4 pennies   (94¢)
50¢ + 1 quarter   (75¢)
10¢ + 1 nickel   (15¢)
75¢ + 1 dime   (85¢)

CLASSWORK AND HOMEWORK SUPPLEMENTS

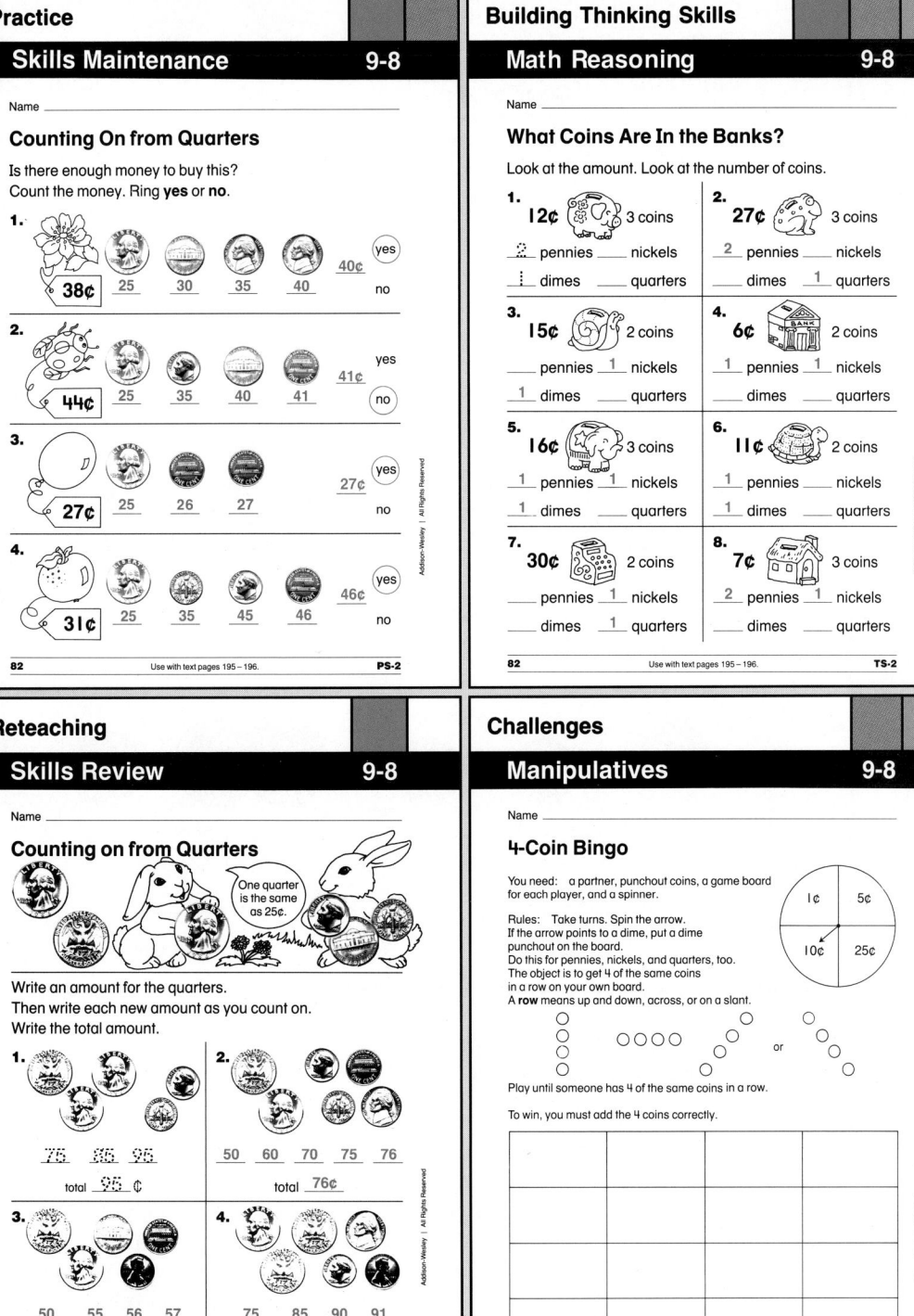

Practice

Skills Maintenance — 9-8

Name

Counting On from Quarters

Is there enough money to buy this?
Count the money. Ring **yes** or **no**.

1. 38¢ — 25 30 35 40 — 40¢ — (yes) no

2. 44¢ — 25 35 40 41 — 41¢ — yes (no)

3. 27¢ — 25 26 27 — 27¢ — (yes) no

4. 31¢ — 25 35 45 46 — 46¢ — (yes) no

82 — Use with text pages 195–196. — PS-2

Building Thinking Skills

Math Reasoning — 9-8

Name

What Coins Are In the Banks?

Look at the amount. Look at the number of coins.

1. 12¢ — 3 coins
   2 pennies — nickels
   1 dimes — quarters

2. 27¢ — 3 coins
   2 pennies — nickels
   — dimes 1 quarters

3. 15¢ — 2 coins
   — pennies 1 nickels
   1 dimes — quarters

4. 6¢ — 2 coins
   1 pennies 1 nickels
   — dimes — quarters

5. 16¢ — 3 coins
   1 pennies 1 nickels
   1 dimes — quarters

6. 11¢ — 2 coins
   1 pennies — nickels
   1 dimes — quarters

7. 30¢ — 2 coins
   — pennies 1 nickels
   — dimes 1 quarters

8. 7¢ — 3 coins
   2 pennies 1 nickels
   — dimes — quarters

82 — Use with text pages 195–196. — TS-2

Reteaching

Skills Review — 9-8

Name

Counting on from Quarters

One quarter is the same as 25¢.

Write an amount for the quarters.
Then write each new amount as you count on.
Write the total amount.

1. 75 85 95 — total 95 ¢

2. 50 60 70 75 76 — total 76¢

3. 50 55 56 57 — total 57¢

4. 75 85 90 91 — total 91¢

82 — Use with text pages 195–196. — RS-2

Challenges

Manipulatives — 9-8

Name

4-Coin Bingo

You need: a partner, punchout coins, a game board for each player, and a spinner.

Rules: Take turns. Spin the arrow.
If the arrow points to a dime, put a dime punchout on the board.
Do this for pennies, nickels, and quarters, too.
The object is to get 4 of the same coins in a row on your own board.
A **row** means up and down, across, or on a slant.

(1¢ 5¢ / 10¢ 25¢)

Play until someone has 4 of the same coins in a row.

To win, you must add the 4 coins correctly.

82 — Use with text pages 195–196. — CS-2

Basic

Exercises All
Calculator Bank, p. 401
More Practice, p. 420, set A

Supplements
Reteaching 82 or
Practice 82
Thinking Skills 82

Average

Exercises All
Calculator Bank, p. 401
More Practice, p. 420, set A

Supplements
Practice 82
Challenges 82 or
Thinking Skills 82

Extended

Exercises All
Calculator Bank, p. 401

Supplements
Challenges 82
Thinking Skills 82

Other Resources:
Mathematics Their Way, p. 333
Workjobs, pp. 224-227
Workjobs For Parents, pp. 106-109

9-8

LESSON PLAN 9-8

OBJECTIVE 9-8
To count quarters, dimes, nickels, and pennies

> **Materials:** punchout quarters, dimes, nickels, and pennies
>
> **Grouping Suggestion:** pairs

1. MOTIVATE AND TEACH

LEARN ABOUT IT

Show students a quarter and tell them that it is worth 25¢. Together, count by 25s to 100 to show that 4 quarters are worth 100¢.

Look at the top of page 195. Describe the coins. (quarters; heads of one quarter, tails of another quarter)

▶ **Why is 50 written under the second quarter?** (Possible answer: That is the value you get when you count on.)

▶ **How can the punchout coins help you find the value of each grouping?** (Possible answer: They can help you keep track of the coins you have counted.)

▶ **How are Exercises 3-6 different from Exercises 1-2?** (Possible answers: Exercises 3-6 use other coins as well as quarters. In Exercises 3-6, you write the amount of all the quarters; but in Exercises 1-2, you count on with quarters.)

▶ **Why do you think we begin with the coin that has the greatest value when we count money amounts?** (Possible answer: It is easier to add larger amounts first, then to count on with smaller numbers like 10s, 5s, and 1s.)

2. CHECK UNDERSTANDING

ERROR ALERT Forgetting to begin counting with the coin of the greatest value.

Name _____

Counting On from Quarters

Work with a partner. Use your punchout coins. Count on by 25s. Write each amount. Then write the total.

Count by 25s.

Two quar are 50¢.

__25__ , __50__   total __50__

1. __25__ , __50__ , __75__

    total __75¢__

2. __25__ , __50__ , __75__ , __10__

    total __100¢__

Write each amount. Then write the total.

3. __50__ , __60__ , __70__

    total __70¢__

4. __75__ , __80__ , __8__

    total __85¢__

5. __25__ , __35__ , __36__

    total __36¢__

6. __50__ , __55__ , __5__

    total __56¢__

Chapter 9   (one hundred ninety-five)

TEACHING OPTIONS

RETEACHING TIPS Have students be bank customers and tellers. Write *2 quarters, 2 nickels*. The customer places each coin in the teller's hand as it is counted. See that quarters are counted first. Partners then switch jobs. Assign Reteaching Supplement 82.

ENRICHMENT **Family Math**
Have students make coin rubbings of quarters, dimes, nickels, and pennies with their family. Practice counting groups of coins and write the value of each group. Ask family members to help them begin counting with the coins of greatest value.

se your punchout coins. Count on.
hen write the total.

> Count coins of greater value first.

Start
1. total 52¢

2. total 76¢

3. total 95¢

4. total 71¢

5. total 46¢

6. total 96¢

RITE ABOUT IT

Fred has two coins in his pocket. The total amount is 35¢. One coin is a dime. Write a sentence to tell what the other coin is.

> penny
> dime
> nickel
> quarter

The other coin is a quarter.

6 (one hundred ninety-six)   More Practice, page 420, set A   Chapter 9

CLOSE AND ASSESS

HOW WHAT YOU KNOW

ave one student in each pair write an mount from 25¢ to 100¢ on a piece paper. The partner reads the mount and chooses punchout coins to tal it. The first student verifies the ins by counting on. Have pairs plore other coin combinations for fferent amounts.

QUICK QUIZ

Count the money. Write the amount.
2 quarters, 3 dimes ___(80¢)___
1 quarter, 2 nickels, 1 penny ___(36¢)___
3 quarters, 2 pennies ___(77¢)___
2 quarters, 1 dime, 2 nickels ___(70¢)___

3. PRACTICE AND APPLY

Basic	All
Average	All
Extended	All

PRACTICE

Which coin will you begin counting with in each of the exercises on page 196? (the coin with the greatest value) *What will you write on the line next to the word **total**?* (the total value of the coins)

APPLY

WRITE ABOUT IT ▶ **What can you use to help you find the answer?** (Possible answer: a punchout quarter, dime, nickel, and penny; draw pictures of each of the coins)
▶ **How will you compare coins to see which one is the correct one?** (Possible answer: You know Fred has 10¢, so you will count on with the other coins until you find one that makes the total 35¢.)

9-8

My Half-Dollar Book

OBJECTIVE 9-9   To count collections of coins including half dollars

PREBOOK ACTIVITIES

QUICK REVIEW

Tell the number of dimes and pennies for each amount.

25	(2 dimes, 5 pennies)	7	(7 pennies)
14	(1 dime, 4 pennies)	53	(5 dimes, 3 pennies)
5	(5 pennies)	39	(3 dimes, 9 pennies)
70	(7 dimes)	44	(4 dimes, 4 pennies)
9	(9 pennies)	16	(1 dime, 6 pennies)

PRIOR KNOWLEDGE

Place a combination of punchout quarters, dimes, nickels, and pennies on the chalk ledge. Ask a pair of students to choose a coin each, stand in order so the coin of greatest value comes first, and count on aloud from the first coin. Increase the number of coins and students by three, four, and five.

COMMUNICATION

Reading and Writing in Math   Write **half dollar** on the chalkboard and read it aloud. Explain that a half dollar is a coin worth 50¢. Let students examine real half dollars. Ask them to identify the words on either side of the coin. Write these words and sentences on the board and have students read them, copy them in their Math Journals, and fill in the blanks.

half dollar   quarter   dime   nickel   penny

1. A (penny) is worth 1¢.
2. A (dime) is worth 10¢.
3. A (half dollar) is worth 50¢.
4. A (quarter) is worth 25¢.
5. A (nickel) is worth 5¢.

EXPLORE AND CONNECT

Materials: punchout half dollar, quarter, dime, nickel, and penny
Grouping Suggestion: pairs
How does the value of a half dollar compare to the value of quarter? (Possible answer: A half dollar is worth 50¢; a quarter is worth 25¢.) Draw a chart labeled *Ways to Make 50¢* on the chalkboard and ask a student in each pair to copy the chart. *Let us explore coin combinations that make 50¢. Can you show one with your coin punchouts?* Get students started by modeling 5 dimes and writing 5 dimes in the chart. Let the pairs explore combinations and record them. Emphasize that they begin counting with the coin of the greater value when they are using different coins to show 50¢. After a period of time, regroup and have pairs share their combinations. Encourage them to copy any combinations that they missed.

CONNECTIONS   Use these anytime.

Problem of the Day

Money   Write a question you could answer after reading the story. Then answer your question.
John bought a pen for 1 quarter.
He bought a pencil for 1 dime.
(Possible answer: How much did he spend in all? 35¢)

Math Connection

Money   Compare the two amounts in each row. Circle the greater amount.
4 nickels or <u>4 dimes</u>
3 dimes or <u>2 quarters</u>
<u>60 pennies</u> or 1 half dollar
<u>1 quarter</u> or 3 nickels
<u>5 nickels</u> or 15 pennies
1 half dollar or <u>3 quarters</u>

Creative Thinking

Physical Education   (Read the directions aloud. Have students interpret the number.)
Turn around 1 penny's worth. (1)
Jump up and down 1 quarter's worth. (25)
Touch your toes 1 dime's worth. (10)
Take a nickel's worth of baby steps. (5)

CLASSWORK AND HOMEWORK SUPPLEMENTS

Practice

Life Skills 9-9

Name

My Half-Dollar Book

Is there enough money to buy this?
Count the money. Ring **yes** or **no**.

1. 75¢ 50 60 65 70 70¢ yes / no

2. 52¢ 50 55 56 57 57¢ yes / no

3. 59¢ 50 55 60 65 65¢ yes / no

4. 70¢ 50 60 65 66 66¢ yes / no

PS-2   Use with text pages 197–198.   83

Reteaching

Skills Review 9-9

Name

My Half-Dollar Book

A half-dollar is the same as 50¢.

1. How many quarters does it take to make a half-dollar?
   Draw circles to show how many. Label them 25¢.

   25¢ 25¢

2. How many dimes does it take to make a half-dollar?
   Draw circles to show how many. Label them 10¢.

   10¢ 10¢ 10¢ 10¢ 10¢

3. How many nickels does it take to make a half-dollar?
   Draw circles to show how many. Label them 5¢.

   5¢ 5¢ 5¢ 5¢
   5¢ 5¢ 5¢ 5¢ 5¢ 5¢

RS-2   Use with text pages 197–198.   83

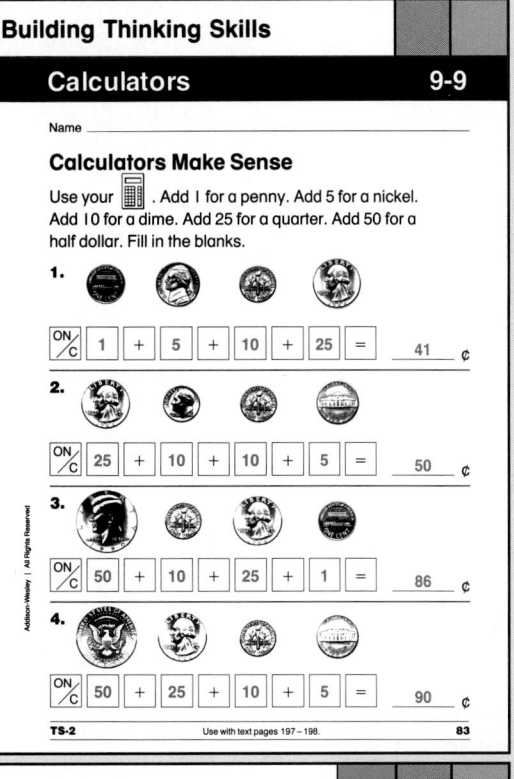

Building Thinking Skills

Calculators 9-9

Name

Calculators Make Sense

Use your [calculator]. Add 1 for a penny. Add 5 for a nickel.
Add 10 for a dime. Add 25 for a quarter. Add 50 for a
half dollar. Fill in the blanks.

1. ON/C 1 + 5 + 10 + 25 = 41 ¢

2. ON/C 25 + 10 + 10 + 5 = 50 ¢

3. ON/C 50 + 10 + 25 + 1 = 86 ¢

4. ON/C 50 + 25 + 10 + 5 = 90 ¢

TS-2   Use with text pages 197–198.   83

Challenges

Family Math 9-9

Name

Savings and Loan

Dear Family,
Your child is learning to recognize and count money. To play this game you will
need $1 in pennies, nickels, dimes, and quarters, and a marker for each player.

Rules: To start, players each get 50¢.
Each player chooses a game board and puts a marker on **Start**.
Flip a penny. If it lands heads up, move 2 spaces.
If it lands tails up, move 1 space. Follow the directions
on the space. Take turns until both players reach **Finish**.
The player with the most money in the bank wins.

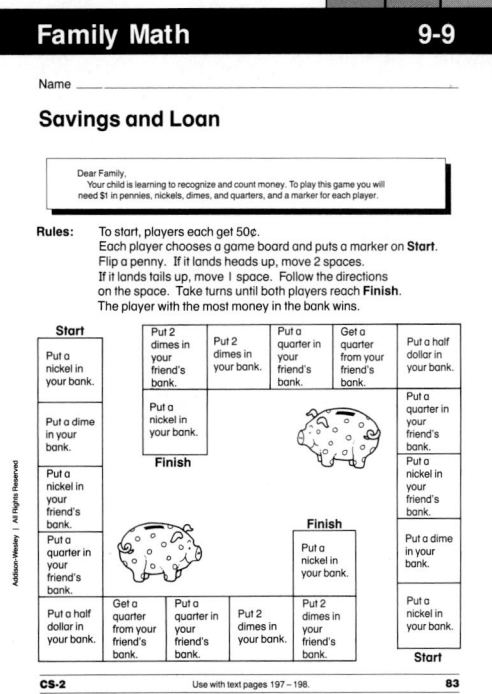

CS-2   Use with text pages 197–198.   83

OPTIONS FOR INDIVIDUAL NEEDS

Basic

Exercises All
Calculator Bank, p. 401

Supplements
Reteaching 83 or
Practice 83
Challenges 83

Average

Exercises All
Calculator Bank, p. 401

Supplements
Practice 83
Challenges 83
Thinking Skills 83

Extended

Exercises All
Calculator Bank, p. 401

Supplements
Challenges 83
Thinking Skills 83

Other Resources:
Mathematics Their Way,
p. 333

9-9

LESSON PLAN 9-9

OBJECTIVE 9-9
To count collections of coins including half dollars

> **Materials:** punchout half dollars, quarter, dimes, nickels, and pennies

1. MOTIVATE AND TEACH

LEARN ABOUT IT

Have students use punchout quarters, dimes, nickels, and pennies to model a grouping of coins worth 50¢. Show the class a half dollar and explain that this coin is worth 50¢.

▶ **When you count a group of coins, with which coin do you begin counting?** (the coin with the greatest value)

▶ **Look at page 197. How will these exercises help you know the value of a half dollar?** (Possible answer: You can compare other coin combinations of 50¢ to a half dollar.)

▶ **How will you know the total value of dimes you colored?** (Possible answer: Count on by 10s.)

▶ **How will you know the total value of the quarters you colored?** (Possible answer: Count on by 25s.)

Explain to students that they will cut on the dashed lines to form the pages of a book they may take home and share with family members.

2. CHECK UNDERSTANDING

ERROR ALERT Not understanding the value of coins equal to a half dollar.

Name _____

Dear Fami
Ask your c
to read this
book to yo

My Half-Dollar Book

A half dollar is 50¢.

half dollar

Use your punchout coins. Find how many dimes it takes to make the same amount as 1 half dollar. Color that many dimes.

Color 5 dimes.
Write the total amount for the coins you colored. __50¢__

Use your punchout coins. Find how many quarters it takes to make the same amount as 1 half dollar. Color that many quarters.

Color 2 quarters.
Write the total amount for the coins you colored. __50¢__

Chapter 9   (one hundred ninety-seven)

TEACHING OPTIONS

RETEACHING TIPS Ask each student to model 1 quarter and 2 dimes. Count on aloud from the quarter. *What do you need to make the value of this grouping 50¢?* (1 nickel or 5 pennies) Repeat to make other coin combinations with a value of 50¢. For further help, use Reteaching Supplement 83.

ENRICHMENT Tell students that they have a half dollar. Have them make coin rubbings to show at least 5 other ways they could have 50 cents. (Possible answers: 5 dimes; 2 quarters; 1 quarter, 2 dimes, 1 nickel; 4 dimes, 2 nickels; 3 dimes, 4 nickels; 50 pennies)

Use your punchout coins. Color 4 coins that total the same amount as 1 half dollar.

Color the quarter, 2 dimes, and 1 nickel.
Write the total amount for the coins you colored. __50¢__

Cover the pictures with your punchout coins as you count on. Write the total. Color the toy that you can buy with exact change.

Color.

75¢

80¢

total amount __75¢__

Cover the pictures with your punchout coins as you count on. Write the total. Color the toy that you can buy with exact change.

75¢

100¢

total amount __100¢__   Color.

198   (one hundred ninety-eight)   Chapter 9

3. PRACTICE AND APPLY

Basic	All
Average	All
Extended	All

PRACTICE

How is the first exercise on page 198 similar to the exercises on page 197? (You are finding a coin combination with the same value as a half dollar.) *How is it different?* (The group will include more than one type of coin.)

APPLY

▶ **Why are you counting the coins in the last two exercises?** (Possible answer: To find the total amount; to find out which toy can be bought with the coins.)
▶ **Analyze the last exercise. What would happen if you used the coins to purchase the parrot?** (Possible answer: You would have a quarter left because the parrot costs only 75¢.)

CLOSE AND ASSESS

SHOW WHAT YOU KNOW   Ask students to name the characters in the chapter story. *Suppose Sara had 1 half dollar, Larry had 1 quarter, Rita had 1 nickel, Bob had 3 pennies, and Ernie had 1 dime. How much money would they have in all? Use punchout money to find the answer.* (93¢)

QUICK QUIZ

Circle the coin that will make the total 50¢.

25¢	dime	quarter	nickel
0¢	penny	half dollar	quarter
40¢	quarter	half dollar	dime

9-9

Making Purchases: Exact Amounts

OBJECTIVE 9-10   To show different ways to pay an exact amount; to identify coins needed to pay an exact amou▮

QUICK REVIEW

Compare. Circle the amount that is less.

1 half dollar	or	8 dimes	1 nickel	or	6 pennies
2 quarters	or	4 dimes	2 quarters	or	2 half dollars
5 dimes	or	15 pennies	4 quarters	or	8 dimes
3 nickels	or	1 quarter	17 pennies	or	2 dimes
1 half dollar	or	4 dimes	6 nickels	or	1 quarter

PRIOR KNOWLEDGE

You are in a toy store and you see a yo-yo with a price of 25¢. Does this mean that the salesperson will accept only a quarter from you? Explain. (No. There are many other coin combinations that total 25¢.) *What are some other combinations that total 25¢?* Have students use punchout money to model the amounts as you write their suggestions on the chalkboard. (Possible answers: 2 dimes, 1 nickel; 5 nickels)

COMMUNICATION

Reading and Discussing Math   Write the words **exact amount** on the chalkboard. Read the words to the students. *What does it mean to give someone the exact amount?* (It means to give them the right amount; nothing more, nothing less.) *If something costs 30¢, what is the exact amount of that toy's cost?* (30¢).Write **1 quarter, 1 nickel and 1 quarter, 1 penny** on the board. Ask a volunteer to circle the amount that is exactly 30¢. (1 quarter, 1 nickel) *Is there more than one way to show an exact amount?* (Yes, different combinations of coins can add up to the same amount.) Discuss other combinations that would give you exactly 30¢. (Possible answers: 1 quarter, 5 pennies; 3 dimes)

EXPLORE AND CONNECT

Materials: punchout half dollars, quarters, dimes, nickels, pennies
Grouping Suggestion: pairs
Give each pair of students 1 half dollar, 2 quarters, 3 dimes, nickels, and 5 pennies. Explain that you will write a money amount on the chalkboard. Students may use only these coins to find at least 2 different ways to show the **exact amount.** Amounts should be less than 100¢, beginning with small amounts and increasing to larger ones. As students explore an▮ find amounts, record them in a chart on the board. The chart should resemble the one on page 199 of the text. *What are some methods you used to find different ways to show the sam▮ amount?* (Possible answers: Guess and check; always begin with the coin of greatest value, then count on.) *How will you know if you have found all the different ways to make an exac▮ amount?* (Possible answer: Make a list.)

CONNECTIONS   Use these anytime.

Problem of the Day

Money   Use punchout pennies to find the amounts and answer the question.
Rob has 2 quarters, 1 dime, and 5 pennies.
Juan has 1 half dollar and 3 nickels.
Do they both have the same amount?
(yes; 65¢)

Number Sense

Mental Math   Write *more* or *less* to tell whether the coins are more or less than the amount at the left.

22¢	1 dime, 3 nickels	(more)
52¢	2 quarters, 1 penny	(less)
14¢	2 nickels, 3 pennies	(less)
39¢	1 quarter, 2 dimes	(more)
54¢	1 half dollar, 1 nickel	(more)
85¢	1 half dollar, 3 dimes	(less)

Counting Patterns

Money   Each row must end with the number 35. Fill in the blanks.
25, _30_ , _35_
10, 20, _25_ , _30_ , _35_
15, 25, 30, 31, _32_ , _33_ , _34_ , _35_
5, 15, _25_ , _35_
25, 30, _31_ , _32_ , _33_ , _34_ , _35_

CLASSWORK AND HOMEWORK SUPPLEMENTS

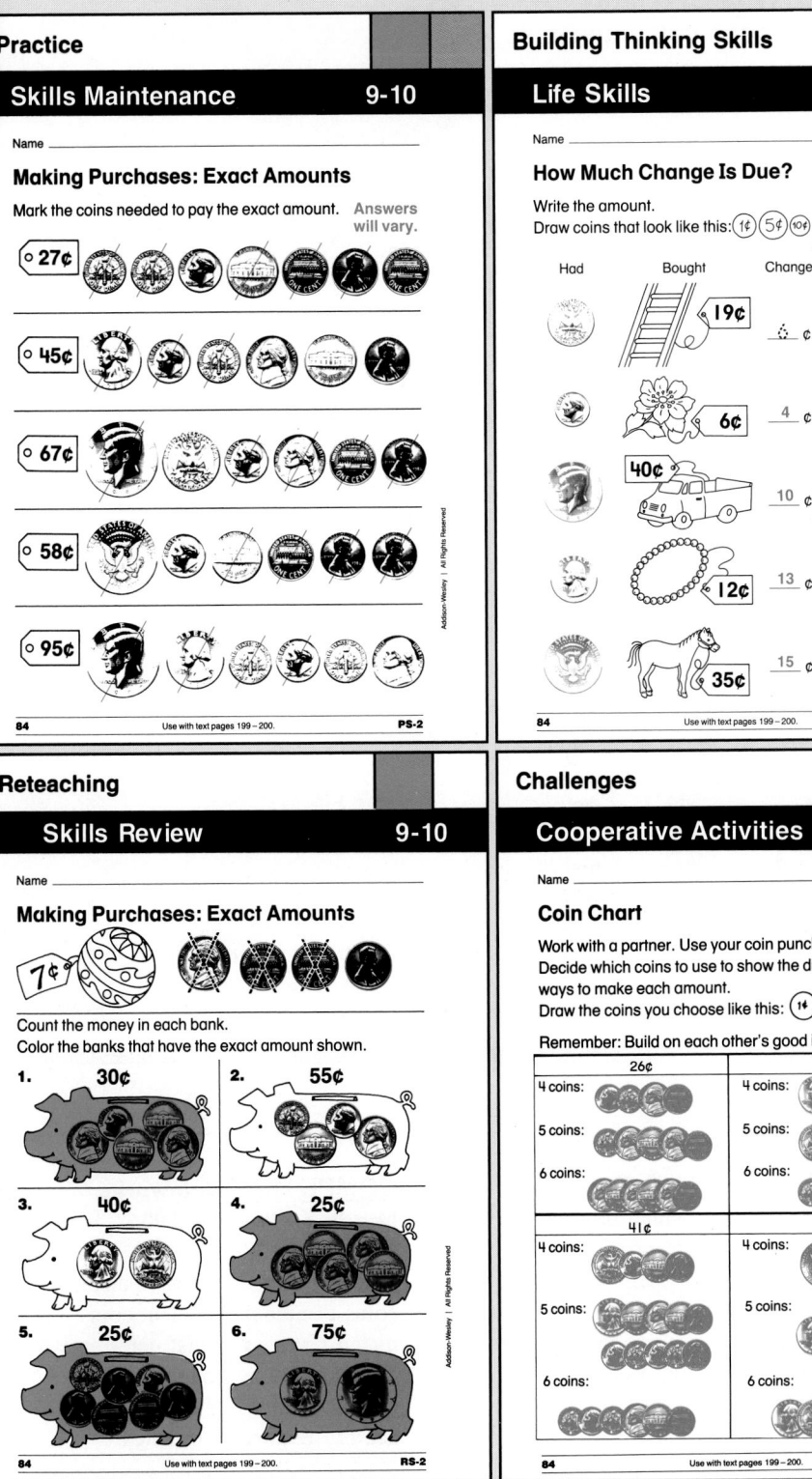

Practice

Skills Maintenance · 9-10

Name _____

Making Purchases: Exact Amounts

Mark the coins needed to pay the exact amount. **Answers will vary.**

- 27¢
- 45¢
- 67¢
- 58¢
- 95¢

84 · Use with text pages 199 – 200. · PS-2

Building Thinking Skills

Life Skills · 9-10

Name _____

How Much Change Is Due?

Write the amount.
Draw coins that look like this: (1¢) (5¢) (10¢)

Answers will vary.

Had	Bought	Change	Coins
	ladder	19¢	6¢	(5¢) (1¢)
	flower	6¢	4¢	1¢ 1¢ / 1¢ 1¢
	truck	40¢	10¢	5¢ 5¢
	beads	12¢	13¢	10¢ 1¢ / 1¢ 1¢
	horse	35¢	15¢	10¢ 5¢

84 · Use with text pages 199 – 200. · TS-2

Reteaching

Skills Review · 9-10

Name _____

Making Purchases: Exact Amounts

7¢

Count the money in each bank.
Color the banks that have the exact amount shown.

1. 30¢
2. 55¢
3. 40¢
4. 25¢
5. 25¢
6. 75¢

84 · Use with text pages 199-200. · RS-2

Challenges

Cooperative Activities · 9-10

Name _____

Coin Chart

Work with a partner. Use your coin punchouts.
Decide which coins to use to show the different
ways to make each amount.
Draw the coins you choose like this: (1¢) (5¢) (10¢) (25¢) (50¢)

Remember: Build on each other's good ideas.

26¢	37¢
4 coins:	4 coins:
5 coins:	5 coins:
6 coins:	6 coins:

41¢	66¢
4 coins:	4 coins:
5 coins:	5 coins:
6 coins:	6 coins:

84 · Use with text pages 199-200. · CS-2

OPTIONS FOR INDIVIDUAL NEEDS

Basic

Exercises All
More Practice, p. 420, set B

Supplements
Reteaching 84 or
Practice 84
Challenges 84

Average

Exercises All
More Practice, p. 420, set B

Supplements
Practice 84
Challenges 84 or
Thinking Skills 84

Extended

Exercises All

Supplements
Challenges 84
Thinking Skills 84

Other Resources:
Math in Stride, p. 42
Mathematics Their Way, p. 225
Explorations, pp. 68, 128-129, 180-184, 267
Problem-Solving Experiences In Mathematics, p. 27
Workjobs, pp. 224-227
Workjobs for Parents, pp. 106-109

9-10

LESSON PLAN 9-10

OBJECTIVE 9-10
To show different ways to pay an exact amount; to identify coins needed to pay an exact amount

> **Materials:** punchout half dollars, quarters, dimes, nickels, and pennies; classroom objects
>
> **Grouping Suggestion:** small groups, pairs

1. MOTIVATE AND TEACH

LEARN ABOUT IT

Place a half dollar, 2 quarters, 3 dimes, 3 nickels, and 3 pennies on a table. Have a student model the exact amount for 72¢ using the coins on the table. Then ask a second student to model a different combination of coins that is also the exact amount for 72¢.

▶ **What are some methods you can use to find the exact amount?**
(Possible answers: Guess and check; begin with half dollars, then count quarters, dimes, nickels, and pennies.)

▶ **Look at the picture on page 199. How would you mark the chart to show coins worth 52¢?** (2 Xs in the quarter column, 2 Xs in the penny column)

▶ **What is another way you could show 52¢?** (Possible answers: 1 quarter, 2 dimes, 1 nickel, 2 pennies; 5 dimes, 2 pennies)

▶ **How can the chart help your group find different ways to show the exact amount?** (Possible answer: We could begin counting with the half dollar and see what coin on the chart can be added to it to get the exact amount. If the half dollar is too much, then we will start with the quarters.)

2. CHECK UNDERSTANDING

ERROR ALERT Not knowing which coin to begin counting with to determine an exact amount; forgetting to mark an X for each coin used.

Name _____

Making Purchases
Exact Amounts

60¢ is too much. I'll try some pennies instead.

Work in a group. Use these coin punchouts.

1 half dollar

2 quarters

3 dimes

3 nickels

3 pennies

Find two ways to pay an exact amount for each patch. Mark an X for each coin you use.
Answers may vary. Sample answers are shown.

1. 31¢ first way			⨉⨉⨉		X
second way		X		X	X
2. 52¢ first way	X				XX
second way		XX			XX
3. 83¢ first way	X		XXX		XXX
second way		XX	XXX		XXX

Chapter 9

(one hundred ninety-nine)

TEACHING OPTIONS

RETEACHING TIPS Attach price tags to small objects. Give each student a set of coins to match a price. Have them count the coins, highest value first, then purchase the object whose price matches the amount. Assign Reteaching Supplement 84.

COMPUTER **Coinworks, Nordic Software © 1986** Easily modified for all student levels. Students match values of displayed coins to numerals, select coins to match given amounts, determine if an item may be bought, and compare values of coin sets. Each activity requires 5 minutes.

ark the coins needed to pay the exact amount.

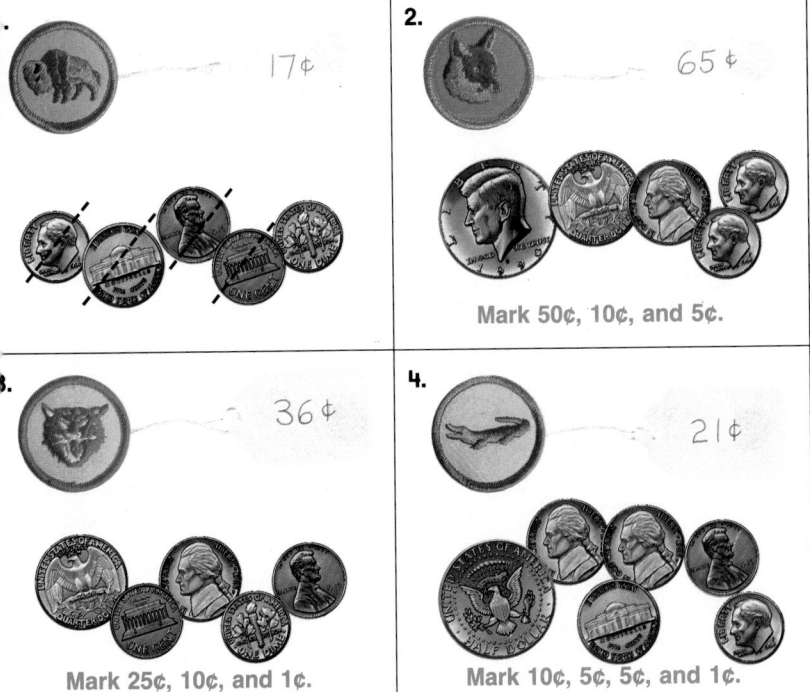

17¢	**2.** 65¢
	Mark 50¢, 10¢, and 5¢.
3. 36¢	**4.** 21¢
Mark 25¢, 10¢, and 1¢.	Mark 10¢, 5¢, 5¢, and 1¢.

MIXED REVIEW

Write > or < in each ◯.   22 ⟩ 19   68 ⟨ 86

dd or subtract.

$12 - 6 = \underline{6}$ $9 + 5 = \underline{14}$ $11 - 7 = \underline{4}$

$9 - 8 = \underline{1}$ $11 - 5 = \underline{6}$ $8 + 4 = \underline{12}$

    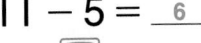   More Practice, page 420, set B   Chapter 9

LOSE AND ASSESS

HOW WHAT YOU KNOW Ask
rtners to cut out pictures of objects
d write a price tag for each one.
hen have one student place a
mbination of coins that is more than
e price of an object in front of its
cture. The other student selects
ins from the group to show the
act amount and counts them out.

QUICK QUIZ

Write the name of the coin that is
needed to show the exact amount.
40¢ 1 quarter, 1 dime, (1 nickel)
56¢ 1 half dollar, 1 nickel, (1 penny)
85¢ 3 quarters, (1 dime)

---

3. PRACTICE AND APPLY

Basic	All, Mixed Review
Average	All, Mixed Review
Extended	All, Mixed Review

PRACTICE

*What coins will you mark in each
exercise on page 200?* (only the ones
needed to pay the exact amount) *How
will you mark these coins?* (by drawing a
line through them)

APPLY

▶ **How could the exercises on page
199 help you find other ways to
make the exact amount for the
exercises on page 200?** (Possible
answers: You could use coin punchouts;
you could set up a chart.)

MIXED REVIEW *What do the
symbols > and < mean?* (greater than,
less than)

9-10

Problem Solving: Using Data from a Chart

OBJECTIVE 9-11   To solve problems using data from a chart

PREBOOK ACTIVITIES

QUICK REVIEW

Write the total amount.
nickel, nickel, nickel, penny   (16¢)
dime, nickel, penny, penny, penny   (18¢)
dime, dime, dime, penny   (31¢)
quarter, dime, nickel, penny   (41¢)
quarter, quarter, nickel, nickel, penny, penny   (62¢)

PRIOR KNOWLEDGE

Who has been to a restaurant where you ordered food from a chart or menu on the wall? What kind of information was on the chart? (the kinds of foods; the prices) *How could you use the information on the chart?* (Possible answers: You could use it to decide what you want to order; you could compare the prices to see if you have enough money to buy what you want.)

COMMUNICATION

Reading and Discussing Math   Write the words **chart** and **table** on the chalkboard and ask students to read the words. Explain that students can read the data on charts and tables to solve story problems. Display several charts and tables from texts or magazines. Have students discuss the kinds of data found in them.

EXPLORE AND CONNECT

COOPERATIVE ACTIVITY

Grouping Suggestion: small groups

Zoo Store Prices

Zoo book	50¢	Zoo pencil	15¢
Map	25¢	Balloon	30¢

Ted bought a book and a pencil. How much did he spend?

TEACHING ACTIONS

 **BEFORE**   ▶ **Describe what you need to know before you can solve this problem.** (Possible answer: You need to know how much the book and the pencil cost.)

▶ **What type of data is found on the chart?** (Possible answer: The chart shows items that are sold at the zoo store and how much they cost.)

 DURING   ▶ **How can you use the chart to plan how to solve the problem?** (Possible answer: Read the chart to find the cost of the book and the pencil. Write these amounts and then decide what operation to use.)

▶ **What can you use to model the action in this story and find the answer?** (Possible answer: Use punchout money to show the amount for each item and then count the total amount of money.)

AFTER   ▶ **Name a way to check your answer.** (Possible answer: Use different combinations of coins to show the amounts; see if you get the same sum.)

Have small groups of students work together counting punchout money to solve other problems using data from the zoo store chart.

CONNECTIONS   Use these anytime.

Problem of the Day

Choose the Operation   Use punchout coins to solve this problem. Jed bought an apple for 35¢. Then he bought an orange for 40¢. How much did he spend all together? (75¢)

Life Skills

Budgeting   Imagine that you own a restaurant. List on a chart food items you will sell for less then 50¢. Ask a partner to be a customer with 90¢ in coins. Your partner orders food from the chart and pays you with the coins. Count the money to be sure it is the correct amount. Then trade roles.

Subject Integration

Physical Education   Make a table to show the following movements:
1 step forward, 2 steps backward
2 steps forward, 4 steps backward
3 steps forward, _(6)_ steps backward
4 steps forward, _(8)_ steps backward
5 steps forward, _(10)_ steps backward

Problem Solving Strategy: Make a Table

To solve problems using the strategy Make a Table

CLASSWORK AND HOMEWORK SUPPLEMENTS

Basic

Exercises All

Supplements
Reteaching 85 or
Practice 85

Practice

Problem Solving 9-11

Name _____

Using Data from a Chart

Food for Sale			
hot dogs	55¢	hamburgers	95¢
milk	25¢	lemonade	25¢
popcorn	35¢	frozen yogurt	50¢

1. Shannon has 80¢. She wants to buy a drink and either a hot dog or a hamburger. What can she buy?
   lemonade or milk and a hot dog

2. Matthew has 45¢. He wants to buy a treat. What can he buy? popcorn

3. Melanie has 90¢. She wants to buy a drink and a treat. What can she buy? lemonade or milk and popcorn or frozen yogurt

4. Michael has 40¢. He wants to buy a drink and some popcorn. If he borrows some money from Matthew, he can get both items. How much money does he need to borrow? 20¢

5. Judy wants a hot dog and a lemonade. How much money does she need? 80¢

6. Jim wants frozen yogurt and a drink. How much money does he need? 75¢

PS-2 Use with text page 201. 85

Building Thinking Skills

Data Analysis 9-11

Name _____

Round and Round You Go

Ride	Price
Carousel	20¢
Ferris Wheel	25¢
Bumper Cars	35¢
Roller Coaster	50¢
Loop-the-Loop	40¢
Parachute Jump	45¢
Moon Walk	15¢

Use the chart to answer the questions. Answers may vary.

1. Maya likes the carousel best. She has 55¢. How do you think she will spend it?
   2 carousel rides and 1 moon walk

2. Karen earns 25¢ a day for helping at home. How many days will it take to earn enough for the moon walk, carousel, and loop-the-loop? 3 days

3. Ricardo's little brother Juan loves the moon walk. The ride is 10 minutes long. How much money will Ricardo need to keep Juan on the moon walk ride for 30 minutes? 45¢

4. If you had 85¢, how would you spend it?
   Answers will vary.

TS-2 Use with text page 201. 85

Average

Exercises All

Supplements
Practice 85
Challenges 85 or
Thinking Skills 85

Reteaching

Critical Thinking 9-11

Name _____

Problem Solving Strategy: Make a Table

Lorena and Tony ran around the track 5 times. The first time Lorena ran, it took her 10 minutes. Each time she ran around the track, it took her 2 minutes more than the time before. Make a table to find out how long it took her to run around the track each time.

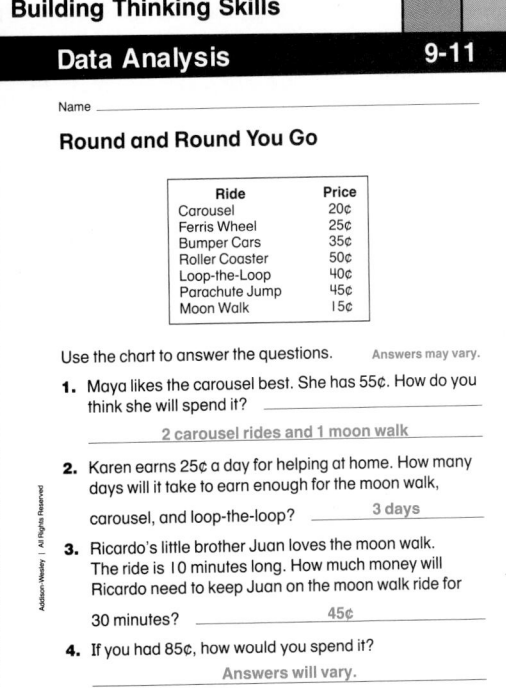

1st time	2nd time	3rd time	4th time	5th time
10 minutes	12 minutes	14 minutes	16 minutes	18 minutes

2 more 2 more 2 more 2 more

The first time Tony ran around the track, it took him 15 minutes. Each time he ran, it took him 1 minute more than the time before. Make a table to find out how long it took him to run around the track each time.

1st time	2nd time	3rd time	4th time	5th time
15 minutes	16 minutes	17 minutes	18 minutes	19 minutes

Compare the tables you made for Lorena and Tony.

Who was the slower runner each time? Tony

RS-2 Use with text page 202. 85

Challenges

Cooperative Activities 9-11

Name _____

What's the Score?

You need: a partner, a number cube, and a spinner.
Rules: Take turns. Write a team name on the scoreboard below.
Spin the spinner and roll the number cube.
The number cube tells the number of runs for your team.
If the spinner lands on **Even**, write the number of runs in an even-numbered inning—2, 4, 6, or 8.
If the spinner lands on **Odd**, write the number of runs in an odd-numbered inning—1, 3, 5, 7, or 9.
If you have filled in all the even innings and the spinner lands on Even, you lose the turn.
Total all the runs for the 9 innings.
The team with the most runs wins.

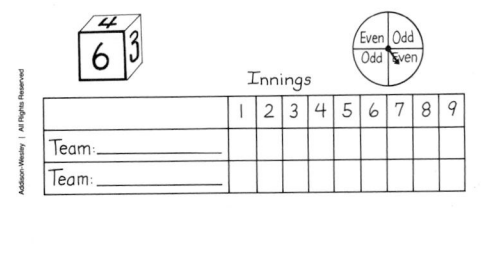

Innings	1	2	3	4	5	6	7	8	9
Team:									
Team:									

CS-2 Use with text page 202. 85

Extended

Exercises All

Supplements
Challenges 85
Thinking Skills 85

Other Resources:
Math in Stride, pp. 138-139
Mathematics Their Way, page 225
Explorations pp. 68, 139, 181-189, 235, 267
Problem-Solving Experiences In Mathematics, pp. 59, 88, 137, 155

9-11

LESSON PLAN 9-11

OBJECTIVE 9-11
To solve problems using data from a chart; to solve problems using the strategy Make a Table

Materials: punchout money

1. MOTIVATE AND TEACH

LEARN ABOUT IT

BEFORE ▶ **How is the chart used to organize information?** (Possible answer: It lists all the jobs of a junior zookeeper along with the pay for each job.)
Why is it a good idea to read the chart before you begin the exercises? (You will understand the data referred to in each exercise.)
▶ **How can you use data from the chart to help you solve Exercise 1?** (Possible answer: Look at the chart to find out how much Raoul received for doing each job and add the amounts.)

DURING ▶ **Describe how you can use punchout coins to find the answer.** (Possible answer: Count out money first for one job and then for the other. Then put the two amounts together and count the total number of coins.)
▶ **When you count money, what is a good rule to remember?** (Always start with the coin that has the greatest value and then add the coins of lesser value.)

AFTER ▶ **How can you check your answers?** (Possible answer: Add the money amounts in a different order.)

2. CHECK UNDERSTANDING

ERROR ALERT **Page 201** Reading the chart incorrectly and adding the wrong amounts.
Page 202 Not relating the correct number of minutes or hours to amount of money shown.

Name _____

Problem Solving
Using Data From a Chart

UNDERSTAND
FIND DATA
PLAN
ESTIMATE
SOLVE
CHECK

Use your coin punchouts. Get coins for each amount in the problem. Count to find the total amount. Then write the answer.

Junior Zoo Keeper Pay Chart	
Job	Pay
Feeding fish	25¢
Sweeping the sidewalk	30¢
Cleaning fish tanks	35¢
Selling bird food	20¢
Picking up litter	45¢
Selling zoo books	40¢

1. Raúl fed the fish and cleaned the fish tanks. What was his total pay?

   His total pay was __60¢__ .

2. Ginger swept the sidewalk and picked up litter. How much money did she earn?

   She earned __75¢__ .

3. Bing sold bird food one day. He sold zoo books the next day. How much did he earn in all?

   He earned __60¢__ in all.

4. Andrea did three jobs. She sold bird food, swept the sidewalk, and cleaned the fish tanks. What was her total pay?

   Her total pay was __85¢__ .

Chapter 9

(two hundred one) 2(

TEACHING OPTIONS

RETEACHING TIPS To help students read charts correctly, have them work in pairs. Have one choose 2 jobs from the chart on page 201 and ask the partner for the total pay in punchout money. They read the chart to verify the amount. For help in making tables, use Reteaching Supplement 85.

ENRICHMENT Group students. Make up a chart that shows items and prices less than 50¢. One student buys 2 items with punchout money and gives the total amount to the other students. The group must decide what combination of 2 items from the chart add up to that amount. Have them take turns.

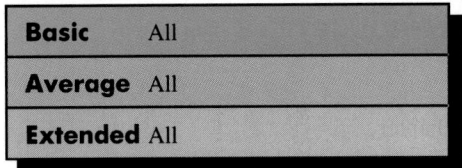

roblem Solving Strategy

ake a Table

ll in each table.

se it to finish

ach sentence.

Darryl and his mother
put in 5 pennies.
They can park for

__10__ minutes.

penny	2 pennies	3 pennies	_4_ pennies	_5_ pennies
_2_ minutes	_4_ minutes	_6_ minutes	_8_ minutes	_10_ minutes

Dennis and his father put in 5 quarters.

They can park for __5__ hours.

quarter	_2_ quarters	_3_ quarters	_4_ quarters	_5_ quarters
_1_ hour	_2_ hours	_3_ hours	_4_ hours	_5_ hours

Rosa put in 5 nickels.

She can park for __50__ minutes.

nickel	2 nickels	_3_ nickels	_4_ nickels	_5_ nickels
_10_ minutes	_20_ minutes	_30_ minutes	_40_ minutes	_50_ minutes

2   (two hundred two)   Chapter 9

3. PRACTICE AND APPLY

Basic	All
Average	All
Extended	All

As you fill in each table on page 202, where do you find the data for the first box? (on the parking meter) *Where will you find the answer to each exercise?* (in the completed table for each exercise)

▶ **How will the information on the parking meter help you complete the tables on this page?** (Possible answer: The data shows the smallest amount paid for the smallest amount of time. You can apply this data to the first box of each table.)

▶ **Compare the first two boxes in Exercise 1. What do you notice about the numbers for the pennies and for the minutes?** (Possible answer: The number of minutes is double the number of pennies.)

▶ **Explain how you can read the table to answer the question in each exercise.** (Possible answer: Look at the table to match the amount of coins that were put in the meter and then look below that number to find the total time.)

CLOSE AND ASSESS

HOW WHAT YOU KNOW

ogether with students, make a chart
at shows items sold at a zoo food
and. All items should be 50¢ or less.
hen make a table that shows certain
umbers of an item and the cost for
ach number. Have pairs use the
hart, table, and punchout money to
ay customer and stand owner.

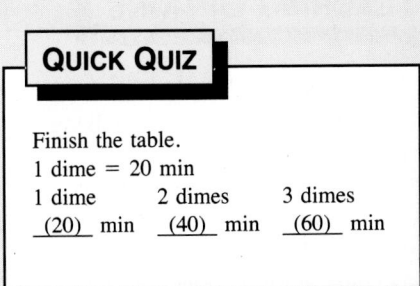

QUICK QUIZ

Finish the table.
1 dime = 20 min

1 dime	2 dimes	3 dimes
_(20)_ min	_(40)_ min	_(60)_ min

CHAPTER 9

WRAP UP

INTRODUCTION The Wrap Up provides activities emphasizing math language and thinking skills for the chapter.

USING PAGE 203

Math Words ▶ **How can you find out if your answers for Exercises 2 and 4 are correct?** (Possible answer: Look at a calendar.)
▶ **What time will it be 10 min after 6:05?** (6:15)
▶ **How can you check your answer?** (Use a punchout or a real clock.)

Math Reasoning ▶ **How can you check to see if you counted the groups of coins correctly?** (Possible answers: Write column addition sentences; add the amounts on a calculator.)
▶ **Which 3 coins are equal in value to a quarter?** (2 dimes and 1 nickel)
▶ **Which coins are equal in value to a half dollar?** (Possible answers: 5 dimes; 2 quarters, 10 nickels)

Name _____

WRAP UP

MATH WORDS

Complete each sentence.
Use a word from the box.

minutes	hours	days	weeks	months	minutes

1. 6:05 is 5 ___minutes___ after 6 o'clock.

2. There are 7 ___days___ in one week.

3. 3:00 is 2 ___hours___ before 5:00.

4. There are 60 ___minutes___ in one hour.

MATH REASONING

5. Ring four groups of coins with a total of 75¢. Do not use a coin more than once. **Hint** Find 2 coins, 3 coins, 4 coins, and 5 coins.

Chapter 9 Wrap Up   (two hundred three) 20

TEACHING OPTIONS

ENRICHMENT Have students make a table as shown. Challenge them to list as many ways as possible to make a set of coins with a total value of 75¢. You may wish to stipulate that students use no pennies in their collections. (Possible answers given.)

Ways to Make 75¢

Half Dollar	Quarter	Dime	Nickel
1	1		
1		2	1
1		1	3
1			5
	3		
	2	2	1

Name _____

CHAPTER REVIEW/TEST

Write the times.

1. 7:05

2. 1:25

3. 6:15

4. 11:45

5. 9:35

6. 12:30

7. Ring the correct clock.

3 hours later

Count the money.

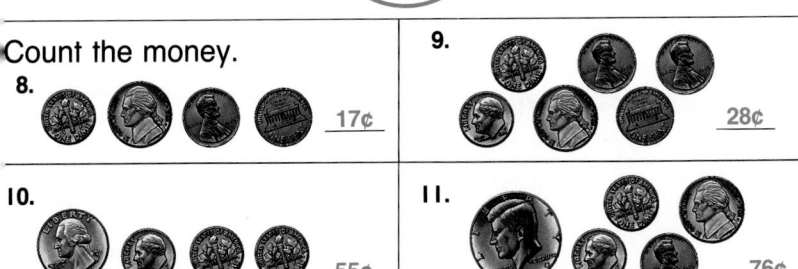

8. 17¢

9. 28¢

10. 55¢

11. 76¢

Gina bought a toy bear and a toy elephant. How much did she spend in all?

She spent __70¢__ in all.

Toy Animal	Price
Zebra	25¢
Bear	30¢
Elephant	40¢

04 (two hundred four)

Chapter 9 Review/Test

CHAPTER 9

ENRICHMENT

INTRODUCTION
Understanding coin values and making coin collections for set amounts will help sharpen students' consumer skills.

USING PAGE 205
This Enrichment page is provided for all students. You may wish to use it after they have completed the Chapter Review/Test on page 204.

▶ **For the group of coins that equals 31¢, what coin must be included every time? Why?** (a penny, because the amount has a 1 in the ones or pennies place)

▶ **Which group of coins will have the fewest coins?** (Possible answer: the group that includes a quarter: 1 quarter, 1 nickel, and 1 penny)

▶ **For the group of coins that equals 1 dollar, list ways that you could use only 1 type of coin.** (Possible answers: 2 half dollars, 4 quarters, 10 dimes, 20 nickels, 100 pennies)

▶ **Which amount has more possible answers? Why?** (the group that equals 1 dollar, because it is a higher value)

EXTENSION
Provide pairs of students with index cards on which you have written money amounts between 11¢ and 99¢. Each pair uses punchout coins to find 2 or more ways to make a group of coins to match the shown value.

Name _____

ENRICHMENT
Showing Equal Amounts of Money

We both have $1.00!

Work with a partner.
Use your coin punchouts.
Show different ways to
make each amount.

Draw ⬤, ⬤, ⬤, or ⬤

to show each way.

Three Ways to Make 31¢		
	Answers may vary.	

Three Ways to Make $1.00		
	Answers may vary.	

Chapter 9   Enrichment: Showing Equal Amounts of Money   (two hundred five)   2

Name _____

CUMULATIVE REVIEW

How many are there?

- ○ 7
- ● 34
- ○ 23

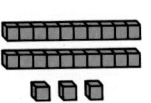

- ○ 32
- ○ 5
- ● 23

Shells Collected					
Brad					
Sara					

Each 🐚 means 5 shells.

How many more shells did Sara collect than Brad?

- ○ 2 more shells
- ○ 5 more shells
- ● 10 more shells

What numbers are missing?

4. 86, ____, ____, 89
   - ○ 90, 91
   - ● 87, 88
   - ○ 84, 85

5. 43, 44, 45, ____
   - ● 46
   - ○ 42
   - ○ 50

6. 9, 12, 15, ____
   - ○ 16
   - ○ 20
   - ● 18

7. ____, ____, 53, 63, 73
   - ○ 51, 52
   - ○ 83, 93
   - ● 33, 43

8. Finish the number sentence.

   71 < ____
   - ○ 17
   - ● 73
   - ○ 65

Amy has 9 books. 2 are new. She gave 4 books to Adam. How many does she have left?

What is the extra data?

- ○ Amy has 9 books.
- ● 2 are new.
- ○ She gave 4 books to Adam.

CUMULATIVE REVIEW

INTRODUCTION The purpose of this Cumulative Review is to maintain previously taught skills and concepts. The emphasis in this Cumulative Review is on Place Value, Chapter 7; and on Number Relationships and Counting Patterns, Chapter 8.

ITEM ANALYSIS The table below correlates the Cumulative Review items with the lesson objectives.

Items	Objectives
1, 2	7-4
3	7-9
4	8-1
5	8-2
6	8-6
7	8-3
8	8-4
9	8-9

Chapter Management

OVERVIEW

Lesson	Pages	Objectives	Subject Integration	Strand Integration
Counting On by Ones	207-208	10-1 To model and add a 2-digit and a 1-digit number	health and fitness: lunch	problem solving
Adding Tens	209-210	10-2 To add tens; to use the commutative property of addition	fine arts: cut & paste	mental math
Counting On by Tens	211-212	10-3 To model and add a 2-digit and a decade number	social studies partner skills	mental math
Making Another Ten	213-214	10-4 To add 2-digit numbers with trading	science: ducks	computation
Problem Solving: Understanding the Operations/Estimating Sums: More or Less than 50c	215-216	10-5 To identify which operation is needed; to estimate sums	social studies: transportation	computation
Same Sum, Different Addends	217-218	10-6 To show different ways to name the same sum	social studies: group skills	place value
Problem Solving: Writing Number Sentences/Problem Solving Strategy: Make a List	219-220	10-7 To write a number sentence; to use the strategy Make a List	language arts: writing	computation

MATHEMATICAL BACKGROUND

Adding 2-Digit Numbers
An algorithm is a sequence of steps that, if followed without error, will lead to the correct answer. In this chapter, students are taught the algorithm for adding 2-digit numbers following this general instructional approach: (1) Introduce the lesson with a real-world story or example. (2) Show and explain the algorithm steps using symbols. (3) Show the reasonableness of the algorithm steps using unifix cubes or related pictures. (4) Practice the algorithm.

The primary focus of this chapter is to add 2-digit numbers with and without trading. The first algorithm step in solving such a problem is to add the ones, trading if necessary. The second step is to add the tens. Students learn to decide whether or not a trade is needed. If the sum of the ones digits has 2 digits, then a trade is needed.

Problem Solving
In this chapter, students write a number sentence and use the strategy Make a List to solve problems.

TIPS FROM TEACHERS

When teaching addition with trading, have students draw on the side of the problem a box labeled HOLD. Tell them to add the ones digits. If the sum is more than 9, then they must put it in the box. To break the ones digit out of the HOLD box, they must write the digit in the ones place of the answer. The digit in the tens place jumps up and around and is added to the sum of the digits in the tens place.

Jack Zewe
Brookline Teacher Center
Pittsburgh, PA

$$
\begin{array}{r}
15 \\
+\,27 \\
\hline
42
\end{array}
$$

HOLD
12

ASSESSMENT

Pretest — Chapter 10, page 1
Multiple-Choice Format

Name _____

1. Count on to add.

$19 + 3 = \underline{?}$
- A 21
- **B** 22
- C 23

2. Add the tens.

$40 + 40 = \underline{?}$
- A 70
- **B** 80
- C 90

3. Start with the number given. Count on by tens.

43

$43 + 20 = \underline{?}$
- A 45
- B 60
- **C** 63

4. Can you make another ten? Ring yes or no.

32   26
- A yes
- **B** no

5. How many are there in all?

36   16

$36 + 16 = \underline{?}$
- **A** 52
- B 46
- C 42

6. Read the story. Would you add or subtract?
28 people are on the bus. 16 people get off. Then how many people are on the bus?
- A add
- **B** subtract

MCT 2   37

Pretest — Chapter 10, page 2
Multiple-Choice Format

Name _____

7. Choose the better estimate for 22¢ + 21¢.
- A more than 50¢
- **B** less than 50¢

8. Which one shows a different way to make the sum?

$30 + 10 = 40$
- **A** 20 + 20
- B 30 + 40
- C 10 + 40

9. 15 red cars and 7 blue cars are in the parking lot. How many cars are there in all?
- A There are 8 cars in all.
- **B** There are 22 cars in all.
- C There are 12 cars in all.

10. Choose the list that shows all the ways to hook the cabs and trailers.

38   MCT 2

ITEM ANALYSIS

Items	Objectives
1	10-1
2	10-2
3	10-3
4, 5	10-4
6, 7	10-5
8	10-6
9, 10	10-7

Note: The item analysis is the same for all pretests and posttests for this chapter.

Posttest — Chapter 10, page 1
Multiple-Choice Format

Name _____

1. Count on to add.

$25 + 1 = \underline{?}$
- A 24
- **B** 26
- C 25

2. Add the tens.

$30 + 30 = \underline{?}$
- A 50
- **B** 60
- C 70

3. Start with the number given. Count on by tens.

32

$32 + 40 = \underline{?}$
- A 36
- B 76
- **C** 72

4. Can you make another ten? Ring yes or no.

18   37
- **A** yes
- B no

5. How many are there in all?

23   35

$23 + 35 = \underline{?}$
- A 85
- B 68
- **C** 58

6. Read the story. Would you add or subtract?
15 people are on the train. 6 more get on. Then how many people are on the train?
- **A** add
- B subtract

MCT 2   39

Posttest — Chapter 10, page 2
Multiple-Choice Format

Name _____

7. Choose the better estimate for 41¢ + 32¢.
- **A** more than 50¢
- B less than 50¢

8. Which one shows a different way to make the sum?

$10 + 30 = 40$
- A 10 + 10
- **B** 20 + 20
- C 30 + 40

9. 17 red cars and 9 blue cars are in the parking lot. How many cars are there in all?
- A There are 8 cars in all.
- **B** There are 26 cars in all.
- C There are 12 cars in all.

10. Choose the list that shows all the ways to hook the cabs and trailers.

40   MCT 2

ALSO AVAILABLE

- ▶ **Free Response Tests**
- ▶ **Alternative Tests**
- ▶ **Thinking Strategies**
- ▶ **Concrete Materials**

CHAPTER 10 UNDERSTANDING 2-DIGIT ADDITION

Optional Chapter Activities

PROJECT AND BULLETIN BOARD

Draw a large hundred chart on the bulletin board and have students use it to solve 2-digit addition exercises. Demonstrate to students how to add 23 and 36 using the chart. Write the addition exercise on the chalkboard vertically and draw a loop around the numbers in the ones column. Point out the greater number. (6) *Start with 6 on the hundreds chart. Count on 3 as you move across 3 spaces: 6 . . . 7, 8, 9.* Point to the tens column in the addition exercise. *Add the tens.* With your finger still at 9 on chart, move down 2 rows to 29. *Add 3 more tens by moving down 3 more rows to 59.*

Have students use the hundred chart to solve the following 2-digit addition exercises.

24	36	71	54	42	15
+ 13	+ 43	+ 17	+ 22	+ 34	+ 72
(37)	(79)	(88)	(76)	(76)	(87)

ADDITION

1	2	3	4	5	6	7	8	9	10
11	12	13	14	15	16	17	18	19	20
21	22	23	24	25	26	27	28	29	30
31	32	33	34	35	36	37	38	39	40
41	42	43	44	45	46	47	48	49	50
51	52	53	54	55	56	57	58	59	60
61	62	63	64	65	66	67	68	69	70
71	72	73	74	75	76	77	78	79	80
81	82	83	84	85	86	87	88	89	90
91	92	93	94	95	96	97	98	99	100

$$\begin{array}{r} 2\,3 \\ +\,3\,6 \\ \hline 5\,9 \end{array}$$

COOPERATIVE LEARNING

Divide the class into groups of 4-6. Identify the group skill: explaining and helping without just giving answers. Ask each group to draw a number line with the numbers 0-100 marked in tens. Assign individual members to choose a multiple of 10 between 0 and 100 but not say it aloud, then to ask another group member to guess the number. If the number is correct, the student chooses another. If it is not correct, help them to guess the right answer by saying *more* or *less*. A third group member will mark the guesses on the number line with counters. Have students exchange tasks and repeat the activity. Some group members may have difficulty with the words *more* and *less*. Remind students to help them by suggesting other words that mean about the same thing, such as *higher* or *greater than* for *more* and *lower* or *fewer than* for *less*. Students may want to use other clues, such as *twice as many* or *20 less*.

You will find grouping suggestions and cooperative learning activities in most lessons throughout this chapter.

LITERATURE

Ross, Pat. *M and M and the Big Bag.* New York: Pantheon Books, 1981.

Mandy and Mimi have a shopping list and $5.00 to spend. The two of them are headed for the local supermarket, The Big Bag. Shopping and counting change does not turn out to be as easy as they thought. Have students make up shopping lists and estimate prices more or less than 50¢. Then ask them to draw pictures of grocery items and price them.

Baba, Noboru. *Eleven Hungry Cats.* Minnesota: Carolrhoda Books, 1988.

Kirn, Ann. *Nine in a Line.* New York: Grosset & Dunlap, 1966.

Sharmat, Mitchell. *The Seven Sloppy Days of Phineas Pig.* New York: Harcourt Brace Jovanovich, 1983.

Chapter 10 Optional Chapter Activities

ENGLISH AS A SECOND LANGUAGE

Students are asked to find different ways to make given sums. Give them a variety of expressions that will help them carry out the task successfully, such as *You could add . . .* and *Why don't you try adding . . .* Encourage students to work together and talk aloud as they find solutions.

Use the exercise requiring students to write number sentences to help ESL students develop their writing skills. Pair ESL students with native speakers and have ESL students write the sentences if they are proficient enough. If ESL students are not ready or confident enough to write the answers in a sentence, ask them to write only the number sentence while their partners write the answer in sentence form. For additional reinforcement, play scrambled sentence games. Write each word in the sentence on a separate slip of paper with the first word capitalized. Have ESL students unscramble *were, 4, boys, than, There, more, girls: There were 4 more boys than girls.*

GIFTED

Mathematically talented students may already understand how to add 2-digit numbers. They will nevertheless likely be interested in many of the strategies presented in this chapter. You may wish to challenge these students, after they have completed their Student Edition work, by having them grocery shop using newspaper ads. For example, after Lesson 5 on estimating sums, have students work in groups to take a shopping trip. Appoint a cashier for each group. Have other students make a shopping list of items with prices less than $1 from newspaper ads and buy the items by writing their costs. Students estimate the total for their shopping list, then check with a calculator. When the total price is calculated, students pay the cashier with punchout coins and bills. If this activity appeals to your students, you may wish to extend it by having students write number sentences to tell what they did or write shopping-trip story problems for their classmates to solve.

STUDENTS AT RISK

The concept of place value is pivotal and receives special attention in the second-grade curriculum. Many learning-disabled students need more practice at the manipulative level than their classmates. The following is a game that all students will enjoy playing together.

The Trading Game requires a place value chart for hundreds, tens, and ones (TA17) and a set of base-ten blocks or objects such as Popsicle sticks or toothpicks bundled into groups of 10. Later on, the bundles of 10 may be bundled into hundreds. You will also need a spinner labeled 1 to 9. Have students take turns spinning and taking that number of ones blocks. After a few turns, students will have enough ones to trade for a ten. The rule of the Trading Game is, *If you can trade, you must trade.* Play continues until all reach 100 or another designated number.

You may also use the Reteaching Supplements and the specific Reteaching Tips from each lesson in this chapter.

Storybook

These pictures and accompanying stories and poems are available as storybooks.

You may want to read and discuss this story with your students before starting the chapter. The first lesson in this chapter includes a question about the story. Lessons 1, 2, 4, and 6 in this chapter have questions in the informal Assessment that refer to the story.

Who's Missing?

Billy Quacker was a careful bus driver. He always counted everyone who got on his bus, including himself. When everyone was seated, Billy sat down behind the wheel, put on his bus-driver hat, and started the bus. Today he was driving students on a field trip to the Tinkerville Train Museum.

When the bus arrived at the museum, Billy announced, "Be back at the bus by 1 o'clock sharp to get a prize. There are 45 of us on the bus. When 45 of us return to the bus, then we can go home."

Teachers and students hurried into the museum. Time passed quickly. A few minutes before 1 o'clock, Billy stood outside the bus, ready to start counting.

The first group arrived with their teacher, Miss Flattail. Billy counted 14. When 4 more came, Billy counted on from 14, "That's 15, 16, 17, 18."

Next came Mr. Pricklyback in a group of 10. Billy added 18 plus 10 and got 28. Three more straggled on. Billy counted "29, 30, 31."

Ms. Hopalong's group of 10 arrived at the bus. Billy added 31 plus 10 and got 41.

Just then, Miss Owl bustled out of the museum with Willy and Milly, the gopher twins. "Just in time," she said. "I checked the museum and we're the last ones. Let's go."

Billy counted, "42, 43, 44." He stepped into the bus and said, "I count only 44. Look around and see who's missing." Everyone looked around. But they could not figure out who was missing.

"Maybe I miscounted," said Billy. "I'll try again." Billy counted the left side of the bus. He counted 24. Then he counted 20 on the right side of the bus. He added 24 plus 20 and got 44. "Oh dear," said Billy.

Billy had another idea. He had everyone go outside the bus and stand in groups of 10. Billy counted 4 groups of 10 and 4 more. That made 44 also.

"I'm sorry," Billy said. "We can't go home until I count 45. That's the rule."

Miss Owl said, "Let me help you count." She counted 21 in her group. Billy counted 22 in his group. Then he added 21 plus 22 and got 43. "This is a mystery!" Billy said. "As soon as Miss Owl stood up to count, there was one more missing."

At that, Billy began to laugh. He laughed so hard that his bus-driver hat fell off. "Boys and girls," he said, still laughing, "let's go back to school. We are all here."

"But whooooo was missing?" Miss Owl asked.

"Nobody," Billy said. "First I forgot to count myself. Then when you stood up to count, you forgot to count yourself. We are all here, and now we can go home."

Everyone on the bus cheered. Billy sat down behind the wheel and put his bus-driver hat back on his head.

On the ride back to school, Miss Owl passed out prizes for everyone. She saved the last prize for Billy Quacker. It was a big red button that said, "I'm #1."

"I won't forget that," said Billy, "ever again."

OBJECTIVE 10-1 To model and add a 2-digit and a 1-digit number by counting on by ones

PREBOOK ACTIVITIES

QUICK REVIEW

Write the missing numbers in each pattern.
16, 17, 18, _(19)_ , _(20)_ , 21
33, 34, 35, _(36)_ , _(37)_ , _(38)_
76, 77, 78, _(79)_ , _(80)_ , _(81)_ , _(82)_

PRIOR KNOWLEDGE

Tell students to imagine that they are train conductors. Explain that they must keep track of the number of passengers that are in their cars. For each situation, ask students to tell if they would count on or count back to find the number of passengers. *You stop at the zoo, and 7 passengers board the train.* (Count on.) *You stop at the museum, and 5 passengers get off.* (Count back.) *You are at the train station, and a passenger runs to catch your train.* (Count on.)

COMMUNICATION

Reading and Discussing Math Write the following sentences on the chalkboard. Have students tell whether or not each sentence is true. For each sentence that is not true, have students tell how they can change it to make it true.
1. When you count on by 1s, the numbers get smaller. (not true; the numbers get larger)
2. You can count on from a number to add. (true)
3. When you count on by 1s, the number of tens cannot change. (not true; the tens will change after you reach 9 ones)
4. If you say 26, 27, 28, 29, 30, you are counting on by ones. (true)

EXPLORE AND CONNECT

Materials: Cube-A-Links, spinners marked 1-5
Grouping Suggestion: pairs
Provide each pair of students with cubes. One student chooses a number between 10 and 30 and shows it with cubes placed the center of his or her work table. The second student spins the spinner and counts on that number from the first number, adding cubes to the group on the table. The first student verifies the accuracy of the partner's work by counting the total number of cubes. Next, students switch roles as the first student spins and counts on, while the second student verifies by counting the total. Students take turns until there are 50 cubes on the table. Encourage students to explain and help each other without just giving answers as they work together.

CONNECTIONS Use these anytime.

Problem of the Day

Logic Jenny counted 33 students on her school bus. There were some adults on the bus, too. If the bus holds no more than 38 people, what is the greatest number of adults that could be on the bus? (5)

Math Connection

Money Make a group of coins with punchout dimes and nickels. Count your coins and write the total. Then ask a classmate to pick a number from 1 to 5. Count on as you add that number of punchout pennies to the group of coins. Find the new total. Write an addition sentence to show what you did.

Mental Math

Addition Use mental math to find the sums.
35 + 3 = _(38)_   42 + 1 = _(43)_
17 + 2 = _(19)_   23 + 3 = _(26)_
54 + 4 = _(58)_   43 + 5 = _(48)_
81 + 3 = _(84)_   75 + 4 = _(79)_
93 + 1 = _(94)_   66 + 2 = _(68)_

CLASSWORK AND HOMEWORK SUPPLEMENTS

OPTIONS FOR INDIVIDUAL NEEDS

Basic

Exercises All

Supplements
Reteaching 86 or
Practice 86

Average

Exercises All

Supplements
Practice 86
Challenges 86 or
Thinking Skills 86

Extended

Exercises All

Supplements
Challenges 86
Thinking Skills 86

Other Resources:
Math in Stride, pp. 64-69, 138
Mathematics Their Way, pp. 305-306
Explorations, pp. 122-123, 127, 131, 144, 271
Workjobs II, p. 119
Developing Number Concepts With Unifix Cubes, p. 148

Practice

Skills Maintenance   10-1

Name _____

Counting On by Ones

Count on to add.
Then write the addition sentence.

1. 97 ▢ ▢

$97 \oplus 2 = 99$

2. 29 ▢ ▢ ▢ ▢

$29 \oplus 4 = 33$

3. 14 ▢ ▢ ▢

$14 \oplus 3 = 17$

4. 68 ▢ ▢ ▢ ▢ ▢

$68 \oplus 5 = 73$

5. 83 ▢ ▢ ▢ ▢

$83 \oplus 4 = 87$

6. 51 ▢ ▢ ▢

$51 \oplus 3 = 54$

7. 36 ▢ ▢ ▢ ▢ ▢

$36 \oplus 5 = 41$

8. 42 ▢ ▢ ▢ ▢

$42 \oplus 4 = 46$

86   Use with text pages 207 – 208.   PS-2

Building Thinking Skills

Number Sense   10-1

Name _____

Price Tag

Read each clue.
Write the answer on the price tag.

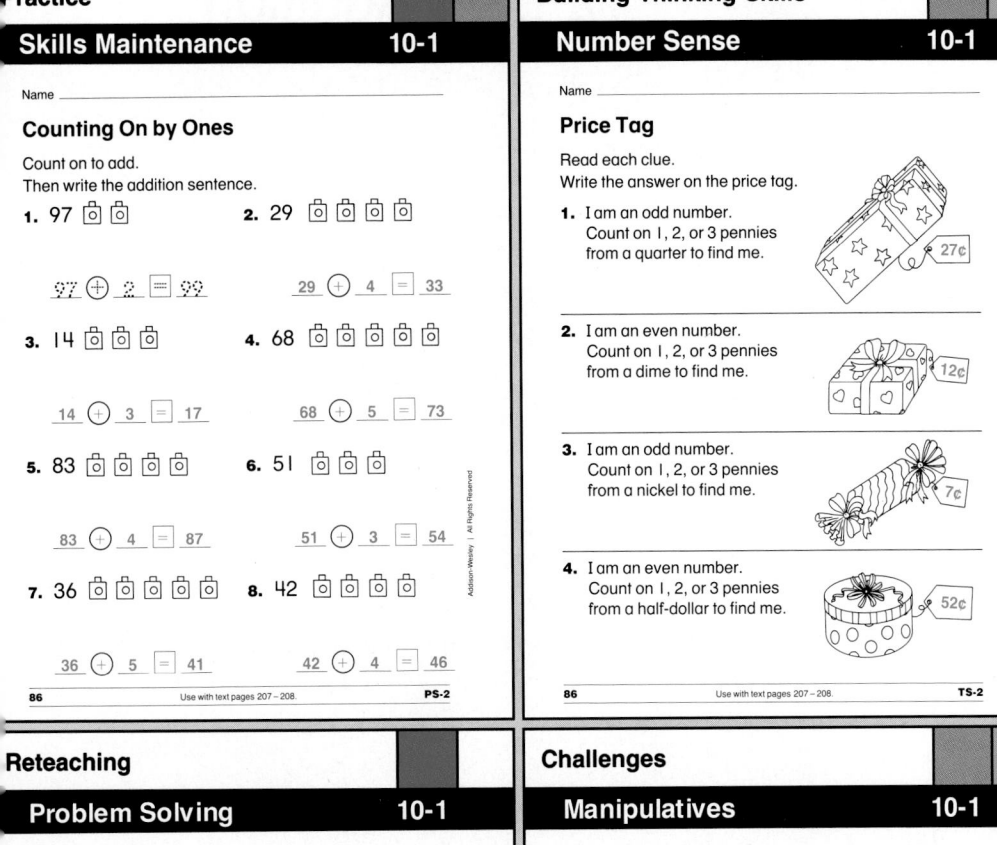

1. I am an odd number.
   Count on 1, 2, or 3 pennies from a quarter to find me.   27¢

2. I am an even number.
   Count on 1, 2, or 3 pennies from a dime to find me.   12¢

3. I am an odd number.
   Count on 1, 2, or 3 pennies from a nickel to find me.   7¢

4. I am an even number.
   Count on 1, 2, or 3 pennies from a half-dollar to find me.   52¢

86   Use with text pages 207 – 208.   TS-2

Reteaching

Problem Solving   10-1

Name _____

Counting On by Ones

Janet had a sack of 26 plums.
She found 7 more.
How many does she have now?

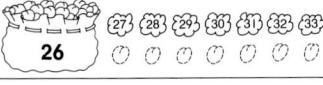

26   ○ ○ ○ ○ ○ ○ ○   33 plums

Draw a picture.
Count on to find the answer.

1. Jack had a box of 47 apples.
   He picked 6 more.
   How many does he have now?

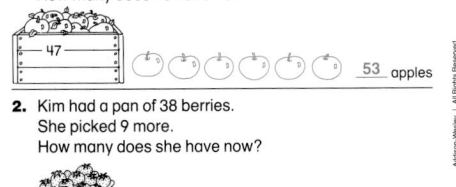

47   ○ ○ ○ ○ ○ ○   53 apples

2. Kim had a pan of 38 berries.
   She picked 9 more.
   How many does she have now?

38   🍓 🍓 🍓 🍓 🍓 🍓 🍓 🍓 🍓   47 berries

86   Use with text pages 207 – 208.   RS-2

Challenges

Manipulatives   10-1

Name _____

The Bigger the Better: A Game for One

You need: 2 number cubes, base-ten blocks.

Rules: Roll the 2 number cubes.
Write the larger 2-digit number you can make on the first line in the Game 1 box below.
Then roll just 1 number cube.
Add it to the big number and find your score.
Use base-ten blocks to check your scores.
Take 3 turns for each game.
Play 2 games.
Ring the highest score in each game with one color.
Ring the lowest game score with another color.

Game 1		Score
1. ___ ___ + ___ = ___		
2. ___ ___ + ___ = ___		
3. ___ ___ + ___ = ___		

Game 2		Score
1. ___ ___ + ___ = ___		
2. ___ ___ + ___ = ___		
3. ___ ___ + ___ = ___		

86   Use with text pages 207 – 208.   CS-2

OBJECTIVE 10-1
To model and add a 2-digit and a 1-digit number by counting on by ones

Materials: Cube-A-Links, base-ten blocks, TA5 (Place Value Chart), punchout number cards 1-5, number cubes

Grouping Suggestions: individual work, pairs, cooperative learning groups of 3

1. MOTIVATE AND TEACH

LEARN ABOUT IT

Read the chapter story to the class. *Billy counted 18 passengers back at the bus. If 3 more arrived, how many would there be?* Have students use cubes to count; then have them write the addition sentence. (18 + 3 = 21) Have students place 16 cubes on the bus pictured on page 207 and 4 cubes on the bench. Tell them to imagine that the school bus stops and picks up the students waiting. Ask them to count on as they move the 4 waiting cubes to the number of cubes already on the bus.
▶ **How can you find the total number of students on the bus?** (Count on or add the 4 students waiting to the number already on the bus.)
▶ **Why is it easier to count on the number of students waiting than to count on the number already on the bus?** (Possible answer: The number waiting is a smaller number; it is easier to add a small number to a large number.)
▶ **How can you find out if your answer is correct?** (Possible answer: Count all the cubes.)

2. CHECK UNDERSTANDING

ERROR ALERT   Adding the ones counted on to the tens place.

10
Understanding 2-Digit Addition

TEACHING OPTIONS

RETEACHING TIPS   Use base-ten blocks, a place value chart, and number cards 1-5. Have students model 33 on the chart. Have them choose a number card, count on to add the number of ones blocks to the ones place, and count tens and ones to check. Use Reteaching Supplement 86.

ENRICHMENT   Have pairs play *Round Up*. One rolls 2 number cubes to make a 2-digit number. The partner tells what number is needed to arrive at the next number ending in 0. For example, if 6 and 1 are rolled, read them as 16 or 61 and say *4 to get to 20* or *9 to get to 70*. Change roles and play again.

...me _____

...ounting On by Ones

...se cubes. Count on to add.
...hen write the addition sentence.

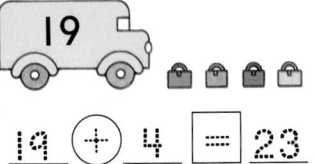

$19 + 4 = 23$

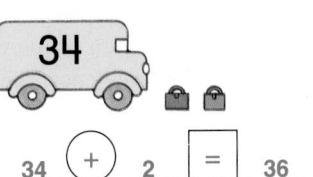

$34 + 2 = 36$

3.

$28 + 3 = 31$

...ount on to add. Then write
...e addition sentence.

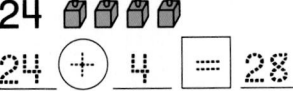

$24 + 4 = 28$

5.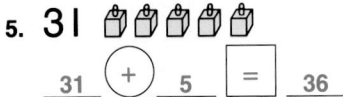

$31 + 5 = 36$

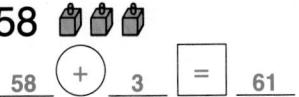

$58 + 3 = 61$

7.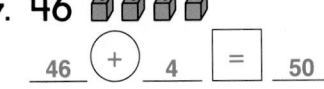

$46 + 4 = 50$

...ROBLEM SOLVING

It is 25 miles to Luna. It is 3 more to Mesa. How
far is it to Mesa? Count on. Use mental math.

It is __28__ miles to Mesa.

Thought bubble: **19**, 20, 21, 22, 23

3. PRACTICE AND APPLY

Basic	All
Average	All
Extended	All

10-1

PRACTICE

*How will you complete each addition
sentence?* (Write the number on the bus
for the first addend, the plus sign, the
number of lunch boxes added for the
second addend; the equal sign; and then
the sum.) *How are Exercises 4 through 7
different from the first 3 exercises?* (You
add cube pictures instead of actual
cubes.)

APPLY

**PROBLEM SOLVING ▶ What do
you need to find out?** (Possible
answer: the distance to Mesa)
**▶ How can you use mental math to
solve the problem?** (You can count on
3 from 25: 25, 26, 27, 28.)
**▶ Identify ways you can check your
answer.** (Possible answers: Use cubes;
enter the addition sentence 25 + 3 on
your calculator.)

...LOSE AND ASSESS

...HOW WHAT YOU KNOW

...emind students of the chapter story,
...ho's Missing? Billy counted 18
...assengers back at the bus. If 3 more
...rrived, how many would there be?
...se cubes to count. Then write the
...ddition sentence. (18 + 3 = 21)
...ncourage students to explain their
...ctions.

QUICK QUIZ

Count on to find the sums.
14 + 5   (19)   25 + 5   (30)
53 + 2   (55)   68 + 2   (70)
48 + 3   (51)   66 + 1   (67)

Adding Tens

OBJECTIVE 10-2   To model and add decade numbers; to use the commutative property of addition

PREBOOK ACTIVITIES

QUICK REVIEW

Write how many tens there are in each number.

40	70	90	10	30	50	80	20	60
(4)	(7)	(9)	(1)	(3)	(5)	(8)	(2)	(6)

PRIOR KNOWLEDGE

Ask students to tell stories about how they use counting by tens in math class and in everyday life. Offer topics such as counting Cube-A-Links, dimes, or fingers; counting things, such as markers, that come in boxes of 10. *Why do you think we count by tens?* (Possible answer: Tens are even; tens are easy to count quickly.)

COMMUNICATION

Reading and Discussing Math   Write **turnaround** on the chalkboard and read the word aloud with students. Then write the addition sentence 2 + 4 = 6 on the board and ask students to tell what they know about the order of the addends and the sum in an addition sentence. (The order of the addends does not change the sum). Ask volunteers to identify the turnaround sentence for 2 + 4 = 6. (4 + 2 = 6)

EXPLORE AND CONNECT

Materials: base-ten blocks (tens), punchout number cards 1–
Grouping Suggestion: pairs
Provide each pair with tens blocks and punchout number card
Ask students to place the cards face down on the table. Each
student draws a card and shows that many tens with tens
blocks. Have partners work together to find the sum of the tw
groups of ten. Ask students to say the addition sentence they
formed together. (for example, 50 + 40 = 90) Then ask then
to show and say the turnaround sentence. (40 + 50 = 90)
Encourage students to explain and help each other without jus
giving the answers. *How do you know that the sum remains t*
same in a turnaround sentence? (Possible answer: because the
addends are the same)

CONNECTIONS   Use these anytime.

Problem of the Day

Family Drive   Keith's grandparents live 60 mi away. Keith and his family drive 50 mi and then stop for lunch. How many miles do they have left to drive? (10) How did you find the answer? (by adding 10; by counting on)

Minute Math

Addition   Write only the answers. How many can you do in 1 min?

4	6	7	9	2
+3	+2	+1	+0	+5
(7)	(8)	(8)	(9)	(7)

1	3	5	8	4
+3	+6	+4	+1	+5
(4)	(9)	(9)	(9)	(9)

Math Connection

Money   Use punchout dimes to show the price for each toy.
Sandy bought a top for 20¢ and a squirt flower for 40¢. Did she spend more or less than 50¢? (more)

CLASSWORK AND HOMEWORK SUPPLEMENTS

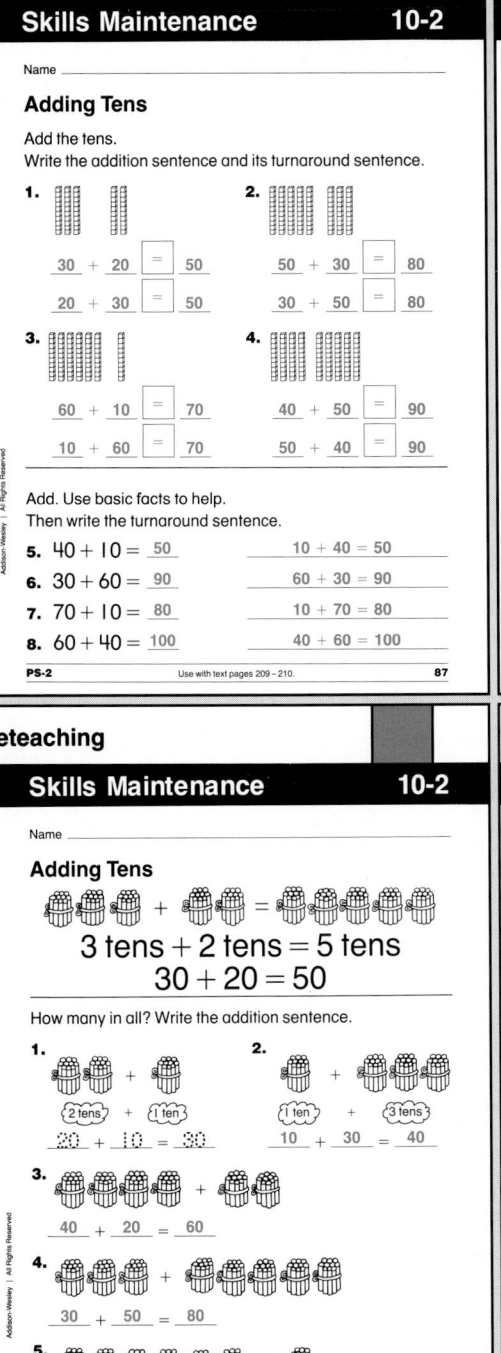

Practice

Skills Maintenance 10-2

Name _____

Adding Tens

Add the tens.
Write the addition sentence and its turnaround sentence.

1. 30 + 20 = 50
   20 + 30 = 50

2. 50 + 30 = 80
   30 + 50 = 80

3. 60 + 10 = 70
   10 + 60 = 70

4. 40 + 50 = 90
   50 + 40 = 90

Add. Use basic facts to help.
Then write the turnaround sentence.

5. 40 + 10 = 50   10 + 40 = 50
6. 30 + 60 = 90   60 + 30 = 90
7. 70 + 10 = 80   10 + 70 = 80
8. 60 + 40 = 100   40 + 60 = 100

PS-2   Use with text pages 209–210.   87

Reteaching

Skills Maintenance 10-2

Name _____

Adding Tens

3 tens + 2 tens = 5 tens
30 + 20 = 50

How many in all? Write the addition sentence.

1. (2 tens) + (1 ten)
   20 + 10 = 30

2. (1 ten) + (3 tens)
   10 + 30 = 40

3. 40 + 20 = 60

4. 30 + 50 = 80

5. 60 + 10 = 70

RS-2   Use with text pages 209–210.   87

Building Thinking Skills

Number Sense 10-2

Name _____

Balance the Scales

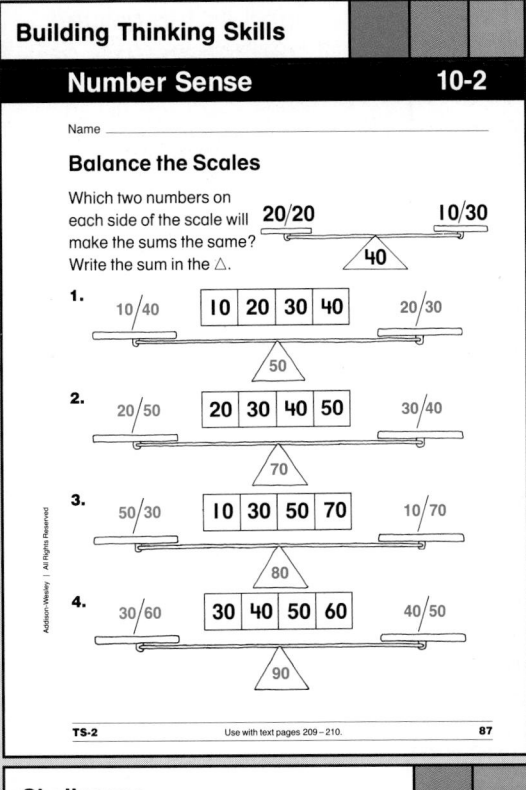

Which two numbers on each side of the scale will make the sums the same? Write the sum in the △.

20/20   10/30
40

1. 10/40 | 10 | 20 | 30 | 40 | 20/30
   50

2. 20/50 | 20 | 30 | 40 | 50 | 30/40
   70

3. 50/30 | 10 | 30 | 50 | 70 | 10/70
   80

4. 30/60 | 30 | 40 | 50 | 60 | 40/50
   90

TS-2   Use with text pages 209–210.   87

Challenges

Data Analysis 10-2

Name _____

Snack Time

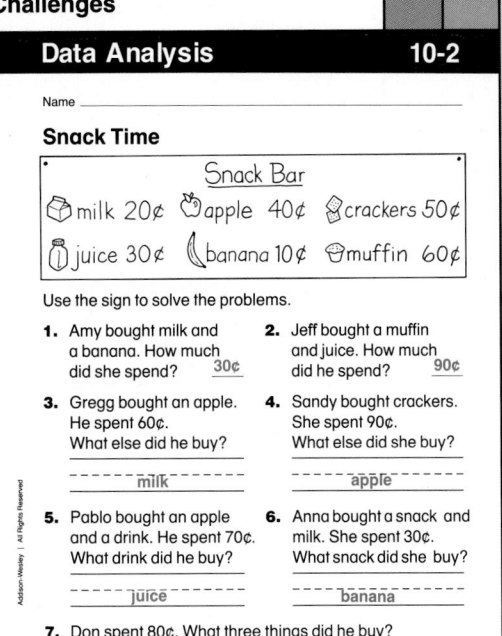

Snack Bar
milk 20¢   apple 40¢   crackers 50¢
juice 30¢   banana 10¢   muffin 60¢

Use the sign to solve the problems.

1. Amy bought milk and a banana. How much did she spend? 30¢

2. Jeff bought a muffin and juice. How much did he spend? 90¢

3. Gregg bought an apple. He spent 60¢. What else did he buy? milk

4. Sandy bought crackers. She spent 90¢. What else did she buy? apple

5. Pablo bought an apple and a drink. He spent 70¢. What drink did he buy? juice

6. Anna bought a snack and milk. She spent 30¢. What snack did she buy? banana

7. Don spent 80¢. What three things did he buy?
   Possible answers: milk, banana, crackers; apple, banana, juice

CS-2   Use with text pages 209–210.   87

OPTIONS FOR INDIVIDUAL NEEDS

Basic

Exercises All

Supplements
Reteaching 87 or
Practice 87
Thinking Skills 87

Average

Exercises All

Supplements
Practice 87
Challenges 87 or
Thinking Skills 87

Extended

Exercises All

Supplements
Challenges 87
Thinking Skills 87

Other Resources:
Math in Stride, pp. 71, 138
Explorations, pp. 100, 116, 173, 266, 271, 275

10-2

OBJECTIVE 10-2

To model and add decade numbers; to use the commutative property of addition

Materials: Cube-A-Links or counters; index cards marked *1 ten-9 tens*, base-ten blocks, number cubes marked in 1–9 tens

Grouping Suggestions: individual work, cooperative groups of 4

1. MOTIVATE AND TEACH

LEARN ABOUT IT

Display the tens cards on the chalk ledge. Hold up two cards, such as 5 tens and 3 tens. Have students use base-ten blocks to find how many tens there are in all. (8 tens) Have students look at the example at the top of page 209.

▶ **Why can you turn the tens around without changing the answer?** (The order of the addends does not change the sum; you can add numbers in any order.)

▶ **Can you change the place of the answer in a turnaround sentence? Explain.** (No; you cannot switch a sum with an addend—an addend is a part and a sum is the whole.)

▶ **For which sentences will there be no turnaround sentence?** (sentences involving doubles)

▶ **How is adding tens like adding ones?** (Possible answer: You join parts to get a whole; you use addition facts to add the tens.)

2. CHECK UNDERSTANDING

ERROR ALERT Adding the zeros and getting a 3-digit sum such as 20 + 60 = 800.

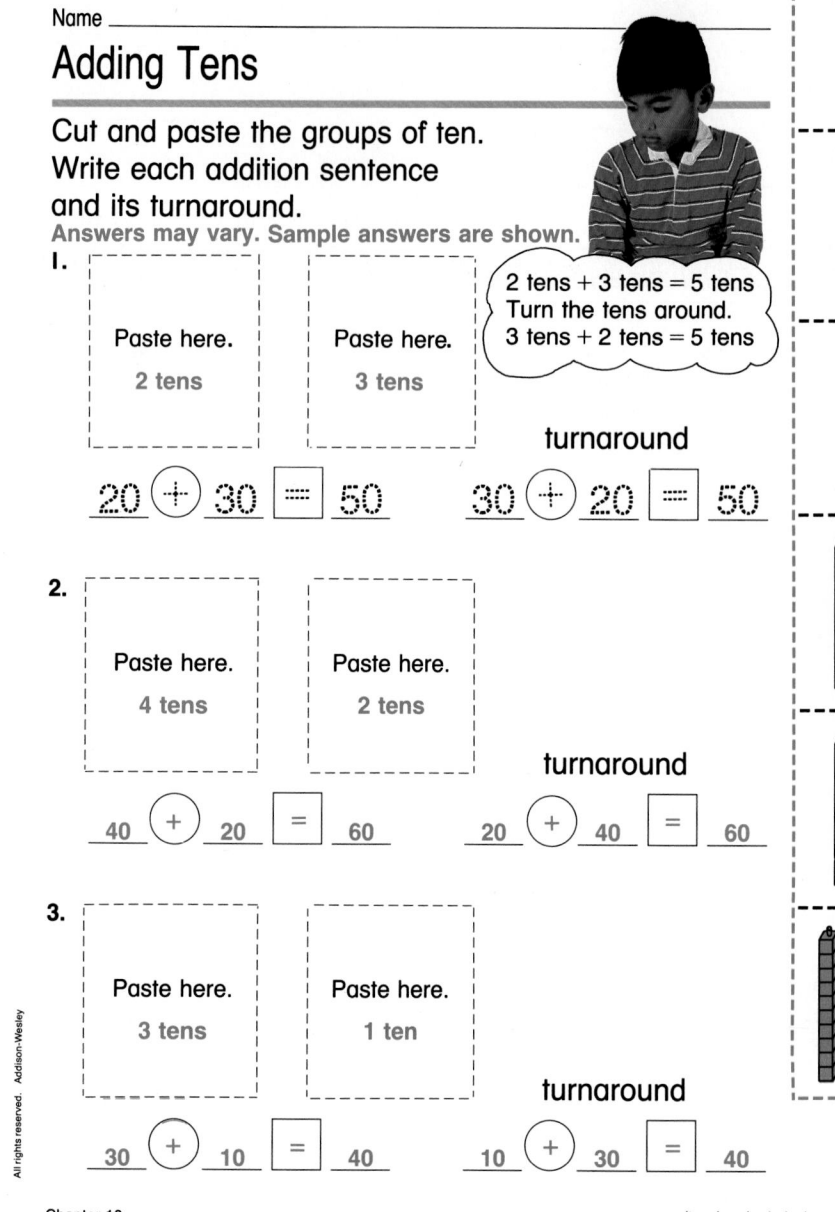

Name _____

Adding Tens

Cut and paste the groups of ten. Write each addition sentence and its turnaround.

Answers may vary. Sample answers are shown.

1.

| Paste here. 2 tens | Paste here. 3 tens |

> 2 tens + 3 tens = 5 tens
> Turn the tens around.
> 3 tens + 2 tens = 5 tens

turnaround

20 (+) 30 = 50   30 (+) 20 = 50

2.

| Paste here. 4 tens | Paste here. 2 tens |

turnaround

40 (+) 20 = 60   20 (+) 40 = 60

3.

| Paste here. 3 tens | Paste here. 1 ten |

turnaround

30 (+) 10 = 40   10 (+) 30 = 40

Chapter 10

(two hundred nine) 20

TEACHING OPTIONS

RETEACHING TIPS Provide students with red and yellow cubes. Have them model 4 tens in yellow and 3 more tens in red. *What number is 4 tens and 3 more tens?* (7 tens) *What is the number for 7 tens?* (70) Write 70 on the chalkboard. Use Reteaching Supplement 87 for additional help.

ENRICHMENT Have students group dried beans in tens and model addition expressions such as 30 + 40, and 20 + 10. Have a partner find the sums and matching turnaround sentences. For example, 30 + 40 = 70, and 40 + 30 = 70. Have both write the addition sentences and their turnarounds.

Use cubes. Add the tens you see.
Write the addition sentence and
its turnaround.

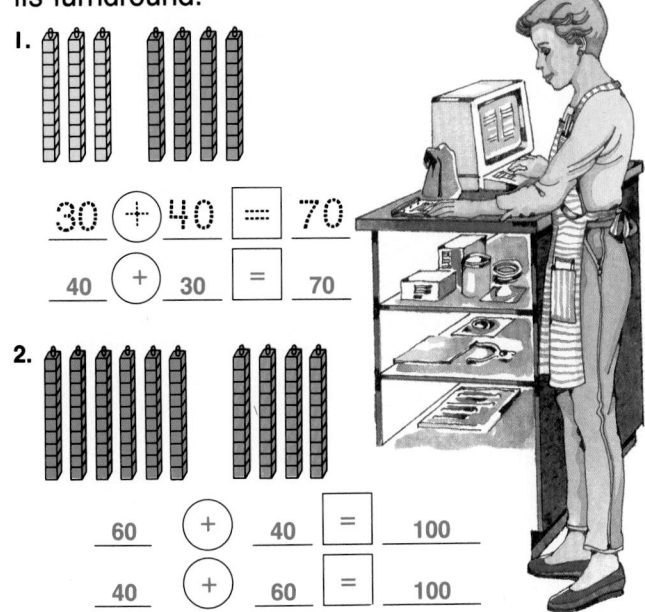

1.

$$30 \; (+) \; 40 \; \boxed{=} \; 70$$

$$\underline{40} \; (+) \; \underline{30} \; \boxed{=} \; \underline{70}$$

2.

$$\underline{60} \; (+) \; \underline{40} \; \boxed{=} \; \underline{100}$$

$$\underline{40} \; (+) \; \underline{60} \; \boxed{=} \; \underline{100}$$

USE MENTAL MATH

Find each sum. Use
basic facts to help.

I know $2 + 7 = 9$.
So 2 tens + 7 tens = 9 tens.

20 + 70 = 90

3. $40 + 50 = \underline{90}$

4. $20 + 80 = \underline{100}$

5. $60 + 30 = \underline{90}$

6. $10 + 90 = \underline{100}$

3. PRACTICE AND APPLY

Basic	All
Average	All
Extended	All

PRACTICE

As students complete page 210, have
them look carefully at their turnaround
sentences. *Which numbers change places
to make a turnaround sentence?* (the two
addends)

APPLY

USE MENTAL MATH ▶ **How can
basic addition facts help you find the
sums?** (Possible answer: The ones place
will be zero since there are no ones, and
the tens can be added as basic facts.)

▶ **How can you show 10 tens? What
is another name for 10 tens?** (10 tens
is the number 10 and a 0; it is called one
hundred.)

▶ **How can turnaround sentences be
made from the number sentences in
Exercises 3-6?** (Change the order of the
addends.)

CLOSE AND ASSESS

SHOW WHAT YOU KNOW

Have students look at the story picture
for *Who's Missing?* and count the
characters. *Suppose Billy counted 10
passengers returning to the bus. Then
30 more arrived. How many
passengers returned in all?* (40) Have
them use cubes to help write the
addition sentence and its turnaround.

QUICK QUIZ

Find the sum and write the turnaround
sentence.
40 + 50   (90; 50 + 40 = 90)
20 + 60   (80; 60 + 20 = 80)
30 + 10   (40; 10 + 30 = 40)

Counting On by Tens

OBJECTIVE 10-3   To model and add a 2-digit and a decade number by counting on by tens

PREBOOK ACTIVITIES

QUICK REVIEW

Copy the number. Then write the next number, counting by tens.

54	(64)	23	(33)
15	(25)	19	(29)
61	(71)	36	(46)

PRIOR KNOWLEDGE

Help students recall that they have learned how to count on by tens and ask them to think about the number patterns they know. *What happens when you count on by 10 one time?* (The number is 10 more.) *What do you think would happen if you counted on by 10 two times?* (The number would be 20 more.) *Why?* (Possible answer: because counting on by 10 two times is the same as adding 2 tens, or 20)

COMMUNICATION

Listening and Discussing Math   Read the following sentences to students. Ask them to show thumbs up if the sentence is true and thumbs down if the sentence is false. Then discuss the responses.

1. When you count on by tens, the numbers get smaller. (false)
2. Counting on by tens once is the same as adding 10. (true)
3. When you count on by tens, the next number after 55 is 66. (false)
4. When you count on by tens, the number in the ones place stays the same. (true)

EXPLORE AND CONNECT

Materials: 2 number cubes, punchout number cards 1-3, base-ten blocks
Group Suggestion: pairs
Provide each pair of students with 2 number cubes, punchout number cards, and base-ten blocks. The number cards are placed face down on the table. One student rolls both number cubes and uses base-ten blocks to model a 2-digit number. The second student draws a number card and adds that many tens blocks to the model. Students work together to determine what new number is represented by the model and then count aloud by 10s from the original number to the new number. Encourage students to explain what they have done and to help each other count accurately.

CONNECTIONS   Use these anytime.

Problem of the Day

Logic   Dora has sold 27 boxes of fruit so far during the fruit sale. She will win a stuffed animal if she sells 50 or more boxes. The fruit comes in 10-box cartons. How many more cartons will Dora have to open in order to sell 50 boxes of fruit? (3)

Math Connection

Patterns   Copy and complete the addition pattern:

30	40	50	60	(70)
+20	+20	+20	+20	(+20)
50	(60)	(70)	(80)	(90)

How do you know what comes next in the pattern? (20 is added to every multiple of 10.)

Subject Integration

Physical Education   Choose a number between 11 and 19. Jump 8 times as you count on by tens. On what number did you finish? Try another number. What is the same about both final numbers? (They both have 9 tens.)

CLASSWORK AND HOMEWORK SUPPLEMENTS

Practice

Skills Maintenance 10-3

Name _____

Counting On by Tens

Use a cube with the numbers 10 to 60.
Roll the cube. Add it to the number given.
Write the sum.
Use base-ten blocks to help.

Answers will vary.

1.
$13 + \_\_\_ = \_\_\_$

2.
$21 + \_\_\_ = \_\_\_$

3.
$31 + \_\_\_ = \_\_\_$

4.
$18 + \_\_\_ = \_\_\_$

5.
$28 + \_\_\_ = \_\_\_$

6.
$38 + \_\_\_ = \_\_\_$

7.
$26 + \_\_\_ = \_\_\_$

8.
$23 + \_\_\_ = \_\_\_$

Are any sums the same?

88   Use with text pages 211–212.   PS-2

Building Thinking Skills

Mental Math 10-3

Name _____

Using Your Head

Use mental math to find the sums.

1. Add 20 to each number.
$33 \;\underline{53}$ $67 \;\underline{87}$
$24 \;\underline{44}$ $58 \;\underline{78}$

2. Add 30 to each number.
$21 \;\underline{51}$ $16 \;\underline{46}$
$52 \;\underline{82}$ $44 \;\underline{74}$

Find the sums.

3. $23 + 10 + 10 = \underline{43}$
4. $56 + 20 + 10 = \underline{86}$
5. $20 + 28 + 20 = \underline{68}$
6. $10 + 40 + 49 = \underline{99}$
7. $30 + 17 + 10 + 10 = \underline{67}$
8. $10 + 20 + 39 + 20 = \underline{89}$

How old will you be?   *Answers may vary.*

9. in 10 years _____
10. in 20 years _____
11. in 30 years _____
12. in 50 years _____

What number was added?

13. $23 \rightarrow 43 \;\underline{20}$
14. $46 \rightarrow 86 \;\underline{40}$
15. $12 \rightarrow 62 \;\underline{50}$
16. $31 \rightarrow 91 \;\underline{60}$

88   Use with text pages 211–212.   TS-2

Reteaching

Skills Review 10-3

Name _____

Counting On by Tens

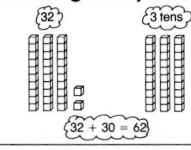

Start with 32.
Count on **3** tens.
32, 42, 52, 62
1 ten 2 tens 3 tens

$32 + 30 = 62$

Start with the number given.
Count on to add the tens shown.
Draw a line to match the sum.

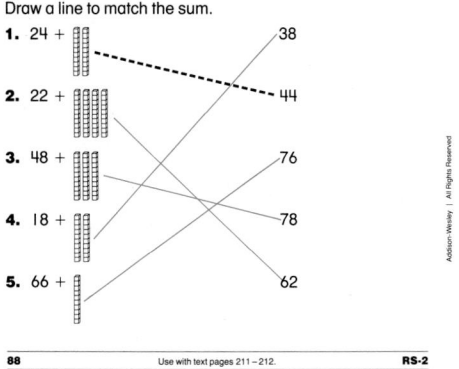

1. $24 +$ 38
2. $22 +$ 44
3. $48 +$ 76
4. $18 +$ 78
5. $66 +$ 62

88   Use with text pages 211–212.   RS-2

Challenges

Cooperative Activities 10-3

Name _____

Spin a Sum

Play with a partner.
Use spinners and a different color crayon for each of you.

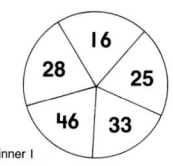
Spinner 1

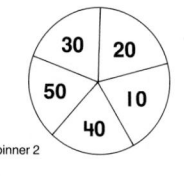
Spinner 2

Spin the first spinner to find the start number.
Spin the second spinner and count on the number of tens.
Color the sum.
Now your partner spins for tens, counts on from the start number,
and colors that sum.
Spin again to change the start number.
Keep playing until one of you colors a whole row of sums.

38	36	43	66	78
83	75	46	35	26
48	53	56	45	73
63	58	65	76	55
96	68	86	56	66

88   Use with text pages 211–212.   CS-2

OPTIONS FOR INDIVIDUAL NEEDS

Basic

Exercises All
Computer Bank, pp. 407-408

Supplements
Reteaching 88 or
Practice 88
Challenges 88

Average

Exercises All
Computer Bank, pp. 407-408

Supplements
Practice 88
Challenges 88 or
Thinking Skills 88

Extended

Exercises All
Computer Bank, p. 407-408

Supplements
Challenges 88
Thinking Skills 88

Other Resources:
Math in Stride, pp. 72-75
Mathematics Their Way, p. 307
Explorations, pp. 131-132

10-3

LESSON PLAN 10-3

OBJECTIVE 10-3
To model and add a 2-digit and a decade number by counting on by tens

---

Materials: toothpicks, rubberbands, number cubes, Cube-A-Links, spinners, base-ten blocks, TA4 (Addition/Subtraction Mats)

Alternative Materials: counters

Grouping Suggestions: pairs, small groups

---

1. MOTIVATE AND TEACH

LEARN ABOUT IT

Begin by writing a 2-digit number that is not a multiple of 10 and a multiple of 10 on the chalkboard. Ask students to show both numbers with cubes. Then have students find the sum by counting on verbally by tens as they add the second number. For example: 26 + 30: 26, 36, 46, 56. Have students look at the cube-train spinner at the top of page 211.

▶ **What is the same about all the numbers shown on the spinner?**
(They are multiples of ten.)

▶ **Why does the number of ones stay the same after counting on tens?**
(Possible answers: No ones are added; 0 ones are added.)

▶ **Suppose the spinner shows 3 tens. How many times will you count on a ten?** (3) **What number will you add to 34?** (30) **Why?** (30 is the same as 3 tens.)

▶ **For Exercises 2-10, what will be different about everyone's work?**
(Possible answer: the tens added; the sum)

▶ **What will be the same about everyone's work?** (Answers will have the same number of ones each time since no ones are being added.)

2. CHECK UNDERSTANDING

ERROR ALERT Adding the spinner number to the ones place.

Name _____

Counting On by Tens

Work in a group.
Use cubes and a spinner.

Start with 34.
Count on by tens.
34, 44, 54

34 + 20 = 54

Show the start number with cubes. Spin.
Use cubes to count on the number of tens.
Finish the addition sentence.
Answers may vary. Check students' work.

	Start Number	Spinner Amount	Sum		Start Number	Spinner Amount	Sum
1.	34	(+) 20	= 54	2.	17	(+) ___	= ___
3.	26	(+) ___	= ___	4.	39	(+) ___	= ___
5.	12	(+) ___	= ___	6.	28	(+) ___	= ___
7.	22	(+) ___	= ___	8.	19	(+) ___	= ___
9.	31	(+) ___	= ___	10.	25	(+) ___	= ___

Chapter 10   (two hundred eleven)

TEACHING OPTIONS

RETEACHING TIPS Provide toothpicks bundled in tens, and number cubes. Have students toss 2 cubes to make a 2-digit number with toothpick tens and ones. Toss one cube, count on to add that many tens, and write the addition sentence. Use Reteaching Supplement 88.

ENRICHMENT Have students use base-ten blocks to play *What Is Missing?* Hold up tens blocks to show the other addend.

43 + _(1 ten)_ = 53
12 + _(2 tens)_ = 32
27 + _(3 tens)_ = 57
36 + _(4 tens)_ = 76
24 + _(5 tens)_ = 74

---

se cubes. Start with the
umber given. Count on by tens.
rite the addition sentence.

38

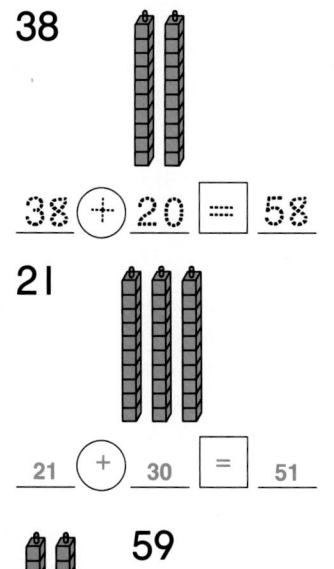

38 (+) 20 = 58

2. 38

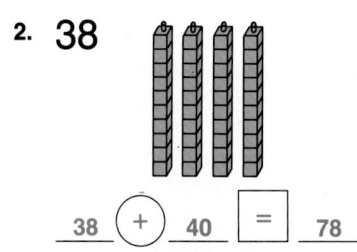

38 (+) 40 = 78

21

21 (+) 30 = 51

4. 21

21 (+) 50 = 71

59

20 (+) 59 = 79

6. 59

40 (+) 59 = 99

SE MENTAL MATH

art with the red number. Count on by tens.

24 + 10 = _34_

8. 34 + 20 = _54_

10 + 52 = _62_

10. 20 + 72 = _92_

3. PRACTICE AND APPLY

Basic	All
Average	All
Extended	All

10-3

PRACTICE

How can you find answers for Exercises 5 and 6 in the same way as you did for Exercises 1 through 4? (Possible answer: You can change the order of the addends so the sentence is written in the same way.)

APPLY

MENTAL MATH ► **Which digit tells you how many times to count on by 10?** (the tens digit)
► **Which digits are added? Which digit stays the same? Why?**
(Possible answer: The tens digits are added; the ones digit remains the same because it is being added to 0.)

LOSE AND ASSESS

HOW WHAT YOU KNOW

ovide each pair with an
dition/subtraction mat and base-ten
ocks. Call out a 2-digit number for
e student to model with the blocks.
ll out a multiple of ten for the
rtner to model. Then have students
mbine the addends and write an
dition sentence.

QUICK QUIZ

Add.

34	53	17	21	40
+20	+10	+30	+30	+23
(54)	(63)	(47)	(51)	(63)

Making Another Ten

OBJECTIVE 10-4   To model and add 2-digit numbers; to decide if trading is needed

PREBOOK ACTIVITIES

As I say an addition exercise, put your thumbs up if the sum is greater than 10. Put your thumbs down if the sum is less than 10.

6 + 5	7 + 6	5 + 4	3 + 9	6 + 3	7 + 7
(greater)	(greater)	(less)	(greater)	(less)	(greater)

PRIOR KNOWLEDGE

Help students recall how to rename 10 ones as 1 ten: Zena is packing markers in plastic bags. Ten markers will fit into one bag. Zena has 14 markers.
Does she have enough for one whole bag? (yes) *How many extra markers will there be?* (4) How do you know that Zena will have enough for one whole bag? (Ten markers will fill one bag, and 14 has 1 ten and 4 ones, or 10 + 4.)

COMMUNICATION

Writing in Math   In their Math Journals, have students copy and complete each sentence using one of the following words or phrases.

less than 10   greater than 10   make another ten   ten ones

1. The sum of 7 and 6 is (greater than 10) .
2. You can (make another ten) with ten ones.
3. The (ten ones) become one ten.
4. If a sum is (less than 10) , you cannot make another ten.

EXPLORE AND CONNECT

Materials: Cube-A-Links in 2 colors
Grouping Suggestion: pairs
Provide students pairs with cubes. Ask one student to tell an addition story that has two 2-digit addends; for example: *I ha▮ 23 stamps. Then I bought 18 more. How many do I now▮* Have the partner model the addends with cubes, using 1 colo▮ for each addend; then have students work together, writing th▮ matching addition sentence and counting cubes to find the sur▮ *When you counted the ones in the addends, were there enoug▮ to make another ten?* (Answers will vary.) *If so, how did you make another ten?* (Possible answer: joined ones cubes to ma▮ a ten) Have students exchange roles, tell another addition stor▮ and join cubes to show the addends and find the sum. For eac▮ story, have them write the addition sentence that tells how many in all. Encourage them to help each other without just giving the answers.

CONNECTIONS   Use these anytime.

Problem of the Day

Adding   You have 27 stamps. 35 stamps fill a page. You buy 7 more stamps. Do you have enough to fill a page? (no)

Counting Patterns

Find the sums. Look for a pattern.

46	46	46	46	46	46
+ 1	+ 2	+ 3	+ 4	+ 5	+ 6
(47)	(48)	(49)	(50)	(51)	(52)

What happened as you added one more? (The answer increased by one.) For which sums did you need to make another ten? (from 46 + 4 on) Why? (There are ten or more ones.)

Math Connection

Estimation   Use punchout pennies and dimes to solve.
Neill has 29¢. He earned 33¢.
Does Neill have close to 50¢ or close to 60¢ now? (close to 60¢)

CLASSWORK AND HOMEWORK SUPPLEMENTS

OPTIONS FOR INDIVIDUAL NEEDS

Basic

Exercises All
More Practice, p. 421, set A

Supplements
Reteaching 89 or
Practice 89
Thinking Skills 89

Average

Exercises All
More Practice, p. 421, set A

Supplements
Practice 89
Challenges 89 or
Thinking Skills 89

Extended

Exercises All

Supplements
Challenges 89
Thinking Skills 89

Other Resources:
Explorations, p. 274
*Developing Number Concepts
with Unifix Cubes*, pp.
149-153

Practice

Skills Maintenance 10-4

Name _____

Adding: Making Another Ten

Add the cubes.
Cross out ones and draw another ten if you can.
Write the number in all.

1. 17   5   _22_ in all
2. 34   14   _48_ in all
3. 23   27   _50_ in all
4. 18   24   _42_ in all
5. 24   39   _63_ in all

PS-2   Use with text pages 213–214.   89

Reteaching

Manipulatives 10-4

Name _____

Adding: Making Another Ten

We took 15.
We added 6.
We linked 10.
Now we have 21.

Work with a partner. Use cubes.
Take some tens and ones. Add some more ones.
Make another ten when you can. Write what you did.

	We took	We added	We have
1.	15	6	2 tens 1 ones / 21 in all
2.	24	7	3 tens 1 ones / 31 in all
3.	46	4	5 tens 0 ones / 50 in all
4.	68	6	7 tens 4 ones / 74 in all

RS-2   Use with text pages 213–214.   89

Building Thinking Skills

Life Skills 10-4

Name _____

Shopping

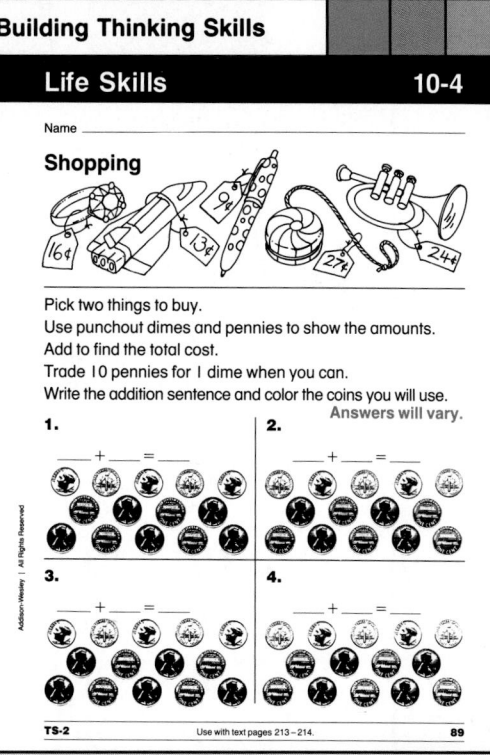

Pick two things to buy.
Use punchout dimes and pennies to show the amounts.
Add to find the total cost.
Trade 10 pennies for 1 dime when you can.
Write the addition sentence and color the coins you will use.
Answers will vary.

1.   2.
3.   4.

TS-2   Use with text pages 213–214.   89

Challenges

Critical Thinking 10-4

Name _____

Crossnumbers

Add the pair of numbers.
When you make another ten, write the sum in its numbered
space in the crossnumber puzzle. The first one is done
for you.

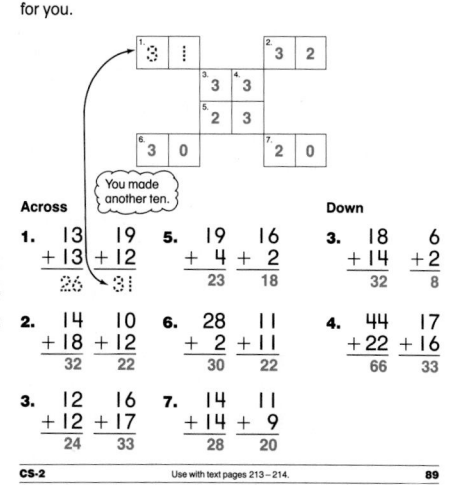

You made another ten.

Across
1. 13 + 13 = 26   19 + 12 = 31
5. 19 + 4 = 23   16 + 2 = 18
2. 14 + 18 = 32   10 + 12 = 22
6. 28 + 2 = 30   11 + 11 = 22
3. 12 + 12 = 24   16 + 17 = 33
7. 14 + 14 = 28   11 + 9 = 20

Down
3. 18 + 14 = 32   6 + 2 = 8
4. 44 + 22 = 66   17 + 16 = 33

CS-2   Use with text pages 213–214.   89

OBJECTIVE 10-4
To model and add 2 digit numbers; to decide if trading is needed

---

Materials: Cube-A-Links of 2 colors, base-ten blocks, number cards 0-9

Alternative Materials: counters

---

1. MOTIVATE AND TEACH

LEARN ABOUT IT

Write 26 + 15 on the chalkboard and have students use cubes of different colors, one for each addend, to model the expression. *Do you have enough ones to make another ten?* (yes) Have students make the ten with the ones cubes, then find the sum. (41) Have students look at the example at the top of page 213.

▶ **Why can you make another ten?** (The 5 red and 8 yellow ones cubes combine to make more than 10.)

▶ **What happens when there are not enough ones to make another ten?** (Possible answer: You add ones, then add tens. There are no new tens.)

▶ **For what sums will you not be able to make another ten?** (sums that are less than 10 in the ones place)

▶ **For what sums will you be able to make another ten?** (sums that have 10 or more in the ones place)

▶ **What happens when there are exactly 10 ones?** (They make another ten with no ones left.)

2. CHECK UNDERSTANDING

ERROR ALERT Neglecting to add another ten to the sum.

Name _____

Making Another Ten

How many cubes are there?

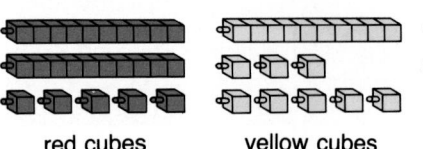

red cubes	yellow cubes	Another ten?	How many in all?
25	18	(yes) no	43

There are 43 cubes.

Work in a group. Use cubes. Add the number of cubes. Can you make another ten? Ring **yes** or **no**. Write the number in all.

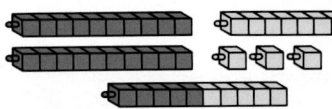

When you add 2-digit numbers you sometimes make another ten

	red cubes	yellow cubes	Another ten?	How many in all?
1.	15	13	yes (no)	28
2.	26	16	(yes) no	42
3.	8	14	(yes) no	22
4.	27	12	yes (no)	39

Make up your own number of cubes.

5.	___	___	yes no	___
6.	___	___	yes no	___

**Answers may vary.
Check students' work.**

Chapter 10

(two hundred thirteen) 2

TEACHING OPTIONS

RETEACHING TIPS Have students use base-ten blocks to model the numbers 27 + 36. As they join blocks to add 7 and 6, have them count 10 ones and trade for a 10. Place the new 10 with the other tens and find the sum. Assign Reteaching Supplement 89.

ENRICHMENT Give students a number cube and a place value chart to play *Top Fifty*. Students toss the cube and write the ones on the chart. As 10 or more ones accumulate, students make another 10 and write it in the tens place. Continue until there are 5 tens on the chart.

se cubes. Can you make another ten?

ng **yes** or **no.** Write the number in all.

		Another ten?	How many in all?

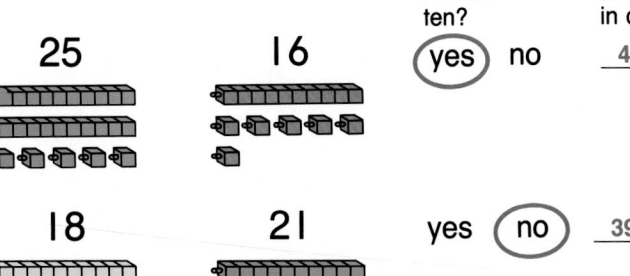

25   16   (yes)   no   <u>41</u>

18   21   yes   (no)   <u>39</u>

MIDCHAPTER REVIEW/QUIZ

'rite the addition sentence for each.

Count on by ones.   **2.** Count on by tens.

49   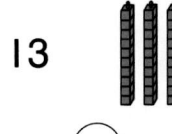   13 

<u>49</u> (+) <u>2</u> [=] <u>51</u>   <u>13</u> (+) <u>30</u> [=] <u>43</u>

'rite the addition sentence and
turnaround sentence.

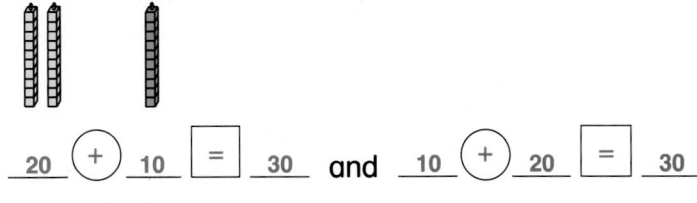

<u>20</u> (+) <u>10</u> [=] <u>30</u> and <u>10</u> (+) <u>20</u> [=] <u>30</u>

LOSE AND ASSESS

HOW WHAT YOU KNOW   Ask
dents to retell the events of the
apter story, *Who's Missing?*
ppose there were 15 passengers on
e bus. Then a group of 19 more
ssengers boarded the bus. How
my passengers were on the bus in
? Have students use cubes to help
m find the answer and write a
mber sentence.

QUICK QUIZ

Model the addends with Cube-A-Links.
Join the cubes. Make another ten if you
need to. Write the sum.
1. 19 + 23 (42)   **2.** 45 + 21 (66)
3. 37 + 14 (51)   **4.** 28 + 16 (44)

---

3. PRACTICE AND APPLY

Basic	All, Midchapter Review/Quiz
Average	All, Midchapter Review/Quiz
Extended	All, Midchapter Review/Quiz

PRACTICE

*As you begin page 214, what will you do
first to find out if you can make another
ten?* (Add the ones.)

APPLY

▶ **At which place will you look to see
if you can make another ten?** (the
ones place)
▶ **How many ones must you have to
make another ten?** (ten or more)
▶ **If you make another ten, where
will you add it?** (to the other tens)

MIDCHAPTER REVIEW/QUIZ

ITEM ANALYSIS   The table
correlates the Midchapter Review/Quiz
items with the lesson objectives.

Items	Objectives
1	10-1
2	10-3
3	10-2

Problem Solving: Understanding the Operations

OBJECTIVE 10-5   To understand the operations of addition and subtraction by identifying which operation is need

PREBOOK ACTIVITIES

QUICK REVIEW

Find the sums.

20	40	60	30	50	60	10	70	30
+30	+10	+30	+30	+20	+10	+40	+10	+50
50	50	90	60	70	70	50	80	80

PRIOR KNOWLEDGE

Read each situation below to the class. Ask students to tell whether they would add or subtract to solve the problem. Discuss their answers.

Randy and Janie put their game tokens together. (add)
Mikala gives some of his tokens to Paul, then counts how many he has left. (subtract)
Janie spends some of her tokens. (subtract)
Randy gets more tokens from his brother. (add)
Mikala and Janie compare the number of tokens each has. (subtract)

COMMUNICATION

Discussing Math   Discuss the following. *When is addition used to solve a problem?* (Possible answer: to join two groups; to find out how many in all) *How can two amounts be compared using subtraction?* (Possible answer: subtract the smaller amount from the larger to find out how many more or to find the difference) *What other kinds of problems can be solved using subtraction?* (Possible answer: problems in which part of a group is taken away) Have students give examples of put-together, compare, and take-away stories.

EXPLORE AND CONNECT

COOPERATIVE ACTIVITY

Grouping Suggestion: small groups
Have students use cubes to solve. Finish the number sentence
27 children were at the party.
6 more children came.
How many children were at the party then?
  (27) (+) (6) = (33)

TEACHING ACTIONS

BEFORE ▶ **What is happening in the story?** (Children are at a party. More children come.)
▶ **How could you use cubes to show the data**
(Show a set of 27 cubes and a set of 6 cubes.)

DURING ▶ **What does the question ask?** (how many children are at the party after 6 more came)
▶ **Should you plan to add or subtract? How do you know?** (add, because you want to find out how man children are at the party in all)
▶ **Why is it a good idea to estimate the sum before adding?** (The estimate can help you decide if your answer is reasonable.)
▶ **How can you use cubes to solve the problem?** (Put together the sets of 27 cubes and 6 cubes, make another ten, count the tens and ones left over to find the answer.)

AFTER ▶ **How can you check your answer?** (Possible answers: Compare it with your estimate; compare answers with a classmate.)
Have groups of students use counters to model similar additio and subtraction story problems with small 2-digit numbers.

CONNECTIONS   Use these anytime.

Problem of the Day
Understanding the Operations
Give a question you could answer for this story. Then solve the problem. (Possible answer: *How much more is the yo-yo?* 12¢)
A yo-yo costs 22¢.
A top costs 10¢.

Number Sense
Estimation   Write these headings on your paper: *About 30, About 40, About 50.* Estimate the sums. List the problems under the correct heading.
1. 10 + 22   **2.** 23 + 31
3. 40 + 13   **4.** 21 + 12
5. 23 + 20   **6.** 11 + 34
7. 34 + 21   **8.** 33 + 12
(30: 1, 4; 40: 5, 6, 8; 50: 2, 3, 7)

Subject Integration
Language Arts   Write a story problem about a trip you would like to take. Read the problem to your partner. Your partner draws a picture for your problem. Together, write an addition or a subtraction sentence for the problem and solve it. Display your illustrated story problem and solution on a bulletin board.

Estimating Sums: More or Less than 50¢

To estimate sums as more or less than 50¢

CLASSWORK AND HOMEWORK SUPPLEMENTS

Practice

Problem Solving 10-5

Name _____

Understanding the Operations

Read each story.
Would you add or subtract? Ring one.

1. 60 oranges were in a basket.
   25 were sold.
   How many oranges were not sold?
   add (subtract)

2. 18 apple trees are in a field.
   42 peach trees are in the same field.
   How many more peach trees than
   apple trees are in the field?
   add (subtract)

3. 14 brown baskets are on a truck.
   26 red baskets are on the same truck.
   Altogether, how many baskets
   are on the truck?
   (add) subtract

4. 35 bananas are yellow.
   24 bananas are green.
   How many more bananas are yellow
   than green?
   add (subtract)

90   Use with text page 215.   PS-2

Building Thinking Skills

Problem Solving 10-5

Name _____

Party Problems

Look at the picture.
Write a number sentence to answer each question.

1. How many children are dressed as robots and monsters?
   2 (+) 2 (=) 4

2. How many children did not dress as a ballerina?
   8 (−) 1 (=) 7

3. How many rainbows and tulips are there?
   7 (+) 6 (=) 13

4. How many more apples are there than children?
   11 (−) 8 (=) 3

5. How many children are dressed in outfits no one
   else had chosen?
   1 (+) 1 (+) 1 (+) 1 (=) 4

90   Use with text page 215.   TS-2

Reteaching

Estimation 10-5

Name _____

Estimating Sums: More or Less than 50¢

Estimate the sums.

18¢ + 26¢   *Think about the number of tens.*   37¢ + 31¢
more than 50¢   (more than 50¢)
(less than 50¢)   less than 50¢

Think about the number of tens.
Ring the better estimate for the sum.

1. 11¢ + 32¢
   more than 50¢
   (less than 50¢)

2. 27¢ + 45¢
   (more than 50¢)
   less than 50¢

3. 52¢ + 24¢
   (more than 50¢)
   less than 50¢

4. 36¢ + 13¢
   more than 50¢
   (less than 50¢)

5. 23¢ + 25¢
   more than 50¢
   (less than 50¢)

6. 44¢ + 32¢
   (more than 50¢)
   less than 50¢

7. 41¢ + 43¢
   (more than 50¢)
   less than 50¢

8. 55¢ + 16¢
   (more than 50¢)
   less than 50¢

90   Use with text page 216.   RS-2

Challenges

Cooperative Activities 10-5

Name _____

Estimation Steps

You need: a friend, 2 counters, a number cube,
and a spinner like this:

Rules: Take turns. Begin at **Start**.
Roll the number cube. Move that many spaces
on the game board. If the space says + **spinner**, spin the spinner.
Estimate the sum of the number on the spinner and the number in
your space. If the estimate is less than 50, go down the slide. If the
estimate is more than 50, go up the steps. The first player to reach
Home wins. You must land exactly on Home to win. If the number
rolled is more than the spaces left on the board, you lose a turn.

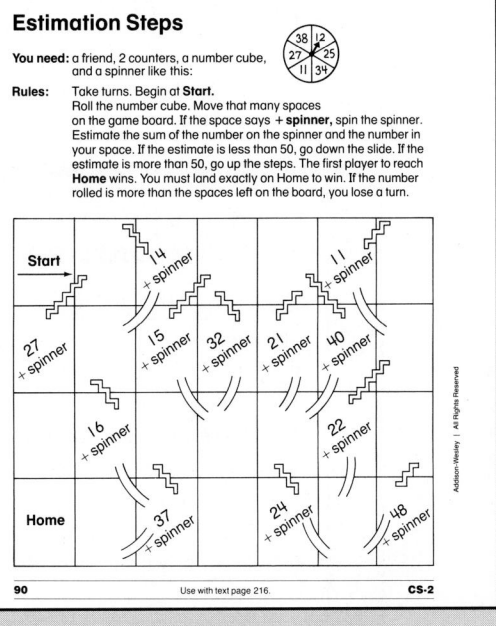

90   Use with text page 216.   CS-2

OPTIONS FOR INDIVIDUAL NEEDS

Basic

Exercises All

Supplements
Reteaching 90 or
Practice 90

Average

Exercises All

Supplements
Practice 90
Challenges 90 or
Thinking Skills 90

Extended

Exercises All

Supplements
Challenges 90
Thinking Skills 90

Other Resources:
Math in Stride, pp. 77-78,
138-139
Mathematics Their Way, p.
317
Explorations, pp. 128-129,
271, 281-283, 296-299

10-5

OBJECTIVE 10-5
To understand the operations of addition and subtraction by identifying which operation is needed; to estimate sums as more or less than 50¢

Materials: Cube-A-Links, counters

1. MOTIVATE AND TEACH

LEARN ABOUT IT

 **BEFORE** ► **Look at Exercise 1. Describe what is happening in the story.**
(Possible answer: Some children were on the bus; then more children got on.)

 **DURING** ► **How can you use cubes to help you plan how to solve the problem?**
(Possible answer: Use cubes to show what is happening; decide whether to add or subtract.)

► **In Exercise 3, what words tell you to subtract?** (The question *How many more?* tells you to compare, or subtract.)

 **AFTER** ► **Describe a method for checking the answer.**
(Possible answers: Write an addition sentence and solve; reread the problem to see if the answer is reasonable.)

2. CHECK UNDERSTANDING
ERROR ALERT
Page 215 Choosing the incorrect operation to solve a problem.
Page 216 Estimating by adding the ones rather than the tens.

Name _____

Problem Solving
Understanding the Operations

Use cubes to show each story.
Read each question. Would you add
or subtract? Ring one.

1. 25 children were on the bus. 5 children got on at the next stop. How many children were on the bus then?

   (add)   subtract

2. 26 cars are on the top. 15 cars are on the bottom. How many cars are on the boat?

   (add)   subtract

3. 16 people are on the top. 9 people are on the bottom. How many more people are there on the top?

   add   (subtract)

Chapter 10   (two hundred fifteen) 21

TEACHING OPTIONS

RETEACHING TIPS Have students put 15 red cubes in 1 yarn ring and 5 yellow cubes in another. *What operation would you use to find the total?* (addition) Ask them to take 8 counters away. *How would you find the number left?* (subtract) For practice estimating sums, use Reteaching Supplement 90.

COMPUTER *Safari Search,* **Sunburst Communications © 1985** Practice problem solving for all. In *Search Out the Seal,* students find the seal in a 5-by-5 grid. A clue is given after each guess. Encourage students to plan using paper and pencil. The recommended game takes 5-10 minutes.

stimating Sums
ore or Less than 50¢

Toy Mat

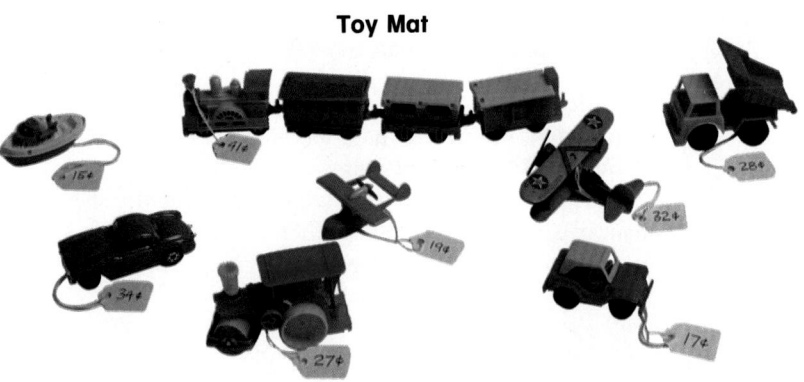

6 tens and some ones.
Estimate more than 50¢.

4 tens and some ones.
Estimate less than 50¢.

41¢ + 28¢

15¢ + 32¢

rop two counters on the mat. Write the
ices for the two nearest toys. Think
out the number of tens. Ring the better
stimate for the sum.

Estimates may vary.
Check students' work.

___¢ + ___¢	more than 50¢	less than 50¢
___¢ + ___¢	more than 50¢	less than 50¢
___¢ + ___¢	more than 50¢	less than 50¢
___¢ + ___¢	more than 50¢	less than 50¢

6 (two hundred sixteen)

Chapter 10

3. PRACTICE AND APPLY

Basic	All
Average	All
Extended	All

*What can you do if your counters do not
land on a toy?* (Possible answers: Move
the counter; throw the counter again; use
the toy that the counter is closest to.)
*How will you compare the cost of the
toys to 50¢?* (Possible answer: Add the
tens and think about the ones to find the
estimated sum for the 2 toys.)

▶ **Why are you supposed to think
about the number of tens as you
estimate each toy's price?** (Possible
answer: Because 50 is equal to 5 tens,
the sum of the tens gives the best
estimate.)

▶ **Explain how you could arrange to
make sums more or less than 50¢.**
(Possible answer: Estimate which toys
would make a sum of either more or less
than 50¢; then drop the counters on those
toys.)

▶ **How can you use the estimates
you made to help you estimate with
other numbers?** (Possible answer: Look
at the tens digits of number pairs that
make a sum of more or less than 50¢;
look for a pattern in those pairs.)

CLOSE AND ASSESS

WRITE WHAT YOU THINK
ave pairs of students write an
ddition and subtraction story that
cludes two 2-digit numbers less than
). Then have them exchange their
ories with other pairs and determine
hat operation is needed to solve the
oblem and whether the answer will
e more or less than 50.

QUICK QUIZ

Write *more than 50* or *less than 50*.
33 + 27 (more)   25 + 12 (less)
26 + 5 (less)   11 + 32 (less)
38 + 35 (more)   45 + 15 (more)
15 + 18 (less)   20 + 41 (more)

Same Sum, Different Addends

OBJECTIVE 10-6   To show different ways to name the same sum

PREBOOK ACTIVITIES

QUICK REVIEW

As I say the sum, write as many addition sentences with that sum as you can.

7   (7 + 0; 6 + 1; 5 + 2; 4 + 3; 3 + 4; 2 + 5; 1 + 6; 0 + 7)

8   (8 + 0; 7 + 1; 6 + 2; 5 + 3; 4 + 4; 3 + 5; 2 + 6; 1 + 7; 0 + 8)

PRIOR KNOWLEDGE

Help students recall the concept of different addends for the same sum. *Marty takes 17 building blocks to the playroom. He uses 2 cartons. How many blocks does he put in each one? Write an addition sentence.* Write students' sentences on the chalkboard. *How do you know that these sentences are correct?* (Possible answer: The sum for each addition sentence is 17.)

COMMUNICATION

Discussing Math   Write this addition pattern on the chalkboard:

$$
\begin{array}{cccccc}
6 & 7 & 8 & 9 & 10 & 11 \\
+12 & +11 & +10 & +9 & +8 & +7
\end{array}
$$

What is the same about all the sums? (They are all 18.) *What patterns do you see?* (Possible answers: The addends in the top row increase by 1 each time; the addends in the bottom row decrease by 1 each time.) *What turnaround facts do you see?* (7 + 11 and 11 + 7; 8 + 10 and 10 + 8) *What is the next addition sentence in the pattern?* (12 + 6 = 18) *How do you know?* (Possible answers: The top addend is one more than 11; it is the turnaround fact for 12 + 6.)

EXPLORE AND CONNECT

Materials: Cube-A-Links
Alternative Materials: base-ten blocks
Grouping Suggestion: pairs

Provide each pair of students with 34 cubes and a sheet of plain paper. Have students fold the paper in half. Show that one way to split the 34 cubes into 2 groups is to put 15 on the left side and 19 on the right side of the paper. *What addition sentence describes the cubes?* (15 + 19 = 34) *What other way could the 34 cubes be separated? What addition sentence describes what you did?* (Possible answers: 20 + 14 = 34, 25 + 9 = 34) As students use cubes to model different addends for 34, record the addition sentences on the chalkboard. Encourage students to explain their ideas to each other.

CONNECTIONS   Use these anytime.

Problem of the Day

Turnarounds   Molly and Eric each had 16 balloons, Molly gave 7 balloons to a friend and Eric gave 9 balloons to his brother. Which two children had the same number of balloons? Why? (Molly and Eric's brother each had 9; 9 + 7 = 16 and 7 + 9 = 16.)

Math Connection

Time   You have 45 min to get ready for school. You must get dressed and eat breakfast. How many minutes will you use for each? Compare your answers with other students' responses. How are your answers the same? (They all equal 45 min.) How are they different? (The addends are different.)

Subject Integration

Art   You need a plain sheet of paper and red and blue crayons. Count to 40 as you draw shapes in each color. When you are finished, count the number of red and blue shapes you made. Write an addition sentence telling about your picture.

CLASSWORK AND HOMEWORK SUPPLEMENTS

Practice

Manipulatives — 10-6

Name _____

Same Sum, Different Addends

1. Use cubes. Ring ways to make the sum of 54.

(10 + 44)	48 + 3	(4 + 50)
(26 + 28)	(22 + 32)	21 + 16
(12 + 42)	37 + 7	(37 + 17)
42 + 16	(24 + 30)	(11 + 43)
(16 + 38)	16 + 48	(40 + 14)

2. Use cubes. Find more ways to make the sum of 54.
Write matching addition sentences. **Answers may vary.**

46 + 8 = 54   8 + 46 = 54

_____   _____

_____   _____

_____   _____

_____   _____

PS-2   Use with text pages 217–218.   91

Building Thinking Skills

Math Reasoning — 10-6

Name _____

Ladders Up

Use the numbers on each ladder to make the sum at
the top of each house.

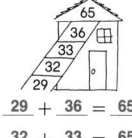

1. (40 / 25 / 22 / 18 / 15)

15 + 25 = 40

18 + 22 = 40

2. (65 / 36 / 33 / 32 / 29)

29 + 36 = 65

32 + 33 = 65

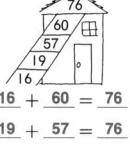

3. (83 / 57 / 47 / 36 / 26)

26 + 57 = 83

36 + 47 = 83

4. (76 / 60 / 57 / 19 / 16)

16 + 60 = 76

19 + 57 = 76

Write numbers on the ladder.
Then write addition sentences.

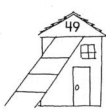

(49)

___ + ___ = 49

___ + ___ = 49

TS-2   Use with text pages 217–218.   91

Reteaching

Manipulatives — 10-6

Name _____

Same Sum, Different Addends

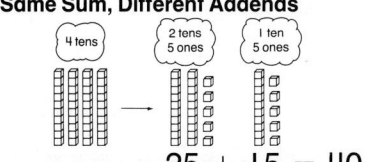

4 tens → 2 tens 5 ones | 1 ten 5 ones

$$25 + 15 = 40$$

Get 40 cubes and a mat.
Break apart the cubes as shown.
Finish the addition sentence.

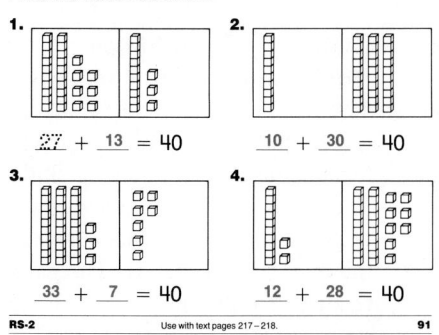

1.   27 + 13 = 40

2.   10 + 30 = 40

3.   33 + 7 = 40

4.   12 + 28 = 40

RS-2   Use with text pages 217–218.   91

Challenges

Family Math — 10-6

Name _____

Same Sum Game

> Dear Family,
> We have just completed a lesson on finding different addends to make the same sum. Play the game below with your child. Have him or her show the addition on another piece of paper.

Take turns with a family member.
Choose a number from 10 to 36.
The first player finds 2 addends in the chart to
make that sum.
The second player finds two other addends to make
the same sum.

10	7	14	19	5
3	9	6	12	11
25	13	16	15	11
15	8	2	20	10

Play again. Pick another number from 10 to 36.
This time player 2 goes first.
Keep playing as long as you wish.

CS-2   Use with text pages 217–218.   91

OPTIONS FOR INDIVIDUAL NEEDS

Basic

Exercises All
More Practice, p. 421, set B

Supplements
Reteaching 91 or
Practice 91
Challenges 91

Average

Exercises All
More Practice, p. 421, set B

Supplements
Practice 91
Challenges 91 or
Thinking Skills 91

Extended

Exercises All

Supplements
Challenges 91
Thinking Skills 91

Other Resources:
Math in Stride, pp. 25-27, 41
Explorations, pp. 50-55,
123-125, 188
*Developing Number Concepts
With Unifix Cubes*, pp.
150-153

OBJECTIVE 10-6
To show different ways to name the same sum

> **Materials:** Cube-A-Links, base-ten blocks, chart paper, magic markers
>
> **Alternate Materials:** counters
>
> **Grouping Suggestion:** small groups

1. MOTIVATE AND TEACH

LEARN ABOUT IT

Provide small groups of students with 28 cubes. Ask students to separate the cubes into 2 groups. Have them write the number of cubes in each group, then write the matching addition sentence. List the sentences on the chalkboard. *How many different ways did you find to make a sum of 28?* (Answers will vary.) Direct students' attention to the example at the top of page 217.

▶ **How does the addition sentence show that a ten was broken up?** (Each 2-digit addend has a number in the ones place.)

▶ **How can you check the addition sentence?** (Combine the cubes; make a ten with the ones and add it to the existing tens.)

▶ **When you know that 37 + 13 = 50, what turnaround addition sentence can you write?** (13 + 37 = 50)

▶ **How might your group's pictures for Exercises 1 and 2 be different from those of other groups? How will they be the same?** (Possible answer: The addends might be different; all the sums will be 50.)

2. CHECK UNDERSTANDING

ERROR ALERT Not understanding how to find more than two different addends for a 2-digit sum.

Name _____

Same Sum, Different Addends

> First I put 50 cubes in tens.

> I broke apart a ten and put the cubes into two groups.

> I drew a picture and wrote an addition sentence to match.

Work in a group. Get 50 cubes.
Find different ways to make a sum of 50.
Draw pictures to show each way.
Write the addition sentences.

Answers may vary. Check students' work.

1. ☐ ☐ ____ (+) ____ (=) 50

2. ☐ ☐ ____ (+) ____ (=) 50

Use your cubes. Find more ways to find a sum of 50. Write the addition sentences.

Answers may vary. Check students' work.

3. _____
4. _____
5. _____
6. _____

Chapter 10   (two hundred seventeen) 2

TEACHING OPTIONS

RETEACHING TIPS Write pairs of addends for 50 on the board. Have students use blocks to model each pair, and write the matching addition sentence and the turnaround sentence for each addition sentence. Assign Reteaching Supplement 91.

COMPUTER *Addition Magician,* Learning Company © 1984 Easily modified for all levels. Students practice addition facts using problem solving skills. They group numbers to add to a target number. The student selects the number of addends. The game requires 15-20 min.

se cubes. Find different
ays to make a sum of 35.
rite addition sentences to
atch.

20 + 15 = 35

_____

_____   **Answers may vary.**
                           Check students' work.

_____   5. _____

_____   7. _____

se cubes. Ring the ways to make each sum.

40	(20 + 20)	33 + 27	(12 + 28)
25	(12 + 13)	20 + 15	(18 + 7)
36	18 + 13	(18 + 18)	(24 + 12)
42	(32 + 10)	(14 + 28)	12 + 40

MIXED REVIEW

d or subtract.

$7 + 4 = \underline{11}$ $5 + 8 = \underline{13}$ $3 + 9 = \underline{12}$

$4 - 1 = \underline{3}$ $17 - 9 = \underline{8}$ $5 + 5 = \underline{10}$

$12 - 3 = \underline{9}$ $9 + 9 = \underline{18}$ $0 + 6 = \underline{6}$

LOSE AND ASSESS

HOW WHAT YOU KNOW
view with students the chapter
ory, *Who's Missing? Find 3 different
ys Billy Quacker could count a
al of 45.* Have small groups of
dents use cubes to explore all of
e possibilities. Encourage them to
lp each other without just giving
swers.

QUICK QUIZ

Use 42 cubes. Find at least 6 different
ways to make a sum of 42. Write
addition sentences to match.

---

3. PRACTICE AND APPLY

Basic	All, Mixed Review
Average	All, Mixed Review
Extended	All, Mixed Review

PRACTICE

*How will you know which pairs of
addends to ring?* (Find the pairs that
have the sum on the left.)

APPLY

▶ **How can turnaround sentences
help you find different ways to make
a sum of 35?** (Possible answer: If you
know 20 + 15 = 35, you also know 15
+ 20 = 35.)

▶ **In Exercises 8-11, what can you do
first to help you decide if a pair of
addends will have the sum shown at
the left?** (Possible answer: You can add
the ones digits of the addends to see if
their sum matches the ones digit of the
sum at the left.)

MIXED REVIEW   *How will you know
whether to add or subtract?* (Look at the
sign in each exercise.)

Problem Solving: Writing Number Sentences

OBJECTIVE 10-7   To solve problems by writing a number sentence

PREBOOK ACTIVITIES

QUICK REVIEW

Write + or − in each ○.

5 ○ 3 = 8 (+)	4 ○ 2 = 2 (−)
12 ○ 3 = 9 (−)	10 ○ 5 = 15 (+)
9 ○ 5 = 4 (−)	3 ○ 7 = 10 (+)
7 ○ 7 = 0 (−)	4 ○ 4 = 8 (+)

PRIOR KNOWLEDGE

For each of the following situations, ask students to tell whether they would use addition or subtraction to solve and which words helped them to know.
Caleb has 15 toy trucks.
His brother Roy has 7 toy trucks.
How many trucks do they have all together? (add; *all together*)
How many more trucks does Caleb have? (subtract; *how many more*)
Caleb loses 4 trucks.
How many does he have left? (subtract; *loses, how many…left*)

COMMUNICATION

Writing in Math   Write the word **list** on the chalkboard and explain that a list can contain all the possible ways things can be combined. Ask students to name things they might list. (Possible answers: lunchbox items, clothing, books, games) List students' ideas on the chalkboard. Have students create their own lists using either one of the ideas on the chalkboard or an idea of their own. Have them share their lists with the class.

EXPLORE AND CONNECT

COOPERATIVE ACTIVITY

Grouping Suggestion: small groups
Jean and Wayne went to a carnival.
Jean won 12 prizes, and Wayne won 7.
1. How many prizes did they win in all?
 (12) (+) (7) (=) (19)   They won (19) prizes.
2. How many more prizes did Jean win than Wayne?
 (12) (−) (7) (=) (5)   Jean won (5) more prizes.

TEACHING ACTIONS

 ► **How are the two questions the same? How are they different?** (Both can be answered with the same data; they ask different information.)

 ► **Which is an addition question? How do you know?** (The first; it asks how many in all.)
► **What kind of question is the second question?** (Subtraction; it asks how many more.)
► **How can you answer the questions using cubes? How are the plans for solving the two questions the same? How are they different?** (Make a group of 12 and a group of 7 for both questions. Join the groups to solve the first question; compare the groups and count how many more for the second.)

 ► **How will you complete the sentences?** (First write the number sentence that tells what you did; then write the answer in a sentence.)
► **How can you check your answers?** (Possible answer: Read the problem and the answer to see if they make sense.) Have students use cubes to model data for story problems and write addition and subtraction sentences to match.

CONNECTIONS   Use these anytime.

Problem of the Day

Write a Question   Write an addition question and a subtraction question.
The children rode the school bus.
6 children sat by the window.
14 children sat on the aisle.
(Wording may vary. Addition: *How many children rode on the school bus?* Subtraction: *How many more children sat on the aisle than by the window?*)

Math Connection

Money   Rita has 38¢. What coins might she have? Use punchout coins. List the ways. (Possible answers given.)

Quarters	Dimes	Nickels	Pennies
1	1	0	3
1	0	2	3
0	3	1	3
0	2	2	8
0	1	5	3

Creative Thinking

How Many Ways?   Work with a partner. List all the ways you can think of to use a can. (Possible answers: Use it to hold pencils; use it to play kick the can; use it for flowers; use it to trace a circle; play drums on it; use it to make a telephone; use it to make a home for a bug.)

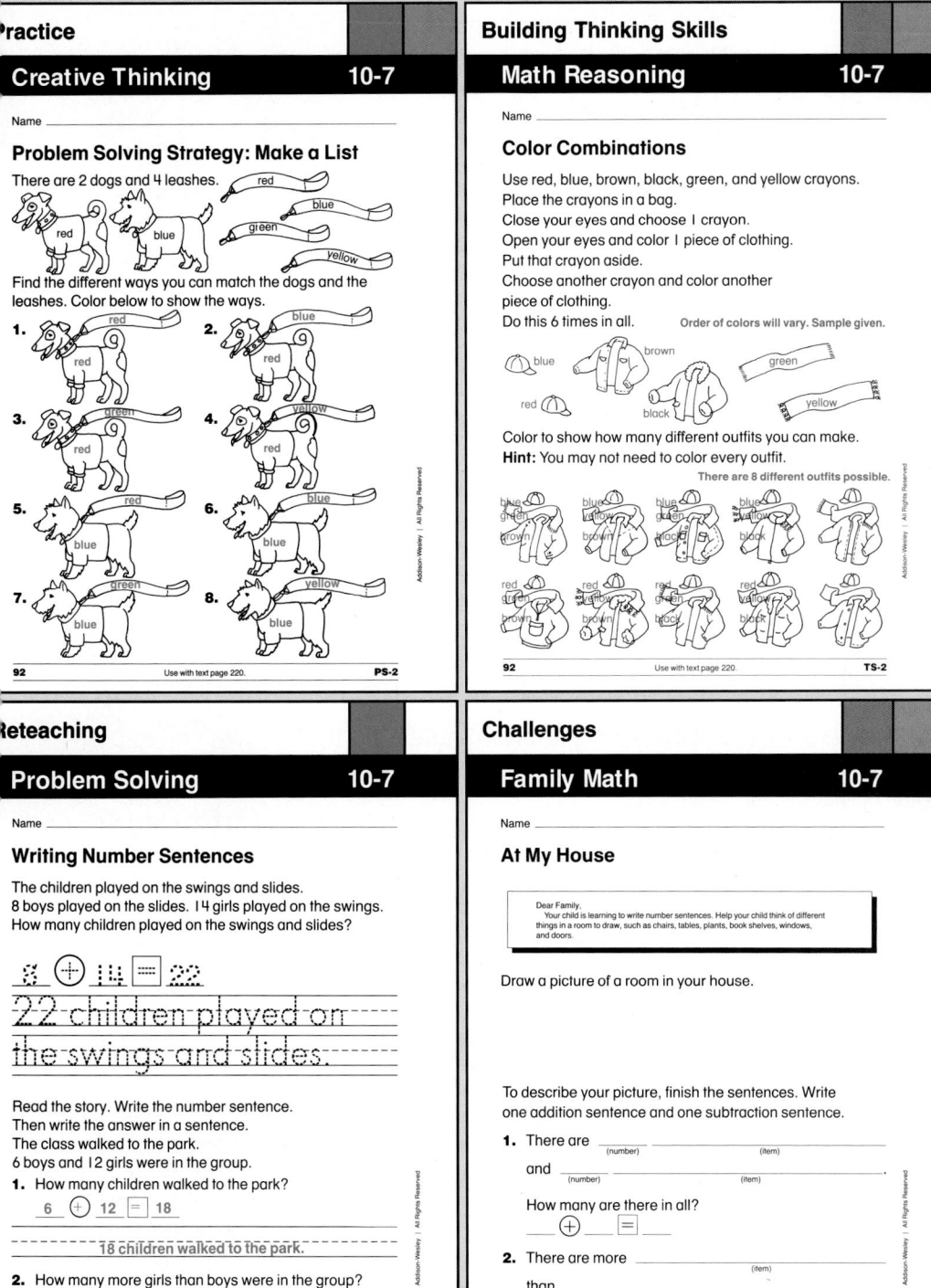

roblem Solving Strategy: Make a List

• solve problems using the strategy Make a List

CLASSWORK AND HOMEWORK SUPPLEMENTS

Practice

Creative Thinking 10-7

Name

Problem Solving Strategy: Make a List
There are 2 dogs and 4 leashes.

Find the different ways you can match the dogs and the leashes. Color below to show the ways.

92   Use with text page 220.   PS-2

Building Thinking Skills

Math Reasoning 10-7

Name

Color Combinations

Use red, blue, brown, black, green, and yellow crayons.
Place the crayons in a bag.
Close your eyes and choose 1 crayon.
Open your eyes and color 1 piece of clothing.
Put that crayon aside.
Choose another crayon and color another
piece of clothing.
Do this 6 times in all.   Order of colors will vary. Sample given.

Color to show how many different outfits you can make.
Hint: You may not need to color every outfit.

There are 8 different outfits possible.

92   Use with text page 220.   TS-2

Reteaching

Problem Solving 10-7

Name

Writing Number Sentences

The children played on the swings and slides.
8 boys played on the slides. 14 girls played on the swings.
How many children played on the swings and slides?

8 ⊕ 14 ⊟ 22

22 children played on
the swings and slides.

Read the story. Write the number sentence.
Then write the answer in a sentence.
The class walked to the park.
6 boys and 12 girls were in the group.

1. How many children walked to the park?

   6 ⊕ 12 ⊟ 18

18 children walked to the park.

2. How many more girls than boys were in the group?

   12 ⊖ 6 ⊟ 6

There were 6 more girls than boys.

92   Use with text page 219.   RS-2

Challenges

Family Math 10-7

Name

At My House

Dear Family,
Your child is learning to write number sentences. Help your child think of different things in a room to draw, such as chairs, tables, plants, book shelves, windows, and doors.

Draw a picture of a room in your house.

To describe your picture, finish the sentences. Write
one addition sentence and one subtraction sentence.

1. There are ___ ___
    (number)   (item)
and ___ ___
  (number)   (item)
How many are there in all?
___ ⊕ ___ ⊟ ___

2. There are more ___
           (item)
than ___
    (item)
How many more are there?
___ ⊖ ___ ⊟ ___

92   Use with text page 219.   CS-2

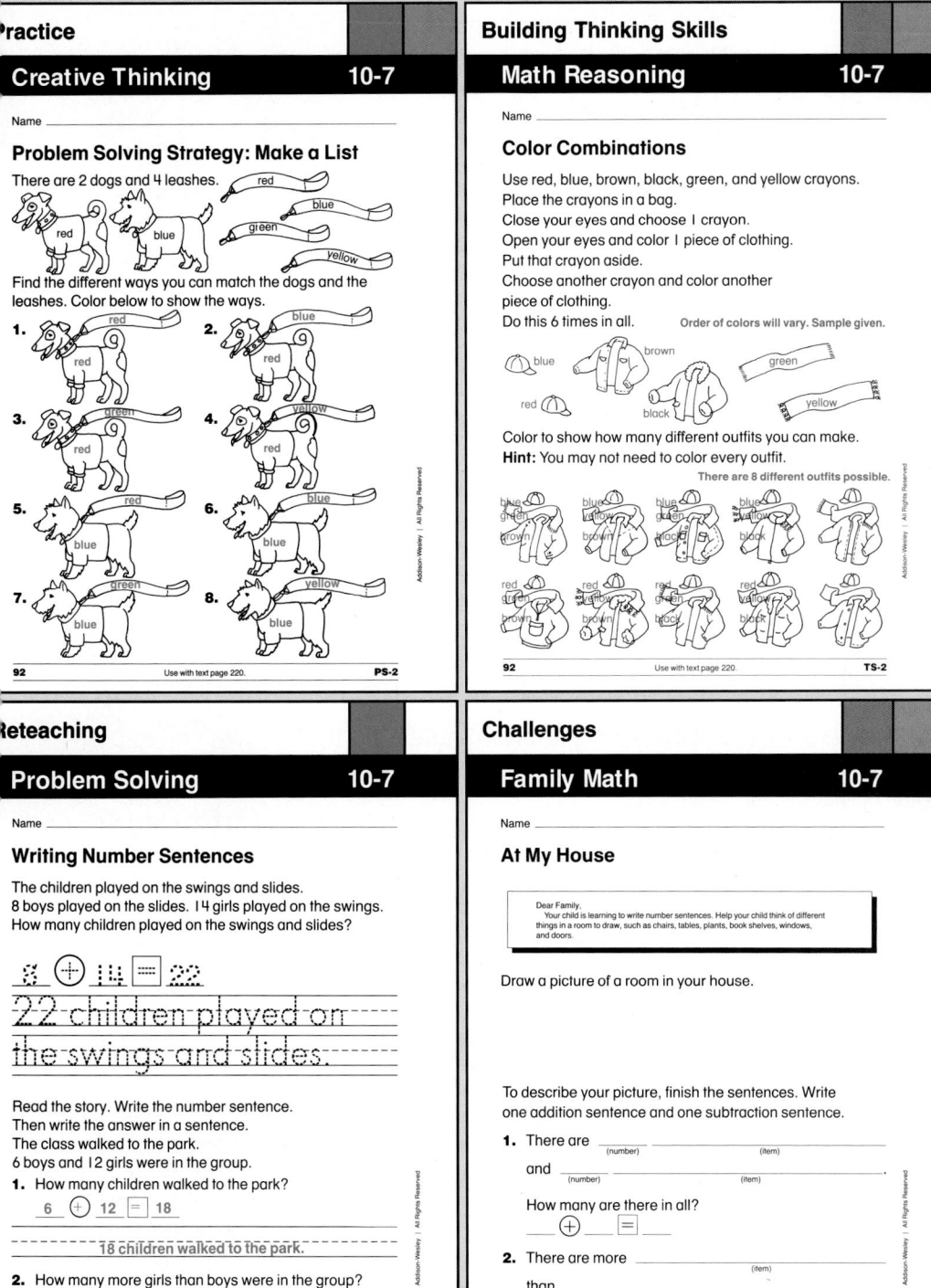

OPTIONS FOR INDIVIDUAL NEEDS

Basic

Exercises All
More Practice, p. 421, set C

Supplements
Reteaching 92 or
Practice 92

Average

Exercises All
More Practice, p. 421, set C

Supplements
Practice 92
Challenges 92 or
Thinking Skills 92

Extended

Exercises All

Supplements
Challenges 92
Thinking Skills 92

Other Resources:
Math in Stride, pp. 77-78
Problem-Solving Experiences In Mathematics, pp. 4, 5, 40, 41, 82, 100, 118, 131, 149, 167

10-7

OBJECTIVE 10-7
To solve problems by writing a number sentence; to solve problems using the strategy Make a List

Materials: cubes or slips of paper in 4 colors: red, blue, green, yellow

 **► Read Story 1. What data do you need to answer the two questions?** (the number of boys and girls on the bus)

 **► How will your plan change as you answer each question for the story?** (Add for the first question; subtract for the second question.)

► How will your plan be different for Story 2? (You must compare and subtract.)

► How will the cubes help you plan your solution? (Possible answer: Decide whether you will add or subtract; work with the cubes; then write a number sentence to solve.)

► How will the cubes help you solve the problems? (Combine cubes to solve addition problems; compare cubes to solve subtraction problems.)

 **► How could you check your answers?** (Use the turnaround addition sentence to check addition; add to check subtraction.)

2. CHECK UNDERSTANDING

ERROR ALERT
Page 219 Writing the incorrect number sentence.
Page 220 Recording impossible combinations.

Name _____

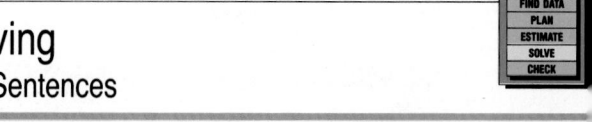

UNDERSTAND
FIND DATA
PLAN
ESTIMATE
SOLVE
CHECK

Problem Solving
Writing Number Sentences

Use cubes to show each story.
Write the number sentence.
Then write the answer in a sentence.
Word sentences may vary.
Sample answers are shown.

The class rode a bus to the lake.
7 boys and 13 girls were on the bus.

1. How many children rode the bus?

$$\underline{7} \; \oplus \; \underline{13} \; \boxed{=} \; \underline{20}$$

20 children rode the bus.

2. How many more girls than boys were on the bus?

$$\underline{13} \; \ominus \; \underline{7} \; \boxed{=} \; \underline{6}$$

There were 6 more girls than boys.

The children went on a boat ride across the lake. It took 12 minutes to go across and 9 minutes to come back.

3. How many more minutes did it take to go than to come back?

$$\underline{12} \; \ominus \; \underline{9} \; \boxed{=} \; \underline{3}$$

It took 3 more minutes to go across the lake.

Chapter 10   More Practice, page 421, set C   (two hundred nineteen)

TEACHING OPTIONS

RETEACHING TIPS Use triangles of 4 colors and red and blue circles. Have students place a red circle beside each triangle and record each pair. Repeat with the blue circle. Count to make sure there are 8 different combinations. For help with number sentences, assign Reteaching Supplement 92.

ENRICHMENT **Family Math** Have students and a family member draw a dart board. Write 15 in the inner circle, 10 in the middle, and 6 in the outer circle. Have them pretend to throw twice and hit the dartboard both times. Then list all of the total scores they could get. (12, 16, 21, 20, 25, 30)

roblem Solving Strategy

ake a List

UNDERSTAND
FIND DATA
PLAN
ESTIMATE
SOLVE
CHECK

here are 2 cabs and 4 trailers.

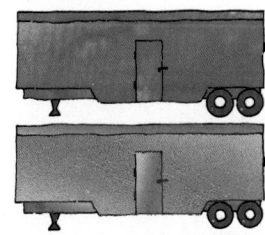
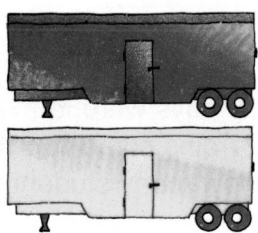

se cubes or slips of colored paper. Find
e 8 ways to hook the cabs and trailers
gether. Color below to show the ways.

Order may vary.

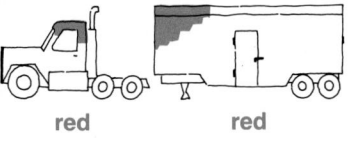

red　　　　red

2.

red　　　　blue

red　　　　green

4.

red　　　　yellow

blue　　　　red

6.

blue　　　　blue

blue　　　　green

8.

blue　　　　yellow

10-7

3. PRACTICE AND APPLY

Basic	All
Average	All
Extended	All

How will you use the cubes or paper slips to help you understand the problem? (Use a red and a blue cube for the cabs; use red, blue, green, and yellow cubes for the trailers.) *What should you do as you find each combination?* (Color to show it.)

▶ **What must you understand about the problem before you plan how to solve it?** (Possible answer: You have to hook one cab with one trailer in as many ways as you can.)

▶ **Describe your plan for solving the problem.** (Possible answer: List each way as you do it.)

▶ **Tell how you can check your list.** (Compare answers with other students; check to make sure all 8 combinations are different.)

CLOSE AND ASSESS

WRITE WHAT YOU KNOW

Display the numbers 2, 3, and 5. Ask students to make up a story problem using the data and write a number sentence to match. Then ask them to choose 2 of the numbers and draw 2 groups of that many different colors. Have them make a list showing all the ways the colors can be combined.

QUICK QUIZ

There are 3 boys named Willie, Marvin, and Ted. There are 2 girls—Nan and Jan. List all the ways to make a pair that has 1 boy and 1 girl each time. (6 combinations)

CHAPTER 10

WRAP UP

INTRODUCTION The Wrap Up provides activities emphasizing math language and thinking skills for the chapter.

USING PAGE 221

Math Words ▶ **How can you tell that this is an addition story?** (Possible answer: The story asks the question *How many?*)

▶ **How can you use cubes to show the story?** (Possible answer: Use the tens strips to show digits in the tens place, ones blocks to show digits in the ones place.)

▶ **Can you make another ten from the ones? Explain.** (Possible answer: No; there are less than 10 ones; there are not enough ones to make another ten.)

▶ **What is a turnaround sentence?** (an addition sentence that has the same addends but in reverse order)

Math Reasoning ▶ **How can you find the numbers that will complete the number sentences so that the sums will be the same?** (Possible answers: Guess and Check; you know the ones digit of the sum is 4, so you can look at the ones digit of each number to find pairs that add to 4.)

Name _____

WRAP UP

MATH WORDS

Work in a group.

38 boys were in the gym.
21 girls came into the gym.
How many students were in the gym?

1. Use cubes to show the story. Write the number sentence.

   <u>38</u> (+) <u>21</u> [=] <u>59</u>

2. Can you make another ten from the ones? Ring **yes** or **no**.

   yes (no

3. Write the turnaround for the number sentence.

   <u>21</u> (+) <u>38</u> [=] <u>59</u>

4. Find a different way to make the same sum. Use cubes to help.

   _____
   Answers may vary.

MATH REASONING

Finish the number sentences so that each has the same sum. Use cubes to help.

5. 34 + <u>10</u> = <u>44</u>

6. 30 + <u>14</u> = <u>44</u>

7. 24 + <u>20</u> = <u>44</u>

8. 22 + <u>22</u> = <u>44</u>

14   20
10   22

y

Chapter 10 Wrap Up

(two hundred twenty-one) 22▶

b

| **TEACHING OPTIONS** |

ENRICHMENT Have students draw a house with several windows and a door. Then ask them to choose a number between 40 and 80. Have students write *House of __* above the door of the house, using their number. Ask them to make as many number pairs as possible that have a sum equal to their number and write the pairs in each window. Display students' work on a bulletin board.

Name _____

CHAPTER REVIEW/TEST

Add.

$43 + 2 = \underline{45}$ $18 + 4 = \underline{22}$ $32 + 3 = \underline{35}$

$10 + 20 = \underline{30}$ $40 + 30 = \underline{70}$ $60 + 30 = \underline{90}$

$42 + 20 = \underline{62}$ $57 + 30 = \underline{87}$ $40 + 23 = \underline{63}$

Use cubes to find how many in all.
Can you make another ten? Ring one.   (yes)   no

17 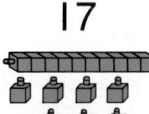   24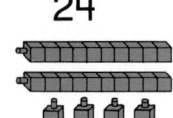

How many in all?

<u>41</u>

Ring the better estimate.

$28¢ + 35¢$

(more than 50¢)
less than 50¢

6. Ring the ways to make 30.

$(15 + 15)$ $(10 + 20)$

$17 + 25$

Write the number sentence. Then
write the answer in a sentence.

There are 14 oak trees and 8 pine
trees in the park. How many trees
are there in the park?

$\underline{14} \; (+) \; \underline{8} \; \boxed{=} \; \underline{22}$

There are 22 trees.

CHAPTER REVIEW/TEST

INTRODUCTION The Review/Test is provided to review and evaluate the skills and concepts presented in Chapter 10.

USING PAGE 222
If you prefer to use this page for review, you may want to use the **Multiple-Choice Posttest** (pages 39-40) or the **Free-Response Posttest** (pages 39-40) to evaluate mastery of chapter objectives.

ITEM ANALYSIS The table below correlates the Chapter Review/Test Items with the lesson objectives.

Items	Objectives
1	10-1
2	10-2
3	10-3
4	10-4
5	10-5
6	10-6
7	10-7

INFORMAL ASSESSMENT

Using Manipulatives Give pairs of students cubes, number cubes, and cards labeled *Yes* or *No*. Students roll number cubes to make two 2-digit numbers and model the numbers with cubes. They estimate whether or not the sum will be greater than 70 and display the *Yes* or *No* card. Then they join the cubes and compare the sum with their estimate.

Communication *Explain the words* make another ten. *How do you make* another ten? How do you know when you can make another ten? (Possible answer: Trade 10 ones for 1 ten. You can make another ten only if you have 10 or more ones.)

Critical Thinking *How do you know that the answer to Problem 7 is found by adding?* (Possible answer: The numbers of oak and pine trees are being combined to find the total number of trees; a total number is found by adding the 2 parts.)

CHAPTER 10

ENRICHMENT

INTRODUCTION   Estimating elapsed time helps students understand time periods such as minutes, hours, days, weeks, and months.

USING PAGE 223
This Enrichment page is provided for all students. You may wish to use it after they have completed the Chapter Review/Test on page 222.

Help students note the elapsed time of different activities they experience during their day.

▶ **Which activity on the page takes the longest amount of time? the shortest amount?** (Sleeping takes the longest amount of time; brushing teeth takes the shortest.)

▶ **Which activity shown may take more or less than the amount of time given?** (Possible answers: Washing the car, sleeping, and eating dinner may take more time; brushing teeth and grocery shopping may take less time.)

EXTENSION   Have students use a sheet of construction paper to make a chart with headings *About 5 Minutes, About 30 Minutes, About 1 Hour, About 8 Hours*. Challenge students to cut out pictures from magazines or draw pictures of their own showing activities that require each elapsed time. Display completed charts in the classroom.

Name _____

ENRICHMENT
Estimating Time

About how long would it take?
Ring the best estimate.

1.

about 10 minutes
(about 1 hour)
about 1 day

2.

(about 5 minutes)
about 2 hours
about 3 days

3.

about 20 minutes
(about 8 hours)
about 1 month

4.

about 5 minutes
(about 1 hour)
about 2 days

5.

(about 30 minutes)
about 3 hours
about 1 day

6.

(about 60 minutes)
about 4 weeks
about 1 week

7.   Talk about the things you can do in 1 hour. Answers may vary

Name _____

CUMULATIVE REVIEW

Finish the number sentences.

1. 23 > ___
   - ○ 24
   - ● 13
   - ○ 33

2. 68 < ___
   - ● 74
   - ○ 53
   - ○ 45

3. Which is the fifth letter?

   A,B,C,D,E,F,G
   - ● E
   - ○ A
   - ○ G

4. What is the time 1 hour later?

   - ○ 8:00
   - ● 10:00
   - ○ 9:30

Give the time.

5.
   - ○ 2:30
   - ○ 3:45
   - ● 3:15

6.
   - ● 12:20
   - ○ 10:30
   - ○ 4:00

7. How many Saturdays are in this month?

S	M	T	W	T	F	S
				1	2	3
4	5	6	7	8	9	10
11	12	13	14	15	16	17
18	19	20	21	22	23	24
25	26	27	28	29	30	

   - ○ 3
   - ● 4
   - ○ 5

8. Count the money.
   - ● 92¢
   - ○ 67¢
   - ○ 97¢

9. It takes Adam 5 minutes to set the table and 11 minutes to walk his dog. How much longer does it take him to walk his dog?
   - ○ 5 minutes
   - ● 6 minutes
   - ○ 16 minutes

Chapter 10 Cumulative Review

CUMULATIVE REVIEW

INTRODUCTION The purpose of this Cumulative Review is to maintain previously taught skills and concepts. The emphasis in this Cumulative Review is on number relationships and counting patterns, Chapter 8; and on time and money, Chapter 9.

ITEM ANALYSIS The table below correlates the Cumulative Review items with the lesson objectives.

Items	Objectives
1,2	8-4
3	8-8
4	9-4
5	9-2
6	9-3
7	9-5
8	9-9
9	9-4

OVERVIEW

Lesson	Pages	Objectives	Subject Integration	Strand Integration
Trading 10 Ones for 1 Ten	225-226	11-1 To trade 10 ones for 1 ten	fine arts: music, bands	estimation
Adding 2-Digit Numbers Using Models	227-228	11-2 To add two 2-digit numbers using models	fine arts: music, drums	critical thinking
Adding 2-Digit Numbers Using Pictures	229-230	11-3 To add two 2-digit numbers using pictures	language arts: verbal expression	place value
Adding 2-Digit Numbers Using Symbols	231-232	11-4 To add two 2-digit numbers using symbols	fine arts: music show	problem solving, data analysis
Estimating Sums	233-234	11-5 To estimate sums using front-end estimation	fine arts: musical instruments	consumer math
Addition Practice	235-236	11-6 To practice adding two 2-digit numbers	social studies: group skills	mental math
Problem Solving: Understanding the Operations/Calculator	237-238	11-7 To use addition and subtraction; to use a calculator to find sums	fine arts: musical instruments	measurement: weight
Problem Solving: Choosing a Calculation Method	239-240	11-8 to choose an appropriate method of calculation	fine arts: music	mental math calculator
Column Addition	241-242	11-9 To add three 2-digit numbers	social studies: radio	place value
Problem Solving: Using Estimation/Problem Solving Strategy: Guess and Check	243-244	11-10 To use estimation; to use the strategy Guess and Check	fine arts: music, bands	consumer math

MATHEMATICAL BACKGROUND

Adding 2-Digit Numbers

The algorithm for adding 2-digit numbers has two steps: Add the ones, then add the tens. When adding ones, students learn to decide whether or not a trade is needed. If the sum of the ones digits is a 2-digit number, then a trade is needed. Students learn to make trades using place value models and related pictures. Manipulating place value models helps students understand the meaning behind the process of adding larger numbers.

Estimation

Lesson 11-5 teaches front-end estimation. In making estimates using front-end numbers, it is assumed that all the addends have the same number of digits (to the tens place). The student then simply adds the front-end, or tens, digits to get the estimate. The estimate can be adjusted, if necessary, by using the numbers in the ones digits of the addends, but students are not asked to do so at this level.

Problem Solving

In this chapter, students solve problems using estimation and by using the strategy Guess and Check.

TIPS FROM TEACHERS

Have students make a Problem of the Day booklet. At the beginning of math class, have students solve 1 sample problem on that day's topic. Set a time limit. Then use the overhead projector to correct the problem as a group.

Nancy Rohrbaugh
Hidden Valley Junior High School
Roanoke, VA

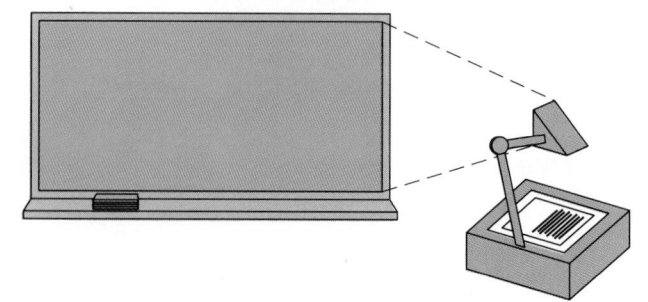

ASSESSMENT

Pretest — Chapter 11, page 1
Multiple-Choice Format

Name _____

1. Think about adding 6 blocks and 5 blocks. Can you trade 10 ones for 1 ten?

6
+5

(A) yes
B no

2. Add. Use the picture or real blocks. Choose the sum.

Tens	Ones
2	5
+1	3

A 33
(B) 38
C 48

3. Look at the picture. Ring and cross out 10 ones to trade if you can. Draw a new ten. Choose the sum.

Tens	Ones
2	5
+1	9

A 64
(B) 44
C 54

4. Add.
55
+37

(A) 92
B 82
C 22

5. Add.
38
+43

A 16
(B) 81
C 71

MCT 2   41

Pretest — Chapter 11, page 2
Multiple-Choice Format

Name _____

6. Estimate.
$21
+$22

A about $60
B about $80
(C) about $40

7. Add.
76
+15

A 61
B 81
(C) 91

8. Guess and check. Which number makes this big double?

□□
+□□
6 6

A 11
B 22
(C) 33

9. Which would you use to solve the problem?

Joy had 2 presents. She got 3 more. How many did she have then?

(A) mental math
B calculator
C paper and pencil

10. Add.
48
16
+23

A 77
(B) 87
C 85

11. Choose the best estimate. Jennifer bought a blouse for $21, a skirt for $24, and a hat for $10. About how much money did she spend?

A about $70
B about $30
(C) about $50

42   MCT 2

Posttest — Chapter 11, page 1
Multiple-Choice Format

Name _____

1. Think about adding 7 blocks and 6 blocks. Can you trade 10 ones for 1 ten?

7
+6

(A) yes
B no

2. Add. Use the picture or real blocks. Choose the sum.

Tens	Ones
2	3
+1	5

A 33
(B) 38
C 48

3. Look at the picture. Ring and cross out 10 ones to trade if you can. Draw a new ten. Choose the sum.

Tens	Ones
2	5
+2	7

A 62
B 42
(C) 52

4. Add.
33
+49

A 92
(B) 82
C 72

5. Add.
37
+45

A 28
(B) 82
C 52

MCT 2   43

Posttest — Chapter 11, page 2
Multiple-Choice Format

Name _____

6. Estimate.
$31
+$22

A about $70
(B) about $50
C about $30

7. Add.
65
+18

A 53
B 73
(C) 83

8. Guess and check. Which number makes this big double?

□□
+□□
4 4

A 11
(B) 22
C 33

9. Which would you use to solve the problem?

Dan had 5 presents. He received 3 more. How many did he have then?

(A) mental math
B calculator
C paper and pencil

10. Add.
37
24
+26

A 77
(B) 87
C 85

11. Choose the best estimate. David bought a pair of jeans for $21, a shirt for $12, and a hat for $10. About how much money did he spend?

(A) about $40
B about $20
C about $60

44   MCT 2

ITEM ANALYSIS

Items	Objectives
1	11-1
2	11-2
3	11-3
4, 5	11-4
6	11-5
7	11-6
8	11-7
9	11-8
10	11-9
11	11-10

Note: The item analysis is the same for all pretests and posttests for this chapter.

ALSO AVAILABLE

► Free Response Tests
► Alternative Tests
► Thinking Strategies
► Concrete Materials

Optional Chapter Activities

PROJECT AND BULLETIN BOARD

Use calculators to practice addition of 2-digit numbers. Display a large model of the students' calculator on the bulletin board and label all the keys. Below the calculator, display an estimating chart similar to the one shown. Instruct students to write two 2-digit numbers on index cards and attach them to the chart. Assist students in writing the decade numbers that are less than and greater than each 2-digit number. Then have them add the pairs of tens. Explain that the sum of the 2-digit numbers will fall between the lowest and the highest tens shown. Have pairs of students use their calculators to find the sum of the 2-digit numbers and decide whether the sum does fall between the 2 sets of tens. In sessions that follow, have students follow the same procedure for adding other 2-digit numbers.

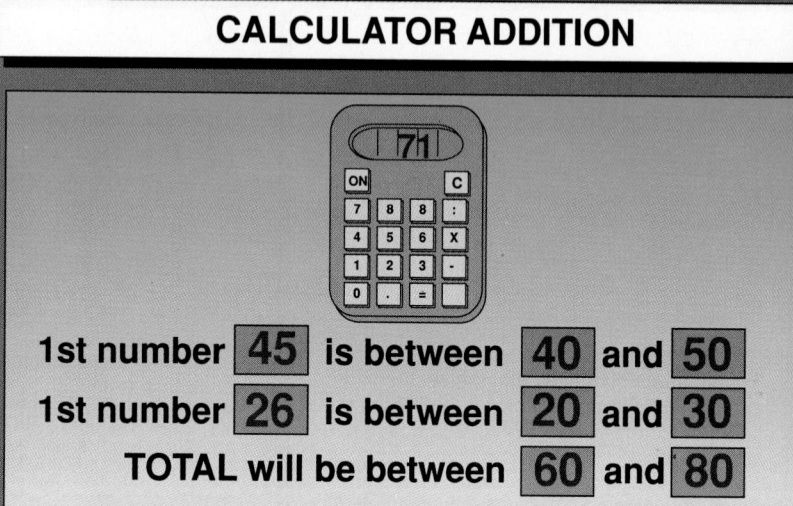

CALCULATOR ADDITION

1st number 45 is between 40 and 50
1st number 26 is between 20 and 30
TOTAL will be between 60 and 80

COOPERATIVE LEARNING

Divide the class into cooperative learning groups of 4-6. Identify the group skill: taking turns. Provide each group with dried beans and 2 small containers. Each group will estimate and record how many beans it thinks each container will hold. Have the groups divide the following tasks among themselves: fill the containers with beans; group the beans in each container by tens and ones; add, trading 10 ones for 1 ten if necessary; record; and compare the estimates to the actual amount of beans in each container and to the total. Repeat the activity using different containers. Encourage students to take turns performing each suggested task.

You will find grouping suggestions and cooperative learning activities in most lessons throughout this chapter.

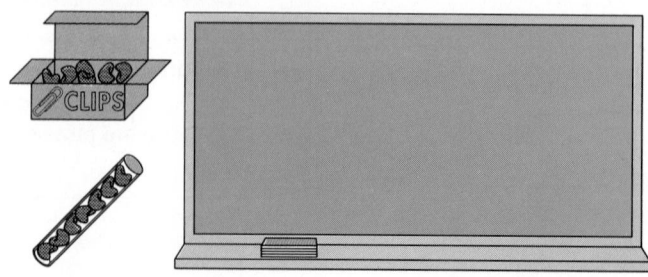

LITERATURE

Anno, Mitsumasa. *Anno's Counting House.* New York: Philomel Books, 1982.

This innovative book lends itself to the study of sets. Ten small people move from one house to another with all their belongings.
Have students use base-ten blocks to represent the people and objects in the story, then add 2-digit numbers.

Mahy, Margaret. *17 Kings and 42 Elephants.* New York: Dial, 1987.

Scott, Louise, and Jesse Thompson. *Rhymes for Fingers and Flannelboards.* New York: McGraw-Hill, 1960.

ENGLISH AS A SECOND LANGUAGE

Help ESL students become familiar with the musical vocabulary necessary for the classification exercise. Assign each student an instrument and have each help the others pronounce the name and show how each instrument is played. Because this chapter focuses on strategies used in addition and problem solving, set up the activities so that students can talk aloud as they think and describe which strategy they have chosen and why. This type of self-reporting will make them aware of their own processing strategies. Take a class survey to see how many students used each strategy, emphasizing the variety of strategies that are available to them. Encourage students to follow the same procedure in small groups, where other students or teachers can help ESL students with language.

Since many of the problems use irregular verb forms and questions in the past tense, give students time to write these verbs on flashcards for future reference.

GIFTED

Mathematically talented students may already understand how to add when trading is necessary. They will nevertheless likely be interested in many of the strategies presented in this chapter. Challenge these students to make a money calendar for the month. Begin by providing students with a calendar. Have them record the money they spend each day, noting the items or food products purchased. (You may wish to have them include lunch or milk money spent in the school cafeteria.) After Lesson 5 on estimating sums and Lesson 9 on column addition, ask students to estimate and solve to find daily totals, 3-day and 4-day totals, weekly totals, and finally a monthly total for expenses. Provide punchout coins and bills for students to work with, if necessary, and allow them to check their totals with a calculator. Encourage students who are gifted writers to make up story problems based on their experiences throughout the month and share them with the class.

STUDENTS AT RISK

Learning-disabled students may need guidance in making a transition from experiences with manipulatives to their pictorial representations and then to their written form. When they begin using manipulatives to show place value, the tens are 10 times as long or 10 times as many as the ones. The next stage introduces a tens counter, which is worth 10 by virtue of its difference in color or shape—for example, using red counters as tens and white counters as ones. When students are able to adjust to this abstraction, the relative values of coins will begin to make sense because a dime is worth 10 times more than a penny without being 10 times larger.

Have students repeat the Trading game (see page 207D) using this more advanced version of place value manipulatives. Have them continue to record their individual transactions as they play the game.

When written exchanges are introduced, it is important to allow students continued access to manipulatives. This helps them confirm that the *new* method yields the same results as the manipulatives.

You may also use the Reteaching Supplements and the specific Reteaching Tips from each lesson in this chapter.

Storybook

PICTURE

These pictures and accompanying stories and poems are available as storybooks.

You may want to read and discuss this story with your students before starting the chapter. The first lesson in this chapter includes a question about the story. Lessons 1, 2, 4, 5, and 9 in this chapter have questions in the informal Assessment that refer to the story.

The Button Shakers

The three little robins read the notice in the newspaper for the second time.

WANTED: Bands for tomorrow's Music Day Parade!

"Oh, that sounds like fun," said Robbie Robin. "We can learn how to play musical instruments and start our own band." Robbie was the oldest of the three robins. She was the one who usually thought up new things for the three robins to do.

"Can I learn how to play the piano for our band?" asked Tootie, who was the youngest in the group.

"Oh Tootie, you know that a piano would be too heavy to carry in the parade," said Robbie. "We will have to think of something that is easy to play and light enough to carry."

"And that won't cost us any money," said Tootie, holding out his empty pockets. "We've already spent our allowances this week."

The three robins thought and thought. And then they thought some more. It was a button popping off Whistle's vest that broke the silence. It made a pleasant sound as it hit an empty jar on the table. "I know! I know! We could make some button shakers and play them in the parade!" said Whistle.

The other two birds thought that was a wonderful idea. They decided to use 10 buttons for each button shaker. They would need 30 buttons in all. "We can find buttons on the playground," said Robbie.

So the three birds flew off to the playground in search of buttons. One hour later, they met back at the house.

They carefully counted their buttons. Whistle announced that he had found 13 red buttons. "That's enough for one button shaker," he said.

Robbie had found 17 blue buttons, and said, "I have enough for one button shaker, too. How many do you have, Tootie?"

And that's when Tootie started to cry. "I thought that we were going to the playground to play. I don't have any buttons. Now I can't be in our band."

But Robbie said, "That's OK, Tootie. We'll think of a way to get a button shaker for you."

And then Whistle carefully counted out 10 of his red buttons. He put them in an empty jar and screwed the lid on tightly. Just to check, he shook the jar, buttons and all. What a lovely sound it would make for the parade!

And then Robbie carefully counted out 10 blue buttons. She put them into another empty jar and screwed the lid on tightly.

When Tootie heard the sounds that Whistle and Robbie made with their button shakers, he started to cry again. But just then, he looked at the table and started jumping up and down with excitement. "Look, look," he shouted, pointing to the table. There were three red buttons and seven blue buttons, enough for a button shaker.

And so Robbie, Whistle, and even Tootie played their button shakers in the Music Day Parade.

LESSON OPTIONS 11-1

Trading 10 Ones for 1 Ten

OBJECTIVE 11-1   To trade 10 ones for 1 ten

PREBOOK ACTIVITIES

QUICK REVIEW

Copy and add.

5	6	3	4	8	9	7	2	5	6	7
+5	+7	+9	+7	+5	+8	+5	+9	+7	+9	+4
10	13	12	11	13	17	12	11	12	15	11

PRIOR KNOWLEDGE

Ask students to imagine that they are filling a sticker book. Explain that each page has room for 10 stickers. Ask students to tell for each situation whether there will be enough stickers to fill a page.

You have 7 stickers. Your sister gives you 3 more. (yes)
You have 4 stickers. Your mother buys you 5 more. (no)
You have 5 stickers. You buy 7 more. (yes)
You have 6 stickers. Your brother gives you 4 more. (yes)

COMMUNICATION

Reading and Discussing Math   Write the word **trade** on the chalkboard. Read the word aloud and explain that to trade means "to give something away and get something back that has the same value." Then write *Sharma traded 10 pennies for 1 dime. Did Sharma make a fair trade?* (yes) *Why do you think so?* (Because 10 pennies equal 10¢; 1 dime also equals 10¢.) *Suppose you had 10 ones. Could you trade them for 1 ten?* (yes) *Why?* (because 10 ones has the same value as 1 ten)

EXPLORE AND CONNECT

Materials: 2-color counters, yarn rings, punchout number cards 4-9
Grouping Suggestion: pairs
Provide each pair with 20 two-color counters and number cards. Each student chooses a number card and models the number with counters. One student uses the red side of the counters while the other student uses the yellow side. Have students combine their counters. *Do you have enough counters to make 1 group of ten? If so, put a yarn ring around them. How many counters, if any, will be left?* Ask students to write an addition sentence showing what they did and to write the number of tens and ones in the sum. If time permits, have students repeat the activity.

CONNECTIONS   Use these anytime.

Problem of the Day

Draw a Picture   Amanda is making a bead necklace. She is using blue beads and pink beads, starting with blue. She changes the color every 10 beads. So far, she has 16 beads on her necklace. If Amanda adds 10 more beads, what colors will she use? (4 pink beads, then 6 blue beads)

Number Sense

Estimation   Take a handful of pennies. Estimate the number of dimes you could trade for the pennies. Then count the pennies and trade 10 pennies for 1 dime when you can. Compare the number of dimes to your estimate. Try the activity again.

Math Connection

Even Trade Game   You will need 19 ones blocks, 5 tens blocks, a place value chart, and a number cube. Roll the number cube and place that number of ones on the place value chart. Repeat. Count the ones after each roll. When you have 10 or more, trade 10 ones for 1 ten and place it on the tens side of the mat. Play until you reach 5 tens.

CLASSWORK AND HOMEWORK SUPPLEMENTS

Practice

Skills Maintenance 11-1

Name _____

Trading 10 Ones for 1 Ten

Add to find the sum. If you need to trade, color a box in the Trading tower **blue**. If you do not trade, color a box in the No Trading tower **red**.

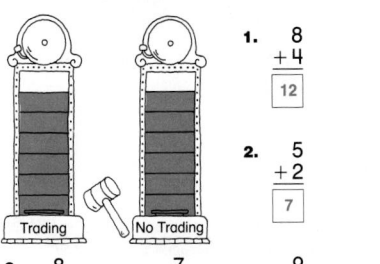

Trading   No Trading

| 1. | 8 +4 = 12 | 7 +2 = 9 |

| 2. | 5 +2 = 7 | 6 +6 = 12 |

| 3. | 8 +1 = 9 | 7 +7 = 14 | 9 +4 = 13 | 3 +3 = 6 |

| 4. | 4 +7 = 11 | 2 +6 = 8 | 8 +8 = 16 | 6 +1 = 7 |

PS-2   Use with text pages 225–226.   93

Reteaching

Skills Review 11-1

Name _____

Trading 10 Ones for 1 Ten

Pick 2 apples. Find the sum. Trade 10 ones for 1 ten when you can. Write the number.

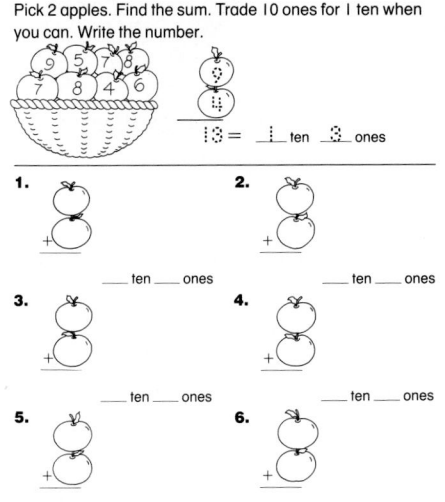

13 = __1__ ten __3__ ones

1.	___ ten ___ ones	2.	___ ten ___ ones
3.	___ ten ___ ones	4.	___ ten ___ ones
5.	___ ten ___ ones	6.	___ ten ___ ones

RS-2   Use with text pages 225–226.   93

Building Thinking Skills

Mental Math 11-1

Name _____

Sports Club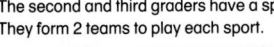

The second and third graders have a sports club. They form 2 teams to play each sport.

Sports Club	Monday	Tuesday	Wednesday	Thursday	Friday
Grade 2 members	10	5	8	13	10
Grade 3 members	12	6	10	10	14

1 baseball team = 9 players   1 basketball team = 5 players
1 soccer team = 11 players

Use the chart to answer the questions.

1. On what days can the club play basketball?
   Monday, Tuesday, Wednesday, Thursday, Friday

2. On what days can they play baseball?
   Monday, Wednesday, Thursday, Friday

3. On what days can they play soccer?
   Monday, Thursday, Friday

4. On what day do they have the right number of players
   for exactly 2 soccer teams? _____ Monday

5. On what day do they have enough players for
   exactly 2 baseball teams? _____ Wednesday

TS-2   Use with text pages 225–226.   93

Challenges

Estimation 11-1

Name _____

Estimate the Sums

Add the ones.
Think about whether you can trade 10 ones for 1 ten.
Ring the better estimate for the sum.
Use blocks to check.

1.	15 +3	15 +6	14 +7
	more than 20 / (less than 20)	(more than 20) / less than 20	(more than 20) / less than 20

2.	16 +8	17 +2	13 +9
	(more than 20) / less than 20	more than 20 / (less than 20)	(more than 20) / less than 20

3.	28 +4	25 +4	26 +7
	(more than 30) / less than 30	more than 30 / (less than 30)	(more than 30) / less than 30

CS-2   Use with text pages 225–226.   93

OPTIONS FOR INDIVIDUAL NEEDS

Basic

Exercises All

Supplements
Reteaching 93 or
Practice 93

Average

Exercises All

Supplements
Practice 93
Challenges 93 or
Thinking Skills 93

Extended

Exercises All

Supplements
Challenges 93
Thinking Skills 93

Other Resources:
Explorations, pp. 122-123, 132, 271
Workjobs II, pp. 116-117
Developing Number Concepts With Unifix Cubes, pp. 148-152

11-1

OBJECTIVE 11-1
To trade 10 ones for 1 ten

Materials: Cube-A-Links, base-ten blocks, punchout dimes and pennies

Grouping Suggestions: pairs

1. MOTIVATE AND TEACH

LEARN ABOUT IT

Read the chapter story to the class. Ask students to explain why there were enough buttons to make a third button shaker. (3 blue buttons combined with 7 red buttons made a total of 10 buttons.) Have students work in pairs. Give each one 9 cubes. Tell each student to place some or all of their cubes in either the blue triangle or the yellow triangle on page 225. Students then add the cubes together by placing them on the bells of the wrist bell.

▶ **How many bells are on the wrist bell?** (10)
▶ **Estimate whether or not there are enough cubes to make a wrist bell.** (Answers will vary.)
▶ **How can you tell, without adding, if there are enough to make a wrist bell?** (You will see, or mentally add, 10 or more cubes.)
▶ **Add. Are there enough to make a wrist bell? How many left over?** (Answers will vary.)
Repeat several times. Encourage students to add mentally and to predict whether they can make a wrist bell.

2. CHECK UNDERSTANDING

ERROR ALERT Counting cubes incorrectly when adding to 10.

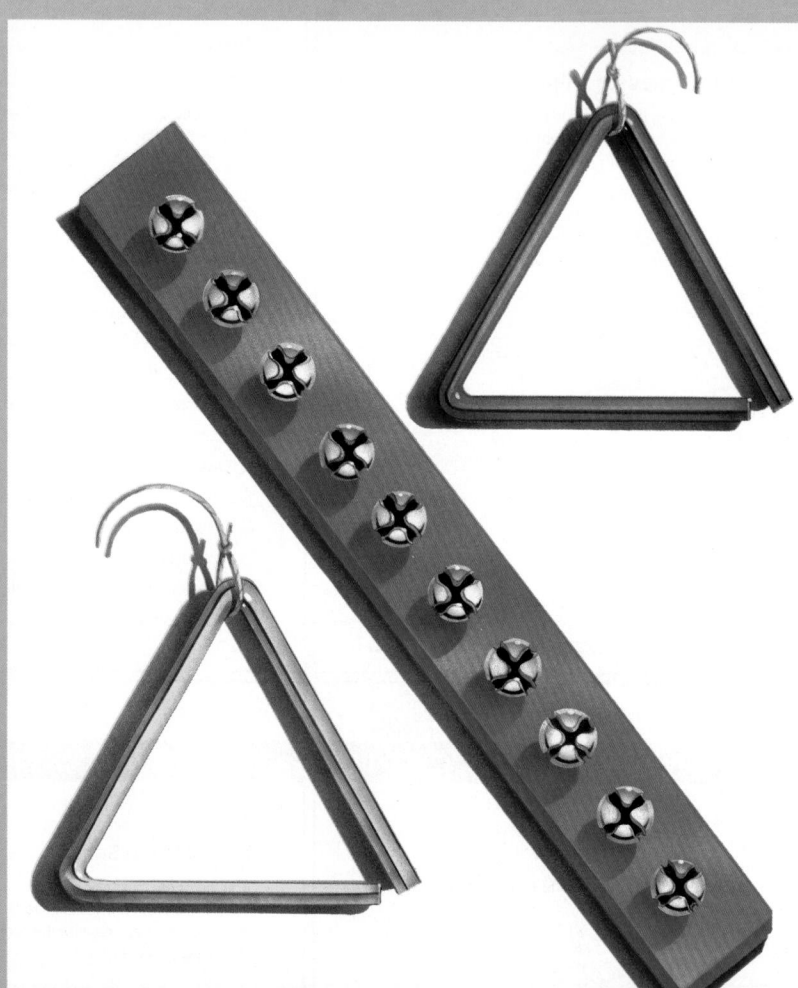

11
Adding 2-Digit Numbers

TEACHING OPTIONS

RETEACHING TIPS Have each student in a pair choose a number between 1 and 9 and model the number by lining up ones blocks beside the tens-stick. Ask them to tell whether or not their combined blocks are enough to make a ten. Repeat several times. Assign Reteaching Supplement 93.

ENRICHMENT Have students work in groups of 3. One student makes a collection of pennies up to 50¢. A second makes a collection of dimes and pennies equal in value to the group of pennies. The third checks to see that the two groups are equal. Repeat, taking turns in each role.

rading 10 Ones for 1 Ten

6 + 7

se blocks to add. Can you trade
) ones for I ten? Ring **yes** or **no**.
'rite the number of tens and ones.

6 + 7   (yes)   no   tens __I__ ones __3__

4 + 8   (yes)   no   tens __1__ ones __2__

9 + 6   (yes)   no   tens __1__ ones __5__

dd. Can you trade 10 ones for I ten?
ng **yes** or **no**. If **yes,** ring 10 ones to show
e trade. Write the number of tens and ones.

7
+5   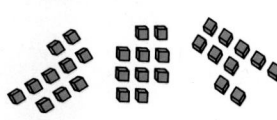   (yes)   no   tens __1__
                                                  ones __2__

4
+5   yes   (no)   tens __0__
                                                   ones __9__

AKE AN ESTIMATE

About how many tens do you think
you could trade for these ones?
Do not count. Ring the best answer.

about 3 tens   (about 6 tens)   about 8 tens

6   (two hundred twenty-six)   Chapter 11

Basic	All
Average	All
Extended	All

11-1

PRACTICE

*How will you know if you can trade 10
ones for 1 ten?* (Possible answer: You
will count 10 or more ones.) *How many
tens will you record if you cannot trade
10 ones for 1 ten? Why?* (0; to show no
tens)

APPLY

MAKE AN ESTIMATE ► **How can
you estimate the number of tens?**
(Possible answer: Look for groups that
might have about 10 cubes.)
► **How can you use the choices to
help you find the answer?** (Possible
answer: Ignore the estimates that are too
low or too high; use the closest
estimate.)
► **How can you check your estimate?**
(Count and ring tens.)
► **How can you use this skill in
everyday life?** (Possible answer: You
can estimate the number of pennies in a
wallet or purse.)

LOSE AND ASSESS

·IOW WHAT YOU KNOW

·ad the chapter story, *The Button
akers,* to students. Have them look
the story picture to find the number
buttons that Whistle and Robbie
llected. *Use counters to show how
ɪny buttons Whistle and Robbie will
·ve left over after they make their
·tton shakers.* (3, 7)

QUICK QUIZ

Add. Can you trade 10 ones for 1 ten?
Write the number of tens and ones.
6 + 8   (yes; 1 ten, 4 ones)
3 + 6   (no; 0 tens, 9 ones)
7 + 4   (yes; 1 ten, 1 one)

Adding 2-Digit Numbers Using Models

OBJECTIVE 11-2 To add two 2-digit numbers using models

PREBOOK ACTIVITIES

QUICK REVIEW

Make a tens and a ones group. As I say a number, the tens group will hold up number cards showing the number of tens and the ones group holds up number cards showing the number of ones.

36	(3 tens and 6 ones)	70	(7 tens and 0 ones)
17	(1 ten and 7 ones)	51	(5 tens and 1 one)
43	(4 tens and 3 ones)	92	(9 tens and 2 ones)

PRIOR KNOWLEDGE

Give the following example to help students recall making another ten.

Quinn can fit 10 packs of colored paper in a carton.
He has 6 packs in one pile and 7 packs in another.
Does he have enough to fill a carton? (yes)
How many extra packs of paper will he have left? (3)
Repeat the question using the following number pairs:
4 + 3 (not enough to fill a carton)
5 + 5 (enough to fill a carton, no extra packs left)
7 + 9 (enough to fill a carton, 6 extra packs left)

COMMUNICATION

Reading and Writing Math Write the following on the chalkboard. Have students write the sentences in order in their Math Journals to show the steps for adding 2-digit numbers.
1. Add the tens.
2. Write the addition sentence.
3. Make another ten if you can.
4. Read the answer.
5. Add the ones.
6. Read the numbers. (6, 2, 5, 3, 1, 4)

EXPLORE AND CONNECT

Materials: TA4 (Addition/Subtraction Mat), Cube-A-Links
Grouping Suggestion: pairs
Provide each pair with an addition mat and cubes. Have one student place 25 cubes in one section of the mat, while the other student places 19 in the other section. Write 25 + 19 vertically on the chalkboard and ask students to combine the ones. *Are there enough ones to make another ten?* (yes) *Make another ten and write the new ten above the other tens. How many ones are left?* (4) *What should you do next?* (Add the tens.) *How many tens in all?* (4) *How did you find your answer?* (added 2 + 1 plus the ten made from the ones) Repeat the activity for the following addends, having partners take turns modeling and adding. 37 + 16 (53); 9 + 54 (63); 24 + 43 (67); 29 + 7 (36); 15 + 41 (56). Remind students that they do not always need to make another ten.

CONNECTIONS   Use these anytime.

Problem of the Day

Estimation Jennifer has 33 stamps on one page of her book and 21 stamps on another page. Does she have more than 50 stamps? (yes) How did you find your answer? (Possible answers: added the tens; estimated each number and added them)

Money Tony has one quarter, one dime, one nickel, and one penny. Does he have enough money to buy a yo-yo for 47¢? (no; 25 + 10 + 5 + 1 = 41¢)

Math Connection

Higher-Level Thinking Use base-ten blocks to help you solve Hedda's problem: Hedda has 27 blocks. What is the smallest number of blocks she can borrow in order to make another ten? (3) What is the largest number of blocks she can get in order to keep all the ones she has without having to make another ten? (2)

CLASSWORK AND HOMEWORK SUPPLEMENTS

Practice

Skills Maintenance 11-2

Name _____

Adding 2-Digit Numbers Using Models

Add the ones. Use blocks to help you.
Can you trade? Ring yes or no.
Add the tens.

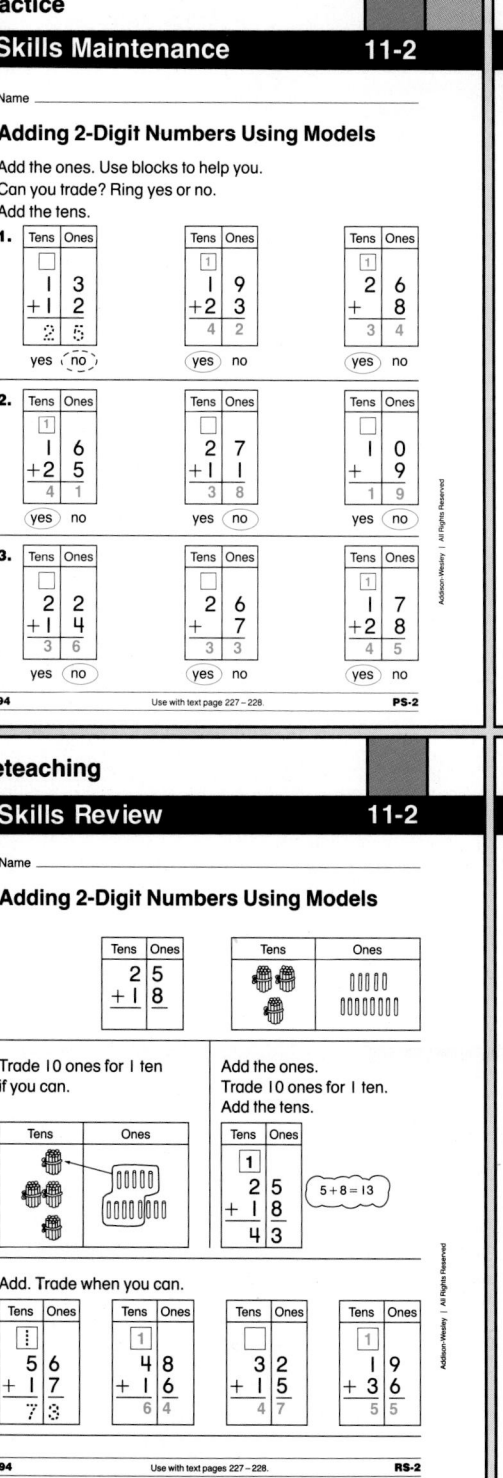

94   Use with text 227–228.   PS-2

Building Thinking Skills

Critical Thinking 11-2

Name _____

Using an Abacus to Add

This is an abacus.
The beads slide up and down.
To add on the abacus, slide a bead toward the middle bar.

Look at each abacus. Write the number. Find the sum.
Then draw beads to show the sum on the last abacus.

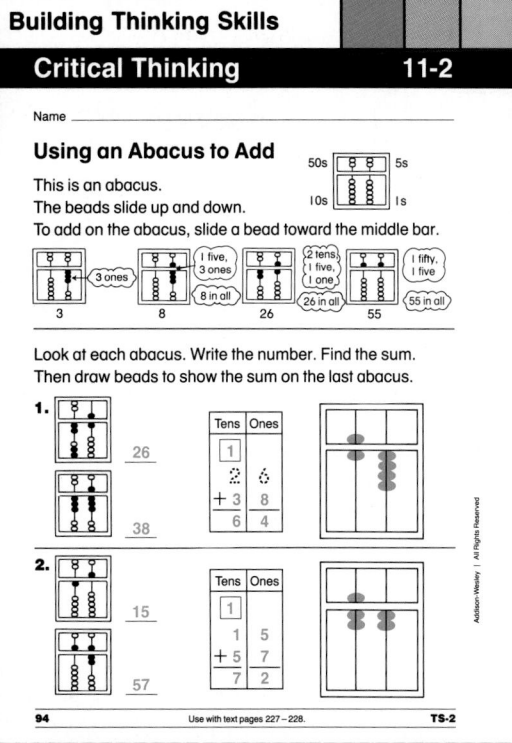

94   Use with text pages 227–228.   TS-2

Reteaching

Skills Review 11-2

Name _____

Adding 2-Digit Numbers Using Models

Tens	Ones
2	5
+1	8

Trade 10 ones for 1 ten if you can.

Add the ones.
Trade 10 ones for 1 ten.
Add the tens.

$5 + 8 = 13$

Add. Trade when you can.

94   Use with text pages 227–228.   RS-2

Challenges

Cooperative Activities 11-2

Name _____

Clothespins and Toothpicks

You need: 1 or more friends, 18 clothespins, and 18 toothpicks.
Rules: Use the clothespins to make tens.
Use the toothpicks to make ones.
Make up an addition problem.

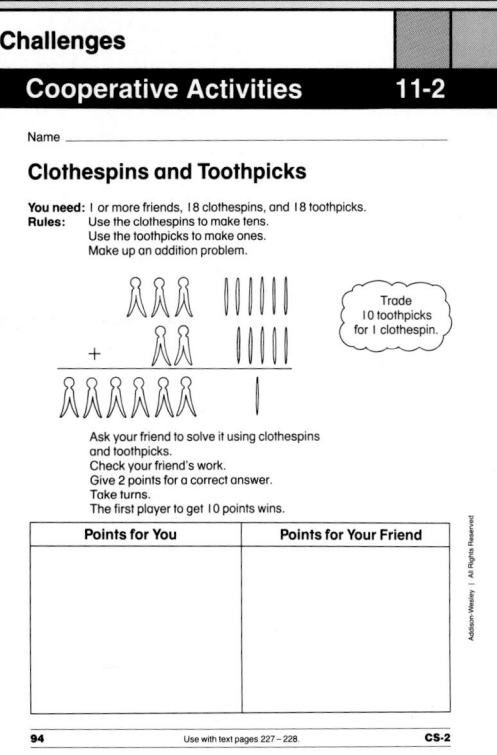

Trade 10 toothpicks for 1 clothespin.

Ask your friend to solve it using clothespins and toothpicks.
Check your friend's work.
Give 2 points for a correct answer.
Take turns.
The first player to get 10 points wins.

Points for You	Points for Your Friend

94   Use with text pages 227–228.   CS-2

Basic

Exercises All
Calculator Bank, p. 402

Supplements
Reteaching 94 or
Practice 94
Thinking Skills 94

Average

Exercises All
Calculator Bank, p. 402

Supplements
Practice 94
Challenges 94 or
Thinking Skills 94

Extended

Exercises All
Calculator Bank, p. 402

Supplements
Challenges 94
Thinking Skills 94

Other Resources:
Math in Stride, pp. 140-141
Mathematics Their Way, p. 313
Explorations, pp. 276-279, 298
Problem-Solving Experiences In Mathematics, pp. 51, 81, 105, 111, 117, 141, 153, 158
Developing Number Concepts With Unifix Cubes, pp. 162-165

11-2

OBJECTIVE 11-2
To add two 2-digit numbers using models

Materials: overhead projector, base-ten blocks, TA5 (Place Value Chart), 2-color counters

Grouping Suggestions: individual work, cooperative learning groups of 4

1. MOTIVATE AND TEACH

LEARN ABOUT IT

Write 16 + 45 on the chalkboard. Have students use blocks to model the numbers on place value charts. Ask a volunteer to show the answer on an overhead projector. Have students check their work. Have students look at the example at the top of page 227.

▶ **Why are the ones added first?** (Possible answers: They are the smaller digits; to see if another ten can be made.)

▶ **How many ones do you need to make another ten?** (10)

▶ **Will you always write a 1 in the extra tens box? Why or why not?** (No; you only write a 1 in the box if you have made another ten.)

▶ **What number will you write in the ones place if you add ones and make exactly 1 ten?** (0)

▶ **How does writing a 1 above the tens place help you when you have made an extra ten?** (Possible answer: It reminds you to add the extra ten to the other tens.)

2. CHECK UNDERSTANDING

ERROR ALERT Failing to add the extra tens.

Name _____

Adding 2-Digit Numbers Using Models

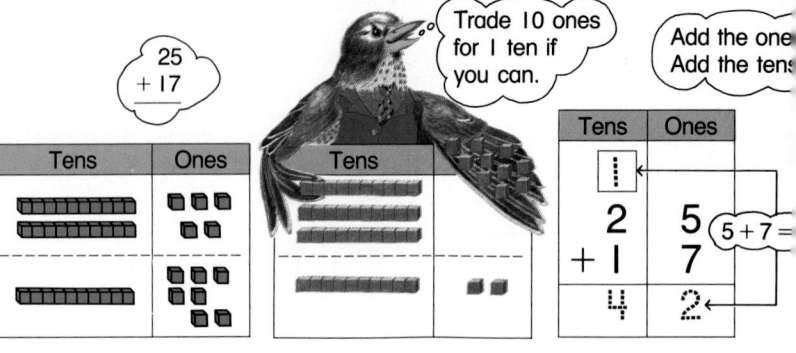

$\begin{array}{r} 25 \\ + 17 \end{array}$

Trade 10 ones for 1 ten if you can.

Add the ones. Add the tens.

Tens	Ones
1	
2	5
+ 1	7
4	2

$5 + 7 =$

Tens	Ones

Find each sum. Use your blocks and the mat above to help.

1.

Tens	Ones
1	
1	4
+ 1	8
3	2

2.

Tens	Ones
☐	
1	3
+ 2	2
3	5

3.

Tens	One
1	
2	5
+	9
3	4

TEACHING OPTIONS

RETEACHING TIPS Have students use 54 two-color counters and a place value chart to model exercises such as 35 + 19. As the ones are added to make another ten, use chalk to write a 1 above the tens place in the example on the board. Assign Reteaching Supplement 94.

ENRICHMENT Have students play *Make Zero Ones*. Roll two number cubes to form a 2-digit number. *What number would you add to your number to reach the next decade number? Give yourself that number of points. Play until you have 10 points.*

se blocks. Answer the questions. Fill in the chart.

1. How many of each block do you need?

   28 __2__ __8__ 🔲

   17 __1__ __7__ 🔲

Tens	Ones
[1]	
2	8
+ 1	7
4	5

2. Add the ones. How many in all? __15__

3. Can you trade? Ring **yes** or **no.** (yes) no

4. Add the tens. How many in all? __4__

5. What is the sum? __45__

6. How many of each block do you need?

   23 __2__ __3__ 🔲

   6 __0__ __6__ 🔲

Tens	Ones
☐	
2	3
+	6
2	9

7. Add the ones. How many in all? __9__

8. Can you trade? Ring **yes** or **no.** yes (no)

9. Add the tens. How many in all? __2__

10. What is the sum? __29__

SE CRITICAL THINKING

. Add each number to 24.
ing those that make a sum
reater than 30.

8 (two hundred twenty-eight)   Chapter 11

---

3. PRACTICE AND APPLY

Basic	All
Average	All
Extended	All

11-2

PRACTICE

Direct students' attention to the exercises on page 228. *How many ones will you need in order to trade for a ten?* (10) *How will you show the new ten that you make?* (Write a 1 in the box above the tens place.)

APPLY

USE CRITICAL THINKING ▶ **How can you find out which numbers will make a sum that is greater than 30?** (Possible answers: Count on from 24; use blocks to show 24 and add blocks until you have more than 30; find what number added to 24 gives a sum of 30 and ring numbers that are greater.)
▶ **How can you tell which numbers will make less than 30?** (Possible answer: Find what number added to 24 gives a sum of 30; ring numbers that are less.)

LOSE AND ASSESS

HOW WHAT YOU KNOW
view with students the chapter
ry, *The Button Shakers*. Have
dents use base-ten blocks to model
e number of buttons that Robbie
und and the number of buttons that
histle found. Ask each student in a
ir to show one of the numbers with
cks and then have pairs combine
cks to find the total. (30)

QUICK QUIZ

Use base-ten blocks to find the sums.

23	45	67	12
+18	+23	+ 8	+66
(41)	(68)	(75)	(78)

Adding 2-Digit Numbers Using Pictures

OBJECTIVE 11-3   To add two 2-digit numbers using pictures

PREBOOK ACTIVITIES

QUICK REVIEW

Add.
$15 + 20 =$ (35) $62 + 20 =$ (82)
$26 + 10 =$ (36) $59 + 40 =$ (99)
$37 + 30 =$ (67) $48 + 40 =$ (88)
$24 + 20 =$ (44) $21 + 50 =$ (71)

PRIOR KNOWLEDGE

Help students recall adding two 2-digit numbers with models. *What numbers do you add first, tens or ones?* (ones) *How do you know if a trade is necessary?* (when there are 10 or more ones) *What happens to the traded ones?* (They make a ten and are added to the other tens.) *What steps would you use to add 45 crayons and 8 crayons?* (**1.** Add the ones. **2.** Trade 10 ones for a ten. **3.** Add the new ten to the other tens.)

COMMUNICATION

Listening and Discussing Math   Read the following sentences and ask students to show thumbs up if the sentence is true and thumbs down if it is false. Then have them explain how they would change the false sentences to make them true.
1. If the number of ones is less than ten, trade to make another ten. (False; the number of ones must be greater than 10.)
2. When you trade 10 ones for 1 ten, a 1 is added to the tens place. (true)
3. Always add the tens first. (False; add the ones first.)
4. If the number of ones is exactly ten, you cannot trade because there would be no number in the ones place. (False; write a zero in the ones place.)

EXPLORE AND CONNECT

Materials: TA 3 (Centimeter Graph Paper), TA 5 (Place Value Chart)
Grouping Suggestion: cooperative learning groups of 3
Provide each group with centimeter graph paper, scissors, paste, crayons, and a place value chart. Have students color and cut tens strips and ones from the graph paper to model two 2-digit numbers under 50. Then have them paste the tens and ones to the place value chart. One student writes the addition exercise on the chalkboard. The second student adds using the model: add ones; cross out a group of ten 10 ones if possible, draw another ten in the tens place; add tens. The third student completes the exercise at the board using the models as a guide. Have students repeat the activity, taking turns in each role.

CONNECTIONS   Use these anytime.

Problem of the Day

Write a Number Sentence   There are 34 first-graders and 47 second-graders singing at the Spring Concert. Write a number sentence to tell how many children are singing in all. Use base-ten blocks to find the answer. ($34 + 47 = 81$)

Counting Patterns

Describe the pattern. Write the next three numbers.
31, 32, 34, 37, 41, (46) , (52) , (59) ($+1, +2, +3, +4, \ldots$)
51, 52, 53, 55, 57, 60, 63, 67, (71) , (76) , (81) ($+1, +1, +2, +2, +3, +3, \ldots$)

Minute Math

Addition   Write only the answers. How many can you do in 1 minute?

7	5	6	9	8	2	4
+5	+6	+7	+2	+1	+3	+5
(12)	(11)	(13)	(11)	(9)	(5)	(9)

6	8	3
+6	+7	+6
(12)	(15)	(9)

CLASSWORK AND HOMEWORK SUPPLEMENTS

Practice

Skills Maintenance 11-3

Name _____

Adding 2-Digit Numbers Using Pictures

Look at the picture.
Ring and cross out 10 ones to trade if you can.
Draw a new ten. Write the sum.

1.
Tens	Ones
2	6
+1	9
4	5

2.
Tens	Ones
1	7
+	8
2	5

3.
Tens	Ones
	7
+4	1
4	8

4.
Tens	Ones
3	4
+1	8
5	2

5.
Tens	Ones
3	6
+1	4
5	0

6.
Tens	Ones
4	2
+2	5
6	7

PS-2   Use with text pages 229–230.   95

Building Thinking Skills

Math Reasoning 11-3

Name _____

Catch the Match

Find a bat and a ball with Xs and Os that add
up to a number on a mitt.
Use 4 colors. Color each set of ball, bat, and
mitt a different color.

Colors will vary.
Sample answers given.

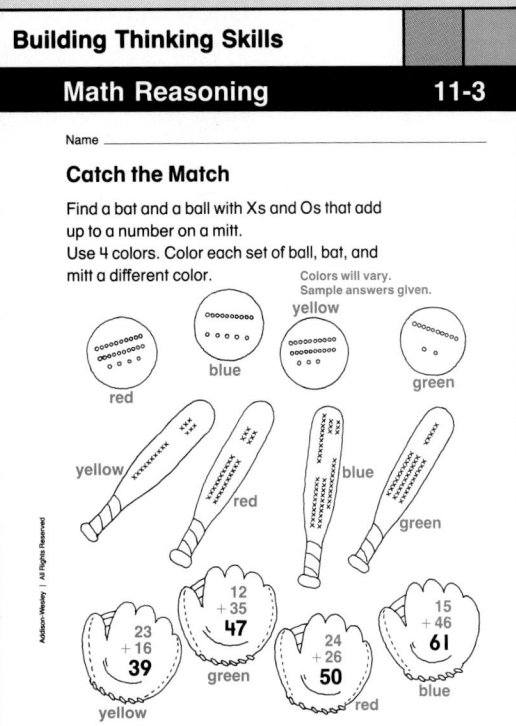

TS-2   Use with text pages 229–230.   95

Reteaching

Skills Review 11-3

Name _____

Adding 2-Digit Numbers Using Pictures

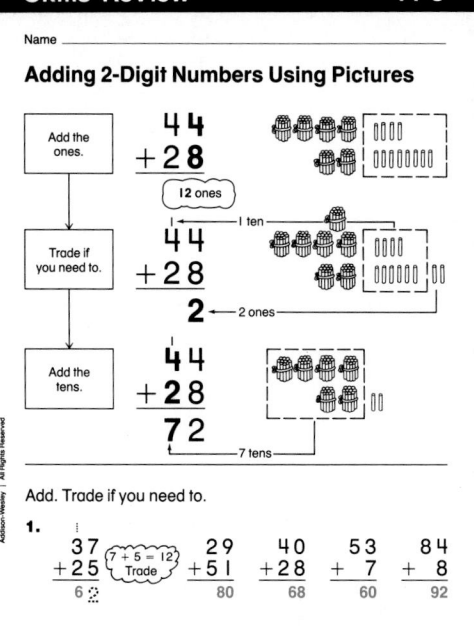

Add the ones.	44 +28
	12 ones
Trade if you need to.	44 +28 — 1 ten — 2 ← 2 ones
Add the tens.	44 +28 72 — 7 tens

Add. Trade if you need to.

1.
$$37 + 25 = 6\!\_ \quad (7+5=12 \text{ Trade})$$
$$29 + 51 = 80$$
$$40 + 28 = 68$$
$$53 + 7 = 60$$
$$84 + 8 = 92$$

RS-2   Use with text pages 229–230.   95

Challenges

Cooperative Activities 11-3

Name _____

Least to Greatest

Work with a friend.
You need a tens spinner labeled 1–4 tens
and a ones number cube labeled 4–9.
Take turns.
Spin the spinner and toss the cube
to make two 2-digit numbers.
Write the numbers in a chart.
Add.
Do this 4 times.

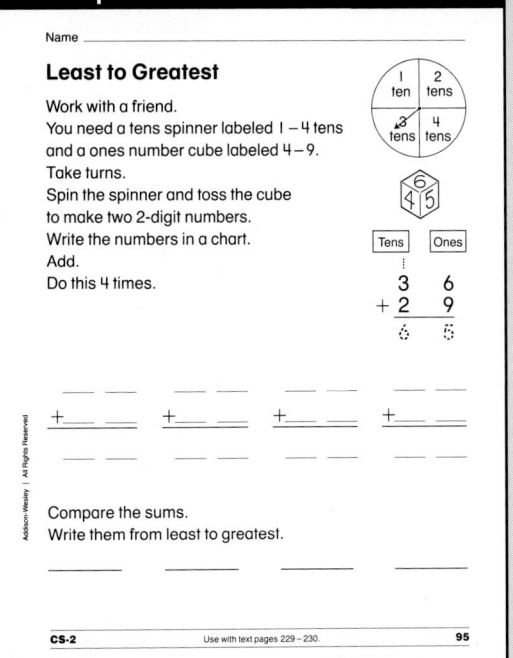

Tens	Ones
3	6
+2	9

___ + ___   ___ + ___   ___ + ___   ___ + ___

Compare the sums.
Write them from least to greatest.

___ ___ ___ ___

CS-2   Use with text pages 229–230.   95

OPTIONS FOR INDIVIDUAL NEEDS

Basic

Exercises All
Calculator Bank, p. 402

Supplements
Reteaching 95 or
Practice 95
Challenges 95

Average

Exercises All
Calculator Bank, p. 402

Supplements
Practice 95
Challenges 95 or
Thinking Skills 95

Extended

Exercises All
Calculator Bank, p. 402

Supplements
Challenges 95
Thinking Skills 95

Other Resources:
Math in Stride, pp. 140-141
Mathematics Their Way, pp. 313, 316
Explorations, pp. 276-279, 298
Developing Number Concepts With Unifix Cubes, pp. 162-165

LESSON PLAN 11-3

OBJECTIVE 11-3
To add two 2-digit numbers using pictures

> **Materials:** TA 5 (Place Value Chart), base-ten blocks, Cube-A-Links, TA 3 (Centimeter Graph Paper)
>
> **Alternative Materials:** counters
>
> **Grouping Suggestions:** individual work, pairs

1. MOTIVATE AND TEACH

LEARN ABOUT IT

Display base-ten blocks to show 27 + 15. Ask a volunteer to write the addition exercise on the chalkboard. Then ask another student to add the ones, trade, and add the tens using the blocks as you complete the addition sentence on the board.

Have students look at the example on page 229. Emphasize that only one exercise is shown on this page, and each picture shows a different step for solving it.

▶ **In Step 1, why is there a box above the tens place?** (It is the place where you write an extra ten when there is a trade.)

▶ **Why are 10 ones circled in Step 2?** (to show that 10 ones are being traded for a ten)

▶ **Why does the arrow point to the tens place?** (A new ten is made from 10 ones; the new ten is added to the other tens.) **What happens to the extra ones?** (They become the ones in the answer.)

▶ **How does the written addition exercise show that another ten has been made?** (A 1 is written in the box above the tens place.)

2. CHECK UNDERSTANDING

ERROR ALERT Writing the sum of the ones in the ones place; not trading for a ten.

Name _____

Adding 2-Digit Numbers Using Pictures

Find the sum of 36 and 18.

1. Show the blocks. Then write the numbers.

What you do.

What you write.

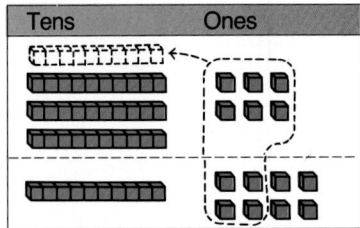

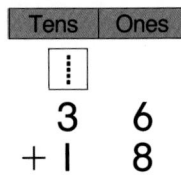

2. Add the ones. Can you trade? (yes) no

3. Add the tens.

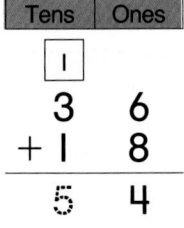

Chapter 11

(two hundred twenty-nine)   2

TEACHING OPTIONS

RETEACHING TIPS Have students use cubes to model 26 + 17 and write the matching addition sentence. Join the ones cubes and move a 10-train to the tens place. *How many ones are left?* (3) *Where did you add the extra ten?* (to the other tens) Assign Reteaching Supplement 95.

ENRICHMENT **Family Math** Have students and family members look through newspapers to find 2 items to purchase with a total price of less than $1. Students draw a picture to show the items, then write an addition sentence and find the sum. Have a family member check their work.

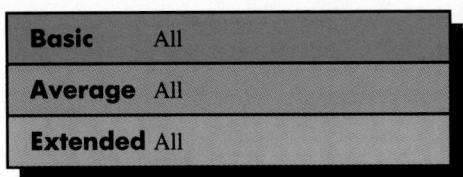

ok at the picture. Ring and cross out
ones to trade if you can. Draw
new ten. Write the sum.

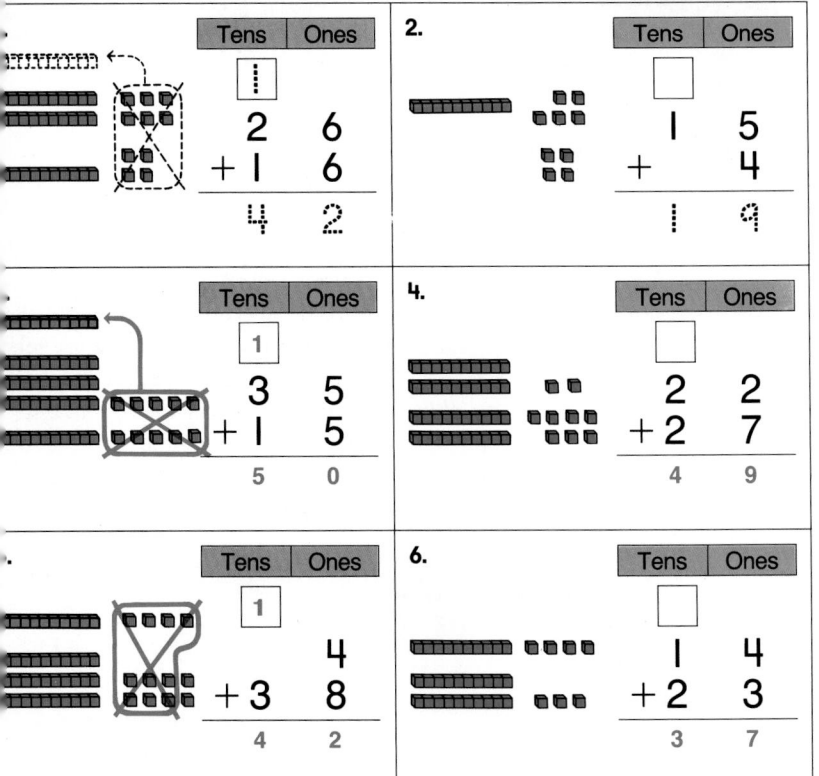

	Tens	Ones
	1	
	2	6
+	1	6
	4	2

2.

	Tens	Ones
	☐	
	1	5
+		4
	1	9

	Tens	Ones
	1	
	3	5
+	1	5
	5	0

4.

	Tens	Ones
	☐	
	2	2
+	2	7
	4	9

	Tens	Ones
	1	
		4
+	3	8
	4	2

6.

	Tens	Ones
	☐	
	1	4
+	2	3
	3	7

ALK ABOUT IT

Tell how adding 9 and
adding 19 are the same.
Tell how they are different.
See teaching notes.

```
  36        36
+  9      +19
  45        55
```

30   (two hundred thirty)   Chapter 11

---

3. PRACTICE AND APPLY

Basic	All
Average	All
Extended	All

PRACTICE

Have students study the picture in
Exercise 1 on page 230. *What should
you do if there are 10 or more ones?*
(Circle a group of ten, cross out the 10
ones to trade, and draw a new ten in the
tens place.)

APPLY

TALK ABOUT IT ► **What is the
same about the numbers 9 and 19?
What is different?** (9 and 19 have the
same digit in the ones place, but 19 has
a 1 in the tens place.)

► **When you add 9 or 19, will the
trading part of the addition process
be the same?** (yes) **Why?** (because the
number of ones is the same)

► **When you add with 19, there is a
one in the tens place. Why do you
need to add another ten?** (The one in
the tens place is part of the number 19;
another ten is needed to show a trade.)

LOSE AND ASSESS

HOW WHAT YOU KNOW

ovide each pair of students with
ntimeter graph paper and base-ten
ocks. Have each student color
uares to show a 2-digit number.
udents use the numbers to form an
ddition exercise. One student uses
ctures or blocks to solve the exercise
the other records the addition on
per.

QUICK QUIZ

Draw pictures. Do you need to trade?
Solve.

```
  35        16        29
+12       +19       +25
(47, no)  (35, yes) (54, yes)
```

Adding 2-Digit Numbers Using Symbols

OBJECTIVE 11-4   To add two 2-digit numbers using symbols

PREBOOK ACTIVITIES

QUICK REVIEW

Tell whether you need to trade ones for a ten in each exercise.

23	38	45	56	74	31	19
+35	+43	+45	+ 9	+18	+46	+ 1
(no)	(yes)	(yes)	(yes)	(yes)	(no)	(yes)

PRIOR KNOWLEDGE

Give students this problem: *Benny has 3 dimes and 4 pennies. He earns 4 dimes and 9 pennies more. He wants to have all his money in dimes and pennies. How many dimes will he have? How can you write the numbers?* (34 + 49) Have students use punchout dimes and pennies. *Which digits will you add first?* (ones) *Can you trade 10 ones for 1 ten?* (yes) *How many dimes will Benny have?* (8) *How many pennies?* (3)

COMMUNICATION

Writing in Math   Have students copy and complete each sentence in their Math Journals using one of the words or phrases in the box below.

trade	ten	tens	line up

1. When you write an addition exercise, you must always __(line up)__ ones with ones and tens with tens.

2. Add the ones first. If there are 10 ones or more, you can __(trade)__ them for a ten.

3. If there are fewer than __(ten)__ ones, you cannot make a trade.

4. You add the __(tens)__ last in an addition exercise.

EXPLORE AND CONNECT

Materials: base-ten blocks
Grouping Suggestion: pairs
Write several vertical addition exercises on the chalkboard, including 2 or 3 that have no trading. Have students use the blocks to model the addends. Then ask them to predict wheth they will have enough ones to trade for a ten in each exercise *How did you know?* (You need to trade when there are 10 on or more.) Have them combine blocks to add, completing the trading when necessary. Then ask them to write the matching addition exercises. *Why must you be sure to line up the ones and tens when you write the exercises?* (Possible answer: so that you can add ones to ones and tens to tens) Encourage students to work cooperatively, taking turns at each task.

CONNECTIONS   Use these anytime.

Problem of the Day

Choose the Operation   There were 36 people in the school band the first year. The second year, 15 more people joined the band. How many people are in the band now?
Write a number sentence and solve it. Use blocks, cubes, or pictures to help.

Counting Patterns

Write the next 3 numbers. Then tell the pattern.
91, 90, 89, __88__, __87__, __86__
(Numbers decrease by 1.)
87, 77, 67, __57__, __47__, __37__
(Numbers decrease by 10.)
Make up your own pattern. Ask a friend to complete it.

Number Sense

Mental Math   Look at the keys on your calculator that have numbers on them. Suppose you wanted to add all these numbers in your head. How could you do it? What is the sum? (find combinations of 10: (9 + 1) + (8 + 2) + (7 + 3) + (6 + 4) + (0 + 5) = 45)

CLASSWORK AND HOMEWORK SUPPLEMENTS

Practice

Skills Maintenance 11-4

Name _____

Adding 2-Digit Numbers Using Symbols

Add. Trade if you need to.

1.
$$\begin{array}{r}1\\28\\+36\\\hline 64\end{array}\quad\begin{array}{r}46\\+21\\\hline 67\end{array}\quad\begin{array}{r}1\\14\\+36\\\hline 50\end{array}\quad\begin{array}{r}42\\+25\\\hline 67\end{array}\quad\begin{array}{r}1\\69\\+22\\\hline 91\end{array}$$

2.
$$\begin{array}{r}8\\+17\\\hline 25\end{array}\quad\begin{array}{r}21\\+38\\\hline 59\end{array}\quad\begin{array}{r}1\\35\\+46\\\hline 81\end{array}\quad\begin{array}{r}27\\+41\\\hline 68\end{array}\quad\begin{array}{r}10\\+17\\\hline 27\end{array}$$

3.
$$\begin{array}{r}1\\16\\+27\\\hline 43\end{array}\quad\begin{array}{r}34\\+25\\\hline 59\end{array}\quad\begin{array}{r}1\\23\\+7\\\hline 30\end{array}\quad\begin{array}{r}1\\16\\+37\\\hline 53\end{array}\quad\begin{array}{r}1\\29\\+29\\\hline 58\end{array}$$

4.
$$\begin{array}{r}1\\31\\+17\\\hline 48\end{array}\quad\begin{array}{r}62\\+24\\\hline 86\end{array}\quad\begin{array}{r}50\\+8\\\hline 58\end{array}\quad\begin{array}{r}1\\16\\+35\\\hline 51\end{array}\quad\begin{array}{r}7\\+40\\\hline 47\end{array}$$

5.
$$\begin{array}{r}43\\+21\\\hline 64\end{array}\quad\begin{array}{r}47\\+8\\\hline 55\end{array}\quad\begin{array}{r}1\\38\\+15\\\hline 53\end{array}\quad\begin{array}{r}20\\+49\\\hline 69\end{array}\quad\begin{array}{r}32\\+16\\\hline 48\end{array}$$

96   Use with text pages 231–232.   **PS-2**

Addison-Wesley | All Rights Reserved

Building Thinking Skills

Mental Math 11-4

Name _____

Math Mountain

Begin at **Start** at the bottom of the page.
Look at the four numbers that lead to each flag.
Decide which two numbers make the sum on the flag.
Ring those numbers. If you traded, color the flag.
Keep going up the mountain until you reach the top.

How many flags did you color? __5__

96   Use with text pages 231–232.   **TS-2**

Addison-Wesley | All Rights Reserved

Reteaching

Skills Review 11-4

Name _____

Adding 2-Digit Numbers Using Symbols

Add the ones.
Trade if you need to.
Add the tens.

$$37+45\quad\begin{array}{r}37\\+45\\\hline 82\end{array}\qquad 24+52\quad\begin{array}{r}24\\+52\\\hline 76\end{array}$$

Copy and add.

1. $$25+16\quad\begin{array}{r}1\\25\\+16\\\hline 41\end{array}$$ 2. $$46+28\quad\begin{array}{r}1\\46\\+28\\\hline 74\end{array}$$

3. $$49+18\quad\begin{array}{r}1\\49\\+18\\\hline 67\end{array}$$ 4. $$54+29\quad\begin{array}{r}1\\54\\+29\\\hline 83\end{array}$$

96   Use with text pages 231–232.   **RS-2**

Addison-Wesley | All Rights Reserved

Challenges

Number Sense 11-4

Name _____

Crossnumber Puzzle Fun

Solve the problems below to fill in the puzzle.

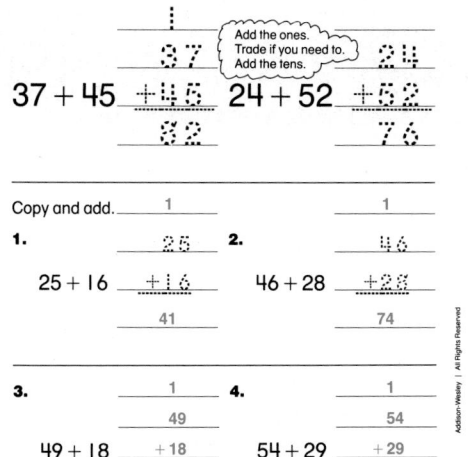

Across		Down	
1. 27 + 25		1. 49 + 7	
3. 9 and 9		2. 6 + 14	
5. 6 tens		3. 7 + 6	
6. 33, 34, 35, □		4. 54 + 32	
7. 18 + 19		7. 29 + 3	
9. 6 ones, 2 tens		8. 75, □, 77	
10. 19 + 28		10. the number after 40	
12. 35 + 27		11. 49 + 26	
14. 6 + 9		12. 4 ones, 6 tens	
15. 5 + 40		13. 5, 10, 15, 20, □	

96   Use with text pages 231–232.   **CS-2**

Addison-Wesley | All Rights Reserved

OPTIONS FOR INDIVIDUAL NEEDS

Basic

Exercises All
Data Bank, p. 399
Calculator Bank, p. 402

Supplements
Reteaching 96 or
Practice 96
Challenges 96

Average

Exercises All
Data Bank, p. 399
Calculator Bank, p. 402

Supplements
Practice 96
Challenges 96 or
Thinking Skills 96

Extended

Exercises All
Data Bank, p. 399
Calculator Bank, p. 402

Supplements
Challenges 96
Thinking Skills 96

Other Resources:
Math in Stride, pp. 140-141
Mathematics Their Way, pp. 313
Explorations, pp. 276-279, 298
Problem-Solving Experiences In Mathematics, pp. 51, 81, 105, 111, 117, 141, 153, 158
Developing Number Concepts With Unifix Cubes, pp. 162-165

11-4

LESSON PLAN 11-4

OBJECTIVE 11-4
To add two 2-digit numbers using symbols

Materials: number cards 0-6, TA4 Addition/Subtraction Mat), TA3 (Centimeter Graph Paper), Cube-A-Links, TA5 (Place Value Chart)

Alternative Materials: base-ten blocks

1. MOTIVATE AND TEACH

LEARN ABOUT IT

Display number cards 0-6 along the chalk ledge. Ask 2 students to make 2-digit numbers. Write an addition exercise on the chalkboard, using the 2 numbers and emphasizing the alignment of the numbers in the ones place. Ask volunteers to help you add the ones, trade if necessary, and add the tens. Have students look at the example at the top of page 231.

► **Why is it important to line up the numbers in the ones and tens places?** (so the ones and tens can be combined with other ones and tens)

► **How will you know if you cannot trade 10 ones for a ten?** (There will be fewer than 10 ones when you add the ones.)

► **How will you line up the numbers in an addition exercise when one of the numbers has only one digit?** (Line up the ones.)

2. CHECK UNDERSTANDING

ERROR ALERT Lining up the ones in a single digit number with the tens when writing addition exercises.

Name _____

Adding 2-Digit Numbers Using Symbols

I sold 28 tickets.

I sold 47 tickets.

How many tickets in all did Nancy and Mike sell for the music show?

| Write the numbers. Line up the ones. Line up the tens. | → | Add the ones. Trade if you can. | → | Add the tens. |

$$\begin{array}{r} 47 \\ + 28 \\ \hline \end{array}$$

$$\begin{array}{r} 47 \\ + 28 \\ \hline 5 \end{array} \quad 7 + 8 = 15$$

$$\begin{array}{r} 47 \\ + 28 \\ \hline 75 \end{array}$$

1 ten + 4 tens + 2 tens = 7 tens

Nancy and Mike sold 75 tickets in all.

Write the numbers. Add.
Did you trade? Ring **yes** or **no.**

1. 42 + 6

yes

(no)

$$\begin{array}{r} 42 \\ + 6 \\ \hline 48 \end{array}$$

2. 58 + 35

(yes)

no

$$\begin{array}{r} 58 \\ + 35 \\ \hline 93 \end{array}$$

3. 67 + 9

(yes)

no

$$\begin{array}{r} 67 \\ + 9 \\ \hline 76 \end{array}$$

4. 5 + 37

(yes)

no

$$\begin{array}{r} 5 \\ + 37 \\ \hline 42 \end{array}$$

5. 14 + 14

yes

(no)

$$\begin{array}{r} 14 \\ + 14 \\ \hline 28 \end{array}$$

6. 28 + 12

(yes)

no

$$\begin{array}{r} 28 \\ + 12 \\ \hline 40 \end{array}$$

Chapter 11   (two hundred thirty-one) 23

TEACHING OPTIONS

RETEACHING TIPS Have students model 37 + 6 with cubes on an addition mat, then write the algorithm. Show the addition by joining cubes to make a ten, then show 6 + 7 ones by ringing the numbers. Use cubes to check. Assign Reteaching Supplement 96.

ENRICHMENT Have students use the lunch menu to solve.
Chicken sandwich .... 52¢
Apple .... 60¢
Milk .... 45¢
Orange juice .... 75¢
Which 2 items could you buy for less than $1.00? (sandwich and milk)

Add. Look at the sums in
each row. Continue the pattern.

3	35	46	22	49	
+ 40	+ 18	+ 17	+ 51	+ 34	
43	53	63	73	83	93

73	46	54	92	68	
+ 18	+ 46	+ 39	+ 2	+ 27	
91	92	93	94	95	96

79	31	23	45	5	
+ 4	+ 51	+ 58	+ 35	+ 74	
83	82	81	80	79	78

44	39	34	29	24	
+ 44	+ 39	+ 34	+ 29	+ 24	
88	78	68	58	48	38

FIND THE DATA

How many tickets
did Randi and Danny
sell in all?

$$\begin{array}{r} 39 \\ + 36 \\ \hline 75 \end{array}$$

They sold __75__ tickets.

Music Show Ticket Sales	
Danny	36
Lee	47
Randi	39
Emily	48

Data Bank How many people can sit in
the first 2 rows of the theater? (See page 399.)

$$\begin{array}{r} 19 \\ + 27 \\ \hline 46 \end{array}$$

__46__ people can sit in the first 2 rows.

3. PRACTICE AND APPLY

Basic	All
Average	All
Extended	All

11-4

PRACTICE

*What do you notice about the sums for
each row on page 232?* (They form a
number pattern.) *How will the number
pattern help you check your work?* (If a
number does not fit into the pattern, the
answer may be incorrect.)

APPLY

__FIND THE DATA__ ▶ **How can you
find the number of tickets sold by
each person?** (Read the table.)
▶ **How can you find the number of
seats in both rows 1 and 2?** (Add.)
▶ **What information in the Data Bank
is not needed for Exercise 6?** (the
number of seats in rows 3-9)

CLOSE AND ASSESS

__SHOW WHAT YOU KNOW__ Ask
students to describe what happens in
the chapter story, *The Button Shakers.*
Suppose Robbie had found 14 buttons
and Whistle had found 15 buttons.
How many buttons did they find in
all? (29) *Would there be enough to
make a button shaker for Tootie?* (no)
Have students use counters to find the
answer.

QUICK QUIZ

Find the sums.
45 + 7	82 + 16
(52)	(98)
27 + 19	39 + 11
(46)	(50)

Estimating Sums

OBJECTIVE 11-5   To estimate sums using front-end estimation

PREBOOK ACTIVITIES

QUICK REVIEW

Write the number of tens.

54	23	43	92	64
(5 tens)	(2 tens)	(4 tens)	(9 tens)	(6 tens)

PRIOR KNOWLEDGE

Help students recall what they know about estimating. Ask questions such as *How much time do you spend getting ready for school? How much money do you spend when you go to the grocery store? How many lunches are sold in school each day?* (Answers will vary.) *Are your answers exact numbers or are they estimates?* (estimates) *Do we need to know exactly how many minutes it takes to walk home or will an estimate give us a reasonable answer?* (Possible answer: An estimate is usually close enough.)

COMMUNICATION

Discussing Math   On the chalkboard, write the following sentence: Eddie estimated that the flute and the harmonica would cost about $50. *What are the clues that tell you that Eddie is estimating?* (Possible answers: *estimated, about*) Have a volunteer underline the words. *Why will it help Eddie to know about how much the instruments will cost?* (Possible answer: He will know how much money he needs to buy them.)

EXPLORE AND CONNECT

Materials: base-ten blocks
Grouping Suggestion: pairs
Have each student draw a picture of a musical instrument on a piece of paper and put a price tag of $22 on one and $43 on the other. *What would be the better estimate for the total cost of both of your instruments—$40, $60, or $80? Why?* (Answers will vary. For example: the better estimate for $22 + $43 is $60; about 2 tens + about 4 tens is about 6 tens.) Have students use base-ten blocks to model the actual numbers; then discuss why each of the other choices is not a good estimate. *How can you estimate the total cost quickly?* (Possible answer: Add the ten digits.) Have each pair work with another pair, using all four pictures to create other combinations of prices and estimating the sums.

CONNECTIONS   Use these anytime.

Problem of the Day

Make a List   What number pairs can be added to make an estimated sum of 40? Make a list of as many as you can. Compare your list with a friend. How are your answers alike? How are they different? (Answers will have a combination of 1 + 3 or 2 + 2 tens; ones will vary.)

Life Skills

Estimation   Use base-ten blocks to help you find the answer. Sara planted 32 orange tulips and 11 yellow tulips. Did she plant closer to 20, 40, or 60 tulips in all? (40)

Math Connection

Calculator   Choose 2 numbers under 50. Write an addition sentence. Add the tens and write the estimated sum. Now add the numbers on the calculator. How close was your estimate? (Answers will vary.)

CLASSWORK AND HOMEWORK SUPPLEMENTS

11-5

Practice

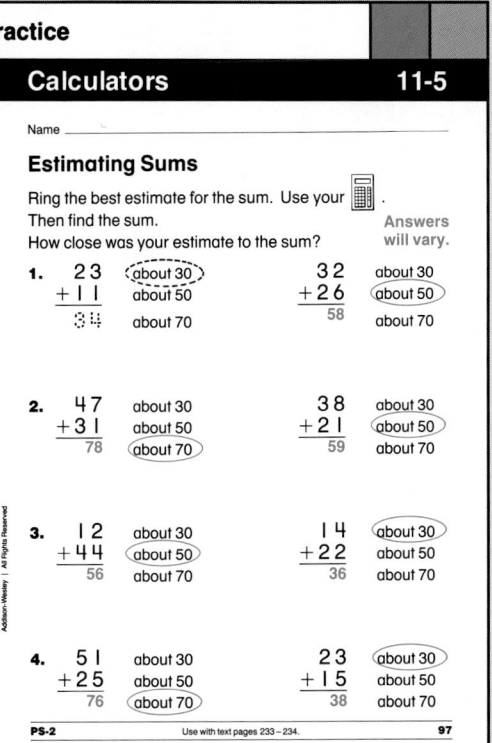

Calculators — 11-5

Name _____

Estimating Sums

Ring the best estimate for the sum. Use your 🖩.
Then find the sum.
How close was your estimate to the sum?

Answers will vary.

1.
```
  23     (about 30)        32    about 30
 +11      about 50        +26   (about 50)
  34      about 70         58    about 70
```

2.
```
  47     about 30         38    about 30
 +31     about 50        +21   (about 50)
  78    (about 70)        59    about 70
```

3.
```
  12     about 30         14   (about 30)
 +44    (about 50)       +22    about 50
  56     about 70         36    about 70
```

4.
```
  51     about 30         23   (about 30)
 +25     about 50        +15    about 50
  76    (about 70)        38    about 70
```

PS-2   Use with text pages 233 – 234.   97

Building Thinking Skills

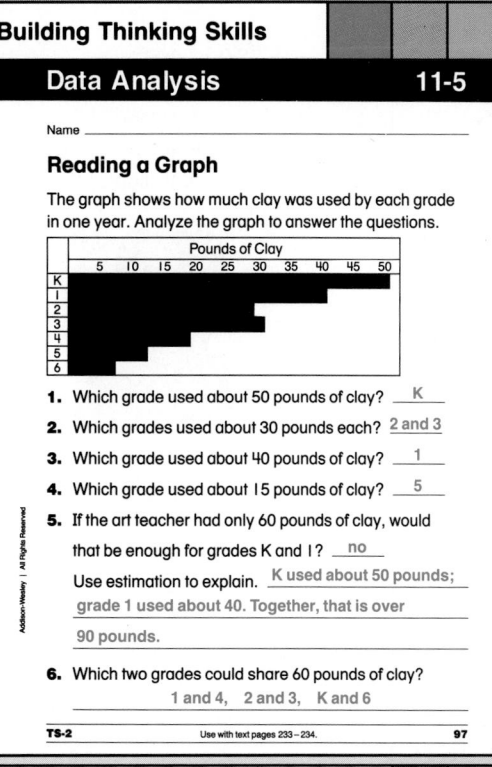

Data Analysis — 11-5

Name _____

Reading a Graph

The graph shows how much clay was used by each grade in one year. Analyze the graph to answer the questions.

1. Which grade used about 50 pounds of clay? __K__
2. Which grades used about 30 pounds each? __2 and 3__
3. Which grade used about 40 pounds of clay? __1__
4. Which grade used about 15 pounds of clay? __5__
5. If the art teacher had only 60 pounds of clay, would that be enough for grades K and 1? __no__
   Use estimation to explain. __K used about 50 pounds; grade 1 used about 40. Together, that is over 90 pounds.__
6. Which two grades could share 60 pounds of clay?
   1 and 4, 2 and 3, K and 6

TS-2   Use with text pages 233 – 234.   97

Reteaching

Skills Review — 11-5

Name _____

Estimating Sums

About how much money do the soccer ball and hockey stick cost in all?

Look at the tens column.

1 ten and 5 tens equal 6 tens. I estimate $60.

$12 ← about $10
+51 ← about +50
[about $60]

Ring the best estimate for the total cost.
Then find the total cost.

				Estimate			Cost
1.	baseball $11	+	mitt $23	$10	($30)	$50	$34
2.	soccerball $12	+	basketball $10	($20)	$40	$60	$22
3.	helmet $21	+	bat $32	$10	$30	($50)	$53
4.	basketball $10	+	mitt $23	$10	($30)	$50	$33
5.	baseball $11	+	helmet $21	$10	($30)	$50	$32

RS-2   Use with text pages 233 – 234.   97

Challenges

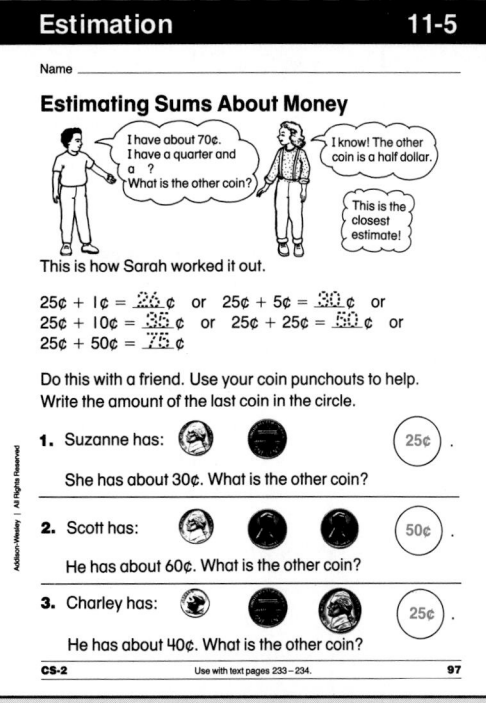

Estimation — 11-5

Name _____

Estimating Sums About Money

I have about 70¢. I have a quarter and a __?__. What is the other coin?

I know! The other coin is a half dollar.

This is the closest estimate!

This is how Sarah worked it out.

25¢ + 1¢ = 26 ¢ or 25¢ + 5¢ = 30 ¢ or
25¢ + 10¢ = 35 ¢ or 25¢ + 25¢ = 50 ¢ or
25¢ + 50¢ = 75 ¢

Do this with a friend. Use your coin punchouts to help.
Write the amount of the last coin in the circle.

1. Suzanne has: ⬤ ⬤ (25¢)
   She has about 30¢. What is the other coin?

2. Scott has: ⬤ ⬤ ⬤ (50¢)
   He has about 60¢. What is the other coin?

3. Charley has: ⬤ ⬤ ⬤ (25¢)
   He has about 40¢. What is the other coin?

CS-2   Use with text pages 233 – 234.   97

OBJECTIVE 11-5

To estimate sums using front-end estimation

> **Materials:** base-ten blocks, calculators, spinners
>
> **Grouping Suggestions:** individual work, cooperative learning groups of 3

1. MOTIVATE AND TEACH

LEARN ABOUT IT

Write 22 + 43 on the chalkboard and have students model the numbers with base-ten blocks. Ask them to estimate whether the sum will be closer to 40, 60, or 80 and to explain their answers. Have students look at the example at the top of page 233.

▶ **Why can you add the first digit to find an estimated sum?** (Possible answer: It has the highest place value; it is worth the most, so it can give the closest estimate.)

▶ **Why are the alternate answers, 40 and 80, incorrect?** (40 is too low, since one of the addends is 40; 80 is too high.)

▶ **How can an estimate help when you find the actual sum?** (An estimate can help you decide whether or not an answer is reasonable.)

▶ **How can you use a calculator to compare the actual sum to your estimate?** (Add the addends and compare the answer, particularly in the tens place, with the estimate.)

2. CHECK UNDERSTANDING

ERROR ALERT Adding the ones to find an estimated sum.

Name _____

Estimating Sums

About how much money do the harmonica and guitar cost in all?

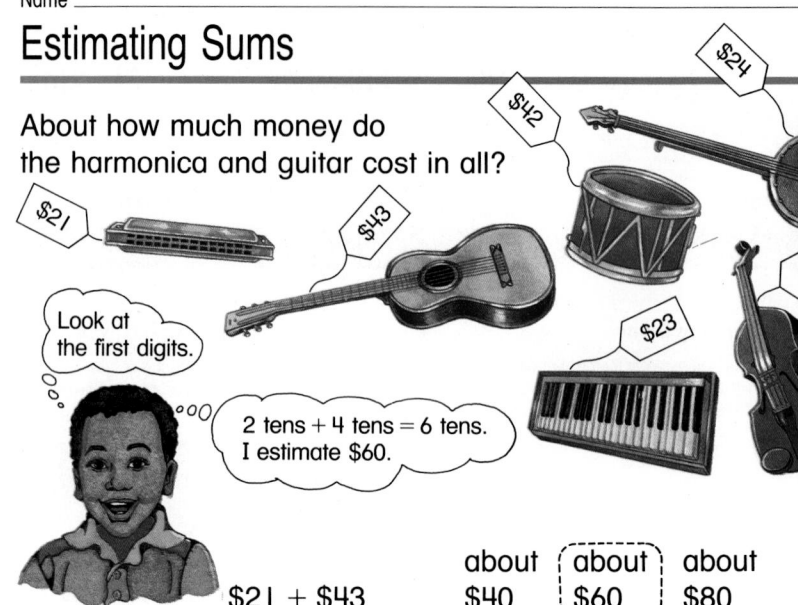

Look at the first digits.

2 tens + 4 tens = 6 tens. I estimate $60.

$21 + $43

| about $40 | about $60 | about $80 |

Ring the best estimate for the total cost.

1. drums   violin

   $ 42 + $ 44   about $40   about $60   **about $80** (circled)

2. banjo   keyboard

   $ 24 + $ 23   **about $40** (circled)   about $60   about $80

3. guitar   banjo

   $ 43 + $ 24   about $40   **about $60** (circled)   about $80

1. $86; 2. $47; 3. $67; Answers may vary.

4. Find each total above. Use your How close was your estimate to the total cost?

TEACHING OPTIONS

RETEACHING TIPS Have students use base-ten blocks to model 2 numbers such as 31 and 43 and estimate the sum by combining the tens. *How many tens are there in all* (7)? *What is the estimated sum?* (70) Repeat for other examples. Assign Reteaching Supplement 97.

COMPUTER Challenge Math, Sunburst Communications © 1984 For use with all levels of students. In *Digitosaurus,* students estimate which of 3 addition problems has the largest answer, then solve that problem. The ones digit is entered before the tens digit. The game requires 15+ minutes.

ing the best estimate for the
um. Then find the sum. Use your
ow close was your estimate to the sum? **Answers may vary.**

36	(about 50)	48	about 50	62	about 50
+ 22	about 70	+ 51	about 70	+ 15	(about 70)
58	about 90	99	(about 90)	77	about 90

$ 8	about $50	$65	about $50	$47	about $50
+ 71	(about $70)	+ 31	about $70	+ 32	( )
$ 79	about $90	$ 96	(about $90)	$ 79	about $90

MIDCHAPTER REVIEW/QUIZ

ing and cross out 10 ones to trade if you can.
raw a new ten. Write the sum.

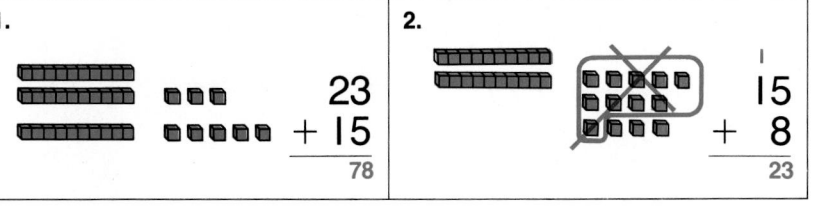

1.

$$\begin{array}{r} 23 \\ + 15 \\ \hline 78 \end{array}$$

2.

$$\begin{array}{r} 15 \\ + 8 \\ \hline 23 \end{array}$$

Add.

24	17	4	52	77	41
+ 24	+ 50	+ 89	+ 18	+ 17	+ 6
48	67	93	70	94	47

3. PRACTICE AND APPLY

Basic	All
Average	All
Extended	All

11-5

PRACTICE

Call students' attention to the dashed line answer and the ringed estimate in Exercise 1 on page 234. *What is the same about both answers?* (They both have a 5 in the tens place.)

APPLY

▶ **How can you estimate each sum?** (Add the tens.)
▶ **How will you know if your estimate is close when you check it with the calculator?** (The number of tens will be the same.)

CLOSE AND ASSESS

ELL WHAT YOU KNOW
eview with students the chapter
ory, *The Button Shakers. If you
timate the sum of 13 and 17, why
ight you think that you have enough
ttons for only 2 button shakers?*
ou would only have 20 buttons.)
sk students to use models as they
plain their answers.

QUICK QUIZ

Estimate each sum: about 30, about 50, about 70, or about 90.
41 + 50 (about 90) 23 + 32 (about 50)
32 + 24 (about 50) 21 + 12 (about 30)
13 + 62 (about 70) 34 + 42 (about 70)

Addition Practice

OBJECTIVE 11-6   To practice adding two 2-digit numbers

PREBOOK ACTIVITIES

QUICK REVIEW

Estimate whether these sums are greater than or less than 50 and then find the sums.

24	36	19	35	22	19
+ 28	+ 27	+ 47	+ 25	+ 18	+ 29
(52)	(63)	(66)	(60)	(40)	(48)

PRIOR KNOWLEDGE

Write 32 + 45 horizontally on the chalkboard. *How can I write these numbers to make them easier to add?* (vertically) Ask a student to rewrite the numbers in vertical form. *What are important things to remember when rewriting these numbers?* (The numbers in the ones and tens places should line up.) *Why is it important to keep the numbers in each column lined up?* (Possible answer: to be sure you add ones to ones and tens to tens) Ask a student to find the sum. (77)

COMMUNICATION

Discussing and Writing Math   Write the following rules for adding two 2-digit numbers on the chalkboard. Ask students to copy the rules in their Math Journals and fill in the blanks.
First, add the digits in the _____ place. (ones)
Then, add the digits in the _____ place. (tens)
Why must you add the ones digits first? (Possible answer: to know if you will trade 10 ones for 1 ten) *When might you need to add two 2-digit numbers?* (Possible answers: in school, adding numbers of students or books; at the store, making a purchase)

EXPLORE AND CONNECT

Materials: strips of yellow and blue construction paper
Grouping Suggestion: groups of 4
Write a 2-digit number less than 50 on a yellow strip and ask students to suggest another 2-digit number less than 50 to wri on the blue strip. Then place one strip above the other and as a volunteer to find the sum. Within each group, 2 students should each have a blue strip and 2 should each have a yellow strip. Ask each student to write a 2-digit number less than 50 on their strips. Then have them take turns pairing the yellow and blue strips to make addition exercises. One student in eac group should record all the different combinations that can be made using the 4 strips of paper. Have the groups find the sums.

CONNECTIONS   Use these anytime.

Problem of the Day

Writing Number Sentences   Read the story. Write the number sentence. Then write the answer in a sentence.
26 students are in Miss Loy's room.
21 students are in Mr. Bean's room.
How many students are there in the 2 rooms?
(26 + 21 = 47; there are 47 students in the 2 rooms.)

Subject Integration

Language Arts   Tell a story about 2 animals or 2 people who need to find the answer to 57 + 28. Tell what the numbers stand for and why the characters in your story must add the numbers together. Be sure that one of the characters finds the sum. (85)

Math Connection

Estimating   Work in groups of 3. Two people each say a number less than 50. The third person estimates the sum by adding tens. All three find the sum to see if the estimate was reasonable. Take turns estimating.

CLASSWORK AND HOMEWORK SUPPLEMENTS

Practice

Skills Maintenance — 11-6

Name _____

Addition Practice

Add. Ring the exercises where you had to trade.

1.
$\begin{array}{r}15\\+\ 6\\\hline 21\end{array}$
$\begin{array}{r}13\\+19\\\hline 32\end{array}$
$\begin{array}{r}24\\+26\\\hline 50\end{array}$
$\begin{array}{r}22\\+\ 9\\\hline 31\end{array}$
$\begin{array}{r}18\\+27\\\hline 45\end{array}$

2.
$\begin{array}{r}28\\+17\\\hline 45\end{array}$
$\begin{array}{r}40\\+19\\\hline 59\end{array}$
$\begin{array}{r}36\\+25\\\hline 61\end{array}$
$\begin{array}{r}18\\+23\\\hline 41\end{array}$
$\begin{array}{r}56\\+12\\\hline 68\end{array}$

3.
$\begin{array}{r}42\\+37\\\hline 79\end{array}$
$\begin{array}{r}35\\+28\\\hline 63\end{array}$
$\begin{array}{r}51\\+19\\\hline 70\end{array}$
$\begin{array}{r}23\\+44\\\hline 67\end{array}$
$\begin{array}{r}38\\+16\\\hline 54\end{array}$

4.
$\begin{array}{r}55\\+35\\\hline 90\end{array}$
$\begin{array}{r}47\\+25\\\hline 72\end{array}$
$\begin{array}{r}33\\+\ 8\\\hline 41\end{array}$
$\begin{array}{r}15\\+54\\\hline 69\end{array}$
$\begin{array}{r}68\\+24\\\hline 92\end{array}$

5.
$\begin{array}{r}77\\+12\\\hline 89\end{array}$
$\begin{array}{r}53\\+38\\\hline 91\end{array}$
$\begin{array}{r}43\\+45\\\hline 88\end{array}$
$\begin{array}{r}33\\+66\\\hline 99\end{array}$
$\begin{array}{r}74\\+\ 9\\\hline 83\end{array}$

98   Use with text pages 235–236.   PS-2

Building Thinking Skills

Math Reasoning — 11-6

Name _____

Number Card Shuffle

Use the numbers on the cards.
Write problems that have the given answers.

1.
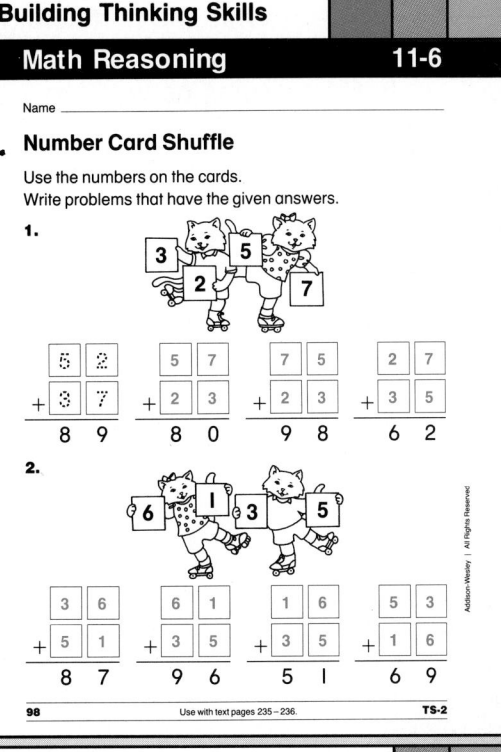

$\begin{array}{r}5\ 2\\+3\ 7\\\hline 8\ 9\end{array}$
$\begin{array}{r}5\ 7\\+2\ 3\\\hline 8\ 0\end{array}$
$\begin{array}{r}7\ 5\\+2\ 3\\\hline 9\ 8\end{array}$
$\begin{array}{r}2\ 7\\+3\ 5\\\hline 6\ 2\end{array}$

2.
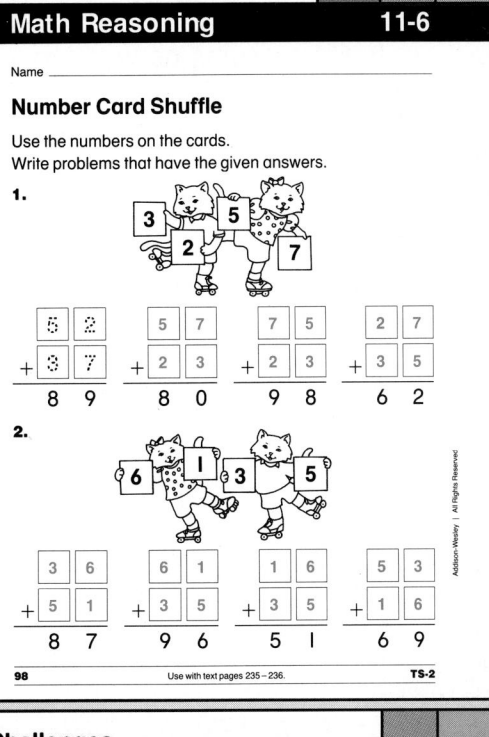

$\begin{array}{r}3\ 6\\+5\ 1\\\hline 8\ 7\end{array}$
$\begin{array}{r}6\ 1\\+3\ 5\\\hline 9\ 6\end{array}$
$\begin{array}{r}1\ 6\\+3\ 5\\\hline 5\ 1\end{array}$
$\begin{array}{r}5\ 3\\+1\ 6\\\hline 6\ 9\end{array}$

98   Use with text pages 235–236.   TS-2

Reteaching

Skills Review — 11-6

Name _____

Addition Practice

How many children are at camp?

Camp Shasta
Tent 1: 36 girls
Tent 2: 45 boys

Add the ones. Trade if you need to.

Then add the tens.

Do not forget the one you traded!
$\begin{array}{r}1\\3\\+4\\\hline 8\ \text{tens}\end{array}$

$\begin{array}{r}36\\+45\\\hline\end{array}$ $\begin{array}{r}36\\+45\\\hline 1\end{array}$

There are 81 children at camp.

Add. Trade if you need to.

1.
$\begin{array}{r}22\\+16\\\hline 38\end{array}$
$\begin{array}{r}41\\+19\\\hline 60\end{array}$
$\begin{array}{r}15\\+33\\\hline 48\end{array}$
$\begin{array}{r}32\\+19\\\hline 51\end{array}$
$\begin{array}{r}25\\+45\\\hline 70\end{array}$

2.
$\begin{array}{r}34\\+32\\\hline 66\end{array}$
$\begin{array}{r}56\\+17\\\hline 73\end{array}$
$\begin{array}{r}63\\+29\\\hline 92\end{array}$
$\begin{array}{r}91\\+\ 7\\\hline 98\end{array}$
$\begin{array}{r}28\\+36\\\hline 64\end{array}$

98   Use with text pages 235–236.   RS-2

Challenges

Family Math — 11-6

Name _____

Sum It Up

5 3 1 0 4 2

Dear Family Member,
    Help your child practice adding 2-digit numbers. You will need 2 sets of number cards marked 0 – 5. Small pieces of paper are fine.

Take turns. Place the number cards face down.
Pick 2 cards. Use the numbers to write the smallest
2-digit number you can. Do this again.
Find the sum of your two numbers. The sum is your score.
Write it below. In each round, add your new sum to your
score to make a new score. The game ends when one
player's score reaches 100.

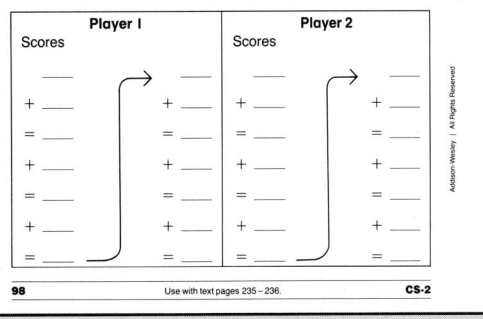

Player 1 Scores	Player 2 Scores
+ ___	+ ___
= ___	= ___
+ ___	+ ___
= ___	= ___
+ ___	+ ___
= ___	= ___

98   Use with text pages 235–236.   CS-2

OPTIONS FOR INDIVIDUAL NEEDS

Basic

Exercises All
Calculator Bank, p. 402
More Practice, p. 422, set A

Supplements
Reteaching 98 or
Practice 98
Thinking Skills 98

Average

Exercises All
Calculator Bank, p. 402
More Practice, p. 422, set A

Supplements
Practice 98
Challenges 98 or
Thinking Skills 98

Extended

Exercises All
Calculator Bank, p. 402

Supplements
Challenges 98
Thinking Skills 98

Other Resources:

Mathematics Their Way, p. 313
Developing Number Concepts With Unifix Cubes, pp. 175-176

11-6

OBJECTIVE 11-6
To practice adding two 2-digit numbers

Materials: number cubes 0-5, newspapers

Grouping Suggestions: groups of 4, pairs

---

1. MOTIVATE AND TEACH

LEARN ABOUT IT

Ask 4 students to come to the chalkboard and each write a 2-digit number that is less than 50. Then ask the first student to write an addition exercise using his or her number and one of the other numbers on the board. Ask the other students to do the same, making sure that their sum is different from the others.

Look at the number cards at the top of page 235. Describe how you are to use these cards on this page. (Possible answer: Members of each group will take turns putting a blue card with a yellow card to make addition exercises that have different sums.)

▶ **Compare the sums of two exercises in which you switch the order of the numbers being added. May you do that on this page? Explain.** (Possible answer: No, because the sums of the two problems would be the same. You are to find as many *different* sums as you can.)

▶ **Look at the examples on this page. What might be a good method for making sure you have tried all the number combinations?** (Possible answer: Begin with a blue card. Use all the yellow cards with it and list the combinations. Then go on to the next number on a blue card and do the same.)

2. CHECK UNDERSTANDING

ERROR ALERT Not aligning ones and tens correctly. Forgetting to trade 10 ones for 1 ten when necessary.

Name _____

Addition Practice

Work in a group. Pick a blue card and a yellow card. Write the numbers. Find their sum. Find as many different sums as you can.

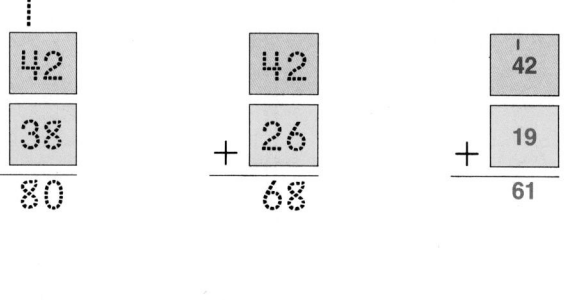

$$\begin{array}{r} 42 \\ +\ 38 \\ \hline 80 \end{array} \qquad \begin{array}{r} 42 \\ +\ 26 \\ \hline 68 \end{array} \qquad \begin{array}{r} 42 \\ +\ 19 \\ \hline 61 \end{array} \qquad \begin{array}{r} 5 \\ +\ 3 \\ \hline 9 \end{array}$$

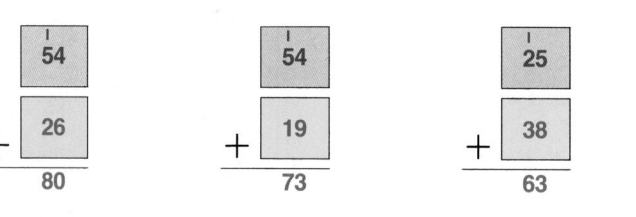

$$\begin{array}{r} 54 \\ +\ 26 \\ \hline 80 \end{array} \qquad \begin{array}{r} 54 \\ +\ 19 \\ \hline 73 \end{array} \qquad \begin{array}{r} 25 \\ +\ 38 \\ \hline 63 \end{array} \qquad \begin{array}{r} 2 \\ +\ 2 \\ \hline 5 \end{array}$$

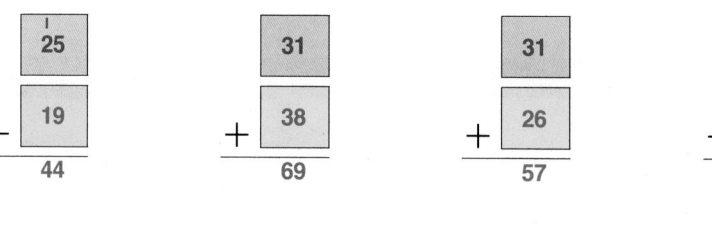

$$\begin{array}{r} 25 \\ +\ 19 \\ \hline 44 \end{array} \qquad \begin{array}{r} 31 \\ +\ 38 \\ \hline 69 \end{array} \qquad \begin{array}{r} 31 \\ +\ 26 \\ \hline 57 \end{array} \qquad \begin{array}{r} 3 \\ +\ 1 \\ \hline 5 \end{array}$$

Chapter 11   (two hundred thirty-five)

TEACHING OPTIONS

RETEACHING TIPS Have students toss a number cube marked 0-5 four times to make two 2-digit numbers. As they toss the numbers, have them write digits in the ones and tens places to form an addition exercise, lining up digits carefully. Have them find the sum. Assign Reteaching Supplement 98.

ENRICHMENT **Family Math** Have students work with a family member. Place a calendar page flat on a table. Take turns dropping 2 paper clips on the page. Have the student write an addition exercise for two of the numbers that the paper clip touches. Then check the sum.

...ld. Cross out each sum in the box to check.

Check Box
45 ~~53~~ ~~67~~
~~46~~ ~~56~~ ~~70~~
~~47~~ ~~60~~ ~~77~~

$$\begin{array}{r} 63 \\ +14 \\ \hline 77 \end{array} \qquad \begin{array}{r} 6 \\ +47 \\ \hline 53 \end{array} \qquad \begin{array}{r} 29 \\ +18 \\ \hline 47 \end{array} \qquad \begin{array}{r} 33 \\ +37 \\ \hline 70 \end{array}$$

$$\begin{array}{r} 25 \\ +35 \\ \hline 60 \end{array} \qquad \begin{array}{r} 41 \\ +26 \\ \hline 67 \end{array} \qquad \begin{array}{r} 38 \\ +7 \\ \hline 45 \end{array} \qquad \begin{array}{r} 28 \\ +28 \\ \hline 56 \end{array}$$

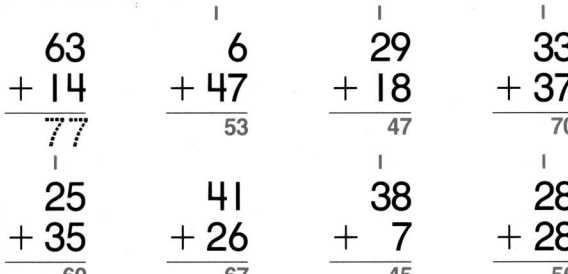

Check Box
~~67¢~~ ~~87¢~~ ~~92¢~~
~~77¢~~ ~~89¢~~ ~~96¢~~
~~80¢~~ ~~91¢~~ ~~99¢~~

$$\begin{array}{r} 27¢ \\ +72¢ \\ \hline 99¢ \end{array} \qquad \begin{array}{r} 63¢ \\ +28¢ \\ \hline 91¢ \end{array} \qquad \begin{array}{r} 48¢ \\ +19¢ \\ \hline 67¢ \end{array} \qquad \begin{array}{r} 62¢ \\ +34¢ \\ \hline 96¢ \end{array}$$

$$\begin{array}{r} 18¢ \\ +62¢ \\ \hline 80¢ \end{array} \qquad \begin{array}{r} 25¢ \\ +62¢ \\ \hline 87¢ \end{array} \qquad \begin{array}{r} 53¢ \\ +39¢ \\ \hline 92¢ \end{array} \qquad \begin{array}{r} 82¢ \\ +7¢ \\ \hline 89¢ \end{array}$$

E MENTAL MATH

...ite each sum. Use mental math.

Count on by ones.	6. Add tens.	7. Count on by tens.
$24 + 3 = \underline{27}$	$30 + 30 = \underline{60}$	$27 + 30 = \underline{57}$
$38 + 2 = \underline{40}$	$20 + 60 = \underline{80}$	$20 + 42 = \underline{62}$

(two hundred thirty-six)   More Practice, page 422, set A   Chapter 11

...LOSE AND ASSESS

...HOW WHAT YOU KNOW Ask ...dents to cut 2-digit numbers less ...n 50 out of the newspaper and ...ste the numbers on a piece of paper ...the form of an addition exercise. ...k students to exchange papers and ...d the sums. Partners check each ...er's answers and mark an X next to ...rcises that involved trading.

QUICK QUIZ

Add. Ring the problems in which you have to trade.

$$\begin{array}{r} 29 \\ +18 \\ \hline (47) \end{array} \quad \begin{array}{r} 56 \\ +11 \\ \hline (67) \end{array} \quad \begin{array}{r} 13 \\ +62 \\ \hline (75) \end{array} \quad \begin{array}{r} 48 \\ +35 \\ \hline (83) \end{array} \quad \begin{array}{r} 37 \\ +23 \\ \hline (60) \end{array}$$

11-6

3. PRACTICE AND APPLY

Basic	All
Average	All
Extended	All

PRACTICE

What are you to do with the numbers in each Check Box on page 236? (Cross out the sum as you solve each problem.)

APPLY

USE MENTAL MATH ▶ **Why are these addition exercises easy to do mentally?** (Possible answers: The strategies for solving them are easy to do in your head; the numbers are simple.)
▶ **Why is it easy to add tens?** (You do not need to add ones; there is a zero in the ones place.)
▶ **When you count on by tens, what do you notice about the digit in the ones place?** (It stays the same.)
▶ **How could you check your work in Exercises 5, 6, and 7?** (Possible answer: Rewrite the problems in vertical form and add.)

Problem Solving: Understanding the Operations/Calculator

OBJECTIVE 11-7 To understand the operations of addition and subtraction by putting together or by taking away

PREBOOK ACTIVITIES

QUICK REVIEW

Add.

6 + 6 (12)   9 + 9 (18)   7 + 7 (14)   5 + 5 (10)
8 + 8 (16)   4 + 4 + 4 (12)   3 + 3 + 3 (9)   6 + 6 + 6 (18)

PRIOR KNOWLEDGE

Write the following data on the chalkboard:

Pages Peg Read
Monday 12   Tuesday 13   Wednesday 19

How many pages did Peg read on Monday and Tuesday? Ask a volunteer to write the addition expression in vertical form on the chalkboard (12 + 13) and have another student solve it. (25) *Did you trade ones for a ten?* (no) *How many pages did Peg read on Tuesday and Wednesday?* (32) Repeat the procedure and ask whether there was a trade. (yes)

COMMUNICATION

Reading and Discussing Math Write the words **double** and **triple** on the chalkboard. *What is a double in math?* (adding 2 of the same numbers, such as 4 + 4 or 9 + 9) *What do you think a triple is?* (Possible answer: adding 3 of the same numbers, such as 4 + 4 + 4)
What are some things other than number problems that you could describe using the word double *or* triple? (Possible answers: double-decker bus, double- or triple-scoop cone, triple jump, double bed, double or triple hit (or play) in baseball, to double or triple a recipe)

EXPLORE AND CONNECT

COOPERATIVE ACTIVITY

Grouping Suggestion: small groups
Mary plays 16 songs on the piano.
Lou plays 5 more songs than Mary.
How many songs does Lou play? (21)

TEACHING ACTIONS

BEFORE
▶ **Does the story tell how many songs Mary plays?** (yes, 16)
▶ **Does the story tell how many songs Lou plays?** (No, it tells that Lou plays 5 more songs than Mary.)
▶ **What are we trying to find out?** (how many songs Lou plays)

DURING
▶ **Will you add or subtract to find the answer? How do you know?** (You will add; since Lou plays more songs than Mary, the answer will be number greater than 16, so you will add.)
▶ **What numbers will you add? Why?** (16 + 5; you add 5 to 16 because Lou plays as many songs as Mary, 16, plus 5 more.)

AFTER
▶ **Explain how you could reread the story in different way to see if your answer makes sense.** (Possible answer: You could change the story to a subtraction story: *Mary plays 16 songs. Lou plays . songs. Lou plays 5 more songs than Mary.*)
Have students in small groups create addition and subtraction story problems about music and share them. Ask the class to decide whether to add or subtract to solve each problem.

CONNECTIONS Use these anytime.

Problem of the Day

Understanding the Operations
Harold's first guitar has 6 strings. Then he gets another guitar that has 6 more strings than the first one. How many strings does his new guitar have? (12)

Creative Thinking

Calculator What number doubled is 134? Make an estimate. Try your number on the calculator. Use the results of your first estimate to estimate again. Use tally marks to count the number of estimates you make until you find the answer. (67) Next, find the number that you can double to get 176. (88) Did you do it in fewer tries?

Minute Math

Addition Copy and solve. How many can you complete in just 1 min?

43	25	37	19	31	48
+16	+25	+38	+28	+42	+27
59	50	75	47	73	75

use a calculator to find two and three 2-digit sums

CLASSWORK AND HOMEWORK SUPPLEMENTS

Practice

Problem Solving 11-7

Name _____

Understanding the Operations

Add or subtract. Then write the answer.

1. Gary did 32 sit-ups with bent knees and 25 sit-ups with his legs straight. How many sit-ups did Gary do?

Gary did __57__ sit ups.

$$\begin{array}{r} 32 \\ +25 \\ \hline 57 \end{array}$$

2. It takes 17 muscles to smile. You use 43 muscles to frown. Tara smiled and then frowned. How many muscles did she use?

Tara used __60__ muscles.

$$\begin{array}{r} \overset{1}{1}7 \\ +43 \\ \hline 60 \end{array}$$

3. Sam walked 6 blocks to the library. He walked 15 blocks to the park. How many more blocks was the trip to the park?

It was __9__ more blocks.

$$\begin{array}{r} 15 \\ -\ 6 \\ \hline 9 \end{array}$$

4. Wendy did 48 jumping jacks. Betty did 7 more jumping jacks than Wendy. How many jumping jacks did Betty do?

Betty did __55__ jumping jacks.

$$\begin{array}{r} \overset{1}{4}8 \\ +\ 7 \\ \hline 55 \end{array}$$

PS-2   Use with text page 237.   99

Building Thinking Skills

Writing Math 11-7

Name _____

Write Your Own

Write your own addition question. Then solve it and write the answer.

Wording may vary.

1.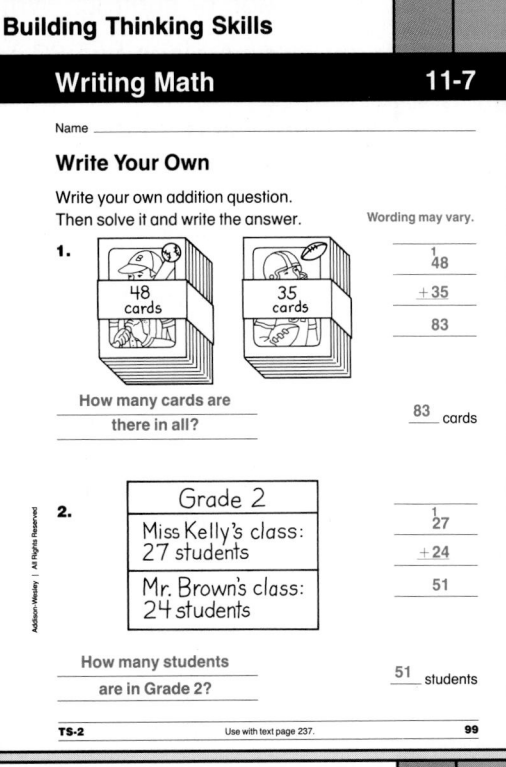

48 cards   35 cards

How many cards are there in all?

$$\begin{array}{r} \overset{1}{4}8 \\ +35 \\ \hline 83 \end{array}$$

__83__ cards

2.

> Grade 2
> Miss Kelly's class: 27 students
> Mr. Brown's class: 24 students

How many students are in Grade 2?

$$\begin{array}{r} \overset{1}{2}7 \\ +24 \\ \hline 51 \end{array}$$

__51__ students

TS-2   Use with text page 237.   99

Reteaching

Calculators 11-7

Name _____

Calculator

You can add 36 + 36 on your [calculator].
Always press ON/C before you start.

| 3 | 36 | 36 | 3 | 36 | 72 |

Press **3** Press **6** Press **+** Press **3** Press **6** Press **=**

Use your [calculator] to add. Write the sum.

1. 16 + 16 __32__
2. 13 + 13 __26__
3. 22 + 22 __44__
4. 25 + 25 __50__
5. 31 + 31 __62__
6. 39 + 39 __78__
7. 11 + 11 + 11 __33__
8. 20 + 20 + 20 __60__
9. 33 + 33 + 33 __99__
10. 12 + 12 + 12 __36__
11. 15 + 15 + 15 __45__
12. 30 + 30 + 30 __90__

RS-2   Use with text page 238.   99

Challenges

Calculator 11-7

Name _____

Washing Dishes

Here is a way to earn a large amount of money in only 12 days. Agree to wash the dishes for 12 days in a row. Charge 1¢ the first day, and each day after that charge twice as much as the day before. Use your calculator to find out how much you will earn each day.

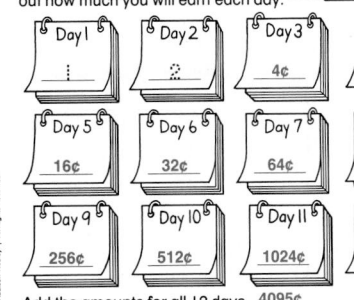

Day 1	Day 2	Day 3	Day 4
1¢	2¢	4¢	8¢

Day 5	Day 6	Day 7	Day 8
16¢	32¢	64¢	128¢

Day 9	Day 10	Day 11	Day 12
256¢	512¢	1024¢	2048¢

Add the amounts for all 12 days. __4095¢__
Turn your paper upside down.

Did you figure out you would earn 2048¢ on the twelfth day? And 4095¢ in all? That is the same as $40.95—more than 40 dollars!

CS-2   Use with text page 238.   99

OPTIONS FOR INDIVIDUAL NEEDS

Basic

Exercises All
Calculator Bank, p. 402

Supplements
Reteaching 99 or
Practice 99

Average

Exercises All
Calculator Bank, p. 402

Supplements
Practice 99
Challenges 99 or
Thinking Skills 99

Extended

Exercises All
Calculator Bank, p. 402

Supplements
Challenges 99
Thinking Skills 99

Other Resources:
Explorations, pp. 280-281, 299
Problem-Solving Experiences In Mathematics, pp. 51, 81, 105, 111, 117, 141, 153, 158
Developing Number Concepts With Unifix Cubes, pp. 174-175

11-7

LESSON PLAN 11-7

OBJECTIVE 11-7
To understand the operations of addition and subtraction by putting together or by taking away; to use a calculator to find two and three 2-digit sums

> **Materials:** calculators
>
> **Grouping Suggestions:** individual work, cooperative learning groups of 4

1. MOTIVATE AND TEACH

LEARN ABOUT IT

 **BEFORE** ▶ **How will you find the data needed to solve the problems?** (Read the problem carefully; look for numbers and words that tell you what to do with the numbers.)

 **DURING** ▶ **What can you use to help you decide whether to add or subtract to solve each problem?** (Possible answers: Use counters or cubes; circle clue words in each problem.)

AFTER ▶ **What number sentences can you use to check your answers?** (Possible answer: Use turnaround sentences to check addition or use related addition sentences to check subtraction.)

2. CHECK UNDERSTANDING

ERROR ALERT
Page 237 Incorrectly aligning the numbers when writing vertical addition and subtraction problems.
Page 238 Doubling the sums instead of doubling addends to find the given sums.

Name _____

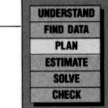
UNDERSTAND
FIND DATA
PLAN
ESTIMATE
SOLVE
CHECK

Problem Solving
Understanding the Operations

Add or subtract. Write the answer.

1. A piano has 52 white keys and 36 black keys. How many keys does a piano have?

   $$\begin{array}{r} 52 \\ + 36 \\ \hline 88 \end{array}$$

   A piano has __88__ keys.

2. A harp has 46 more strings than a guitar. A guitar has 6 strings. How many strings does a harp have?

   $$\begin{array}{r} 1 \\ 46 \\ + 6 \\ \hline 52 \end{array}$$

   A harp has __52__ strings.

3. A tuba weighs 12 pounds. A drum weighs 5 pounds. How much more does a tuba weigh than a drum?

   $$\begin{array}{r} 12 \\ - 5 \\ \hline 7 \end{array}$$

   A tuba weighs __7__ more pounds.

4. An accordian has 14 black keys and 20 white keys. How many keys does an accordian have?

   $$\begin{array}{r} 14 \\ + 20 \\ \hline 34 \end{array}$$

   An accordian has __34__ keys.

Chapter 11   (two hundred thirty-seven)

TEACHING OPTIONS

RETEACHING TIPS Make up stories that require adding a 1-digit to a 2-digit number or subtracting a 1-digit from a 2-digit number. Have students model with blocks, then write the problems in vertical form. For help using a calculator to guess and check, assign Reteaching Supplement 99.

ENRICHMENT Have students use a calculator to play *Double, Double.* Begin with a number such as 25, double it, then double the new number and tell the total. (100) *How many times would you have to add your number to reach the total?* (4) Repeat with other numbers, such as 30 (120) and 15 (60).

alculator

nd some big doubles. Use your

33	12	18	24
+ 33	+ 12	+ 18	+ 24
66	**24**	**36**	**48**

25	35	49	31
+ 25	+ 35	+ 49	+ 31
50	**70**	**98**	**62**

nd some big triples. Use your

22	15	20	25
22	15	20	25
+ 22	+ 15	+ 20	+ 25
66	**45**	**60**	**75**

---

3. PRACTICE AND APPLY

Basic	All
Average	All
Extended	All

11-7

What do you know about the numbers you will write in the 2 or 3 boxes in each exercise? (In each problem, the numbers, or addends, will be the same.) *If your first guess gives a sum that is too low or too high, what will you do?* (Choose a higher number or a lower number to double or triple.)

▶ **What is a double?** (2 of the same number added together)

▶ **What is a triple?** (3 of the same number added together)

▶ **Describe a plan for finding the doubles or triples.** (Possible answer: Double or triple a *guess* number on the calculator. Use the result to make another estimate. Guess and check until you solve.)

▶ **How can you check your answer?** (Add the doubles or triples on paper; compare the sum.)

CLOSE AND ASSESS

HOW WHAT YOU KNOW

ave students work in groups of 4.
ne student rolls 2 number cubes
ice to form an addition expression.
e second makes up a story to match
e numbers, and the third solves the
oblem. The fourth student verifies
e answer with a calculator. Have
udents switch roles.

QUICK QUIZ

Use a calculator.
Find doubles for each number.
30 (15)   36 (18)   90 (45)   52 (26)
Find triples for each number.
90 (30)   51 (17)   69 (23)   84 (28)

Problem Solving: Using a Calculation Method

OBJECTIVE 11-8 To choose an appropriate method of calculation

PREBOOK ACTIVITIES

QUICK REVIEW

Find the sums in your head.

3 + 4 = __(7)__	2 + 6 = __(8)__
30 + 40 = __(70)__	20 + 60 = __(80)__
30 + 43 = __(73)__	20 + 66 = __(86)__
10 + 50 = __(60)__	4 + 4 = __(8)__
10 + 55 = __(65)__	40 + 49 = __(89)__

PRIOR KNOWLEDGE

Help students recall using mental math to solve problems. Pose situations such as the following and ask students whether they could use mental math to add or subtract or whether they would need paper and pencil. (Suggested answers are provided.) *There are 5 trombones and 6 trumpets in the band.* (mental math) *The string instruments include 36 violins and 12 cellos.* (paper and pencil) *The band plays in 27 concert halls and 49 stadiums.* (paper and pencil) *There are 30 men and 30 women in the orchestra.* (mental math)

COMMUNICATION

Discussing Math Write the words **calculation method** on the chalkboard. Read the words aloud and explain that to choose a calculation method means to plan a way to solve a problem. Point out that calculation methods may include using mental math, paper and pencil, or a calculator. *What kinds of addition exercises could you solve using mental math?* [Possible answers: addition facts; adding tens (40 + 20); counting on by tens (20 + 63); and counting on by ones (3 + 47)] *What kind of exercise might you choose a calculator to solve?* (Possible answer: addition with 3-digit numbers)

EXPLORE AND CONNECT

COOPERATIVE ACTIVITY

Grouping Suggestion: small groups
There were 37 people in the Traveling Whistlers Club. Then 42 more people joined the club. How many people belong to the club now?

TEACHING ACTIONS

BEFORE ▶ **Describe what is happening in the story.** (Possible answer: A group of people are in the Traveling Whistlers Club and more people join the club.)

▶ **Identify the important data in the story.** (the number of people in the club to begin with; the number of people who joined later)

DURING ▶ **What operation will you use to solve the problem? How do you know?** (Addition; you want to find out how many people are in the club after the others join.)

▶ **Can you use mental math to solve this problem, or will you need paper and pencil? Explain your choice.** (Possible answer: paper and pencil, because two 2-digit numbers that are not tens are too hard to add mentally)

AFTER ▶ **How can you check your answer?** (Possible answers: Add the numbers in reverse order; add using a calculator.)

Ask students to write 2 addition exercises they might solve using mental math and 2 exercises they might solve using paper and pencil or a calculator.

CONNECTIONS Use these anytime.

Problem of the Day

Choose a Calculation Method
Solve. Tell whether you used mental math, paper and pencil, or a calculator.
  Jason read 34 pages of his book after school. He read 26 more pages just before going to sleep. How many pages of his book did Jason read that day? He read __(60)__ pages in all.
(Calculation methods may vary.)

Number Sense

Mental Math Use mental math to solve. Write only the answers.
1. Add 3 to each number.
23 (26) 45 (48) 67 (70)
16 (19) 99 (102) 88 (91)
2. Add 30 to each number.
10 (40) 50 (80) 60 (90)
44 (74) 36 (66) 52 (82)

Math Connection

Calculator Use your calculator to add.

Press  ON/C 1 0 1 + 5 4 =

101	67	105	75
+ 54	+103	+ 88	+102
(155)	(170)	(193)	(177)

CLASSWORK AND HOMEWORK SUPPLEMENTS

11-8

Practice

Problem Solving — 11-8

Name _____

Choosing a Calculation Method

Solve.
Ring the method you used: mental math, paper and pencil, or a 🖩 .

Calculation methods may vary.

1. How much does it cost for the two toys?
30¢ 50¢
They cost _80_ cents in all.
I used   mental math.
   paper and pencil.
   a calculator.

2. How far is it from Kent to Dent?
Kent 36 miles Gent 27 miles Dent
It is _63_ miles in all.
I used   mental math.
   paper and pencil.
   a calculator.

3. How long did it take Dan to watch both movies?
103 minutes   96 minutes
It took _199_ minutes in all.
I used   mental math.
   paper and pencil.
   a calculator.

4. How many liters are there in all?
2 liters   22 liters
There are _24_ liters in all.
I used   mental math.
   paper and pencil.
   a calculator.

100   Use with text pages 239–240.   PS-2

Building Thinking Skills

Mental Math — 11-8

Name _____

Match Up

Use mental math.
Color pairs of tags that add up to $1.00 (100¢) the same color.
Use a different color for each pair.   Check students' work.
Check using paper and pencil or a calculator.

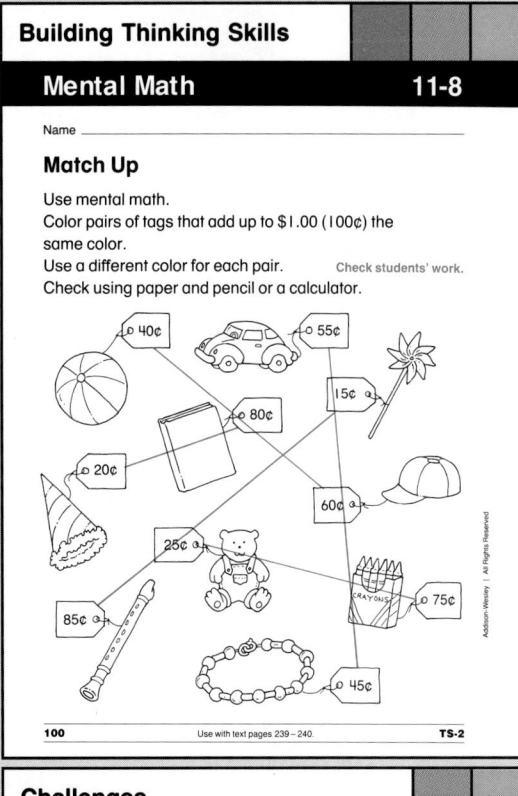

40¢ 55¢ 80¢ 15¢ 20¢ 60¢ 25¢ 75¢ 85¢ 45¢

100   Use with text pages 239–240.   TS-2

Reteaching

Problem Solving — 11-8

Name _____

Choosing a Calculation Method

? Mental Math   ✏ Paper and Pencil   🖩 Calculator

42	42	61	103
+ 3	+20	+35	+ 27

(Count on 1s.) (Count on 10s.) (Add 2-digit numbers.) (Add a 3-digit number and a 2-digit number.)

Choose mental math ? , paper and pencil ✏ , or a calculator 🖩 .

Then add. Check the method you used.

1. 30   ✓ ?
 +40
 70

2. 54   ?
 +25   ✓
 79

3. 56   ✓ ?
 + 3
 59

4. 104   ?
 + 67
 171   ✓

100   Use with text pages 239–240.   RS-2

Challenges

Problem Solving — 11-8

Name _____

Data Search

Use mental math, paper and pencil, or a calculator to solve.
Finish the sentence.

🍊 juice 35¢
🍎 apple 30¢
🧁 muffin 60¢

1. Ann spent 95¢ in all.
She bought ___ juice and a muffin

Mr. Reed's class: 26 students
Mrs. Rivera's class: 27 students
Miss Rice's class: 32 students

2. Two classes went to the zoo.
53 children went in all.
The classes that went to the zoo are ___
Mr. Reed's and Mrs. Rivera's

Fairview 24 miles Hope 42 miles Lokeville 16 miles Trent

3. The Chong family drove 58 miles in all.
They drove from ___ Hope to Trent

Freckle Juice 40 pages   Arthur's Pen Pal 64 pages   Beezus and Ramona 123 pages

4. Will read 2 books.
He read 163 pages in all.
Will read ___ Freckle Juice and
Beezus and Ramona

100   Use with text pages 239–240.   CS-2

OBJECTIVE 11-8
To choose an appropriate method of calculation

Materials: Scissors, paste, calculators, base-ten blocks, TA5 (Place Value Chart)

1. MOTIVATE AND TEACH

LEARN ABOUT IT

 **BEFORE** ► **Why do you use a different calculation method to solve different problems?** (Possible answer: Some problems are more easily solved using one method than using another.)

 **DURING** ► **How would you decide which method to use when planning to solve a problem?** (Possible answer: Read the problem; solve mentally if possible; use pencil and paper if you can; use a calculator if the math is too hard.)

 **AFTER** ► **How can you check your answer?** (Use another calculation method; compare results.)

► **Why might your paper look different from someone else's?** (Possible answer: Students might choose different methods.)

2. CHECK UNDERSTANDING

ERROR ALERT Adding incorrectly using mental math or paper and pencil.

Name _____

Problem Solving
Choosing a Calculation Method

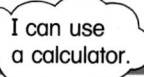

Cut out the exercises. Sort them into the three groups shown. Paste. Then add.

Groups may vary. Sample groups are shown.

My Mental Math Exercises		My Paper and Pencil Exercises	
20 +50 70	56 + 2 58	47 +32 79	55 +37 92
45 +10 55	30 +43 73		

My Calculator Exercises	
105 + 87 192	103 + 79 182

Chapter 11   (two hundred thirty-nine) 23

TEACHING OPTIONS

RETEACHING TIPS Have students model an expression such as 35 + 37 using base-ten blocks and a place value chart. Guide them through the addition in the ones and tens places. Then write the addition sentence. Repeat, using some that can be solved mentally. Assign Reteaching Supplement 100.

ENRICHMENT Have students choose mental math, paper and pencil, or a calculator to solve each exercise as a partner keeps the time. Make a table showing their times. Which method took the most time? The least? Explain why.

30   51   29
+17 (47) +46 (97) +48 (77)

Solve. Ring if you used
mental math, paper and pencil, or a
Calculation methods may vary.

1. How long did it take Jay to play
both tapes?

25 minutes long   20 minutes long

It took __45__ minutes in all. I used:

mental math   paper and pencil   a calculator

2. How long did Sandy spend
practicing the piano this week?

Tuesday	45 minutes
Thursday	32 minutes

She practiced __77__ minutes in all. I used:

mental math   paper and pencil   a calculator

MIXED REVIEW
Add or subtract.

3. $11 - 7 =$ __4__ $9 + 4 =$ __13__ $18 - 9 =$ __9__

4.
$$\begin{array}{r} 3 \\ 3 \\ +3 \\ \hline 9 \end{array} \qquad \begin{array}{r} 1 \\ 8 \\ +5 \\ \hline 14 \end{array} \qquad \begin{array}{r} 4 \\ 3 \\ +7 \\ \hline 14 \end{array} \qquad \begin{array}{r} 0 \\ 5 \\ +2 \\ \hline 7 \end{array} \qquad \begin{array}{r} 6 \\ 2 \\ +6 \\ \hline 14 \end{array}$$

3. PRACTICE AND APPLY

Basic	All
Average	All
Extended	All

*What will you do after solving each
problem?* (Ring the calculation method
you used.)

▶ **What do you need to understand
about each problem before you
plan?** (what the problem is asking; what
numbers are being added together)

▶ **How will you decide on a
calculation method?** (Possible answer:
Use mental math if you can; if not, use
paper and pencil. If you cannot do the
math, use a calculator.)

▶ **Why should you use mental math if
you can?** (It is quicker than the other
methods.)

▶ **What methods can you use to
check your answers?** (Possible
answers: Compare your answers with
another student's answers; check using
another method.)

MIXED REVIEW   *What calculation
method can you use to solve the
exercises?* (mental math)

CLOSE AND ASSESS

TELL WHAT YOU KNOW   Have
the class play *What's My Method?*
Give each student a slip of paper
labeled with one method of
calculation. Have students create a
story problem that they would solve
using that method. Ask volunteers to
read their problems aloud and have
the class vote on which method they
would use to solve it.

QUICK QUIZ

Choose a calculation method. Solve:
The Big Band needs 13 trucks and 28
vans to carry all the musicians and
their equipment. How many vehicles
do they need in all? (41)

Chapter 11 Lesson 8   **240**

Column Addition

OBJECTIVE 11-9 To add three 2-digit numbers

PREBOOK ACTIVITIES

QUICK REVIEW

Add these numbers in your head. Look for pairs of numbers that add to 10.

8	6	5	7	6	9	2
7	3	8	9	6	1	6
+ 2	+ 7	+ 5	+ 3	+ 4	+ 2	+ 8
(17)	(16)	(18)	(19)	(16)	(12)	(16)

PRIOR KNOWLEDGE

Help students recall the steps to follow when adding two 2-digit numbers. *What do you add first?* (Add the ones first. Then trade if you need to.) *What do you add next?* (Add the tens.) On the chalkboard, write addition problems that require both trading and no trading. Ask volunteers to find the sums using the steps they have just described.

COMMUNICATION

Reading and Discussing Math Write the words **column addition** on the chalkboard. Read the words aloud and explain that column addition is a name for exercises that have more than two 2-digit addends. Write an example of column addition on the board, such as 43 + 17 + 12. *Why do you think this is called column addition?* (Possible answer: The numbers are written in column form.) *When might you use column addition?* (Possible answer: when you buy 3 items and need to know what they will cost)

EXPLORE AND CONNECT

Materials: base-ten blocks or Cube-A-Links
Let students get used to adding three 2-digit numbers by first having them mentally add such exercises as 30 + 40 + 20 = (90); 34 + 20 + 10 = (64); 46 + 2 + 1 = (49); and 35 + 10 + 3 = (48).
On the chalkboard, write a column addition exercise with a sum less than 100 that does not require trading. Remind students that the steps they followed to add two 2-digit numbers also apply to adding 3 numbers. Encourage them to use blocks or cubes to find the answer. Write additional exercises on the board, including some that involve trading. *What are some things to look for as you add the digits in the ones column?* (Possible answer: Look for doubles facts; look for sums of 10.)

CONNECTIONS Use these anytime.

Problem of the Day

Understanding the Operations
Add or subtract. Write the answer.
A collie weighs 50 lb.
A cocker spaniel weighs 22 lb.
How much more does the collie weight?
(50 − 22 = 28; 28 lb)

Life Skills

Map Reading Make a map that shows at least 3 roads and City A, City B, and City C. Write a number less than 30 near each road to show how many miles it is between cities. Exchange maps with a friend and find out how many miles it is round trip from City A to cities B and C and back to City A again.

Mental Math

Find the sums in your head.
50 + 10 + 20 = (80)
26 + 20 + 40 = (86)
14 + 3 + 1 = (18)
67 + 10 + 2 = (79)
7 + 30 + 60 = (97)
25 + 10 + 4 = (39)

CLASSWORK AND HOMEWORK SUPPLEMENTS

Practice

Skills Maintenance   11-9

Name

Column Addition

Add. Trade if you need to.

1.
```
  7    61    33    26    55
 14    12    17    31     4
+23   + 4   +24   +12   +14
──    ──    ──    ──    ──
 44    77    74    69    73
```

2.
```
  8     3    42    60    51
  9    25    37    30    16
+15   +12   + 4   + 9   + 5
──    ──    ──    ──    ──
 32    40    83    99    72
```

3.
```
 16     5    72    21    36
  7     8     6     5     7
+24   +43   + 4   +19   +11
──    ──    ──    ──    ──
 47    56    82    45    54
```

4.
```
 21    17    15    44    20
 33     1    37     7    40
+16   +27   + 5   +10   +39
──    ──    ──    ──    ──
 70    45    57    61    99
```

PS-2   Use with text pages 241–242.   101

Building Thinking Skills

Writing Math   11-9

Name

Cards, Children, and Miles

Write your own addition problem. Then solve.

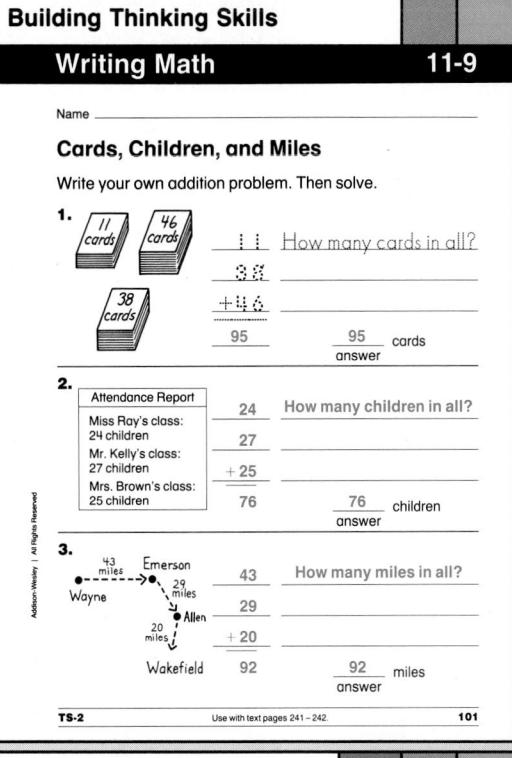

1.
```
 11
 38
+46
──
 95
```
How many cards in all? 95 cards answer

2.
Attendance Report
Miss Ray's class: 24 children
Mr. Kelly's class: 27 children
Mrs. Brown's class: 25 children
```
 24
 27
+25
──
 76
```
How many children in all? 76 children answer

3.
```
 43
 29
+20
──
 92
```
How many miles in all? 92 miles answer

Wayne → Emerson 43 miles, 29 miles → Allen, 20 miles → Wakefield

TS-2   Use with text pages 241–242.   101

Reteaching

Skills Review   11-9

Name

Column Addition

Add the ones. Trade if you need to. → Then add the tens.

```
35          35
12          12
+28         +28
──          ──
 5          75
```
5+2+8 = 15 ones or 1 ten 5 ones

Add. Trade if you need to.

1.
```
27    24    17    33    52
24     8    16    47    24
+13   + 5   +15   +12   + 3
──    ──    ──    ──    ──
64    37    48    92    79
```
7+4+3 = 14 ones or 1 ten 4 ones

2.
```
14     5    22    14     7
13    16    39    13    32
+59   + 8   +25   +25   + 9
──    ──    ──    ──    ──
86    29    86    52    48
```
4+3+9 = 16 ones or 1 ten 6 ones

RS-2   Use with text pages 241–242.   101

Challenges

Cooperative Activities   11-9

Name

Go, Go, Go Fish

You need: a friend, a bowl, 18 paper clips, a horseshoe magnet, string, and a ruler.
Make 18 paper fish.

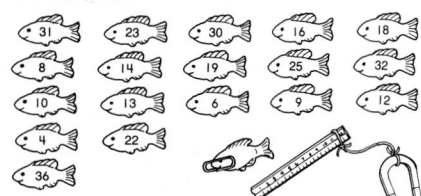

Fish numbers: 31, 23, 30, 16, 18, 8, 14, 19, 25, 32, 10, 13, 5, 9, 12, 4, 22, 36

Put a paper clip on each fish.
Put all the fish in the bowl.
Make a fishing pole.

Rules: Take turns. Use the fishing pole to catch 3 fish.
Add the numbers on the fish to find the sum.
You get: 1 point if the sum is even.
          1 point if the sum is odd.
          2 points if you traded.
          3 points if the sum ends in zero.
Then put the 3 fish back in the bowl.
After 5 turns, the player with the most points wins.

CS-2   Use with text pages 241–242.   101

OPTIONS FOR INDIVIDUAL NEEDS

Basic

Exercises All
Calculator Bank, p. 402
More Practice, p. 422, set B

Supplements
Reteaching 101 or
Practice 101
Challenges 101

Average

Exercises All
Calculator Bank, p. 402
More Practice, p. 422, set B

Supplements
Practice 101
Challenges 101 or
Thinking Skills 101

Extended

Exercises All
Calculator Bank, p. 402

Supplements
Challenges 101
Thinking Skills 101

Other Resources:
Explorations, pp. 163-164, 169, 172
Problem-Solving Experiences in Mathematics, p. 83

11-9

OBJECTIVE 11-9
To add three 2-digit numbers

Materials: flannelboard, felt numbers, newspapers

Grouping Suggestions: individual work, pairs

1. MOTIVATE AND TEACH

LEARN ABOUT IT

Write the following exercises on the chalkboard in column form: 3 + 3 + 6, 9 + 6 + 1, 7 + 2 + 6. *Look at each exercise. What clues can you find to help you add quickly?* (Possible answer: The first exercise has a doubles fact. The second has a sum of 10. The third exercise must be added one digit at a time.) Remind students to consider these clues as they add the digits in the ones column in column addition.

▶ **What might happen if you do not line up the ones and tens correctly when writing a column addition exercise?** (Possible answer: A ones digit may be added as part of the tens column and you would get a wrong answer.)

▶ **Why is it a good idea to write a small 1 at the top of the tens column when you trade 10 ones for 1 ten?** (Possible answer: to help you remember to add the new ten when you total the tens column)

▶ **How can finding doubles facts and sums of 10 help you do column addition?** (Possible answer: Doubles facts and sums of 10 are easy to remember, so it will seem as if you are only adding 2 numbers instead of 3.)

2. CHECK UNDERSTANDING

ERROR ALERT Not recording the extra ten to show that trading was needed. Forgetting to include the new ten when adding the tens column.

Name _____

Column Addition

Add 24 + 5 + 34.

| Write the numbers. Line up the ones. Line up the tens. | → | Add the ones. Trade if you can. | → | Add the tens. |

$$\begin{array}{r} 24 \\ 5 \\ + 34 \\ \hline \end{array}$$

$$\begin{array}{r} 24 \\ 5 \\ + 34 \\ \hline 3 \end{array} \quad (4 + 5 + 4 = 13)$$

$$\begin{array}{r} 24 \\ 5 \\ + 34 \\ \hline 63 \end{array}$$

Add.

I looked for doubles.

1.
$$\begin{array}{r} 24 \\ 3 \\ + 34 \\ \hline 61 \end{array} \quad (4 + 4 = 8 \text{ and } 3 \text{ more make } 11.)$$
$$\begin{array}{r} 36 \\ 16 \\ + 22 \\ \hline 74 \end{array}$$
$$\begin{array}{r} 61 \\ 25 \\ + 5 \\ \hline 91 \end{array}$$

I looked for sums of 10.

2.
$$\begin{array}{r} 33 \\ 16 \\ + 34 \\ \hline 83 \end{array} \quad (6 + 4 = 10 \text{ and } 3 \text{ more make } 13.)$$
$$\begin{array}{r} 8 \\ 21 \\ + 12 \\ \hline 41 \end{array}$$
$$\begin{array}{r} 21 \\ 29 \\ + 15 \\ \hline 65 \end{array}$$

I added one digit at a time.

3.
$$\begin{array}{r} 46 \\ 15 \\ + 31 \\ \hline 92 \end{array} \quad (6 + 5 = 11 \text{ and } 1 \text{ more make } 12.)$$
$$\begin{array}{r} 25 \\ 23 \\ + 22 \\ \hline 70 \end{array}$$
$$\begin{array}{r} 34 \\ 13 \\ + 39 \\ \hline 86 \end{array}$$

Chapter 11

(two hundred forty-one)

TEACHING OPTIONS

RETEACHING TIPS Show a column addition exercise with trading on a flannelboard. Have students use felt numbers to add the digits in the ones column, placing the ones digit below and the extra ten above the tens column. Then complete the addition. Assign Reteaching Supplement 101.

COMPUTER Math Practice Level 1, IBM Educational Systems © **1985** Extra practice for all students. In Lesson 3, students add 2-digit numbers vertically, with some regrouping. In the answer, students must enter the ones digit before the tens digit. The lesson takes 15 minutes.

ing [crayon] each exercise where doubles can help.
ing [crayon] each exercise where sums of 10 can help.
hen add.

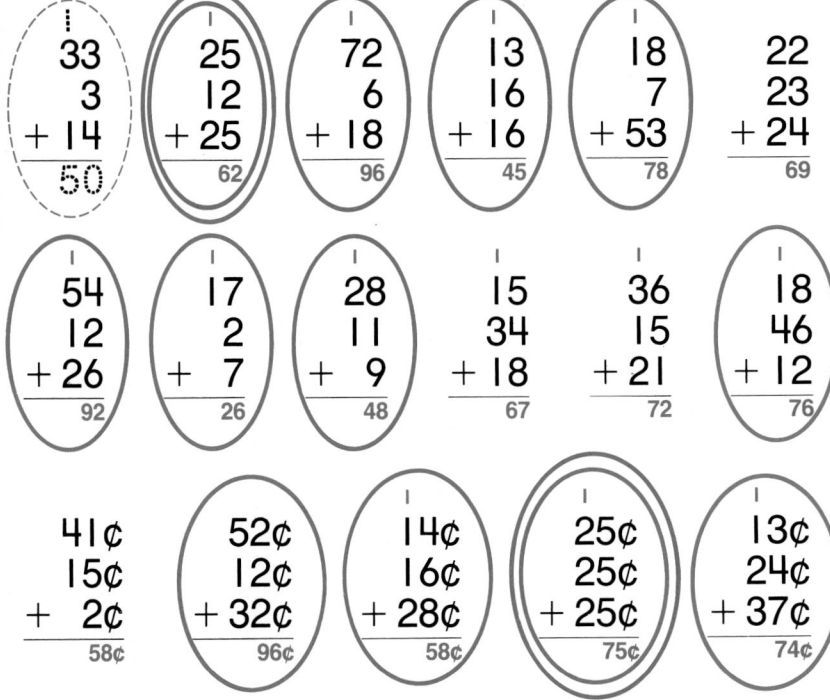

33 3 + 14 50	25 12 + 25 62	72 6 + 18 96	13 16 + 16 45	18 7 + 53 78	22 23 + 24 69
54 12 + 26 92	17 2 + 7 26	28 11 + 9 48	15 34 + 18 67	36 15 + 21 72	18 46 + 12 76
41¢ 15¢ + 2¢ 58¢	52¢ 12¢ + 32¢ 96¢	14¢ 16¢ + 28¢ 58¢	25¢ 25¢ + 25¢ 75¢	13¢ 24¢ + 37¢ 74¢	

ROBLEM SOLVING

The radio station played 3 tapes. The first was 18 minutes long. The second was 24 minutes long. The third was 17 minutes long.
How many minutes did it take to play all 3 tapes?

It took __59__ minutes in all.

18
24
+ 17
59

42 (two hundred forty-two) 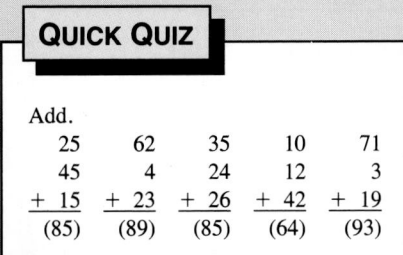 More Practice, page 422, set B   Chapter 11

---

3. PRACTICE AND APPLY

Basic	All
Average	All
Extended	All

PRACTICE

How do you show an exercise for which doubles can help? (Draw a red ring around it.) *How do you show an exercise for which a sum of 10 can help?* (Draw a blue ring around it.) *Look at the second exercise in the first row. What do you see in the ones column?* (both a sum of 10 and a doubles fact)

APPLY

PROBLEM SOLVING ▶ **How can you tell whether the problem requires addition or subtraction?** (Possible answer: It asks for the total number of minutes for all 3 tapes. It is a put-together problem, so it requires addition.)
▶ **If you did not read this problem carefully, what might happen when you write the numbers?** (Possible answer: You might record the number 3 as one of the addends and get a wrong answer.)

CLOSE AND ASSESS

HOW WHAT YOU KNOW

emind students of the events in the apter story. *Suppose Tootie had und 9 buttons. How many buttons ould they have found in all?* (39) ave students work in pairs and use ocks to solve addition problems with addends.

QUICK QUIZ

Add.

25	62	35	10	71
45	4	24	12	3
+ 15	+ 23	+ 26	+ 42	+ 19
(85)	(89)	(85)	(64)	(93)

Problem Solving: Using Estimation

OBJECTIVE 11-10   To solve problems using estimation

PREBOOK ACTIVITIES

QUICK REVIEW

Tell the number of tens in each number.

52	(5)	47	(4)	92	(9)	25	(2)	70	(7)
35	(3)	29	(2)	51	(5)	42	(4)	67	(6)
89	(8)	91	(9)	57	(5)	83	(8)			

PRIOR KNOWLEDGE

Help students recall what they know about estimating sums using front-end estimation.
Miles pays $21 for a music stand.
He buys a music book for $11.
About how much does Miles spend in all? ($30) *How can you estimate the total?* (Add the tens.)

COMMUNICATION

Discussing and Writing Math   Write the following sentence on the chalkboard: *About how many in all?* Read the sentence aloud and ask students to imagine that it is the last sentence in a story problem they have just read. *What clue words do you see in the sentence?* (about, in all) *What does the word* **about** *tell about the answer you are looking for?* (*About* means that the answer will be an estimate.) *What do the words* **in all** *tell about the answer?* (You will be joining groups, or looking for a sum.) Ask students to write a story problem which includes the sentence on the chalkboard. Have students share their stories with the class.

EXPLORE AND CONNECT

COOPERATIVE ACTIVITY

Grouping Suggestion: small groups
John writes 33 new songs every year.
Paul writes 21 new songs every year.
About how many songs do John and Paul write each year?
(about 50)

TEACHING ACTIONS

BEFORE
▶ **Identify the important data in the story.** (John writes 33 songs. Paul writes 21.)
▶ **How do you know that you need to find a sum?** (Possible answer: because the question asks for the total number of songs for both John and Paul)

DURING
▶ **Describe how the word** *about* **will affect your plan for solving the problem.** (Possible answer: The word *about* means that an estimate, rather than an exact answer, is asked for. The plan will be to estimate the sum.)
▶ **How can you estimate the sum of two 2-digit numbers?** (Add the tens digits; write the number that means that many tens.)

AFTER
▶ **Describe how you can check the estimate.** (Possible answers: Add the actual numbers and compare to the estimate; compare the number of tens in the answer to the number of tens in the estimate.) Have groups write 2-digit addition sentences. Have them create story problems to match the numbers and then estimate the sums by adding tens.

CONNECTIONS   Use these anytime.

Problem of the Day

Using Estimation   Think about the tens to estimate the answer.
Hal read 22 books in July and 41 books in August. About how many books did Hal read during the 2 months? (about 60)

Math Connection

Calculator   Guess and Check using your calculator. Which 3 numbers have a sum of 96?
23   37   41
26   32   22
(23, 41, 32)

Creative Thinking

Money   Imagine that you have 80¢. What can you buy? Write 4 ways you can spend your money on different things. Buy 2 or 3 things each time.

marble	10¢	sticker	10¢
car	50¢	top	20¢
pen	30¢	ring	60¢

(car, pen; top, ring; marble, sticker, ring; marble, car, top)

Problem Solving Strategy: Guess and Check

use the problem solving strategy Guess and Check

CLASSWORK AND HOMEWORK SUPPLEMENTS

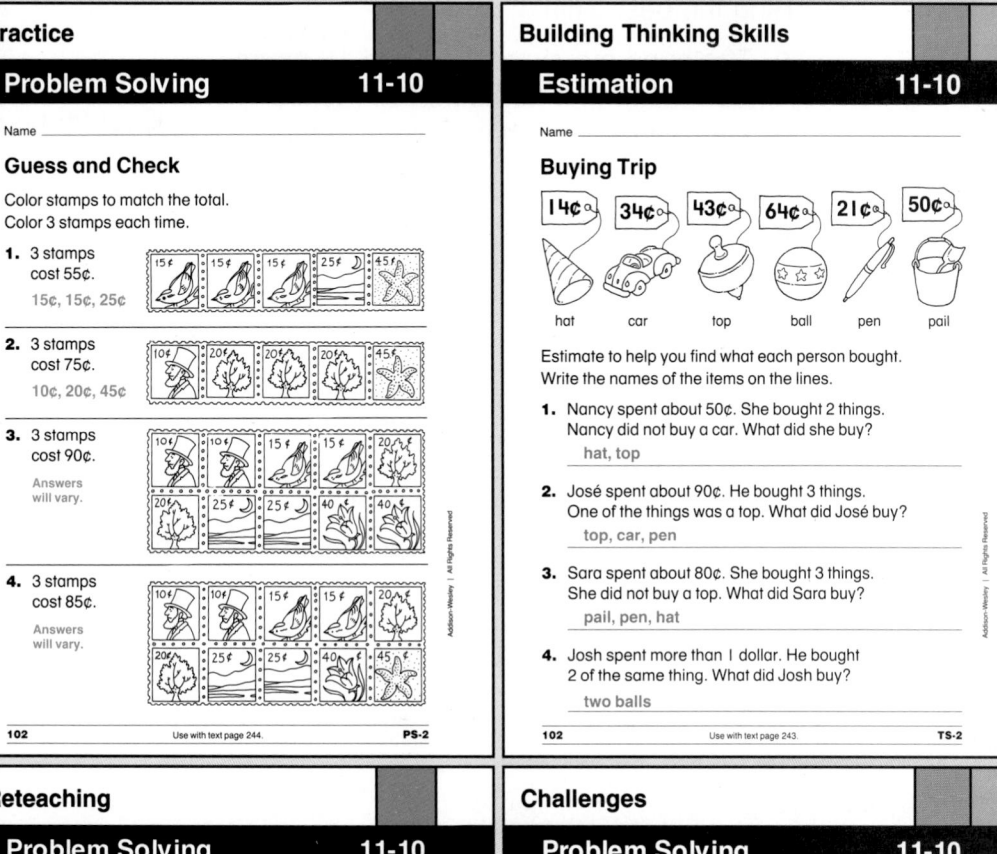

Practice

Problem Solving   11-10

Name

Guess and Check

Color stamps to match the total.
Color 3 stamps each time.

1. 3 stamps cost 55¢.
   15¢, 15¢, 25¢

2. 3 stamps cost 75¢.
   10¢, 20¢, 45¢

3. 3 stamps cost 90¢.
   Answers will vary.

4. 3 stamps cost 85¢.
   Answers will vary.

102   Use with text page 244.   PS-2

Building Thinking Skills

Estimation   11-10

Name

Buying Trip

14¢ hat   34¢ car   43¢ top   64¢ ball   21¢ pen   50¢ pail

Estimate to help you find what each person bought.
Write the names of the items on the lines.

1. Nancy spent about 50¢. She bought 2 things.
   Nancy did not buy a car. What did she buy?
   hat, top

2. José spent about 90¢. He bought 3 things.
   One of the things was a top. What did José buy?
   top, car, pen

3. Sara spent about 80¢. She bought 3 things.
   She did not buy a top. What did Sara buy?
   pail, pen, hat

4. Josh spent more than 1 dollar. He bought
   2 of the same thing. What did Josh buy?
   two balls

102   Use with text page 243.   TS-2

Reteaching

Problem Solving   11-10

Name

Using Estimation

About how many children are there in all?

23 girls
21 boys

Add the tens.
2 tens + 2 tens = 4 tens.
4 tens = 40

about 20
(about 40)
about 60

Ring the best estimate.

1. Tickets Sold
   Bob   13
   Sue   24

   About how many tickets were sold in all?

   1 ten + 2 tens
   That is 3 tens.

   about 10 tickets
   (about 30 tickets)
   about 50 tickets

2. 12 grape juice
   14 apple juice

   About how many cans of juice in all?

   (about 20 cans)
   about 40 cans
   about 60 cans

3. 44¢   32¢

   About how much for both?

   about 30¢
   about 50¢
   (about 70¢)

4. 22 roses were picked.
   13 tulips were picked.
   30 daisies were picked.

   About how many flowers were picked in all?

   about 20 flowers
   about 40 flowers
   (about 60 flowers)

102   Use with text page 243.   RS-2

Challenges

Problem Solving   11-10

Name

Ball Toss Game

You throw 3 balls at the board and try to get them in the holes. Each hole is worth a different number of points.

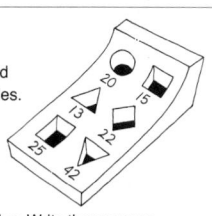

Use Guess and Check to solve. Write the answers.

1. Lee scored 75 points. He threw all 3 balls into the same hole. In which hole did Lee throw the balls?
   25

2. Trina scored 75 points. She threw the ball into 3 different holes. In which holes did she throw the balls?
   13, 20, 42

3. David scored 57 points. He threw the ball into 3 different holes. In which holes did he throw the balls?
   22, 20, 15

4. Rita scored 68 points. 2 of the balls went into the same hole. In which holes did she throw the balls?
   13, 13, 42

5. What are two different ways you could get a score of 72?
   25, 25, 22   and   15, 15, 42

102   Use with text page 244.   CS-2

OPTIONS FOR INDIVIDUAL NEEDS

Basic

Exercises All
More Practice, p. 422, set C

Supplements
Reteaching 102 or
Practice 102

Average

Exercises All
More Practice, p. 422, set C

Supplements
Practice 102
Challenges 102 or
Thinking Skills 102

Extended

Exercises All

Supplements
Challenges 102
Thinking Skills 102

Other Resources:
Explorations, pp. 260-261, 281-283
Problem-Solving Experiences In Mathematics, pp. 10-11, 46-47, 83, 101, 119, 150, 168
Workjobs, pp. 225-227
Workjobs For Parents, pp. 106-109

11-10

OBJECTIVE 11-10
To solve problems using estimation; to solve problems using the strategy Guess and Check

> **Materials:** scissors, paste
>
> **Grouping Suggestions:** pairs

1. MOTIVATE AND TEACH

LEARN ABOUT IT

How will you estimate the answer in each problem? (Add the tens in each number.) *How will you know if your estimate is reasonable?* (It will match one of the given estimates.)

 **BEFORE** ▶ **Look at Exercise 1. Identify the data you are combining in this story.**
(the number of hours the band members practiced last month and this month)

 **DURING** ▶ **What is your plan for finding the estimated sum?** (Add the number of tens in each number.)
▶ **Can you use mental math to find the answer?** (Yes; since you are adding only the tens, it is like adding 1-digit numbers.)

 **AFTER** ▶ **How can you check to see if your answer is reasonable?** (Possible answers: Compare your answer with the other choices; add the actual numbers and compare the number in the tens place with the estimated sum.)

2. CHECK UNDERSTANDING

ERROR ALERT **Page 243** Adding both digits in the numbers instead of adding just tens to estimate.
Page 244 Not understanding how different sets of numbers can be combined to get a sum.

Name _____

Problem Solving
Using Estimation

UNDERSTAND
FIND DATA
PLAN
ESTIMATE
SOLVE
CHECK

Ring the best estimate.

1. The band members practiced 14 hours last month and 23 hours this month. About how many hours did they practice in the 2 months?

   about 10 hours
   (about 30 hours)
   about 50 hours

2. The band bought new uniforms. The jacket cost $31. The pants cost $22. The hat cost $10. About how much did all 3 pieces cost?

   about $20
   about $40
   (about $60)

3. The band members rode two buses to the parade. 36 members rode one. 22 members rode the other. About how many members rode buses?

   about 30
   (about 50)
   about 70

4. The band marched 12 blocks south and then 13 blocks east. About how many blocks did they march in the parade?

   (about 20 blocks)
   about 40 blocks
   about 60 blocks

Chapter 11   More Practice, page 422, set C   (two hundred forty-three) 2

TEACHING OPTIONS

RETEACHING TIPS Write 15, 20, 25, 30, 35, and 40 on the board. Ask students to choose 3 numbers with a sum of 90, then check by adding. If the guess does not match the sum, repeat. Have them recheck with a calculator or blocks. For help with estimation, use Reteaching Supplement 102.

ENRICHMENT Draw pictures of toys or games for each of the following prices: 43¢, 24¢, 31¢, 51¢, 62¢, 42¢, 21¢, and 64¢. Have students imagine they have 70¢ to spend and write a problem about 2 toys that cost about 70¢. Then have them write a story problem about 3 toys that cost about 90¢.

me _____

roblem Solving Strategy
uess and Check

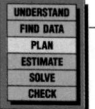

UNDERSTAND
FIND DATA
PLAN
ESTIMATE
SOLVE
CHECK

ork with a partner. Cut out the pictures.
aste them to make each band.

Answers may vary.
Check students' work.

Music Makers Marching Band

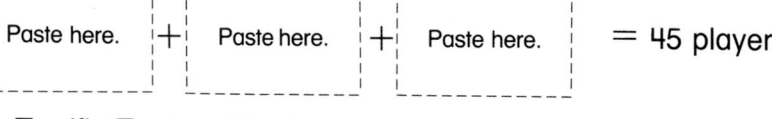

Paste here. $+$ Paste here. $+$ Paste here. $= 45$ players

Terrific Tooters Marching Band

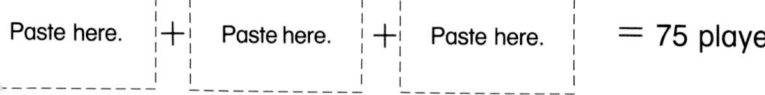

Paste here. $+$ Paste here. $+$ Paste here. $= 75$ players

Nifty Notes Marching Band

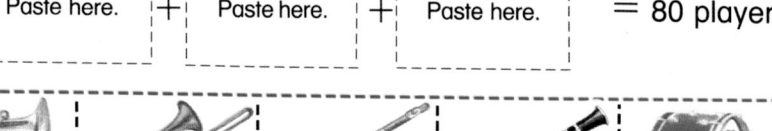

Paste here. $+$ Paste here. $+$ Paste here. $= 80$ players

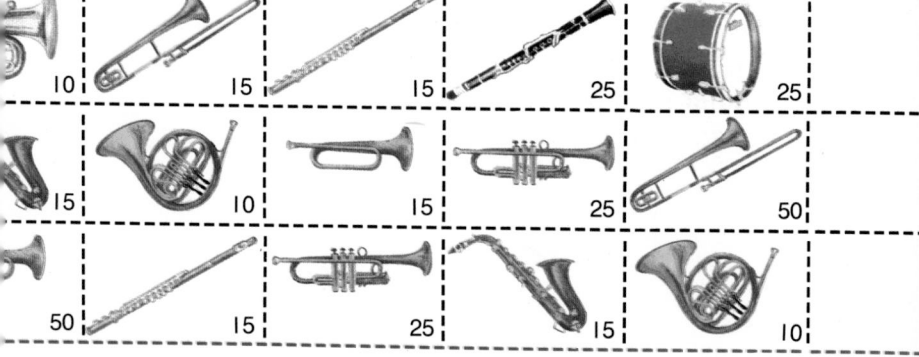

10	15	15	25	25
15	10	15	25	50
50	15	25	15	10

4 (two hundred forty-four)   Chapter 11

---

3. PRACTICE AND APPLY

Basic	All
Average	All
Extended	All

*Why should you cut out the pictures
before you begin to solve the problems?*
(Possible answer: You can move the
squares around to find the solutions.)
*What should you do before you begin to
paste?* (Plan each solution; solve and
check the problems.)

▶ **What must you understand about
each band?** (Possible answers: Each
band is made up of a combination of
different instruments; each band has a
different number of players.)

▶ **How would an estimate help you
find the answer?** (Possible answer: An
estimate would help you decide if your
guess is reasonable.)

▶ **When is the best time to check your
work on this page?** (before you paste)

▶ **How will you check your answers?**
(Possible answers: Make sure your bands
are made up of 3 different instruments;
add the numbers to make sure the
addends match the sum.)

LOSE AND ASSESS

RITE WHAT YOU KNOW

efer students to page 243. Have
em rewrite the problems so that one
the other estimates is correct.
artners may exchange papers and
lve. Then have pairs choose a sum
etween 50 and 99 and use the guess
d check method to find three
ddends that total the sum.

QUICK QUIZ

Find 3 numbers with a sum of 80 and
3 numbers with a sum of 90.
20 40 10 50 15 25 35 45.
(Possible answers: 80: 10, 20, 50; 90:
15, 35, 40)

CHAPTER 11

WRAP UP

INTRODUCTION The Wrap Up provides activities emphasizing math language and thinking skills for the chapter.

USING PAGE 245

Math Words ▶ **Why do you add ones first?** (Possible answer: so you can trade for another 10 if you need to)
▶ **What should you do if there are not enough ones to trade for another ten?** (Possible answer: Write the total number of ones; do not add an extra 10 in the tens place.)

Math Reasoning ▶ **How can you predict which numbers will make it necessary to trade?** (Possible answer: Think of the numbers that when added to 5 make a sum of 10 or more.)
▶ **Which number when added to 45 makes a sum of exactly 50?** (5)

Name _____

WRAP UP

MATH WORDS

1. Number the sentences in order. Show how to add 2-digit numbers when trading ones.

    __3__ Write the ones digit.

    __5__ Add the tens.

    __1__ Add the ones.

    __2__ Check to see if you should trade.

    __4__ Write the traded tens digit above.

    __6__ Write the tens digit.

Tens	Ones
1	
3	9
+ 1	7
5	6

2. Use the steps above. Add 39 + 17.

MATH REASONING

3. Add each number to 45. Ring the numbers that make a sum greater than 50. Tell when you traded 10 ones for 1 ten. **45 + 5 = 50; 45 + 6 = 51; 45 + 7 = 52; 45 + 8 = 53; 45 + 9 = 54**

  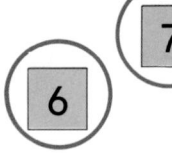  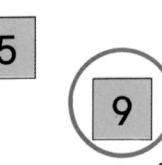

Chapter 11 Wrap Up   (two hundred forty-five) 2▶

TEACHING OPTIONS

ENRICHMENT Give each student up to 9 punchout dimes and 19 punchout pennies. Have students use the dimes and pennies as tens and ones to model addition exercises. For each exercise, have them decide if a trade is necessary and then find the answer.

For example:

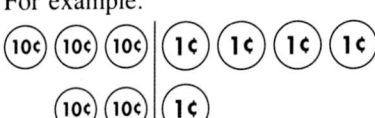

```
  34
+ 21
  55    no trade
```

Name _____

CHAPTER REVIEW/TEST

Ring and cross out 10 ones to trade if
you can. Draw a new ten. Write the sum.

 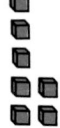 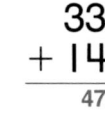

$$\begin{array}{r} 33 \\ + 14 \\ \hline 47 \end{array}$$

2.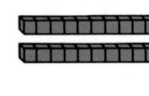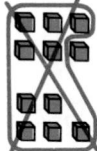

$$\begin{array}{r} 26 \\ + 5 \\ \hline 31 \end{array}$$

Ring the best estimate for the sum.
Then find the sum.

3.
$$\begin{array}{r} 32 \\ + 32 \\ \hline 64 \end{array}$$

about 40
(about 60)
about 80

4.
$$\begin{array}{r} 61 \\ + 23 \\ \hline 84 \end{array}$$

about 40
about 60
(about 80)

Add.

5.
$$\begin{array}{r} 59 \\ + 12 \\ \hline 71 \end{array}$$
$$\begin{array}{r} 26 \\ + 17 \\ \hline 43 \end{array}$$
$$\begin{array}{r} 30 \\ + 54 \\ \hline 84 \end{array}$$
$$\begin{array}{r} 49 \\ + 25 \\ \hline 74 \end{array}$$
$$\begin{array}{r} 82 \\ + 8 \\ \hline 90 \end{array}$$
$$\begin{array}{r} 29 \\ + 20 \\ \hline 49 \end{array}$$

6.
$$\begin{array}{r} 25 \\ 2 \\ + 25 \\ \hline 52 \end{array}$$
$$\begin{array}{r} 25 \\ 32 \\ + 18 \\ \hline 75 \end{array}$$
$$\begin{array}{r} 13 \\ 24 \\ + 33 \\ \hline 70 \end{array}$$
$$\begin{array}{r} 49 \\ 10 \\ + 25 \\ \hline 84 \end{array}$$
$$\begin{array}{r} 5 \\ 12 \\ + 14 \\ \hline 31 \end{array}$$
$$\begin{array}{r} 23 \\ 12 \\ + 8 \\ \hline 43 \end{array}$$

7. Randy bought
these.

 26¢ 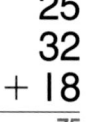 64¢

How much did
she spend?

____90____ ¢

Ring one. I used:
mental math
paper and pencil

 **Calculation
methods
may vary.**

CHAPTER REVIEW/TEST

INTRODUCTION The Review/Test is
provided to review and evaluate the skills
and concepts presented in Chapter 11.

USING PAGE 246
If you prefer to use this page for review,
you may want to use the
Multiple-Choice Posttest (pages 43-44)
or the **Free Response Posttest** (pages
43-44) to evaluate mastery of chapter
objectives.

ITEM ANALYSIS The table below
correlates the Chapter Review/Test Items
with the lesson objectives for the
chapter.

Items	Objectives
1, 2	11-1; 11-2; 11-3
3, 4	11-5
5	11-4; 11-6
6	11-9
7	11-8

INFORMAL ASSESSMENT

Using Manipulatives Have each
student write a 2-digit number on 2
slips of paper and trade 1 slip with a
partner. The first student adds by
joining blocks, and the second adds
with a calculator. Students compare
answers to check. Have them
exchange tasks and repeat the activity.

Communication *When might you
use mental math to solve a problem?
When might you use paper and pencil
or a calculator?* (Possible answers:

Use mental math when you can find
the answer in your head; use paper
and pencil when you need to trade 10
ones for a ten or 1 ten for 10 ones;
use a calculator when you are working
with large numbers or want to check
an answer.)

Critical Thinking *Why do you
always begin to solve an addition
exercise in the ones place?* (Possible
answer: to see if the combined ones
will make another ten)

CHAPTER 11

ENRICHMENT

INTRODUCTION Continuing number sequences helps students recognize and identify number patterns and develops number sense.

USING PAGE 247
This Enrichment page is provided for all students. You may wish to use it after they have completed the Chapter Review/Test on page 246.

Help students see some of the other number patterns that can be identified by looking across or down; for example, even and odd numbers, skip counting, and patterns of ones digits.

▶ **Why does the first pattern start over again at 90?** (Possible answer: You are adding 9; 81 + 9 = 90.)

▶ **What do you think would happen if the pattern continued for another row?** (Possible answer: 108 would be circled because it is the next number diagonally to the left after 99.)

▶ **How could you predict the last 4 numbers in the second pattern after completing the first 5 numbers?** (Possible answer: Continue along the diagonal line made by the number pattern; notice that both the tens and ones digits increase by 1 each time.)

EXTENSIONS Provide students with hundred charts and crayons. Have them ring a number between 3 and 8 on the chart, and choose a target number, such as 4, 5, 10, or 12. Then ask them to add their target number and color the new number. Tell students to continue to add and color until they reach the bottom of the chart. Have them share their charts with a friend and tell what patterns they see. Encourage students to look up, down, and diagonally to identify patterns.

Name _____

ENRICHMENT
Addition Patterns

1	2	3	4	5	6	7	8	9	10
11	12	13	14	15	16	17	18	19	20
21	22	23	24	25	26	27	28	29	30
31	32	33	34	35	36	37	38	39	40
41	42	43	44	45	46	47	48	49	50
51	52	53	54	55	56	57	58	59	60
61	62	63	64	65	66	67	68	69	70
71	72	73	74	75	76	77	78	79	80
81	82	83	84	85	86	87	88	89	90
91	92	93	94	95	96	97	98	99	100

1. Ring 9.
   Add 9 and ring the new number.
   Continue to add 9 and ring the numbers. Look for a pattern.
   Talk about the patterns you see. diagonals from 9 to 81, 90 to 9

2. Box 1.
   Add 11 and box the new number.
   Continue to add 11 and box the numbers. Look for a pattern.
   Talk about the patterns you see. diagonals from 1 to 100

Name _____

UMULATIVE REVIEW

ve the time.

- ○ 9:10
- ● 2:45
- ○ 3:30

- ○ 4:45
- ● 9:20
- ○ 10:20

ount the money.

- ● 46¢
- ○ 41¢
- ○ 55¢

- ○ 41¢
- ○ 57¢
- ● 70¢

Snacks	
popcorn	25¢
nuts	15¢
apple	5¢
banana	10¢

5. Find another way to make the sum.

$17 + 8$

- ● $12 + 13$
- ○ $13 + 4$
- ○ $15 + 12$

Add.

6. 28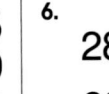

$28 + 4 = $ ___

- ● 32
- ○ 30
- ○ 34

7. 33 ▬▬▬

$33 + 30 = $ ___

- ○ 36
- ○ 43
- ● 63

8.

$40 + 30 = $ ___

- ○ 60
- ● 70
- ○ 80

Andy bought an apple and nuts. How much did he spend?

- ○ 25¢
- ● 20¢
- ○ 30¢

CUMULATIVE REVIEW

INTRODUCTION   The purpose of this Cumulative Review is to maintain previously taught skills and concepts. The emphasis in this Cumulative Review is on time and money, Chapter 9; and on understanding 2-digit addition, Chapter 10.

ITEM ANALYSIS   The table below correlates the Cumulative Review items with the lesson objectives.

Items	Objectives
1	9-2
2	9-8
3	9-9
4	10-6
5	10-1
6	10-3
7	10-2
8	10-4
9	9-11

CHAPTER 12 GEOMETRY

Chapter Management

MATHEMATICAL BACKGROUND

Geometry

At the elementary school level, the study of geometry should begin with an introduction to the variety of geometric shapes and figures we encounter in our daily lives. Initial geometric experiences should involve an analysis of the geometric characteristics of real-world objects, followed by an introduction to the mathematical name for each shape. The study of plane shapes should evolve from students' experience with real-world objects. After students develop the relationships between real-world objects and their mathematical representations, they are ready to analyze and compare these mathematical objects. Two types of analyses and comparisons are appropriate for students at this level: studying shapes with respect to the number of sides and the numbers of corners and studying pairs of shapes to determine whether they are the same size or shape.

Symmetric and Congruent Figures

Geometric figures of the same size and shape are congruent. Symmetric figures consist of two congruent halves.

Problem Solving

In this chapter, students use data from a number pair graph and the strategy Look for a Pattern to solve problems.

TIPS FROM TEACHERS

Have each student create a 9-in. by 9-in. symmetrical design on oaktag paper. Transfer the design to a fabric square. Then sew all the design squares together to make a patchwork quilt of symmetrical designs.

Phyllis Smith
Bell School
Marblehead, MA

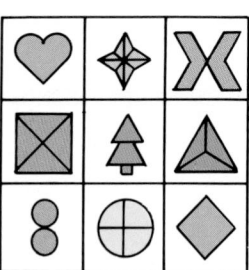

ASSESSMENT

ITEM ANALYSIS

Items	Objectives
1	12-1
2	12-2
3	12-3
4	12-4
5	12-5
6	12-6
7	12-7
8	12-8

Note: The item analysis is the same for all pretests and posttests for this chapter.

Pretest — Chapter 12, page 1
Multiple-Choice Format

Name _____

1. Choose the shape and name that match the picture.
   - A cylinder
   - B cone
   - C cube

2. What shape would this pattern make if you cut and pasted it?
   - A triangular prism
   - B pyramid
   - C cone

3. What plane figure is being drawn?
   - A rectangle
   - B triangle
   - (C) circle

4. How many sides are there?
   - A 2 sides
   - (B) 4 sides
   - C 6 sides

MCT 2   45

Pretest — Chapter 12, page 2
Multiple-Choice Format

Name _____

5. Imagine how the first figure will look when you turn the board as shown. Will it look like the second picture?
   - (A) yes
   - B no

6. This figure was cut from folded paper. Find the other half of the figure.
   - (A)
   - B
   - C

7. Could you use the 2 triangles to make a figure congruent to the shaded figure?
   - (A) yes
   - B no

8. Use the data from the graph. Write the prices. Then find the total cost.

   start

   over up
   Jo bought something at [3] [2]. price ____
   She bought something at [2] [1]. price ____
   What was the total cost?
   - (A) 71¢
   - B 61¢
   - C 21¢

46   MCT 2

Posttest — Chapter 12, page 1
Multiple-Choice Format

Name _____

1. Choose the shape and name that match the picture.
   - A cylinder
   - B cone
   - (C) cube

2. What shape would this pattern make if you cut and pasted it?
   - A triangular prism
   - B pyramid
   - (C) cube

3. What plane figure is being drawn?
   - (A) rectangle
   - B triangle
   - C circle

4. How many sides are there?
   - A 2 sides
   - (B) 4 sides
   - C 6 sides

MCT 2   47

Posttest — Chapter 12, page 2
Multiple-Choice Format

Name _____

5. Imagine how the first figure will look when you turn the board as shown. Will it look like the second picture?
   - (A) yes
   - B no

6. This figure was cut from folded paper. Find the other half of the figure.
   - A
   - B
   - (C)

7. Could you use the 2 triangles to make a figure congruent to the shaded figure?
   - (A) yes
   - B no

8. Use the data from the graph. Write the prices. Then find the total cost.

   start

   over up
   Mel bought something at [2] [3]. price ____
   He bought something at [1] [2]. price ____
   What was the total cost?
   - A 41
   - (B) 32
   - C 45

48   MCT 2

ALSO AVAILABLE

▶ Free Response Tests
▶ Alternative Tests
▶ Thinking Strategies
▶ Concrete Materials

PROJECT AND BULLETIN BOARD

Provide a variety of fruits and vegetables, tempera paint, plastic picnic knives, and shallow aluminum tins. Help small groups of students cut through the center of each fruit and vegetable. Observe the shape of each side of the fruit. *Are the halves alike in size, shape, and position? If so, they are symmetrical.* Have students dip the half pieces of fruits and vegetables into aluminum tins containing thin paint, then press the pieces on paper to make prints. Display the prints under the appropriate headings on the bulletin board. Have students look for pictures of other symmetric and nonsymmetric shapes and add them to the bulletin board display.

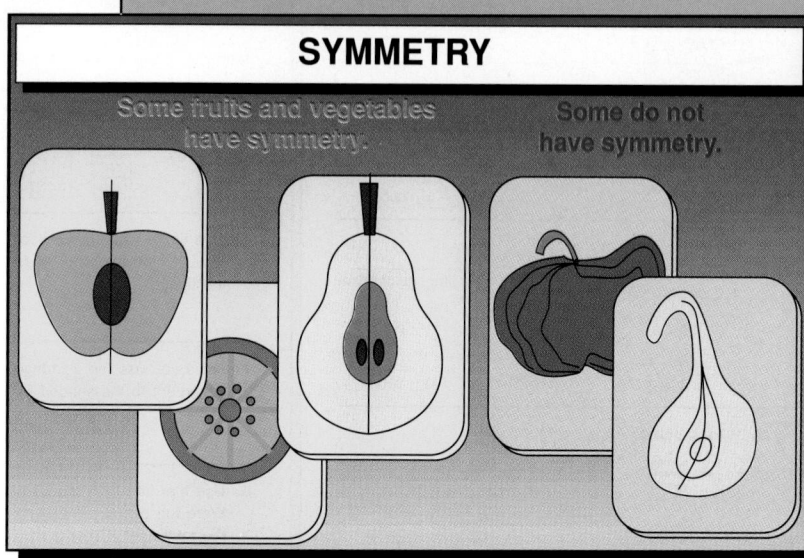

COOPERATIVE LEARNING

Divide the class into 5 or 6 groups. Identify the group skill: reaching a group decision. Distribute attribute blocks to each group. Ask students to use the shapes to create a picture of a single object, such as a house, an arrow, a dog, or a tree. Each group should practice arranging the pieces and making simple objects. The members of each group should then demonstrate at least 3 simple shapes they created. Group members should observe, discuss, and agree on the object they would like to show to the class. Members of the group plan the presentation and share the following tasks: arrange the shapes on a piece of black paper to show the finished object, trace the outline of the object in white chalk, label the object, and trace the outline and the individual shapes on white paper. Each group displays the black outline drawing of its object and challenges other groups to create the shape using their own attribute blocks. Share the white answer sheet so the groups can check their work.

You will find grouping suggestions and cooperative learning activities in most lessons throughout this chapter.

LITERATURE

Anno, Mitsumasa. *Anno's Alphabet.* New York: Thomas Y. Crowell, 1975.

In this highly imaginative book students will enjoy playful 3-dimensional images of various shapes. Have students identify the different solid figures, then draw the plane shapes that form the faces of the solid shapes. Have them compare their shapes to the ones in *Anno's Alphabet.*

Pienkowski, Jan. *Shapes.* New York: Harvey House, 1975.

Reit, Seymour. *All Kinds of Signs.* New York: Western Publishing, 1970.

Seuss, Dr. *The Shape of Me and Other Stuff.* New York: Random House, 1973.

ENGLISH AS A SECOND LANGUAGE

Chapter 12 provides hands-on activities with solid and plane figures. The concepts and related vocabulary introduced are new for all students, putting ESL students on a par with native speakers. Make sure that ESL students understand *can slide,* and *can roll* before asking them to classify the objects. When students are asked to reach inside a box and describe objects without seeing them, invite native speakers to go first so that ESL students have time to listen to the language before having to produce it.

Vary the developmental activities by asking native speakers to set down the conditions for the ESL students to follow in making plane figures on a geoboard. Then, if ESL students are ready, reverse the roles and have them give the conditions. Similarly, vary the game where partners make congruent figures so that one student gives directions for the partner to follow.

Use large visual aids and encourage students to speak aloud and point to figures when comparing figures.

GIFTED

Mathematically talented students may already understand solid and plane figures. Many of the activities presented in this chapter may interest them, however. You may wish to challenge these students, after they have completed their book work, to discover more about plane figures with which they are familiar. For example, after Lesson 4 on corners and sides, draw a 4-sided figure on the chalkboard. Demonstrate how to find the perimeter by measuring each side from corner to corner, recording the number of inches, and finding the sum of the measures. Then provide students with centimeter rulers and challenge them to find perimeters for the plane figures in their Student Editions. After Lesson 6 on symmetry and Lesson 7 on congruence, have students measure figures to see if equal perimeters always reflect congruent shapes. If this appeals to your students, you may wish to have them estimate perimeters for irregular shapes or have the artistically gifted create their own shapes and calculate perimeters and lines of symmetry.

STUDENTS AT RISK

Have students use a length of rope to make plane figures on the classroom floor. Have them tie knots at the corners and count the number of sides and knots on the completed shapes.

Provide a pair of students with a geoboard and have the first student make a shape using a rubber band. Then have the second student make a congruent figure.

Take a walk through the school or the neighborhood to hunt for shapes. Have students note different plane and solid shapes they have studied and look carefully for unusual ways shapes are used. For example, they might note that a fire hydrant is a cylinder, a covered bus stop is a cube, and so on. When you return to the classroom, have them make a graph or an illustrated chart of the different shapes.

You may also use the Reteaching Supplements and the specific Reteaching Tips from each lesson in this chapter.

PICTURE

These pictures and accompanying stories and poems are available as storybooks.

You may want to read and discuss this story with your students before starting the chapter. The first lesson in this chapter includes a question about the story. Lessons 1, 3, and 4 in this chapter have questions in the informal Assessment that refer to the story.

Candle Crafts

"What can we make for the crafts fair next week?" asked Ken. The three Koala brothers sat in their tree fort thinking hard.

"Maybe we can sew puppets," suggested Leo, the middle brother.

"Yes! I love puppets! Let's make puppets!" cried Joey, the youngest.

"But we don't know how to sew," Ken reminded them. "There must be something we can do." The three sat and thought some more.

"How about stringing beads to make necklaces?" offered Leo.

"Oh yes! I love bright beads! Let's make necklaces!" exclaimed Joey.

"That's not a bad idea, but our neighbors, Gretchen and Barbara, are making necklaces. We should do something different," replied Ken. The three sat with their heads in their hands.

Suddenly Leo leapt up. "I've got it! Let's make candles. Remember last year Dad said he'd help us and we never got around to making them?"

"Yes! I love candles! Let's make candles!" chimed Joey.

"Good idea," said Ken excitedly. "We need to collect objects to form the candles. Let's meet in the kitchen in 20 minutes. Bring as many different shaped objects as you can find." The three brothers scurried off in three different directions.

Twenty minutes later Ken and Leo showed up with their father. "Dad, I found an empty milk carton, an empty soup can, and an old cup. Can we use these objects to make candles?" asked Leo.

"Yes, son. Those objects will work just fine," smiled his father.

"Hey, I found an empty orange juice carton, a small bucket, and a drinking glass. These will work, won't they, Dad?" questioned Ken.

"Yes, I think you both found some good objects," replied Dad. "But where is Joey? Wasn't he supposed to find some objects too?" Before either Ken or Leo could answer, they heard a noise. "Thump, plop...thump, plop, thump, plop," went the sound. Then around the corner came Joey bouncing a red rubber ball and catching it inside a funnel. "Thump, plop...thump, plop...thump, plop."

"Hey, look what I found!" exclaimed Joey with glee.

"Great, Joey," said Ken with disgust. "We can't make candles with a rubber ball and a funnel." Joey lowered his head dejectedly.

His father laughed. "Oh, I don't know about that. I think Joey has found good objects. I can poke a hole in the ball and use the funnel to pour the wax into it. After the wax hardens, I can carefully cut the rubber off. Then I can plug the funnel's spout and pour wax into it. Yes, I think Joey has found the most interesting objects."

Joey held up his head proudly and beamed. "I like candles. I like candles of different shapes!"

Identifying Solid Figures

OBJECTIVE 12-1   To identify and sort solid figures

PREBOOK ACTIVITIES

QUICK REVIEW

Tell the name of each shape

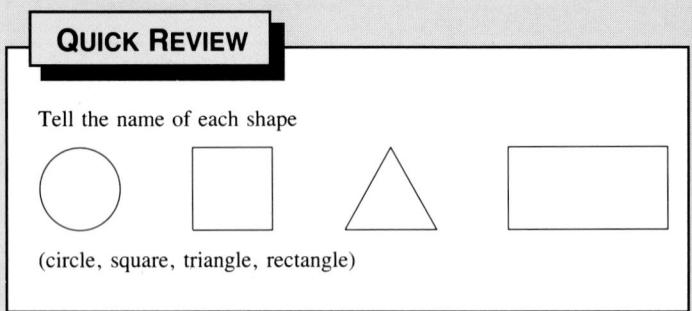

(circle, square, triangle, rectangle)

PRIOR KNOWLEDGE

Display several classroom objects of different shapes, such as a number cube, a covered can, a shoe box, and a ball. Give shape clues such as the following and ask students to name the object that matches.

It is round all over. (ball)
It is small and square. (number cube)
It has a rectangle as its top and bottom. (shoe box)
It has a circle as its top and bottom. (covered can)

Ask students to discuss other characteristics of each object.

COMMUNICATION

Reading and Discussing Math   Write the words **solid figures, sphere, cone, cylinder, triangular prism, rectangular prism, triangular pyramid,** and **rectangular pyramid** on the chalkboard. Point to the term *solid figures* and explain that these are figures that can be held. Then read the other terms, one at a time, as you hold up the corresponding geometric solid block. *Suppose you want to describe a sphere, What words would you use?* (Possible answers: *round; can roll; shaped like a ball*) Have students write in their Math Journals a description of one of the solid figures.

EXPLORE AND CONNECT

Materials: graphing mat, geometric solid blocks, index card labeled with the names of solids
Grouping Suggestion: small groups

Make a large graphing mat out of a sheet of paper or plastic with columns for the geometric solids introduced in the lesso Spread the mat on the floor and place a solid and a label at t top of each column. Point to and name each solid. Tell students that there are many objects in the classroom that hav the same shape as the solid blocks. Assign a geometric solid each group and have students go on a scavenger hunt and br back objects shaped like their solid. Have students place the objects appropriately on the graphing mat. Talk about the solids that were easiest and hardest to find. *Which ones can slide?* (any solids with flat faces) *Which ones can roll?* (any solids that are round or curved)

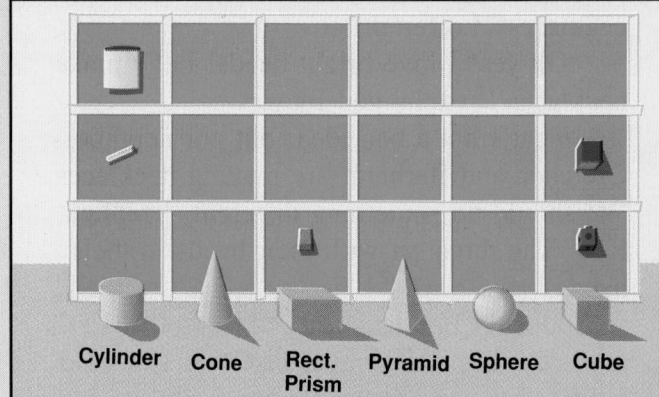

Cylinder   Cone   Rect. Prism   Pyramid   Sphere   Cube

CONNECTIONS   Use these anytime.

Problem of the Day

Guess and Check   Cut a hole in a shoe box. Secretly place a solid block in the box. Have a classmate reach inside the box without looking and guess which block you hid. Show the block to check. Now have your classmate hide a block so you can guess and check.

Subject Integration

Language Arts   Play a guessing game with some other students. Choose a solid geometric block and describe it, using words that tell about its shape, about its flat faces, and whether it can slide or roll. The other students in your group are to guess which block you are describing. The one who guesses correctly describes the next block.

Math Connection

Shape Patterns   Use solid blocks. Place blocks in a row to make a pattern. Read your pattern aloud to a partner. Then see if your partner can add blocks to continue the pattern. Take turns starting and finishing shape patterns. Draw pictures of your patterns and show them to the class.

CLASSWORK AND HOMEWORK SUPPLEMENTS

Practice

Skills Maintenance   12-1

Name _____

Identifying Solid Figures

Color solid figures and objects that match the same color.
Use a different color for each pair.   Check students' work.

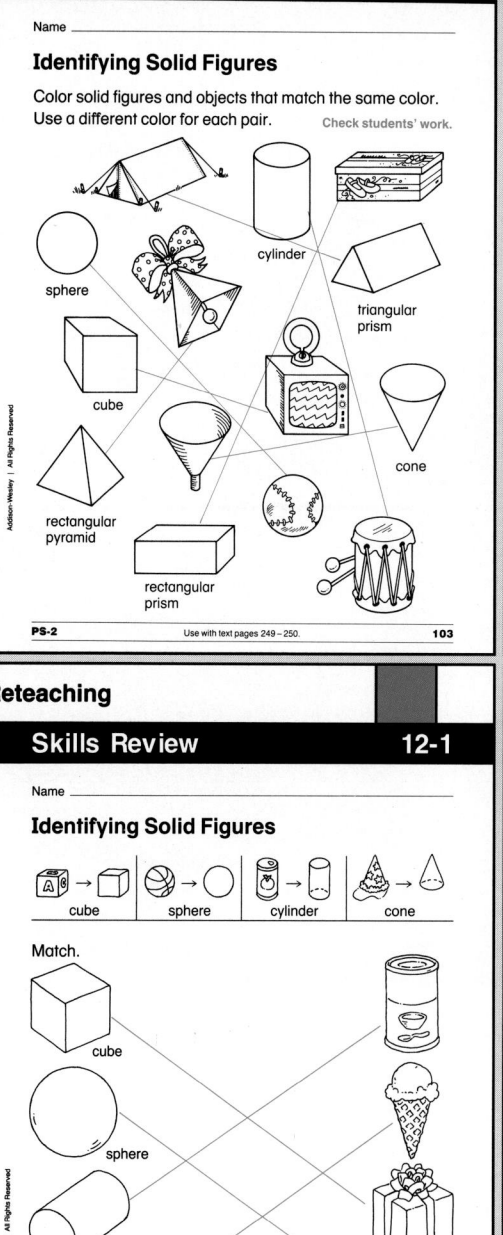

sphere
cylinder
triangular prism
cube
cone
rectangular pyramid
rectangular prism

PS-2   Use with text pages 249–250.   103

Building Thinking Skills

Family Math   12-1

Name _____

Solids at Home

> Dear Family,
> In our math class we are learning to identify solid figures and match them to real-world objects. Help your child match solids to objects around the house and complete the chart.

Look around your house.
Find objects with the same shape as the solids on the chart.
Ask a family member to help you write the names of the objects to finish the chart.

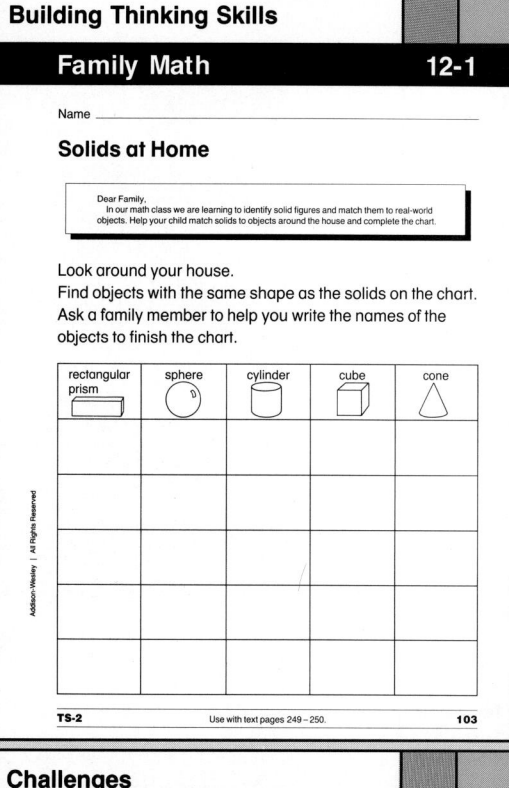

rectangular prism	sphere	cylinder	cube	cone

TS-2   Use with text pages 249–250.   103

Reteaching

Skills Review   12-1

Name _____

Identifying Solid Figures

→ cube	→ sphere	→ cylinder	→ cone
cube	sphere	cylinder	cone

Match.

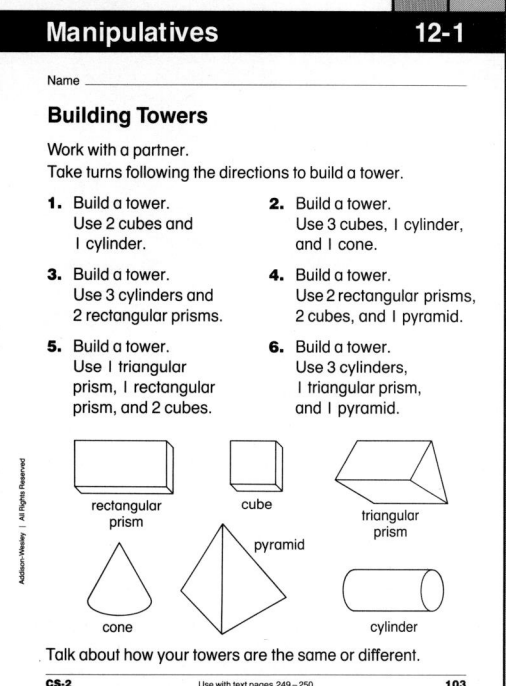

cube
sphere
cylinder
cone

RS-2   Use with text pages 249–250.   103

Challenges

Manipulatives   12-1

Name _____

Building Towers

Work with a partner.
Take turns following the directions to build a tower.

1. Build a tower.
Use 2 cubes and
1 cylinder.

2. Build a tower.
Use 3 cubes, 1 cylinder,
and 1 cone.

3. Build a tower.
Use 3 cylinders and
2 rectangular prisms.

4. Build a tower.
Use 2 rectangular prisms,
2 cubes, and 1 pyramid.

5. Build a tower.
Use 1 triangular
prism, 1 rectangular
prism, and 2 cubes.

6. Build a tower.
Use 3 cylinders,
1 triangular prism,
and 1 pyramid.

rectangular prism
cube
triangular prism
cone
pyramid
cylinder

Talk about how your towers are the same or different.

CS-2   Use with text pages 249–250.   103

OPTIONS FOR INDIVIDUAL NEEDS

Basic

Exercises All

Supplements
Reteaching 103 or
Practice 103

12-1

Average

Exercises All

Supplements
Practice 103
Challenges 103 or
Thinking Skills 103

Extended

Exercises All

Supplements
Challenges 103
Thinking Skills 103

Other Resources:
Explorations, pp. 80-89, 96,
100, 173, 235, 302
*Problem-Solving Experiences
In Mathematics,* p. 107
Workjobs, pp. 214-215
Workjobs For Parents, pp.
68-69
Mathematics Book A, p. 78

OBJECTIVE 12-1
To identify and sort solid figures

Materials: solid geometric blocks, cans, boxes, balls, party hats, cones, and other classroom objects.

Grouping Suggestions: individual work, cooperative learning groups

1. MOTIVATE AND TEACH

LEARN ABOUT IT

Read the chapter story to the class. Have students identify the geometric shapes shown in the picture. Then have them match geometric solids to the appropriate pictures.

Have students turn to page 249 and ask them to place a solid geometric block on top of the matching candle picture as you discuss the story. Have them read the name of each shape as they place the block on the page.

▶ **Which shape was most difficult to keep in place on the page? Why?** (The sphere; it has no flat sides.)

▶ **Why do you need to place the cylinder on end in order to get it to stay on the paper?** (Possible answer: so that it does not roll)

▶ **How are the cone and the rectangular pyramid alike? How are they different?** (Possible answer: Both have a pointed top and get wider at the bottom; the pyramid has flat sides, the cone does not; the cone has a circle bottom, and the pyramid has a rectangle bottom.)

2. CHECK UNDERSTANDING

ERROR ALERT Confusing faces on solid shapes with curved surfaces. Being unable to identify the shape of a flat face.

12
Geometry

TEACHING OPTIONS

RETEACHING TIPS Display boxes, cans, balls, and cones and have students identify each as a solid. Hold up a box; look at each face and ask what shapes they are. Repeat for others. Explain that a solid shape may have different kinds of faces. Assign Reteaching Supplement 103.

ENRICHMENT Have pairs gather a collection of real-world solid objects in the shapes of cylinders, cubes, cones, rectangular prisms, triangular prisms, and pyramids. Trace on paper each face of a solid they like. Compare the traced shapes with a partner's and discuss their characteristics.

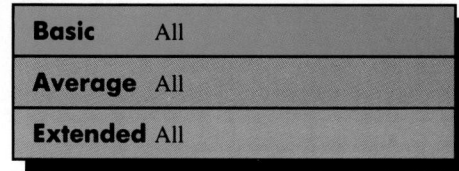

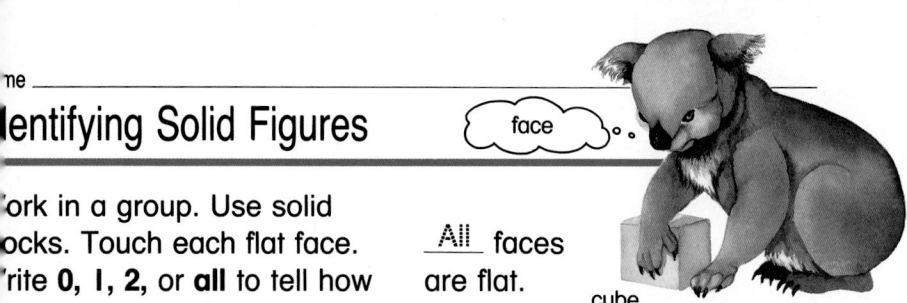

...me _____

...entifying Solid Figures

face

...ork in a group. Use solid
...ocks. Touch each flat face.
...rite **0, 1, 2,** or **all** to tell how
...any faces are flat.

__All__ faces
are flat.

cube

 sphere

__0__ faces are flat.

2. cone

__1__ face is flat.

 cylinder

__2__ faces are flat.

4. 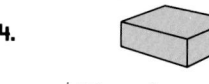 rectangular prism

__All__ faces are flat.

Match.

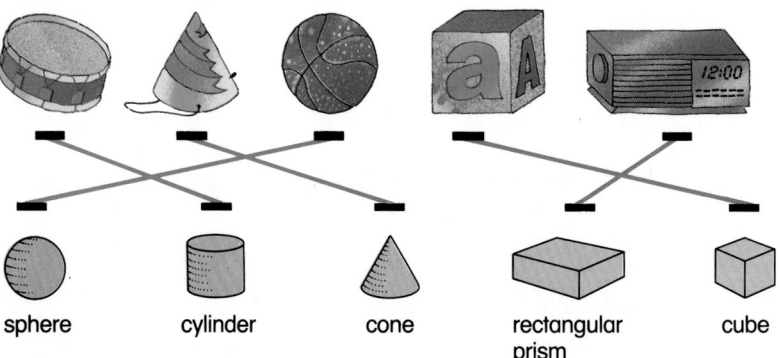

| sphere | cylinder | cone | rectangular prism | cube |

...LK ABOUT IT

Tell how a rectangular prism
and a cube are alike.
See teaching notes.

 cube

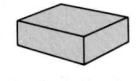 rectangular prism

Chapter 12

---

3. PRACTICE AND APPLY

Basic	All
Average	All
Extended	All

12-1

PRACTICE

How can you tell if a surface is flat?
(Possible answers: A surface is flat if it
does not roll; if you can stack something
on top of it.) *How will you write the
answers in Exercise 2?* (Draw lines from
the solids to the matching objects.)

APPLY

TALK ABOUT IT ▶ **What do you
have to do to answer the question?**
(Compare the cube to the rectangular
prism.)
▶ **How might you find the things that
are alike?** (Possible answers: Look at
the drawings in your book; hold one
block in each hand and compare.)
▶ **How are the blocks' faces the
same? How are they different?**
(Possible answers: Both blocks have 6
faces; the opposite faces are the same for
both blocks; the cube has 6 faces that are
the same, but the rectangular prism has 2
different-sized faces.)

...LOSE AND **ASSESS**

...HOW WHAT YOU KNOW

...emind students of the chapter story,
...ndle Crafts and have them identify
...e geometric shapes shown in the
...ory picture. Ask them to match
...ncrete geometric solids to the
...propriate picture and to name the
...gure as they match it.

QUICK QUIZ

Name each solid I hold up.

○ ⬡ ⬭ ▽

(sphere, cube, cylinder, cone)

Making a Solid Figure

OBJECTIVE 12-2   To make a solid figure; to count the number of corners, edges, or faces

PREBOOK ACTIVITIES

QUICK REVIEW

Name an object found at school or at home that has the same shape.
sphere   (baseball, beachball, orange)
cone   (party hat, funnel)
cylinder   (paint can, wastebasket)
cube   (television set, box)
rectangular prism   (tissue box, digital clock)

PRIOR KNOWLEDGE

Show students everyday objects in the shapes of a sphere, cube, cylinder, and cone. After students have examined the objects, ask them to discuss and compare qualities of the shapes. *Is there a sharp place on the shape? Can you roll the shape? Can you stack the shape?* Ask students to group the shapes by their qualities, noting how they are alike and how they are different.

COMMUNICATION

Reading and Writing in Math   Write **corner, edge,** and **face** on the chalkboard. As you say each word, show what it is by pointing to it on a solid figure. Draw the following shape with answer lines on the board.

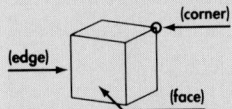

Call on volunteers to label the parts of the shape using the vocabulary words *corner, edge,* and *face.* Have students use the labeled figures to write their own definitions of *corner, edge,* and *face* in their Math Journals.

EXPLORE AND CONNECT

Materials: small objects in shapes of a sphere, cube, cylinder, cone, triangular pyramid, triangular prism, rectangular prism; shoeboxes
Grouping Suggestion: groups of 4
Hold up a cube. Point to each **corner** as you count aloud. *How many corners does a cube have?* (8) Repeat for the **edges** and **faces** of the cube. Give each small group a shoebox with a hole cut in the top that will allow a small hand to fit through. Give each group a variety of solid shapes that will fit in the box. Ask one student to choose a shape without letting the others see it and place it in the box. Ask the second student to feel the shape; describe the number of corners, edges, and faces; and then try to identify it. Have the third student record the answer and the fourth open the box and verify the shape. As a group, students decide if the number of corners, edges, and faces is correct. Then have students change roles.

CONNECTIONS   Use these anytime.

Problem of the Day

Understand the Operation   Add or subtract? Write the answer.
Bill has 17 cone-shaped blocks.
He has 29 cube-shaped blocks.
How many blocks does Bill have?
(add, 46 blocks)

Creative Thinking

Building with Shapes   Using building blocks of all shapes and sizes, design a house of the future. Try to use as many different shapes as possible. Share your house with the class and identify some of the solid figures you used.

Minute Math

Geometry Riddles   I have no corners, edges, or faces.
I look like something you bounce.
Guess my shape. (sphere)
I am made up of 4 triangles.
I look like a tent.
Guess my shape. (pyramid)

CLASSWORK AND HOMEWORK SUPPLEMENTS

Practice

Manipulatives 12-2

Name _____

Making a Solid Figure

Work in a group. Use solid blocks. Fill in the chart.
Then answer the questions.

		How many flat faces?	How many corners?	How many edges?
⬭	sphere	0	0	0
⬭	cylinder	2	0	0
⬭	cube	6	8	12
⬭	pyramid	4	4	6
⬭	rectangular prism	6	8	12
⬭	triangular prism	5	6	9

1. Which two solids have the most faces? The fewest?

rectangular prism, cube; sphere, cylinder

2. Which solid has the same number of faces, corners, and edges? Why? sphere; it has 0

3. Which solids have more edges than corners?

cube, pyramid, rectangular prism, triangular prism

104   Use with text pages 251 – 252.   **PS-2**

Building Thinking Skills

Critical Thinking 12-2

Name _____

Sort the Solids

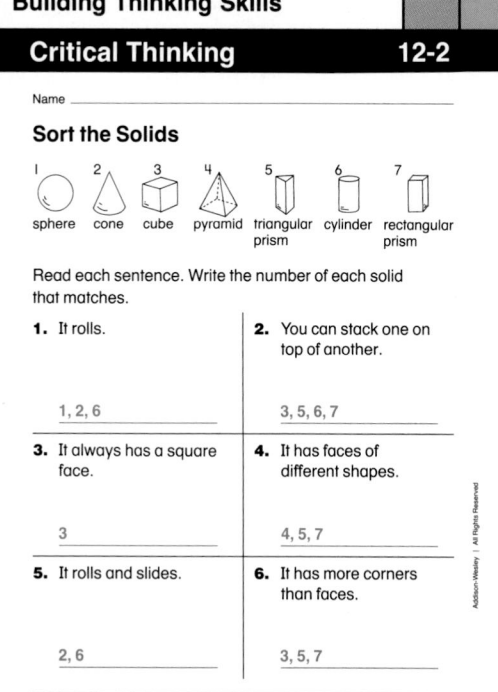

1 sphere 2 cone 3 cube 4 pyramid 5 triangular prism 6 cylinder 7 rectangular prism

Read each sentence. Write the number of each solid
that matches.

1. It rolls.

1, 2, 6

2. You can stack one on top of another.

3, 5, 6, 7

3. It always has a square face.

3

4. It has faces of different shapes.

4, 5, 7

5. It rolls and slides.

2, 6

6. It has more corners than faces.

3, 5, 7

104   Use with text pages 251 – 252.   **TS-2**

Reteaching

Manipulatives 12-2

Name _____

Making a Solid Figure

corner — edge — face

Use solid blocks. Ring the answer.

1. Which has no flat faces?

2. Which has more corners?

3. Which has 6 faces?

4. Which has more edges?

5. Which has 2 flat faces?

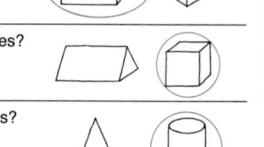

104   Use with text pages 251 – 252.   **RS-2**

Challenges

Creative Thinking 12-2

Name _____

What Is My Name?

Look at the pattern for each solid figure.
Write the name of the solid you could make from
the pattern.

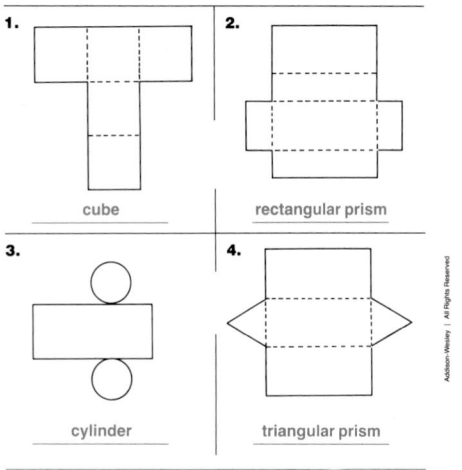

1. cube

2. rectangular prism

3. cylinder

4. triangular prism

104   Use with text pages 251 – 252.   **CS-2**

OPTIONS FOR INDIVIDUAL NEEDS

Basic

Exercises All
More Practice, p. 423, set A

Supplements
Reteaching 104 or
Practice 104

Average

Exercises All
More Practice, p. 423, set A

Supplements
Practice 104
Challenges 104 or
Thinking Skills 104

Extended

Exercises All

Supplements
Challenges 104
Thinking Skills 104

Other Resources:
Explorations, pp. 89, 96, 173
Mathematics Book A, p. 78

12-2

OBJECTIVE 12-2

To make a solid figure; to count the numbers of corners, edges, or faces

> **Materials:** objects in the shapes of spheres, cones, cubes, cylinders, rectangular prisms, triangular prisms, and triangular pyramids; colored tape; geometric shape blocks
>
> **Grouping Suggestions:** individual work, pairs

1. MOTIVATE AND TEACH

LEARN ABOUT IT

Place 3 different-shaped objects in a paper bag. Invite a student to reach into the bag and choose the shape after you describe the number of **corners, edges,** and **faces** that it has. After the student has chosen the correct shape, take out the other 2 shapes and compare them to the first one. Discuss how they are alike and how they are different.

▶ **Look at the box at the top of page 251. Explain the difference between the face, the edge, and the corner of the box.** (Possible answer: The face is a flat surface. The edge is the line where two faces meet. The corner is the point where the edges meet.)

▶ **How do you think the solid figure you make will differ from the picture?** (Possible answer: The picture is flat; the solid figure will be an object.) Remind students to cut on only the dashed lines. Some may find it easier to use tape to secure the sides instead of glue.

▶ **How many corners does the pyramid have?** (4)

▶ **How many edges does it have?** (6)

▶ **How many flat faces does it have?** (4)

▶ **How is the cone different from the pyramid?** (It has only one corner and one flat face; its bottom face is a circle.)

2. CHECK UNDERSTANDING

ERROR ALERT Difficulty counting corners, edges, and faces.

Name _____

Making a Solid Figure

Cut out the figure below along the dashed lines. Fold and paste the figure so the faces show. Count the number of **corners, edges,** and **faces.** Write the numbers.

1. corners ___4___

2. edges ___6___

3. faces ___4___

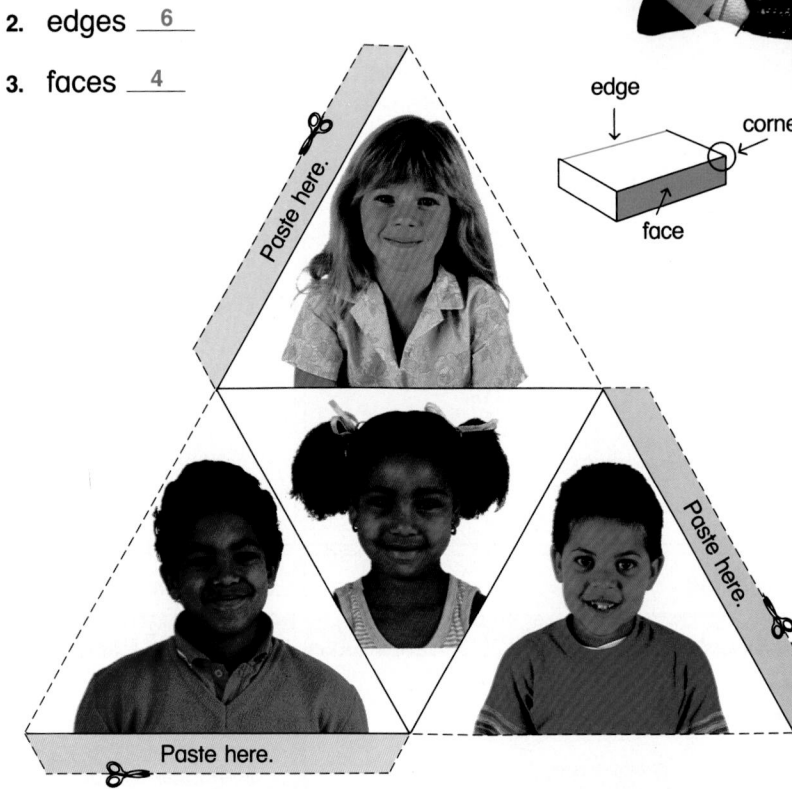

Chapter 12   (two hundred fifty-one)

TEACHING OPTIONS

RETEACHING TIPS Give students colored tape and geometric blocks. Have them place a piece of tape over each corner, edge, or face of a block as they count it, to see which parts they have counted and which are left. Repeat with different shapes. Use Reteaching Supplement 104.

ENRICHMENT **Family Math** After a shopping trip with a family member, students sort packages and cans by their shapes and group like shapes. Have them name the shapes and count the corners, edges, and faces of each box or can. Discuss reasons why some shapes are not practical for packaging.

What shape did you make? Ring it.

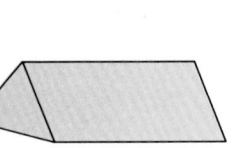 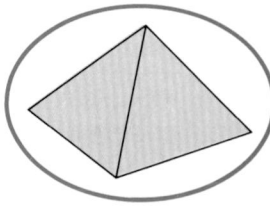 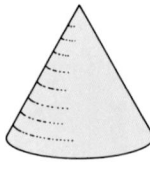

How many edges meet at each corner? __3__ edges

How many faces meet at each edge? __2__ faces

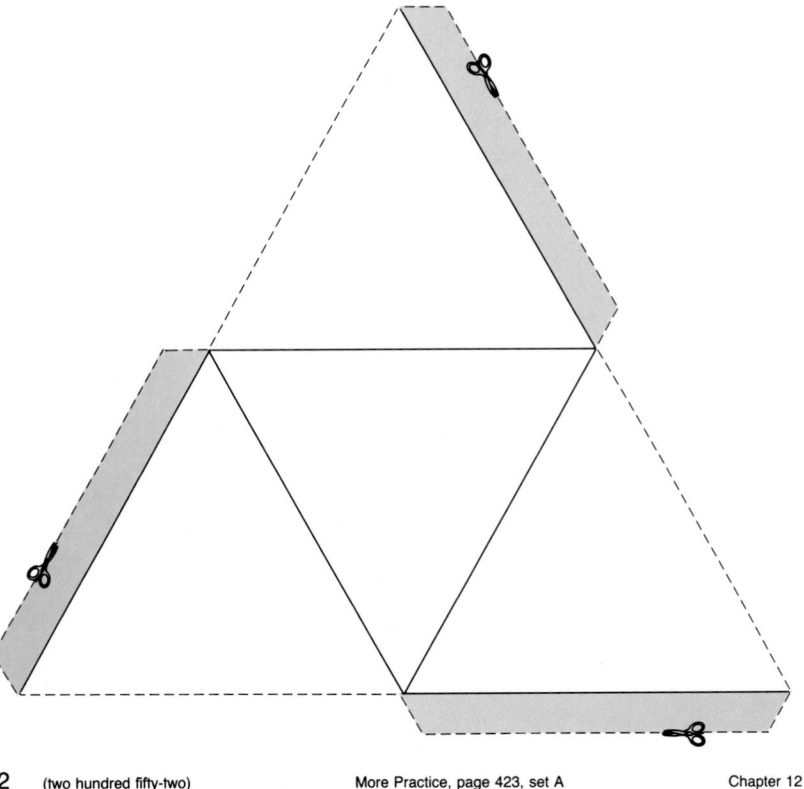

3. PRACTICE AND APPLY

Basic	All
Average	All
Extended	All

PRACTICE

How can you tell how many edges meet at each corner? (First, touch each edge of the figure and trace it with your finger to where it meets a corner. Then count the number of edges that meet at that corner.)

APPLY

▶ **Describe how the figure you made differs from the pictures of the triangular prism and the cone found on page 252.** (Possible answer: The pyramid has a different-shaped base; the pyramid has all flat faces; the cone has only 1 flat face.

▶ **How are the three solid figures alike?** (Possible answer: They all have a triangular shape.)

▶ **Compare your triangular pyramid to a rectangular pyramid. How are they different?** (Possible answer: The rectangular pyramid would have a square base and 4 sides; the triangular pyramid has a triangular base and 3 sides.)

12-2

LOSE AND ASSESS

AY WHAT YOU THINK Have e student in each pair count and ite the number of corners, faces, d edges of one particular geometric ape block. Then have the student ce that block in a group with 2 ferent blocks. Have the second dent use the first student's data to ntify the correct block.

QUICK QUIZ

Write the answer for each shape.
sphere __(0)__ corners
cone __(1)__ flat face(s)
cube __(12)__ edges
triangular prism __(6)__ corners

Drawing Plane Figures from Solids

OBJECTIVE 12-3 To identify plane shapes on solids

PREBOOK ACTIVITIES

QUICK REVIEW

Write the number of flat faces that are found on each solid figure.

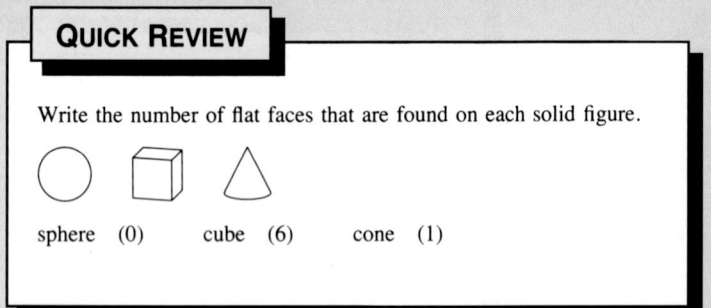

sphere (0)   cube (6)   cone (1)

PRIOR KNOWLEDGE

Help students recall the names of plane figures by drawing on the chalkboard a simple house that includes a square, rectangle, triangle, and circle. Draw a line to each shape and ask volunteers to identify each and write its name on the line. Then ask other students to add trees, flowers, and people drawn with those shapes.

COMMUNICATION

Reading and Discussing Math   Display a triangular pyramid and a plane figure of a triangle. Write **solid figure** and **plane figure** on the chalkboard. Read each word aloud and hold up the matching shape. Then ask students to read the word that goes with the shape you point to.
How is a plane figure different from a solid figure? (Possible answer: A plane figure is flat. It is like one of the faces of the solid figure.) *What other plane figures can you identify?* (Possible answer: circle, square, rectangle) *What other solid figures can you identify?* (Possible answer: sphere, cube, cone, rectangular prism, pyramid) Have students look around the room to name examples of plane and solid figures.

EXPLORE AND CONNECT

Materials: geometric solids or objects shaped like solids
Explain to students that **a plane figure** is actually a flat face of a **solid figure.** As an example, hold up a cube and then trace around one of its faces on the chalkboard. *What shape have I drawn?* (square) Identify the cube as the solid figure and the square as the plane figure. Distribute a geometric solid to every student. If possible, include an oval can or oval solid. Ask each student to draw around one of the faces of the solid. Then collect the drawings and redistribute them, making sure students do not get their own. Challenge students to match the plane figure picture with the solid that was used to draw it. *Could more than one solid figure have the same type of face?* (Possible answer: Yes, a cube and a rectangular pyramid could each have a square face.) *What plane figure do you get when you trace this (oval) can?* (oval)

CONNECTIONS   Use these anytime.

Problem of the Day

Using Estimation   Ring the best estimate.
Roy painted 11 cubes purple and 14 cones green. About how many solid shapes did he paint in all?
about 60 shapes
about 40 shapes
(about 20 shapes)

Subject Integration

Physical Education   With a group of friends, think of ways that you can use your bodies to show plane figures such as circles, squares, rectangles, and triangles. Try starting with a small shape and then add people to make it larger.

Life Skills

Reading a Map   Make a map of a pretend city. Use different plane figures to show buildings in the town, such as the school, the library, and the fire station. At the bottom of your map, tell what each plane figure stands for. Share your map with a friend. Have your friend use the key to name the buildings on your map.

CLASSWORK AND HOMEWORK SUPPLEMENTS

12-3

Practice

Skills Maintenance   12-3

Name

Drawing Plane Figures from Solids

Color each triangle blue.
Color each rectangle red.
Color each square orange.
Color each circle yellow.

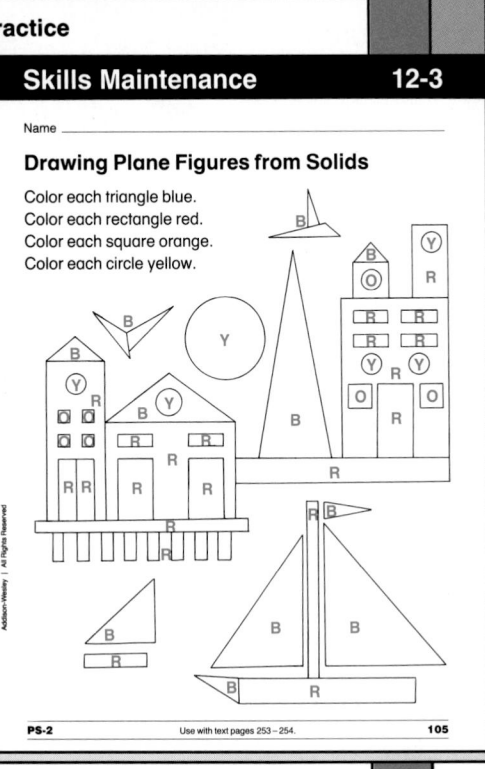

PS-2   Use with text pages 253–254.   105

Building Thinking Skills

Data Analysis   12-3

Name

Picture This

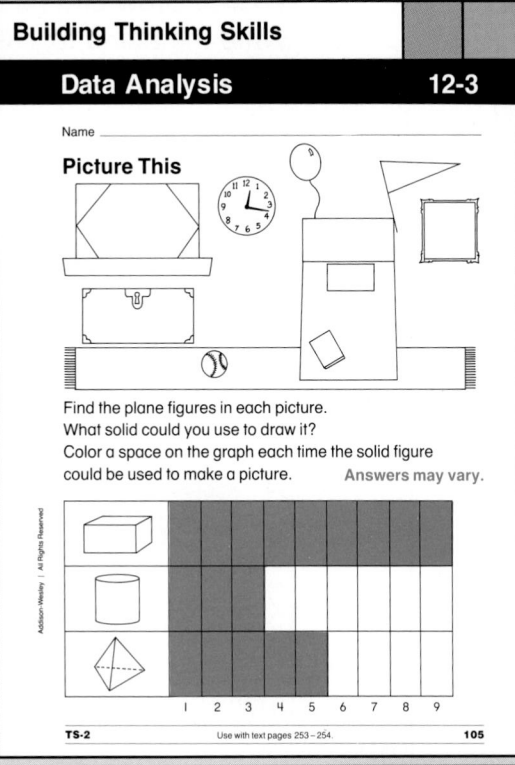

Find the plane figures in each picture.
What solid could you use to draw it?
Color a space on the graph each time the solid figure could be used to make a picture.   **Answers may vary.**

TS-2   Use with text pages 253–254.   105

Reteaching

Skills Review   12-3

Name

Drawing Plane Figures from Solids

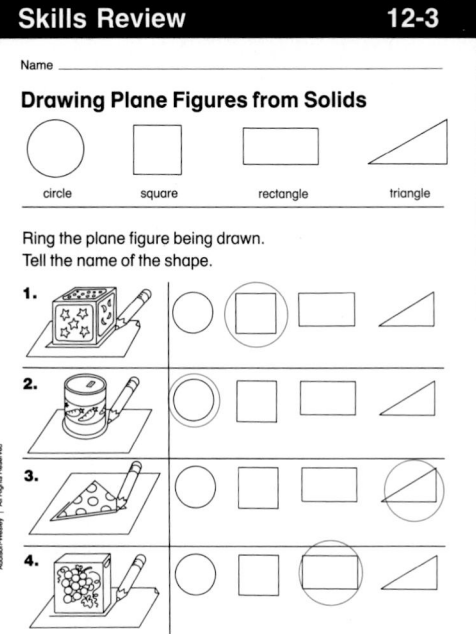

Ring the plane figure being drawn.
Tell the name of the shape.

RS-2   Use with text pages 253–254.   105

Challenges

Family Math   12-3

Name

Shapes All Around

Dear Family,
We have just finished a geometry lesson on drawing plane figures from real-world objects. Work with your child to discover things in your home that you can trace to make the shapes on the chart. You may also provide your child with pictures from magazines or newspapers to cut.

Find things you can draw around to make these shapes.
Make a picture graph.

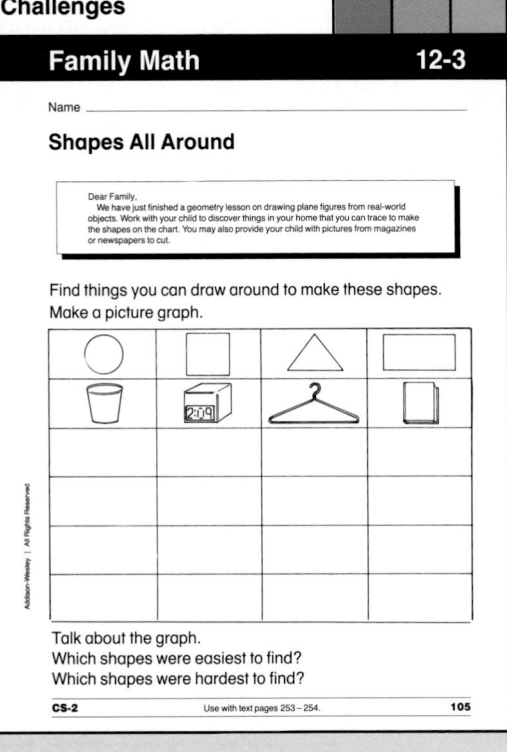

Talk about the graph.
Which shapes were easiest to find?
Which shapes were hardest to find?

CS-2   Use with text pages 253–254.   105

LESSON PLAN 12-3

OBJECTIVE 12-3
To identify plane shapes on solids

> **Materials:** pattern blocks, commercial solid objects of all shapes, geometric solids, index cards
>
> **Grouping Suggestions:** individual work, pairs

1. MOTIVATE AND TEACH

LEARN ABOUT IT

Show students a cereal box and ask them to focus on the front face of the box. Ask a student to draw the shape of that face on the chalkboard. Explain that the face is a plane figure. Place 3 different solids on a table. Have students close their eyes while you draw a face of one of the objects. Then ask them to match the plane figure picture to its solid figure.

▶ **How can you make sure that the object you draw around matches the solid figure in each exercise?** (Possible answers: by matching the number of corners, edges, and faces shown; by visually comparing the solid figure and the object)

▶ **Explain what you would do if you could not find a solid figure small enough to trace around in each exercise?** (Possible answer: Imagine what the shape of the face would be for the solid; draw it freehand.)

▶ **Analyze the solid figure in each exercise. Do any of the solid figures contain more than one plane figure? Explain.** (Possible answer: Yes, the triangular prism contains triangles and rectangles; the rectangular prism contains rectangles and squares.)

▶ **Compare the oval to other plane figures. Which shape is it most like? Why?** (Possible answer: circle; neither has straight edges)

2. CHECK UNDERSTANDING

ERROR ALERT Difficulty relating the flat face of the solid figure to the appropriate plane figure.

253   Chapter 12 Lesson 3

Name _____

Drawing Plane Figures from Solids

Use a solid figure like the one shown. Draw around a flat face. Write the name for the plane figure you drew. Check students' work.

1. square	2. triangle
3. rectangle	4. circle

5. Kara drew around a piece of jewelry. Write and say the name of the plane figure.

oval

Chapter 12   (two hundred fifty-three) 25

TEACHING OPTIONS

RETEACHING TIPS Make cards with solid figures and names on side 1, and plane figure(s) that make the solid on side 2. Display side 1. Have students use solids and pattern blocks to name the solid figure and the plane figure(s) they see in it. Repeat for side 2. Use Reteaching Supplement 105.

ENRICHMENT Ask students to cut a picture of a solid object, such as a television set or a refrigerator, out of a magazine and paste it on a piece of paper. Next to it, have them draw all the plane figures that make up the object and draw arrows to the picture to show where each plane figure is located.

ng the plane figure being drawn.

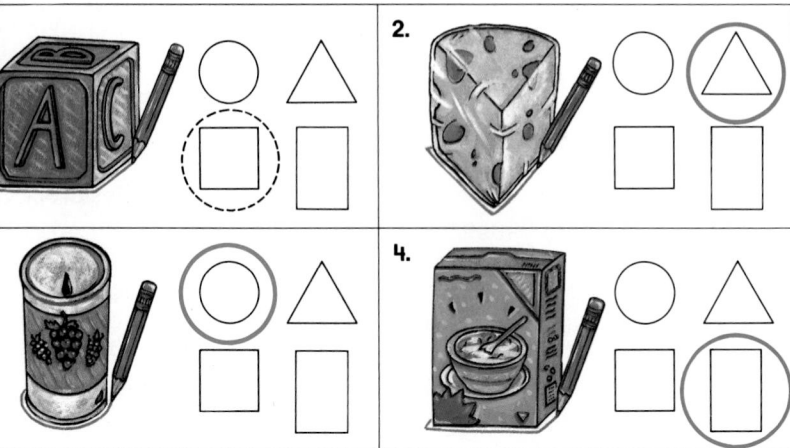

2.

4.

MIDCHAPTER REVIEW/QUIZ

Match.

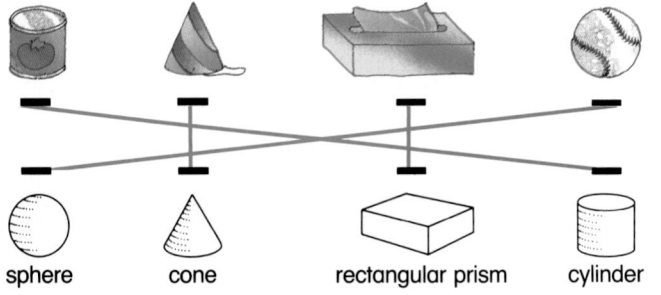

| sphere | cone | rectangular prism | cylinder |

Use solid blocks. Finish the chart.

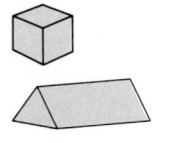

corners	edges	faces
8	12	6
6	9	5

(two hundred fifty-four)   More Practice, page 423, set B   Chapter 12

---

3. PRACTICE AND APPLY

Basic	All; Midchapter Review/Quiz
Average	All; Midchapter Review/Quiz
Extended	All; Midchapter Review/Quiz

PRACTICE

How are the exercises on page 254 different from the ones on the previous page? (Instead of drawing the plane figure, you must circle the plane figure that matches the one being drawn.) *Identify the solid figure with faces that are all the same shape.* (cube)

APPLY

▶ **What could you do to help you decide which plane figure is being drawn?** (Possible answers: Shade in the top face of each solid figure because it matches the bottom face; find a solid to match and compare its faces to the face being drawn.)

MIDCHAPTER REVIEW/QUIZ

ITEM ANALYSIS The table is a correlation for the Midchapter Review/Quiz.

Items	Objectives
1	12-1
2	12-2

LOSE AND ASSESS

HOW WHAT YOU KNOW   Ask
dents to tell what objects the Koala
others used to make their candles in
e chapter story. *Suppose Leo drew
ound the bottom of the soup can.
at shape would he have drawn?*
rcle) Have students draw around the
se of a cylinder to show this.

QUICK QUIZ

Write the name of each plane figure.

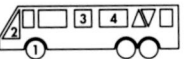

1. (circle)
2. (triangle)
3. (square)
4. (rectangle)

Making Plane Figures: Corners and Sides

OBJECTIVE 12-4   To make plane shapes using a geoboard; to count the number of sides and corners; to find poin

PREBOOK ACTIVITIES

QUICK REVIEW

Ring the plane figures.

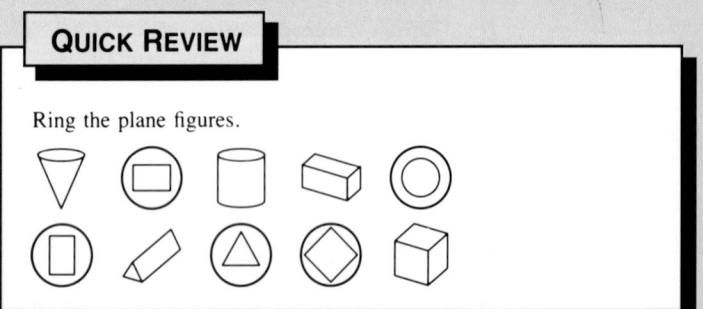

PRIOR KNOWLEDGE

Display geometric solids: cube, rectangular prism, triangular prism. Hold up one of the blocks and point to one of its faces. *Is this a corner, an edge, or a face?* Repeat by having students identify a corner and an edge of the block. *Can we count the corners, edges, and faces on all these blocks?*(yes) Next, trace the faces of each block on a piece of construction paper and cut them out. Have students name the plane figures. (square, rectangle, triangle) Talk about how these shapes are different from the blocks. (They are flat.) *Can we count the corners, edges, and faces on these shapes?* (only the corners) Have students count the corners as you point to them. Then show students how to count sides.

COMMUNICATION

Reading and Discussing Math   Write the words **pentagon** and **hexagon** on the chalkboard and draw each figure under its name. Have students count the sides of the pentagon as you go over each side with colored chalk. Repeat for the hexagon. Draw different-shaped pentagons and hexagons and discuss the fact that a pentagon can be any 5-sided closed figure and a hexagon can be any 6-sided closed figure.

EXPLORE AND CONNECT

Materials: 1 geoboard and 1 rubber band for each student
Grouping Suggestion: small groups
Have students use the rubber bands to make a closed shape o the geoboard. Have the groups ask these questions to discuss each other's figures: *How many sides does it have? How man corners? Which shapes are alike? How are they alike? How are they different? Which are shapes that we know?* (Answer: will vary.) Next, ask students to make different 3-sided figure then different 4-sided ones. *Are all the 3-sided figures triangles? Are any of the 4-sided figures rectangles? Are any squares? How can we decide?* (Answers will vary.) Have one student in each group make a pentagon or a hexagon and hav the others duplicate it. *Do your figures exactly match the firs one?* Suggest that students come to a group decision on how they will decide this. (the number of pegs on, inside, and outside the figure)

CONNECTIONS   Use these anytime.

Problem of the Day

Logic   Use the clues to color the shapes.

○ □ △

Each shape is red, blue, or green. The blue shape has the most sides. The red shape does not have 3 corners. (circle = red; square = blue; triangle = green)

Creative Thinking
Guess the Rule

These are gleggs:

These are not gleggs:

Is this a glegg?
Why or why not? (No, gleggs have straight sides and are closed shapes.)

Subject Integration

Art   Use circles, squares, triangles, and rectangles cut from construction paper. Glue the shapes onto a large piece of paper to make a picture or design. Ask a friend to find the different shapes in your picture.

side, outside, and on

CLASSWORK AND HOMEWORK SUPPLEMENTS

12-4

Basic

Exercises All, Mixed Review
Computer Bank, pp. 405-408

Supplements
Reteaching 106 or
Practice 106
Thinking Skills 106

Average

Exercises All, Mixed Review
Computer Bank, pp. 405-408

Supplements
Practice 106
Challenges 106 or
Thinking Skills 106

Extended

Exercises All, Mixed Review
Computer Bank, pp. 405-408

Supplements
Challenges 106
Thinking Skills 106

Other Resources:
Math in Stride, pp. 34-40
Mathematics Their Way, pp. 12-13, 17, 32, 37, 72-73, 76-77, 80, 241
Explorations, pp. 210-211, 214, 216-217

Practice

Creative Thinking 12-4

Name _____

Making Plane Figures: Corners and Sides

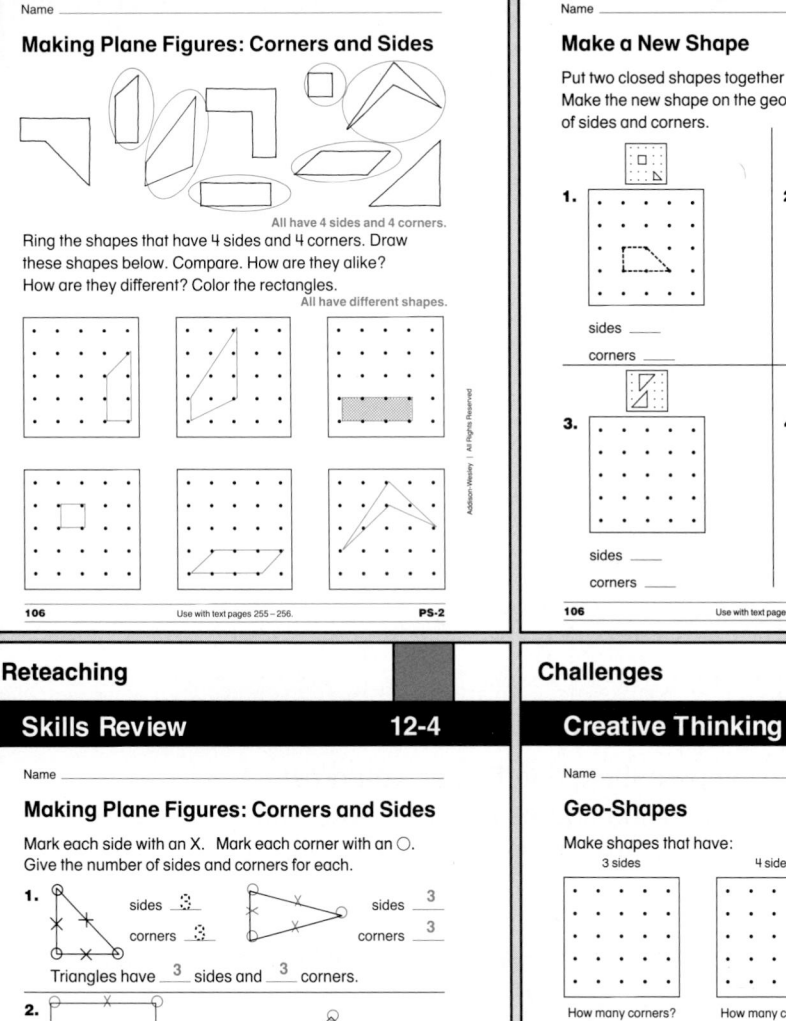

All have 4 sides and 4 corners.

Ring the shapes that have 4 sides and 4 corners. Draw these shapes below. Compare. How are they alike? How are they different? Color the rectangles.

All have different shapes.

106   Use with text pages 255 – 256.   **PS-2**

Building Thinking Skills

Critical Thinking 12-4

Name _____

Make a New Shape   Answers may vary.

Put two closed shapes together to make a new shape. Make the new shape on the geoboard. Write the number of sides and corners.

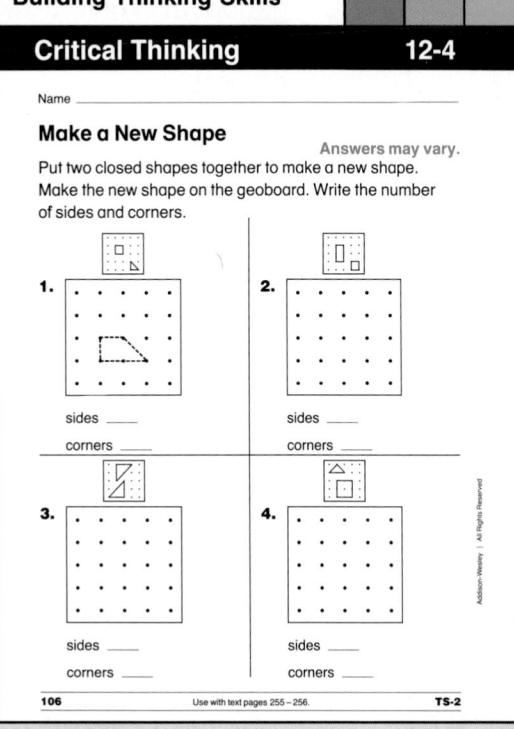

1.   sides _____   corners _____

2.   sides _____   corners _____

3.   sides _____   corners _____

4.   sides _____   corners _____

106   Use with text pages 255 – 256.   **TS-2**

Reteaching

Skills Review 12-4

Name _____

Making Plane Figures: Corners and Sides

Mark each side with an X. Mark each corner with an ○. Give the number of sides and corners for each.

1.   sides 3   corners 3   sides 3   corners 3

Triangles have 3 sides and 3 corners.

2.   sides 4   corners 4   sides 4   corners 4

Squares have 4 sides and 4 corners.

3.   sides 4   corners 4   sides 4   corners 4

Rectangles have 4 sides and 4 corners.

106   Use with text pages 255 – 256.   **RS-2**

Challenges

Creative Thinking 12-4

Name _____

Geo-Shapes

Make shapes that have: Shapes may vary.

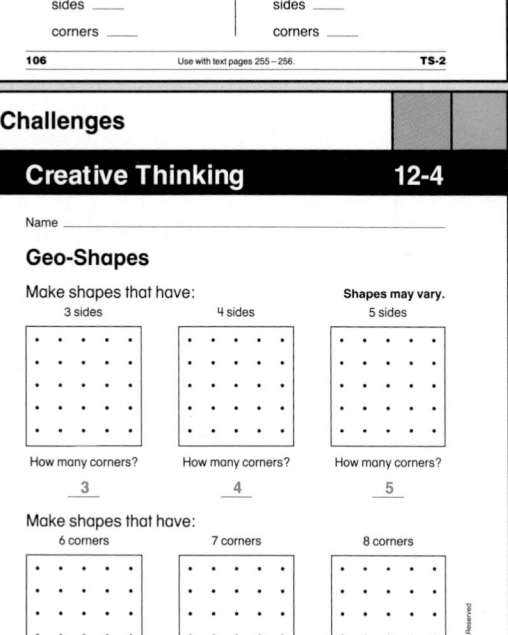

3 sides	4 sides	5 sides
How many corners?	How many corners?	How many corners?
3	4	5

Make shapes that have:

6 corners	7 corners	8 corners
How many sides?	How many sides?	How many sides?
6	7	8

Is there a pattern in the number of sides and corners? What is the pattern?

The number of sides and corners is always the same.

106   Use with text pages 255 – 256.   **CS-2**

OBJECTIVE 12-4
To make plane shapes using a geoboard; to count the number of sides and corners; to find points inside, outside, and on

Materials: 1 geoboard and 1 rubber band for each student; Tinker Toys or straws and clay; TA11 (Dot Paper)

1. MOTIVATE AND TEACH

LEARN ABOUT IT

Have students make 3-, 4-, 5-, and 6-sided figures on their geoboards and identify the number of sides and corners of their figures. Direct their attention to the names of the figures they are to make on page 255.

▶ **What do you notice about the number of sides and corners for each shape?** (There are the same number of sides as corners for each shape.)

▶ **How are the square and the rectangle alike?** (Both have 4 sides and 4 corners.)

▶ **How are they different?** (All the sides of the square are the same length. Only the opposite sides of the rectangle are the same length.)

▶ **How are the figures you draw alike?** (Possible answers: They all have straight lines; some have the same number of sides and corners.)

▶ **How are the figures different?** (Possible answers: The shapes are different sizes; the sides are different lengths; one has a different number of sides and corners.)

2. CHECK UNDERSTANDING

ERROR ALERT Having difficulty identifying the corners and sides of a figure made on the geoboard.

Name _____

Making Plane Figures
Corners and Sides

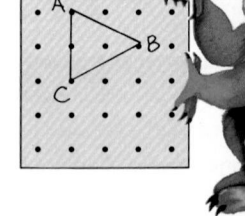

Pegs A, B, and C are **corners**. From A to B is one **side**.

Make each plane figure on your geoboard. Then draw it below. Write the number of sides and corners.

sides _3_   corners _3_

1. square		2. triangle	
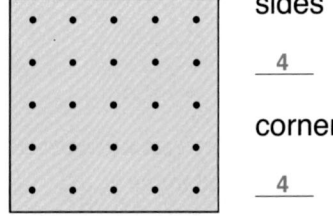	sides _4_ corners _4_		sides _3_ corners _3_
3. rectangle		4. a different rectangle	
	sides _4_ corners _4_	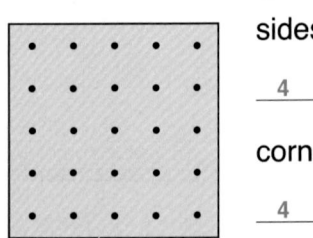	sides _4_ corners _4_

5. Compare the plane figures you drew. Tell how the figures are alike. Then tell how they are different. Answers may vary. See teaching notes.

Chapter 12   (two hundred fifty-five) 255

TEACHING OPTIONS

RETEACHING TIPS Use Tinker Toys or straws and clay. Have students construct figures with 3, 4, 5, and 6 sides and then identify the numbers of corners and sides.

Assign Reteaching Supplement 106.

COMPUTER Trap-a-zoid, Designware © 1983 Five levels of play for all students. Drill and game formats are combined, encouraging students to generate geometric figures. Games reinforce concepts of triangles and quadrilaterals. Each game requires 3-10 minutes.

nswers may vary. Check students' work.
se your geoboard. Make the plane figure
escribed. Then draw it below.

Each corner must be at a peg.

3 sides and 3 corners

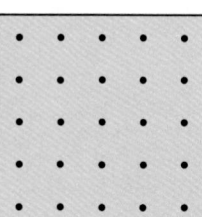

2. 4 sides and 4 corners

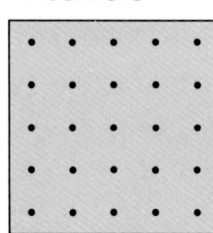

lake up your own plane figure.
rite the number of pegs that are inside,
utside, and on the lines you drew.
nswers may vary. Check students' work.

The red pegs are **inside.**
The blue pegs are **on.**
The yellow pegs are **outside.**

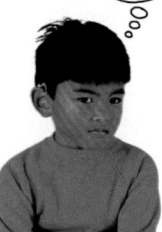

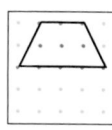

inside _____
outside _____
on _____

MIXED REVIEW

Write the time.

10:30   1:10

5. Count the money. Write the amount.

36¢

6 (two hundred fifty-six)

Chapter 12

---

3. PRACTICE AND APPLY

Basic	All, Mixed Review
Average	All, Mixed Review
Extended	All, Mixed Review

12-4

PRACTICE

How will you do Exercises 1 and 2 on page 256? (Make a figure on the geoboard with the given number of sides and corners.) *How will you do Exercise 3 on page 256?* (Make up a figure, then tell which pegs are inside, outside, and on the lines.)

APPLY

▶ **How many dots are inside, outside, and on the figure you drew for Exercise 1 on page 256?** (Answers will vary.)
▶ **Which pegs—inside, outside, or on the figure—show the actual shape of the figure?** (the pegs *on* the figure)
▶ **Are the corners of the figure inside, outside, or on the pegs?** (on the pegs)

MIXED REVIEW *What will you do in Exercise 4 on page 256?* (Write the times shown on the clocks.) *What will you do in Exercise 5?* (Count up all the money that is shown.)

LOSE AND ASSESS

HOW WHAT YOU KNOW

eview with students the chapter
ory, *Candle Crafts.* Suppose Ken
rew around the bottom of the orange
ice carton. *What shape would he
ave drawn?* (square) *How many sides
nd corners would it have?* (4, 4)
ave students draw around the base of
ube shapes to find the answers.

QUICK QUIZ

Write how many sides and corners
each figure has.

△ ⬡ ⬠ ▢

triangle, hexagon, pentagon, rectangle
(3, 3; 6, 6; 5, 5; 4, 4)

Problem Solving: Understanding the Operations

OBJECTIVE 12-5   To understand the operation of subtraction by finding the missing part

PREBOOK ACTIVITIES

Write the missing addend.
1. $2 + \underline{(3)} = 5$ 2. $4 + \underline{(4)} = 8$ 3. $3 + \underline{(6)} = 9$
4. $5 + \underline{(4)} = 9$ 5. $3 + \underline{(7)} = 10$ 6. $8 + \underline{(3)} = 11$

EXPLORE AND CONNECT

COOPERATIVE ACTIVITY

Grouping Suggestion: pairs
Distribute a piece of adding-machine tape or strip of paper either 10, 11, or 12 in. long to each pair of students. Have students use their inch rulers to measure the length of the paper and record the measurement. Then have them roll up part of the strip and tape it in place. *How can you find the length of the rolled-up part?*

PRIOR KNOWLEDGE

Help students recall measuring to the nearest inch. *Imagine that you need to measure the length of a ribbon. What tool will you use to measure?* (an inch ruler) *How will you measure?* (Possible answer: Place the edge of the ruler at one end of the ribbon. Look to see what number most closely matches the other end of the ribbon.) *What if the ribbon ends between 2 numbers?* (The length is the number that the end of the ribbon is closer to.)

TEACHING ACTIONS

 ► **What data do you already know?** (the total length of the strip)
► **What data can you find using your inch ruler?** (You can measure to find the length of the unrolled part.)

 ► **How will you use the data to plan a solution? Tell whether you will add or subtract and why.** (If you know the whole and one part, you can find the other part; subtract the length of the unrolled part from the total length to find the length of the rolled-up part.)

COMMUNICATION

Listening and Discussing Math   Provide each student with dot paper. Create a figure on a geoboard and do not show the class. Describe the figure, including its shape and position on the geoboard. Direct students to listen to the description and draw what they hear. After all students have completed their drawings, have them work in pairs to compare and discuss each other's figures. Then show the class your geoboard and have them correct their papers if necessary. Repeat the activity to encourage students to improve their thinking and listening skills.

AFTER ► **How can you check your answer?** (Possible answers: Add the length of the unrolled part and the length of the rolled-up part to check that the sum matches the total length; mark where the unrolled part begins, unroll the paper, and then measure the part that was rolled.)
Have students find the length of the rolled-up part of their paper strips.

CONNECTIONS   Use these anytime.

Problem of the Day
Understanding the Operations
Andrea has 15 in. of ribbon. She cuts the ribbon into 2 pieces. One piece measures 9 in. How long is the other piece? (6 in.)

Subject Integration
Fine Arts   Make a triangle on your geoboard. Copy it onto dot paper. Turn your figure on its side. Copy it again. Turn and copy until you are back at the first position. Color each part of your design a different color. What does it look like?

Math Connection
Measurement   First guess each length. Then measure to the nearest inch. (Answers will vary.)
1. your pencil
2. your little finger
3. your shoe
4. a pair of scissors
5. a chalkboard eraser

sing Critical Thinking

● use critical thinking to make visual predictions

CLASSWORK AND HOMEWORK SUPPLEMENTS

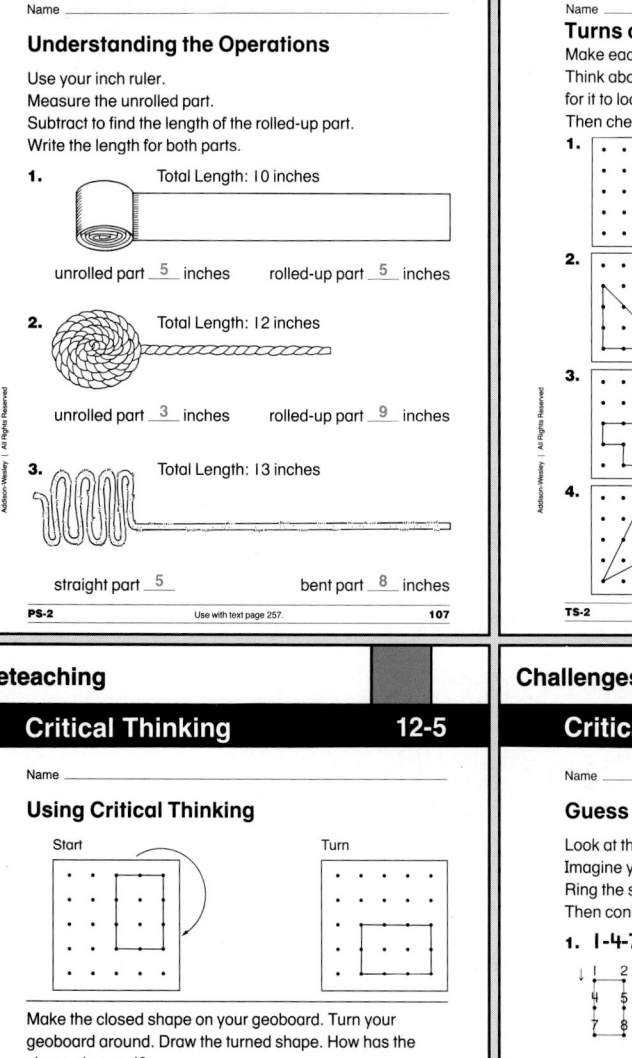

Practice

| Problem Solving | 12-5 |

Name _____

Understanding the Operations

Use your inch ruler.
Measure the unrolled part.
Subtract to find the length of the rolled-up part.
Write the length for both parts.

1. Total Length: 10 inches

unrolled part __5__ inches   rolled-up part __5__ inches

2. Total Length: 12 inches

unrolled part __3__ inches   rolled-up part __9__ inches

3. Total Length: 13 inches

straight part __5__   bent part __8__ inches

PS-2   Use with text page 257.   107

Reteaching

| Critical Thinking | 12-5 |

Name _____

Using Critical Thinking

Start   Turn

Make the closed shape on your geoboard. Turn your
geoboard around. Draw the turned shape. How has the
shape changed?

1.

2.

RS-2   Use with text page 258.   107

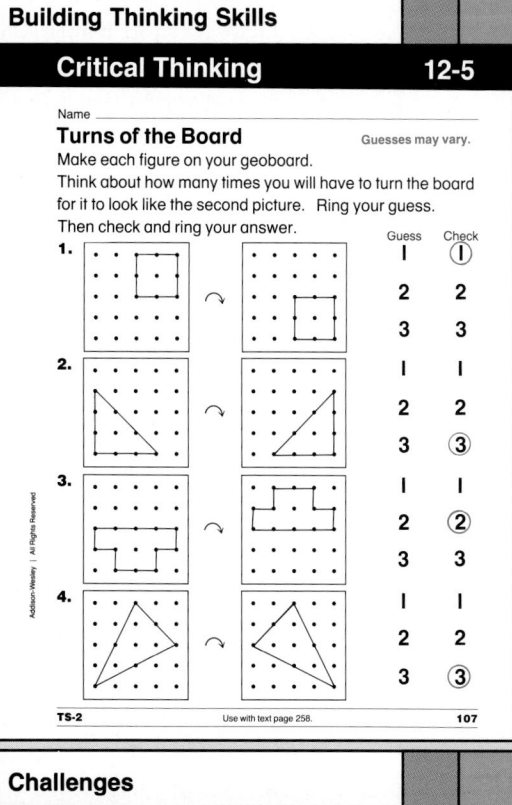

Building Thinking Skills

| Critical Thinking | 12-5 |

Name _____

Turns of the Board   Guesses may vary.
Make each figure on your geoboard.
Think about how many times you will have to turn the board
for it to look like the second picture. Ring your guess.
Then check and ring your answer.

	Guess	Check
1.	1	(1)
	2	2
	3	3
2.	1	1
	2	2
	3	(3)
3.	1	1
	2	(2)
	3	3
4.	1	1
	2	2
	3	(3)

TS-2   Use with text page 258.   107

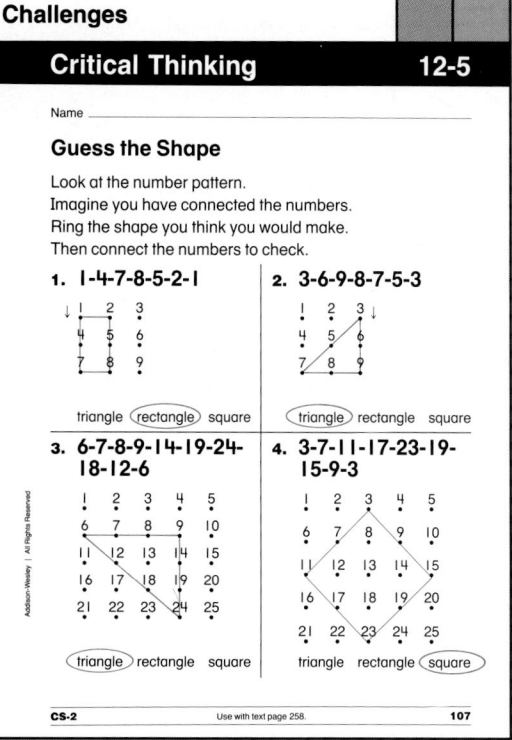

Challenges

| Critical Thinking | 12-5 |

Name _____

Guess the Shape

Look at the number pattern.
Imagine you have connected the numbers.
Ring the shape you think you would make.
Then connect the numbers to check.

1. 1-4-7-8-5-2-1

triangle (rectangle) square

2. 3-6-9-8-7-5-3

(triangle) rectangle square

3. 6-7-8-9-14-19-24-18-12-6

(triangle) rectangle square

4. 3-7-11-17-23-19-15-9-3

triangle rectangle (square)

CS-2   Use with text page 258.   107

Basic

Exercises All
More Practice, p. 423, set C

Supplements
Reteaching 107 or
Practice 107

Average

Exercises All
More Practice, p. 423, set C

Supplements
Practice 107
Challenges 107 or
Thinking Skills 107

Extended

Exercises All

Supplements
Challenges 107
Thinking Skills 107

Other Resources:
Explorations, pp. 165-167,
235

LESSON PLAN 12-5

OBJECTIVE 12-5
To understand the operation of subtraction by finding the missing part; to use critical thinking to make visual predictions

Materials: rulers, 10-in. paper strips, geoboards, rubber bands, TA 11, (Dot Paper)

1. MOTIVATE AND TEACH

LEARN ABOUT IT

Read the following stories to students.
1. *Ruth, DeAnne, and Paul are helping Mr. Jennings decorate the bulletin board. Paul says that there is a 9-in. roll of ribbon they can use. Ruth unrolls part of the ribbon. How long is the rolled-up part?*
2. *DeAnne begins to unroll the paper needed to back the bulletin board. She knows there are 11 in. on the roll. She measures the unrolled part. How long is the rolled-up part?*
3. *The bulletin board is almost finished. Paul unrolls a small part of the 12-in. banner for the top of the board. How long is the rolled-up part?*

 **BEFORE** ▶ **What are we trying to find out?** (the length of ribbon or paper still rolled up)

 **DURING** ▶ **Describe your plan for solving the problem.** (Measure the unrolled part and subtract from the total length; write an addition number sentence and find the missing addend.)

AFTER ▶ **How will you check your answer?** (Add the rolled-up amount to the unrolled measure; the sum should match the total length.)

2. CHECK UNDERSTANDING

ERROR ALERT **Page 257** Finding the sum of the whole and part.
Page 258 Visualizing the rotated geometric shape incorrectly.

Name _____

Problem Solving
Understanding the Operations

Listen to the story. How long is each rolled-up part? Use your inch ruler to measure the unrolled part. Write the length for both parts.

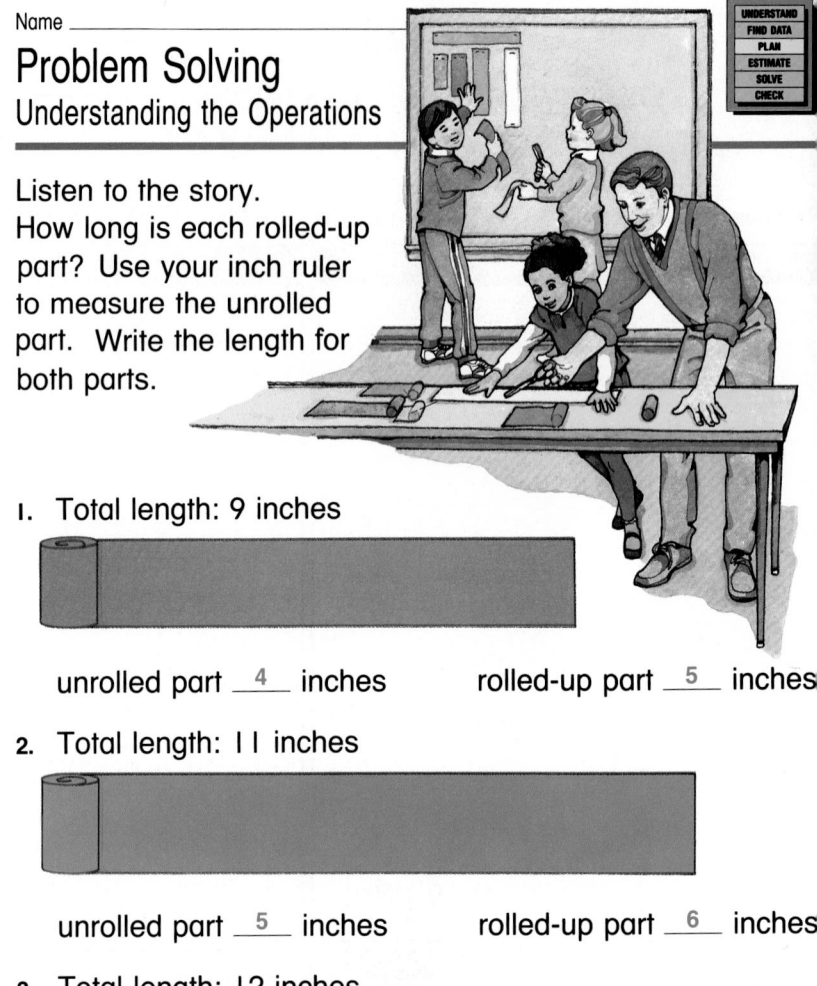

1. Total length: 9 inches

unrolled part __4__ inches   rolled-up part __5__ inches

2. Total length: 11 inches

unrolled part __5__ inches   rolled-up part __6__ inches

3. Total length: 12 inches

is Fun!

unrolled part __3__ inches   rolled-up part __9__ inches

Chapter 12   More Practice, page 423, set C   (two hundred fifty-seven) 2

TEACHING OPTIONS

RETEACHING TIPS Partly roll 10-in. paper strips and fasten with paper clips. Have students draw a line next to the clip, measure the unrolled part, and write a subtraction sentence to find the length of the rolled-up part. Unroll the strips and measure to check answers. Assign Reteaching Supplement 107.

ENRICHMENT Have one student in a pair make a figure on the geoboard. Ask the partner to study the shape and try to draw it from memory on dot paper without looking at the geoboard. (Students may refer to the shape as often as necessary in order to recreate it.) Repeat, having students take turns.

sing Critical Thinking

ake each figure on your geoboard.
hink about how it will look when
u turn the board as shown. Will it
ok like the second picture? Guess
st. Then check. Ring your answer.

Start | **Turn**

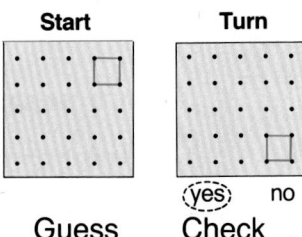

(yes) no

Make this.	Will it look like this?	Guess	Check

Guesses may vary.

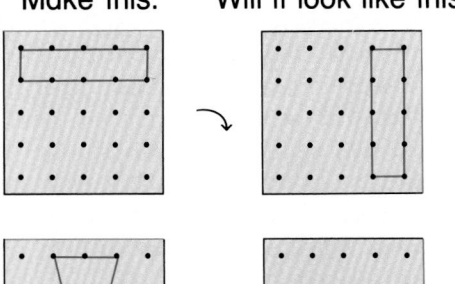

yes | (yes)

no | no

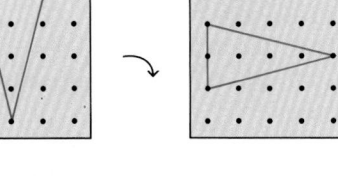

yes | yes

no | (no)

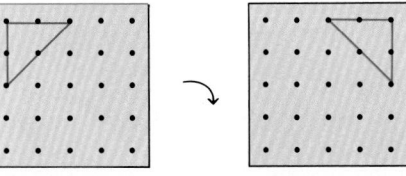

yes | (yes)

no | no

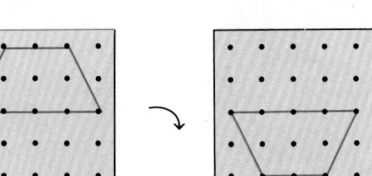

yes | yes

no | (no)

---

3. PRACTICE AND APPLY

Basic	All
Average	All
Extended	All

*You can guess how each figure will look
after the board is turned on its side.
How could you guess how the figures
would look if the board were turned once
more in the same direction?* (Possible
answer: Predict how the figures would
look upside-down.)

▶ **Explain what you are trying to
predict for each geometric figure.**
(Possible answer: what the figure will
look like after the board is turned)

▶ **Describe your plan for solving
each problem.** (Possible answer:
Imagine how the figure will look when
the board is turned; see if it matches the
second picture.)

▶ **How can you check your guess?**
(Turn your geoboard.)

12-5

LOSE AND ASSESS

HOW WHAT YOU KNOW

splay a geoboard with a rectangle
r students to copy. Ask them to
edict what the geoboard will look
ke if it is turned on its side and draw
eir predictions on dot paper. Have
udents then turn their geoboards to
eck their results. Repeat for a
angle and a trapezoid. Vary the
tivity by having students predict
hat the geoboard will look like
rned upside-down or to the left.

QUICK QUIZ

Jamie had a bookmark that was 8 in.
long. When she put it in her book, 2
in. of the bookmark were showing.
How long was the part that was
hidden? (6 in.)

My Book of Symmetry

OBJECTIVE 12-6   To make symmetric figures

PREBOOK ACTIVITIES

Draw the other half. What shape did you make?

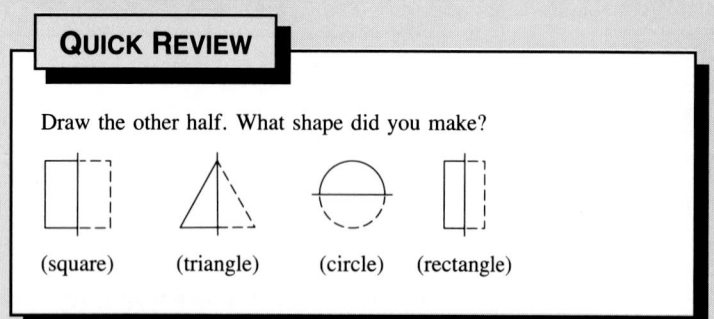

(square)   (triangle)   (circle)   (rectangle)

PRIOR KNOWLEDGE

Discuss the fact that many things have two matching parts. Display a variety of objects and pictures of objects that have matching halves, such as a blade of grass, a leaf, a butterfly, an airplane, and a sandwich. Ask students to imagine a line down the center of the objects. *Would that divide them into two matching parts?* (yes) If mirrors are available, have students hold a mirror along the middle of some of the objects until they can see what looks like the whole object.

COMMUNICATION

Discussing and Listening in Math   Cut a square from construction paper and draw a line down the center. Display the shape. *Do the two parts on either side of the line match?* (yes) How can we check that? (by folding the paper on the line) Explain that there is a special name for figures that can be folded so that one half fits exactly on the other half. *We say that the figure is* **symmetrical.** *Is the square symmetrical?* (yes) Point to the fold line down the center. Tell students that the fold line is called the **line of symmetry** when it divides an object into two matching parts.

EXPLORE AND CONNECT

Materials: scissors, squares of construction paper
Grouping Suggestion: small groups
Have each student fold a square of construction paper in half and cut out a figure that begins and ends at the fold line. Have group members help each other if one or more students do not understand how to do this. Before they unfold their papers, ask group members to predict what each whole figure will look like. Have them draw each figure or describe it orally. Encourage students to reach a group decision. Then have them unfold their papers and compare the figures to their predictions. *How can you check that each figure is* **symmetrical?** (by folding it again to make sure both sides match) *Can you point out the* **line of symmetry?** (the fold line) *Are there any figures that can be folded in another way to make two other sides match? Draw another line of symmetry if you can.*

CONNECTIONS   Use these anytime.

Problem of the Day

A Fair Share   Larry and Tony were sharing their lunches from home in the lunchroom at school. They both wanted a fair share of everything they had:

Copy the pictures. Draw lines to show where they cut the foods to be fair.

Creative Thinking

Art   Fold and unfold a piece of drawing paper. Put some blobs of paint on one side of the fold line. Fold your paper once more and rub lightly. Then unfold your paper. What does your design look like?

Subject Integration

Movement   Work with a partner. Face each other and make believe you are looking in a mirror. Each of you take a turn moving slowly. The other should pretend to be the reflection and move the same way. After a while, switch roles.

CLASSWORK AND HOMEWORK SUPPLEMENTS

Practice

Math Reasoning   **12-6**

Name _____

My Book of Symmetry

Ring the figure that shows the fold in the correct place.

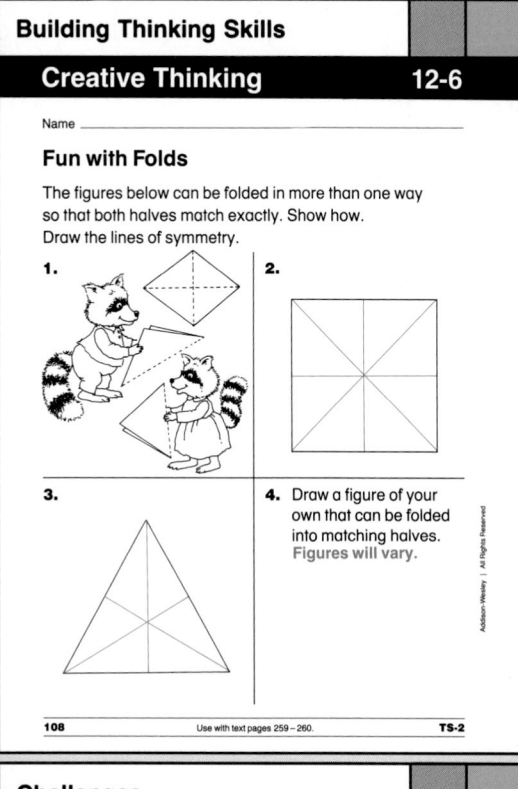

108   Use with text pages 259–260.   **PS-2**

Reteaching

Skills Review   **12-6**

Name _____

My Book of Symmetry

the same   A   P   not the same   E   the same

Ring the letters with parts that match.

B C D F G
H I J K L
M N O Q R
S T U V W
X Y Z

108   Use with text pages 259–260.   **RS-2**

Building Thinking Skills

Creative Thinking   **12-6**

Name _____

Fun with Folds

The figures below can be folded in more than one way so that both halves match exactly. Show how.
Draw the lines of symmetry.

1.

2.

3.

4. Draw a figure of your own that can be folded into matching halves.
Figures will vary.

108   Use with text pages 259–260.   **TS-2**

Challenges

Cooperative Activities   **12-6**

Name _____

Symmetry Squares   Sample answer for first row given.

Work with a partner. Use different colored crayons.
Color some squares on one side of the line.
Your partner colors the other half to match the squares
you colored. Color one row at a time. Take turns going first.

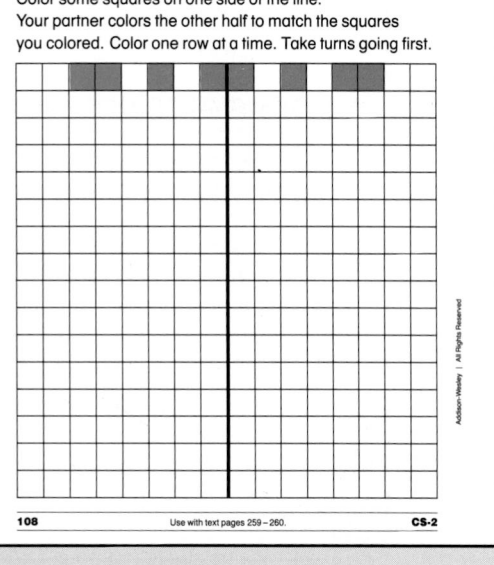

108   Use with text pages 259–260.   **CS-2**

OPTIONS FOR INDIVIDUAL NEEDS

12-6

Basic

Exercises All
More Practice, p. 424, set A

Supplements
Reteaching 108 or
Practice 108

Average

Exercises All
More Practice, p. 424, set A

Supplements
Practice 108
Challenges 108 or
Thinking Skills 108

Extended

Exercises All

Supplements
Challenges 108
Thinking Skills 108

Other Resources:
Math in Stride, pp. 34-40,
145-146
Explorations, pp. 223-225,
230-231, 303

LESSON PLAN 12-6

OBJECTIVE 12-6
To make symmetric figures

> **Materials:** 3-in. by 4-in. pieces of construction paper, pattern blocks, paper mats with center line, TA 3 (Centimeter Graph Paper); symmetrical and nonsymmetrical objects and shapes

1. MOTIVATE AND TEACH

LEARN ABOUT IT

If your students did not do the Explore and Connect activity, have them make symmetrical figures by folding squares of construction paper, then drawing a figure that begins and ends on the fold. Have other students predict what the whole figure will look like, then compare the prediction to the figure after it is cut out. Focus students' attention on page 259 and remind them to paste only half the figure, so they can draw their prediction of what the other half will look like.

▶ **Does the heart figure have another line of symmetry?** (no) **Explain your answer.** (There is no other way you could fold the heart and get two matching parts.)

▶ **Does the butterfly figure have another line of symmetry?** (no) **Explain your answer.** (same as above)

▶ **Name two figures that *do* have more than one line of symmetry.** (Possible answers: circle, square, rectangle)

2. CHECK UNDERSTANDING

ERROR ALERT Having difficulty understanding the concept of symmetry and visualizing and drawing the matching half of a figure

---

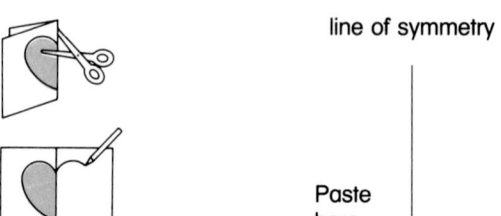

Name _____

My Book of Symmetry

Dear Family, Ask your child to tell you about the symmetric figures in this book.

Cut out a figure from folded paper. Paste the fold line along the **line of symmetry.** Draw the other half of the figure. Unfold to check. See teaching notes.

line of symmetry

Paste here.

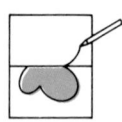

Paste here.

line of symmetry

Chapter 12

(two hundred fifty-nine) 2

TEACHING OPTIONS

RETEACHING TIPS Use pattern blocks and a mat with a line drawn down the center. Have students put 1 block on one side of the line, then add blocks to make the model symmetrical. Assign Reteaching Supplement 108.

COMPUTER Logo Works, Terrapin © 1985 For those with some experience with Logo. Using Chapter 4 of this software package (with 7 activities), students will generate symmetrical geometric figures through guided activities. Each activity requires 35-50 minutes.

Paste here.

_____ line of symmetry

- - - - - - - - - - - - - - - - - - - -

Make up your own figure.

line of symmetry

Paste
here.

3. PRACTICE AND APPLY

Basic	All
Average	All
Extended	All

PRACTICE

What are you to do at the bottom of page 260? (Cut a figure from folded paper, paste half along the line of symmetry, then draw the other half.) Help students cut on the dashed line and staple the halves to make a book.

12-6

APPLY

► **How do you know that the figure you made up is symmetrical?** (When it is folded, the parts will fit exactly on top of each other.)

► **Can you fold your figure in any other way to make two matching parts?** (Answers will vary.)

► **When you make a figure in this way from a folded piece of paper, will it always be symmetrical? Why?** (Yes; by cutting a folded piece of paper, you are making the same figure on both sides of the fold.)

► **When we draw a line of symmetry, what fraction of the whole figure is each part?** (Possible answer: one half)

CLOSE AND ASSESS

SHOW WHAT YOU KNOW

Collect symmetrical and nonsymmetrical objects such as dominos (doubles and non-doubles), number cards, and paper shapes. Have students make a chart with the headings *Symmetrical* and *Not Symmetrical*. Have them write the object names under the appropriate heading.

QUICK QUIZ

Which figures show the line of symmetry in the correct place? (1, 4, 5)

1. 2. 3. 4. 5.

Making Congruent Figures

OBJECTIVE 12-7   To identify and make congruent figures

PREBOOK ACTIVITIES

QUICK REVIEW

Find all the squares. Then find all the triangles.

PRIOR KNOWLEDGE

Discuss the previous lesson about symmetry. *What makes a figure or object symmetrical?* (two matching halves) *Do you think that if we cut a symmetrical figure along the fold line, the two pieces would be the same? Why?* (Yes, because the fold line is the line of symmetry, or the line that divides the figure into two matching parts.) Demonstrate this by cutting a triangle from a folded piece of paper, then cutting the triangle along the fold line. *Do the two smaller triangles match? Are they exactly the same size and shape? How can we check?* (by putting one over the other)

COMMUNICATION

Reading and Listening in Math   Write the word **congruent** on the chalkboard. Tell students that the word *congruent* is the word we use to describe two or more figures that are exactly the same size and shape. Review the word **symmetrical.** Remind students that we use the word *symmetrical* to describe *one* figure that has matching halves. Have students orally complete sentences such as these with one of the words.
1. That butterfly is (symmetrical) .
2. Those two big squares are (congruent) .

EXPLORE AND CONNECT

Materials: construction paper, paper clips, templates or attribute blocks for tracing, drawing paper
Grouping Suggestion: pairs
Have each student trace figures on construction paper, then cli
that paper to another piece of a different color. Have them cut out the figures, cutting through both pieces of paper. *For each figure you cut out, is there another that is exactly the same siz and shape?* Have them paste all the shapes of one color on a piece of drawing paper. Have pairs exchange papers and the other set of figures, then find the **congruent** figures by matching the cutouts to the figures on the paper. Extend this activity by having students choose one type of figure and make pairs of cutouts of that figure in various sizes. Have them ask their partners to identify congruent figures. *Are congruent figures the same shape?* (yes) *the same size?* (yes) *What make figures congruent?* (They are the same size and shape.)

CONNECTIONS   Use these anytime.

Problem of the Day

Draw a Picture   Jamal made a wooden scratching post for his kitten. The post is 18 in. high and 6 in. wide. He wants to cover one side of the post with carpet. Jamal found 4 old carpet squares, each of them 6 in. square. How many of the carpet squares does he need to cover one side of the post? (3)

Math Connection

Geometry   Work with a partner and take turns going first. Use a geoboard and one rubber band to make a closed figure. Ask your partner to make one just like it. Check to make sure the figures are the same size and shape. Try making figures that are the same size and shape but in different positions on the geoboard.

Life Skills

Arranging Books   Go to a bookshelf in the classroom. Arrange the books in size order, beginning with the largest book. Which books are exactly the same size and shape?

CLASSWORK AND HOMEWORK SUPPLEMENTS

Basic

Exercises All

Supplements
Reteaching 109 or
Practice 109

12-7

Average

Exercises All

Supplements
Practice 109
Challenges 109 or
Thinking Skills 109

Extended

Exercises All

Supplements
Challenges 109
Thinking Skills 109

Other Resources:
Math in Stride, pp. 34-40
Mathematics Their Way, p. 241
Explorations, pp. 215-217, 231, 234

Practice

Manipulatives 12-7

Name _____

Making Congruent Figures

Make a closed shape on your geoboard. Shapes will vary.
Turn your geoboard. Record the shape with each turn.

Are your shapes congruent? yes

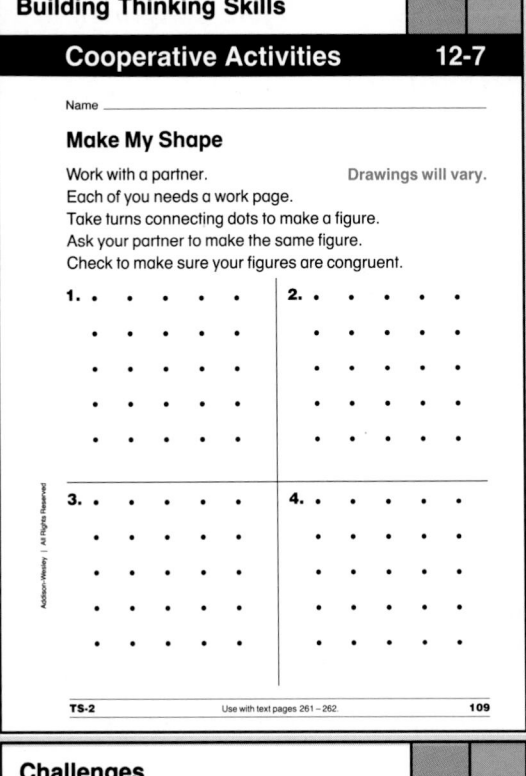

1. 2. 3.

Ring the shape on each board that is not congruent.

4. 5. 6.

Draw a shape that is congruent to the one shown.
Positions will vary.

7. 8. 9.

PS-2   Use with text pages 261 – 262.   109

Building Thinking Skills

Cooperative Activities 12-7

Name _____

Make My Shape

Work with a partner.   Drawings will vary.
Each of you needs a work page.
Take turns connecting dots to make a figure.
Ask your partner to make the same figure.
Check to make sure your figures are congruent.

1.   2.

3.   4.

TS-2   Use with text pages 261 – 262.   109

Reteaching

Skills Review 12-7

Name _____

Making Congruent Figures

same size
same shape
These figures are congruent!

Trace figures A, B, C, D, and E on another piece of paper.
Use the tracing to match each figure to another figure on the page.
Mark the congruent figure with the same letter.

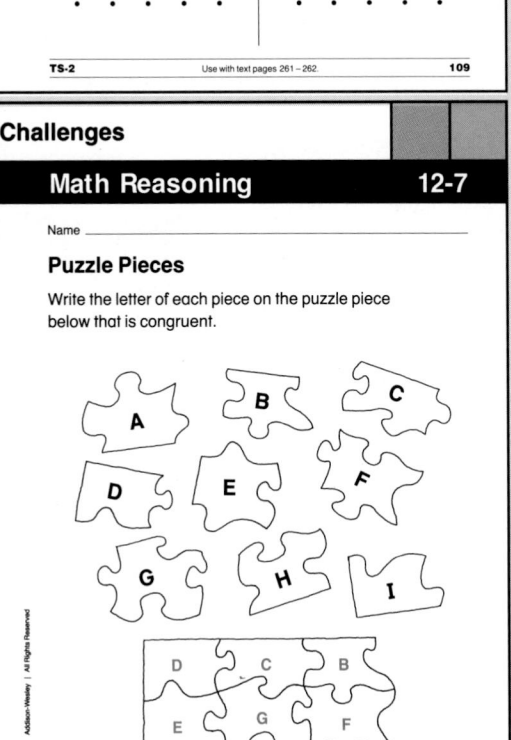

RS-2   Use with text pages 261 – 262.   109

Challenges

Math Reasoning 12-7

Name _____

Puzzle Pieces

Write the letter of each piece on the puzzle piece below that is congruent.

A   B   C
D   E   F
G   H   I

D   C   B
E   G   F
I   A   H

CS-2   Use with text pages 261 – 262.   109

OBJECTIVE 12-7
To identify and make congruent figures

Materials: pattern blocks, geoboards, rubber bands

Grouping Suggestion: pairs

---

1. MOTIVATE AND TEACH

LEARN ABOUT IT

Have students trace around a pattern block twice, then cut out one of the figures. Ask them to place the cutout on top of the traced figure. *Are the figures congruent?* (yes)
▶ **What does it mean when you say two figures are congruent?** (They are the same size and the same shape.)
Go over the directions for page 261.
▶ **How do you know that the two figures in each exercise are congruent?** (Possible answer: The two triangles used for the second figure fit exactly on top of the blue figure.)
▶ **What can you say about the side that the two triangles share in each figure?** (Possible answer: It is a line of symmetry for each of the figures.)
▶ **Will congruent figures have the same line(s) of symmetry?** (yes)
▶ **Explain your answer.** (If the figures have the same shape, they must have the same line that divides them into two matching parts.)

2. CHECK UNDERSTANDING

ERROR ALERT Thinking that figures are congruent when they are only similar.

Name _____

Making Congruent Figures

Cut out the red triangles. Use two triangles to make a figure **congruent** to each blue figure. Paste the figures.

Congruent figures have the same size and shape.

Check students' work. Sample answers are shown.

1.

Paste here.

2.

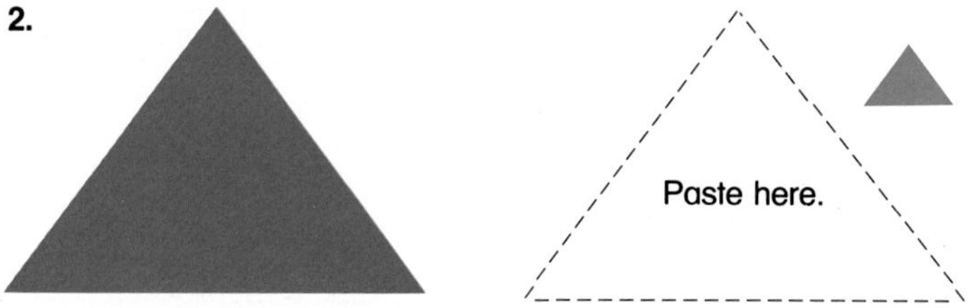

Paste here.

3.

Paste here.

Chapter 12

(two hundred sixty-one) 2

TEACHING OPTIONS

RETEACHING TIPS Have students place 2 trapezoid pattern blocks on top of a hexagon. *Are the figures congruent? Why?* (yes; same size and shape) Have them compare 2 different-sized squares. *Are these figures congruent? Why?* (no; same shape, different size) Assign Reteaching Supplement 109.

COMPUTER Moptown Parade, Learning Company © 1985 For use with all levels of students. In *Make My Twin* and *What's the Same?* students develop preliminary skills needed to investigate congruency. Use *Club House* with advanced students. Each lesson takes 15-20 minutes.

Check students' work.
Draw a figure congruent to the one shown.
Ring **yes** or **no** to answer each question.

1.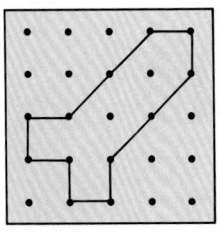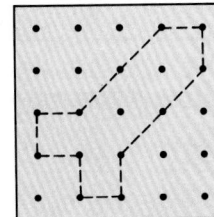
Is it the same size and shape?

yes   no

2.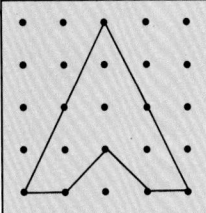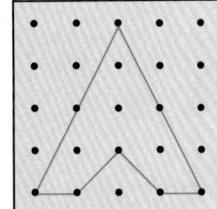
Is it the same size and shape?

yes   no

3.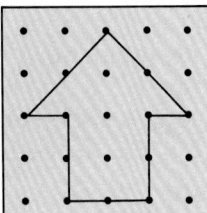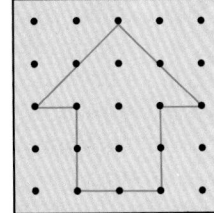
Is it the same size and shape?

yes   no

PROBLEM SOLVING

4. Barb took 4 cubes out of the box. How many cubes are still in the box?

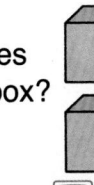 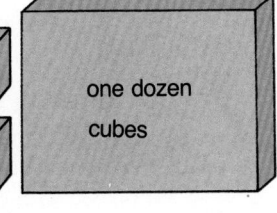

one dozen cubes

___8___ cubes

62 (two hundred sixty-two)   Chapter 12

3. PRACTICE AND APPLY

Basic	All
Average	All
Extended	All

PRACTICE

How can you find out whether the figures are congruent? (Possible answer: Match the dots on the outlines of the figures.)

APPLY

PROBLEM SOLVING *What does the picture tell you?* (There are 4 cubes outside a box that holds 12.) *What do you know?* (the whole and one part) *What must you find?* (the other part)

▶ **What operation begins with the whole and one part?** (subtraction)
▶ **Is there a way to use addition for this problem?** (yes; think 4 + how many = 12)
▶ **What if there were 8 cubes outside the box, how many cubes would still be inside?** (4)
▶ **Is there a quick way, or strategy, to know this?** (Use the turnaround fact.)
▶ **What other combinations of 12 cubes can you create inside and outside the box?** (3 + 9, 9 + 3, 5 + 7, 7 + 5, 6 + 6, 1 + 11, 11 + 1, 2 + 10, 10 + 2)

12-7

CLOSE AND ASSESS

SHOW WHAT YOU KNOW.

Have one student in a pair make a figure on a geoboard, keeping it hidden from the partner. Then the student gives the partner directions on how to make a congruent figure. Directions might include how many pegs are inside, outside, and on the figure. Partners should check to see if the figures are congruent.

QUICK QUIZ

Ring the answers. Congruent figures must have <u>same size</u>, same color, <u>same number of corners</u>, <u>same number of sides</u>. <u>same shape</u>, same line of of symmetry, same position.

Problem Solving: Using Data From a Number Pair Graph

OBJECTIVE 12-8   To solve problems using data from a number pair graph

PREBOOK ACTIVITIES

QUICK REVIEW

Continue the pattern.
1, 2, 3, _(4)_ , _(5)_ , _(6)_
3, 6, 9, _(12)_ , _(15)_ , _(18)_
10, 20, 30, _(40)_ , _(50)_ , _(60)_
5, 10, 15, _(20)_ , _(25)_ , _(30)_

PRIOR KNOWLEDGE

If classroom chairs are in rows, assign row and seat numbers and have students identify the students at a given location. For example: *Who is sitting in the third seat in row 1?* Vary the activity by having students identify their own desk or chair locations.

COMMUNICATION

Reading and Discussing Math   Display TA6 (Hundred Chart) on the overhead projector. Then write the words **over** and **up** on the chalkboard. Place your finger on 31 and move it to the right to 34. *Did I move up or over?* (over) *How many spaces did I move over?* (3) Then move your finger to 24. *What did I do that time?* (moved up 1 space) Choose a different starting point at the left of the chart, such as 61. Have students locate a given number by following your directions. For example: *Go over 2 numbers. Go up 1 number. What number are you at now?* (53) Continue with other numbers.

EXPLORE AND CONNECT

COOPERATIVE ACTIVITY

Grouping Suggestion: small groups
Draw the following on the chalkboard. Have students give number pairs to show the location of the moon, star, and sun.

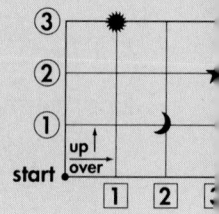

TEACHING ACTIONS

BEFORE
▶ **What does the graph show?** (a moon, a star, and a sun on a grid)
▶ **What data does the graph have?** (numbers at the bottom and on the side of the grid)
▶ **How can 2 numbers tell the location of an object on the graph?** (One number tells the location **over**; the other number tells the location **up**.)

DURING
▶ **Give the 2 numbers that tell where the moon is. First give the number that tells how many spaces over from Start. Then give the number that tells how many spaces up.** (2, 1)
▶ **Can you use the same plan to tell where the star and the sun are?** (yes; star: 3, 2; sun: 1, 3)

AFTER
▶ **How can you check your answers?** (Possible answer: Use the number pairs to check the location of each object on the grid.)
Have students in groups make their own grids and locate 2 or 3 places on the grid.

CONNECTIONS   Use these anytime.

Problem of the Day

Look for a Pattern   Draw a picture or make a table to solve this problem. Look for a pattern.
Amy made party bags for the children coming to her party. She put 3 toys in each bag. How many toys did she use for 6 bags? (18)

Life Skills

Following Directions   Work with a partner. Each of you makes 4 rows of dots with 4 dots in each row. Draw a shape. Then give your partner directions for drawing the same shape. For example: 1) Start at the first dot in the top row. 2) Go over 2 dots. 3) Go down 2 dots. 4) Go back (left) 2 dots. 5) go up 2 dots.

Creative Thinking

Patterns   Get 20 cubes. Think of a pattern you can use to build a tower with all 20 cubes. Tell how many cubes you used on each floor and what the pattern is. Then find another way to build a tower with all the cubes but with a different pattern. (Answers will vary. Possible arrangements: 5, 5, 5, 5; 8, 6, 4, 2; 6, 5, 4, 3, 2)

Problem Solving Strategy: Look for a Pattern

- solve problems using the strategy Look for a Pattern

CLASSWORK AND HOMEWORK SUPPLEMENTS

Practice

Problem Solving   12-8

Name _____

Look for a Pattern

Look for a pattern. Finish the table.
Then answer the question.

1. The desks in the classroom were set up in rows.
   Each row had 4 desks. There were 6 rows.
   How many desks were there in all?

Row	1	2	3	4	5	6
Desks in all	4	8	12	16	20	24

There were __24__ desks in all.

2. Betty planted 8 rows of seeds.
   She planted 40 seeds in row 1.
   She planted 35 seeds in row 2.
   She planted 30 seeds in row 3.
   Betty continued this pattern.
   How many seeds did she plant in row 7?

Row	1	2	3	4	5	6	7	8
Seeds in that row	40	35	30	25	20	15	10	5

Betty planted __10__ seeds in row 7.

110   Use with text page 264.   **PS-2**

Building Thinking Skills

Mental Math   12-8

Name _____

How Much?

Use skip counting to solve. Make a table if you need to.

1. Lisa wants to buy
   5 stickers. Each one
   costs 2¢. How much
   does Lisa need?
   __10¢__

2. The rides at the fair
   cost 3¢ each. How
   much would it cost
   for 4 rides.?
   __12¢__

3. Kareem earns 5¢ a day
   for setting the table.
   How much will he earn
   after 5 days?
   __25¢__

4. Roger bought
   7 marbles. Each one
   cost 2¢. How much
   did Roger spend?
   __14¢__

5. Yung-Su wants to mail
   4 letters. Each letter
   needs a 10¢ stamp.
   How much will Yung-Su
   have to pay for the
   stamps?
   __40¢__

6. At Sally's Sewing Store
   buttons come in packs
   of 2 for 5¢. How much
   would it cost for
   8 buttons?
   __20¢__

110   Use with text page 264.   **TS-2**

Reteaching

Problem Solving   12-8

Name _____

Using Data from a Number Pair Graph

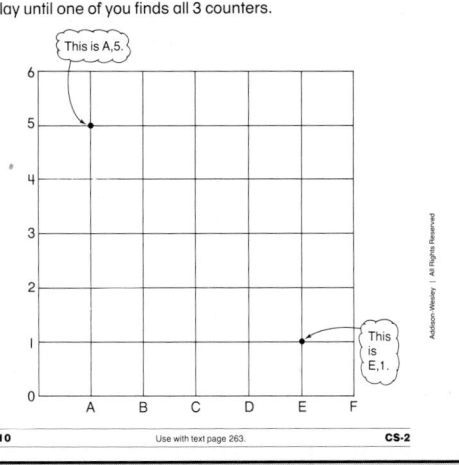

Start at ●.
Go over 3. Go up 2.
The 🚲 is at
3 2

↑ up
over →
Start

| 1 | 2 | 3 | 4 | 5 |

Match.

| 4 | 1 | | 1 | 2 | | 2 | 4 | | 5 | 3 | | 3 | 5 |

110   Use with text page 263.   **RS-2**

Challenges

Data Analysis   12-8

Name _____

Hidden Counters

Play with a partner. Stand a book between you to keep your
game boards hidden. Each player places 3 counters on
points on the board. Then take turns guessing where your
partner has placed them. Make a guess like this: *Is it at A,3?*
Mark an X on the point for each wrong guess.
Play until one of you finds all 3 counters.

This is A,5.

This is E,1.

110   Use with text page 263.   **CS-2**

Addison-Wesley | All Rights Reserved

OPTIONS FOR INDIVIDUAL NEEDS

Basic

Exercises All
Calculator Bank, p. 401
Computer Bank, pp. 405-408

Supplements
Reteaching 110 or
Practice 110

Average

Exercises All
Calculator Bank, p. 401
Computer Bank, pp. 405-408

Supplements
Practice 110
Challenges 110 or
Thinking Skills 110

Extended

Exercises All
Calculator Bank, p. 401
Computer Bank, pp. 405-408

Supplements
Challenges 110
Thinking Skills 110

Other Resources:

*Problem-Solving Experiences
In Mathematics,* pp. 17,
22-23, 52-53, 58-59, 88, 106,
137, 155, 162
Explorations, p. 335

12-8

OBJECTIVE 12-8

To solve problems using data from a number pair graph; to solve problems using the strategy Look for a Pattern

Materials: Cube-A-Links, TA7 (Blank Hundred Chart), punchout pennies and nickels

1. MOTIVATE AND TEACH

LEARN ABOUT IT

Look at the example. Why are the numbers 3 and 2 inside different shapes? (Possible answer: The box tells the number over, the circle tells the number up.)

 **BEFORE** ▶ **How can you find the data in order to solve the problems?** (Possible answer: Read the numbers that tell the location over and up.)

 **DURING** ▶ **What is your plan for solving the problems?** (Possible answer: First, read the graph to find each price. Then write an addition exercise using the 2 prices and solve to find the total cost.)

 **AFTER** ▶ **What steps will you take to check your work?** (Possible answer: Compare the number pairs to the graph to make sure you wrote the right prices; add the numbers in reverse order to check the addition.)

2. CHECK UNDERSTANDING

ERROR ALERT **Page 363**
Reversing the *over* and *up* movement of locating points on the graph.
Page 364 Misinterpreting a pattern and continuing it incorrectly.

Name _____

Problem Solving
Using Data from a Number Pair Graph

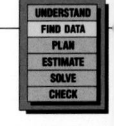

Use data from the graph. Write the prices. Find the total cost.

1. Bo bought something at ☐2, ①.   price __56¢__   56
   He bought something at ☐1, ③.   price __25¢__   + 25
   What was the total cost?   total cost __81¢__   81

2. Lucas bought something at ☐4, ④.   price __16¢__   16
   He bought something at ☐2, ⑤.   price __27¢__   + 27
   What was the total cost?   total cost __43¢__   43

3. Mari bought something at ☐4, ①.   price __55¢__   55
   She bought something at ☐5, ③.   price __43¢__   + 43
   What was the total cost?   total cost __98¢__   98

Chapter 12   (two hundred sixty-three)   2

TEACHING OPTIONS

RETEACHING TIPS ▪Have students make a pattern with 1, 2, 3, and 4 nickels; then place 5 pennies below 1 nickel, 10 below 2 nickels, and so on. *How many pennies are there for every nickel?* (5) Make a table to show the pattern. For help with number pairs, use Reteaching Supplement 110.

ENRICHMENT Have students make a simple drawing on a 10-by-10 grid, drawing dots at the points where the outline crosses grid intersections. Beginning at (0, 0), have them name the points in the order they were drawn. Have them exchange lists and draw each other's pictures on new 10-by-10 grids.

roblem Solving Strategy
ook for a Pattern

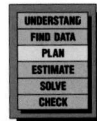

UNDERSTAND
FIND DATA
PLAN
ESTIMATE
SOLVE
CHECK

se cubes. Look for a pattern. Finish
e table. Then answer the question.

Joan built a tower with 3 cubes
on each floor. The tower was
8 floors tall. How many cubes
did Joan use?

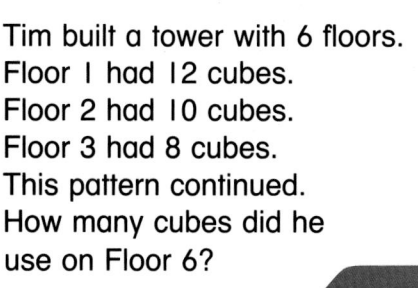

Floor	1	2	3	4	5	6	7	8
Cubes in all	3	6	9	12	15	18	21	24

Joan used __24__ cubes for her tower.

Tim built a tower with 6 floors.
Floor 1 had 12 cubes.
Floor 2 had 10 cubes.
Floor 3 had 8 cubes.
This pattern continued.
How many cubes did he
use on Floor 6?

Floor	1	2	3	4	5	6
Cubes on Floor	12	10	8	6	4	2

Tim used __2__ cubes on Floor 6.

4 (two hundred sixty-four)   Chapter 12

---

3. PRACTICE AND APPLY

Basic	All
Average	All
Extended	All

How can cubes help you complete the table? (Possible answer: They will help you see the number pattern.) *How can you use the table to find the number of cubes on Floor 6?* (Possible answer: Continue the pattern to complete the table; find the number of cubes for the floor.)

▶ **Where can you find the data for building the towers?** (Possible answers: Read the problem; look at the numbers already shown in the tables.)

▶ **How will you show each floor of the towers? Explain.** (Possible answer: Use cubes of different colors to see the pattern more easily.)

▶ **Identify methods for checking your work.** (Possible answers: Build the towers with cubes to see if the answer is correct; see if the number patterns get larger or smaller in the same way throughout the table.)

12-8

LOSE AND ASSESS

HOW WHAT YOU KNOW

raw a grid on the chalkboard. Write
e number pair (2, 5) on the board.
sk a student to draw a circle at the
cation identified by the number pair.
ave another student check the
cation. Continue with other
rections, such as: *Mark an X at (2,
; draw a heart at (4, 1).* Give each
dent a chance either to draw a
gure or to check another student's
ork.

QUICK QUIZ

Use cubes to help you finish the table.

1	2	3	(4)	(5)	(6)	(7)
5	10	15	(20)	(25)	(30)	(35)

CHAPTER 12

WRAP UP

INTRODUCTION The Wrap Up provides activities emphasizing math language and thinking skills for the chapter.

USING PAGE 265

Math Words ▶ **Compare the space figures with the plane figures. How are they alike? How are they different?** (Possible answers: Shapes such as the circle and the sphere or the square and the cube are similar, but the plane figure shows only 1 face and the space figure shows several faces. Other figure pairs, such as the triangle and cone, look similar but have no common faces.)
▶ **Which of the plane figures in Exercise 2 are similar? Why are they alike?** (square, triangle, rectangle; they all have sides and corners)

Math Reasoning ▶ **Why can there be more than one way to show a figure on the geoboard?** (The figure can be constructed in different positions.)
▶ **How will all solutions be the same?** (Possible answer: They will all have sides and corners.)

Name _____

WRAP UP

MATH WORDS

1. Match.

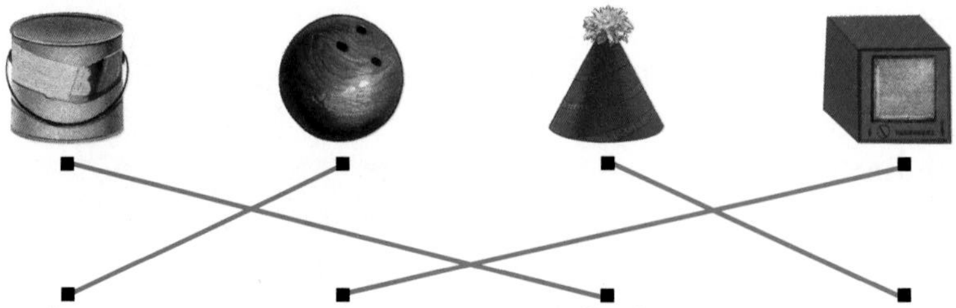

| sphere | cube | cylinder | cone |

2. Draw pictures to match.

circle	square	triangle	rectangle
 ◯	▢	 △	 ▭

MATH REASONING

Make these figures on a geoboard. Then copy them on the page.

Answers may vary. Sample answers are shown.

3. 4 sides
   no pegs inside

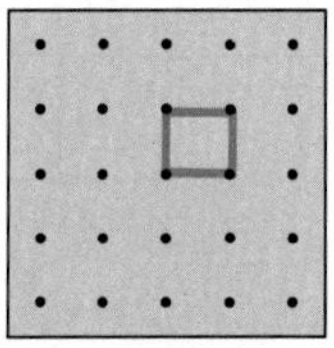

4. 5 sides
   3 pegs inside

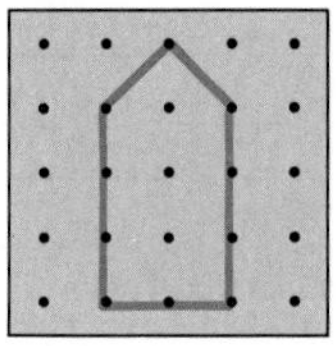

5. 6 sides
   2 pegs inside

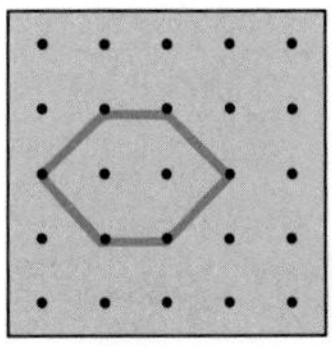

Chapter 12 Wrap Up

(two hundred sixty-five) 2

TEACHING OPTIONS

ENRICHMENT Have students work in pairs. Have the first student make a shape on the geoboard with a rubber band. Instruct the student's partner to make a second shape that uses one side of the first shape and has double the number of dots inside. Students should work together to determine the shape formed by both figures. *How many sides does it have? How many dots are inside?* (Answers will vary.)

Name _____

CHAPTER REVIEW/TEST

Match.

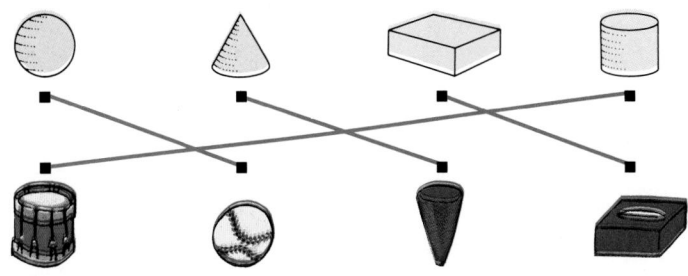

Ring the plane figure being drawn.

Find a congruent figure for each. Color to match.

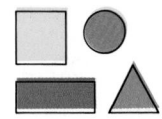

3. Write the number of each.

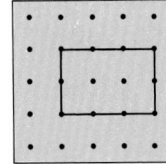

sides ___4___

corners ___4___

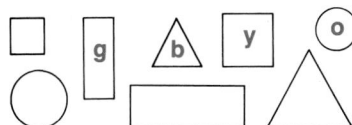

David did 8 push-ups the first day, 10 the second day, and 12 the third day. This pattern continued. How many push-ups did he do on the eighth day?

Day 1	Day 2	Day 3	Day 4	Day 5	Day 6	Day 7	Day 8
8	10	12	14	16	18	20	22

David did ___22___ push-ups on the eighth day.

INTRODUCTION   The Review/Test is provided to review and evaluate the skills and concepts presented in Chapter 12.

USING PAGE 266
If you prefer to use this page for review, you may want to use the **Multiple-Choice Posttest** (pages 47-48) or the **Free-Response Posttest** (pages 47-48) to evaluate mastery of chapter objectives.

ITEM ANALYSIS   The table below correlates the Chapter Review/Test Items with the lesson objectives.

Items	Objectives
1	12-1
2	12-3
3	12-4
4	12-7
5	12-8

INFORMAL ASSESSMENT

Using Manipulatives   Provide groups of 4 with geometric solid blocks. One student names the solid and passes it to the student on the right, who names a real-life object shaped like the block. The block is passed again and the other 2 students name other real-life objects. Repeat, having a different student name the solid each time.

Communication   *Explain to a friend the difference between symmetry and congruence.* (Possible answer: The half-figures on either side of a line of symmetry are exactly the same. Two figures are congruent if both are exactly the same.)

Critical Thinking   *Suppose that you made a rectangle on a geoboard and then turned the geoboard on its side. What can you predict about the figure you see?* (Possible answers: It will be a rectangle; it will be congruent to the original shape.

CHAPTER 12

ENRICHMENT

INTRODUCTION Adding numbers in different order helps students understand and apply the associative property to larger numbers.

USING PAGE 267
This Enrichment page is provided for all students. You may wish to use it after they have completed the Chapter Review/Test on page 266.
Help students note that each pair of number sentences are the same, but are combined in a different order.
▶ **What happens to the sum when the order of addition changes?** (The sum remains the same.)
▶ **What do you think would happen to the sum if you wrote the numbers in the number sentence in a different order? Why?** (It would stay the same, because the numbers can be added in any order and the sum will not change.)

EXTENSION Provide small groups of students with a collection of coins. Have each student select 4 coins and find the total value. Then have them each write an addition sentence, using first the value of their own coins and then the values of the group members' coins. Have students add with paper and pencil or a calculator to find the total of all of the collections, then compare their totals.

Name _____

ENRICHMENT
Order and Grouping

Find each sum. Add the red numbers first.

1. $2 + 3 + 5 =$ __10__
    $2 + 3 + 5 =$ __10__

2. $6 + 4 + 5 =$ __15__
    $6 + 4 + 5 =$ __15__

3. $8 + 0 + 7 =$ __15__
    $8 + 0 + 7 =$ __15__

4. $2 + 7 + 2 =$ __11__
    $2 + 7 + 2 =$ __11__

Find each sum. Add the red numbers first. Use your 🖩.

5. $22 + 44 + 16 =$ __82__
    $22 + 44 + 16 =$ __82__

6. $30 + 25 + 18 =$ __73__
    $30 + 25 + 18 =$ __73__

7. $16 + 37 + 22 =$ __75__
    $16 + 37 + 22 =$ __75__

8. $29 + 42 + 11 =$ __82__
    $29 + 42 + 11 =$ __82__

9. Look at the exercises above. Does it matter which pair of numbers you add first? Tell why or why not. See teaching notes.

10. Ring the ones that give the same sum. as $12 + 42 + 37$. Tell how you know. See teaching notes.

    $42 + 11 + 35$ $\boxed{42 + 37 + 12}$

    $\boxed{37 + 12 + 42}$ $\boxed{12 + 37 + 42}$

Chapter 12 Enrichment: Order and Grouping   (two hundred sixty-seven) 26

Name _____

CUMULATIVE REVIEW

Add.

37 ▱▱▱▱

37 + 4 = ___

- ○ 47
- ● 41
- ○ 42

20 + 30 = ___

- ● 50
- ○ 60
- ○ 70

Mark the best estimate.

$$\begin{array}{r} 23 \\ + 41 \end{array}$$

- ○ about 20
- ○ about 40
- ● about 60

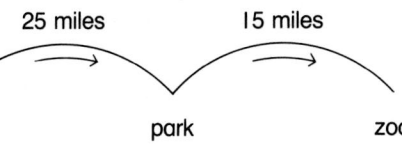

- ○ less than 50¢
- ○ 50¢
- ● more than 50¢

Add.

5.
$$\begin{array}{r} 33 \\ + 18 \end{array}$$
- ○ 45
- ● 51
- ○ 68

6.
$$\begin{array}{r} 38 \\ + 47 \end{array}$$
- ○ 64
- ○ 46
- ● 85

7.
$$\begin{array}{r} 35 \\ 11 \\ + 25 \end{array}$$
- ○ 63
- ● 71
- ○ 89

8.
$$\begin{array}{r} 17 \\ 23 \\ + 42 \end{array}$$
- ○ 70
- ○ 59
- ● 82

The school bus went from school to the zoo. How far did it go?

- ○ 21 miles
- ● 40 miles
- ○ 19 miles

25 miles   15 miles

□ ⟶   ⟶

school   park   zoo

CUMULATIVE REVIEW

INTRODUCTION The purpose of this Cumulative Review is to maintain previously taught skills and concepts. The emphasis in this Cumulative Review is on understanding 2-digit addition, Chapter 10; and on addition of 2-digit numbers, Chapter 11.

ITEM ANALYSIS The table below correlates the Cumulative Review items with the lesson objectives.

Items	Objectives
1	10-1
2	11-3
3	11-5
4	10-5
5, 6	11-4
7, 8	11-9
9	11-8

Chapter Management

OVERVIEW

Lesson	Pages	Objectives	Subject Integration	Strand Integration
Counting Back by Ones	269-270	13-1 To subtract a 1-digit from a 2-digit number	social studies: mail	mental math
Subtracting Tens	271-272	13-2 To model and subtract decade numbers	social studies: letters/stamps	mental math
Counting Back by Tens	273-274	13-3 To subtract from a 2-digit number by counting back by tens	social studies: group skills	computation
Related Subtraction Sentences	275-276	13-4 To show different ways to name the same difference	social studies: group skills	computation
Problem Solving: Understanding the Operations/Estimating Differences: More or Less than 50¢	277-278	13-5 To compare or find the missing part; to estimate differences	language arts: writing	consumer math
Breaking Apart a Ten	279-280	13-6 To subtract two 2-digit numbers with trading	science: dinosaurs	computation, number sense, problem solving
Problem Solving: Finding Missing Data/Problem Solving Strategy: Draw a Picture	281-282	13-7 To find missing data; to use the strategy Draw a Picture	social studies: mail delivery	computation, logic

MATHEMATICAL BACKGROUND

Subtraction of 2-Digit Numbers
This chapter begins by introducing subtraction of a 1-digit number from a 2-digit number by counting back by ones. Students also model and subtract decade numbers (multiples of 10). The next step is to have students subtract a decade number from a 2-digit number. The use of models and related pictures helps students develop a foundation for understanding the concept of subtracting 2-digit numbers with and without trading.

Estimation
Lesson 13-5 has students use front-end estimation. In making estimates using front-end numbers, it is assumed that all the addends have the same number of digits (to the tens place). The student then simply adds the front-end (tens place) digits to get the estimate.

Problem Solving
In this chapter, students solve problems by finding missing data and using the strategy Use a Picture.

TIPS FROM TEACHERS

Clip a sheet of clear plastic over several 2-digit subtraction exercises. Have students use colored pens to color the ones digit of the top number of each exercise in which a trade is needed.

Linda Sheppard
Lincoln Elementary School
Van Buren, ID

ART: 2-13-Interleaf-1-1

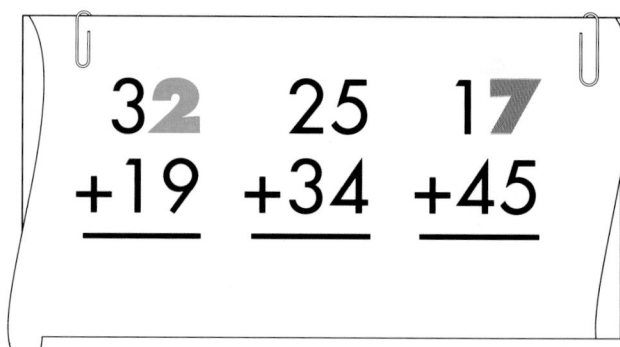

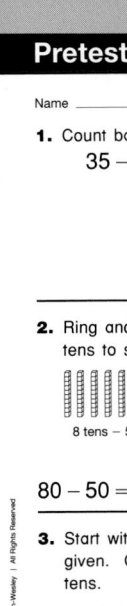

for pages 269-286

ASSESSMENT

Pretest — Chapter 13, page 1

Multiple-Choice Format

Name _____

1. Count back to subtract.

$35 - 3 = \underline{?}$

- **A** 32
- **B** 22
- **C** 38

2. Ring and cross out tens to subtract.

8 tens − 5 tens

$80 - 50 = \underline{?}$

- **A** 20
- **B** 40
- **C** 30

3. Start with the number given. Count back by tens.

55

$55 - 30 = \underline{?}$

- **A** 15
- **B** 25
- **C** 35

4. Choose the related subtraction sentence.

$51 - 23 = 28$

- **A** $51 - 23 = 28$
- **B** $51 - 28 = 23$
- **C** $28 - 23 = 5$

5. Jo has 65 stamps. 21 are car stamps. The rest are boat stamps. How many boat stamps does Jo have?

- **A** 44 boat stamps
- **B** 86 boat stamps
- **C** 34 boat stamps

MCT 2 — 49

Pretest — Chapter 13, page 2

Multiple-Choice Format

Name _____

6. Choose the better estimate for your change.

— 75¢

- **A** more than 50¢
- **B** less than 50¢

7. How many are left? Break apart a ten.

Number to start	Number to take away
32	13

- **A** 19
- **B** 29
- **C** 45

8. Karla had 18 fish. She gave some fish to Pierre. How many fish did she have left?

Is there enough data to solve the problem?

- **A** yes
- **B** no

9. Finish the picture to solve the problem.

There are 4 black mailboxes and some white mailboxes on Elm Street. Each white mailbox is between 2 black mailboxes. How many mailboxes are there on Elm Street?

- **A** 6 mailboxes
- **B** 8 mailboxes
- **C** 7 mailboxes

50 — MCT 2

Posttest — Chapter 13, page 1

Multiple-Choice Format

Name _____

1. Count back to subtract.

$28 - 4 = \underline{?}$

- **A** 14
- **B** 24
- **C** 32

2. Ring and cross out tens to subtract.

6 tens − 2 tens

$60 - 20 = \underline{?}$

- **A** 40
- **B** 30
- **C** 80

3. Start with the number given. Count back by tens.

48

$48 - 20 = \underline{?}$

- **A** 38
- **B** 18
- **C** 28

4. Choose the related subtraction sentence.

$45 - 27 = 18$

- **A** $45 - 27 = 18$
- **B** $45 - 18 = 27$
- **C** $27 - 18 = 9$

5. Beau has 67 stars. 32 are gold. The rest are silver. How many silver stars does Beau have?

- **A** 79 silver stars
- **B** 45 silver stars
- **C** 35 silver stars

MCT 2 — 51

Posttest — Chapter 13, page 2

Multiple-Choice Format

Name _____

6. Choose the better estimate for your change.

— 35¢

- **A** more than 50¢
- **B** less then 50¢

7. How many are left? Break apart a ten.

Number to start	Number to take away
65	29

- **A** 44
- **B** 36
- **C** 46

8. Noelle had 18 fish. She gave 9 fish to Chantay. How many fish did she have left?

Is there enough data to solve the problem?

- **A** yes
- **B** no

9. Finish the picture to solve the problem.

There are 3 white mailboxes and some black mailboxes on Elm Street. Each black mailbox is between 2 white mailboxes. How many mailboxes are there on Elm Street?

- **A** 3 mailboxes
- **B** 4 mailboxes
- **C** 5 mailboxes

52 — MCT 2

ITEM ANALYSIS

Items	Objectives
1	13-1
2	13-2
3	13-3
4	13-4
5, 6	13-5
7	13-6
8, 9	13-7

Note: The item analysis is the same for all pretests and posttests for this chapter.

ALSO AVAILABLE

▶ **Free Response Tests**
▶ **Alternative Tests**
▶ **Thinking Strategies**
▶ **Concrete Materials**

Optional Chapter Activities

PROJECT AND BULLETIN BOARD

You will need styrofoam packing "worms," plastic bags, twist ties, push pins, and a plastic pail. Put 10 worms in each of 9 plastic bags and tie with a twist tie. Place the remaining worms in the pail. On the bulletin board, have students paint a fishing scene. Pin a tens and ones chart on the board. Demonstrate breaking apart tens to make extra ones with 31 − 17 = ___. Pin 3 bags of worms in the tens place and 1 single worm in the ones place. Since 7 single worms cannot be taken away from 1 worm, open a bag of worms and pin them on the ones side of the chart to show breaking apart a ten. Finish the subtraction and write the answer. During the next 6 to 8 math sessions, have small groups of students go subtraction fishing for the answers to subtraction exercises.

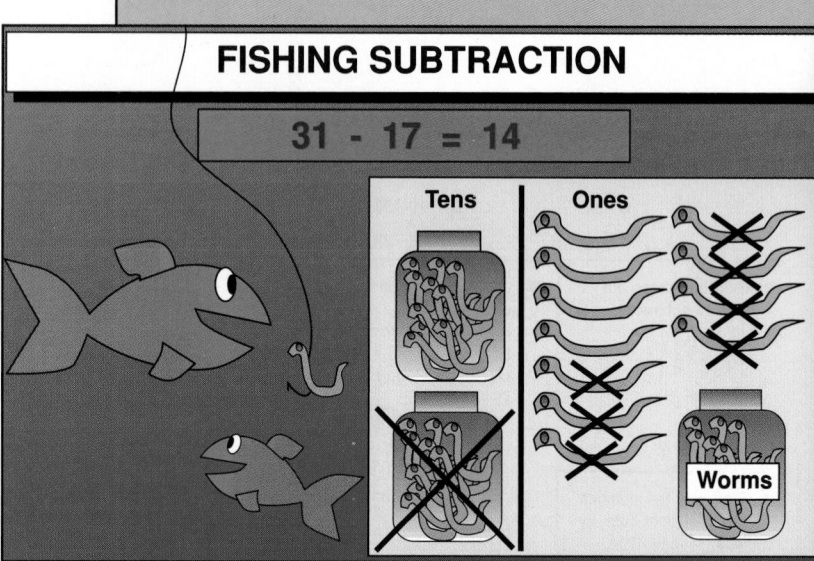

FISHING SUBTRACTION

31 - 17 = 14

Tens   Ones

Worms

COOPERATIVE LEARNING

Divide the class into groups of 4 or 5. Identify the group skill: listening to each other. Draw a gameboard, similiar to the one shown, on a piece of butcher paper or chart paper. Have 2 students stand 5 ft back from the gameboard. Instruct the first student to toss a red beanbag onto the board and have the second student toss a blue beanbag onto the board. Have other members of the group share the following tasks: write the numbers on the chalkboard, with the greater number over the lesser number; show the greater number with base-ten blocks; and take away base-ten blocks to count back the amount shown by the lesser number. As students observe members of their group counting back by tens, encourage them to listen carefully to check that what they say matches what is shown by the blocks. Repeat counting back to subtract tens and have students change tasks.

You will find grouping suggestions and cooperative learning activities in most lessons throughout this chapter.

LITERATURE

Rockwell, Anne. "The Travels of a Fox," from *The Old Woman and Her Pig and 10 Other Stories.* New York: Thomas Y. Crowell, 1975.

A clever fox outwits several people in his travels, but he is outwitted in the end.
Have students use numbers from the story to write number sentences.

Peppe, Rodney. *Humphrey the Number Horse.* New York: Viking, 1975.

Testa, Fulvio. *Leaves.* New York: Peter Bedrick Books, 1980.

ENGLISH AS A SECOND LANGUAGE

Talking aloud is a useful technique for mental math and problem solving. Model the language needed to complete these tasks, practicing questions and short responses. Ask students to write subtraction sentences patterned after those given. Ask native speakers to help ESL students with comprehension of word problems. When complex linguistic structures are used to frame questions *(How many more homes than stores did she bring mail to? How many boxes are being mailed to Florida?)*, have the native speakers read the questions aloud and try to paraphrase them. Give the ESL students a chance to paraphrase as well. If they are unable to do so at the start, give them another chance to perform successfully.

In the activity for which students draw a picture to solve a problem, group 1 ESL student with 2 native speakers at the chalkboard, where native speakers will tell ESL students what to draw. Carrying out the task accurately will show that the ESL students have understood the directions.

GIFTED

Mathematically talented students may already understand how to break apart a ten to subtract. They will nevertheless likely be interested in many of the strategies presented in this chapter. Challenge these students, after they have completed their book work, by showing them how to subtract on a calendar. Provide them with a calendar for the school year and display a calendar showing the (previous) month of September. Block out the weekends and holidays and have students add or count to find the total number of school days. Show them how to subtract by counting back from the total number of days in the month to find the number of days they attended school. Have students repeat the procedure for the remaining school months. With the data they have collected, students may calculate the number of school days remaining in the school year using repeated addition or subtraction. If this activity appeals to students, challenge them to find the number of days until their birthday or their favorite holiday.

STUDENTS AT RISK

Learning-disabled students may have particular difficulty subtracting 2-digit numbers. Continue to provide experiences for students to think aloud as they subtract, so that they can focus on their own thinking processes and you can guide their work.

Also provide manipulative materials for students' use. Students should be allowed to use these materials for their actual computation as long as they express a desire to do so. It is important to remember that development of the trading/place value concept progresses at very different rates. You can help students with this difficult skill by focusing their attention on a few critical parts of subtraction computation. Remind them to begin by subtracting ones. Have them look at the top number first to avoid the mistake of subtracting the lower number from the higher number. It may be helpful to mark the top number in the ones place with a different color. Ask questions such as these: *Do you have enough ones to subtract? If not, then trade 1 ten for 10 ones. Do you have enough tens to subtract?*

You may also use the Reteaching Supplements and the specific Reteaching Tips from each lesson in this chapter.

Storybook

PICTURE

These pictures and accompanying stories and poems are available as storybooks.

You may want to read and discuss this story with your students before starting the chapter. The first lesson in this chapter includes a question about the story. Lessons 1, 3, 6, and 7 in this chapter have questions in the informal Assessment that refer to the story.

Rover's Surprise

Manuel called and called. His dog was nowhere in sight. He called again, "Rover, Ro-ver!" Still no dog.

Rover was hiding behind a big tree across the street. He liked to be out in front of the house where he could watch people and cars pass by.

Maria, Manuel's sister, jumped off the porch steps. "We sure gave that dog the right name—Rover."

"We sure did. He roves around the neighborhood whenever we forget to shut the gate to the back yard," Manuel said.

"I bet Rover wanders because it's boring in the back yard," said Maria.

"Mom told me that there is a surprise for Rover coming in the mail this week," Manuel said. "She said that it will make him happy. I wonder what it could be."

"Here comes the mail carrier now," said Maria. "Maybe she has the surprise."

"Hi, Mrs. Stampley," Manuel said. "How many letters do you have left in your mailbag?"

"I have 25 letters left to deliver," answered Mrs. Stampley.

"Mrs. Stampley always sings while she delivers letters," Maria whispered. "Listen."

"I'll deliver 3 to Ms. McGoo, and then that leaves me 22," Mrs. Stamply warbled as she strolled to the next mailbox. She sang in a high, shrill voice.

Rover threw his head back and almost started to howl. Then he realized that Manuel would hear him and find his hiding place. So Rover kept quiet.

Mrs. Stampley continued singing as she went from mailbox to mailbox. "I'll take out 10 for Mr. Shelve. The remainder left is only 12. And 10 more here and I'll soon be through. Now that leaves me only 2."

Maria and Manuel waited patiently for Mrs. Stampley to come to their mailbox. Rover wagged his tail and watched from behind the tree.

Mrs. Stampley smiled at the children as she passed right by their mailbox. "I'm sorry to say what's left is 2, but neither one is mailed to you."

"Zero, zip, zonk!" Manuel groaned. "No surprise today."

Mrs. Stampley delivered the remaining 2 letters to the next mailbox. Then she turned back toward Manuel and Maria and opened the bag up wide. "Zero letters are left. You can see with your own two eyes. But way down in the bottom, there is one surprise."

Manuel and Maria peeked into the mailbag. "Zero letters, but one surprise!" they exclaimed.

Mrs. Stampley pulled a small package out of the mailbag and gave it to Manuel. Manuel opened the box. Maria clapped her hands with delight. "A collar and leash for Rover! Now we can take him for walks all over town. He'll be able to see everything!"

Manuel called for Rover again. This time Rover romped across the street. He sat between Maria and Manuel, waiting for his new collar to be fastened. Then Rover and the children set off down the street, with Mrs. Stampley as their guide.

Counting Back by Ones

OBJECTIVE 13-1   To model and subtract a 1-digit number from a 2-digit number by counting back by ones

PREBOOK ACTIVITIES

QUICK REVIEW

Subtract.

11	8	13	15	10	9	14	12
− 3	− 5	− 7	− 9	− 2	− 4	− 6	− 3
(8)	(3)	(6)	(6)	(8)	(5)	(8)	(9)

PRIOR KNOWLEDGE

Tell students to imagine that they are mail carriers. Explain that they must keep track of the packages they collect and deliver. For each situation, have students tell whether they would count on or count back to keep track of the number of packages in their mail truck.

You pick up 3 packages from Mrs. Rosen. (count on)
You drop off 4 packages at Smith's Store. (count back)
One package falls off the truck! (count back)
You deliver a package to Mr. Chan. (count back)

COMMUNICATION

Listening in Math   *Listen to the paragraph as I read it aloud. See if you can find the mystery buzzword.*
We use buzz *every day.* Buzz *helps us figure out how much change we get at the grocery store. We can use* buzz *to compare how much money we have before and after we get our allowance, or how many more jumping jacks we do than someone else. Counting back is one way we can find the solution to a* buzz *problem. What is the mystery* buzzword? (subtraction)

EXPLORE AND CONNECT

Materials: Cube-A-Links, punchout number cards 1-5
Grouping Suggestion: pairs
Provide each pair of students with a quantity of Cube-A-Links. The first student says a number between 20 and 50 and shows it with cubes. The second student chooses a punchout number card between 1 and 5 to subtract from the first number. The first student counts back verbally to tell how many are left after subtracting while removing that number of cubes. The partner checks by counting the remaining cubes. Students switch roles and repeat, making up a story to go with their problem each time. Encourage students to listen to each other and follow each other's suggestions if they have difficulty completing the activity.

CONNECTIONS   Use these anytime.

Problem of the Day

Choose the Operation   Write the number sentence and solve. Use cubes to check.
Jason has 32 newspapers to deliver. So far he has delivered 3 of them. How many more newspapers does he have to deliver? (32 − 3 = 29)

Counting Patterns

Counting Back by Ones   Finish each pattern. Write the pattern in your Math Journal.
1. 69, 68, 67, (66) , (65) , (64)
2. 54, 53, 52, (51) , (50) , (49)
3. 32, 31, (30) , (29) , 28, (27)
4. 80, (79) , (78) , (77) , 76, 75
5. 41, (40) , (39) , 38, (37) , 36

Mental Math

Subtraction   Count back by ones to find the differences.
25 − 2 = (23)   53 − 1 = (52)
39 − 5 = (34)   60 − 3 = (57)
47 − 4 = (43)   90 − 1 = (89)
56 − 3 = (53)   31 − 4 = (27)
22 − 2 = (20)   45 − 5 = (40)

CLASSWORK AND HOMEWORK SUPPLEMENTS

Basic

Exercises All

Supplements
Reteaching 111 or
Practice 111

Average

Exercises All

Supplements
Practice 111
Challenges 111 or
Thinking Skills 111

Extended

Exercises All

Supplements
Challenges 111
Thinking Skills 111

Other Resources:
Mathematics Their Way, pp. 188-189
Explorations, pp. 42, 74, 100, 127, 131, 285
Problem Solving Experiences In Mathematics, pp. 129, 147
Developing Number Concepts With Unifix Cubes, p. 168

Practice

Skills Maintenance — 13-1

Name _____

Counting Back by Ones

Count back to subtract.
Check each cube as you count.
Then write the subtraction sentence.

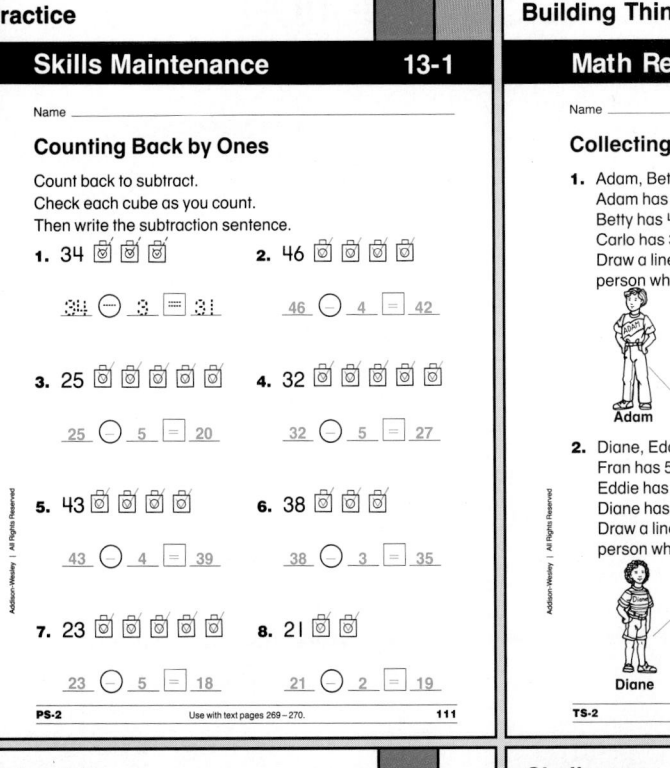

1. 34 □□□ 34 ⊖ 3 = 31

2. 46 □□□□ 46 ⊖ 4 = 42

3. 25 □□□□□ 25 ⊖ 5 = 20

4. 32 □□□□□ 32 ⊖ 5 = 27

5. 43 □□□□ 43 ⊖ 4 = 39

6. 38 □□□ 38 ⊖ 3 = 35

7. 23 □□□□□ 23 ⊖ 5 = 18

8. 21 □□ 21 ⊖ 2 = 19

PS-2   Use with text pages 269-270.   **111**

Building Thinking Skills

Math Reasoning — 13-1

Name _____

Collecting

1. Adam, Betty, and Carlo collect stamps.
   Adam has 42 stamps.
   Betty has 4 less than Carlo.
   Carlo has 3 less than Adam.
   Draw a line between each box of stamps and the person who owns it.

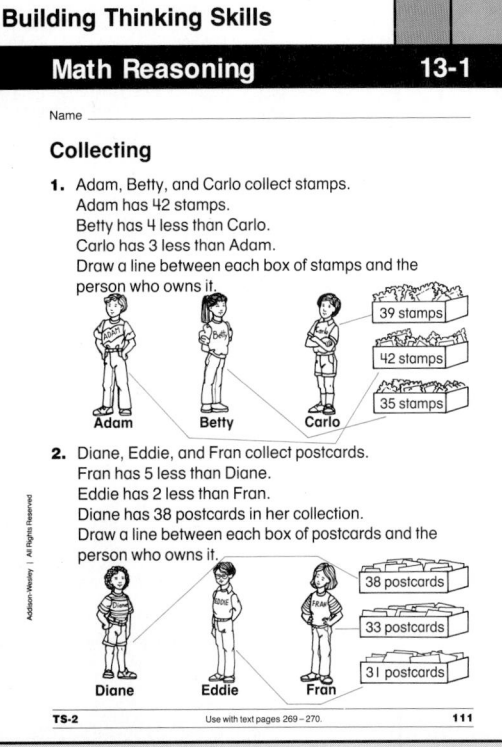

39 stamps
42 stamps
35 stamps

Adam   Betty   Carlo

2. Diane, Eddie, and Fran collect postcards.
   Fran has 5 less than Diane.
   Eddie has 2 less than Fran.
   Diane has 38 postcards in her collection.
   Draw a line between each box of postcards and the person who owns it.

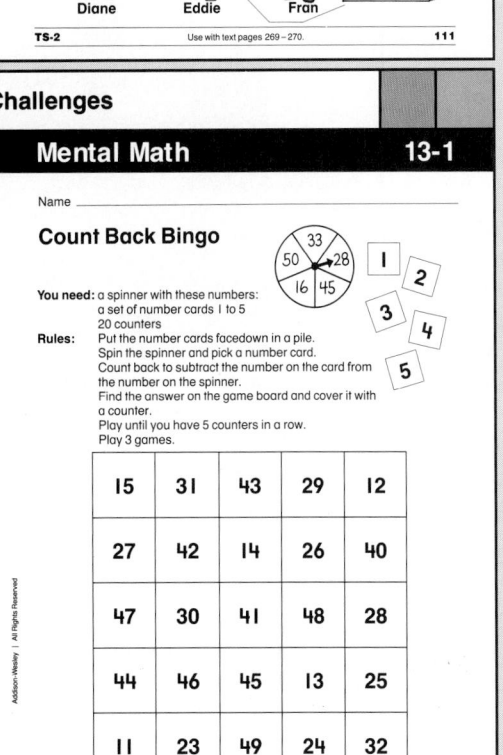

38 postcards
33 postcards
31 postcards

Diane   Eddie   Fran

TS-2   Use with text pages 269-270.   **111**

Reteaching

Skills Review — 13-1

Name _____

Counting Back by Ones

Take away 1 cube to count back 1.

24, 23   36, 35, 34

24 ⊖ 1 = 23   36 ⊖ 2 = 34

Count back to subtract.
Then write the subtraction sentence.

1.   27 ⊖ 3 = 24

2.   45 ⊖ 2 = 43

3.   58 ⊖ 5 = 53

4.   39 ⊖ 4 = 35

RS-2   Use with text pages 269-270.   **111**

Challenges

Mental Math — 13-1

Name _____

Count Back Bingo

Spinner: 33, 28, 45, 16, 50

Cards: 1, 2, 3, 4, 5

You need: a spinner with these numbers:
a set of number cards 1 to 5
20 counters

Rules: Put the number cards facedown in a pile.
Spin the spinner and pick a number card.
Count back to subtract the number on the card from the number on the spinner.
Find the answer on the game board and cover it with a counter.
Play until you have 5 counters in a row.
Play 3 games.

15	31	43	29	12
27	42	14	26	40
47	30	41	48	28
44	46	45	13	25
11	23	49	24	32

CS-2   Use with text pages 269-270.   **111**

OBJECTIVE 13-1

To model and subtract a 1-digit number from a 2-digit number by counting back by ones

> **Materials:** Cube-A-Links, spinner labeled 1-5, number cards 31-40, subtraction sentence cards (2-digit minus 1-digit)
>
> **Grouping Suggestions:** individual work, cooperative groups of 3

1. MOTIVATE AND TEACH

LEARN ABOUT IT

Read the chapter story to the class. *Suppose Mrs. Stampley had started with 37 letters and delivered 4. How many would she have left? (33)*

Have students turn to page 269. Ask them to place cubes in the mail pouch in ten-stacks and ones to represent the number of letters in all. As letters are delivered, have students take cubes out of the pouch and place them in the mailbox, counting back by ones to find the number still in the pouch. Repeat for different numbers of letters and deliveries.

▶ **How can you find the number of letters left in the pouch?** (Count back, or subtract, the number of letters that were delivered.)

▶ **Why is it easier to count back the number of letters delivered than to count the remaining letters in the pouch?** (Possible answer: The number of letters delivered, or taken away, is a smaller number, so it is easier to count.)

▶ **How can you find out if your answer is correct?** (Possible answers: Count the cubes left in the pouch; add to check.)

2. CHECK UNDERSTANDING

ERROR ALERT Counting on instead of counting back.

13
Understanding 2-Digit Subtraction

TEACHING OPTIONS

RETEACHING TIPS Use a spinner labeled 1-5. Students model a 2-digit number with cubes, then spin and take away that number of cubes from the original number, counting back as they remove each cube. Check answer by counting the remaining cubes. Assign Reteaching Supplement 111.

ENRICHMENT One student in a group is banker. Place number cards 31-40 face down. The others draw a card without looking, and model it with cubes. The banker calls out *25*. The others remove cubes as they count back to 25. The player with the fewest removed is banker next, and calls a new number.

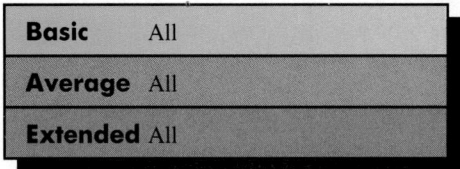

ne _____

ounting Back by Ones

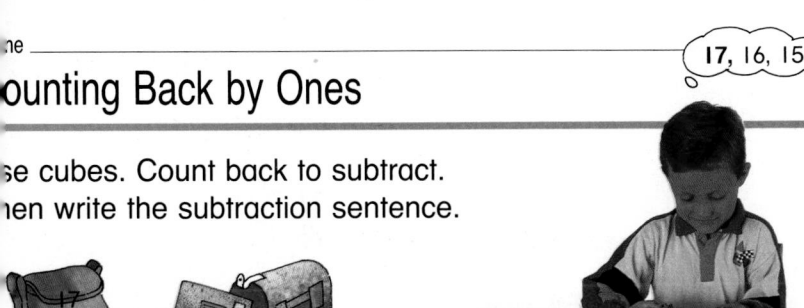

(17, 16, 15)

se cubes. Count back to subtract.
hen write the subtraction sentence.

17 ⊖ 2 = 15

25 ⊖ 5 = 20

3. 20 ⊖ 4 = 16

ount back to subtract. Check each cube as
u count. Then write the subtraction sentence.

24 ⊖ 3 = 21

5.  38 ⊖ 4 = 34

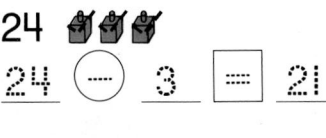

29 ⊖ 5 = 24

7. 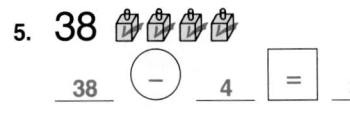 30 ⊖ 2 = 28

SE MENTAL MATH

ount back by ones. Write the difference.

21 − 1 = __20__   50 − 2 = __48__   45 − 3 = __42__

---

3. PRACTICE AND APPLY

Basic	All
Average	All
Extended	All

PRACTICE

How can you find the information needed to write and solve Exercises 1-3? (The number on the mail pouch is the first number; the number of letters in the picture is the number to be subtracted; the remaining number is the difference.)

APPLY

USE MENTAL MATH ▶ **How can you solve these exercises without using cubes or pictures?** (Use mental math by counting back the number of ones taken away from the number to start.)
▶ **How can you use counting on to check your answers?** (Start with the answer, or difference, and count on the number of ones taken away to make sure it matches the number to start.)

13-1

LOSE AND ASSESS

HOW WHAT YOU KNOW Give
ch group Cube-A-Links and a
btraction sentence card. One student
inks of a problem to ask the group,
second models the problem with
bes, and a third counts back as the
bes are removed. The second and
ird students then state the answer;
e first shows the subtraction
ntence card to check.

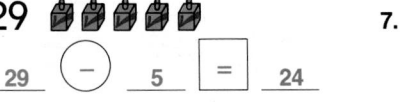

QUICK QUIZ

Use cubes. Count back to find the differences.

17 − 2 (15)	39 − 5 (34)
48 − 5 (43)	62 − 3 (59)
40 − 2 (38)	56 − 1 (55)

Chapter 13 Lesson 1   **270**

Subtracting Tens

OBJECTIVE 13-2   To model and subtract decade numbers

PREBOOK ACTIVITIES

$9 - 4 = \underline{(5)}$ $8 - 6 = \underline{(2)}$ $3 - 1 = \underline{(2)}$
$7 - 5 = \underline{(2)}$ $7 - 3 = \underline{(4)}$ $8 - 3 = \underline{(5)}$
$6 - 2 = \underline{(4)}$ $5 - 1 = \underline{(4)}$ $9 - 2 = \underline{(7)}$

PRIOR KNOWLEDGE

Have students count on by tens from 0 to 90. Then have them count back by tens from 90 to 0. *Which way is like adding tens?* (counting on) *Why?* (The numbers get bigger.) *Which way is like subtracting tens? Why?* (counting back, because the numbers get smaller) *When you count on by tens, how much are you adding as you say each number?* (1 ten) *When you count back by tens, how much are you subtracting as you say each number?* (1 ten) Call out random multiples of ten, such as 50. Have students count back 1 ten and say the new number. (40)

COMMUNICATION

Writing in Math   Write the following on the chalkboard and have students write the numeral and name of each number in their Math Journals: 1 ten (10, ten), 2 tens (20, twenty), 3 tens (30, thirty), 4 tens (40, forty), 5 tens (50, fifty), 6 tens (60, sixty), 7 tens (70, seventy), 8 tens (80, eighty), 9 tens (90, ninety)

Materials: Cube-A-Links; TA 12 (Spinners), marked 2-5 and 6-9
Grouping Suggestion: pairs
Have each student spin one of the spinners and show that many tens by linking 10 cubes. *Which partner has the larger number of tens? Who has the smaller number? Which number of tens can you subtract from the other?* (the smaller from the larger) Encourage students to listen to each other's ideas when they decide which number to subtract from the other. Have partners show the subtraction by taking away the smaller number of 10-trains from the larger number. *How can we write that subtraction sentence?* (6 tens − 4 tens = 2 tens) *What basic subtraction fact is this like?* (6 − 4 = 2) *What number sentence is the same as 6 tens − 4 tens = 2 tens?* (60 − 40 = 2

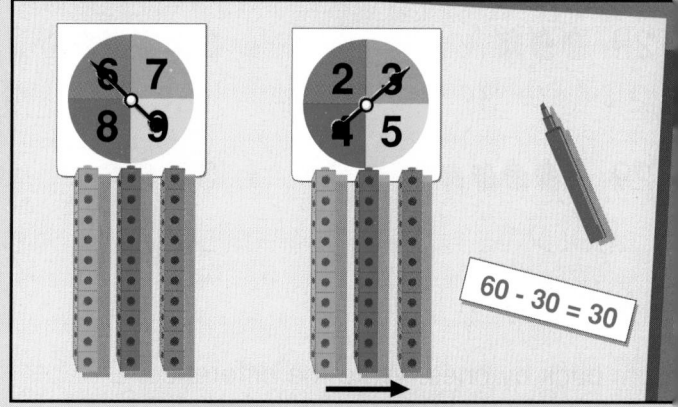

CONNECTIONS   Use these anytime.

Problem of the Day

Make a Table   Tammy and her brother, Doug, take turns doing the jobs at home. They earn 1 dime every time they set the table and 2 dimes every time they wash the dishes. For the last 2 nights, Tammy washed the dishes and Doug set the table. Which one earned more money? (Tammy) How much more? (2 dimes or 20 cents)

Counting Patterns

Counting by Tens   What is the next number in the pattern?
90, 80, 70, 60, 50, __(40)__
100, 70, 40, __(10)__
100, 80, 60, 40, __(20)__
70, 80, 50, 60, 30, 40, __(10)__

Math Connection

Graphing   Mitch is using a pictograph to keep track of the books he reads every month. On it, each book = 10 books. Mitch read 20 books in March, 30 books in April, and 50 books in May. Draw the graph. How many more books did he read in May than in April? than in March? (20 more than in April, 30 more than in March)

CLASSWORK AND HOMEWORK SUPPLEMENTS

13-2

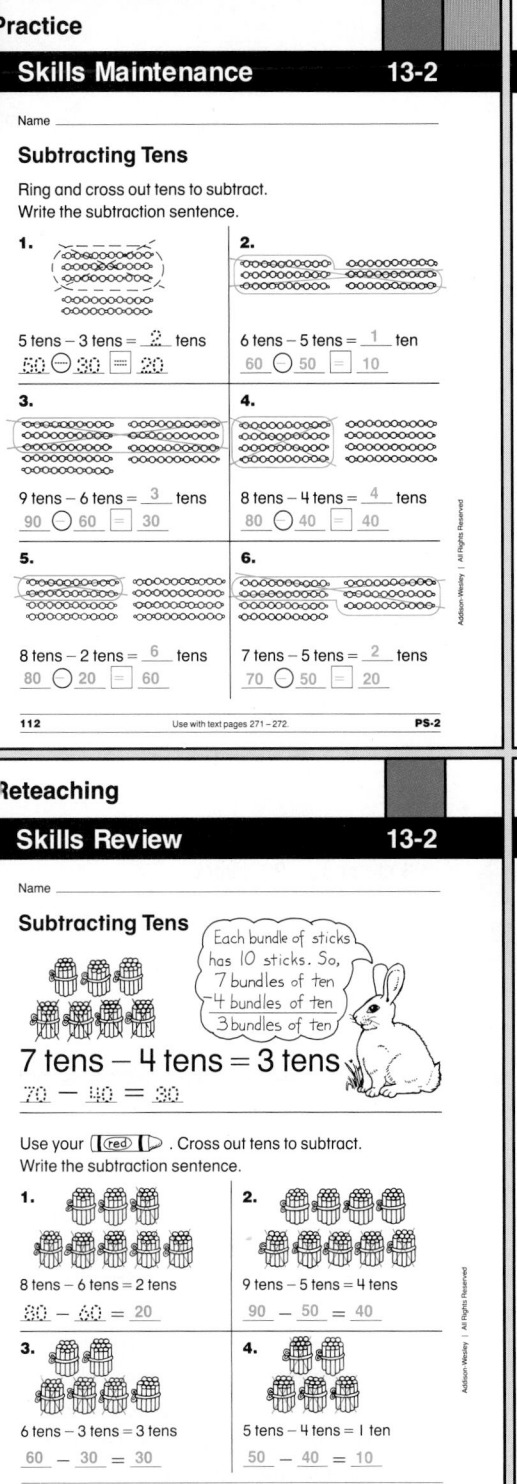

Practice

Skills Maintenance 13-2

Name _____

Subtracting Tens

Ring and cross out tens to subtract.
Write the subtraction sentence.

1.
5 tens – 3 tens = __2__ tens
50 ⊖ 30 ▯ 20

2.
6 tens – 5 tens = __1__ ten
60 ◯ 50 = 10

3.
9 tens – 6 tens = __3__ tens
90 ◯ 60 = 30

4.
8 tens – 4 tens = __4__ tens
80 ⊖ 40 ▯ 40

5.
8 tens – 2 tens = __6__ tens
80 ◯ 20 ▯ 60

6.
7 tens – 5 tens = __2__ tens
70 ◯ 50 ▯ 20

112   Use with text pages 271 – 272.   **PS-2**

Reteaching

Skills Review 13-2

Name _____

Subtracting Tens

Each bundle of sticks has 10 sticks. So, 7 bundles of ten – 4 bundles of ten = 3 bundles of ten

7 tens – 4 tens = 3 tens

70 — 40 = 30

Use your [red] . Cross out tens to subtract.
Write the subtraction sentence.

1.
8 tens – 6 tens = 2 tens
80 — 60 = 20

2.
9 tens – 5 tens = 4 tens
90 — 50 = 40

3.
6 tens – 3 tens = 3 tens
60 — 30 = 30

4.
5 tens – 4 tens = 1 ten
50 — 40 = 10

112   Use with text pages 271 – 272.   **RS-2**

Building Thinking Skills

Manipulatives 13-2

Name _____

What Did I Buy?

Use your coin punchouts.
Match each story to the toy that was bought.

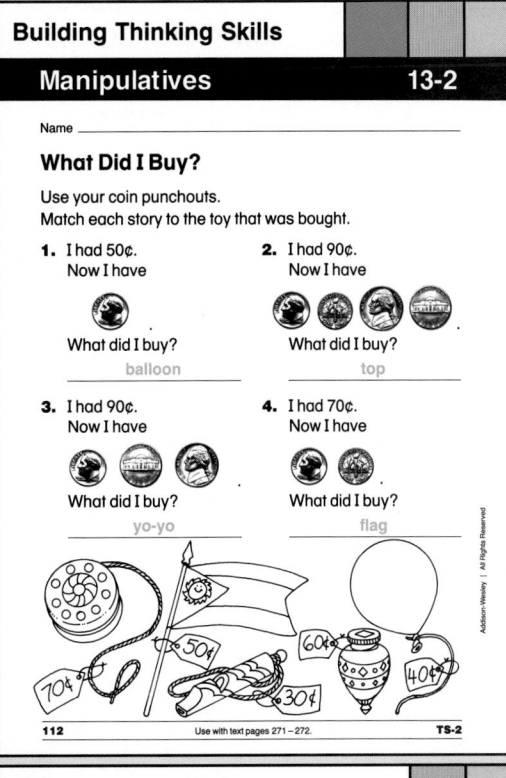

1. I had 50¢.
Now I have

What did I buy?
balloon

2. I had 90¢.
Now I have

What did I buy?
top

3. I had 90¢.
Now I have

What did I buy?
yo-yo

4. I had 70¢.
Now I have

What did I buy?
flag

112   Use with text pages 271 – 272.   **TS-2**

Challenges

Family Math 13-2

Name _____

Bowling for Tens

Dear Family,
Your child has just completed a lesson on subtracting tens. To play this game you will need a number cube marked in tens — 10 – 60 — or small cards marked 10 – 60.

Take turns.
The first player rolls the number cube or draws a card.
Read the number on the top of the cube or on the card.
Cross out one pin to subtract each ten.
For example, if you roll a 30, cross out 3 pins.
If the number on the cube is more than the number of pins you have left, you lose your turn.
The first player to cross out all the pins wins.

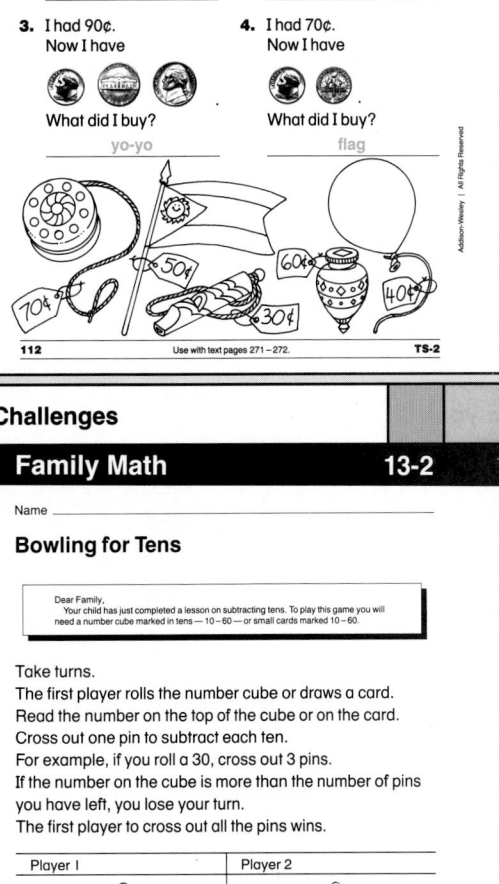

Player 1	Player 2

112   Use with text pages 271 – 272.   **CS-2**

Basic

Exercises All

Supplements
Reteaching 112 or
Practice 112
Thinking Skills 112

Average

Exercises All

Supplements
Practice 112
Challenges 112 or
Thinking Skills 112

Extended

Exercises All

Supplements
Challenges 112
Thinking Skills 112

Other Resources:
Math In Stride, pp. 138-139
Explorations, pp. 131, 285

Chapter 13 Lesson 2   **271B**

OBJECTIVE 13-2

To model and subtract decade numbers

> **Materials:** Cube-A-Links, decade number cards 10-90
>
> **Grouping Suggestion:** pairs

1. MOTIVATE AND TEACH

LEARN ABOUT IT

Have partners make cube 10-trains for 2 different numbers of tens, then take away the smaller number of tens from the larger number. Have them write a subtraction sentence to show what they did:

_____ tens − _____ tens = _____ tens.

Discuss the example at the top of page 271. Have students use cubes if they need to.

▶ **Why are we subtracting 30 to find out how many stamps will be left?** (Since there are 30 letters and each letter gets one stamp, 30 is the number of stamps that will be used.)

▶ **Why is 8 tens − 3 tens = 5 tens the same as 80 − 30 = 50?** (8 tens is the same as 80, 3 tens is the same as 30, and 5 tens is the same as 50.)

▶ **What basic subtraction fact can you use to find the answer to 80 − 30? Why does this work?** (8 − 3 = 5; since there are 0 ones in each number, you always know the ones place will be 0, so you do not have to subtract.)

▶ **What if you had 10 more letters? How many stamps would you have left over?** (10 fewer stamps, or 40)

2. CHECK UNDERSTANDING

ERROR ALERT Writing the expanded form instead of using numbers in the subtraction sentences.

Name _____

Subtracting Tens

You have 80 stamps and 30 letters.
You want to put a stamp on each letter.
How many stamps will you have left?

8 tens − 3 tens = 5 tens

You will have 50 stamps left.

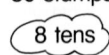 80 stamps  30 letters

8 tens   3 tens

Work with a partner. Cross out tens to subtract. Write the subtraction sentence.

1.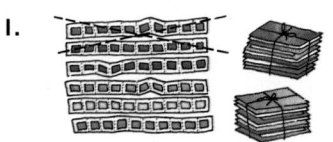

60 stamps   20 letters

__6__ tens − __2__ tens = __4__ tens

60 ⊖ 20 ▢= 40

2.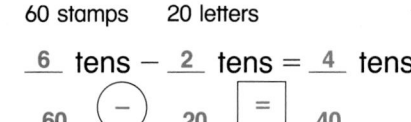

50 stamps   30 letters

__5__ tens − __3__ tens = __2__ tens

50 ⊖ 30 ▢= 20

3.

90 stamps   20 letters

__9__ tens − __2__ tens = __7__ tens

90 ⊖ 20 ▢= 70

Chapter 13

(two hundred seventy-one) 2

TEACHING OPTIONS

RETEACHING TIPS Have students use Cube-A-Links to make 10-trains, one at a time. After they make each ten, ask: *How many tens? What number is that?* Have students write each form of the number: *1 ten, 10.* Use Reteaching Supplement 112 for additional help with this skill.

COMPUTER **Milt's Math Drills, Hartley Courseware © 1986** Review for all students, timed or untimed. In *Addition/Subtraction Disk 2,* students practice addition and subtraction with sums and minuends 0-18, with doubles, and by building tens sums 11-18. The lesson requires 10-15 minutes.

...oss out tens to subtract.
...rite the subtraction sentence.

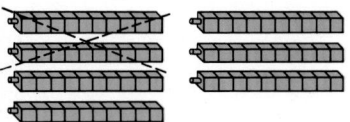

7 tens − 2 tens = __5__ tens

$\underline{70}$ ⊝ $\underline{20}$ ▣ $\underline{50}$

2.

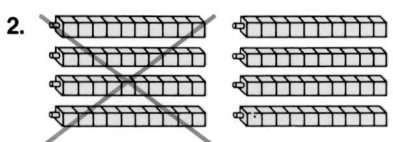

8 tens − 4 tens = __4__ tens

$\underline{80}$ ⊝ $\underline{40}$ = $\underline{40}$

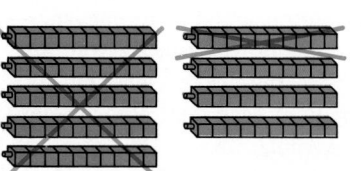

9 tens − 6 tens = __3__ tens

$\underline{90}$ ⊝ $\underline{60}$ ▣ $\underline{30}$

4.

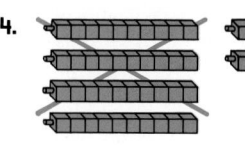

6 tens − 3 tens = __3__ tens

$\underline{60}$ ⊝ $\underline{30}$ = $\underline{30}$

I know 9 − 7 = 2.
So 9 tens − 7 tens = 2 tens.

90 − 70 = 20

...E MENTAL MATH

...nd each difference.
...e basic facts to help.

__ 60 − 20 = __40__   **6.** 70 − 40 = __30__

__ 50 − 20 = __30__   **8.** 80 − 60 = __20__

__ 90 − 50 = __40__   **10.** 60 − 50 = __10__

2 (two hundred seventy-two)

Chapter 13

...LOSE AND ASSESS

...Y WHAT YOU THINK Provide
...rs of students with number cards
...owing multiples of ten, 10-90. Have
...h student draw a large subtraction
...tence with blanks on a piece of
...per: _____ − _____ = _____.
...ve students arrange number cards to
...m a subtraction sentence, using
...h card only once.

QUICK QUIZ

Subtract.
70 − 60 = __(10)__   90 − 30 = __(60)__
80 − 20 = __(60)__   60 − 40 = __(20)__
50 − 10 = __(40)__   70 − 50 = __(20)__
90 − 50 = __(40)__   80 − 70 = __(10)__

---

for pages 271-272

3. PRACTICE AND APPLY

Basic	All
Average	All
Extended	All

PRACTICE

*How will you know how many tens to
cross out in the exercises on page 272?*
(The sentence tells how many tens to
subtract.)

APPLY

USE MENTAL MATH ▶ **What
basic subtraction fact would you use
to find the difference in Exercise 5?**
(6 − 2 = 4)

▶ **Is the difference in 60 − 20 the
same as the difference in the basic
subtraction fact? Explain.** (No, you
have to add a zero to show that the
answer is 4 tens, or 40, not just 4, which
is 4 ones.)

▶ **How can you check the
subtraction?** (Possible answers: Use
cubes; add 2 tens and 4 tens; count on 2
tens from 40.)

13-2

Chapter 13 Lesson 2   **272**

LESSON OPTIONS 13-3

Counting Back by Tens

OBJECTIVE 13-3 To model and subtract a decade number from a 2-digit number by counting back by tens

PREBOOK ACTIVITIES

PRIOR KNOWLEDGE

Hold up a number card showing a 2-digit number that is not a multiple of ten, such as 98. *Can we count back by tens from this number?* Begin the count—98, 88, 78—and ask students to join in. Hold up another number, such as 84. *If we count back by tens from this number, will we say 64? 56? 44? How do you know?* (We will say 64 and 44 but not 56; we will say only numbers that end in 4 because the ones stay the same.) Have students count back by tens from 84 to 14 to check.

COMMUNICATION

Reading and Discussing Math Write 90 − 30 = ____ on the chalkboard. Remind students that they learned how to count back by tens to subtract. *Which number tells you how many tens to count back?* (30) Explain that you can count back by tens to subtract as long as the number being subtracted is a multiple of ten. Write the following on the chalkboard. Have students tell whether you can count back by tens to subtract.

1. 90 − 50 = (yes)   2. 88 − 40 = (yes)
3. 60 − 48 = (no)   4. 43 − 36 = (no)
5. 67 − 20 = (yes)   6. 54 − 44 = (no)
7. 76 − 60 = (yes)   8. 50 − 21 = (no)

EXPLORE AND CONNECT

Materials: Cube-A-Links
Grouping Suggestion: pairs
On the chalkboard, write a 2-digit number from 41 to 99 (other than a multiple of 10), such as 54. Ask partners to show the number with cubes. Encourage students to listen to each other while discussing how many ten-trains and extra ones they need to show the number. How could you subtract 30 from *this number?* (Possible answer: by taking away 3 tens) Have the first partner count back verbally as each ten-train is removed by the second partner—for example: **54,** 44, 34, 24. *How many tens do you count back to take away 30?* (3) *How do you know?* (30 is 3 tens.) Suggest other numbers for students to show with cubes and other multiples of 10 to subtract, encouraging them to count back the appropriate number of tens by removing the matching number of ten-trains.

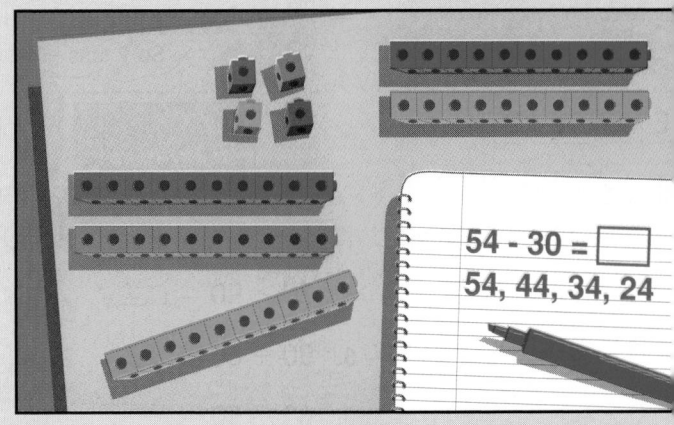

CONNECTIONS   Use these anytime.

Problem of the Day

Draw a Picture The houses on Park Street are numbered by tens. The last house on the street is number 82. Amy lives 2 houses before the last house. Craig lives 3 houses before Amy. At what numbers do Amy and Craig live?
(62, 32)

 32 Craig   42   52   62 Amy   72   82

Counting Patterns

Counting Back by 10s Write the number that comes next. Tell how many tens were counted back in all.
81, 71, 61, (51) (3 tens)
69, 59, 49, 39, (29) (4 tens)
33, 23, 13, (3) (3 tens)
56, 46, 36, 26, (16) (4 tens)

Math Connection

Time

What time was it 10 min ago? (4:34)
30 min ago? (4:14)
Draw 2 clocks of your own. Show 2 times that are 20 min apart.

CLASSWORK AND HOMEWORK SUPPLEMENTS

ractice

Skills Maintenance   13-3

Name _____

Counting Back by Tens

Start with the number given.
Count back by tens.
Write the difference.

1.   56   **56**
  − 30
    26

2.   28   **28**
  − 10
    18

3.   74   **74**
  − 20
    54

4.   85   **85**
  − 40
    45

5.   32   **32**
  − 20
    12

6.   47   **47**
  − 10
    37

PS-2   Use with text pages 273–274.   **113**

Building Thinking Skills

Mental Math   13-3

Name _____

Tens Count Back

Write the answers in the blanks.

78 40 less → 38	54 20 less → 34	38 10 less → 28	46 30 less → 16
66 10 less → 56	97 30 less → 67	11 10 less → 1	39 20 less → 19
59 40 less → 19	86 10 less → 76	26 20 less → 6	75 40 less → 35
17 10 less → 7	41 10 less → 31	53 30 less → 23	18 10 less → 8
22 10 less → 12	63 40 less → 23	89 40 less → 49	

Find these answers above:
34   28   76   67   6   7   23   31   23
Color the spaces yellow. What does the picture show?

___ a bell ___

TS-2   Use with text pages 273–274.   **113**

eteaching

Skills Review   13-3

Name _____

Counting Back by Tens

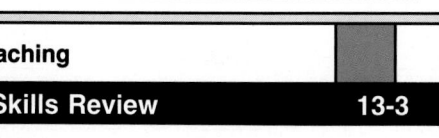

Start with 34. Count back by tens. 34, 24, 14

$$34 - 20 = 14$$

Count back by 10s to subtract.
Write the subtraction sentence.

1.   66 −
  66 − 20 = 46

2.   48 −
  48 − 10 = 38

3.   75 −
  75 − 30 = 45

4.   53 −
  53 − 40 = 13

5.   82 −
  82 − 10 = 72

6.   94 −
  94 − 20 = 74

RS-2   Use with text pages 273–274.   **113**

Challenges

Cooperative Activities   13-3

Name _____

Tens Checkers

Rules: 1. Each player puts 6 counters on the 6 white squares nearest the top or bottom edge of the checkerboard.
2. Take turns. Move 1 counter to a subtraction square. Solve the exercise aloud.
3. If your answer is right, stay on the square. If your answer is wrong, move back to the white square.
4. Move your counters to the opposite side of the board by moving from one subtraction square to the next.
5. The first player to reach the opposite side with all 6 counters wins.

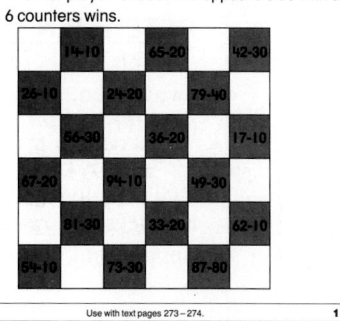

CS-2   Use with text pages 273–274.   **113**

OPTIONS FOR INDIVIDUAL NEEDS

Basic

Exercises All, Midchapter Review/Quiz
More Practice, p. 424, set B

Supplements
Reteaching 113 or
Practice 113
Challenges 113

Average

Exercises All, Midchapter Review/Quiz
More Practice, p. 424, set B

Supplements
Practice 113
Challenges 113 or
Thinking Skills 113

Extended

Exercises All, Midchapter Review/Quiz

Supplements
Challenges 113
Thinking Skills 113

Other Resources:
Developing Number Concepts With Unifix Cubes, p. 175

13-3

OBJECTIVE 13-3
To model and subtract a decade number from a 2-digit number by counting back by tens

---

Materials: Cube-A-Links, spinners; home-made tens cards showing multiples of ten in different forms: ten-trains, numerals, word names, numbers of tens

Grouping Suggestion: small groups

---

1. MOTIVATE AND TEACH

LEARN ABOUT IT

Write a 2-digit number on the chalkboard and ask pairs of students to show the number with cubes. Then have them subtract 30 from the original number by counting back tens as they take away 3 ten-trains. Direct students' attention to Exercise 1 on page 273, which is modeled at the top of page. *How is the start number, 58, shown in cubes?* (5 ten-trains and 8 single cubes)

▶ **Why is the boy taking away 3 of the ten-trains?** (He spun 30, which means to subtract 30 from 58; 30 is the same as 3 tens.)

▶ **How many numbers do you say after the start number when you count back 30 by tens?** (3) **What does the 3 stand for?** (3 tens)

▶ **When you subtract an amount of tens from a 2-digit number, what is the same about the start number and the difference? Why?** (The number in the ones place is the same, because an amount of tens has 0 ones. The ones do not change.)

▶ **If the spinner had a section with 5 tens, could you do Exercise 5 if you spun that amount? Why or why not?** (No, because 5 tens is 50, and 50 is larger than 49. You cannot subtract a large number from a small number.)

2. CHECK UNDERSTANDING

ERROR ALERT Not understanding that removing a number of ten-trains is the same as subtracting tens in a subtraction sentence.

Name _____

Counting Back by Tens

Work in a group.
Use cubes and a spinner.

I spun 30.
Count back ten
58, 48, 38, 28

Start with 58.

$$58 - 30 = 28$$

Show the start number with cubes. Spin. Use cubes to count back the spinner amount. Finish the subtraction sentence.

Answers may vary.
Check students' wo

	Start Number	Spinner Amount	Difference		Start Number	Spinner Amount	Differen
1.	58	30	28	2.	74		
3.	62			4.	55		
5.	49			6.	85		
7.	93			8.	67		
9.	81			10.	46		

Chapter 13

(two hundred seventy-three)

TEACHING OPTIONS

RETEACHING TIPS Have students make 9 ten-trains, then take away 1 ten. *What number is 1 ten?* (10) *Write the subtraction sentence to show this.* (90 − 10 = 80) Continue in this way, subtracting up to 9 tens. Use Reteaching Supplement 113 for additional help.

ENRICHMENT Have students make challenge sheets. Under the headings *Count Back (2, 3, or 4) Tens* list 2-digit numbers. Have pairs exchange and complete the sheets by writing subtraction sentences. Discuss any subtraction that cannot be completed.

e cubes. Start with the number
en. Count back by tens. Write
e subtraction sentence.

36 | | | 2. **49** | | |

36 ⊝ 20 ▭ 16   49 ⊝ 30 ▯ 19

68 | | | | 4. **25** |

68 ⊝ 40 ▯ 28   25 ⊝ 10 ▯ 15

MIDCHAPTER REVIEW/QUIZ

rite the subtraction sentences.

1. Count back by ones.   2. Count back by tens.

34 🎲🎲🎲🎲   **89** ▭▭

34 ⊝ 4 ▯ 30   89 ⊝ 20 ▯ 69

oss out tens to subtract.
en write the subtraction sentence.

4.

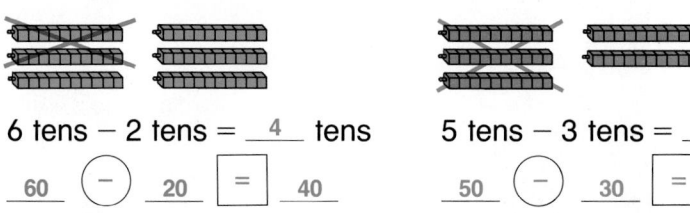

6 tens − 2 tens = __4__ tens   5 tens − 3 tens = __2__ tens

60 ⊝ 20 ▯ 40   50 ⊝ 30 ▯ 20

3. PRACTICE AND APPLY

Basic	All, Midchapter Review/Quiz
Average	All, Midchapter Review/Quiz
Extended	All, Midchapter Review/Quiz

PRACTICE

In Exercises 1-4 on page 274, what number will you subtract from the start number? (the number that stands for the ten-trains shown)

APPLY

▶ **How is counting back by tens different from counting on by tens?**
(In counting on, you add tens to make the start number larger; in counting back, you subtract tens to make the start number smaller.)

MIDCHAPTER REVIEW/QUIZ The table is a correlation of the Midchapter Review/Quiz.

Items	Objectives
1	13-1
2	13-3
3,4	13-2

13-3

LOSE AND ASSESS

HOW WHAT YOU KNOW

view with students the chapter
ry, *Rover's Surprise*. Mrs.
mpley had 73 letters in her
ilbag. She delivered 40. How many
she have left? (33) Have students
rk together using cubes to find the
swer and write a number sentence.

QUICK QUIZ

Count back 5 tens from each number.
Show the counting back.
94 (94, 84, 74, 64, 54, 44)
63 (63, 53, 43, 33, 23, 13)
87 (87, 77, 67, 57, 47, 37)

Related Subtraction Sentences

OBJECTIVE 13-4   To show different ways to name the same difference

PREBOOK ACTIVITIES

QUICK REVIEW

These are related subtraction sentences: $8 - 5 = 3$ and $8 - 3 = 5$.
Write the related subtraction sentence for each.

1. $9 - 2 = 7$ $(9 - 7 = 2)$ **2.** $7 - 6 = 1$ $(7 - 1 = 6)$
3. $10 - 4 = 6$ $(10 - 6 = 4)$ **4.** $8 - 3 = 5$ $(8 - 5 = 3)$
5. $9 - 4 = 5$ $(9 - 5 = 4)$ **6.** $6 - 4 = 2$ $(6 - 2 = 4)$

PRIOR KNOWLEDGE

Review with students what they know about addition and
subtraction of basic facts. *What addition fact can you write
using the numbers 5, 4, and 9?* $(5 + 4 = 9)$ *Is there another
addition fact you can write?* $(4 + 5 = 9)$ *Can you always
reverse the addends to make another addition fact? Why?* (Yes;
one part plus the other part always gives the same sum; it does
not matter in what order you add the parts) *What subtraction
fact can you write if you subtract 5 from the whole?* $(9 - 5 =
4)$ *How can you write another subtraction fact?* (Subtract 4;
$9 - 4 = 5$) *How are these subtraction sentences related?*
(They have the same whole and parts.)

COMMUNICATION

Writing in Math   Write the following Word Bank on the
chalkboard: *whole, part, more, less, take away, left, minus,*
and *subtract.*
Ask small groups of students to write a paragraph explaining to
a pen pal from outer space when and how people on Earth do
subtraction. Tell students that they may use the words in the
Word Bank to help them.

EXPLORE AND CONNECT

Materials: Cube-A-Links
Grouping Suggestion: pairs
Have partners explore the idea of related subtraction sentence
1 whole minus 1 part equals the other part; the whole minus
the second part equals the first part. Have them snap apart a
ten-train into different parts—5 and 5, 6 and 4, 7 and 3, 8 a
2, or 9 and 1—and write the 2 related subtraction sentences.
Which combination has only 1 subtraction sentence? Why?
$(10 - 5 = 5$; the parts are the same) Repeat with a larger
2-digit number, such as 25. Show it with cubes, then break
them in 2 parts—for example, 12 and 13. *What 2 subtraction
sentences can you write?* $(25 - 12 = 13; 25 - 13 = 12)$ *Ar
they related subtraction sentences? Why?* (Yes; the whole is
the same and the 2 parts are the same.) Put the 25 back
together, find another way to make 2 parts, and write the
related subtraction sentences.

CONNECTIONS   Use these anytime.

Problem of the Day

How Much More?   Lucas and David
have each saved some money. Their
father promised to give them enough
money so that each would have 75¢.
Lucas has 4 dimes and 4 pennies. How
much does his father have to give him?
(31¢) David has the amount that their
father gave Lucas. How much more does
David need? (44¢)

Subject Integration

Language Arts   Which 2 sentences
say the same thing?
1. Jane and Andy like to jump and hop.
2. Jane and Andy like to hop.
3. Andy likes to hop, and Jane likes to
jump.
4. Andy and Jane like to hop and jump.
5. Andy and Jane like to hop and skip.
(1 and 4)

Number Sense

Mental Math   Do this in your head.
Since $96 - 47 = 49$, how much is
$96 - 49$? (47) How could you do such a
difficult exercise in your head? (The parts
are the same, so the answer is the other
part, 47.) Make up another difficult
subtraction. Use a calculator to find the
difference. Have a partner tell you the
related subtraction.

CLASSWORK AND HOMEWORK SUPPLEMENTS

Practice

Writing Math 13-4

Name _____

Related Subtraction Sentences

Match the related subtraction sentences.
Use cubes to check.

1. $36 - 14 = 22$ $21 - 14 = 7$
2. $28 - 17 = 11$ $45 - 19 = 26$
3. $21 - 7 = 14$ $40 - 21 = 19$
4. $45 - 26 = 19$ $36 - 22 = 14$
5. $40 - 19 = 21$ $28 - 11 = 17$

6. Which number stays the same in related subtraction sentences? Why? Possible answer: the number to start, because it stands for the whole

7. Which numbers changes places? Why can they change places? Possible answer: the number taken away and the number left, because each stands for one part

8. Do related subtraction sentences always have the same three numbers? yes

114   Use with text pages 275–276.   PS-2

Building Thinking Skills

Number Sense 13-4

Name _____

How Many Ways?

Get 30 cubes.
How many different ways do you think there are to separate the cubes into 2 groups?

Write your guess here. Guesses will vary.
Separate the cubes into 2 equal groups.
Add 1 to the first group and take away 1 from the second group each time. Write the numbers.

15 and 15	20 and 10	25 and 5
16 and 14	21 and 9	26 and 4
17 and 13	22 and 8	27 and 3
18 and 12	23 and 7	28 and 2
19 and 11	24 and 6	29 and 1

How many ways are there? 15
How close was your guess? Answers will vary.
What do you notice about the number of ways and the number in each group at the start?

It is the same.

Try one on your own. Use an even number of cubes.
(An even number ends in 0, 2, 4, 6, or 8.)

114   Use with text pages 275–276.   TS-2

Reteaching

Manipulatives 13-4

Name _____

Related Subtraction Sentences

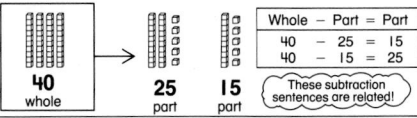

Whole − Part = Part
$40 - 25 = 15$
$40 - 15 = 25$

These subtraction sentences are related!

Use 40 cubes. Make the two groups. Take away one group from 40. Then take away the other group from 40. Finish the subtraction sentences to show what you did.

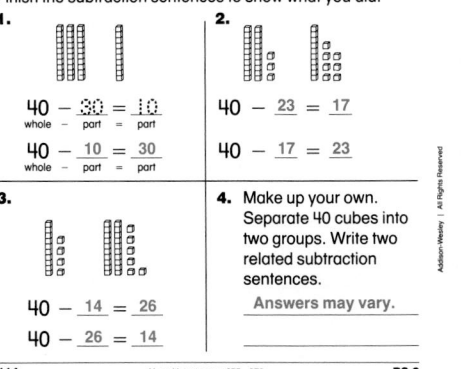

1. $40 - 30 = 10$
   whole − part = part
   $40 - 10 = 30$
   whole − part = part

2. $40 - 23 = 17$
   $40 - 17 = 23$

3. $40 - 14 = 26$
   $40 - 26 = 14$

4. Make up your own. Separate 40 cubes into two groups. Write two related subtraction sentences.
   Answers may vary.

114   Use with text pages 275–276.   RS-2

Challenges

Family Math 13-4

Name _____

Color the Squares

Dear Family,
Your child has just learned about related subtraction sentences for 2-digit numbers. Work together on these grids to explore this skill.

Color the squares on each grid. Write a subtraction sentence that tells how many squares are colored. Then write a sentence that tells how many are not colored.

Use the 50-block grid.

1. Color 20 squares.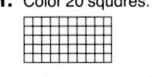
   $50 - 30 = 20$
   $50 - 20 = 30$

2. Color 17 squares.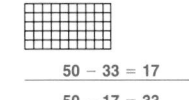
   $50 - 33 = 17$
   $50 - 17 = 33$

Use the 100-block grid.

3. Color 25 squares.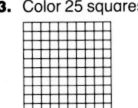
   $100 - 75 = 25$
   $100 - 25 = 75$

4. Color 40 squares.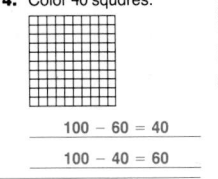
   $100 - 60 = 40$
   $100 - 40 = 60$

114   Use with text pages 275–276.   CS-2

OPTIONS FOR INDIVIDUAL NEEDS

Basic

Exercises All, Mixed Review
Calculator Bank, p. 403

Supplements
Reteaching 114 or
Practice 114
Challenges 114

Average

Exercises All, Mixed Review
Calculator Bank, p. 403

Supplements
Practice 114
Challenges 114 or
Thinking Skills 114

Extended

Exercises All, Mixed Review
Calculator Bank, p. 403

Supplements
Challenges 114
Thinking Skills 114

Other Resources:
Math in Stride, pp. 28-29, 46
Mathematics Book A, p. 28

13-4

LESSON PLAN 13-4

OBJECTIVE 13-4
To show different ways to name the same difference

> **Materials:** Cube-A-Links, chart paper, jars or bowls
>
> **Grouping Suggestion:** small groups, pairs

1. MOTIVATE AND TEACH

LEARN ABOUT IT

Have students show 25 with cubes using 2 sets of 10 and a set of 5. Next, have them split the 25 into 2 parts and write 2 subtraction sentences, showing the subtraction of each of the parts. Discuss how these sentences are related. Discuss the example at the top of page 275. *What groups did the students make when they broke apart a ten?* (2 groups of 5)

► **Which numbers in the subtraction sentences stand for the 2 parts?** (15 and 35)

► **Which number stays the same in the related subtraction sentences? Why?** (50; you always start with the whole.)

► **What if you split the 50 cubes into 2 groups of 25? Would there be 2 related subtraction sentences? Why or why not?** (There would be only 1 sentence, 50 − 25 = 25, since the parts are the same.)

► **How could you use addition to check the subtraction sentences in the example exercise?** (15 + 35 = 50; 35 + 15 = 50) **Are these sentences related? Why?** (Yes, they have the same parts and the same whole.)

2. CHECK UNDERSTANDING

ERROR ALERT Writing the related subtraction sentences but not understanding the relationship on the concrete level.

Name _____

Related Subtraction Sentences

Put 50 cubes in groups of ten.

Break apart a ten. Separate the 50 cubes into two groups.

Write two related subtraction senten about what you di

$$50 - 15 = 35$$
$$50 - 35 = 15$$

Work in a group. Use cubes. Find different ways to separate 50 cubes into two groups. Write two related subtraction sentences.

Answers may vai Check students' woi

1. $50 - 15 = 35$
   $50 - 35 = 15$

2. _____

3. _____

4. _____

5. _____

6. _____

7. _____

8. _____

Chapter 13

(two hundred seventy-five) 2

TEACHING OPTIONS

RETEACHING TIPS Write Whole − Part = Part. Have students make a 2-digit number with cubes. Put 1 set under *Whole*. Separate another set and place each group under *Part*. Place a third set of the same 2 groups, reversing the parts. Use Reteaching Supplement 114.

ENRICHMENT Have students collect interesting 2-digit numbers about themselves: their height in inches, their weight, their age in months, the number of teeth they have, and so on. Show these with cubes, break them into 2 groups, and write 2 related subtraction sentences for each.

...nd different ways to separate
... cubes into two groups.
...ite two related
...btraction sentences. *Answers may vary. Check students' work.*

1. $35 - 17 = 18$

   $35 - 18 = 17$

3. _____

   _____

5. _____

   _____

...nd different ways to separate 42 cubes
...o two groups. Write two related
...btraction sentences. **Answers may vary. Check students' work.**

7. _____

   _____

9. _____

   _____

MIXED REVIEW

...d or subtract.

23	15	8	17	15	24
$+19$	-7	$+79$	-8	$+13$	$+16$
42	8	87	9	$+25$	$+9$
				53	49

$24 + 3 = \underline{27}$ $9 - 9 = \underline{0}$ $13 - 5 = \underline{8}$

3. PRACTICE AND APPLY

Basic	All, Mixed Review
Average	All, Mixed Review
Extended	All, Mixed Review

PRACTICE

How will you do Exercises 2-5 on page 276? (Show 35, using cubes, then separate the cubes to show 2 parts of 35 and write the 2 related subtraction sentences.) *How will you do Exercises 6-9?* (the same way as the other exercises, using 42)

APPLY

▶ **Could you break 42 cubes into 2 even groups to give you only 1 subtraction sentence?** (yes) **Show the groups with the cubes. What is the number of cubes in each group?** (21)
▶ **Could you do the same with 35 cubes?** (no) **Why not?** (The closest we can get to breaking 35 apart evenly is 17 and 18.)

MIXED REVIEW *How will you know whether to add or subtract in Exercises 10 and 11?* (by looking at the sign; if it is a plus sign, add; if it is a minus sign, subtract)

13-4

CLOSE AND ASSESS

SHOW WHAT YOU KNOW Give ...rtners a jar filled with an unknown ...ount of cubes. Have them find the ...mber by making as many ten-trains ... possible, then counting the tens and ...tra ones. Have students record the ...mber, separate the cubes into 2 ...oups, and write the 2 related ...btraction sentences. Then have them ...place cubes and exchange them with ...other pair of students. Have pairs ...mpare the sentences they wrote.

QUICK QUIZ

Model the start number. Take away 28. Write the related sentence.
$76 - 28 = (48)$ $(76 - 48 = 28)$
$54 - 28 = (26)$ $(54 - 26 = 28)$
$62 - 28 = (34)$ $(62 - 34 = 28)$

Problem Solving: Understanding the Operations

OBJECTIVE 13-5   To understand the operation of subtraction by comparing or by finding the missing part

PREBOOK ACTIVITIES

QUICK REVIEW

Count back to subtract.

25 − 3 = (22)	39 − 4 = (35)	22 − 1 = (21)
18 − 2 = (16)	33 − 3 = (30)	20 − 3 = (17)
35 − 5 = (30)	26 − 4 = (22)	45 − 2 = (43)
60 − 3 = (57)	49 − 1 = (48)	23 − 3 = (20)

PRIOR KNOWLEDGE

Pretend that you are a gardener. Your customer wants 2 kinds of flowers in one part of the garden. There is room for 55 plants. You already have 22 petunia plants. How will you decide how many zinnia plants to bring? (Possible answers: If you know the total and one part of the total, you subtract to find the other part.) *Draw a picture of the garden and count how many more plants you need.* (33)

COMMUNICATION

Writing and Discussing Math   Write **whole** and **part** on the chalkboard. Tell students to think about these words as they read the numbers in story problems. In their Math Journals, have them copy this sentence and fill in the blank: *If I know the whole and one part, I _____ to find the other part.* (subtract)

When might you need to estimate how much money you have? (Possible answer: to see if you have enough money to buy several items; to see how much change you will get back)

EXPLORE AND CONNECT

COOPERATIVE ACTIVITY

Grouping Suggestion: small groups
The kennel boarded 27 dogs.
13 were small dogs. The rest were large dogs.
How many large dogs were at the kennel?

TEACHING ACTIONS

BEFORE ▶ **What are you asked to compare in this problem?** (Possible answer: the number of large dogs to the number of small dogs)

▶ **Describe the data in the story.** (Possible answer: You know the total number of dogs and the number of small dogs. You do not know the number of large dogs.)

DURING ▶ **How can you use the data to plan the solution?** (Possible answer: If you know the whole and one part, you can subtract to find the other part.)

▶ **How might you use estimation to find an answer?** (Possible answer: 27 is close to 30, and 13 is close to 10. 30 − 10 is 20.)

AFTER ▶ **Explain how you could use cubes to check the answer to this problem.** (Possible answer: Use cubes to show the total amount and then take away 13 to see how many are left.)

Have students work together in small groups using cubes to solve verbal problems like the one on this page.

CONNECTIONS   Use these anytime.

Problem of the Day

Understand the Operations   Use cubes to solve the problem. Write the number sentence and the answer.
James had a collection of 36 buttons.
14 buttons were from old clothes.
The rest were found outside.
How many buttons were found outside?
(36 − 14 = 22; 22 buttons were found outside.)

Number Sense

Estimation   Ring the best answer for each item.
1. weight of a bicycle
more than 1 kilogram
less than 1 kilogram
2. height of a door
more than 1 meter
less than 1 meter

Subject Integration

Physical Education   Mark off a distance in the gym or on the playground. Estimate how many giant steps it will take to cover that distance and then check your guess. Tell whether your guess was more or less than the actual number. Repeat this activity using baby steps and hops.

Estimating Differences: More or Less than 50¢

To estimate differences as more or less than 50¢

CLASSWORK AND HOMEWORK SUPPLEMENTS

Practice

Writing Math   13-5

Name _____

Understanding the Operations

Solve. Write the number sentence.
Then write the answer in a sentence.

1. Reza had 22 swimming lessons last summer.
Pedro had 10 swimming lessons last summer.
How many more swimming lessons did Reza have?

$$22 \ominus 10 = 12$$

Reza had 12 more lessons.

2. Margaret had 32 diving lessons.
Caroline had 18 diving lessons.
How many more diving lessons did Margaret have?

$$32 \ominus 18 = 14$$

Margaret had 14 more lessons.

PS-2   Use with text page 277.   115

Building Thinking Skills

Patterns   13-5

Name _____

Chicken Pox!

There are 39 students in the second grade.
Each day more students stayed home with chicken pox.
Look at the chart.
How many students stayed home each day?
Write the number sentence and your answer for each day in the chart.

	Students at School	Number Sentence	Students with Chicken Pox
Mon.	28	39 – 28 = 11	11
Tues.	25	39 – 25 = 14	14
Wed.	22	39 – 22 = 17	17
Thurs.	19	39 – 19 = 20	20
Fri.	16	39 – 16 = 23	23

What pattern do you notice in the answers?

Every day 3 more students caught chicken pox.

TS-2   Use with text page 277.   115

Reteaching

Estimation   13-5

Name _____

**Estimating Differences:
More or Less Than 50¢**

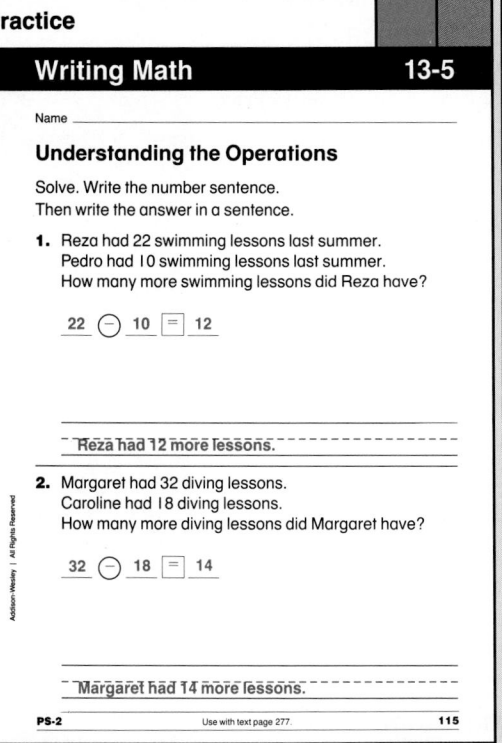

I spent more than 50¢. So my change is less than 50¢.

Estimated Change

more than 50¢
(less than 50¢)

$ – 80¢

Ring the better estimate for your change.

Then find each difference with your 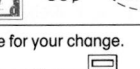.

		Estimated Change	Exact Change
1.	– 30¢	(more than 50¢) / less than 50¢	70¢
2.	– 45¢	(more than 50¢) / less than 50¢	55¢
3.	– 75¢	more than 50¢ / (less than 50¢)	25¢
4.	– 90¢	more than 50¢ / (less than 50¢)	10¢

RS-2   Use with text page 278.   115

Challenges

Estimation   13-5

Name _____

Name Change

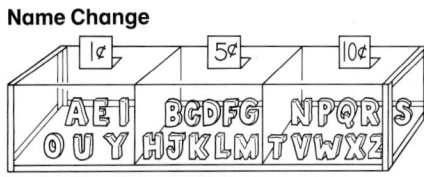

1¢   5¢   10¢

AEI OUY   BCDFG HJKLM   NPQRS TVWXZ

1. Buy the letters in your first name.

How much does your name cost? _____
Start with $1.01. Ring the best estimate for your change.

more than 50¢   less than 50¢

2. Buy the letters in a friend's first name.

How much does the name cost? _____
Start with $1.01. Ring the best estimate for your change.

more than 50¢   less than 50¢

3. Buy the letters in a relative's first name.

How much does the name cost? _____
Start with $1.01. Ring the best estimate for your change.

more than 50¢   less than 50¢

Work Space

Answers will vary.

CS-2   Use with text page 278.   115

OPTIONS FOR INDIVIDUAL NEEDS

Basic

Exercises All

Supplements
Reteaching 115 or
Practice 115

Average

Exercises All

Supplements
Practice 115
Challenges 115 or
Thinking Skills 115

Extended

Exercises All

Supplements
Challenges 115
Thinking Skills 115

Other Resources:
Mathematics Their Way, p. 225
Explorations, pp. 128-130, 292-293, 296-297
Problem-Solving Experiences In Mathematics, pp. 93, 123, 129, 147, 159
Workjobs, pp. 224-227
Workjobs for Parents, pp. 106-109
Developing Number Concepts with Unifix Cubes, pp. 168-169

13-5

LESSON PLAN 13-5

OBJECTIVE 13-5
To understand the operation of subtraction by comparing or by finding the missing part; to estimate differences as more or less than 50¢

Materials: Cube-A-Links

1. MOTIVATE AND TEACH

LEARN ABOUT IT

BEFORE ▶ **Apply the data in Exercise 1 to this rule: If you know a whole and one part, you can find the other part.** (Possible answer: You know the whole is 42 stamps and one part is 30 stamps. You subtract 30 from 42 to find the other part.)

DURING ▶ **What can you use to help you find the answer?** (Possible answer: Use cubes to show the whole and take away the part you know to find the other part.)
▶ **How might you work with a partner to solve the problem?** (Let one person count out the total number of cubes and the other person take away the part that you know. Then count how many are left together.)
▶ **Which number in each story is always going to be the whole?** (the largest number)

AFTER ▶ **Give reasons why you might need to know how many items are in each part of the whole.** (Possible answers: You might want to compare the amounts to see how much more you have of one part. You might want to know if you have enough of one part.)

2. CHECK UNDERSTANDING

ERROR ALERT **Page 277** Not understanding the concept of subtracting the part from the whole to find the other part.
Page 278 Estimating change incorrectly when the amount spent is close to 50¢.

277   Chapter 13 Lesson 5

Name _____

Problem Solving
Understanding the Operations

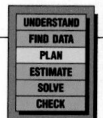
UNDERSTAND
FIND DATA
PLAN
ESTIMATE
SOLVE
CHECK

Work with a partner. Use cubes to solve. Write the number sentence. Then write the answer.
Word sentences may vary. Sample answers are shown.

1. Ollie's father gave him 42 stamps. 30 were butterfly stamps. The others were duck stamps. How many duck stamps did Ollie have?

   42 — 30 = 12

   Ollie had 12 duck stamps.

2. Maya has 38 stamps. She has 15 clown stamps. The rest are dog stamps. How many dog stamps does Maya have?

   38 – 15 = 23

   Maya has 23 dog stamps.

3. Tracy has 12 dinosaur stamps. The rest are buffalo stamps. She has 25 stamps in all. How many are buffalo stamps?

   25 — 12 = 13

   13 are buffalo stamps.

Chapter 13   (two hundred seventy-seven)   27

All rights reserved. Addison-Wesley

TEACHING OPTIONS

RETEACHING TIPS Have pairs use cubes to make up a subtraction story problem about stamps. Have them model the problem, then write a number sentence to match. For help in estimating differences, use Reteaching Supplement 115.

ENRICHMENT Have students take turns giving each other an amount of change from a purchase that is either over 50¢ or under 50¢. The one who gets the change must estimate whether the price of the item was more or less than 50¢, then count on to $1 to show how much the item cost.

stimating Differences
ore or Less than 50¢

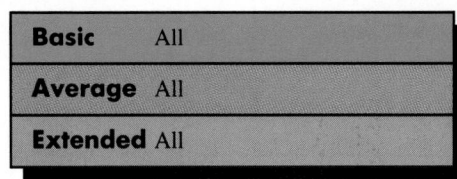

Decide if you spent more than or less than 50¢.

u have [money] to mail the package.
'ill your change be more than or less
an 50¢? Estimate to find out.

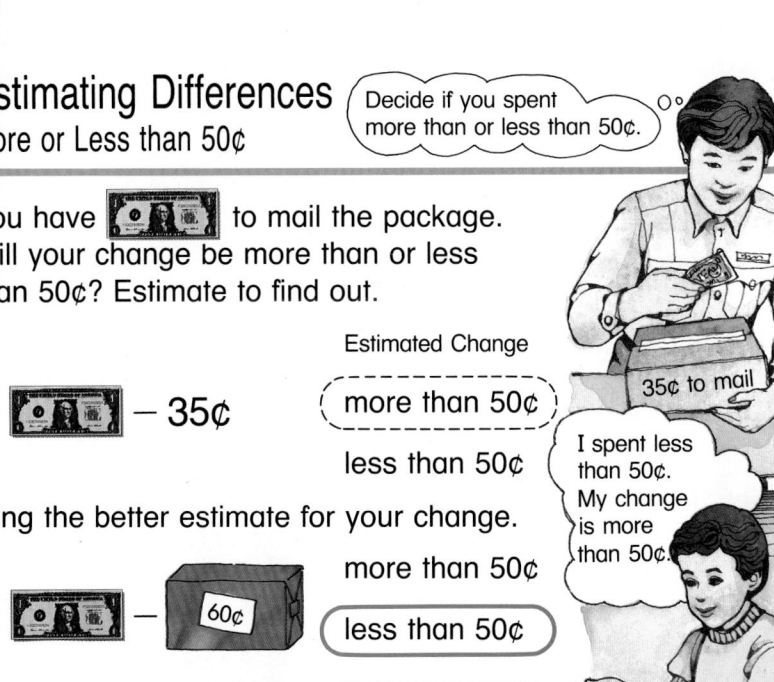

35¢ to mail

I spent less than 50¢. My change is more than 50¢.

Estimated Change

[money] — 35¢

(more than 50¢)

less than 50¢

ing the better estimate for your change.

[money] — | 60¢ |
    more than 50¢
    (less than 50¢)

[money] — | 25¢ |
    (more than 50¢)
    less than 50¢

[money] — | 85¢ |
    more than 50¢
    (less than 50¢)

[money] — | 55¢ |
    more than 50¢
    (less than 50¢)

Find each difference with your .
How close was your estimate
to the exact change?

1. 40¢; 2. 75¢; 3. 15¢; 4. 45¢
Answers may vary.

'8 (two hundred seventy-eight)

Chapter 13

3. PRACTICE AND APPLY

Basic	All
Average	All
Extended	All

Discuss estimating change with students.
How many cents are in a dollar? (100)
*How much will your change be if you
spend more than 50¢?* (less than 50¢)
*How much will your change be if you
spend less than 50¢?* (more than 50¢)
*How will you use a calculator to find
each difference?* (Subtract the amount
spent from 100.)

▶ **Look at the example. Why might
you think about whether you spent
more than 50¢?** (Possible answer: 50¢
+ 50¢ = $1. If you spent more than
50¢, your change will be less than 50¢.)

▶ **How can you use punchout money
to help you find the answers?**
(Possible answer: Show the amount you
spent, then count on to 100. Ask
yourself if the second amount is more or
less than 50¢.)

▶ **How will using a calculator in
Exercise 5 help you check your
estimate?** (Possible answer: You can
compare your estimate to the exact
amount of change.)

13-5

LOSE AND ASSESS

HOW WHAT YOU KNOW

ogether with students, write story
oblems about stamps like those on
age 277. Ask students to read each
oblem, model the whole, take away
e part they know, and write the
umber sentence for the problem.
hen have students subtract from $1
d estimate whether the difference
ill be more or less than 50¢.

QUICK QUIZ

Ring the better estimate for change.
1. $1.00 − 35¢   <u>more than 50¢</u>
                less than 50
2. $1.00 − 70¢   more than 50
                <u>less than 50¢</u>

Breaking Apart a Ten

OBJECTIVE 13-6   To subtract two 2-digit numbers using models; to decide if trading is needed

PREBOOK ACTIVITIES

QUICK REVIEW

Write two related subtraction sentences for each group of numbers.

54, 12, 42	$(54 - 12 = 42)$	28, 8, 20	$(28 - 8 = 20)$
	$(54 - 42 = 12)$		$(28 - 20 = 8)$
14, 75, 61	$(75 - 14 = 61)$	10, 22, 32	$(32 - 10 = 22)$
	$(75 - 61 = 14)$		$(32 - 22 = 10)$

PRIOR KNOWLEDGE

Tell students the following story and ask them for solutions to the problem: *Julie only has 1 dime. She owes her friend Joe 4 pennies. What can Julie do?* (Possible answers: Julie can trade the dime for 10 pennies and then give Joe 4 pennies. She can give Joe the dime and ask Joe to give her 6 pennies.) Discuss the fact that either way, Julie has to trade the 1 dime for 10 pennies.

COMMUNICATION

Reading and Discussing Math   Write **breaking apart a ten** on the chalkboard and read the phrase to the students. Hold up a bundle of 10 toothpicks tied together with a twist tie. Ask a student to break apart the bundle of ten. Together count the 10 ones. Write the following sentence on the board. Ask students to read it and fill in the blank: *Breaking apart a ten makes* _____ *ones.* (10)

EXPLORE AND CONNECT

Materials: red and blue Cube-A-Links
Grouping Suggestion: pairs

Write 43 on the chalkboard. Have students use red cubes to make 4 tens and blue cubes to make 3 ones. *Suppose we wan. to subtract 15. How can we show this? We could take away 1 ten and the 3 ones; but then we have subtracted only 13. Wha should we do?* (Possible answer: Break apart a ten.) Have students break apart a red ten to make 10 red ones. Place 2 of the red ones with the 3 blue ones. *Look at the cubes. How ca you tell we had to break apart a 10?* (Possible answer: There are red cubes with blue cubes; the red represents a 10 that had to be broken apart.) *How many ones are left?* (8) Have students work in pairs to repeat this activity using numbers tha require breaking apart a ten. Encourage students to listen to each other as they explain how many tens and ones are neede to show each problem.

CONNECTIONS   Use these anytime.

Problem of the Day

Understanding the Operations

Use cubes to solve. Write the number sentence. Then write the answer.
   Kyle has 15 large dinosaurs.
   The rest are small dinosaurs.
   He has 26 dinosaurs in all.
   How many are small dinosaurs?
$(26 - 15 = 11$; There are 11 small dinosaurs.)

Math Connection

Money   With a partner, price small objects for less than 99¢. Use punchout pennies and dimes. Your partner is the storekeeper and has pennies. You have 10 dimes. Buy something and use as many dimes as you can. Then trade 1 dime for 10 pennies from your partner to make the exact amount. Continue to buy until you run out of coins. Trade roles.

Counting Patterns

Counting Back   Count back by tens to 0, starting with each number below:

50	(50, 40, 30, 20, 10, 0)
30	(30, 20, 10, 0)
100	(100, 90, 80, 70, 60, 50, 40, 30, 20, 10, 0)
20	(20, 10, 0)
70	(70, 60, 50, 40, 30, 20, 10, 0)
40	(40, 30, 20, 10, 0)

CLASSWORK AND HOMEWORK SUPPLEMENTS

Practice

Skills Maintenance   13-6

Name _____

Breaking Apart a Ten

Look at each picture.
Cross out the number to take away. Write how many
are left. Put a ✔ in the box if you had to
break apart a ten.

		Number to start	Number to take away	Number left	
1.		24	15	9	✔
2.		33	18	15	✔
3.		28	11	17	☐
4.		42	24	18	✔
5.		37	16	21	☐
6.		26	19	7	✔

116   Use with text pages 279–280.   **PS-2**

Addison-Wesley | All Rights Reserved

Building Thinking Skills

Critical Thinking   13-6

Name _____

Break Apart a Ten?

Imagine you have the cubes shown.
Ring the amounts you could take away without breaking
apart a ten.
Use cubes to check.

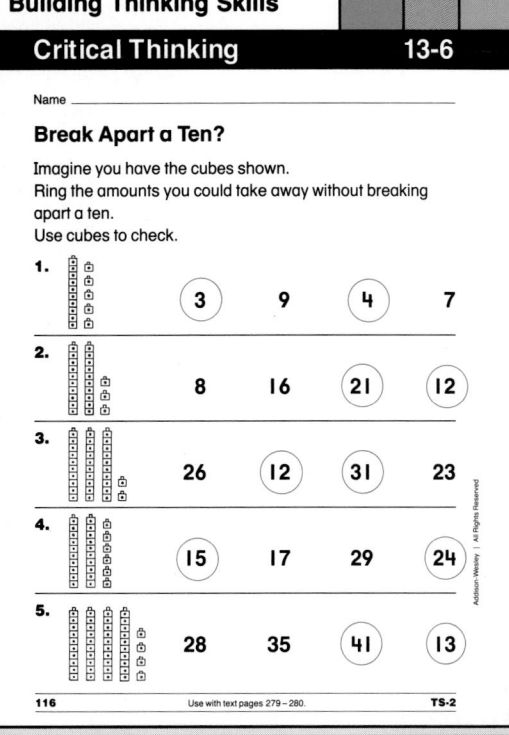

1.	3	9	4	7
2.	8	16	21	12
3.	26	12	31	23
4.	15	17	29	24
5.	28	35	41	13

116   Use with text pages 279–280.   **TS-2**

Addison-Wesley | All Rights Reserved

Reteaching

Manipulatives   13-6

Name _____

Breaking Apart a Ten

Start with 25.

Take away 7.   *Not enough to take away 7 ones.*

Break apart a ten.

Now take away 7.

How many left?   1 ten and 8 ones → 18 are left.

Use cubes to find out how many are left.
Break apart a ten when you need to.

	Number to start	Number to take away	Break apart a ten?	How many left?
1.	22	6	yes no	16
				1 ten and 6 ones
2.	24	12	yes no	12
3.	36	19	yes no	17
4.	21	13	yes no	8
5.	28	16	yes no	12

116   Use with text pages 279–280.   **RS-2**

Addison-Wesley | All Rights Reserved

Challenges

Life Skills   13-6

Name _____

What Did they Buy?

Use punchout dimes and pennies to subtract.
Draw lines to show what each one bought.

1. Juan had 25¢.
   Now he has 7¢.
   What did he buy?

2. Karen had 38¢.
   She has 22¢ left.
   What did she buy?

3. Nick had 30¢.
   He got 17¢ change.
   What did he buy?

4. Julie had 26¢.
   She has 9¢ left.
   What did she buy?

16¢   18¢   17¢   13¢

116   Use with text pages 279–280.   **CS-2**

Addison-Wesley | All Rights Reserved

OPTIONS FOR INDIVIDUAL NEEDS

Basic

Exercises All
Calculator Bank, p. 403

Supplements
Reteaching 116 or
Practice 116
Thinking Skills 116

Average

Exercises All
Calculator Bank, p. 403

Supplements
Practice 116
Challenges 116 or
Thinking Skills 116

Extended

Exercises All
Calculator Bank, p. 403

Supplements
Challenges 116
Thinking Skills 116

Other Resources:
Explorations, pp. 287-291
*Problem Solving Experiences
In Mathematics* p. 159
*Developing Number Concepts
With Unifix Cubes*, pp.
150-151

13-6

LESSON PLAN 13-6

OBJECTIVE 13-6
To subtract two 2-digit numbers using models; to decide if trading is needed

Materials: Cube-A-Links in 2 colors, TA 5 (Place Value Charts), small cards

1. MOTIVATE AND TEACH

LEARN ABOUT IT

Have students use cubes to model 24, using red for tens and blue for ones. Then ask them to subtract 16 from 24. *You know you already have 4 ones. What can you do to get 2 more ones to make 6 ones?* (Possible answer: Break apart a ten.) Help students show 1 red ten, 4 blue ones, and 2 red ones taken away. *How many ones are left?* (8)
▶ **Look at the top of page 279. Why must Sean break apart a ten?** (Possible answer: He does not have enough ones to take away.)
▶ **How do the two colors help you to see that Sean had to break apart a ten?** (Possible answer: You can see the blue cubes that show the ones Sean started with and the red cubes that show a ten after it has been broken apart.)
▶ **In Exercises 1-5, how will you know whether or not you will need to break apart a ten?** (Possible answers: by using cubes to model the numbers; by comparing the numbers in the ones columns)
▶ **Are you adding or subtracting in these exercises? Identify clue words.** (Possible answer: You are subtracting on this page. Clues include **take away** and **How many are left?**)

2. CHECK UNDERSTANDING

ERROR ALERT Incorrectly counting the number of cubes that are left as they complete Exercises 1-6.

Name _____

Breaking Apart a Ten

Sean had 35 toy dinosaurs. He mailed 17. How many were left?

Break apart 1 ten. Then take away 17.

Start with 35   Take away 17

Dinosaurs mailed   Dinosaurs left

18 left

Work with a partner. Use cubes to show the start number. Take away the dinosaurs mailed. Did you break apart a ten? Ring **yes** or **no**. Write the number of dinosaurs left.

	Dinosaurs to start	Dinosaurs mailed	Break apart a ten?	How many are left?
1.	23	18	(yes) no	5
2.	17	12	yes (no)	5
3.	32	26	(yes) no	6

Make up your own numbers of dinosaurs mailed. **Answers may vary. Check students' work.**

4.	19	___	yes no	___
5.	38	___	yes no	___

Chapter 13   (two hundred seventy-nine) 2

TEACHING OPTIONS

RETEACHING TIPS Use 2 place value charts. On one, have students use cubes to show 24, then take away 17 cubes and place them on the second chart. Look back at the first chart to find how many cubes are left. Assign Reteaching Supplement 116.

ENRICHMENT **Family Math**
Have students and family members make up stories about number expressions such as 35 − 17 and 42 − 11. Tie sets of 10 toothpicks with a twist tie to show tens. Use the toothpicks to model the subtraction and tell if they need to break apart a ten.

se cubes. Find how many are left.

	Number to start	Number to take away	Break apart a ten?		How many are left?
	34	15	(yes)	no	19
	23	12	yes	(no)	11
	42	14	(yes)	no	28
	28	19	(yes)	no	9

ROBLEM SOLVING

se cubes. Ring and finish the correct
umber sentence. Then write the
nswer in a sentence.
ord sentences may vary. A sample answer is shown.

Mr. Jones had 24 boxes. He mailed
15 to Texas and the rest to Florida.
How many did he mail to Florida?

$24 + 15 =$ ___

$(24 - 15 = \underline{9})$

He mailed 9 boxes to Florida.

---

for pages 279-280

3. PRACTICE AND APPLY

Basic	All
Average	All
Extended	All

PRACTICE

*How can you use cubes to help you find
the answer in Exercises 1-4?* (Possible
answers: Use the cubes to model the
numbers and take away the number of
cubes shown by the second number;
break apart the cubes when you need to
break a ten.)

APPLY

PROBLEM SOLVING ▶ **Describe
how you can use cubes to solve
Exercise 5.** (Possible answer: Use cubes
to show the tens and ones that make up
the total number of boxes. Then take
away cubes to show the boxes going
to Texas. Last, count the cubes to show
how many boxes are going to Florida.)
▶ **How can you decide whether this is
an addition or subtraction number
sentence using your cubes?** (Possible
answer: Try both adding and subtracting
cubes from the total number of boxes to
see which answer would make sense.)

13-6

CLOSE AND ASSESS

HOW WHAT YOU KNOW Ask
udents to describe the characters in
e chapter story, *Rover's Surprise.*
uppose Mrs. Stampley had 57 letters
her mail bag. She delivered 29.
ow many remained in her bag? (28)
se cubes. Did you break apart a 10?
es)

QUICK QUIZ

Use cubes to decide if you need to
break apart a ten. Circle the answer.
$47 - 16$ yes <u>no</u>
$23 - 15$ <u>yes</u> no
$51 - 12$ <u>yes</u> no

Problem Solving: Finding Missing Data

OBJECTIVE 13-7   To solve problems by finding missing data

PREBOOK ACTIVITIES

QUICK REVIEW

Fill in the missing data in each pattern.

40, 50, _(60)_ , _(70)_ , _(80)_ , 90

25, _(35)_ , _(45)_ , _(55)_ , _(65)_ , 75

62, _(64)_ , 66, _(68)_ , _(70)_ , 72

80, 75, _(70)_ , _(65)_ , _(60)_ , _(55)_ , 50

_(33)_ , 43, 53, 63, _(73)_ , _(83)_ , 93

PRIOR KNOWLEDGE

Have you ever tried to finish a jigsaw puzzle that had one piece missing? How did that make you feel? Have students share experiences of working on projects where a piece of information or a particular piece of equipment was missing. Ask them to explain how they knew something was missing and then tell how they solved their problem.

COMMUNICATION

Reading and Discussing Math   Write **missing data** on the chalkboard. Have students read the phrase and use it in a sentence. Remind students that you have just discussed how missing data can affect a project. *How might missing data affect a story problem you are trying to solve?* (Possible answer: There may not be enough information in the problem to let you know which operation to use.)

If you were taking a trip, how might drawing a picture help you plan where you are going? (Possible answer: You could draw a map of the roads you will take; you might draw the location of buildings that you want to see.)

EXPLORE AND CONNECT

COOPERATIVE ACTIVITY

Grouping Suggestion: small groups

John ran 11 mi on Wednesday. On Thursday, he ran farther. How many more miles did he run on Thursday? He ran _____ more mi on Thursday.

TEACHING ACTIONS

BEFORE ▶ **What does the question in this problem ask you to do?** (Possible answer: Compare the number of miles John ran on Wednesday and Thursday and tell how many more he ran on Thursday.)

▶ **Identify any important data that are missing in this problem.** (Possible answer: You need to know how many miles John ran on Thursday before you can solve the problem

DURING ▶ **Describe a plan you can use to find an answer:** (Possible answer: Make up a sentence that tells how many miles John ran on Thursday replace the missing data.)

▶ **How can you use cubes to model the number sentence for this problem?** (Possible answer: Show the greater numbe of miles and the smaller number of miles with cubes. Count how many more cubes are in the greater set to find the answer.)

AFTER ▶ **If more than one group is working on this problem, why might there be more than one correct answer?** (Possible answer: Each group might use a different number of miles for the Thursday run.) Have small groups of students use cubes to solve other additic and subtraction problems with missing data.

CONNECTIONS   Use these anytime.

Problem of the Day

Finding Missing Data   Give the missing data needed to solve this problem. Then use cubes to find the answer.
Jean had 36¢.
She bought a small container of milk How much money did she have left?
(Answers will vary.)

Creative Thinking

Jobs   Many people work at jobs in which they need to find missing data. Look at the jobs below. Tell what kind of data this person might look for to help him or her solve a problem.

police officer   postal worker
detective   telephone operator
scientist   accountant
(Answers will vary.)

Minute Math

Draw a Picture   Read the riddle. Then draw a picture to solve it.
My pattern has 2 colors, red and green. Red starts and ends my pattern. Green appears 4 times. On each side of every 2 greens there is a red. What does my pattern look like? (R/G/G/R/G/G/R)

roblem Solving Strategy: Draw a Picture

solve problems using the strategy Draw a Picture

CLASSWORK AND HOMEWORK SUPPLEMENTS

Practice

Creative Thinking   13-7

Name _____

Problem Solving Strategy: Draw a Picture

Draw a picture to solve each problem.
Finish the picture.

1. At the seal and sea lion show, there are 4 sea
lions in a row. Each sea lion is between 2 seals. How
many seals and sea lions are there in the show?

There are __9__ seals and sea lions in the show.

2. At the whale and dolphin show, there is a whale
at each corner of the rectangular pool. There are
2 dolphins on each side of the pool between the whales.
How many whales and dolphins are there in all?

There are __12__ whales and dolphins in all.

PS-2   Use with text page 282.   117

Building Thinking Skills

Critical Thinking   13-7

Name _____

Pet Problems

Liane takes care of all the pets on Park Street.
<u>First</u> she walks a dog named Gus. He lives in the 5th house
on the street.
<u>Next</u> she feeds a cat named Snow. Snow lives next to Sam.
<u>Then</u> she cleans Elsa's birdcage. Elsa lives between the
fish and Gus.
<u>After that</u> she feeds the fish, Harry and Hilda. They live in
the middle house on the street.
<u>Finally</u> she cleans the aquarium for a turtle named Sam. He
lives in the 2nd house on the street.
Draw 5 ⌂ .
Use the clues to write the name of the animal that lives in
each house. Then number the houses to show the order
Liane follows when she cares for the pets.

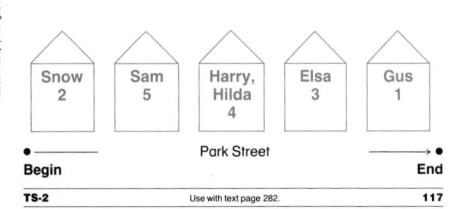

| Snow 2 | Sam 5 | Harry, Hilda 4 | Elsa 3 | Gus 1 |

● Begin   Park Street   End ●

TS-2   Use with text page 282.   117

Reteaching

Problem Solving   13-7

Name _____

Finding Missing Data

Read the story.	Molly swam for 43 minutes. Jay swam for less time. How much longer did Molly swim?
Is there enough data to solve the problem?	yes (no)
Write the data you need.	Jay swam for 25 minutes.
Finish the number sentence. Then write the answer.	43 – 25 = 18 Molly swam 18 minutes longer.

1. Mai Lee jumped rope
15 times. Eric jumped
rope more times than
Mai Lee did. How many
more times did Eric
jump rope? Answers will vary.

Is there enough data?   yes
Missing data: (no)
Eric jumped 23 times.

23 ⊖ 15 = 8

Eric jumped 8 more times.

2. Dan rode his bike
21 miles. Sue rode her
bike farther than Dan.
How much farther did
Sue ride her bike?
Answers will vary.

Is there enough data?   yes
Missing data: (no)
Sue rode 35 miles.

35 ⊖ 21 = 14

Sue rode 14 miles farther.

RS-2   Use with text page 281.   117

Challenges

Family Math   13-7

Name _____

Scavenger Hunt

> Dear Family,
> Your child is learning to solve word problems by finding missing data. Help your child
> use the missing data to write subtraction sentences.

1. Living room: Count the number of chairs. Count
the number of tables. We have ____ chairs and
____ tables. How many more chairs than tables does
your family have?   Answers will vary.

____ ⊖ ____ = ____

2. Bathroom: Count the number of towels. Count the
number of facecloths. We have ____ towels and
____ facecloths. How many more towels than
facecloths does your family have?   Answers will vary.

____ ⊖ ____ = ____

3. Bedroom: Count the number of pillows. Count
the number of blankets. We have ____ pillows and
____ blankets. How many more pillows than blankets
does your family have?   Answers will vary.

____ ⊖ ____ = ____

CS-2   Use with text page 281.   117

Addison-Wesley | All Rights Reserved

OPTIONS FOR INDIVIDUAL NEEDS

Basic

Exercises All
Computer Bank, p. 407
More Practice, p. 424, set C

Supplements
Reteaching 117 or
Practice 117

Average

Exercises All
Computer Bank, p. 407
More Practice, p. 424, set C

Supplements
Practice 117
Challenges 117 or
Thinking Skills 117

Extended

Exercises All
Computer Bank, p. 407

Supplements
Challenges 117
Thinking Skills 117

Other Resources:
Explorations, pp. 292, 297, 299
Problem Solving Experience In Mathematics, p. 93
Mathematics Book A, p. 29

13-7

LESSON PLAN 13-7

OBJECTIVE 13-7

To solve problems by finding missing data; to solve problems using the strategy Draw a Picture

Materials: Cube-A-Links, flannelboard, felt shapes

1. MOTIVATE AND TEACH

LEARN ABOUT IT

 **BEFORE** ▶ **Look at Exercise 1. Describe clues that show there is data missing.** (Possible answer: There is only one number in the problem; to answer the question you need more information.)

 **DURING** ▶ **How can you decide which information at the bottom of the page fits each problem?** (Possible answer: Read all the data and then decide which sentence has something in common with the problem.)

 **AFTER** ▶ **How can you use cubes to model each problem?** (Possible answer: After deciding which action is taking place, use cubes to model the amounts given in the problem and either put the cubes together or take some away.)

2. CHECK UNDERSTANDING

ERROR ALERT

Page 281 Being unable to identify whether a problem has missing data.
Page 282 Drawing the items mentioned in a problem in the wrong order.

Name _____

Problem Solving
Finding Missing Data

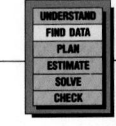

UNDERSTAND
FIND DATA
PLAN
ESTIMATE
SOLVE
CHECK

Is there enough data? Ring **yes** or **no**.
Cut out the data below if you need to.
Paste. Then use cubes to solve.

1. Mrs. Adams mailed 15 boxes and some letters. How many more letters did she mail?

   She mailed __10__ more letters.
   Mrs. Adams mailed 25 letters.

   Is there enough data
   yes (no)

   Paste here if needed.

2. Mrs. Adams bought 27 car stamps. She bought more train stamps. How many stamps did she buy in all?

   She bought __57__ stamps in all.
   Mrs. Adams bought 30 train stamps.

   Is there enough data
   yes (no)

   Paste here if needed.

3. Mrs. Adams had 18 eagle stamps. She used 14 of them. How many did she have left?

   She had __4__ stamps left.

   Is there enough data
   (yes) no

   Paste here if needed.

| Mrs. Adams had 20 owl stamps. | Mrs. Adams mailed 25 letters. | Mrs. Adams bought 30 train stamps. |

Chapter 13   (two hundred eighty-one) 2

TEACHING OPTIONS

RETEACHING TIPS Use felt shapes in 2 colors to make pictures on a flannelboard for problems. Have students read each sentence, lay out the pieces they need, make a plan to arrange them, and make a picture on the flannelboard. For help in finding missing data, use Reteaching Supplement 117.

COMPUTER Blockers and Finders, Sunburst Communications © 1987 Problem solving practice for all students. The *Finder* travels through a 4-by-4 grid. The locations of the *tilties,* arrows, and detours are found based on their effect on the *Finder*. The game takes 10-20 minutes.

Problem Solving Strategy
Draw a Picture

UNDERSTAND
FIND DATA
PLAN
ESTIMATE
SOLVE
CHECK

Draw a picture to solve each problem.
Finish the sentence.

There are 5 red mailboxes and some
blue mailboxes on Elm Street. Each
blue mailbox is between 2 red ones.
How many mailboxes are there?

blue   red   blue   red   blue   red

Elm Street

There are __9__ mailboxes.

There is a red house
on each corner. There
are 3 blue houses on
each street between
the corner houses.
How many houses are
on the block in all?

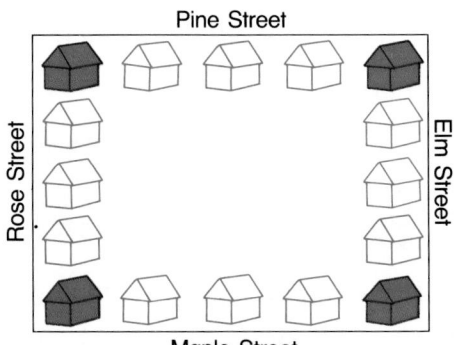

Pine Street

Rose Street

Elm Street

Maple Street

There are __16__ houses on the block.

Basic	All
Average	Average
Extended	All

*How will you show the solution to each
problem?* (by drawing a picture) *Does it
matter what color you use?* (yes, because
you are showing a pattern)

▶ **As you read Exercise 1, what can
you do to help you understand the
pattern?** (Possible answer: Take time to
absorb the data in each sentence and
visualize the pattern in your head.)

▶ **How might you plan your drawing
before actually making it?** (Possible
answer: Use cubes in 2 colors to work
out each step of the pattern and then
draw it.)

▶ **Describe a good way to check your
drawing.** (Possible answer: Use the
problem as a checklist and mentally
check off every piece of given data that
is shown correctly on your drawing.)

13-7

CLOSE AND ASSESS

SHOW WHAT YOU KNOW
Remind students of the chapter story.
*Mrs. Stampley delivered 10 boxes and
some magazines. How many more
magazines did she deliver?* Have
students decide if there is enough data
to solve the problem. If not, have
them make up some data and use a
drawing to solve the problem.

QUICK QUIZ

Draw a picture to solve the problem.
There are 7 black cars and some red
cars on the lot. Each black car is
between 2 red cars. How many cars
are on the lot? (15)

Chapter 13 Lesson 7   **282**

CHAPTER 13

WRAP UP

INTRODUCTION The Wrap Up provides activities emphasizing math language and thinking skills for the chapter.

USING PAGE 283

Math Words ▶ **What will you think about as you decide how you will subtract?** (Possible answers: Count back by 1s if subtracting 5 or less; count back by 10s if subtracting a decade number; break apart a 10 if the other 2 ways will not help solve the problem.)
▶ **For which of the 2 methods might you use mental math?** (counting back by ones and tens)

Math Reasoning ▶ **Where can you find information to help you answer the questions?** (Possible answer: Look at the price tags of the gifts.)
▶ **For which problems do you need to add? to subtract?** (add: Exercise 7; subtract: Exercises 8 and 9)

MATH WORDS

Decide how you would subtract.
Put an **X** in the box.

	Count Back by Ones	Count Back by Tens	Break Apart a Ten
1. $51 - 3$	X		
2. $80 - 40$		X	
3. $64 - 30$		X	
4. $28 - 2$	X		
5. $50 - 15$			X

MATH REASONIING

Answer the questions. Use coins to help.

Mia and Helen went shopping.

Mia bought a .   Helen bought a .

Together they had    left over.

6. How much money did they spend in all? _____ 59¢

7. How much money did they have in all to start? _____ 86¢

8. What can they buy with the money left over? _____ hat

Chapter 13 Wrap Up   (two hundred eighty-three) 2

TEACHING OPTIONS

ENRICHMENT Have small groups of students shop at the gift store shown on the page. Each student begins with 50¢ and chooses an item to buy. Then students add to find the total amount spent by their group. Next, have them find out how much change they each have left from their 50¢. Finally, ask who has the most change and why. (The person with the most change will be the one who bought the least expensive item.)

Name _____

CHAPTER REVIEW/TEST

Write the subtraction sentence.

1. Count back by ones.

33

33 (−) 4 [=] 29

2. Count back by tens.

76

76 (−) 40 [=] 36

Cross out tens to subtract.
Then write the subtraction
sentence.

8 tens − 3 tens = __5__ tens

80 (−) 30 [=] 50

Find different ways to separate
40 cubes into two groups. Write two
related subtraction sentences.

_____ 40 − 19 = 21 _____

_____ 40 − 21 = 19 _____

**Answers may vary. Sample
answers are shown.**

Draw a picture to solve. Finish the sentence.

There are 6 blue cars and some white
cars on First Street. Each white
car is between 2 blue cars. How many
cars are there on First Street?

There are __11__ cars.

CHAPTER REVIEW/TEST

INTRODUCTION   The Review/Test is
provided to review and evaluate the skills
and concepts presented in Chapter 13.

USING PAGE 284
If you prefer to use this page for review,
you may want to use the
Multiple-Choice Posttest (pages 51-52)
or the **Free-Response Posttest** (pages
51-52) to evaluate mastery of chapter
objectives.

ITEM ANALYSIS   The table below
correlates the Chapter Review/Test Items
with the lesson objectives.

Items	Objectives
1	13-1
2	13-3
3	13-2
4	13-4
5	13-7

INFORMAL ASSESSMENT

Using Manipulatives   Give pairs
[cu]bes, index cards with decade
[n]umbers, and number cards 1-5. The
[fi]rst student chooses a decade card
[a]nd models the number with cubes.
[T]he second draws a number card, and
[b]reaks apart a ten to subtract the
[n]umber on the card from the decade
[n]umber.

Communication   Tell what it means
[to] break apart a ten. When do you
[b]reak apart a ten? What happens to
[th]e ones? (Possible answer: Separate a

ten into 10 ones; break apart a ten
when there are not enough ones to
subtract from the ones place. When
you break apart a ten, add 10 ones to
the ones place.)

Critical Thinking   How are 2 related
subtraction sentences alike? What
addition sentences are related to
them? (Possible answers: Related
subtraction sentences have the same 3
numbers; related addition sentences
also have the same numbers. They
make a family.)

CHAPTER 13

ENRICHMENT

INTRODUCTION Identifying the rules that govern operations helps students understand and extend number relationships and patterns.

USING PAGE 285
This Enrichment page is provided for all students. You may wish to use it after they have completed the Chapter Review/Test on page 284.
Help students understand that relationships between numbers can be found by looking at number pairs and finding the operation that causes them to change in the same way. Point out that the relationship between Ann's and Tad's counters stays the same in each round of the game.

▶ **If Ann and Tad continue to play the same game, what will the ninth round show?** (Ann would show 10 counters; Tad would show 12.)

▶ **How could Ann say the rule?** (She puts in 2 fewer counters than Tad each time.)

▶ **How does your rule differ from the rule Tad made for his game?** (Answers will vary but should include adding or subtracting the same amount of counters for each entry in the table.)

EXTENSIONS Have pairs of students make a table as shown on page 285 and write their names at the top. Each student spins the spinner labeled 1-6 once and writes the number in the first row of the table. Students work together to make up rules that describe the relationship between the 2 numbers. Next, the first student spins and writes the number in the second row. The second student uses the rule to complete the row. For the third row, the second student spins and the first student uses the rule to complete the row. Have students play 4 more rounds.

Name _____

ENRICHMENT
What's My Rule?

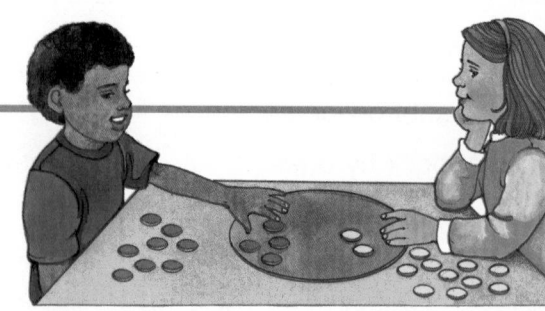

1. Ann and Tad played a game. Tad made up a rule. When Ann put in 2 yellow counters, Tad put in 4 red counters. When Ann put in 3, Tad put in 5. When Ann put in 4, Tad put in 6.

   Can you guess Tad's rule? Follow the rule. Fill in the table.
   Tad put in 2 more than Ann.

Ann	Tad
2	4
3	5
4	6
5	7
6	8
7	9
8	10

2. Make up your own rule. Play the game with a partner. Use two-color counters. Record what you did.
   Answers may vary.

Chapter 13 Enrichment: What's My Rule?   (two hundred eighty-five) 28

Name _____

CUMULATIVE REVIEW

Add.

$$\begin{array}{r} 18 \\ + 7 \\ \hline \end{array}$$
○ 16
● 25
○ 34

$$\begin{array}{r} 34 \\ + 28 \\ \hline \end{array}$$
● 62
○ 46
○ 59

$$\begin{array}{r} 47 \\ + 47 \\ \hline \end{array}$$
○ 86
● 94
○ 78

$$\begin{array}{r} 29 \\ 22 \\ + 15 \\ \hline \end{array}$$
○ 70
○ 53
● 66

5. How many faces are flat?

○ 1 face
● 2 faces
○ 3 faces

6. How many corners does the figure have?

● 4 corners
○ 6 corners
○ 2 corners

7. Which plane figure is being drawn?

○ □
○ ○
● △

8. Which one shows a line of symmetry?
A   B   C
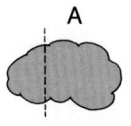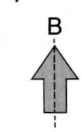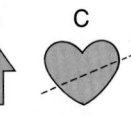
○ A
● B
○ C

The children in Ms. Moore's class held a bake sale. They earned $21 in the morning and $32 in the afternoon. About how much money did they earn all day?
○ about $30
● about $50
○ about $70

CUMULATIVE REVIEW

INTRODUCTION The purpose of this Cumulative Review is to maintain previously taught skills and concepts. The emphasis in this Cumulative Review is on addition of 2-digit numbers, Chapter 11; and on geometry, Chapter 12.

ITEM ANALYSIS The table below correlates the Cumulative Review items with the lesson objectives.

Items	Objectives
1-3	11-4; 11-6
4	11-9
5	12-1
6	12-2
7	12-3
8	12-6
9	11-10

Chapter Management

MATHEMATICAL BACKGROUND

Subtraction of 2-Digit Numbers
The algorithm for subtracting 2-digit numbers has two steps: subtract the ones (trading if necessary); then subtract the tens. This chapter begins by having students subtract 2-digit numbers using models, pictures, and, finally, symbols. Chapter 13 provided students with a basic understanding of the concept of subtracting 2-digit numbers. This chapter builds on the strategies taught and helps students make the transition to 2-digit subtraction using symbols (numbers).

Estimation
Lesson 14-5 teaches students to estimate differences using front-end estimation. When students make estimates using front-end numbers, it is assumed that all the addends have the same number of digits (to the tens place). The student then adds the front-end (tens place) digits to get the estimate.

Problem Solving
In this chapter, students solve problems using estimation and using the strategy Use Logical Reasoning.

TIPS FROM TEACHERS

Teach students to use the **BBB Rule** *to decide whether subtraction exercises require regrouping: When the Bottom number is Bigger, then you Break apart a ten.*

Donna Martinez
Zavala School
McAllen, Texas

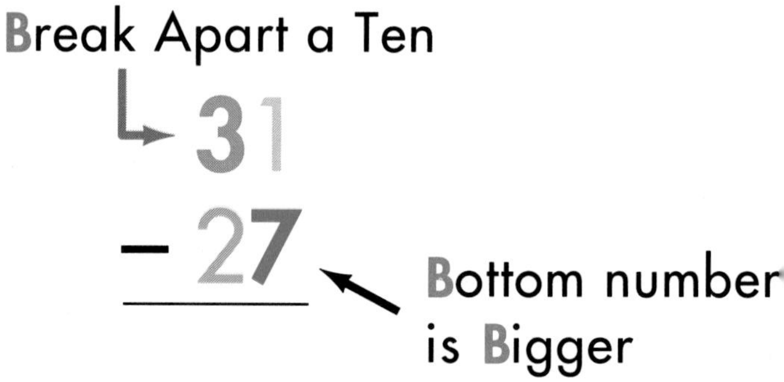

Break Apart a Ten

$$\llcorner\, 31$$
$$-\, 27$$

← **B**ottom number
is **B**igger

ASSESSMENT

Items	Objectives
1	14-1
2	14-2
3	14-3
4	14-4
5	14-5
6	14-6
7	14-7
8	14-8
9	14-9
10, 11	14-10
12	14-11

Note: The item analysis is the same for all pretests and posttests for this chapter.

Pretest — Chapter 14, page 1

Multiple-Choice Format

Name _____

1. Trade I ten for 10 ones. Choose the new numbers.

Tens	Ones
3	4

Ⓐ
Tens	Ones
2	14

B
Tens	Ones
3	14

2. Subtract. Use the picture or real blocks.

47
− 23

Cross out 2 tens.
Cross out 3 ones.

A 23
B 42
Ⓒ 24

3. Look at the picture. If you need to trade, cross out a ten and draw ten ones. Then cross out to subtract. Choose the difference.

34
− 16

A 23
Ⓑ 18
C 38

4. Subtract.

83
− 74

Ⓐ 9
B 11
C 19

5. Choose the best estimate for the difference.

72
− 13

A 50
Ⓑ 60
C 70

MCT 2   53

Pretest — Chapter 14, page 2

Multiple-Choice Format

Name _____

6. Subtract. Choose the add-to-check exercise.

85
− 7

Ⓐ
7
+78

B
7
+82

7. A pen costs 45¢. You have 29¢. How much more money do you need?

A You need 24¢ more.
Ⓑ You need 16¢ more.

8. Subtract. What is the difference pattern?

9   9   9
−4 −5 −6

A one more
Ⓑ one less

9. Ring how you would solve the problem.

9 − 8 = _?_

Ⓐ mental math
B paper and pencil

10. Subtract.

67
− 62

A 15
B 9
Ⓒ 5

11. Add.

49
+ 34

A 15
B 73
Ⓒ 83

12. Estimate. About how many players are on the two teams?

Team 1	Team 2
21 players	10 players

A about 20 players
Ⓑ about 30 players
C about 40 players

54   MCT 2

Posttest — Chapter 14, page 1

Multiple-Choice Format

Name _____

1. Trade I ten for 10 ones. Choose the new numbers.

Tens	Ones
4	5

A
Tens	Ones
4	15

Ⓑ
Tens	Ones
3	15

2. Subtract. Use the picture or real blocks.

48
− 22

Cross out 2 tens.
Cross out 2 ones.

A 46
B 36
Ⓒ 26

3. Look at the picture. If you need to trade, cross out a ten and draw ten ones. Then cross out to subtract. Choose the difference.

32
− 16

A 36
Ⓑ 16
C 26

4. Subtract.

45
− 16

Ⓐ 29
B 39
C 31

5. Choose the best estimate for the difference.

92
− 64

A 50
B 40
Ⓒ 30

MCT 2   55

Posttest — Chapter 14, page 2

Multiple-Choice Format

Name _____

6. Subtract. Choose the add-to-check exercise.

68
− 9

A
9
+49

Ⓑ
9
+59

7. A pen costs 97¢. You have 59¢. How much more money do you need?

Ⓐ You need 38¢ more.
B You need 42¢ more.

8. Subtract. What is the difference pattern?

9   9   9
−8 −7 −6

Ⓐ one more
B one less

9. Ring how you would solve the problem.

9 − 7 = _?_

Ⓐ mental math
B paper and pencil

10. Subtract.

45
− 41

A 14
Ⓑ 4
C 83

11. Add.

63
+ 28

Ⓐ 91
B 45
C 35

12. Estimate. About how many points did the two teams score?

Team A	Team B
32 players	21 players

Ⓐ about 50
B about 60
C about 70

56   MCT 2

▶ **Free Response Tests**
▶ **Alternative Tests**
▶ **Thinking Strategies**
▶ **Concrete Materials**

PROJECT AND BULLETIN BOARD

Prepare the Terrific Triangles as shown and post them on the bulletin board. Direct students to subtract down side 1 and then down side 2 and write the answers in the open circles. Next, subtract from left to right across side 3 and check the subtraction by adding up each side. The sums should be the number written in the circle at the top of the triangle. In another session, post the starred triangles. Have students subtract sides 1 and 2. Then have them count back to find the missing number on side 3. Add along each side to check subtraction. Challenge students to make up their own Terrific Triangles.

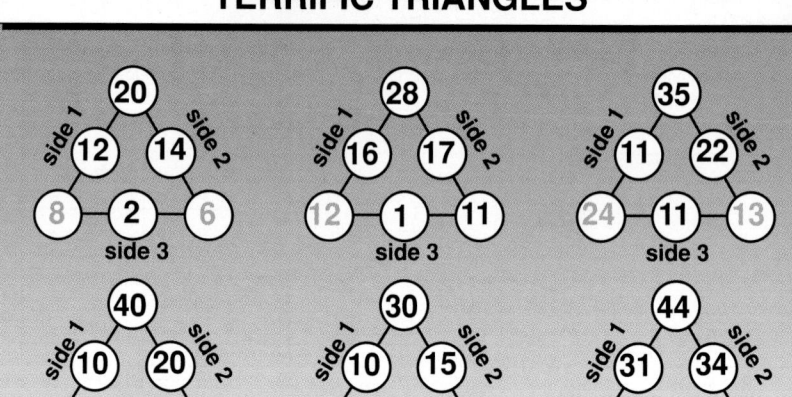

TERRIFIC TRIANGLES

COOPERATIVE LEARNING

Divide the class into groups of 4 or 5. Identify the group skill: summarizing and checking with others for agreement and understanding. Instruct members of each group to measure each other's height to the nearest inch. Have each student stand beside a measuring tape while another marks the height. A second group member will record the heights on a chart similar to the one shown. The third and fourth group members will write subtraction stories about the results of the measuring, and a fifth will hang the completed stories in the classroom. Members should explain their tasks to make sure they all understand what they are to do.

You will find grouping suggestions and cooperative learning activities in most lessons throughout this chapter.

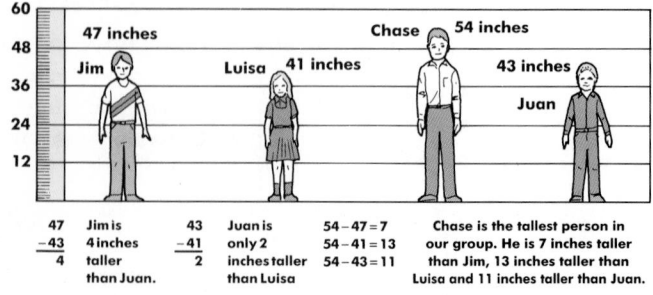

LITERATURE

Blos, Joan. *Martin's Hats.* New York: Morrow, 1984.

Martin has a whole wardrobe of hats to fit every fantasy and occasion.
Have students write number sentences, using base-ten blocks to represent Martin's hats.

Ormerod, Jan. *101 Things to Do With a Baby.* Lothrop, 1984.

Hawkins, Colin. *One More and One Less.* New York: Crown, 1974.

ENGLISH AS A SECOND LANGUAGE

One focus of this chapter is writing subtraction sentences with words. Have ESL students dictate the sentences to native speakers, who will write them down.

Before reading the tortoise and the hare story, explain that students will hear information that will help them solve the problem and that they must listen selectively for the clues. Have them listen in groups to encourage collaboration and sensitivity to any problems ESL students might have. Have them discuss their hypotheses and then share their answers with the whole class. Provide the language needed to state probabilities by using expressions such as *it could be 23, it is probably,* and *it must be.*

The developmental activities are interactive and provide many speaking opportunities for ESL students. Have students give each other direction for drawing sports equipment. Encourage pairs to discuss the prices they would set for each item.

GIFTED

Mathematically talented students may already understand units of measure and be able to work with them readily. They will nevertheless likely be interested in many of the activities presented in this chapter. Challenge these students, after they have completed their Student Edition work, by having them create their own story problems involving subtraction. Provide students with a tape recorder, a cassette, and punchout coins. After Lesson 4 on subtracting 2-digit numbers with symbols, have students write the script for a story problem involving money amounts. Offer an example, such as *Shelly bought a book for 59¢ and gave the sales clerk 3 quarters. How much change will the sales clerk give Shelly?* After they complete their scripts, have students record the problems. Then, working with partners, have them listen to each other's story problems and model them with the appropriate punchout coins. Have students count on to find the correct change, reviewing the procedure if necessary; then have them write and solve a related sentence to check their work. After Lesson 6 on adding to check subtraction, students may write the add-to-check sentence as an alternative means for checking.

STUDENTS AT RISK

Write two 2-digit numbers side by side on the chalkboard. Ask which number should be written on top to subtract. Have students point with their thumbs to show which side has the larger number. Refer to a hundred chart and a number line to provide concrete proof. Have a student write the numbers, with the larger number on top. Then model the subtraction using manipulatives and have another student write the answer.

Ask the group to show thumbs up or down to tell whether the answer is right. If it is incorrect, ask a volunteer to correct the error.

To give students an opportunity to work with calculators to solve 2-digit subtraction problems, have them solve the same exercise with a calculator and with manipulatives. At this point, students need proof that the calculator can do the same subtraction and get the same answer that they can.

You may also use the Reteaching Supplements and the specific Reteaching Tips from each lesson in this chapter.

Storybook

PICTURE

These pictures and accompanying stories and poems are available as storybooks.

You may want to read and discuss this story with your students before starting the chapter. The first lesson in this chapter includes a question about the story. Lessons 1, 2, 4, 5, and 6 in this chapter have questions in the informal Assessment that refer to the story.

Baseball Business

Joey Kangaroo was so excited! Today was the opening day of his new sporting goods store. He could hardly wait for his first customer to arrive. Once more he carefully counted the 31 baseballs he had on the shelf. There were three boxes of 10 balls each and 1 single ball in a basket by itself.

Just then the door opened, and in came Peter Platypus. "Good morning, Joey, I'd like to buy 15 baseballs."

"Let's see," said Joey. "You want one box of 10 and 5 single balls." He carefully looked at the shelf, and then shook his head. "I'm sorry, Peter. I can sell you 10 or 11, 20 or 21. But I can't sell you 15 because I have just one single ball."

"No," said Peter, "I need 15 baseballs. It just won't do to buy 10 or 11, 20 or 21." And then he left without buying even one ball.

After Peter left, Joey was worried. "Perhaps," he thought to himself, "I should have ordered more single balls to sell."

Before he could think about it much longer, the door opened again, and Wilda Wombat walked in. "What a nice store you have, Joey," she said. "I'm here to buy 23 baseballs."

"Let's see," said Joey. "You want two boxes of 10 and 3 single balls." He again carefully looked at the shelf, and then shook his head. "I'm sorry, Wilda. I can sell you 10 or 11, 20 or 21. But I can't sell you 23 because I have just one single ball."

"No," said Wilda. "I need 23 baseballs. It just won't do to buy 10 or 11, 20 or 21." And then she also left without buying even one ball.

After Wilda left, Joey was very worried. "I never knew it would be so hard to sell baseballs," he thought to himself.

Before he could think about it much longer, the door opened again, and Rachel Raccoon came in. "I need to buy 18 baseballs," she said.

"Let's see," said Joey. "You want one box of 10 and 8 single balls." Once again he looked carefully at the shelf. And with a very sad look on his face, he said, "I'm sorry, Rachel. I can sell you 10 or 11, 20 or 21. But I can't sell you 18 because I have just one single ball."

"No," said Rachel, "that just won't do. I really do need to buy 18 balls from you." At that very moment, Joey turned and his tail knocked one box of baseballs off the shelf. Ten balls spilled out of the box and onto the floor. The box was torn and of no use at all, so Joey picked up the 10 balls and put them in the basket with the 1 single ball.

And then Rachel said once again, "I need to buy 18 baseballs."

Joey carefully looked at his 31 balls. Now there were two boxes of 10 balls and 11 single balls. And Joey said, "Of course."

LESSON OPTIONS 14-1

Trading 1 Ten for 10 Ones

OBJECTIVE 14-1   To trade 1 ten for 10 ones

PREBOOK ACTIVITIES

QUICK REVIEW

Write the number of tens and ones.
45 (4 tens, 5 ones)   62 (6 tens, 2 ones)   50 (5 tens, 0 ones)
 6 (0 tens, 6 ones)   71 (7 tens, 1 one)   17 (1 ten, 7 ones)

PRIOR KNOWLEDGE

Remind students that they already know how to subtract 2-digit numbers using cubes. *Suppose that you had 35 cubes. How would you show them in tens and ones?* (3 tens and 5 ones) *Now you want to take away 17 cubes. Can you take away 1 ten and 7 ones? Why?* (no, because 7 ones is more than 5 ones) *What do you have to do first?* (Break apart a ten.) Explain that breaking apart a ten is the same as trading 1 ten for 10 ones.

COMMUNICATION

Listening and Discussing Math   Tell students to listen as you read the following story. *Rita needs pennies for the superball machine at the variety store. She has only 1 dime. Mr. King, the store owner, lets Rita trade her dime for 10 pennies. Now Rita can use the machine. What did Rita and Mr. King do?* (They traded 1 dime for 10 pennies.) *Did Rita and Mr. King make a fair trade?* (yes) *How do you know?* (Possible answer: 1 dime has the same value as 10 pennies.) *Suppose that in a subtraction problem you had to take away more ones than you had. Could you trade 1 ten to get 10 more ones without changing the problem?* (yes) *Why?* (because 1 ten has the same value as 10 ones)

EXPLORE AND CONNECT

Materials: base-ten blocks, TA5 (Place Value Chart)
Grouping Suggestion: pairs
Provide each pair with base-ten blocks and a place value char
Have one student in each pair choose a number between 20 a
50 to model with blocks. The student writes the number of te
and ones. Next, the partner trades 1 ten for 10 ones and tells
how many tens and ones there are now. *Do you still have the
same amount?* (yes) Have the first student trade back 10 ones
for 1 ten to check. If the trades have been completed correctl
the original number will be modeled once again with blocks.
Encourage students to check with each other as they work fo
agreement and understanding.

CONNECTIONS   Use these anytime.

Problem of the Day

Use Objects   Use punchout dimes and pennies to solve this problem.
Holly has 4 dimes and 5 pennies.
She trades 1 dime for 10 pennies.
What coins does she have now?
(3 dimes and 15 pennies)

Math Connection

Numeration   How many ways can you show tens and ones equal to 76? Use blocks to find the answer. Here are 2 ways to get you started: 0 tens, 76 ones and 1 ten, 66 ones.
(Students continue the pattern to find 6 more ways.)

Subject Integration

Social Studies   A long time ago, people did not use money. They got things they needed by trading one thing for another. Work with a partner. Name something you would like to have. Imagine that your partner has that thing. Tell your partner what you would trade for it. Talk about whether it is a fair trade.

CLASSWORK AND HOMEWORK SUPPLEMENTS

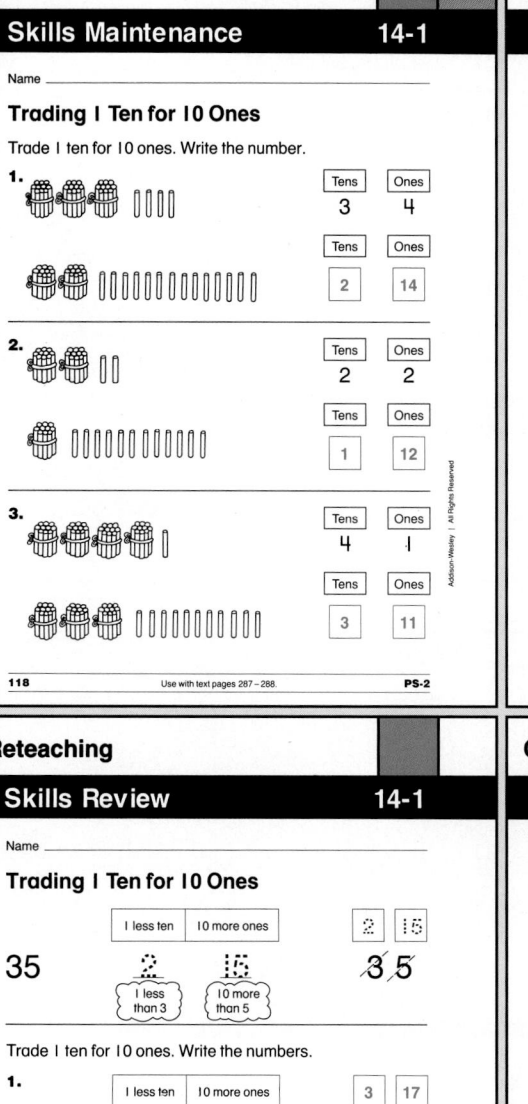

Practice

Skills Maintenance   **14-1**

Name _____

Trading 1 Ten for 10 Ones

Trade 1 ten for 10 ones. Write the number.

1.

Tens	Ones
3	4

Tens	Ones
2	14

2.

Tens	Ones
2	2

Tens	Ones
1	12

3.

Tens	Ones
4	1

Tens	Ones
3	11

118   Use with text pages 287–288.   PS-2

Reteaching

Skills Review   **14-1**

Name _____

Trading 1 Ten for 10 Ones

	1 less ten	10 more ones		
35	2 (1 less than 3)	15 (10 more than 5)		3 5

Trade 1 ten for 10 ones. Write the numbers.

1.

	1 less ten	10 more ones		
47	3 (1 less than 4)	17 (10 more than 7)		4 7

2.

	1 less ten	10 more ones		
60	5 (1 less than 6)	10 (10 more than 0)		6 0

3.

	1 less ten	10 more ones		
55	4 (1 less than 5)	15 (10 more than 5)		5 5

118   Use with text pages 287–288.   RS-2

Building Thinking Skills

Mental Math   **14-1**

Name _____

Trading

Finish the table.

Number	Before the Trade Tens and Ones	After the Trade Tens and Ones	Number
52	5 tens 2 ones	4 tens 12 ones	4 12 / 5 2
65	6 tens 5 ones	5 tens 15 ones	5 15 / 6 5
83	8 tens 3 ones	7 tens 13 ones	7 13 / 8 3
46	4 tens 6 ones	3 tens 16 ones	3 16 / 4 6
78	7 tens 8 ones	6 tens 18 ones	6 18 / 7 8
62	6 tens 2 ones	5 tens 12 ones	5 12 / 6 2

118   Use with text pages 287–288.   TS-2

Challenges

Cooperative Activities   **14-1**

Name _____

Tens and Ones Bingo   Tens   Ones

You need: a friend, 2 spinners like these: 40 counters, and 2 game boards.

Rules: Take turns. Spin both spinners.
Read the number like this: ___ tens and ___ ones.
If a number on your game board can be traded to make the spinner number, put a counter on the number.
For example, 2 tens and 12 ones = 32.

spinner numbers   game board numbers

The first player to cover 5 numbers in a row wins.

22	65	38	80	35
51	34	26	91	83
98	62	40	87	71
47	69	94	56	29
78	75	53	44	67

118   Use with text pages 287–288.   CS-2

OPTIONS FOR INDIVIDUAL NEEDS

Basic

Exercises All

Supplements
Reteaching 118 or
Practice 118

Average

Exercises All

Supplements
Practice 118
Challenges 118 or
Thinking Skills 118

Extended

Exercises All

Supplements
Challenges 118
Thinking Skills 118

Other Resources:
Explorations, p. 287
Developing Number Concepts With Unifix Cubes, pp. 165-166

14-1

OBJECTIVE 14-1

To trade 1 ten for 10 ones

> **Materials:** base-ten blocks, punchout ones, TA5 (Place Value Chart), number cubes labeled 1-6 and 4-9
>
> **Grouping Suggestions:** individual work, pairs

1. MOTIVATE AND TEACH

LEARN ABOUT IT

Read the chapter story to the class. Have students use blocks to show how Joey could have traded 1 box of 10 for 10 single baseballs in each situation. Have students turn to page 287. Tell them that the sporting goods store has 4 boxes of 10 baseballs and a basket of 3 single baseballs. Ask them to model the baseballs by placing 4 tens sticks in the carton and 3 ones blocks in the basket. *How many tens and ones are there?* (4 tens, 3 ones)

▶ **Suppose that the owner wanted to place 10 more baseballs in the basket. How could you show that on the page?** (Take away 1 tens stick and place 10 ones in the basket.)

▶ **How many tens and ones are there now?** (3 tens, 13 ones) **Are there still the same number of baseballs in all? Explain.** (Yes, because 1 ten has the same value as 10 ones.)

▶ **How many more times could the owner trade 1 box for 10 balls to put into the basket? How do you know?** (3 more times, because there are 3 tens left after the first trade.)

Continue several times. Encourage students to trade 1 ten for 10 ones each time and tell the new number of tens and ones.

2. CHECK UNDERSTANDING

ERROR ALERT Neglecting to change the value of the tens or the ones after a trade.

14
Subtracting 2-Digit Numbers

BASEBALLS
$2.79

TEACHING OPTIONS

RETEACHING TIPS Give each student base-ten blocks to model numbers such as 23, 45, and 36. In each case, ask them to trade 1 ten for 10 ones and name the new number of tens and ones. Have students continue until they can name trades easily. Assign Reteaching Supplement 118.

ENRICHMENT Have students roll number cubes labeled 1-6 and 4-9 and use the digits to write the largest and smallest possible 2-digit numbers. Ask if they would have to trade 1 ten for 10 ones in order to subtract the smaller number from the larger. Have them write at least 5 problems.

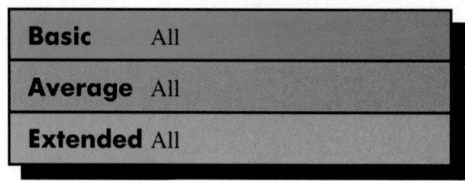

ading 1 Ten for 10 Ones

e blocks to show the tens and ones.
en trade 1 ten for 10 ones. Cross out
d write the new numbers.

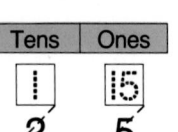 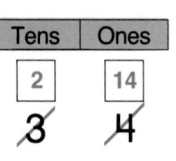 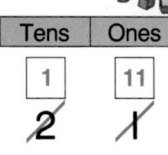 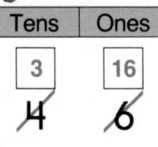

Tens	Ones		Tens	Ones		Tens	Ones		Tens	Ones
1	15		2	14		1	11		3	16
2	5		3	4		2	1		4	6

e your punchouts. Paste 10 ones over
en to show a trade. Cross out and
ite the new numbers.

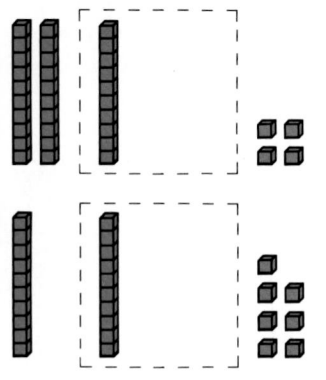

Tens	Ones
2	14
3	4

Tens	Ones
1	17
2	7

OW WITH BLOCKS

Use blocks. Trade 10 ones for
1 ten when you can. Show that
these are the same amounts.

4 tens 15 ones __55__

5 tens 5 ones __55__

3 tens 25 ones __55__

(two hundred eighty-eight) Chapter 14

---

3. PRACTICE AND APPLY

Basic	All
Average	All
Extended	All

PRACTICE

When you cross out the number in the tens place, what do you know about the new tens digit? (It will be 1 less.) *What do you know about the new digits in the ones place?* (They will be 10 more.)

APPLY

SHOW WITH BLOCKS ▶ **What clues help you see that all 3 numbers are the same amount?** (Possible answer: They all have 5 ones; the number of tens is the same if you add the tens shown in the ones place to the tens in the tens place.)

▶ **How can you prove that all 3 numbers are the same?** (Possible answer: For 4 tens and 15 ones, trade 10 ones for 1 ten; for 3 tens and 25 ones, trade 20 ones for 2 tens; model 55 as 5 tens and 5 ones. All 3 numbers have 5 tens and 5 ones.

▶ **What other ways could be used to name 5 tens and 5 ones?** (Possible answers: 2 tens and 35 ones; 1 ten and 45 ones; 55 ones)

14-1

LOSE AND ASSESS

OW WHAT YOU KNOW

ovide pairs with 2 number cubes,
se-ten blocks, and a place value
art. One student rolls the cubes,
kes a 2-digit number, writes it, and
dels it on the chart with tens sticks
d ones. The other student trades 1
for 10 ones and writes the new
ounts for tens and ones. Students
tch roles and repeat. Have students
ord their work on a chart in their
th Journals.

Subtracting 2-Digit Numbers Using Models

OBJECTIVE 14-2   To subtract 2-digit numbers using models

PREBOOK ACTIVITIES

QUICK REVIEW

Ask students to give the number of tens and ones for each number.

54	(5 tens, 4 ones)	23	(2 tens, 3 ones)
32	(3 tens, 2 ones)	75	(7 tens, 5 ones)
19	(1 ten, 9 ones)	50	(5 tens, 0 ones)
9	(0 tens, 9 ones)	46	(4 tens, 6 ones)
98	(9 tens, 8 ones)	66	(6 tens, 6 ones)

PRIOR KNOWLEDGE

Present a situation such as the following to help students recall breaking apart a ten.

Jerry has 21 models to build.
14 models are of cars.
The rest are of ships.
How many models are ships?

Ask a student to model 21 with Cube-A-Links. *Do we need to break apart a ten to take away 14?* (yes) *How many models are ships?* (7 models are ships.)

COMMUNICATION

Reading and Writing in Math   Write the word **trade** on the chalkboard. Read it and ask students to name things that they trade with each other. *What are some reasons we trade?* (Possible answers: We trade because we need something or because we want something.) List student responses on the board. *What do we trade 1 ten for?* (10 ones) *Why do we need to trade 1 ten in math?* Ask students to answer the question by writing the following sentence in their Math Journals and filling in the blank. *When more ones are needed, _____ 1 ten for 10 ones.* (trade)

EXPLORE AND CONNECT

Materials: TA 5 (Place Value Chart), Cube-A-Links
Provide students with place value charts and cubes. Ask them to model the number 35 on the chart with cubes. (3 tens and ones) Then ask students to subtract 14 cubes as you write 35 − 14 in vertical form on the chalkboard. *Are there enough ones in 35 to subtract 4 ones?* (yes) As students are taking away the ones, record the answer on the chalkboard. *Subtract ten. How many tens are left?* (2 tens) Again record the answer. Repeat this process using an example that requires trading 1 ten for 10 ones, such as 24 − 16. Then ask students to suggest other subtraction exercises, to use the cubes to decide if trading is necessary, and to show how to do it.

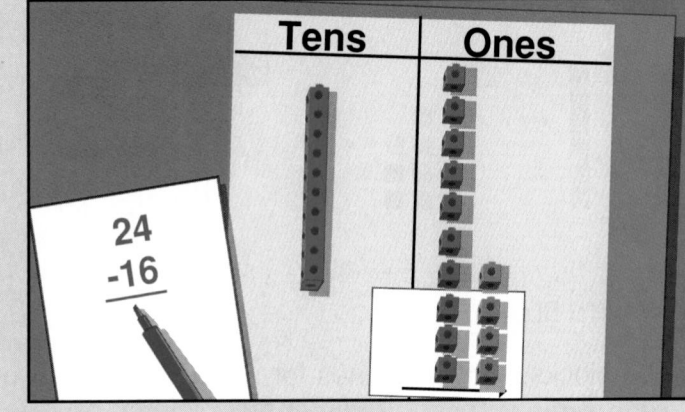

CONNECTIONS   Use these anytime.

Problem of the Day

Draw a Picture   Draw a picture to solve the problem. Finish the sentence. There are 4 yellow flowers and some red flowers in the flower box. Each red flower is between 2 yellow flowers. How many flowers are in the flower box? There are __(7)__ flowers.

Math Connection

Operation   Read each situation. Tell whether you would add or subtract.
You lose a nickel of your lunch money. (subtract)
You win 2 prizes. (add)
You give away 5 shirts. (subtract)
You put 10 dollars in the bank. (add)
You take 10 dollars out of the bank. (subtract)

Mental Math

Money   Write the difference.
1 nickel − 2 pennies   (3¢)
2 dimes − 1 dime   (10¢)
1 quarter − 1 dime   (15¢)
2 quarters − 2 dimes   (30¢)
3 nickels − 1 nickel   (10¢)
1 half-dollar − 1 dime   (40¢)
7 pennies − 1 nickel   (2¢)

CLASSWORK AND HOMEWORK SUPPLEMENTS

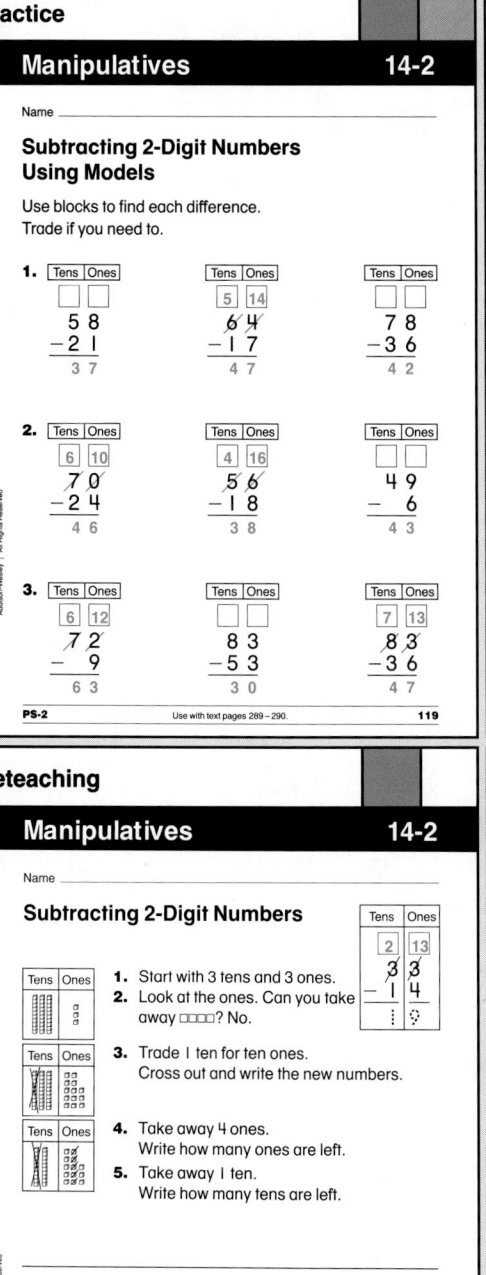

Practice

Manipulatives 14-2

Name _____

Subtracting 2-Digit Numbers Using Models

Use blocks to find each difference.
Trade if you need to.

1.

Tens	Ones
5	8
− 2	1
3	7

Tens	Ones
5	14
6̶	4̶
− 1	7
4	7

Tens	Ones
7	8
− 3	6
4	2

2.

Tens	Ones
6	10
7̶	0̶
− 2	4
4	6

Tens	Ones
4	16
5̶	6̶
− 1	8
3	8

Tens	Ones
4	9
−	6
4	3

3.

Tens	Ones
6	12
7̶	2̶
− 1	
6	3

Tens	Ones
8	3
− 5	3
3	0

Tens	Ones
7	13
8̶	3̶
− 3	6
4	7

PS-2 · Use with text pages 289–290. · **119**

Reteaching

Manipulatives 14-2

Name _____

Subtracting 2-Digit Numbers

Tens	Ones
2	13
3̶	3̶
− 1	4

1. Start with 3 tens and 3 ones.
2. Look at the ones. Can you take away ☐☐☐☐? No.
3. Trade 1 ten for ten ones. Cross out and write the new numbers.
4. Take away 4 ones. Write how many ones are left.
5. Take away 1 ten. Write how many tens are left.

Use blocks to find the difference.

1.

Tens	Ones
3	3
− 1	1
2	2

Take away the ones.
Take away the tens.

no trade

2.

Tens	Ones
1	14
2̶	4̶
−	6
1	8

Trade 1 ten for 10 ones. Take away the ones. How many ones and tens are left?

trade

RS-2 · Use with text pages 289–290. · **119**

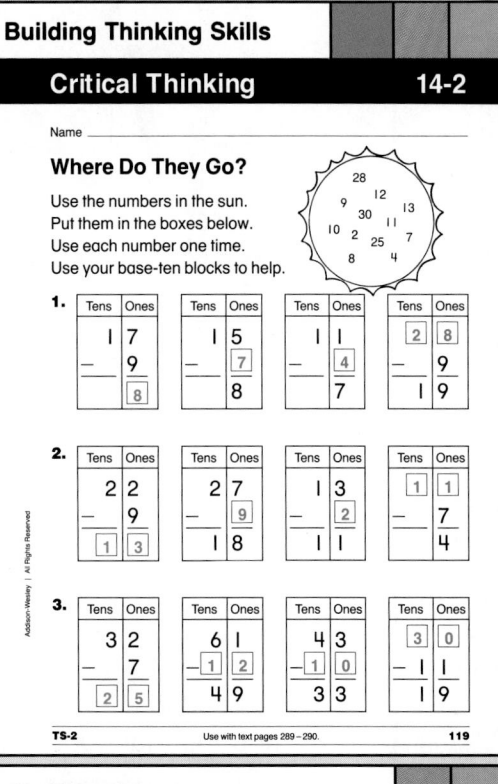

Building Thinking Skills

Critical Thinking 14-2

Name _____

Where Do They Go?

Use the numbers in the sun.
Put them in the boxes below.
Use each number one time.
Use your base-ten blocks to help.

(Sun numbers: 28, 9, 12, 13, 30, 11, 10, 2, 7, 8, 25, 4)

1.

Tens	Ones
1	7
−	9
	8

Tens	Ones
1	5
−	7
	8

Tens	Ones
1	1
−	4
	7

Tens	Ones
2	8
−	9
1	9

2.

Tens	Ones
2	2
−	9
1	3

Tens	Ones
2	7
−	9
1	8

Tens	Ones
1	3
−	2
1	1

Tens	Ones
1	1
−	7
	4

3.

Tens	Ones
3	2
−	7
2	5

Tens	Ones
6	1
− 1	2
4	9

Tens	Ones
4	3
− 1	0
3	3

Tens	Ones
3	0
− 1	1
1	9

TS-2 · Use with text pages 289–290. · **119**

Challenges

Family Math 14-2

Name _____

Making Change

> Dear Family,
> Your child has just learned about subtracting 2-digit numbers using models. Have your child show 99¢ in dimes and pennies. Provide newspaper ads for grocery items and have your child pick something to buy and subtract to find the change.

Pick something to buy that costs less than 99¢.
Take away pennies and dimes to subtract the cost.
Trade 1 dime for 10 pennies when you need to.
Write how much money is left.

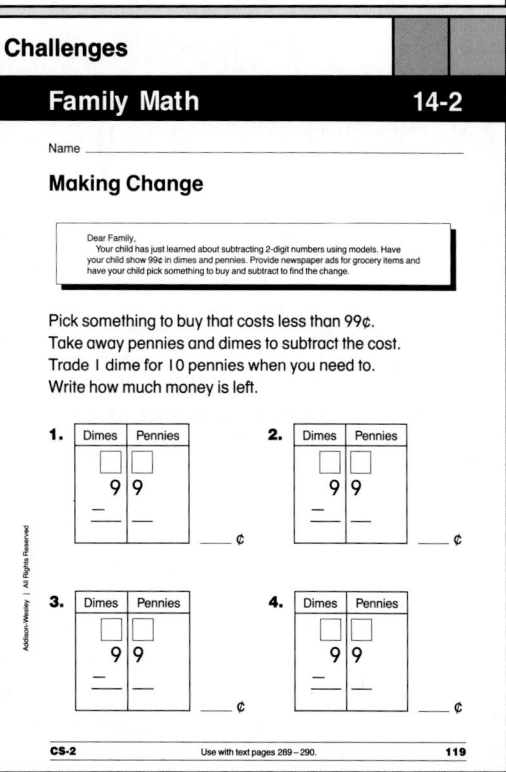

1.

Dimes	Pennies
9	9
−	
	____ ¢

2.

Dimes	Pennies
9	9
−	
	____ ¢

3.

Dimes	Pennies
9	9
−	
	____ ¢

4.

Dimes	Pennies
9	9
−	
	____ ¢

CS-2 · Use with text pages 289–290. · **119**

OPTIONS FOR INDIVIDUAL NEEDS

Basic

Exercises All

Supplements
Reteaching 119 or
Practice 119
Thinking Skills 119

Average

Exercises All

Supplements
Practice 119
Challenges 119 or
Thinking Skills 119

Extended

Exercises All

Supplements
Challenges 119
Thinking Skills 119

Other Resources:
Explorations, pp. 288-291
Problem Solving Experiences In Mathematics, pp. 93, 123, 129
Developing Number Concepts With Unifix Cubes, pp. 116, 174
Mathematics Book A, pp. 26-27

14-2

OBJECTIVE 14-2
To subtract 2-digit numbers using models

Materials: bundles of 10 wooden sticks, Cube-A-Links

Grouping Suggestions: individual work, pairs

---

1. MOTIVATE AND TEACH

LEARN ABOUT IT

Ask a volunteer to model the number 23 using bundles of wooden sticks. Next to this model, ask another student to show what happens when 15 is subtracted from 23. Write 23 − 15 in vertical form on the chalkboard. *Look at the before and after models. Did we need to break apart a ten to have enough ones to subtract 5 ones?* (yes) *How many ones sticks were left?* (8) Write the answer on the board. *How can each step in the subtraction you modeled be written in the exercise?* (Possible answer: Cross out tens, write 1 less ten, write 1 more ten over the ones column.) Direct students' attention to the top of page 289. *What is being shown in the picture?* (trading 1 ten for 10 ones)
▶ **What are the numbers that appear in the boxes over the tens and ones columns?** (Possible answer: the total number of ones and the total number of tens after trading a ten)
▶ **Look at the number in the box above the ones column. Why does that number contain a ten?** (Possible answer: You had to trade a ten in order to subtract 5 ones.)
▶ **Examine Exercises 1–3. What will appear in the boxes if trading is not necessary?** Explain. (The boxes will be blank because you do not need to trade a 10. There are enough ones in the top number to subtract the ones in the bottom number.)

2. CHECK UNDERSTANDING

ERROR ALERT Forgetting to cross out a ten to show it has been traded to the ones column.

Name _____

Subtracting 2-Digit Numbers Using Models

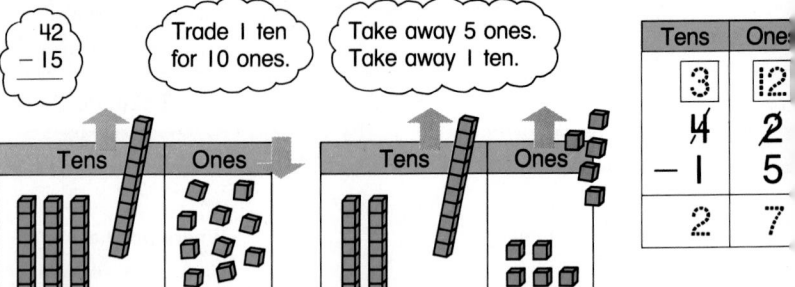

Tens	Ones
3	12
4̶	2̶
− 1	5
2	7

Tens	Ones

Find each difference. Use your blocks and the mat above to help.

1.

Tens	Ones
2	14
3̶	4̶
− 1	6
1	8

2.

Tens	Ones
☐	☐
2	8
− 1	2
1	6

3.

Tens	Ones
3	11
4̶	1̶
−	5
3	6

Chapter 14   (two hundred eighty-nine) 2

TEACHING OPTIONS

RETEACHING TIPS Ask 2 students to model 31 with cubes. Write 31 − 17 in a chart like the one on page 289. Have the *tens* student hand over 1 ten, cross out the 3, and write 2 in the tens section. Have the *ones* student complete the subtraction. Assign Reteaching Supplement 119.

ENRICHMENT Draw a large round target on the chalkboard. Label the three rings −15, −10, and −5. Label the bullseye +25. Each student starts with 50 points and has 2 throws of an eraser from a designated line at the target. All students should add or subtract the score after each throw.

swer the questions. Fill in the chart.

1. How many of each block do you need?

to start ___3___ 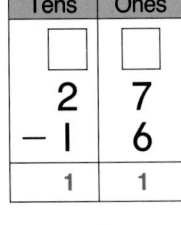 ___2___ ▱

to take away ___1___ ___4___ ▱

Tens	Ones
2	12
3̶	2̶
−1	4
1	8

2. Do you need to trade? (yes) no

3. Subtract the ones. How many are left? ___8___

4. Subtract the tens. How many are left? ___1___

5. What is the difference? ___18___

6. How many of each block do you need?

to start ___2___ 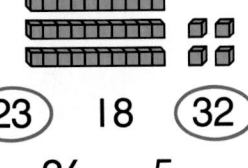 ___7___ ▱

to take away ___1___ ___6___ ▱

Tens	Ones
☐	☐
2	7
−1	6
1	1

7. Do you need to trade? yes (no)

8. Subtract the ones. How many are left? ___1___

9. Subtract the tens. How many are left? ___1___

10. What is the difference? ___11___

SE CRITICAL THINKING

1. Ring the amounts you can subtract from these blocks without trading 1 ten for 10 ones.

(23) 18 (32)

26 5

90 (two hundred ninety) Chapter 14

3. PRACTICE AND APPLY

Basic	All
Average	All
Extended	All

PRACTICE

On page 290, what do Exercises 1-5 show? (Possible answer: The steps used to solve a problem.) *Look at Exercise 5. What does difference mean?* (the answer in a subtraction sentence)

APPLY

USE CRITICAL THINKING ▶ **How many blocks are there?** (34)
▶ **What will you look at in each number to decide if you must trade a ten?** (Possible answer: the ones column to identify numbers with four or less)
▶ **How can you prove which numbers can be subtracted from 34 without trading?** (Possible answer: Use cubes to model each sentence.)
▶ **Which numbers subtracted from 34 would leave the greatest difference? Explain.**
(5; it is the smallest amount to be taken away)

14-2

LOSE AND ASSESS

HOW WHAT YOU KNOW

eview the chapter story with
udents. Have them use cubes to act
t each subtraction problem in the
ory: 31 − 15; 31 − 23; 31 − 18.
alk about why Joey kept saying he
uld sell 10 or 11, 20 or 21. Ask
hat other numbers he could sell
ithout opening another box. (30, 31)

QUICK QUIZ

Use cubes to find the difference.
1. ☐☐ (4) (12) 2. ☐☐
    5 2   6 7
  −3 3 (19)   −2 5 (42)

Chapter 14 Lesson 2   **290**

LESSON OPTIONS 14-3

Subtracting 2-Digit Numbers Using Pictures

OBJECTIVE 14-3   To subtract 2-digit numbers using pictures

PREBOOK ACTIVITIES

QUICK REVIEW

Ring the amounts you can take away from these cubes without trading 1 ten for 10 ones. Use cubes if you need help.

(3)   24   37   5   (11)   (42)

PRIOR KNOWLEDGE

Write 21 − 13 vertically on the chalkboard. Ask one student to model the tens by holding 2 rows of 10 cubes and another to stand next to the first student and hold 1 one. *Do we need to trade 1 ten in order to subtract?* (yes) The *tens* student should hand 1 ten to the *ones* student, who can now display 11 ones. Record what took place on the board. As the class subtracts the ones and tens, the two students should take away 3 ones and 1 ten. Ask a student to read the difference. (8)

COMMUNICATION

Discussing and Writing Math   Draw on the chalkboard pictures of cubes to show tens and ones. For example, 5 tens, 3 tens, 1 one, 6 ones. *What do these pictures show?* (tens, ones) Ask a student to come to the board and write a label for each picture. (5 tens, 3 tens, 1 one, 6 ones)
How do pictures help us understand things? (Possible answer: Pictures help us to actually see what is going on instead of having to imagine it.) *Name ways that we use pictures in math.* (Possible answer: counting money, giving directions, adding and subtracting 2-digit numbers, graphing, drawing shapes)

EXPLORE AND CONNECT

Materials: TA3 (Graph Paper), TA5 (Place Value Chart)
Remind students that they have used cubes to model subtraction exercises and explain that now they will use pictures. Write 42 on the chalkboard. Ask students to cut strip of tens from their graph paper to represent the tens and square to represent the ones in this number and then place them on a place value chart. Write 42 − 16 on the board. *Do you need trade 1 ten for 10 ones?* (yes) Have students cut the individua squares from 1 row of 10 and place them in the ones column. Then have them paste the strips and squares to the chart and cross out 6 ones and 1 ten to show what was subtracted. *Cou how many squares are left. What is the difference?* (26) Reco all the steps on the board. Repeat this activity, asking student to make up the subtraction exercises. Make sure students use graph paper to explore subtraction that does not involve tradi as well.

CONNECTIONS   Use these anytime.

Problem of the Day

Finding Missing Data   Rewrite this problem and add the information that is missing. Then solve.
Trey has 19 pet birds. Then he let some of them go. How many birds does he have now?
(Include the number of birds he let go. Then subtract to find the answer.)

Mental Math

Subtraction   Subtract 10 from each of the numbers below. Do not use pencil and paper. Say the answer.

33	(23)	46	(36)
50	(40)	75	(65)
37	(27)	66	(56)
14	(4)	28	(18)
12	(2)	99	(89)

Math Connection

Operation   Fill in the chart. Subtract down and add across in the direction of the arrows.

(+) →

(−)	26	(13)	39
	9	(5)	14
	(17)	(8)	(25)

CLASSWORK AND HOMEWORK SUPPLEMENTS

Practice

| Skills Maintenance | 14-3 |

Name

Subtracting 2-Digit Numbers Using Pictures

Cross out a ten and draw 10 ones if you need to trade.
Then cross out ones and tens to subtract.

1.
	Tens	Ones
	2	9
	− 1	5
	1	4

2.
	Tens	Ones
	2	12
	3 2	
	− 1	8
	1	4

3.
	Tens	Ones
	1	14
	2 4	
	−	7
	1	7

4.
	Tens	Ones
	4	4
	− 2	1
	2	3

120   Use with text pages 291 – 292.   **PS-2**

Building Thinking Skills

| Problem Solving | 14-3 |

Name

Weigh In

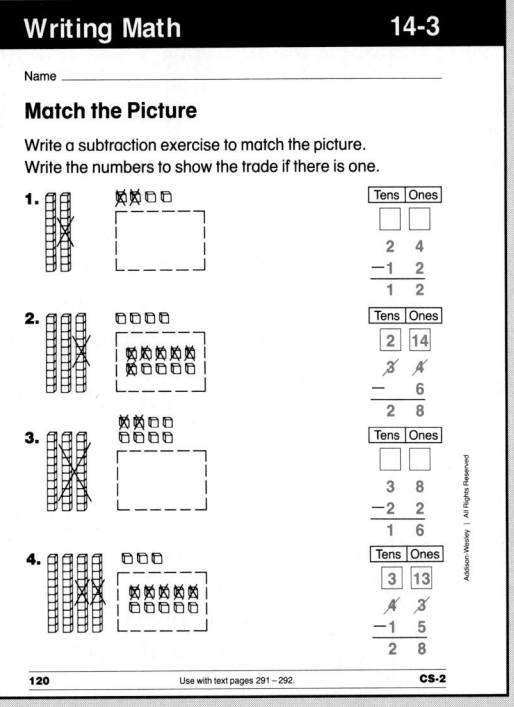

Papa	Mama	Sam	Sal	Sue
84 lbs	57 lbs	31 lbs	26 lbs	11 lbs

Use the weights of the Seal family to answer the questions.

1. How much more does Sal weigh than Sue? __15 lbs__

2. How many pounds would Sue have to gain to weigh the
   same as Sam? __20 lbs__

3. How much would Mama Seal weigh if she lost
   35 pounds? __22 lbs__

4. Which two seals together weigh the same as
   Mama Seal? __Sam and Sal__

5. How much would Sam weigh if he lost 5 pounds?
   __26 lbs__

6. Which seal weighs about 30 pounds less than
   Mama Seal? __Sal__

7. How much less does Mama Seal weigh than
   Papa Seal? __27 lbs__

120   Use with text pages 291 – 292.   **TS-2**

Reteaching

| Skills Review | 14-3 |

Name

Subtracting 2-Digit Numbers

Tens	Ones			Tens	Ones	
2	11					
3 1				3	5	
− 1	6	trade		− 2	1	no trade
1	5			1	4	

First decide whether to trade.
Ring **yes** or **no**. Then subtract.

1.
	Tens	Ones
	3	13
43	4 3	
− 15	− 1 5	
Trade? (yes) no	2 8	

2.
	Tens	Ones
65	6 5	
− 22	− 2 2	
Trade? yes (no)	4 3	

3.
	Tens	Ones
76	7 6	
− 34	− 3 4	
Trade? yes (no)	4 2	

4.
	Tens	Ones
	5	10
60	6 0	
− 25	− 2 5	
Trade? (yes) no	3 5	

120   Use with text pages 291 – 292.   **RS-2**

Challenges

| Writing Math | 14-3 |

Name

Match the Picture

Write a subtraction exercise to match the picture.
Write the numbers to show the trade if there is one.

1.
Tens	Ones
2	4
− 1	2
1	2

2.
Tens	Ones
2	14
3	4
−	6
2	8

3.
Tens	Ones
3	8
− 2	2
1	6

4.
Tens	Ones
3	13
4	3
− 1	5
2	8

120   Use with text pages 291 – 292.   **CS-2**

OPTIONS FOR INDIVIDUAL NEEDS

Basic

Exercises All

Supplements
Reteaching 120 or
Practice 120
Challenges 120

Average

Exercises All

Supplements
Practice 120
Challenges 120 or
Thinking Skills 120

Extended

Exercises All

Supplements
Challenges 120
Thinking Skills 120

Other Resources:
Explorations, pp. 288-291
*Problem Solving Experiences
In Mathematics*, p. 147
*Developing Number Concepts
With Unifix Cubes*, pp.
166-167, 174

14-3

Chapter 14 Lesson 3   **291B**

LESSON PLAN 14-3

OBJECTIVE 14-3
To subtract 2-digit numbers using pictures

Materials: base-ten blocks; TA12 (Spinners), TA3 (Graph Paper)

Grouping Suggestions: individual work, pairs, cooperative learning groups of 3

1. MOTIVATE AND TEACH

LEARN ABOUT IT

Write the number 26 on the chalkboard and ask a student to draw a picture of it. (2 tens, 6 ones) Then write 26 − 17 in vertical form on the board. *Do you need to trade 1 ten before you can subtract 7 ones?* (yes) *How can you show the trade?* (Possible answer: Erase one row of tens and draw 10 ones next to the 6 ones.) *How can you show that 17 has been subtracted?* (Cross out 7 ones and 1 ten.) *What is the difference?* (9) Show all the steps on the board. Have students look at the exercises on page 291.
▶ **What do you notice about these exercises?** (Possible answer: They are all the same; they show the steps for subtracting the numbers.)
▶ **What does the picture show in Exercise 1?** (the number of ones and tens)
▶ **Look at the boxes above 34 in Exercise 2. What do these numbers mean?** (Possible answer: another name for 3 tens and 4 ones; 2 tens and 14 ones)
▶ **How will the picture change in Exercise 2?** (Possible answer: It will show 2 tens and 14 ones; it will show 6 ones crossed out.)
▶ **How does crossing out the ones and tens help you solve the problem?** (Possible answer: It is easier to count how many are left.)

2. CHECK UNDERSTANDING

ERROR ALERT Forgetting to reduce the number of tens by 1 to show that trading has taken place.

Name _____

Subtracting 2-Digit Numbers Using Pictures

Find the difference between 34 and 16.

1. Show the blocks. Then write the numbers.

What you do.

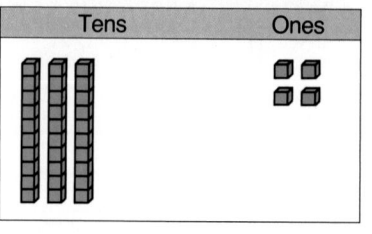

What you write.

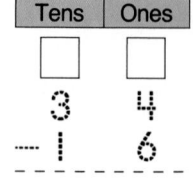

2. Do you need to trade? If yes, paste your punchout. Subtract the ones. Cross out to show it.

Students should paste 10 ones and cross out 6 ones.

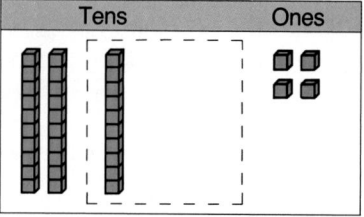

3. Subtract the tens. Cross out to show it.

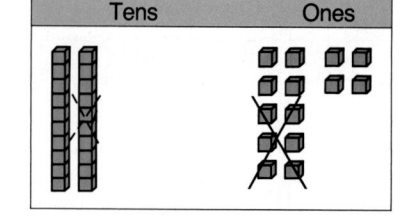

Chapter 14

(two hundred ninety-one) 29

TEACHING OPTIONS

RETEACHING TIPS Ask pairs to use blocks and a place value chart to show the tens and ones in 43. *Subtract 15. Do you need to trade?* (yes) Have one student trade a ten while the other removes 15 blocks. Count to find the answer. Repeat. For further review, assign Reteaching Supplement 120.

ENRICHMENT Have students collect data on the ages of older friends, siblings, and adults. Have them write subtraction exercises to show how much older each person is than they are. Compare differences to see who knows the oldest person.

se your punchouts. Paste 10 ones over
ten if you need to trade. Cross out blocks
subtract. Write the difference.

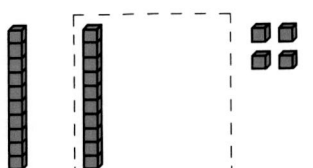

Students should paste 10 ones
and cross out 5 ones.

Tens	Ones
1	14
2	4
−	5
1	9

Students should cross out 4 ones
and 2 tens.

Tens	Ones
□	□
2	7
−2	4
	3

Students should paste 10 ones
and cross out 5 ones and 1 ten.

Tens	Ones
2	13
3	3
−1	5
1	8

ROBLEM SOLVING

Solve. Use blocks to help. Miguel
picked up 14 blocks. They have a
value of 32. How many of each
block did he pick up?

__2__    __12__ ▢

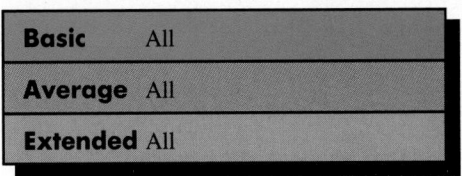

3. PRACTICE AND APPLY

Basic	All
Average	All
Extended	All

PRACTICE

*Why are there boxes above each
exercise?* (Possible answer: so you can
show when a trade is made) *What do you
notice about Exercise 2 on page 292?*
(Possible answer: You do not have to
trade.)

APPLY

PROBLEM SOLVING ▶ **Tell why
this is a guess and check problem.**
(Possible answer: You know Miguel has
only 14 blocks, so you need to guess
which combination of 14 blocks has a
value of 32. You can check your guesses
by using blocks.)
▶ **Could you have more than 3 tens
blocks? Why or why not?** (Possible
answer: No, because 4 tens blocks have
a value of 40, which is more than 32.)
▶ **Could Miguel have 14 ones blocks?
Why or why not?** (No, because Miguel
has only 14 blocks; if only ones blocks
are used, the value will not total 32.)

14-3

CLOSE AND ASSESS

WRITE WHAT YOU KNOW

ave students work in small groups.
ne uses a spinner to identify
umbers for a 2-digit subtraction
roblem. A second makes a picture of
e subtraction using graph paper
rips for tens and squares for ones. A
ird student summarizes the process
y recording each step.

QUICK QUIZ

Use pictures to find each difference.
1. □□   **2.** □□   (6) (12)
   8 4   7 2
 − 3 3   − 2 4
 (5 1)   (4 8)

Subtracting 2-Digit Numbers Using Symbols

OBJECTIVE 14-4   To subtract 2-digit numbers using symbols

PREBOOK ACTIVITIES

QUICK REVIEW

Trade 1 ten for 10 ones. Then write the number of tens and ones after the trade.

3 tens, 6 ones   (2 tens, 16 ones)
4 tens, 2 ones   (3 tens, 12 ones)
7 tens, 0 ones   (6 tens, 10 ones)
1 ten, 3 ones   (0 tens, 13 ones)

PRIOR KNOWLEDGE

You have been selling lemonade and have made 91¢. So far, you have spent 53¢ on supplies. How much money do you have left? *Do you add or subtract to find the answer?* (subtract) Ask students to write the subtraction for this story. (91 − 53) *Do you need to trade 1 ten for 10 ones?* (yes) Suggest that students use cubes or graph paper if they need help in finding the difference. (38¢)

COMMUNICATION

Writing and Discussing Math   Display the following:

1.	Tens/Ones	2.	Tens/Ones	3.	Tens/Ones
	( ) ( )		(3) (13)		(3) (13)
	4 3		4 3		4 3
	−2 7		−2 7		−2 7
			6		1 6

Discuss the steps. Have students write a phrase in their Math Journals to tell what is happening in each step. Use cubes to model the steps if necessary. Discuss student explanations of each step.

EXPLORE AND CONNECT

Materials: base-ten blocks
Write 8 subtraction exercises in horizontal form on the chalkboard. Include a 2-digit minus a 1-digit exercise and exercises with and without trading. Ask students to copy each exercise on a slip of paper, making sure that the tens and ones are properly aligned. Point to an exercise that involves trading. *Will a trade be necessary to find the answer?* Listen to the predictions, then do the exercise with students, saying each step aloud. Suggest that students use base-ten blocks to check their work. Repeat this activity using an exercise that does not need a trade. Then ask students to sort the remaining 6 exercises into two groups: those that need a trade and those that do not. Discuss their reasons for sorting the exercises and have them find the differences.

CONNECTIONS   Use these anytime.

Problem of the Day

Using Estimation   Ring the best estimate. Mr. Eliot invited 37 guests to lunch. Only 15 were able to come. About how many guests did not come to lunch?
  about 10 guests
  about 20 guests
  about 30 guests

Life Skills

Budgeting   You have saved 95¢. You want to buy a book that costs 45¢ and a ball that costs 39¢. Use subtraction to find out whether you can afford both of these items or only one of them. (You can afford both and have 10¢ left.)

Mental Math

Subtraction   Write the number that was subtracted.

4 8	9 5	5 1
− (4)	− (2)	− (9)
4 4	9 3	4 2

CLASSWORK AND HOMEWORK SUPPLEMENTS

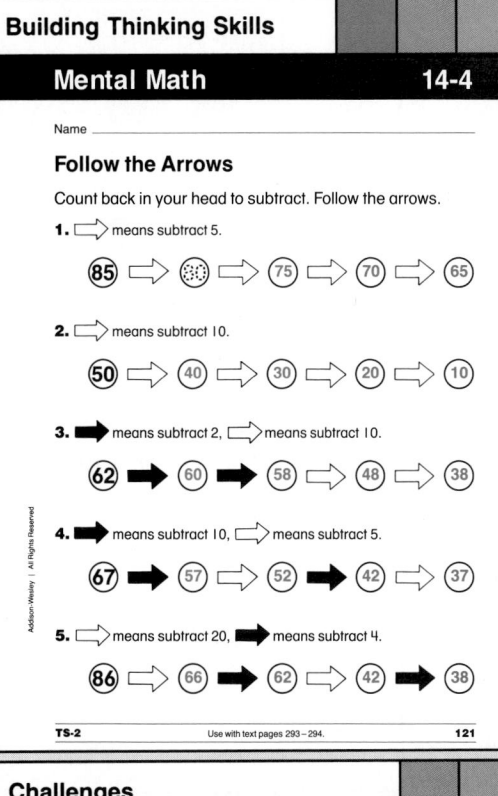

Practice

Skills Maintenance   14-4

Name _____

Subtracting 2-Digit Numbers Using Symbols

Subtract. Trade if you need to.

1.
$\begin{array}{r} {\scriptstyle 3\ \ 13} \\ 4\!\!\!/3 \\ -2\,7 \\ \hline 16 \end{array}$
$\begin{array}{r} {\scriptstyle 2\ \ 12} \\ 3\!\!\!/2 \\ -1\,6 \\ \hline 16 \end{array}$
$\begin{array}{r} {\scriptstyle \ \ } \\ 36 \\ -1\,5 \\ \hline 21 \end{array}$
$\begin{array}{r} {\scriptstyle \ \ } \\ 84 \\ -3\,3 \\ \hline 51 \end{array}$
$\begin{array}{r} {\scriptstyle 6\ \ 15} \\ 7\!\!\!/5 \\ -2\,6 \\ \hline 49 \end{array}$

2.
$\begin{array}{r} {\scriptstyle \ \ } \\ 44 \\ -1\,3 \\ \hline 31 \end{array}$
$\begin{array}{r} {\scriptstyle \ \ } \\ 83 \\ -6\,2 \\ \hline 21 \end{array}$
$\begin{array}{r} {\scriptstyle 4\ \ 14} \\ 5\!\!\!/4 \\ -2\,9 \\ \hline 25 \end{array}$
$\begin{array}{r} {\scriptstyle 5\ \ 13} \\ 6\!\!\!/3 \\ -2\,8 \\ \hline 35 \end{array}$
$\begin{array}{r} {\scriptstyle 6\ \ 10} \\ 7\!\!\!/0 \\ -4\,6 \\ \hline 24 \end{array}$

3.
$\begin{array}{r} {\scriptstyle 3\ \ 15} \\ 4\!\!\!/5 \\ -1\,7 \\ \hline 28 \end{array}$
$\begin{array}{r} {\scriptstyle 2\ \ 11} \\ 3\!\!\!/1 \\ -1\,5 \\ \hline 16 \end{array}$
$\begin{array}{r} {\scriptstyle 6\ \ 12} \\ 7\!\!\!/2 \\ -2\,4 \\ \hline 48 \end{array}$
$\begin{array}{r} {\scriptstyle \ \ } \\ 85 \\ -6\,4 \\ \hline 21 \end{array}$
$\begin{array}{r} {\scriptstyle 4\ \ 11} \\ 5\!\!\!/1 \\ -1\,6 \\ \hline 35 \end{array}$

4.
$\begin{array}{r} {\scriptstyle 7\ \ 14} \\ 8\!\!\!/4 \\ -5\,8 \\ \hline 26 \end{array}$
$\begin{array}{r} {\scriptstyle \ \ } \\ 31 \\ -1\,1 \\ \hline 20 \end{array}$
$\begin{array}{r} {\scriptstyle 3\ \ 18} \\ 4\!\!\!/8 \\ -1\,9 \\ \hline 29 \end{array}$
$\begin{array}{r} {\scriptstyle 4\ \ 10} \\ 5\!\!\!/0 \\ -3\,7 \\ \hline 13 \end{array}$
$\begin{array}{r} {\scriptstyle \ \ } \\ 96 \\ -6\,1 \\ \hline 35 \end{array}$

PS-2   Use with text pages 293–294.   121

Building Thinking Skills

Mental Math   14-4

Name _____

Follow the Arrows

Count back in your head to subtract. Follow the arrows.

1. ⇨ means subtract 5.

(85) ⇨ (80) ⇨ (75) ⇨ (70) ⇨ (65)

2. ⇨ means subtract 10.

(50) ⇨ (40) ⇨ (30) ⇨ (20) ⇨ (10)

3. ➡ means subtract 2, ⇨ means subtract 10.

(62) ➡ (60) ➡ (58) ⇨ (48) ⇨ (38)

4. ➡ means subtract 10, ⇨ means subtract 5.

(67) ➡ (57) ⇨ (52) ➡ (42) ⇨ (37)

5. ⇨ means subtract 20, ➡ means subtract 4.

(86) ⇨ (66) ➡ (62) ⇨ (42) ➡ (38)

TS-2   Use with text pages 293–294.   121

Reteaching

Skills Review   14-4

Name _____

Subtracting 2-Digit Numbers

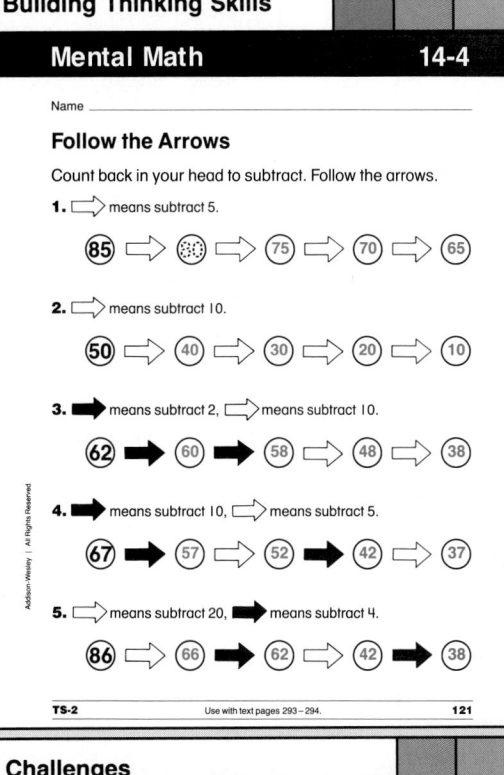

Trade	No Trade
$\begin{array}{r}{\scriptstyle 3\ \ 12}\\ 4\!\!\!/2\\ -27\\ \hline 15\end{array}$ not enough ones	$\begin{array}{r} 35\\ -12\\ \hline 23\end{array}$ 5 is greater than 2.

Do you need to trade? Ring **yes** or **no**. Then subtract.

1.
$\begin{array}{r} {\scriptstyle 4\ \ 14} \\ 5\!\!\!/4 \\ -2\,8 \\ \hline 2\,6 \end{array}$ 4 is less than 8. Trade. (yes) no
$\begin{array}{r} 43 \\ -1\,2 \\ \hline 31 \end{array}$ 3 is greater than 2. yes (no)

2.
$\begin{array}{r} 67 \\ -4\,6 \\ \hline 21 \end{array}$ 7 is greater than 6. yes (no)
$\begin{array}{r} {\scriptstyle 7\ \ 12} \\ 8\!\!\!/2 \\ -5\,3 \\ \hline 29 \end{array}$ 2 is less than 3. (yes) no

3.
$\begin{array}{r} 34 \\ -1\,2 \\ \hline 22 \end{array}$ yes (no)
$\begin{array}{r} {\scriptstyle 4\ \ 10} \\ 5\!\!\!/0 \\ -2\,2 \\ \hline 28 \end{array}$ (yes) no
$\begin{array}{r} {\scriptstyle 5\ \ 12} \\ 6\!\!\!/2 \\ -3\,8 \\ \hline 24 \end{array}$ (yes) no

RS-2   Use with text pages 293–294.   121

Challenges

Algebra   14-4

Name _____

What Is Missing?

Find the missing numbers.
See how fast you can reach the end of each path.

1. $47 - \underline{14} = 33$
   $ - \underline{13}$
   $20 - \underline{8} = 12$
   $ - \underline{6}$
   $6 - \underline{6} = 0$

2. $94 - \underline{14} = 80$
   $ - \underline{30}$
   $50 - \underline{12} = 38$
   $ - \underline{18}$
   $20 - \underline{20} = 0$

3. $64 - \underline{3} = 61$
   $ - \underline{40}$
   $21 - \underline{11} = 10$
   $ - \underline{7}$
   $3 - \underline{3} = 0$

4. Make up your own.

   ___ − ___ = ___

   $ - $ ___

   ___ − ___ = ___

   $ - $ ___

   ___ − ___ = 0

   Answers may vary.

CS-2   Use with text pages 293–294.   121

OPTIONS FOR INDIVIDUAL NEEDS

Basic

Exercises All
More Practice, p. 425, set A

Supplements
Reteaching 121 or
Practice 121
Thinking Skills 121

Average

Exercises All
More Practice, p. 425, set A

Supplements
Practice 121
Challenges 121 or
Thinking Skills 121

Extended

Exercises All

Supplements
Challenges 121
Thinking Skills 121

Other Resources:
Explorations, pp. 288-291
Developing Number Concepts With Unifix Cubes, pp. 166-167, 174

14-4

Chapter 14 Lesson 4   **293B**

OBJECTIVE 14-4
To subtract 2-digit numbers using symbols

Materials: chalk in 2 colors, TA5 (Place Value Chart)

Grouping Suggestions: individual work, pairs

1. MOTIVATE AND TEACH

LEARN ABOUT IT

Ask a student to choose two 2-digit numbers to subtract and write the exercise on the chalkboard. Have the rest of the class copy it. *Are the ones lined up? Are the tens lined up? Do you need to trade 1 ten for 10 ones?* If so, have the student at the board use a different-colored chalk to cross out the tens and ones digits and write the new numbers above. *What is the next step?* (Subtract ones, then subtract tens.) Have students read the problem at the top of page 293.

▶ **Is this an addition or a subtraction problem? How do you know?** (Possible answer: subtraction, because you need to find out how many baseballs the store has left)

▶ **Why will you rewrite the exercises in vertical form?** (Possible answers: to line up the ones and the tens; to make it easier to see if you need a trade)

▶ **What are important steps to remember when you rewrite subtraction exercises in vertical form?** (Possible answers: Copy the numbers correctly; be sure the tens and the ones are aligned.)

▶ **Describe one way you know when you need to trade.** (Possible answer: When the number in the ones column of the bottom number is greater than the number in the ones column of the top number, you need to trade.)

2. CHECK UNDERSTANDING

ERROR ALERT Incorrectly aligning ones and tens when copying exercises in vertical form.

Name _____

Subtracting 2-Digit Numbers Using Symbols

The Sport Shop had 45 baseballs.
It sold 26. How many does it have now?

Write the numbers. Line up the ones. Line up the tens.	→	Trade if you need to. Subtract the ones.	→	Subtract the tens.

$$\begin{array}{r} 45 \\ -26 \\ \hline \end{array} \qquad \begin{array}{r} {}^{3\,15} \\ \cancel{45} \\ -26 \\ \hline 9 \end{array} \qquad \begin{array}{r} {}^{3\,15} \\ \cancel{45} \\ -26 \\ \hline 19 \end{array}$$

The Sport Shop has 19 baseballs left.

Write the numbers. Do you need to trade? Ring **yes** or **no.** Then subtract.

1. 38 − 6

yes
(no)

$$\begin{array}{r} 38 \\ -\ 6 \\ \hline 32 \end{array}$$

2. 41 − 15

(yes)
no

$$\begin{array}{r} {}^{3\,11} \\ \cancel{41} \\ -15 \\ \hline 26 \end{array}$$

3. 26 − 8

(yes)
no

$$\begin{array}{r} {}^{1} \\ 2\cancel{6} \\ -\ \ \\ \hline 18 \end{array}$$

4. 39 − 7

yes
(no)

$$\begin{array}{r} 39 \\ -\ 7 \\ \hline 32 \end{array}$$

5. 24 − 17

(yes)
no

$$\begin{array}{r} {}^{1\,14} \\ \cancel{24} \\ -17 \\ \hline 7 \end{array}$$

6. 85 − 67

(yes)
no

$$\begin{array}{r} {}^{7} \\ 8\cancel{5} \\ -67 \\ \hline 18 \end{array}$$

Chapter 14   (two hundred ninety-three)   2

TEACHING OPTIONS

RETEACHING TIPS Write 42 − 1 and 42 − 10 horizontally on the board. Have students copy them vertically on place value charts. *When the number you subtract has 1 digit, where does it go?* (ones column) Solve and compare differences. Assign Reteaching Supplement 121.

COMPUTER Math Practice Level 1, IBM Educational Systems © **1985** For use with all levels. In Lesson 4, students subtract 2-digit numbers with some trading. The problems are presented vertically. In the answer, they enter the 1s digit before the 10s digit. The lesson takes 15 minutes.

Subtract. Trade if you need to.

	8 11			6 10	
87	9̷1̷	58	96	7̷0̷	53
− 24	− 64	− 5	− 46	− 8	− 21
63	27	53	50	62	32

	7 12	3 13	6 13		
66	8̷2̷	4̷3̷	7̷3̷	87	44
− 23	− 23	− 25	− 9	− 37	− 12
43	59	18	64	50	32

	4 10		2 12	1 15	
63	5̷0̷	76	3̷2̷	2̷5̷	93
− 13	− 19	− 5	− 14	− 17	− 41
50	31	71	18	8	52

5 15			7 10	2 18	
6̷5̷¢	75¢	48¢	8̷0̷¢	3̷8̷¢	79¢
− 7¢	− 25¢	− 27¢	− 15¢	− 9¢	− 18¢
58¢	50¢	21¢	65¢	29¢	61¢

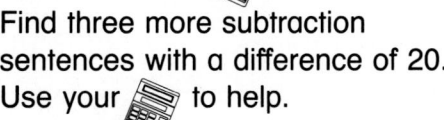

TRY A CALCULATOR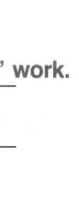

Find three more subtraction sentences with a difference of 20. Use your ▨ to help.

$$35 − 15 = 20$$
$$38 − 18 = 20$$
$$32 − 12 = 20$$

Answers may vary. Check students' work.

_____

_____

CLOSE AND ASSESS

WRITE WHAT YOU KNOW

Discuss the chapter story with students. Have them write each subtraction problem mentioned in the story. Ask partners to make sure they have lined up the tens and the ones. Have students solve the problems and trade if they need to.

QUICK QUIZ

Ring the exercise if you need to trade. Then subtract.

81 − 56 (25)	24 − 12 (12)
74 − 17 (57)	43 − 34 (9)
66 − 54 (12)	38 − 32 (6)

3. PRACTICE AND APPLY

Basic	All
Average	All
Extended	All

PRACTICE

On page 294, what is different about Exercise 4? (The exercises all have a cents sign after each number.) _Does this change the way the exercises are solved?_ (no)

APPLY

TRY A CALCULATOR ▶ **What number can you subtract from the ones digit that will always give a difference of 0?** (the same number)
▶ **What do you notice about the digit in the tens place in each exercise?** (Possible answers: They are 3 and 1. They have a difference of 2 when you subtract the tens.)
▶ **How can you use these clues to help you find more subtraction sentences with a difference of 20?** (Possible answer: Make sure the ones digits are the same number and the first tens digit is greater than the second tens digit by 2.)

14-4

Estimating Differences

OBJECTIVE 14-5   To estimate differences using front-end estimation

PREBOOK ACTIVITIES

Find the sums.

32	43	19	47	56	8
+25	+ 8	+50	+52	+23	+51
(57)	(51)	(69)	(99)	(79)	(59)

PRIOR KNOWLEDGE

Pose a situation such as the following to help students recall estimating sums: *Karen has 22 marbles. Brian has 31 marbles. When they add their marbles, do they have about 40, 50, or 60 marbles?* (about 50) *How did you figure that out?* (by adding 2 tens and 3 tens, or 20 and 30) *Is this the exact amount or an estimate?* (an estimate)

COMMUNICATION

Discussing and Listening in Math   Discuss the idea that sometimes we need to know the exact difference, and other times we can get the information we need just by estimating the difference. Read the following situations aloud. Have students tell whether the exact amount is needed or an estimate is enought.
1. Maria sold lemonade for 25 cents a glass at her stand. A woman gave Maria a half dollar and asked for 1 glass. How much change should Maria give her? (exact amount)
2. Paul had 75 cents. He bought a pack of baseball cards for 20 cents. About how much does he have left? (estimate)

Materials: base-ten blocks
Grouping Suggestion: pairs
Provide each pairs with crayons, paper, and base-ten blocks. Have each student draw a picture of a piece of sports equipment and put a price tag on it of $25, $33, $47, or $53. Have them use base-ten blocks to show the number of tens in the dollar prices. *How can partners estimate the total cost of their two items?* (by adding tens) Ask partners to use their ten blocks to estimate the difference in price between their two items. *How did you find out?* (by subtracting the tens) *How is this kind of estimating different from finding the exact amount* (You subtract only the tens digits; to find the exact amount, you subtract the ones, then tens.) Have a pair of students wor with another pair, using all 4 pictures to create other problem and estimate differences. Encourage them to summarize and check with others for agreement and understanding.

CONNECTIONS   Use these anytime.

Problem of the Day

Guess and Check   Estimate the difference. Then solve to check.
83 people were at the game.
When it began to rain, some people went home.
Now only 24 people are left.
About how many people went home? (60)
Exactly how many people went home? (59)

Math Connection

Calculator   Choose two numbers under 90. Write a subtraction sentence. Subtract the tens to estimate the difference. Now subtract the numbers on the calculator. How close was your estimate? (Answers will vary.)

Number Sense

Estimation   Use place value models. Which problems have a difference of about 40?
1. 90 − 52   **2.** 82 − 34   **3.** 76 − 32
4. 68 − 43   **5.** 69 − 26   **6.** 44 − 11
7. 55 − 12   **8.** 88 − 45   **9.** 73 − 51
(1, 3, 5, 7, 8)

CLASSWORK AND HOMEWORK SUPPLEMENTS

OPTIONS FOR INDIVIDUAL NEEDS

Basic

Exercises All
Computer Bank, p. 407
More Practice, p. 425, set B

Supplements
Reteaching 122 or
Practice 122
Challenges 122

Average

Exercises All
Computer Bank, p. 407
More Practice, p. 425, set B

Supplements
Practice 122
Challenges 122 or
Thinking Skills 122

Extended

Exercises All
Computer Bank, p. 407

Supplements
Challenges 122
Thinking Skills 122

Other Resources:
Exploration, p. 293
Developing Number Concepts With Unifix Cubes, p. 174

14-5

Practice

Estimation 14-5

Name

Estimating Differences

Estimate the difference.

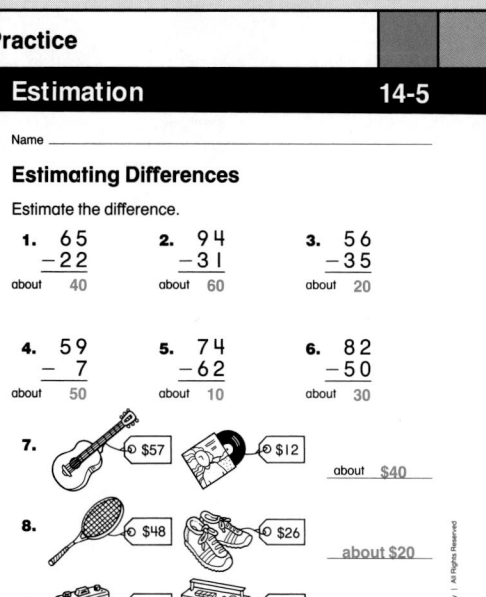

1. 65
   −22
   about 40

2. 94
   −31
   about 60

3. 56
   −35
   about 20

4. 59
   − 7
   about 50

5. 74
   −62
   about 10

6. 82
   −50
   about 30

7. $57 $12   about $40

8. $48 $26   about $20

9. $99 $47   about $50

10. $45 $11   about $30

122   Use with text pages 295 – 296.   PS-2

Building Thinking Skills

Estimation 14-5

Name

Make a Difference!

Ring the two numbers whose difference is close to the number given.

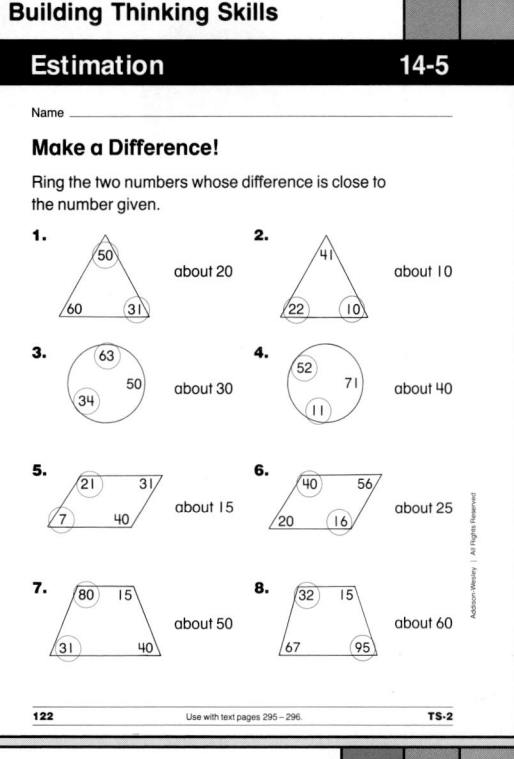

1. 50 60 31   about 20

2. 41 22 10   about 10

3. 63 34 50   about 30

4. 52 71 11   about 40

5. 21 31 7 40   about 15

6. 40 56 20 16   about 25

7. 80 15 31 40   about 50

8. 32 15 67 95   about 60

122   Use with text pages 295 – 296.   TS-2

Reteaching

Estimation 14-5

Name

Estimating Differences

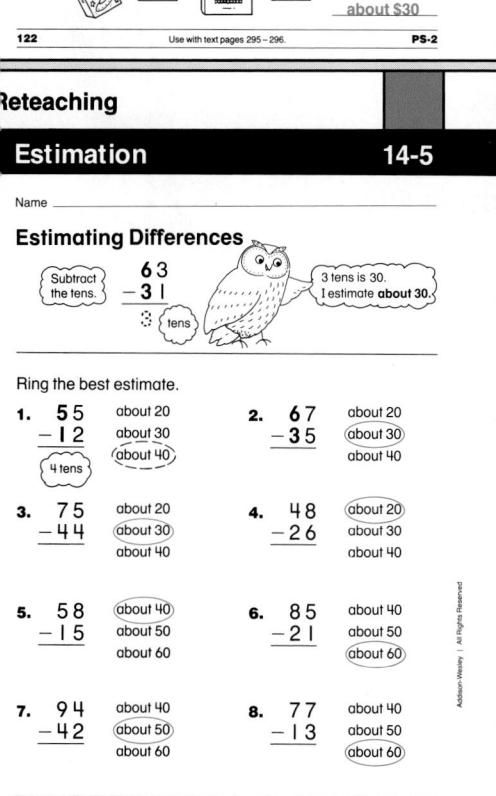

Subtract the tens.
 63
−31
 ∷ tens

3 tens is 30. I estimate **about 30.**

Ring the best estimate.

1. 55
   −12
   about 20
   about 30
   (about 40)
   4 tens

2. 67
   −35
   about 20
   (about 30)
   about 40

3. 75
   −44
   about 20
   (about 30)
   about 40

4. 48
   −26
   (about 20)
   about 30
   about 40

5. 58
   −15
   (about 40)
   about 50
   about 60

6. 85
   −21
   about 40
   about 50
   (about 60)

7. 94
   −42
   about 40
   (about 50)
   about 60

8. 77
   −13
   about 40
   about 50
   (about 60)

122   Use with text pages 295 – 296.   RS-2

Challenges

Math Reasoning 14-5

Name

Make a Problem

Choose a number to go in the box.
Answers will vary. Possible answers given.

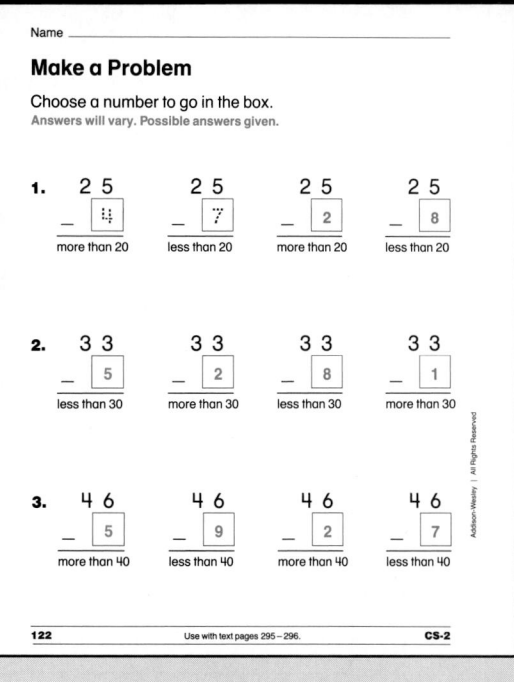

1. 25
   − 4
   more than 20

   25
   − 7
   less than 20

   25
   − 2
   more than 20

   25
   − 8
   less than 20

2. 33
   − 5
   less than 30

   33
   − 2
   more than 30

   33
   − 8
   less than 30

   33
   − 1
   more than 30

3. 46
   − 5
   more than 40

   46
   − 9
   less than 40

   46
   − 2
   more than 40

   46
   − 7
   less than 40

122   Use with text pages 295 – 296.   CS-2

LESSON PLAN 14-5

OBJECTIVE 14-5
To estimate differences using front-end estimation

> **Materials:** base-ten blocks, Cube-A-Links, number cubes labeled 1-6 and 4-9

1. MOTIVATE AND TEACH

LEARN ABOUT IT

Write the subtraction sentence $64 − $32 on the chalkboard. Have students model the numbers at their desks with base-ten blocks. Ask them to estimate whether the answer will be closer to $10, $30, or $50. ($30) *How did you figure that out?* (by subtracting the tens) Have students look at the problem at the top of page 295.

▶ **Why do you subtract the first digits to estimate a difference?** (The tens have a higher place value than the ones, so subtracting them gives the closest estimate.)

▶ **How can estimating the difference help you find the actual difference?** (The estimated difference can tell you whether or not the actual difference is reasonable.)

▶ **Why are $20 and $30 not good estimates for the problem?** (Both estimates are too low, because 6 tens − 2 tens is 4 tens, or $40.)

▶ **How can you check to see if your estimate is close to the actual difference?** (Possible answers: Subtract the actual numbers; use a calculator to subtract.)

2. CHECK UNDERSTANDING

ERROR ALERT Subtracting the ones instead of the tens to find the estimated differences.

Name _____

Estimating Differences

About how much more money does the helmet cost than the football?

> Look at the first digits.
> 6 tens − 2 tens = 4 tens
> I estimate $40.

about $20
about $30
about $40

$64 − $21

The helmet costs about $40 more.
Ring the best estimate.

			Estimate
1.	pads	pants	about $20
			about $30
	$36 − $13		about $40
2.	shoes	pants	about $20
			about $30
	$55 − $13		about $40
3.	shoes	football	about $20
			about $30
	$55 − $21		about $40

4. Check to see if your estimate is close to the difference.

TEACHING OPTIONS

RETEACHING TIPS Have students use cubes to model a number such as 86. Ask them to estimate 86 − 25 by taking 2 tens away and telling how many tens are left. (6) Explain that 6 tens, or 60, is the *estimated* difference. Assign Reteaching Supplement 122.

ENRICHMENT Write *About 20, About 30, About 40,* and *About 50* on the board. Display subtraction exercises similar to those on page 295. Have students choose which category the answer to each exercise fits.

ng the best estimate.
olor the box to match.

about 40 about 50 about 60

red 75 − 21	blue 84 − 42	blue 63 − 25	red 82 − 34
about 40 (about 50) about 60	(about 40) about 50 about 60	(about 40) about 50 about 60	about 40 (about 50) about 60
yellow 91 − 33	red 67 − 18	red 96 − 42	yellow 78 − 15
about 40 about 50 (about 60)	about 40 (about 50) about 60	about 40 (about 50) about 60	about 40 about 50 (about 60)
red 86 − 33	blue 76 − 38	blue 59 − 16	red 91 − 43
about 40 (about 50) about 60	(about 40) about 50 about 60	(about 40) about 50 about 60	about 40 (about 50) about 60

Ring the color pattern above.

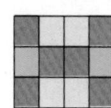 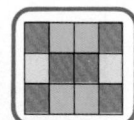 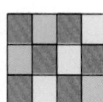

SE MENTAL MATH

ubtract. Count back by tens. Use mental math.

$35 - 10 = \underline{25}$ $27 - 10 = \underline{17}$ $42 - 20 = \underline{22}$

$53 - 20 = \underline{33}$ $56 - 30 = \underline{26}$ $71 - 30 = \underline{41}$

LOSE AND ASSESS

RITE WHAT YOU KNOW

view with students the chapter
ry, *Baseball Business. About how
ny balls did Joey have left after he
de his sale to Rachel?* Have
dents write the subtraction sentence
d solve it. ($31 - 18 = 13$) Have
m use blocks to help them trade 1
 for 10 ones.

QUICK QUIZ

Estimate each difference.

$65 - 42$ (20)	$87 - 79$ (10)
$41 - 15$ (30)	$76 - 38$ (40)
$94 - 27$ (70)	$62 - 13$ (50)

3. PRACTICE AND APPLY

Basic	All
Average	All
Extended	All

PRACTICE

Call students' attention to Exercises 1-3
on page 296. *How can you find the best
estimate for each difference?* (Subtract
the numbers in the tens place.)

APPLY

USE MENTAL MATH ▶ **How is
counting back by tens like estimating
differences?** (You are subtracting tens.)
▶ **How can you check to see if your
answers are correct?** (Possible
answers: Use a calculator; do the
subtraction; add to check.)
▶ **Will you find the exact difference
or an estimate in these exercises?
Why?** (an exact difference, because you
are subtracting a round number, or a
number with zero ones)

14-5

Adding to Check Subtraction

OBJECTIVE 14-6   To add to check subtraction

PREBOOK ACTIVITIES

Write the number sentences for each fact family.

6, 7, 13	8, 6, 14	9, 8, 17
(6 + 7 = 13)	(8 + 6 = 14)	(9 + 8 = 17)
(7 + 6 = 13)	(6 + 8 = 14)	(8 + 9 = 17)
(13 − 7 = 6)	(14 − 8 = 6)	(17 − 8 = 9)
(13 − 6 = 7)	(14 − 6 = 8)	(17 − 9 = 8)

PRIOR KNOWLEDGE

Ask a student to subtract 16 − 7. (9) *What addition fact can be used to check the subtraction?*   (7 + 9 = 16) Write the subtraction expression 82 − 24 vertically on the chalkboard and ask a volunteer to solve it. (58) *What numbers can we add to check the subtraction?* (24 + 58) Have a student write the add-to-check sentence on the chalkboard and solve. *Does the sum match the first number in the subtraction sentence?* (yes) *Can addition be used to check subtraction with larger numbers?* (yes)

COMMUNICATION

Discussing and Listening in Math   Read the following sentences to students. Ask them to show thumbs up if the sentence is true and thumbs down if the sentence is false. Ask students how they would make the false statement true.
1. You can write the addends in an addition sentence in any order.   (true)
2. You can write the numbers in a subtraction sentence in any order.   (False; you must write the greater number first.)
3. The add-to-check sentence should have exactly the same numbers as the subtraction sentence it is checking.   (true)

Materials: 2 blue and 2 yellow index cards for each group; Cube-A-Links
Grouping Suggestion: cooperative learning groups of 4
Ask one pair of students in the group to write two 2-digit numbers greater than 50 on the blue index cards. Have the other pair of students write two 2-digit numbers less than 50 on the yellow index cards. Have the groups find, write, and solve as many different subtraction problems as they can using 1 blue card and 1 yellow card each time. Remind them to start with the number on the blue card (the greater number). Have students check the subtraction by modeling with cubes. Then have them add the difference to the number on the yellow card. *Is the sum the same as the number on the blue card? Why?* (The sum in an addition sentence and the first number in a subtraction sentence both stand for the whole.) Encourage students to summarize what they did.

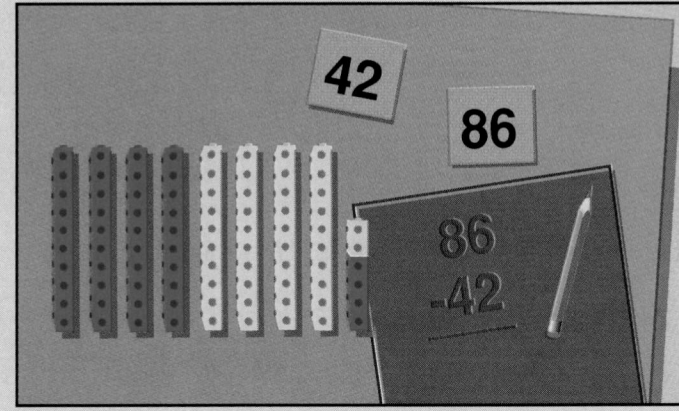

CONNECTIONS   Use these anytime.

Problem of the Day

Make a Table   Andy practiced running around the track. Each day he ran 4 s faster than the day before. Finish the table.

Day 1	Day 2	Day 3	Day 4	Day 5
54	50	(46)	(42)	(38)

How much faster did Andy run Day 5 than on Day 1? (16 s)

Minute Math

Subtraction   Subtract, then compare answers with a partner. Add to check any answers that do not match.

47	82	54	35	77	68
−16	−36	−49	−21	−38	−55
(31)	(46)	(5)	(14)	(39)	(13)

Life Skills

Following Directions   Imagine that you are driving to Deer Lake. These are the directions: Drive west on Route 7 for 34 mi. Go south on Highway 2 for 21 mi. Go east on Deer Road for 12 mi. You have driven 60 mi so far. Which road are you on? (Deer Road) How do you know? (60 is more than 34 + 21, so you must be on Deer Road.)

CLASSWORK AND HOMEWORK SUPPLEMENTS

Practice

Skills Maintenance   14-6

Name _____

Adding to Check Subtraction

Subtract. Then check by adding.

1.
$$\overset{6\ 16}{\cancel{7}\cancel{6}} \over -58$$ 18 +58 18 76

2.
$$\overset{7\ 11}{\cancel{8}\cancel{1}} \over -46$$ 35 +46 35 81

3.
$$59 \over -12$$ 47 +12 47 59

4.
$$\overset{8\ 10}{\cancel{9}0} \over -45$$ 45 +45 45 90

5.
$$\overset{4\ 13}{\cancel{5}\cancel{3}} \over -38$$ 15 +38 15 53

6.
$$\overset{6\ 12}{\cancel{7}\cancel{2}} \over -\ 7$$ 65 +7 65 72

7.
$$\overset{4\ 12}{\cancel{5}\cancel{2}} \over -29$$ 23 +29 23 52

8.
$$\overset{5\ 11}{\cancel{6}\cancel{1}} \over -13$$ 48 +13 48 61

9.
$$\overset{7\ 15}{\cancel{8}\cancel{5}} \over -66$$ 19 +66 19 85

10.
$$\overset{4\ 13}{\cancel{5}\cancel{3}} \over -17$$ 36 +17 36 53

11.
$$68 \over -22$$ 46 +22 46 68

12.
$$\overset{7\ 12}{\cancel{8}\cancel{2}} \over -55$$ 27 +55 27 82

PS-2   Use with text pages 297 – 298.   123

Building Thinking Skills

Family Math   14-6

Name _____

Magic Squares

> Dear Family,
> Your child has been learning how to add to check subtraction. Work with your child on these addition-subtraction boxes to develop this skill.

Finish each box by subtracting and adding.
Subtract and add in the directions shown by the arrows.
Then check.   The first one has been done for you.

1.
26	15	11
17	12	5
9	3	6

2.
| 42 | 11 |
| 20 | 9 |

3.
| | 30 | 35 |
| 30 | | 15 |

4.
79		
	4	
54	32	

5.
	48	
53	32	
39		

6. Try your own!

Answers:

2. 42|11|31, 3. 65|30|35, 4. 79|53|26, 5. 92|48|44
20|9|11, 6|11|5, 5|15|20, 25|21|4, 53|32|21
22|0|22, 35|15|20, 54|32|22, 39|16|23

TS-2   Use with text pages 297 – 298.   123

Reteaching

Skills Review   14-6

Name _____

Adding to Check Subtraction

Total ← 6 4
Part ← − 4 1
Part ← 2 3   It checks!

2 3 → Part
+ 4 1 → Part
6 4 → Total

Subtract. Then add to check.

1.
$$59 \over -38$$ 21 +38
21 59

2.
$$\overset{5\ 10}{\cancel{6}0} \over -24$$ 36 +24
36 60

3.
$$\overset{6\ 15}{\cancel{7}\cancel{5}} \over -59$$ 16 +59
16 75

4.
$$\overset{1\ 13}{2\cancel{3}} \over -\ 6$$ 17 +6
17 23

5.
$$46 \over -21$$ 25 +21
25 46

6.
$$\overset{7\ 14}{8\cancel{4}} \over -36$$ 48 +36
48 84

RS-2   Use with text pages 297 – 298.   123

Challenges

Cooperative Activity   14-6

Name _____

Check It Out!

Work with a friend.
Your friend chooses a number.
You subtract, then add as shown below to get the
same number. Take turns.   **Answers will vary.**

1. Choose a number greater than 50. ___

   Subtract 20. ___

   Add 10. ___   Are these numbers the same?

   Add 10. ___

2. Choose a number greater than 30. ___

   Subtract 10. ___

   Add 5. ___

   Add 5. ___

3. Choose a number greater than 40. ___

   Subtract 18. ___

   Add 6. ___

   Add 6. ___

   Add 6. ___

4. Make up your own with your friend.

CS-2   Use with text pages 297 – 298.   123

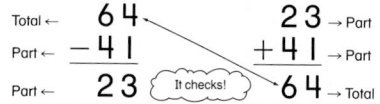

OPTIONS FOR INDIVIDUAL NEEDS

Basic

Exercises All, Midchapter
Review/Quiz
Computer Bank, p. 406

Supplements
Reteaching 123 or
Practice 123
Challenges 123

Average

Exercises All, Midchapter
Review/Quiz
Computer Bank, p. 406

Supplements
Practice 123
Challenges 123 or
Thinking Skills 123

Extended

Exercises All, Midchapter
Review/Quiz
Computer Bank, p. 406

Supplements
Challenges 123
Thinking Skills 123

Other Resources:
Explorations, pp. 278-283,
289-293
Math Book A, p. 28

14-6

OBJECTIVE 14-6
To add to check subtraction

Materials: base-ten blocks,
Cube-A-Links, TA 4
(Addition/Subtraction Mat)

Grouping Suggestions: individual
work, pairs

1. MOTIVATE AND TEACH

LEARN ABOUT IT

Write a 2-digit subtraction exercise on
the chalkboard and ask students to find
the difference using base-ten blocks.
Have a volunteer write the add-to-check
exercise that matches the subtraction as
students use base-ten blocks to find the
sum.
▶ **Which number must you write in
the top box each time? Why?** (the
number on the blue card, because it is
greater than the number on the yellow
card)
▶ **Why do the numbers in the blue
boxes match for each exercise?** (They
are the numbers that tell the whole.)
▶ **How can you use the add-to-check
exercise to correct an error in a
subtraction exercise?** (Compare the
sum of the add-to-check exercise with
the first number in the subtraction
exercise. If it does not match, the
subtraction must be repeated. Use the
sum of the add-to-check exercise to
guess how you will need to change the
subtraction.)

2. CHECK UNDERSTANDING

ERROR ALERT Subtracting
incorrectly. Writing the add-to-check
exercise incorrectly.

Name _____

Adding to Check Subtraction

Work in a group. Pick a blue card and
a yellow card. Write the numbers.
Find their difference. Then check
by adding. Find as many different ways
to subtract as you can. Order of answers may vary.

44	53	62
25	32	
		17

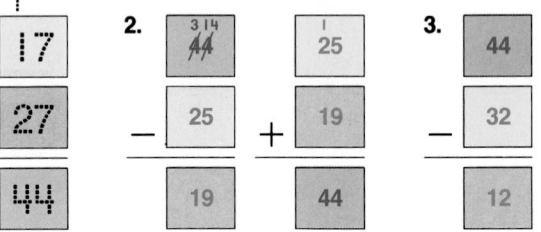

1.
$$\begin{array}{r}{}^{3}\!\!\not{4}\,{}^{14}\!\!\not{4}\\-\ 17\\\hline 27\end{array}\qquad\begin{array}{r}{}^{1}\!\!\not{1}\,7\\+\ 27\\\hline 44\end{array}$$

2.
$$\begin{array}{r}{}^{3}\!\!\not{4}\,{}^{14}\\-\ 25\\\hline 19\end{array}\qquad\begin{array}{r}25\\+\ 19\\\hline 44\end{array}$$

3.
$$\begin{array}{r}44\\-\ 32\\\hline 12\end{array}\qquad\begin{array}{r}32\\+\ 12\\\hline 44\end{array}$$

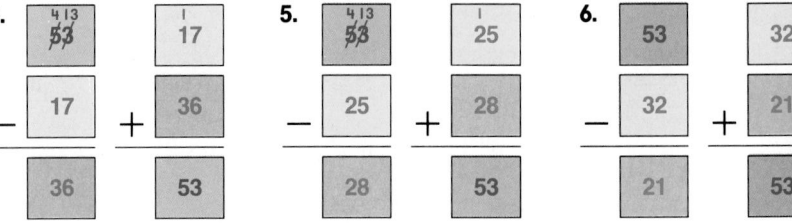

4.
$$\begin{array}{r}{}^{4}\!\!\not{5}\,{}^{13}\!\!\not{3}\\-\ 17\\\hline 36\end{array}\qquad\begin{array}{r}17\\+\ 36\\\hline 53\end{array}$$

5.
$$\begin{array}{r}{}^{4}\!\!\not{5}\,{}^{13}\!\!\not{3}\\-\ 25\\\hline 28\end{array}\qquad\begin{array}{r}25\\+\ 28\\\hline 53\end{array}$$

6.
$$\begin{array}{r}53\\-\ 32\\\hline 21\end{array}\qquad\begin{array}{r}32\\+\ 21\\\hline 53\end{array}$$

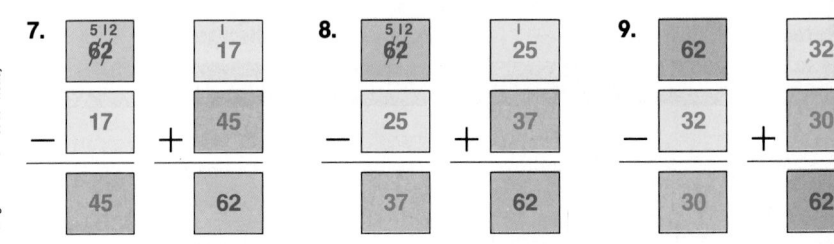

7.
$$\begin{array}{r}{}^{5}\!\!\not{6}\,{}^{12}\!\!\not{2}\\-\ 17\\\hline 45\end{array}\qquad\begin{array}{r}17\\+\ 45\\\hline 62\end{array}$$

8.
$$\begin{array}{r}{}^{5}\!\!\not{6}\,{}^{12}\!\!\not{2}\\-\ 25\\\hline 37\end{array}\qquad\begin{array}{r}25\\+\ 37\\\hline 62\end{array}$$

9.
$$\begin{array}{r}62\\-\ 32\\\hline 30\end{array}\qquad\begin{array}{r}32\\+\ 30\\\hline 62\end{array}$$

Chapter 14

(two hundred ninety-seven) 29

TEACHING OPTIONS

RETEACHING TIPS Write 86
− 45 on the chalkboard and ask
students to find the difference using
cubes. (41) Next, have students join
cubes to add the parts as you write
the add-to-check exercise and
identify the whole and the parts in
each exercise. Assign Reteaching
Supplement 123.

ENRICHMENT **Family Math**
Have parents gather small objects
and put price tags of between 10¢
and 40¢ on them. Have them give
the student coins between 50¢ and
90¢. The student buys an item,
subtracts to find the change, then
writes an addition sentence to check.
Repeat with other items.

Subtract. Match the add-to-check
exercise. Then add.

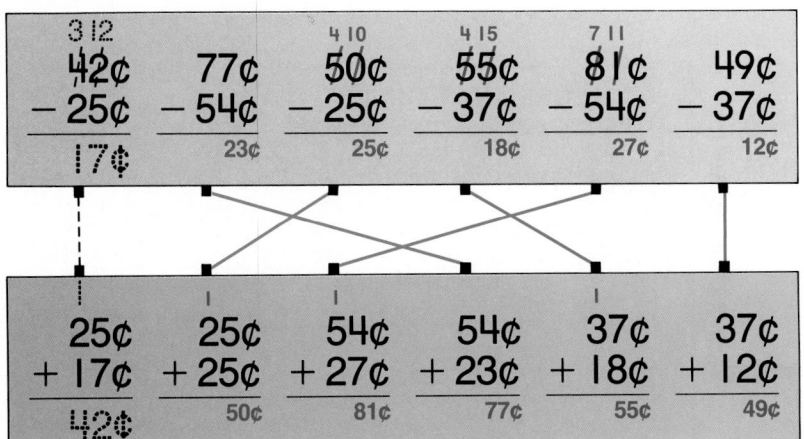

MIDCHAPTER REVIEW/QUIZ

Trade 1 ten for 10 ones.
Write the numbers.

Tens	Ones	Tens	Ones
5	13	8	10

6̸   3̸   9̸   0̸

2. Cross out to subtract.

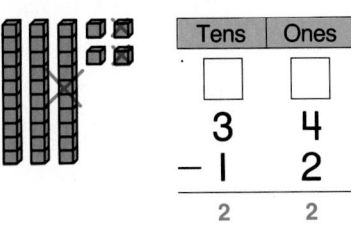

	Tens	Ones
	☐	☐
	3	4
−	1	2
	2	2

Subtract.

6 15
7̸5̸
− 26
49

19
− 7
12

3 14
4̸4̸
− 17
27

4. Ring the best estimate.

$56
− 29

(about $30)
about $40
about $50

---

3. PRACTICE AND APPLY

Basic	All; Midchapter Review/Quiz
Average	All; Midchapter Review/Quiz
Extended	All; Midchapter Review/Quiz

PRACTICE

*How will you know which add-to-check
exercise matches after you subtract?*
(The two *parts* in each exercise will
match.)

APPLY

▶ **If you need to trade 1 ten for 10
ones to solve a subtraction exercise,
what do you know about the
add-to-check exercise?** (You will have
to trade 10 ones for 1 ten.)

MIDCHAPTER REVIEW/QUIZ

ITEM ANALYSIS   The following
table correlates the Midchapter
Review/Quiz items with lesson
objectives.

Items	Objectives
1	14-1
2	14-3
3	14-4
4	14-5

14-6

CLOSE AND ASSESS

SHOW WHAT YOU KNOW

Remind students of the events that
took place in the chapter story. Have
partners work together to solve the
subtraction problems from the story
and then use addition to check their
answers. Problems include 31 − 15,
31 − 23, and 31 − 18.

QUICK QUIZ

Subtract. Then add to check.
78 (46)   53 (27)   62 (48)
−46 (+32) −27 (+26) −48 (+14)
(32) (78) (26) (53) (14) (62)

Problem Solving: Understanding the Operations/Calculator

OBJECTIVE 14-7 To understand the operation of subtraction by finding how many more are needed; to use a

PREBOOK ACTIVITIES

QUICK REVIEW

Subtract. Trade if you need to.

1.
69	81	96	65	43	72
−33	−35	−84	−29	−16	−34
(36)	(46)	(12)	(36)	(27)	(38)

2. 81 − 63 = (18)   56 − 34 = (22)

PRIOR KNOWLEDGE

Present the following situation to students. *Tony has 25¢. He wants to buy a ball that costs 79¢. What question could you ask about this situation?* (Possible answer: How much more money does Tony need?) *How could you find the answer to your question?* (Subtract.)

COMMUNICATION

Discussing Math *Suppose that I ask you how many more paper cups I need to buy for a party. What data do I already know? What data do I want to know?* (Possible answer: You know how many people are coming and how many cups you have. You want to know how many cups you need.) Write the following exercises on the chalkboard: 14 − 7 = 7, 4 − 2 = 2, 8 − 4 = 4, 16 − 8 = 8. *How are these subtraction facts alike?* (They are all doubles facts.) *What is a doubles fact?* (one in which the 2 parts are the same) *Name some other doubles facts you know.* (Possible answers: 6 − 3 = 3; 12 − 6 = 6; 18 − 9 = 9; 10 − 5 = 5)

EXPLORE AND CONNECT

COOPERATIVE ACTIVITY

Grouping Suggestion: small groups
Jay wants a book that costs $24.
He has $18.
How much more money does he need?

TEACHING ACTIONS

BEFORE ▶ **What is this problem about? What does it ask you?** (Possible answer: A boy does not have enough money to buy something; he has to find out how much more money he needs.)

▶ **What data do you know? What data are you trying to find?** (Possible answer: You know the total number or the co of the book is $24 and one part, the money Jay has, is $18. You are trying to find the other part, the money Jay needs.)

DURING ▶ **How could you use cubes to show the data to solve this problem?** (Possible answer: Use 2 cubes to show the total amount Jay needs. Set apart 18 of the cubes to show how much money he has. The number of cubes remaining is how much more money he needs.)

AFTER ▶ **How can you check your answer by drawing a picture?** (Possible answer: Draw 24 dollar signs and circle 18 to see how many more dollars you need.)

Have small groups of students work together using cubes to solve other story problems like the one on this page.

CONNECTIONS Use these anytime.

Problem of the Day
Understanding the Operation
Solve. Use cubes to help. Write the answer in a sentence.
43 students are needed to fill the bus. There are 26 students already on the bus. How many more students are needed to fill the bus?
(17 more students)

Subject Integration
Physical Education Have everyone stand behind a line in the gym or on the playground. Ask a classmate to call out a number between 1 and 9. When you hear the number, double it and take that many steps. Change the game by changing the size of the steps. Take turns being the caller.

Minute Math
How Many More Riddle Read the riddle and tell how many more.
I am an even number between 1 and 5. If you double me I am 8. I want to be added to a second number to make 10. What number am I and how many more do I need to make 10? (4, 6)

lculator to find differences

CLASSWORK AND HOMEWORK SUPPLEMENTS

Practice

Calculators 14-7

Name _____

Calculator

Use your 🖩.

Find a number to subtract so that the difference is that same number.
Cross out each number you use.

20	42	26
31	25	27
49	19	48
24	18	37
11	36	22

1.

22 − 11 = 11	38 − 19 = 19	40 − 20 = 20	54 − 27 = 27

2.

96 − 48 = 48	62 − 31 = 31	84 − 42 = 42	72 − 36 = 36

3.

44 − 22 = 22	52 − 26 = 26	74 − 37 = 37	98 − 49 = 49

124   Use with text page 300.   PS-2

Building Thinking Skills

Math Reasoning 14-7

Name _____

Play Ball!

Kim, Jim, and Tim need new sports equipment.
Read the clues to find out what each one will buy.
Write the answer in the sentence.
Then find out how much more money each one needs.

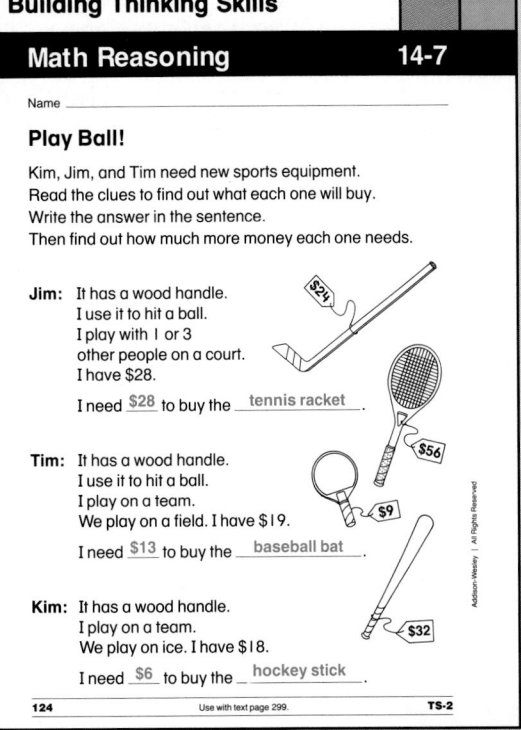

Jim: It has a wood handle.
I use it to hit a ball.
I play with 1 or 3
other people on a court.
I have $28.

I need $28 to buy the __tennis racket__

Tim: It has a wood handle.
I use it to hit a ball.
I play on a team.
We play on a field. I have $19.

I need $13 to buy the __baseball bat__

Kim: It has a wood handle.
I play on a team.
We play on ice. I have $18.

I need $6 to buy the __hockey stick__

124   Use with text page 299.   TS-2

Reteaching

Problem Solving 14-7

Name _____

Understanding the Operations

Write the number sentences. Solve.
Then write the answer in a sentence.

1. Sam's dad gave him 32 lessons on how to ride
a bike. Shoshana had only 13 lessons. How many
more lessons did Sam have?

You know: Sam's lessons = 32
Shoshana's lessons = 13

You need to find how many more Sam had.
Subtract.

$$32 - 13 = 19$$

Sam had 19 more lessons.

2. Juan's dad gave him 15 lessons on flying a kite.
Ricardo's dad gave him 31 lessons.
How many more lessons did Ricardo have?

$$31 \bigcirc 15 = 16$$

Ricardo had 16 more lessons.

124   Use with text page 299.   RS-2

Challenges

Cooperative Activities 14-7

Name _____

Shape Race

You need a friend, 2 🖩, and 2 number cubes labeled 1 to 6.

Take turns. Roll the 2 number cubes twice.
Write two 2-digit numbers. Subtract the smaller from the greater number.
If the difference is between 0 – 20, write the subtraction sentence

in the ◯

If the difference is between 21 – 30, write the subtraction sentence

in the △

If the difference is between 31 – 55, write the subtraction sentence

in the ▢

The first player to fill all 3 shapes wins.

Hint: Decide which shape you want to fill, then think about what
the difference should be. Use your 🖩 to check.

124   Use with text page 300.   CS-2

Exercises All
Calculator Bank, p. 403

Supplements
Reteaching 124 or
Practice 124

Average

Exercises All
Calculator Bank, p. 403

Supplements
Practice 124
Challenges 124 or
Thinking Skills 124

14-7

Extended

Exercises All
Calculator Bank, p. 403

Supplements
Challenges 124
Thinking Skills 124

Other Resources:
Explorations, pp. 292-293,
296-299
*Problem Solving Experiences
In Mathematics,* pp. 123, 129,
147, 159
*Developing Number Concepts
With Unifix Cubes,* pp.
167-169, 174-175

LESSON PLAN 14-7

OBJECTIVE 14-7

To understand the operation of subtraction by finding how many more are needed; to use a calculator to find differences

Materials: base-ten blocks, calculators

1. MOTIVATE AND TEACH

LEARN ABOUT IT

 **BEFORE** ▶ **What do you know about the data in Exercise 1?** (Possible answer: 25 students want to go to a show, but they only have 17 tickets. You need to find out how many more tickets they need.)
▶ **How do you know whether to add or subtract?** (You need to know a part, or how much more, so you subtract.)

 **DURING** ▶ **What action could you show with your blocks to solve this problem?**
(Possible answer: Take away the number they have from the number they want.)

 **AFTER** ▶ **How can you use blocks to check your answer?** (Possible answer: Add the number needed to the number they have to see if it equals the number they want.)

2. CHECK UNDERSTANDING

ERROR ALERT **Page 299** Not understanding which operation to use.
Page 300 Forgetting that the difference must be equal to the number subtracted.

Name _____

Problem Solving
Understanding the Operations

UNDERSTAND
FIND DATA
PLAN
ESTIMATE
SOLVE
CHECK

Solve. Use blocks to help.
Write the answer in a sentence.
Word sentences may vary. Sample answers are shown.

1. 25 students want to see the ice show. They have 17 tickets already. How many more tickets do they need?

   They need 8 more tickets

2. The total cost of the tickets is $50. The students have $22. How much more money do they need?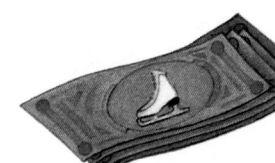

   They need $28 more.

3. One student wants to buy a book about the ice show. It costs 75¢. She has 50¢ in her pocket. How much more money does she need?

   She needs 25¢ more.

TEACHING OPTIONS

RETEACHING TIPS Give students doubles subtraction facts to solve by modeling with base ten blocks. When they understand that the number being subtracted and the difference are the same, have them model doubles subtraction using larger numbers. Assign Reteaching Supplement 124.

ENRICHMENT Have students use their calculators to answer the following questions:
1. What number doubled is 50? (25)
2. What number doubled is 76? (38)
3. Choose 4 other numbers to double. Are the sums odd or even? (even)

:alculator

se your 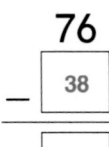. Find a number ▸ subtract so that the difference ◂ that same number. Cross ut each number you use.

~~15~~	~~21~~	~~29~~	~~36~~
16	~~23~~	~~30~~	~~38~~
~~17~~	~~24~~	~~32~~	~~45~~
18	~~25~~	~~34~~	~~46~~
19	~~28~~	~~35~~	47

```
  48            56            60            30
- [24]        - [28]        - [30]        - [15]
  [24]          [28]          [30]          [15]

  34            42            50            72
- [17]        - [21]        - [25]        - [36]
  [17]          [21]          [25]          [36]

  58            70            64            90
- [29]        - [35]        - [32]        - [45]
  [29]          [35]          [32]          [45]

  76            68            92            46
- [38]        - [34]        - [46]        - [23]
  [38]          [34]          [46]          [23]
```

3. PRACTICE AND APPLY

Basic	All
Average	All
Extended	All

Which keys will you press on your calculator to solve the first exercise in Row 1? (Press 48, −, 24, = in that order to show the answer 24.) *Count the number of exercises and the numbers in the box. Will you use all of the numbers in the box?* (no) *How will you show if you have used a number?* (Cross it out.)

▶ **How will the numbers you write in the boxes be similar for each exercise?** (Possible answer: The 2 numbers in each exercise will be the same; the numbers will be doubles.)

▶ **How can you use the numbers in the box at the top of the page to help you solve the problems?** (Possible answer: Use your calculator to subtract each one from the top number in an exercise until you find a number that has its double as the answer.)

▶ **What do you notice about all the numbers that you subtract from on this page? How are they alike?** (Possible answer: They all end in 0, 2, 4, 6, or 8. They are even numbers.)

14-7

CLOSE AND ASSESS

SHOW WHAT YOU KNOW Ask .mall groups of students to write a .ory problem similar to the ones on .age 299. Have them model the action ith base-ten blocks and write a .umber sentence to tell how many .ore are needed. Then have them .hoose 2-digit even numbers and use .eir calculators to create exercises .ke those on page 300.

QUICK QUIZ

Solve. Use blocks to help. The total cost of a coat is $35. Brad has $24. How much more money does he need? ($11)

Subtraction Patterns

OBJECTIVE 14-8 To find subtraction patterns

PREBOOK ACTIVITIES

QUICK REVIEW

Complete the patterns.

34, 33, 32, ____, ____, 29, 28, ____ (31, 30, 27)

85, 80, ____, 70, ____, ____, 55, ____ (75, 65, 60, 50)

25, 27, ____, 31, ____, ____, 37, ____ (29, 33, 35, 39)

PRIOR KNOWLEDGE

Help students recall patterns in addition and subtraction facts. *How is the sum of a double-plus-one different from the sum of a double?* (The sum is one more than the sum of a double.) *Why does that happen?* (One of the addends is 1 larger, so the sum is 1 larger.) *How does the difference change in a subtraction fact of a doubles-plus-one sum?* (The difference is 1 larger than it would be for a doubles subtraction fact because the number you begin with is 1 larger.)

COMMUNICATION

Reading and Discussing Math Write the following number pattern on the chalkboard: 20, 22, 24, 26, 28, 30, 32. Have students read the pattern aloud. *What can you tell about the number pattern?* (Possible answers: The numbers increase; the pattern is counting on by twos; it is an even number pattern going from smaller numbers to larger numbers.) Write additional number patterns on the chalkboard and have students describe them.

1. 88, 86, 84, 82, 80, 78   **2.** 20, 30, 40, 50, 60, 70

3. 30, 33, 36, 39, 42, 45   **3.** 60, 56, 52, 48, 44, 40

5. 75, 80, 85, 90, 95, 100   **6.** 11, 22, 33, 44, 55, 66

EXPLORE AND CONNECT

Material: Cube-A-Links

Grouping Suggestion: pairs

Have pairs of students use cubes to show 65. *How many cube would you take away to get a difference of 50?* (15) Ask a volunteer to write the subtraction sentence on the chalkboard. (65 − 15 = 50) *What do you think will happen if you subtrac 1 more than 15 from 65? Will you have as much left? Will yo have more left? Use cubes to find out.* (not as much left; whe subtracting exactly 15, the difference is 50; if you take 1 mor than 15 away, you will have 1 less than 50, or 49, left.) Record the new subtraction sentence beside the original sentence. (65 − 16 = 49) *What if you subtract 1 less than 15 from 65?* (You will have 1 more than 50, or 51.) Record the new sentence above the original sentence. (65 − 14 = 51) *What rule can you make about this subtraction pattern?* (As the number taken away gets larger, the difference gets smalle

CONNECTIONS   Use these anytime.

Problem of the Day

Choose the Operation Harold scored 35 points in the basketball game. Greg scored 51 points. How many fewer points did Harold score? (16) How did you find your answer? (by subtracting 51 − 35)

Math Connection

Patterns Guess what the pattern will be. Subtract to find out.

41	43	45	47	49
−22	−22	−22	−22	−22
(19)	(21)	(23)	(25)	(27)

(The difference gets larger by 2.)

Number Sense

Mental Math Which subtraction problem will have the largest difference? The smallest? Which will have the same? Subtract to check.

1. 85	**2.** 85	**3.** 85	**4.** 86
−64	−38	−51	−52
(21)	(47)	(34)	(34)

(**2,** largest difference; **1,** smallest difference; **3** and **4,** the same)

CLASSWORK AND HOMEWORK SUPPLEMENTS

Practice

Patterns   14-8

Name _____

Subtraction Patterns

Subtract. Look for a pattern.

1.
```
 4 13      4 13      4 13      4 13
  5̷3̷       5̷3̷       5̷3̷       5̷3̷        5 3
 -2 6     -2 7     -2 8     -2 9      -3 0
 ────     ────     ────     ────      ────
  2 7      2 6      2 5      2 4       2 3
```

2.
```
            1 14      2 14      3 14      4 14
  1 4       2̷4̷       3̷4̷       4̷4̷       5̷4̷
 -  6      -  6      -  6      -  6      -  6
 ────      ────      ────      ────      ────
    8        18        28        38        48
```

3.
```
            1 13      2 13              2 13      2 13
  1 3       2̷3̷       3̷3̷      (Be       3̷3̷       3̷3̷
 -  9      -  9      -  9    careful!) -1 9      -2 9
 ────      ────      ────              ────      ────
    4        14        24               14         4
```

4.
```
  7 10               7 10               7 10
  8̷0̷       8 0       8̷0̷       8 0       8̷0̷
 -1 5      -2 0      -2 5      -3 0      -3 5
 ────      ────      ────      ────      ────
  6 5       6 0       5 5       5 0       4 5
```

5.
```
            6 11                          7 12      5 13
  4 7       7̷1̷       5 4       8̷2̷       6̷3̷
 -3 6      -4 9      -2 1      -3 8      -  8
 ────      ────      ────      ────      ────
  1 1        22        33        44        55
```

PS-2   Use with text pages 301 – 302.   125

Reteaching

Patterns   14-8

Name _____

Subtraction Patterns

```
  2 5       2 6       2 7       2 7       2 7       2 7
 -1 4      -1 4      -1 4      -1 4      -1 5      -1 6
 ────      ────      ────      ────      ────      ────
  1 1       1 2       1 3       1 3       1 2       1 1
```

Start number is 1 more so difference is 1 more.

Number subtracted is 1 more, so difference is 1 less.

Subtract. The answers have a pattern.
Check your answers by finding the pattern.

1.
```
  5 12      5 13      5 14
  6̷2̷       6̷3̷       6̷4̷       6 5       6 6
 -2 5      -2 5      -2 5      -2 5      -2 5
 ────      ────      ────      ────      ────
  3 7        38        39        40        41
```

2.
```
  8 9       8 9       8 9       8 9       8 9
 -3 7      -3 8      -3 9      -4 0      -4 1
 ────      ────      ────      ────      ────
  5 2        51        50        49        48
```

3.
```
            1 14      2 14      3 14      4 14
  1 4       2̷4̷       3̷4̷       4̷4̷       5̷4̷
 -  6      -  6      -  6      -  6      -  6
 ────      ────      ────      ────      ────
    8        18        28        38        48
```

RS-2   Use with text pages 301 – 302.   125

Building Thinking Skills

Writing Math   14-8

Name _____

Predicting Patterns

Find the pattern. Write what happens to the difference.

Wording may vary.

1.
```
  7 6       7 7       7 8       7 9       8 0
 -5 8      -5 8      -5 8      -5 8      -5 8
 ────      ────      ────      ────      ────
```
The difference will be 1 more each time.

2.
```
  5 2       5 2       5 2       5 2       5 2
 -1 6      -1 8      -2 0      -2 2      -2 4
 ────      ────      ────      ────      ────
```
The difference will be 2 less each time.

3.
```
  7 1       7 2       7 3       7 4       7 5
 -1 2      -1 3      -1 4      -1 5      -1 6
 ────      ────      ────      ────      ────
```
The difference will be the same each time.

4.
```
  4 8       5 8       6 8       7 8       8 8
 -2 3      -2 3      -2 3      -2 3      -2 3
 ────      ────      ────      ────      ────
```
The difference will be 10 more each time.

TS-2   Use with text pages 301 – 302.   125

Challenges

Calculators   14-8

Name _____

That's Odd!

Here are some rules about odd and even numbers.
Use your calculator and check to see if they are true.
Record 2 problems for each rule.   Problems will vary.

1. Pick any two odd numbers.
   Add them.   _____

   The answer will be an even number.   _____

2. Subtract any odd number from
   any other odd number.   _____

   The answer will be an even number.   _____

3. Subtract any even number from
   any odd number.   _____

   The answer will be an odd number.   _____

Think of the rules. Ring the answers. Check with your calculator.

4. Which two numbers have
   a sum of 78?   62   53   24   25   56

5. Which two numbers have
   a difference of 33?   19   24   62   23   57

6. Which two numbers have
   a difference of 48?   99   88   96   51   44

CS-2   Use with text pages 301 – 302.   125

OPTIONS FOR INDIVIDUAL NEEDS

Basic

Exercises All
Data Bank, p. 400
Calculator Bank, p. 403
More Practice, p. 425, set C

Supplements
Reteaching 125 or
Practice 125
Challenges 125

Average

Exercises All
Data Bank, p. 400
Calculator Bank, p. 403
More Practice, p. 425, set C

Supplements
Practice 125
Challenges 125 or
Thinking Skills 125

Extended

Exercises All
Data Bank, p. 400
Calculator Bank, p. 403

Supplements
Challenges 125
Thinking Skills 125

Other Resources:
*Developing Number Concepts
With Unifix Cubes*, p. 175

LESSON PLAN 14-8

OBJECTIVE 14-8
To find subtraction patterns

Materials: Cube-A-Links, base-ten blocks, punchout number cards 0-9

Grouping Suggestions: pairs, individual work

1. MOTIVATE AND TEACH

LEARN ABOUT IT

Provide each student pair with 13 cubes. Ask them to take away 9 cubes and find the difference. (4) Repeat the activity, having students take away 8, then 7. Ask students to say each new difference and describe the pattern. (5, 6; when the amount taken away is 1 less each time, the difference is one more.) Ask students to predict the next fact in the pattern. (13 − 6 = 7) Direct student's attention to Exercise 1 on page 301.

▶ **How are these exercises related?** (They are all differences from the same number, 84.)

▶ **How is the pattern of the numbers subtracted opposite from the pattern of the differences?** (The amount subtracted gets larger by one, the difference gets smaller by one.)

▶ **How can finding patterns be helpful in subtraction?** (Possible answers: If you see a pattern, you can predict what will happen next; it can make subtraction easier because you can predict or estimate the answer.)

2. CHECK UNDERSTANDING

ERROR ALERT Trading unnecessarily when subtracting the ones digits.

Name _____

Subtraction Patterns

Subtract. Then ring the correct answer.

1.

$\overset{7\,14}{84}$	$\overset{7\,14}{84}$	$\overset{7\,14}{84}$	$\overset{7\,14}{84}$	84	8
− 26	− 27	− 28	− 29	− 30	− 3
58	57	56	55	54	5

When the amount subtracted is 1 more each time, what happens to the difference?
- stays the same
- is 1 more
- (is 1 less)

2.

$\overset{6\,16}{76}$	$\overset{6\,17}{77}$	78	79	$\overset{7\,10}{80}$	$\overset{7}{8}$
− 68	− 68	− 68	− 68	− 68	− 68
8	9	10	11	12	

When the amount to start is 1 more each time, what happens to the difference?
- stays the same
- (is 1 more)
- is 1 less

3.

$\overset{4\,13}{53}$	$\overset{4\,14}{54}$	$\overset{4\,15}{55}$	56	57	5
− 47	− 48	− 49	− 50	− 51	− 52
6	6	6	6	6	

When the amount to start and the amount subtracted are 1 more each time, what happens to the difference?
- (stays the same)
- is 1 more
- is 1 less

Chapter 14

(three hundred one) 3(

TEACHING OPTIONS

RETEACHING TIPS Have students use base-ten blocks to model 64 and take 48 away. *Is trading necessary?* (yes) Have students subtract 49, 50, and 51 from 64. *Which problems do not need a trade?* (50 and 51) Assign Reteaching Supplement 125.

ENRICHMENT Have students make number cards to show 2-digit numbers that are multiples of ten (10, 20, 30, . . .). Choose a pair of numbers and ask students to find the difference mentally. Then have them choose other pairs of numbers that have the same difference.

ubtract. Look at the differences in
ch row. Continue the pattern.

$\overset{5\ 13}{\cancel{63}}$	$\overset{4\ 12}{\cancel{52}}$	$\overset{5\ 10}{\cancel{60}}$	59	$\overset{5\ 16}{\cancel{66}}$	
-45	-24	-22	-11	$-\ 8$	
18	28	38	48	58	$\boxed{68}$

46	$\overset{3\ 12}{\cancel{42}}$	$\overset{6\ 12}{\cancel{72}}$	69	$\overset{7\ 10}{\cancel{80}}$	
-24	$-\ 9$	-28	-14	-14	
22	33	44	55	66	$\boxed{77}$

$\overset{6\ 11}{\cancel{71}}$	$\overset{5\ 10}{\cancel{60}}$	84	$\overset{3\ 16}{\cancel{46}}$	59	
-29	-19	-44	$-\ 7$	-21	
42	41	40	39	38	$\boxed{37}$

$\overset{6\ 18}{\cancel{78}}$	68	$\overset{4\ 18}{\cancel{58}}$	48	$\overset{2\ 18}{\cancel{38}}$	
-39	-34	-29	-24	-19	
39	34	29	24	19	$\boxed{14}$

ND THE DATA

How many more points did
the Giants score than
the Beetles?

Data Bank   How many
more points did the
Bulldogs score than the
Whales? (See page 400.)

$$\begin{array}{r} \overset{2\ 10}{\cancel{30}} \\ -\ 13 \\ \hline 17 \end{array}$$

_17_ more points

$$\begin{array}{r} 35 \\ -\ 21 \\ \hline 14 \end{array}$$

_14_ more points

Scores	
Giants	30
Beetles	13

02   (two hundred two)   More Practice, page 425, set C   Chapter 14

3. PRACTICE AND APPLY

Basic	All
Average	All
Extended	All

PRACTICE

*What will you do after subtracting each
row on page 302?* (Find the pattern,
write the next difference.) *How can the
patterns help you check the subtraction?*
(If the pattern is broken, the subtraction
may be incorrect.)

APPLY

FIND THE DATA ▶ **Why is
subtraction used to answer the
question *How many more*?** (When you
compare two numbers, you are finding
the *difference* between them.)
▶ **What information in the Data Bank
is not needed for solving Problem 6?**
(the scores of the Beetles/Groundhogs
and the Bulldogs/Groundhogs games)
▶ **How could you check your work in
Problem 6?** (add 21 and 14)
▶ **Look at the Data Bank. Which team
won 2 games?** (The Groundhogs)
**Which team did the Groundhogs beat
by 7 points?** (the Beetles)

14-8

CLOSE AND ASSESS

HOW WHAT YOU KNOW
ovide each pair with a set of
mber cards 0-9. Each student draws
o cards to make two 2-digit
mbers, then the pair writes and
lves a subtraction exercise using the
mbers. Have them write 3 more
ercises, keeping one of the original
mbers the same to see what pattern
ey can make.

QUICK QUIZ

Subtract. Then write an exercise to
continue the pattern.

84	74	64	54	(44)
-15	-15	-15	-15	(-15)
(69)	(59)	(49)	(39)	(29)

Problem Solving: Choosing a Calculation Method

OBJECTIVE 14-9   To choose an appropriate method of calculation

PREBOOK ACTIVITIES

Ring the best estimate for the difference.

33	88	75
− 12	− 56	− 38
about 10	about 10	about 30
about 20	about 20	about 40
about 30	about 30	about 50

PRIOR KNOWLEDGE

On the chalkboard, write exercises similar to the following. $9 - 2 = 7$, $8 - 4 = 4$, $7 + 3 = 10$, $8 + 5 = 13$. *What strategies have you learned that can help you solve these exercises?* List students' answers on the board under the appropriate exercise. (count back; doubles; sums of 10; make 10 and add extra) *How can you decide what operation to use when you solve a story problem?* (Possible answer: Read the problem to see whether the action tells you to add or subtract.)

COMMUNICATION

Discussing and Writing Math   Explain to students that they can use mental math to do some subtraction exercises but might need paper and pencil or a calculator to help them solve problems with larger numbers. *Why is it important to know how to use all 3 methods for solving problems?* (Possible answer: so you can choose the one that can help you solve the problem quickly and correctly) Have students copy and complete the following sentence in their Math Journals (TA 2). *I can solve problems by using _____, _____, and _____.* (mental math; paper and pencil; a calculator)

EXPLORE AND CONNECT

COOPERATIVE ACTIVITY
Grouping Suggestion: small groups

70	40	93	33	106
− 30	− 2	− 40	− 17	− 39
(40)	(38)	(53)	(16)	(67)

TEACHING ACTIONS

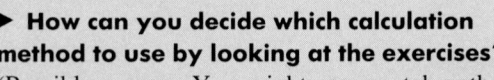

BEFORE ▶ **Look at the exercises. How are they alike? How are they different?** (Possible answer: They are all subtraction; some involve subtracting 10s; some involve trading; there are 1-, 2-, and 3-digit numbers.)
▶ **What are some methods could you use to solve these exercises?** (Possible answer: mental math; paper and pencil; calculator)

DURING ▶ **How can you decide which calculation method to use by looking at the exercises?** (Possible answer: You might use mental math if you are subtracting tens or counting back by tens or ones. If a problem has a 3-digit number, you might use a calculator to solve it. Otherwise, you can use paper and pencil.)
▶ **Why does it matter which calculation method you use?** (Possible answer: You want to find the method that will help you solve the problem quickly and correctly.)

AFTER ▶ **How can you check your answer?** (Possible answer: Use another calculation method to see if your answer is the same.)
Have small groups of students choose a calculation method and solve the exercises.

CONNECTIONS   Use these anytime.

Problem of the Day

Understanding the Operation
Solve. Use a calculator to help. Write the answer in a sentence.
103 people in a tour group want to see an exhibit.
They have 59 tickets already.
How many more tickets do they need?
(They need 44 more tickets.)

Number Sense

Mental Math   Use mental math to find a related addition exercise for each subtraction exercise.
$90 - 30 = 60$ $(60 + 30 = 90)$
$85 - 2 = 83$ $(83 + 2 = 85)$
$105 - 17 = 88$ $(88 + 17 = 105)$
$58 - 49 = 9$ $(49 + 9 = 58)$

Counting Patterns

Identify the counting pattern you would use to solve each problem using mental math.
$62 - 40$ (Count back by tens.)
$70 - 20$ (Count back by tens.)
$35 - 3$ (Count back by ones.)
$59 - 30$ (Count back by tens.)
$76 - 2$ (Count back by ones.)

CLASSWORK AND HOMEWORK SUPPLEMENTS

Practice

Problem Solving   14-9

Name _____

Choosing a Calculation Method

Solve.   Calculation methods may vary.
Ring the method: mental math, paper and pencil, or a 🖩 .

1. The campers went to the lake. The red bus carried 30 children. The blue bus carried 20 children. How many more children went on the red bus?

   __10__ more on the red bus
   I used ⟨mental math⟩
   paper and pencil.
   a calculator.

2. 33 children went in the water right away. 17 children played on the sand. How many more children went right in the water?

   __16__ went right in the water.
   I used   mental math.
   ⟨paper and pencil⟩
   a calculator.

3. There were 127 children at the lake that day. 50 children were from Montclair Camp. How many children were not?

   __77__ children were not.
   I used   mental math.
   paper and pencil.
   ⟨a calculator.⟩

4. 32 children had goggles to wear. 18 children had tubes to play with. How many more children had goggles?

   __14__ more had goggles.
   I used   mental math.
   ⟨paper and pencil⟩
   a calculator.

126   Use with text pages 303 – 304.   PS-2

Building Thinking Skills

Mental Math   14-9

Name _____

Summer Rentals

Draw a line to show what each person can rent.
Use mental math to solve.

55¢   75¢   90¢   45¢   50¢

I have 3 quarters, I dime, and I nickel.
I have I half dollar and 5 pennies.
I have I half dollar, 2 dimes, and 5 pennies.
I have 3 dimes and 3 nickels.
I have 10 nickels.

126   Use with text pages 303 – 304.   TS-2

Reteaching

Problem Solving   14-9

Name _____

Choosing a Calculation Method

Exercises like this I can solve using mental math.	Exercises like this I can solve using paper and pencil.	Exercises like this I can solve using a calculator.
70 −40 30	82 −19 63	122 −67 55

Cross out the exercises you solve using mental math.
Ring the exercises you solve using paper and pencil.
Draw a ✔ on the exercises you solve using a 🖩 .

1. 90 −50 = 40   111 −22 = 89   ⟨72 −53 = 19⟩   108 −63 = 45

2. ⟨84 −48 = 36⟩   80 −30 = 50   119 −74 = 45   10 −10 = 0

3. 70 −60 = 10   ⟨93 −77 = 16⟩   10 −0 = 10   126 −89 = 37

126   Use with text pages 303 – 304.   RS-2

Challenges

Cooperative Activities   14-9

Name _____

Spin to Win

START	60 −20 = 40	44 −30 = 14	131 −68 = 63	Go back I space.	57 −28 = 29	80 −30 = 50	113 −76 = 37	Spin again.

			126 −89 = 37
FINISH	You need: I or more friends, I spinner, I marker		50 −40 = 10
77 −50 = 27	for each player, paper and pencil, and a 🖩 .		
Go back 2 spaces.	(spinner: 1 2 5 3 4)		72 −54 = 18
26 −17 = 9	Rules: Put your marker on START. Spin the spinner. Move that number of spaces. Decide if the exercise on the space can be solved using mental math,		Lose I turn.
164 −99 = 65	paper and pencil, or a 🖩 .		97 −60 = 37
60 −30 = 30	Solve it. All players need to agree that the answer is right. Take turns. The first person to get to FINISH wins. **Calculation methods will vary.**		83 −45 = 38
Lose I turn.			Go back to start.

153 −65 = 88	88 −70 = 18	20 −20 = 0	44 −27 = 17	Spin again.	178 −87 = 91	91 −66 = 25	146 −97 = 49

126   Use with text pages 303 – 304.   CS-2

OPTIONS FOR INDIVIDUAL NEEDS

Basic

Exercises All, Mixed Review
Calculator Bank, pp. 402-403

Supplements
Reteaching 126 or
Practice 126
Challenges 126

Average

Exercises All, Mixed Review
Calculator Bank, pp. 402-403

Supplements
Practice 126
Challenges 126 or
Thinking Skills 126

Extended

Exercises All, Mixed Review
Calculator Bank, pp. 402-403

Supplements
Challenges 126
Thinking Skills 126

Other Resources:
Developing Number Concepts With Unifix Cubes, pp. 172-174

14-9

OBJECTIVE 14-9
To choose an appropriate method of calculation

1. MOTIVATE AND TEACH

LEARN ABOUT IT

 **BEFORE** ► **For what types of subtraction exercises do you think it is best to use mental math?** (Possible answer: subtracting tens; counting back by tens; counting back by ones)

 **DURING** ► **How can you decide which calculation method you should use?** (Possible answer: Look at the problem. If you cannot do it mentally, decide if you can do it with paper and pencil. If not, then use a calculator.)

 **AFTER** ► **Explain how to subtract using a calculator.** (Possible answer: Press *on/c*, then the digits in the top number, the minus sign, the digits in the bottom number, and the equal sign.)
Where are the exercise that you will cut out? (on the side of the page) *What should you do with the exercises before you paste them on the page?* (For each exercise, decide which method to use and paste it under that heading.) *What should you do after you paste the pictures under the right heading for you?* (Solve the problem using the method named by the heading.)

2. CHECK UNDERSTANDING

ERROR ALERT Being unable to choose an appropriate method of calculation.

Name _____

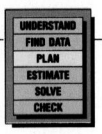

Problem Solving
Choosing a Calculation Method

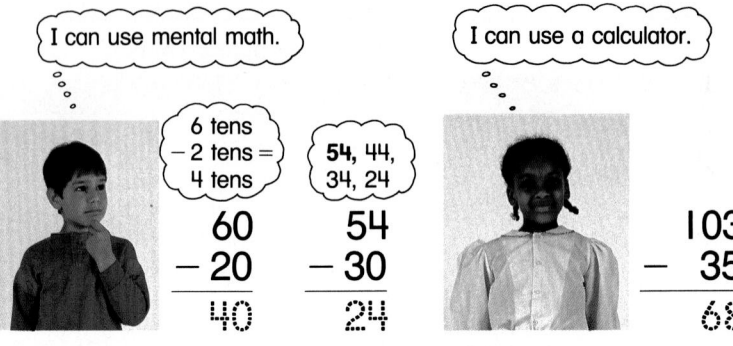

Press [ON/C] [1] [0] [3] [−] [3] [5] [=]

Cut out the exercises. Sort them into the three groups shown. Paste. Then subtract. **Calculation methods may vary.**

My Mental Math Exercises			My Paper and Pencil Exercises		
35 − 2 33	38 − 20 18	50 − 30 20	43 − 21 22	414 54 − 27 27	318 48 − 39 9

My Calculator Exercises					
101 − 28 73	104 − 87 17				

Chapter 14   (three hundred three) 3

TEACHING OPTIONS

RETEACHING TIPS Write subtraction exercises on cards. Have pairs draw an exercise and choose a method to solve it. One student uses that method while the second solves it differently. Compare results and discuss preferences. Assign Reteaching Supplement 126.

ENRICHMENT Have students choose 3 cards with 3-digit numbers and 3 cards with 2-digit numbers. Estimate which combinations of 2 cards will produce the greatest difference and the smallest difference. They may use their calculators to solve the exercises. Are the estimates reasonable?

Solve. Ring if you used mental math,
paper and pencil, or a . Calculation methods may vary.

1. How many minutes
did the game last?

It lasted __90__ minutes.

| 1st half | 42 minutes |
| 2nd half | 48 minutes |

I used   mental math.

paper and pencil.

calculator.

2. Julie's family drove
from Palm Harbor to
Brandon for the game.
How far did they drive?

They drove __48__ miles.

Palm Harbor • — 28 miles — • — 20 miles — • Brandon
Tampa

I used   mental math.

paper and pencil.

calculator.

MIXED REVIEW

Add or subtract.

3.
$$\begin{array}{r} 7\ 11 \\ 8\cancel{1} \\ -27 \\ \hline 54 \end{array}$$
$$\begin{array}{r} 45 \\ +19 \\ \hline 64 \end{array}$$
$$\begin{array}{r} 15 \\ +15 \\ \hline 30 \end{array}$$
$$\begin{array}{r} 26 \\ 14 \\ + 8 \\ \hline 48 \end{array}$$
$$\begin{array}{r} 12 \\ 42 \\ +14 \\ \hline 68 \end{array}$$

4.
$$\begin{array}{r} 48 \\ -38 \\ \hline 10 \end{array}$$
$$\begin{array}{r} 17 \\ +46 \\ \hline 63 \end{array}$$
$$\begin{array}{r} 2\ 13 \\ 3\cancel{3} \\ -28 \\ \hline 5 \end{array}$$
$$\begin{array}{r} 16 \\ +79 \\ \hline 95 \end{array}$$
$$\begin{array}{r} 5\ 13 \\ 6\cancel{3} \\ -47 \\ \hline 16 \end{array}$$

14-9

3. PRACTICE AND APPLY

Basic	All, Mixed Review
Average	All, Mixed Review
Extended	All, Mixed Review

▶ **Why is choosing a calculation method important to solving a subtraction story problem?** (Possible answer: After you plan how to organize the data, you need to choose a method of calculation to solve the problem.)

▶ **Explain how the 3 methods can also be used with an addition story problem.** (Possible answer: First decide if you can do the problem mentally. If not, decide if you need paper and pencil or a calculator.)

▶ **Why might different people use different calculation methods?** (Possible answer: because some people may find it is easier to use paper and pencil than to use a calculator or mental math) *Where do you find the data for the problems on this page?* (in the picture for each problem)

MIXED REVIEW *Which exercises do you think you can solve using mental math?* (Possible answers: Row 3, Exercises 3 and 5; Row 4, Exercise 1)

CLOSE AND ASSESS

SAY WHAT YOU THINK On the chalkboard, write several exercises that can be solved mentally, with paper and pencil, and with a calculator. Call on individual students to choose an exercise, tell how they would solve it, and use that method to find the answer. Discuss reasons why one method might be better than another for each exercise.

QUICK QUIZ

Solve. Which method did you use?
The Hawks scored 60 points. The
Eagles scored 30 points. How many
more points did the Hawks score? (30;
mental math)

Addition and Subtraction Practice

OBJECTIVE 14-10   To practice adding and subtracting 2-digit numbers

PREBOOK ACTIVITIES

QUICK REVIEW

Give the missing numbers in each pattern.

74, 75, _(76)_ , _(77)_ , 78   83, 86, _(89)_ , _(92)_ , 95

32, 34, _(36)_ , _(38)_ , 40   27, 26, _(25)_ , _(24)_ , 23

45, 50, _(55)_ , _(60)_ , 65   95, 90, _(85)_ , _(80)_ , 75

PRIOR KNOWLEDGE

What does it mean to add 2 numbers? (Possible answer: to find the total; to find how many there are all together) *Describe a situation when you had to add 2 things.* (Descriptions will vary.) *What does it mean to subtract 2 numbers?* (to find how many there are left; to find the difference) *Describe a situation when you had to subtract.* (Descriptions will vary.)

COMMUNICATION

Discussing Math   Write the word **predict** and the following number pattern on the chalkboard: 5, 10, 15, 20, 25, —, —. *What does it mean to predict something?* (Possible answer: to tell whether or not it will happen) *Can you predict what 2 numbers will come next in the number pattern?* (yes—30, 35) Next, display 4 red blocks and 1 blue block, then put them in a paper bag. *If I take out 1 block without looking, can you predict what color it will be?* (Answers will vary.) *What color block will I be more likely to take out? Why?* (Possible answer: Red; there are more red blocks in the bag.)

EXPLORE AND CONNECT

Materials: punchout number cards 3, 7, and 8 for each pair, base-ten blocks

Grouping Suggestions: pairs

Have students in pairs use number cards to find and record 6 different addition problems for a 2-digit number plus a 1-digit number. Have them use base-ten blocks to model the addends and find each sum. *What is the greatest sum you could find?* (90) *the least sum?* (45) *Compare each addend to the sum. What do you notice?* (Possible answer: The sum is greater than the addend.) Repeat, subtracting a 1-digit number from a 2-digit number. *What is the greatest difference you could find?* (84) *the least difference?* (29) *If you compare the difference to the amount you started with each time, what do you notice?* (Possible answer: The difference is always less.)

CONNECTIONS   Use these anytime.

Problem of the Day

Logic   I guessed there were 65 beans in a jar. My guess was off by 20. My friend guessed there were 35 beans in the jar. She was off by 10. How many beans are in the jar? (45) How did you find your answer? (If you subtract 20 from 65, you get 45, which is the same as adding 10 to 35.)

Number Sense

Mental Math   When you add with pencil and paper, you usually start at the right and work to the left. When you add in your head, sometimes it is easier to start at the left. For example, in 38 + 23, you can think: 30 + 20 = 50, 8 + 3 = 11; 50 + 11 = 61. Now try 48 + 27. Make up another addition exercise and add the numbers in your head.

Minute Math

Carmen and Lheng played a game of Ping-Pong. Carmen won the game with a score of 21. She won by 7 points. What was Lheng's score? (14)

CLASSWORK AND HOMEWORK SUPPLEMENTS

Basic

Exercises All
Calculator Bank, pp. 402-403

Supplements
Reteaching 127 or
Practice 127
Thinking Skills 127

Practice

Skills Maintenance 14-10

Name _____

Addition and Subtraction Practice

Add or subtract.

1.
$\begin{array}{r}{}^{4\ 12}\\ 5\,2\\ -1\,8\\ \hline 34\end{array}$
$\begin{array}{r}{}^{6\ 14}\\ 7\,4\\ -3\,6\\ \hline 38\end{array}$
$\begin{array}{r}{}^{1}\\ 4\,8\\ +2\,6\\ \hline 74\end{array}$
$\begin{array}{r}{}^{1}\\ 3\,7\\ +1\,9\\ \hline 56\end{array}$
$\begin{array}{r}{}^{2\ 15}\\ 3\,5\\ -1\,7\\ \hline 18\end{array}$

2.
$\begin{array}{r} 3\,6\\ +2\,3\\ \hline 59\end{array}$
$\begin{array}{r}{}^{7\ 11}\\ 8\,1\\ -3\,9\\ \hline 42\end{array}$
$\begin{array}{r} 4\,7\\ +1\,6\\ \hline 63\end{array}$
$\begin{array}{r}{}^{3\ 13}\\ 4\,3\\ -1\,4\\ \hline 29\end{array}$
$\begin{array}{r}{}^{3\ 17}\\ 4\,7\\ -1\,9\\ \hline 28\end{array}$

3.
$\begin{array}{r}{}^{5\ 13}\\ 6\,3\\ -2\,5\\ \hline 38\end{array}$
$\begin{array}{r}{}^{8\ 14}\\ 9\,4\\ -5\,7\\ \hline 37\end{array}$
$\begin{array}{r}{}^{1}\\ 1\,4\\ +2\,7\\ \hline 41\end{array}$
$\begin{array}{r}{}^{1}\\ 2\,8\\ +5\,6\\ \hline 84\end{array}$
$\begin{array}{r}{}^{1}\\ 7\,7\\ +\ \ 8\\ \hline 85\end{array}$

4.
$\begin{array}{r}{}^{5\ 10}\\ 6\,0\\ -3\,7\\ \hline 23\end{array}$
$\begin{array}{r}{}^{6\ 12}\\ 7\,2\\ -4\,3\\ \hline 29\end{array}$
$\begin{array}{r} 9\,3\\ +\ \ 8\\ \hline 101\end{array}$
$\begin{array}{r}{}^{1}\\ 3\,5\\ +1\,5\\ \hline 50\end{array}$
$\begin{array}{r}{}^{7\ 10}\\ 8\,0\\ -3\,1\\ \hline 49\end{array}$

5.
$\begin{array}{r}{}^{1}\\ 1\,9\\ +6\,7\\ \hline 86\end{array}$
$\begin{array}{r}{}^{1}\\ 4\,3\\ +1\,7\\ \hline 60\end{array}$
$\begin{array}{r}{}^{8\ 16}\\ 9\,6\\ -4\,7\\ \hline 49\end{array}$
$\begin{array}{r}{}^{7\ 15}\\ 8\,5\\ -\ \ 6\\ \hline 79\end{array}$
$\begin{array}{r}{}^{1}\\ 2\,9\\ +3\,2\\ \hline 61\end{array}$

PS-2   Use with text pages 305–306.   127

Building Thinking Skills

Critical Thinking 14-10

Name _____

Sums and Differences

Use these numbers to write 6 addition and 6 subtraction problems. Make each problem different.   Order may vary.

| 48 | 23 | 56 | 17 |

1.
$\begin{array}{r}{}^{1}\\ 4\,8\\ +2\,3\\ \hline 7\,1\end{array}$
2.
$\begin{array}{r}{}^{1}\\ 4\,8\\ +5\,6\\ \hline 1\,0\,4\end{array}$
3.
$\begin{array}{r}{}^{1}\\ 4\,8\\ +1\,7\\ \hline 6\,5\end{array}$
4.
$\begin{array}{r} 2\,3\\ +5\,6\\ \hline 7\,9\end{array}$

5.
$\begin{array}{r} 4\,8\\ -2\,3\\ \hline 2\,5\end{array}$
6.
$\begin{array}{r} 4\,8\\ -1\,7\\ \hline 3\,1\end{array}$
7.
$\begin{array}{r}{}^{1}\\ 2\,3\\ +1\,7\\ \hline 4\,0\end{array}$
8.
$\begin{array}{r}{}^{1}\\ 5\,6\\ +1\,7\\ \hline 7\,3\end{array}$

9.
$\begin{array}{r}{}^{1\ 13}\\ 2\,3\\ -1\,7\\ \hline 6\end{array}$
10.
$\begin{array}{r}{}^{4\ 16}\\ 5\,6\\ -4\,8\\ \hline 8\end{array}$
11.
$\begin{array}{r} 5\,6\\ -2\,3\\ \hline 3\,3\end{array}$
12.
$\begin{array}{r}{}^{4\ 16}\\ 5\,6\\ -1\,7\\ \hline 3\,9\end{array}$

TS-2   Use with text pages 305–306.   127

Average

Exercises All
Calculator Bank, pp. 402-403

Supplements
Practice 127
Challenges 127 or
Thinking Skills 127

14-10

Reteaching

Skills Review 14-10

Name _____

Addition and Subtraction Practice

Adding 2-digit Numbers	Subtracting 2-digit Numbers
• Add the ones.	• See if you need more ones.
• Trade if you need to.	• Trade if you need to.
• Then add the tens.	• Subtract the ones.
	• Subtract the tens.

Add or subtract.

1. (Trade 1 ten for 10 ones.)
$\begin{array}{r}{}^{3\ 12}\\ 4\,2\\ -\ \ 7\\ \hline 3\,5\end{array}$
2. (Trade 10 ones for 1 ten.)
$\begin{array}{r}{}^{1}\\ 7\,6\\ +1\,5\\ \hline 9\,1\end{array}$
3.
$\begin{array}{r}{}^{5\ 10}\\ 6\,0\\ -1\,8\\ \hline 4\,2\end{array}$

4.
$\begin{array}{r}{}^{6\ 11}\\ 7\,1\\ -5\,5\\ \hline 1\,6\end{array}$
5.
$\begin{array}{r} 2\,3\\ -1\,2\\ \hline 1\,1\end{array}$
6.
$\begin{array}{r} 7\,2\\ +2\,7\\ \hline 9\,9\end{array}$
7.
$\begin{array}{r}{}^{1}\\ 5\,4\\ +3\,6\\ \hline 9\,0\end{array}$

8.
$\begin{array}{r}{}^{1}\\ 2\,9\\ +5\,9\\ \hline 8\,8\end{array}$
9.
$\begin{array}{r}{}^{2\ 13}\\ 3\,3\\ -1\,8\\ \hline 1\,5\end{array}$
10.
$\begin{array}{r} 6\,8\\ -2\,5\\ \hline 4\,3\end{array}$
11.
$\begin{array}{r}{}^{8\ 15}\\ 9\,5\\ -3\,9\\ \hline 5\,6\end{array}$

RS-2   Use with text pages 305–306.   127

Challenges

Number Sense 14-10

Name _____

Crossnumber Puzzle

Solve the puzzle.

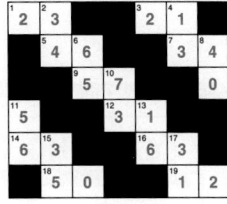

Across
1. 61 − 38
3. 7 + 7 + 7
5. 6 ones, 4 tens
7. 82 − 48
9. 60, 59, 58, □
12. 50 − 19
14. 27 + 36
16. 70 − 7
18. 5 tens
19. 3, 6, 9, □

Down
2. 93 − 59
4. 4 + 3 + 4 + 2
6. 70 − 5
8. 10, 20, 30, □
10. 58 + 15
11. 4 less than 60
13. 7 more than 9
15. 64 − 29
17. 34, 33, 32, □

CS-2   Use with text pages 305–306.   127

Extended

Exercises All
Calculator Bank, pp. 402-403

Supplements
Challenges 127
Thinking Skills 127

Other Resources:
Explorations, pp. 298-299
Developing Number Concepts With Unifix Cubes, pp. 175-176
Using the Math Explorer Calculator: A Source Book for Teachers, Chapter 14

OBJECTIVE 14-10
To practice adding and subtracting
2-digit numbers

> **Materials:** spinners, number cards 0-9,
> paperbags
>
> **Grouping suggestions:** individual
> work, cooperative learning groups of 4

Direct students' attention to the spinner
on page 305. *What will the spinner tell
you?* (whether to add or subtract)
▶ **How will you decide whether you
are more likely to spin plus more
often or to spin minus more often?**
(Possible answer: Look at the spaces on
the spinner.)
Discuss with students how they
responded to Exercise 5.
▶ **Do you think it is possible to spin
more pluses than minuses? Why?**
(Yes; answers will vary.)
▶ **Do you think it is possible to spin
plus and minus the same number of
times?** (yes)
▶ **Why do you think it is more likely
that you will spin minus more often?**
(The section of the spinner for minus is
larger.)

2. CHECK UNDERSTANDING

ERROR ALERT Subtracting the
smaller digit from the larger digit even
though the larger digit is part of the
smaller number—for example, $35 - 9 =$
34.

Name _____

Addition and Subtraction Practice

Use your spinner. Spin. Write + or −
in the ☐. Then add or subtract.

1. Answer before you spin.
   Ring which is more likely to happen.

   I will spin + more often.

   I will spin − more often.

   I will spin + and − the same
   number of times.

   Answers may vary. Check students' wor

2. ☐ 43   ☐ 62   ☐ 19   ☐ 35   ☐ 74   ☐ 3
      25   31   16   9   16   1

3. ☐ 58   ☐ 80   ☐ 24   ☐ 46   ☐ 18   ☐ 7
      26   17   8   34   12   2

4. ☐ 47   ☐ 39   ☐ 62   ☐ 24   ☐ 53   ☐ 3
       7   24   15   18   27   2

5. Ring which happened.

   I spun + more often.

   I spun − more often.

   I spun + and − the same
   number of times.

Chapter 14

(three hundred five) 3(

TEACHING OPTIONS

RETEACHING TIPS Write
vertical subtraction exercises on the
chalkboard. Have students use
base-ten blocks to show the
difference. Ask them to take away
the number of blocks named by the
bottom number and tell whether or
not trading is necessary. Assign
Reteaching Supplement 127.

ENRICHMENT Provide pairs
with a paper bag containing 3
crayons of 1 color and 2 of another
color. Ask them to take turns
drawing 1 crayon from the bag, first
predicting its color, then returning
the crayon to the bag. Ask them to
keep a record and compare
predictions and results.

Add or subtract. Fill in the puzzle.

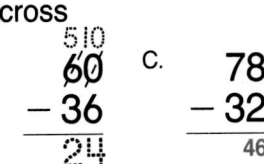

Across

$$\begin{array}{r}{\scriptstyle 5\,10}\\ \not{6}\not{0}\\ -36\\ \hline 24\end{array}$$
C. $\begin{array}{r}78\\ -32\\ \hline 46\end{array}$

$\begin{array}{r}46\\ +37\\ \hline 83\end{array}$
I. $\begin{array}{r}{\scriptstyle 4\,12}\\ \not{5}\not{2}\\ -39\\ \hline 13\end{array}$

$\begin{array}{r}{\scriptstyle 6\,11}\\ \not{7}\not{1}\\ -\ 9\\ \hline 62\end{array}$
M. $\begin{array}{r}58\\ +14\\ \hline 72\end{array}$

O. $45 + 20 = \underline{65}$
Q. $34 - 20 = \underline{14}$
R. $40 + 50 = \underline{90}$

Down

$\begin{array}{r}34\\ +14\\ \hline 48\end{array}$
D. $\begin{array}{r}13\\ +48\\ \hline 61\end{array}$
E. $\begin{array}{r}{\scriptstyle 2\,15}\\ \not{3}\not{5}\\ -27\\ \hline 8\end{array}$
F. $\begin{array}{r}27\\ +29\\ \hline 56\end{array}$
H. $\begin{array}{r}{\scriptstyle 4\,10}\\ \not{5}\not{0}\\ -13\\ \hline 37\end{array}$

$30 + 6 = \underline{36}$
L. $51 - 30 = \underline{21}$

$49 - 20 = \underline{29}$
P. $10 + 40 = \underline{50}$

PROBLEM SOLVING

The coach wants to have 24 players on the team. She already has 15. How many more players does she need?

Word sentences may vary. Sample answer is shown.

$$\begin{array}{r}{\scriptstyle 1\,14}\\ \not{2}\not{4}\\ -15\\ \hline 9\end{array}$$

She needs 9 more players.

06 (three hundred six)   Chapter 14

---

3. PRACTICE AND APPLY

Basic	All
Average	All
Extended	All

PRACTICE

When must you trade in subtraction? (Possible answer: When the number of ones in the larger number is less than the number of ones in the smaller number.) *What do you do when you are adding and you have 10 or more ones?* (Trade for 1 ten.)

APPLY

PROBLEM SOLVING ▶ **What words in the problem tell you whether to add or subtract?** (*How many more* tells you to subtract.)
▶ **Did you have to trade in order to solve the problem? Why or why not?** (yes; there are not enough ones in 24 to subtract a 5.)

14-10

CLOSE AND ASSESS

SHOW WHAT YOU KNOW

Organize students in groups of 4. Have 2 students arrange number cards to form 2 addition and subtraction exercises. The third and fourth students use base-ten blocks to model each exercise and find the sum or difference. Have group members check for agreement and understanding of each exercise. Then have them exchange roles and repeat the activity for a new set of exercises.

QUICK QUIZ

Add or subtract.
$37 + 6 = (43)$ $45 + 7 = (52)$
$86 - 9 = (77)$ $23 - 6 = (17)$
$24 + 16 = (40)$ $96 - 28 = (68)$
$78 - 6 = (72)$ $59 + 7 = (66)$

LESSON OPTIONS 14-11

Problem Solving: Using Estimation

OBJECTIVE 14-11 To solve problems using estimation

PREBOOK ACTIVITIES

QUICK REVIEW

Mentally subtract 10 from each number.

57 (47)	82 (72)	36 (26)	91 (81)
14 (4)	77 (67)	32 (22)	63 (53)

Mentally add 10 to each number.

16 (26)	55 (65)	79 (89)	33 (43)
20 (30)	89 (99)	45 (55)	61 (71)

PRIOR KNOWLEDGE

Show students a length of 6 inches on a ruler. Then ask them to look around the room for an object that they estimate is 6 in. long. *Compare your object to this book. Do you estimate that it is longer or shorter?* (Answers will vary.) Have students measure the book and the objects. *Was your estimate reasonable?* (Answers will vary.)

COMMUNICATION

Writing Math   Write **estimate** and **logical reasoning** on the chalkboard. Read the words aloud and ask students to tell what they mean. (Possible answers: *Estimate* means *to make a reasonable guess*. Using *logical reasoning* means *making a plan for using data to solve a problem.*) Have students copy and complete these sentences in their Math Journals. *When I* (estimate), *I make a reasonable guess. When I use* (logical reasoning), *I make a plan for using data to solve a problem.*

EXPLORE AND CONNECT

COOPERATIVE ACTIVITY

Grouping Suggestions: small groups
About how much taller is Dave than Dan?
about 10 in.   <u>about 20 in.</u>   about 30 in.

Growth Chart	
Dave	56 in.
Dan	38 in.

TEACHING ACTIONS

 **BEFORE** ▶ **Explain what you are asked to do in this problem.** (Possible answer: Use the data in the chart to compare the heights of 2 people.)

▶ **Must you give an exact answer?** (no; an estimate)

▶ **Look at the data in the growth chart and the data in the answers you can choose from. How are the numbers different?** (Possible answer: The growth chart shows the actual heights. The numbers in the answers are estimates; they have zeros in the ones position.)

 **DURING** ▶ **How can you change the data in the chart to help you estimate the answer?** (Possible answer: Think of 56 as 5 tens and 38 as 3 tens.)

▶ **How will you use the estimated data to find the answer?** (Possible answer: Subtract 30 from 50 because you are comparing numbers to find which is greater.)

AFTER ▶ **What would be a good way to check your answer?** (Possible answer: Subtract the numbers shown in the chart to see if the estimate you chos is close to the actual answer.) Have groups estimate difference for this and similar comparison problems.

CONNECTIONS   Use these anytime.

Problem of the Day

Estimating   Ring the best estimate. There are 32 students in Mr. Loy's class. There are 21 students in Ms. Britt's class. About how many students are there in the 2 classes?
about 30 students
about 40 students
<u>about 50 students</u>

Life Skills

Estimating Prices   Work with a partner. Make price tags less than 50¢ for small classroom objects. You each have 90¢ to buy 3 items. Estimate the cost of the items you want, then add to find the total. Was your estimate reasonable? Did you spend 90¢ or less? (Answers will vary.)

Math Connection

Logical Reasoning   Use logical reasoning to solve these problems.

$$\begin{array}{r} 63 \\ -(46) \\ \hline 17 \end{array} \qquad \begin{array}{r} 17 \\ -(\ 9) \\ \hline 8 \end{array}$$

roblem Solving Strategy: Use Logical Reasoning

o solve problems using the strategy Use Logical Reasoning

CLASSWORK AND HOMEWORK

Practice

Problem Solving   14-11

Name _____

Using Estimation

Ring the best estimate.
Answer the question.

1. About how much taller is the
mother than the child?

about 10 inches

(about 20 inches)

about 30 inches

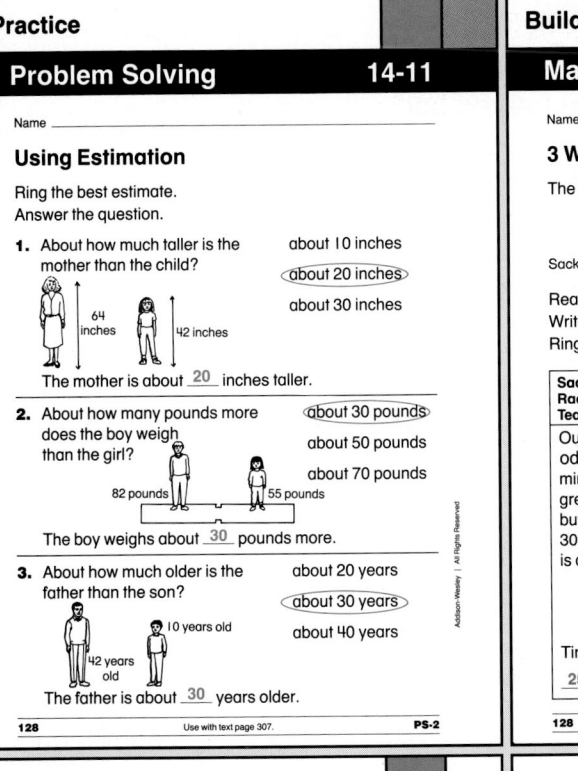

64 inches   42 inches

The mother is about __20__ inches taller.

2. About how many pounds more
does the boy weigh
than the girl?

(about 30 pounds)

about 50 pounds

about 70 pounds

82 pounds   55 pounds

The boy weighs about __30__ pounds more.

3. About how much older is the
father than the son?

about 20 years

(about 30 years)

about 40 years

42 years old   10 years old

The father is about __30__ years older.

128   Use with text page 307.   PS-2

Building Thinking Skills

Math Reasoning   14-11

Name _____

3 Winners

The winners of 3 different races compared their times.

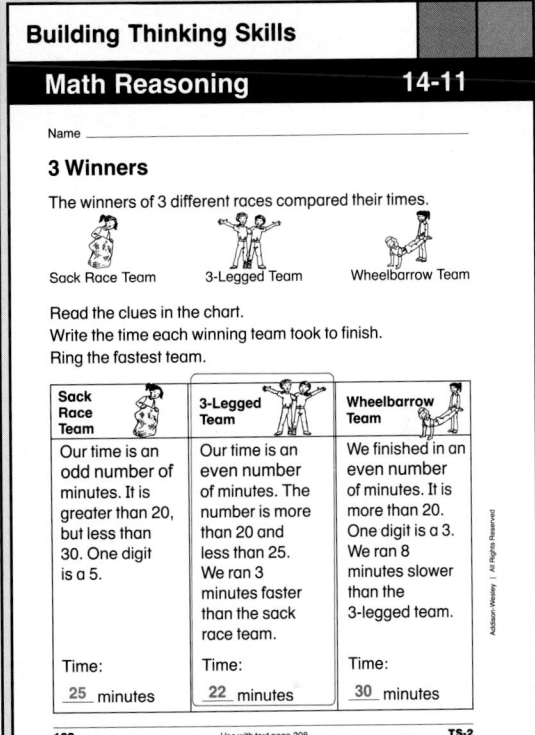

Sack Race Team   3-Legged Team   Wheelbarrow Team

Read the clues in the chart.
Write the time each winning team took to finish.
Ring the fastest team.

Sack Race Team	3-Legged Team	Wheelbarrow Team
Our time is an odd number of minutes. It is greater than 20, but less than 30. One digit is a 5.	Our time is an even number of minutes. The number is more than 20 and less than 25. We ran 3 minutes faster than the sack race team.	We finished in an even number of minutes. It is more than 20. One digit is a 3. We ran 8 minutes slower than the 3-legged team.
Time: __25__ minutes	Time: __22__ minutes	Time: __30__ minutes

128   Use with text page 308.   TS-2

Reteaching

Problem Solving   14-11

Name _____

Use Logical Reasoning

Read the story.   Find out who won the race.   Cross out numbers that will not work.

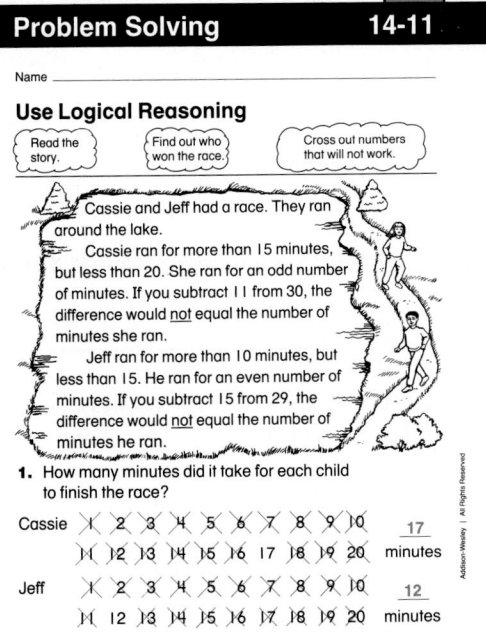

Cassie and Jeff had a race. They ran around the lake.

Cassie ran for more than 15 minutes, but less than 20. She ran for an odd number of minutes. If you subtract 11 from 30, the difference would <u>not</u> equal the number of minutes she ran.

Jeff ran for more than 10 minutes, but less than 15. He ran for an even number of minutes. If you subtract 15 from 29, the difference would <u>not</u> equal the number of minutes he ran.

1. How many minutes did it take for each child to finish the race?

Cassie ~~1~~ ~~2~~ ~~3~~ ~~4~~ ~~5~~ ~~6~~ ~~7~~ ~~8~~ ~~9~~ ~~10~~
~~11~~ ~~12~~ ~~13~~ ~~14~~ ~~15~~ ~~16~~ 17 ~~18~~ ~~19~~ ~~20~~   __17__ minutes

Jeff ~~1~~ ~~2~~ ~~3~~ ~~4~~ ~~5~~ ~~6~~ ~~7~~ ~~8~~ ~~9~~ ~~10~~
~~11~~ 12 ~~13~~ ~~14~~ ~~15~~ ~~16~~ ~~17~~ ~~18~~ ~~19~~ ~~20~~   __12__ minutes

2. Ring the name of the person who won.   (Jeff)   Cassie

128   Use with text page 308.   RS-2

Challenges

Family Math   14-11

Name _____

Estimate and Measure

> Dear Family,
>   Your child is learning to use estimation to solve word problems. Help your child read each problem and make an estimate. Together, use a measuring tape or ruler to find the measurement in inches.

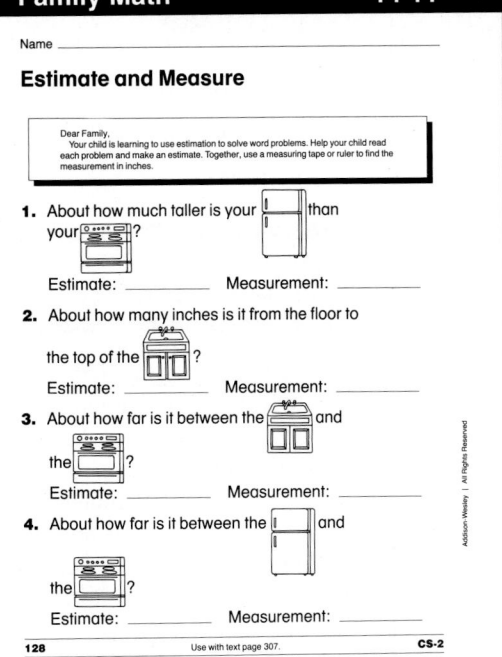

1. About how much taller is your [stove] than your [refrigerator]?

Estimate: _____   Measurement: _____

2. About how many inches is it from the floor to the top of the [cabinet]?

Estimate: _____   Measurement: _____

3. About how far is it between the [cabinet] and the [stove]?

Estimate: _____   Measurement: _____

4. About how far is it between the [refrigerator] and the [stove]?

Estimate: _____   Measurement: _____

128   Use with text page 307.   CS-2

14-11

OBJECTIVE 14-11

To solve problems using estimation; to solve problems using the strategy Use Logical Reasoning

1. MOTIVATE AND TEACH

LEARN ABOUT IT

 **BEFORE** ▶ **Before you can estimate in each exercise, how will you use the plan step?** (Possible answer: to plan what operation to use to solve the problem)

▶ **How will you decide if you need to add or subtract?** (If you need to put 2 numbers together, you add; if you are comparing 2 numbers, you subtract.)

 **DURING** ▶ **How did you find your estimate in Exercise 1?** (Possible answer: by estimating 42 as 4 tens and 24 as 2 tens—40 − 20 = 20)

 **AFTER** ▶ **Describe a situation when you might estimate answers to problems like the ones on this page.** (Possible answer: when you need an approximate answer; when you do not have paper and pencil to find an exact answer)

2. CHECK UNDERSTANDING

ERROR ALERT **Page 307** Being unable to change an actual number into an estimated number.

Page 308 Forgetting to consider all clues before finding an answer.

Name _____

Problem Solving
Using Estimation

Ring the best estimate.
Answer the question.

1. About how much longer is the brown bat than the red bat?

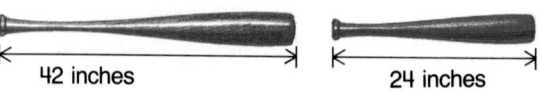

   about 20 inches
   about 30 inches
   about 40 inches

The brown bat is about __20__ inches longer.

2. About how many players are on the two teams?

Number of Players	
Chipmunks	24
Bulldogs	21

   about 20 players
   about 40 players
   about 60 players

There are about __40__ players in all.

3. About how many ounces more does a basketball weigh than a baseball?

   about 10 ounces
   about 20 ounces
   about 30 ounces

23 ounces   5 ounces

A baseball weighs about __20__ ounces more.

Chapter 14   (three hundred seven) 30?

TEACHING OPTIONS

RETEACHING TIPS Remind students to use the tens digit when they are estimating. As you tell a story problem, have students write the data. Have volunteers identify the operation, cross out the ones digit and apply the operation to the tens digits. Assign Reteaching Supplement 128.

COMPUTER **Path Tactics, MECC © 1986** Problem solving practice for all. Choose the operation to be practiced. Given 3 numbers, students will create an equation whose solution is the number of steps the Robot needs to reach the end of the path. The game requires 10 minutes.

oblem Solving Strategy

e Logical Reasoning

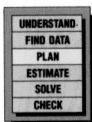

UNDERSTAND·
FIND DATA
PLAN
ESTIMATE
SOLVE
CHECK

sten to the story. Find out who won
e race. Cross out numbers
at will not work.

How many minutes did it take for each animal
to finish the race?

tortoise ~~1~~ ~~2~~ 3 ~~4~~ ~~5~~ ~~6~~ ~~7~~ 8 ~~9~~ ~~10~~

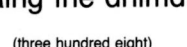 11 ~~12~~ ~~13~~ ~~14~~ ~~15~~ ~~16~~ ~~17~~ ~~18~~ ~~19~~ 20

___11___ minutes

hare ~~1~~ ~~2~~ ~~3~~ ~~4~~ ~~5~~ ~~6~~ ~~7~~ ~~8~~ ~~9~~ ~~10~~

~~11~~ ~~12~~ ~~13~~ ~~14~~ ~~15~~ 16 ~~17~~ 18 ~~19~~ 20

___16___ minutes

Ring the animal that won.

8 (three hundred eight)

Chapter 14

---

3. PRACTICE AND APPLY

Basic	All
Average	All
Extended	All

Read the following story. Ask students to listen carefully to the data. Have a volunteer write the data on the chalkboard as you read.

This story is about a race between a tortoise and a hare. The hare is so sure that he will win the race, he even takes a nap while the race is going on. It takes the hare an even number of minutes to finish the race. His total time is more than 15 min and less than 20 min. The ones digit is a 6. The tortoise plods slowly along the race course. He never stops. It takes the tortoise an odd number of minutes to finish. His total time is more than 10 min but less than 13 min. Who won the race? (the tortoise) *What should you listen carefully for during the story?* (data that will help you solve the problem) *How will it help to cross out numbers as you think about each piece of data?* (You will see which numbers match the data and which do not.)

▶ **How can logical reasoning help you find the answer?** (Possible answer: You can consider each piece of data and cross out all numbers that do not apply.)

14-11

LOSE AND ASSESS

AY WHAT YOU THINK Ask
dents to pretend that they are
spectors in Tinytown, where nothing
n be longer than an imaginary
easuring stick of 24 in. Have small
oups of students find and measure
jects and estimate how much shorter
 longer they are than their imaginary
easuring stick. Remind them to use
timated lengths for the measuring
ck (20 in.) and the objects before
ey subtract.

QUICK QUIZ

Ring the best estimate.
Mrs. James sold 43 large drinks and
22 small drinks. About how many
drinks did she sell in all?
about 50   __about 60__   about 70

CHAPTER 14

WRAP UP

INTRODUCTION The Wrap Up provides activities emphasizing math language and thinking skills for the chapter.

USING PAGE 309

Math Words ▶ **Why do you always begin to solve a subtraction problem in the ones place?** (Possible answer: You need to know how many ones to subtract first because you may need to trade 1 ten for 10 ones.)

▶ **How do you know when a trade is needed? How do you trade?** (Possible answer: A trade is needed if you need more ones to subtract; trade 1 ten for 10 ones.)

Math Reasoning ▶ **How will the sum across the top row help you find the missing number?** (Possible answer: Once you know the sum, you can subtract the numbers you know to find the missing numbers.)

▶ **How can you check to see if your answers are correct?** (Possible answer: Add across and down, all rows should have the same sum.)

Name _____

Wrap Up

MATH WORDS

1. Number the steps in order. Show how to subtract 2-digit numbers.

   [2] Trade 1 ten for 10 ones if you need to.

   [4] Subtract the tens. Write how many are left.

   [1] See if there are enough ones to subtract.

   [3] Subtract the ones. Write how many are left.

Tens	Ones
3	13
4̶	3̶
− 2	9
1	4

2. Use the order you chose. Find the difference for 43 − 29.

MATH REASONING

3. Write a number for each blank square.

   Use a  to help. Each row and

   each column should have the same sum.

	row ⟶		
column ↓	16	37	46
	54	22	23
	29	40	30

Chapter 14 Wrap Up   (three hundred nine) 3●

TEACHING OPTIONS

ENRICHMENT Challenge students to make their own subtraction squares similar to the one shown on page 309. Have them fill all squares in first. Then tell students to trace the square onto another sheet of paper and fill numbers in for only 1 row plus 3 other numbers. Have students exchange papers with a classmate and solve.

Name _____

Chapter Review/Test

1. Trade 1 ten for 10 ones. Cross out. Write the new numbers.

Tens	Ones		Tens	Ones
1	16		5	13
2	6		6	3

2. Cross out to subtract. Write the difference.

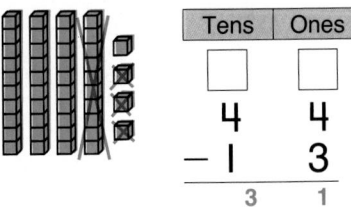

Tens	Ones
4	4
−1	3
3	1

3. Ring the best estimate.

$48
−17

about $20
(about $30)
about $40

4. Subtract. Check by adding.

```
  4 12          1
  52           29
 −29         + 23
  23           52
```

Subtract.

```
 5 14      8 12                 5 11     2 12
 64        92      60      61      32      59
−18       −45     −30     −24     − 8     − 9
 46        47      30      37      24      50
```

Solve. Use blocks to help. Write the answer in a sentence.

Li wants a set of 25 airplanes. He already has 16. How many more airplanes does he need?

Word sentences may vary. Sample answer is shown.

Li needs 9 more airplanes.

INTRODUCTION The Review/Test is provided to review and evaluate the skills and concepts presented in Chapter 14.

USING PAGE 310
If you prefer to use this page for review, you may want to use the **Multiple-Choice Posttest** (pages 55-56) or the **Free-Response Posttest** (pages 55-56) to evaluate mastery of chapter objectives.

ITEM ANALYSIS The table below correlates the Chapter Review/Test Items with the lesson objectives.

Items	Objectives
1	14-1
2	14-2, 14-3
3	14-5
4	14-6
5	14-4, 14-10
6	14-7

INFORMAL ASSESSMENT

Using Manipulatives Give students base-ten blocks and a place value chart (TA 5). Write 61 − 37 on the chalkboard and ask students to find the difference using blocks. When students are finished, ask them to explain how they found their answers.

Communication *Tell how you can estimate a difference. Explain how an estimate is helpful.* (Possible answers: subtract the tens digits. An estimate will tell you if the actual difference is reasonable.)

Critical Thinking *If you find that your answer to a subtraction problem is incorrect, what might you have done wrong?* (Possible answers: forgot to trade; traded when it was not needed, subtracted incorrectly)

CHAPTER 14

ENRICHMENT

INTRODUCTION Identifying patterns in addition helps students understand the relationship between addends and sums, and develops number sense.

USING PAGE 311
This Enrichment page is provided for all students. You may wish to use it after they have completed the Chapter Review/Test on page 310.
Help students verbalize what they know about addends and sums and number patterns they have already discovered.

▶ **If you wanted to continue the patterns in the exercises, how would you know which addends to use? How could you predict the sum?**
(Possible answer: Follow the patterns for each addend and sum; see if they are staying the same, getting larger, or getting smaller.)

▶ **Which pattern is easiest to continue? What makes you think so?**
(Answers will vary. Accept all reasonable responses.)

EXTENSIONS Distribute practagons (TA 18) to students. Challenge students to make a practagon with 11 in the center section and consecutive numbers from 55 to 62 around the middle sections. Have students compute the sums and describe the pattern they see. As an additional challenge, tell students to write 75 in the middle section and 58 in one of the outside sections. First, have students find the missing number for the middle section; then ask them to complete all other sections in the practagon. Emphasize that a pattern must be made for each addend and the sum must remain at 75.

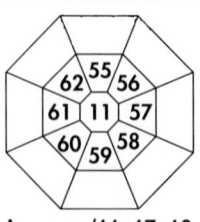

Answers: (66, 67, 68, 69, 70, 71, 72, 73)   (Possible answer)

ENRICHMENT
Addition Patterns

Add. Then ring the correct answer.

1.
| $\begin{array}{r}65\\+22\\\hline 87\end{array}$ | $\begin{array}{r}65\\+23\\\hline 88\end{array}$ | $\begin{array}{r}65\\+24\\\hline 89\end{array}$ | $\begin{array}{r}65\\+25\\\hline 90\end{array}$ | $\begin{array}{r}65\\+26\\\hline 91\end{array}$ | $\begin{array}{r}6\\+2\end{array}$ |

When the amount added is 1 more each time, what happens to the sum?
- stays the same
- (is 1 more)
- is 1 less

2.
| $\begin{array}{r}38\\+18\\\hline 56\end{array}$ | $\begin{array}{r}37\\+18\\\hline 55\end{array}$ | $\begin{array}{r}36\\+18\\\hline 54\end{array}$ | $\begin{array}{r}35\\+18\\\hline 53\end{array}$ | $\begin{array}{r}34\\+18\\\hline 52\end{array}$ | $\begin{array}{r}3\\+1\end{array}$ |

When the amount to start is 1 less each time, what happens to the sum?
- stays the same
- is 1 more
- (is 1 less)

3.
| $\begin{array}{r}54\\+19\\\hline 73\end{array}$ | $\begin{array}{r}55\\+18\\\hline 73\end{array}$ | $\begin{array}{r}56\\+17\\\hline 73\end{array}$ | $\begin{array}{r}57\\+16\\\hline 73\end{array}$ | $\begin{array}{r}58\\+15\\\hline 73\end{array}$ | $\begin{array}{r}5\\+1\end{array}$ |

When the amount to start is 1 more each time and the amount added is 1 less, what happens to the sum?
- (stays the same)
- is 1 more
- is 1 less

Chapter 14   Enrichment: Addition Patterns   (three hundred eleven)   3

Name _____

CUMULATIVE REVIEW

What is this shape?
- ○ cube
- ● sphere
- ○ cone

How many sides are there?
- ○ 5
- ● 6
- ○ 7

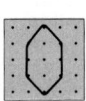

How many pegs are inside the figure?
- ○ 4
- ○ 9
- ● 1

Which figures are congruent?
- ○ A and B
- ● A and C
- ○ B and C

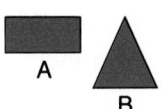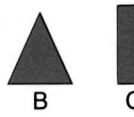

A   B   C

---

5. Subtract.

41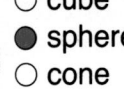

$41 - 3 =$ ___
- ○ 37
- ● 38
- ○ 44

6.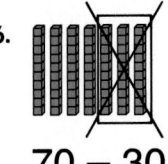

$70 - 30 =$ ___
- ● 40
- ○ 70
- ○ 30

7. 88

$88 - 20 =$ ___
- ○ 78
- ● 68
- ○ 50

8. Which is the related subtraction sentence?

$32 - 18 = 14$
- ● $32 - 14 = 18$
- ○ $32 - 20 = 12$
- ○ $32 - 16 = 16$

Which picture would you use to solve this problem?

Evan put a photo in each corner of a bulletin board. He put 2 others along each edge. How many photos did he put on the board in all?

- ○
- ○
- ●

CUMULATIVE REVIEW

INTRODUCTION   The purpose of this Cumulative Review is to maintain previously taught skills and concepts. The emphasis in this Cumulative Review is on geometry, Chapter 12; and on understanding 2-digit subtraction, Chapter 13.

ITEM ANALYSIS   The table below correlates the Cumulative Review items with the lesson objectives.

Items	Objectives
1	12-1
2, 3	12-4
4	12-7
5	13-1
6	13-2
7	13-3
8	13-4
9	13-7

CHAPTER 15 FRACTIONS

Chapter Management

MATHEMATICAL BACKGROUND

Fractions

In the early grades, students should encounter a fraction as part of a region and as part of a group or set. Since the meaning of a fraction as part of a region is easier for young students to grasp, instruction should begin with and emphasize the region model. Students must understand, first, that the region represents 1 whole and, second, that the whole is divided into a certain number of equal parts. The third idea to be grasped is that each of the equal parts that make up the whole is a fraction of the whole.

Next, students are introduced to naming fractions. The first step is to identify the number of equal parts, which tells us how to name the fractional parts of the whole. The next step is to identify how many of the equal parts are being named.

Finally, students should become familiar with the symbols for naming the fractional parts: 3 of the 4 equal parts of a whole are written as $\frac{3}{4}$ and read as *3 fourths*.

Problem Solving

In this chapter, students solve problems using the strategy Use Objects and learn how to determine whether an answer is reasonable.

TIPS FROM TEACHERS

Help students identify the numerator and the denominator. The <u>d</u>enominator can be thought of as the <u>d</u>own number; it is found beneath the numerator.

Pat Miller
N. Ward Elementary School
St. Petersburg, FL

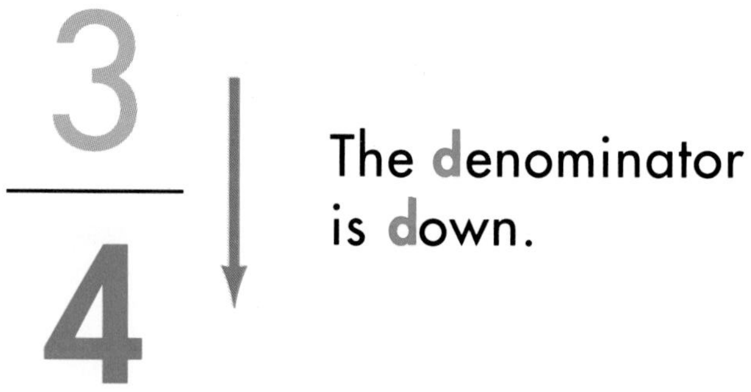

$$\frac{3}{4}$$

The **d**enominator is **d**own.

ASSESSMENT

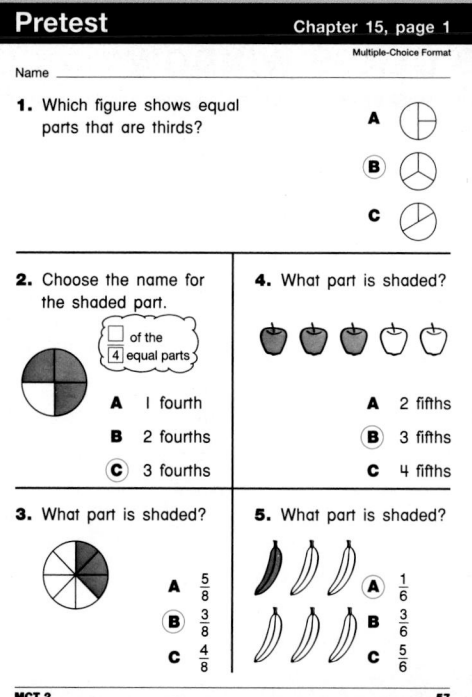

Pretest — Chapter 15, page 1

Multiple-Choice Format

Name _____

1. Which figure shows equal parts that are thirds?

- A ⊘
- B ⊘
- C ⊘

2. Choose the name for the shaded part.

▢ of the 4 equal parts

- A 1 fourth
- B 2 fourths
- **C 3 fourths**

3. What part is shaded?

- A $\frac{5}{8}$
- **B $\frac{3}{8}$**
- C $\frac{4}{8}$

4. What part is shaded?

- A 2 fifths
- **B 3 fifths**
- C 4 fifths

5. What part is shaded?

- **A $\frac{1}{6}$**
- B $\frac{3}{6}$
- C $\frac{5}{6}$

MCT 2   57

Pretest — Chapter 15, page 2

Multiple-Choice Format

Name _____

6. Estimate if more than $\frac{1}{2}$ or less than $\frac{1}{2}$ of the tiles are shaded.

- **A more than $\frac{1}{2}$ shaded**
- B less than $\frac{1}{2}$ shaded

7. Choose the picture that has $\frac{5}{10}$ shaded.

- A
- B
- **C**

8. Felix ate $\frac{1}{4}$ of a meat pie.

Mia ate $\frac{3}{4}$ of a meat pie.

How much did they eat in all?

Answer: 1 whole meat pie

Does the answer make sense?

- **A yes**
- B no

58   MCT 2

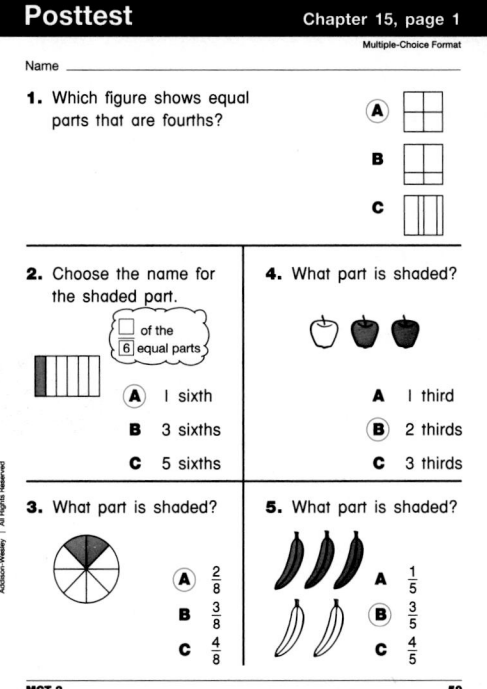

Posttest — Chapter 15, page 1

Multiple-Choice Format

Name _____

1. Which figure shows equal parts that are fourths?

- **A** ▦
- B ▤
- C ▥

2. Choose the name for the shaded part.

▢ of the 6 equal parts

- **A 1 sixth**
- B 3 sixths
- C 5 sixths

3. What part is shaded?

- **A $\frac{2}{8}$**
- B $\frac{3}{8}$
- C $\frac{4}{8}$

4. What part is shaded?

- A 1 third
- **B 2 thirds**
- C 3 thirds

5. What part is shaded?

- A $\frac{1}{5}$
- **B $\frac{3}{5}$**
- C $\frac{4}{5}$

MCT 2   59

Posttest — Chapter 15, page 2

Multiple-Choice Format

Name _____

6. Estimate if more than $\frac{1}{2}$ or less than $\frac{1}{2}$ of the tiles are shaded.

- A more than $\frac{1}{2}$ shaded
- **B less than $\frac{1}{2}$ shaded**

7. Choose the picture that has $\frac{3}{8}$ shaded.

- A
- B
- **C**

8. Marco ate $\frac{1}{2}$ of an apple.

Lori ate $\frac{1}{2}$ of a apple.

How much did they eat in all?

Answer: 1 whole apple

Does the answer make sense?

- **A yes**
- B no

60   MCT 2

ITEM ANALYSIS

Items	Objectives
1	15-1
2	15-2
3	15-3
4, 5	15-4
6	15-5
7	15-6
8	15-7

Note: The item analysis is the same for all pretests and posttests for this chapter.

ALSO AVAILABLE

- ▶ **Free Response Tests**
- ▶ **Alternative Tests**
- ▶ **Thinking Strategies**
- ▶ **Concrete Materials**

CHAPTER 15 FRACTIONS

Optional Chapter Activities

PROJECT AND BULLETIN BOARD

Divide the class into 4 groups. Assign each group a fraction—thirds, fourths, fifths, or sixths—and have the group design and make a stained-glass window to illustrate the fraction. Direct groups to glue 1-in. strips of black paper together to form the window frame and the strips between each piece, then cut and glue colored tissue paper for each piece of colored glass. Hang the finished windows in the center of the bulletin board or where light can shine through them. A border can be made for the bulletin board by having students use the same technique to make individual stained-glass windows to show given fractions. Provide index cards (for frame and strips), tissue, and glue. Look at the finished stained-glass display. Students may want to regroup the pictures by fractions.

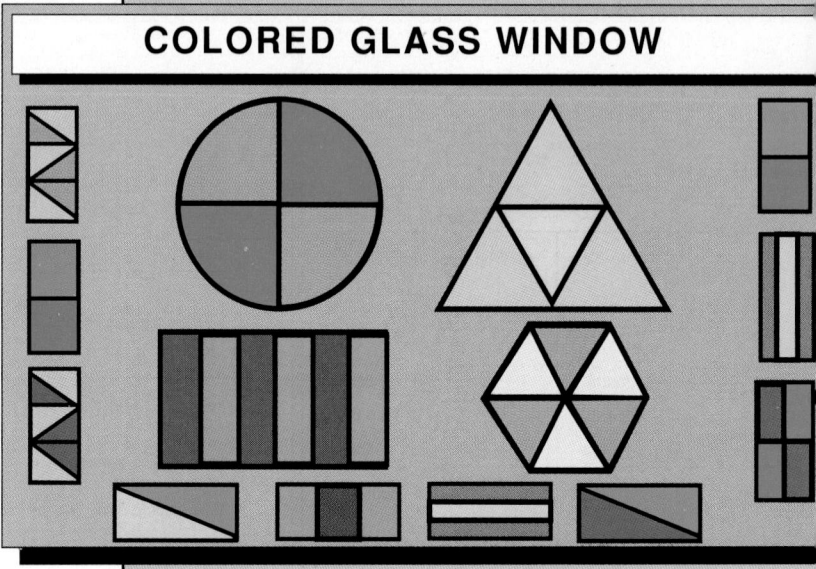

COLORED GLASS WINDOW

COOPERATIVE LEARNING

Divide the class into groups of 4 or 5. Identify the group skill: explaining and helping without just giving answers. Have students plan and present a continuous filmstrip story about fractions. On rolls of wide adding-machine paper or long paper strips, have each group draw a fraction story about thirds, fourths, fifths, sixths, or tenths and write a short script. Assign individual students the following tasks:

Make projector (1 or 2 students): Use 2 dowel rods or chubby pencils to spool the filmstrip. Cut a hole in a cardboard box larger than the frames on the filmstrip. Place the filmstrip on the rods inside the projector box and roll it for a ''moving'' picture show.

Edit filmstrip: Check that each fraction story is correct. Add a title frame and a closing frame to the filmstrip.

Provide sound: Record scripts on cassette tape. Play the tape during the presentation. Add music if desired.

Introduce project: Invite another class to see the presentation. When it is time for the presentation to begin, introduce the members of your group.

You will find grouping suggestions and cooperative learning activities in most lessons throughout this chapter.

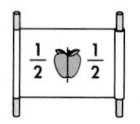 

LITERATURE

Mathews, Louise. *Gator Pie.* New York: Dodd, Mead, 1979.

Fractions are used in the story when two alligators decide to divide a pie among their friends.
Have students draw pies and divide them into halves, fourths, thirds and sixths.

Greenaway, Kate. *A-Apple Pie.* New Jersey: Castle Books, 1979.

Leonni, Leo. *Pezzettino.* New York: Pantheon, 1975.

ENGLISH AS A SECOND LANGUAGE

The language of fractional parts is emphasized in this chapter. The only difficulty for the ESL students here is in pronouncing these fractions. In developmental activities, encourage ESL students to repeat the fractions as much as possible. Work on the difference between the numbers and the fractions (eight versus eighth) both for listening and speaking. Exaggerate the endings of the words to point out the differences. Have students tape record themselves while doing the activities and keep the tape in the cassette file so that they can practice comprehension and expression.

The problem-solving feature contains questions in past and future tenses. Have students write their answers on the chalkboard and point out variations, such as *They each got, Each of them got, Susan got, Her mother got.* When students are asked if an answer makes sense, have them think out loud and discuss why the answer makes sense or not.

GIFTED

Mathematically talented students may already understand fractions and be able to work with them readily. They will nevertheless likely be interested in many of the activities presented in this chapter. Challenge these students to make designs based on fractional parts. For example, after Lesson 4, provide students with 2 sheets of colored paper and show them how to fold 1 paper to show fourths and the other to show eighths. Next, ask them to cut on the folds to make fraction pieces. Have them write the fractions on the pieces in numbers and in words—for example, $\frac{3}{8}$ and three eighths. Then ask them to make a design by pasting fraction pieces to a third sheet of colored paper. If this appeals to your students, have them create other designs, using different fractional parts. Have students compare and discuss their designs.

STUDENTS AT RISK

For Fraction Concentration, prepare a set of index cards with pictures of fractional parts colored in (halves, thirds, fourths) and a set of cards with the corresponding fractions in written form. Have students mix up the cards and lay them face down. Students alternate turning over 2 cards. If they show a fraction and its matching picture, they keep the cards and take another turn. If the cards do not match, the student places them face down again. The student with the most pairs wins the round.

 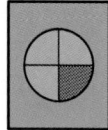 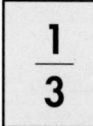 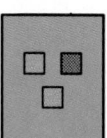

Provide an opportunity for students to follow a simple recipe that requires them to use fractional parts of cups, teaspoons, and tablespoons. Have them read the recipe and measure the correct quantities. Provide copies of the recipe for students to make under supervision at home. Making fruit salad is an excellent project for exploring fractions.

You may also use the Reteaching Supplements and the specific Reteaching Tips from each lesson in this chapter.

Chapter 15 Optional Chapter Activities   **313D**

Storybook

PICTURE

These pictures and accompanying stories and poems are available as storybooks.

You may want to read and discuss this story with your students before starting the chapter. The first lesson in this chapter includes a question about the story. Lessons 1, 2, 4, and 5 in this chapter have questions in the informal Assessment that refer to the story.

Roberta's Birthday Lunch

Roberta Rabbit ate a nice breakfast of carrot juice and strawberry waffles. Then she made some cornbread for lunch. "Now I will just sit outside and wait for my friends to visit me," she said to herself. Roberta was quite sure that her four best friends would come to see her this particular morning because today was her birthday. When they came, she was going to ask them to have a birthday lunch with her.

Roberta waited. And she waited. And then she waited some more. But nobody came to wish her happy birthday. She looked up and saw that the sun was all the way up in the sky. "Why, it's already noon," she thought, "and time for lunch. I guess I'll just have to eat by myself. My friends must have forgotten all about my birthday."

On the table she put a head of lettuce, some cornbread in a round tin, and some radishes. Just as Roberta was about to sit down at the table, she heard a knock at the door. "Why, it must be my four friends coming to visit," she thought. But instead it was the mail carrier. As he turned to go, Roberta asked, "Would you like to stay and share some lunch with me?"

"That would be very nice," he replied. Roberta carefully cut the head of lettuce into two equal pieces. And then Roberta and her guest each ate one of the halves.

Roberta was about to cut the cornbread when there was another knock at the door. "Why, it must be my four friends coming to visit," she thought. But instead it was the milk deliverer. "Would you like to come in and share some lunch with us?" asked Roberta.

"I would enjoy that very much," she replied. Roberta then carefully cut the cornbread into three equal pieces. Then she and her two guests each ate one of the thirds.

Roberta was looking at the four radishes wondering how she could divide them into thirds, too, when there was yet another knock at the door. "Oh, it's finally my friends," she said. But no, it was the friendly neighborhood policeman.

"Would you like to share some lunch with us?" she asked.

"I'd be delighted to join you," he said.

So again Roberta counted. She found that she needed to divide the radishes into fourths. And then everyone ate one radish.

Roberta's guests were telling her what a delicious lunch it was, when there was another knock at the door. Roberta wondered to herself, "Who could be coming now? It certainly will not be my four friends, because they have forgotten my birthday." But when Roberta opened the door, there stood her four friends holding a beautiful birthday carrot cake complete with birthday candles. "Happy birthday!" they cried. They had not forgotten her birthday after all.

Everybody sang *Happy Birthday* to Roberta. And then it was time for her to cut the cake. She counted her guests. "Seven of you and one of me," she said, and then carefully cut the cake into 8 equal pieces.

As each of the animals ate one of the eighths, Roberta said, "This was the best birthday of all. Instead of four friends I now have seven."

LESSON OPTIONS 15-1

Finding Equal Parts of a Whole

OBJECTIVE 15-1   To find equal parts of a whole

PREBOOK ACTIVITIES

PRIOR KNOWLEDGE

On the chalkboard, draw an apple, a banana, an orange, and some grapes. *Suppose that you want to share these fruits equally with a friend. How might you cut them so that you each get the same amount?* (apple: cut it down the middle; banana: cut it in the middle or slice it lengthwise; orange: cut it down the middle or count the pieces and give half to your friend; grapes: count them and give half to your friend)

COMMUNICATION

Writing and Listening in Math   Write **equal parts** and **unequal parts** on the chalkboard. Ask students what they think these words mean. Then have them use the words to complete these sentences in their Math Journals.
1. Parts that are the same size are (equal) parts.
2. Parts that are different sizes are (unequal) parts.
Explain that 1 whole thing can be divided equally into 2 parts called **halves,** 3 parts called **thirds,** or 4 parts called **fourths.** Ask students to hold up fingers to show how many equal parts each shows: halves, thirds, fourths. (2, 3, 4)

EXPLORE AND CONNECT

Materials: paper shapes, string, straws, clay
Grouping Suggestions: small groups
Demonstrate equal and unequal parts by cutting pieces of string or a straw. Hold up 1 item that has been cut into thirds. *If I gave 1 piece of this to 3 people, would the sharing be fair? Why or why not?* (Possible answer: Yes, because the parts are equal.) Repeat this activity for both equal and unequal parts. Then distribute paper cut into squares, rectangles, and circles; lengths of string; and chunks of clay to students. *How can you divide each of these items into 2, 3, or 4 equal parts?* Allow students to explore ways of dividing the items. Then ask them to choose 1 item and describe or show how they would divide it. Ask students to use the term **halves** if they make 2 equal parts, **thirds** if they make 3 equal parts, and **fourths** if they make 4 equal parts.

CONNECTIONS   Use these anytime.

Problem of the Day
Understanding the Operations

Find the answer. Then write a number sentence.
The Twins scored 63 home runs last season.
The Bills scored 57 home runs.
How many more home runs did the Twins score? (63 − 57 = 6; the Twins scored 6 more home runs.)

Math Connection

Equal or Unequal   With 3 friends, divide a block of clay into 4 equal parts. Each person should make an object with his or her part of the clay. Compare the objects. Do all the objects contain an equal amount of clay? Explain your answer.

Subject Integration

Fine Arts   On paper, design a shape that can be divided into equal parts. Cut it out and ask a classmate to fold it into halves, thirds, or fourths. Make another shape that cannot be divided equally. Ask another friend to tell which shape can be divided in equal parts and which cannot.

CLASSWORK AND HOMEWORK SUPPLEMENTS

Basic

Exercises All

Supplements
Reteaching 129 or
Practice 129

Average

Exercises All

Supplements
Practice 129
Challenges 129 or
Thinking Skills 129

Extended

Exercises All

Supplements
Challenges 129
Thinking Skills 129

Other Resources:
Math In Stride, pp. 94-96
Explorations, pp. 226-228
Mathematics Book A, pp. 81-82

15-1

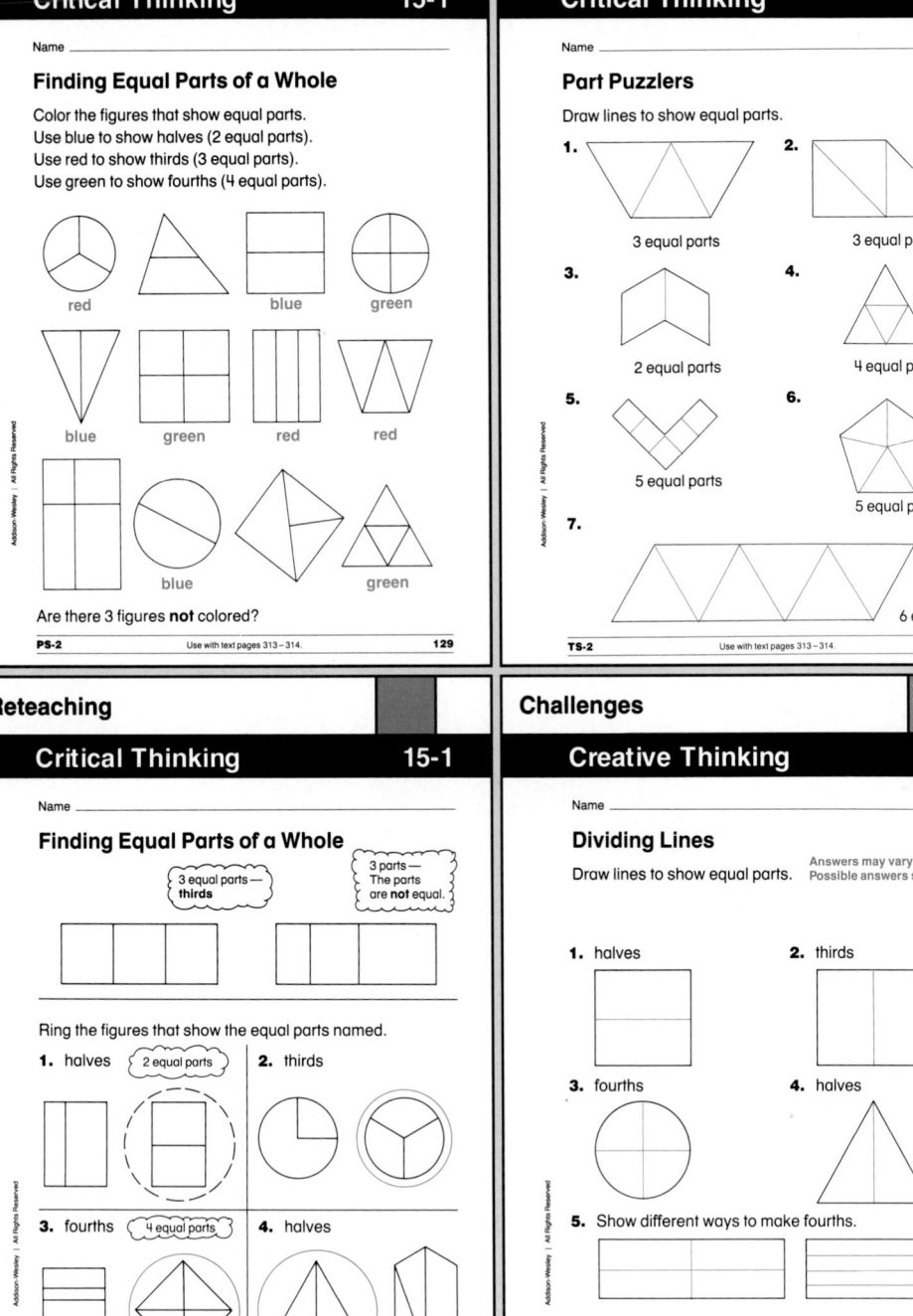

Practice

Critical Thinking 15-1

Name _____

Finding Equal Parts of a Whole

Color the figures that show equal parts.
Use blue to show halves (2 equal parts).
Use red to show thirds (3 equal parts).
Use green to show fourths (4 equal parts).

red blue green
blue green red red
blue green

Are there 3 figures **not** colored?

PS-2   Use with text pages 313–314.   129

Building Thinking Skills

Critical Thinking 15-1

Name _____

Part Puzzlers

Draw lines to show equal parts.

1. 3 equal parts
2. 3 equal parts
3. 2 equal parts
4. 4 equal parts
5. 5 equal parts
6. 5 equal parts
7. 6 equal parts

TS-2   Use with text pages 313–314.   129

Reteaching

Critical Thinking 15-1

Name _____

Finding Equal Parts of a Whole

3 equal parts — **thirds**

3 parts — The parts **are not** equal.

Ring the figures that show the equal parts named.

1. halves   2 equal parts
2. thirds
3. fourths   4 equal parts
4. halves

RS-2   Use with text pages 313–314.   129

Challenges

Creative Thinking 15-1

Name _____

Dividing Lines

Draw lines to show equal parts.   Answers may vary. Possible answers shown.

1. halves
2. thirds
3. fourths
4. halves
5. Show different ways to make fourths.

CS-2   Use with text pages 313–314.   129

OBJECTIVE 15-1
To find equal parts of a whole

Materials: fraction pieces, clay

1. MOTIVATE AND TEACH

LEARN ABOUT IT

Read the story about Roberta Rabbit to the students. *In how many pieces did Roberta divide the lettuce?* (2) *Were they equal pieces?* (yes) Have students show the 2 equal pieces with their fraction pieces. Direct students' attention to the picture of cornbread on page 313 and ask then to use their fraction pieces to cover the bread with the least number of pieces.

▶ **How did you decide which pieces to use? What are these pieces called?** (Possible answer: The least number of pieces that would cover the bread is 2. 2 equal pieces are called halves.)

▶ **Model and explain how other equal pieces can be used to cover the bread.** (Possible answer: The bread can also be covered by 4 fourths or 3 thirds.)

▶ **Explore ways to use unequal pieces to cover the whole. Describe your findings.** (Possible answer: 1 half, 2 fourths)

▶ **If you were really hungry, would you rather have 2 thirds or 1 half of the bread? Why? Use your pieces to model each fraction.** (Possible answer: 2 thirds, because it is more than 1 half)

2. CHECK UNDERSTANDING

ERROR ALERT Being unable to understand how 1 whole can be divided into different kinds of equal parts.

15
Fractions

TEACHING OPTIONS

RETEACHING TIPS Use 4 same-size sheets of paper. Have students fold 1 in half and cut on the fold, then fold and cut another in fourths. Have them paste the halves and fourths on the other 2 papers to show that a whole can be divided in more than 1 way. Assign Reteaching Supplement 128.

ENRICHMENT Have students pretend they work in a pizza parlor. Tell them to fold and cut paper circles to find different combinations of equal parts, then prepare a menu that shows the size and price of each slice. Have them think about how the price might correspond to the size of the slice.

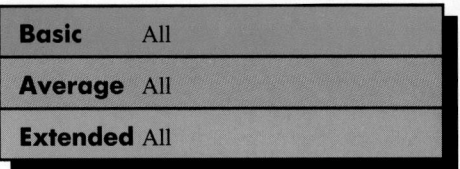

...inding Equal Parts of a Whole

Use your fraction pieces.
How many pieces will
cover the white whole?
Match to show equal parts.

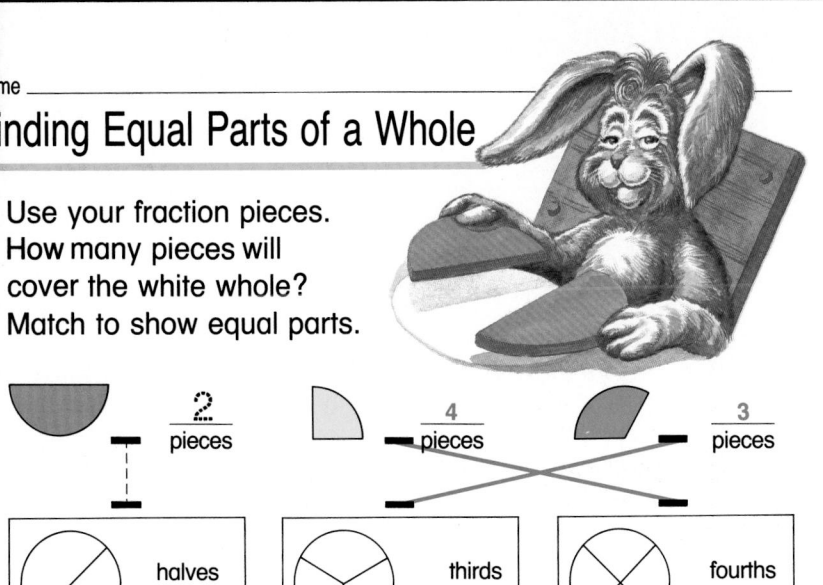

$\underline{2}$ pieces	$\underline{4}$ pieces	$\underline{3}$ pieces
halves	thirds	fourths
2 equal parts	3 equal parts	4 equal parts

...olor the figures that show the equal parts named.

fourths   **3. thirds**   **4. halves**

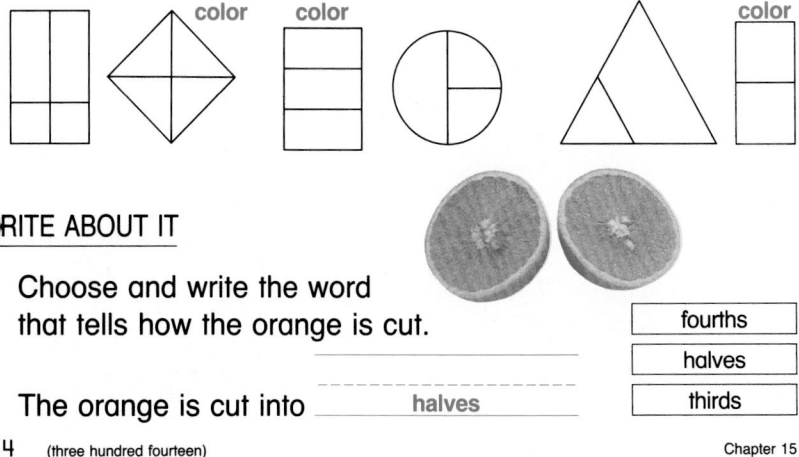

color   color   color

...RITE ABOUT IT

Choose and write the word
that tells how the orange is cut.

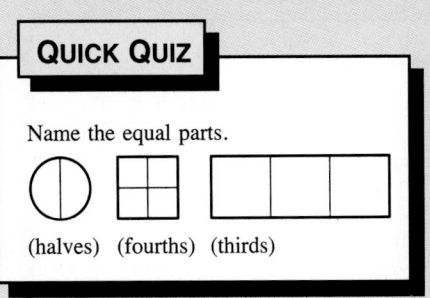

| fourths |
| halves |
| thirds |

The orange is cut into _____ halves

---

3. PRACTICE AND APPLY

Basic	All
Average	All
Extended	All

PRACTICE

What are you to do in Exercise 1? (Write
the number of pieces that will cover the
whole and then draw a line to match
equal parts.) *What 2 things should you
look for as you do Exercises 2-4?* (Look
for equal parts and for the number named
in each exercise.)

APPLY

WRITE ABOUT IT ▶ **Describe how
you can be sure your answer is
correct for Exercise 5.** (Possible answer:
Choose your answer. Then draw pictures
of the orange as it would look if it were
divided into the other equal parts named.
If the pictures do not match the one
shown on the page, then your answer is
correct.)

15-1

...LOSE AND ASSESS

...HOW WHAT YOU KNOW

...rite the words *halves, thirds,* and
...urths on cards. Ask students to take
...rns choosing 1 of the words. Have
...em choose a way to show their
...umber of equal parts. They might
...aw a whole shape and divide it into
...ual parts, use clay to illustrate the
...actions, or use the fraction pieces in
...e kit. Have them share their display,
...d use their word in a sentence.

QUICK QUIZ

Name the equal parts.

(halves) (fourths) (thirds)

Modeling and Recording Fractional Parts

OBJECTIVE 15-2 To identify fractions of a whole for halves, thirds, fourths, and sixths

PREBOOK ACTIVITIES

QUICK REVIEW

Add or subtract.
1. $43 + 12 =$ (55)   **2.** $29 - 19 =$ (10)
3. $39 + 8 =$ (47)   **4.** $45 - 18 =$ (27)
5. $72 - 14 =$ (58)   **6.** $24 + 17 =$ (41)

PRIOR KNOWLEDGE

Show students 2 sheets of paper. Fold the first into halves and fold the second into 2 unequal parts. *Which paper shows 2 equal parts? How do you know the parts are equal?* (The sheet folded in half; they are the same size.) *What do we call these parts?* (halves) *What other names for equal parts do you know? How many equal parts does your word name?* (Possible answer: fourths; 4 equal parts)

COMMUNICATION

Discussing Math Write the words *halves, thirds, fourths, fifths,* and *sixths* on the chalkboard. Read the words aloud. *Halves are 2 equal parts of 1 whole. Which word means 3 equal parts?* (thirds) *How many equal parts do you think fourths are?* (4) *What are fifths? sixths?* (5 equal parts; 6 equal parts) *When might you want to break something into halves? thirds? fourths? fifths? sixths?* (Possible answer: when you need to share something equally with that many people)

EXPLORE AND CONNECT

Materials: 4 paper strips per pair
Grouping Suggestions: pairs
Have students in pairs take turns folding strips of paper in halves, thirds, fourths, and sixths. Then have students mark t equal parts of each fraction strip. Write the fractions $\frac{1}{2}$, $\frac{1}{3}$, $\frac{2}{4}$, a $\frac{2}{6}$ on the chalkboard. Have students color individual strips to show each fraction and have them label the colored part. *How can you be sure the parts you make are equal?* (Possible answer: Cut and place each part on top of the others to check the size.) *What do you notice about the colored parts showing 1 half and 2 fourths?* (They are the same size.) *Which strip h a colored part the same size as 1 third?* (2 sixths) *Which is larger—1 of 2 parts or 1 of 3 parts?* (1 of 2 parts) *How do y know?* (because the colored part of the strip showing 1 half is larger than the colored part of the strip showing 1 third)

CONNECTIONS Use these anytime.

Problem of the Day

Logic Mrs.Fugua hired Joe to rake her yard for $8. On the first day, Joe raked half of the yard. On the second day, Joe asked his friend for help. Joe and his friend finished raking the yard. How much should Joe pay his friend? ($2)

Math Connection

Estimation About what fraction of your height is your arm length? Estimate first and then check.

Life Skills

Sharing Draw a picture to help you solve this problem. If there are 6 people at a party and you have 2 pies, would you cut each pie in halves, thirds, or fourths? Why? (thirds; each person would get 1 piece.)

CLASSWORK AND HOMEWORK SUPPLEMENTS

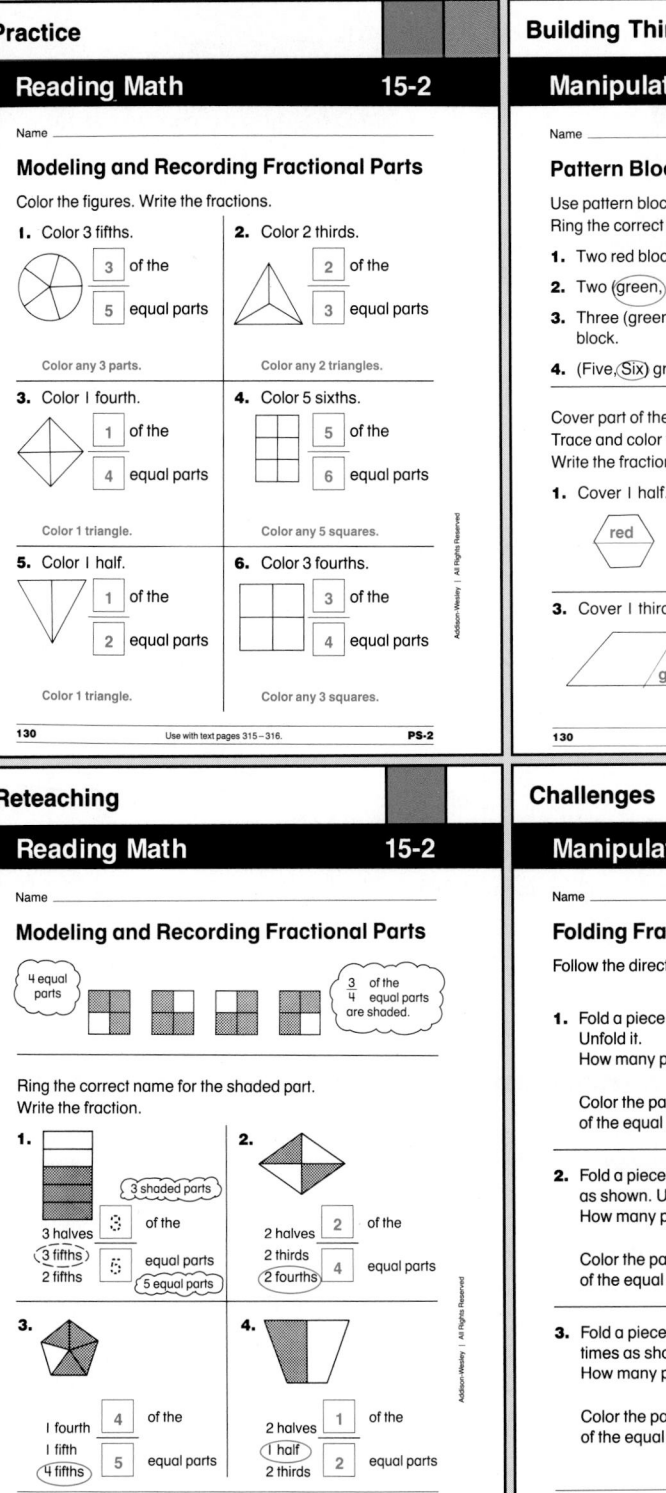

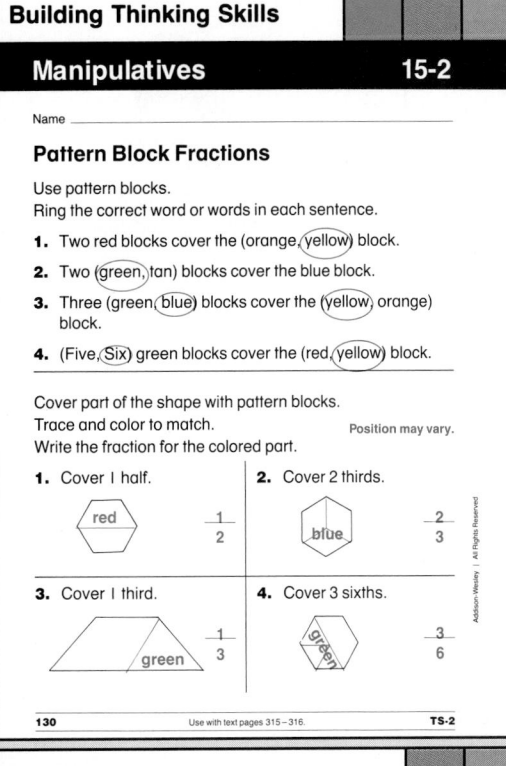

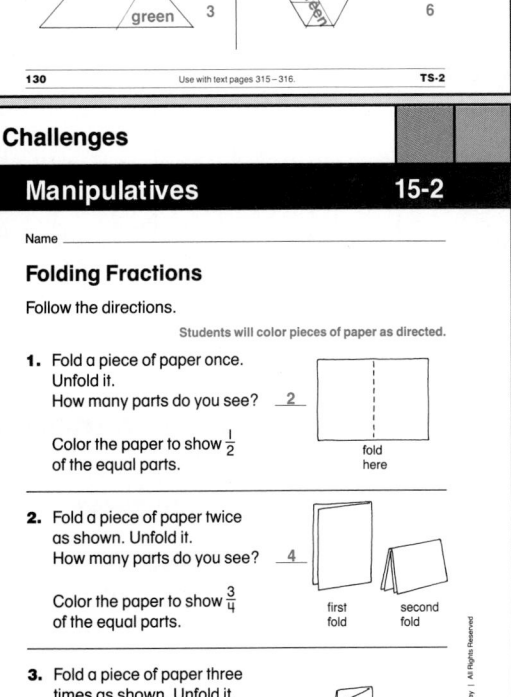

OPTIONS FOR INDIVIDUAL NEEDS

Basic

Exercises All
More Practice, p. 426, set A

Supplements
Reteaching 130 or
Practice 130
Thinking Skills 130

Average

Exercises All
More Practice, p. 426, set A

Supplements
Practice 130
Challenges 130 or
Thinking Skills 130

Extended

Exercises All

Supplements
Challenges 130
Thinking Skills 130

Other Resources:
Math In Stride, p. 94-97
Explorations, p. 228
Mathematics Book A, pp. 81-82

15-2

LESSON PLAN 15-2

OBJECTIVE 15-2
To identify fractions of a whole for halves, thirds, fourths and sixths

> **Materials:** fraction pieces, pattern blocks
>
> **Grouping Suggestion:** pairs

1. MOTIVATE AND TEACH

LEARN ABOUT IT

Write the fractions $\frac{1}{2}$, $\frac{2}{3}$, $\frac{1}{4}$, $\frac{1}{6}$, $\frac{3}{6}$, and $\frac{5}{6}$ on the chalkboard. Have students in pairs take turns modeling each fraction using their fraction pieces.

▶ **In Exercises 1–4 on page 315, which fraction is largest? Which is smallest?** ($\frac{2}{2}$, $\frac{1}{3}$)

▶ **How would you put the fractions in order from least to greatest?** ($\frac{1}{3}$, $\frac{3}{4}$, $\frac{5}{6}$, $\frac{2}{2}$)

▶ **Would you rather have $\frac{2}{6}$ or $\frac{1}{3}$ of something you like? Why?** (Either; they are the same amount.)

▶ **Why is $\frac{2}{2}$ the same as 1 whole?** ($\frac{2}{2}$ means 2 of the 2 equal parts; it is the same as 1 whole.)

▶ **How many more equal parts would you need to make $\frac{3}{4}$ into 1 whole?** ($\frac{1}{4}$)

2. CHECK UNDERSTANDING

ERROR ALERT Being unable to see fractions, such as 3 thirds, as 1 whole divided into equal parts from a drawing or a diagram.

Name _____

Modeling and Recording Fractional Parts

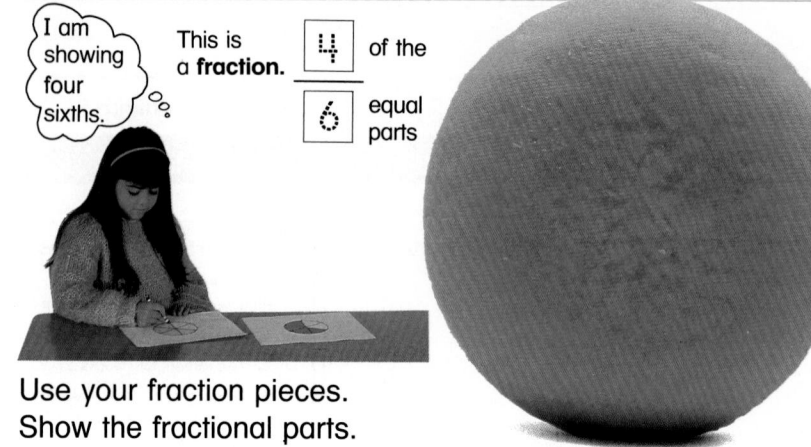

Use your fraction pieces.
Show the fractional parts.
Color to match. Write the fraction.

Check students' work.

1. Show one third.

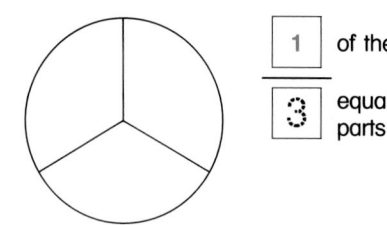

2. Show three fourths.

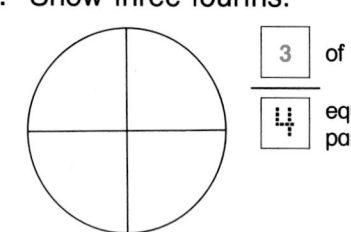

3. Show five sixths.

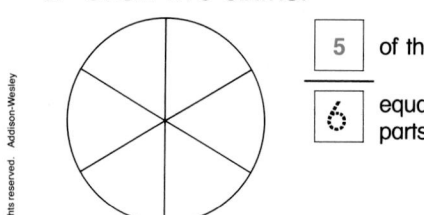

4. Show two halves.

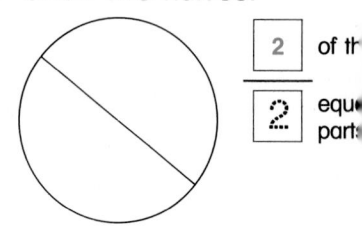

Chapter 15

(three hundred fifteen) 3|

TEACHING OPTIONS

RETEACHING TIPS Have students use the yellow hexagon block as a base and cover it with other blocks. Have them find 1 half of the hexagon (red trapezoid), 1 third (blue parallelogram), and 1 sixth (green triangle). Assign Reteaching Supplement 130.

ENRICHMENT Have students draw and color a picture in which 1 △ is $\frac{1}{6}$ of their design. (Designs will vary but should be 6 times larger than 1 △ .) Ask them what fraction of their design is 1 △△ . ($\frac{1}{2}$)

ing the correct name for the colored part.
rite the fraction.

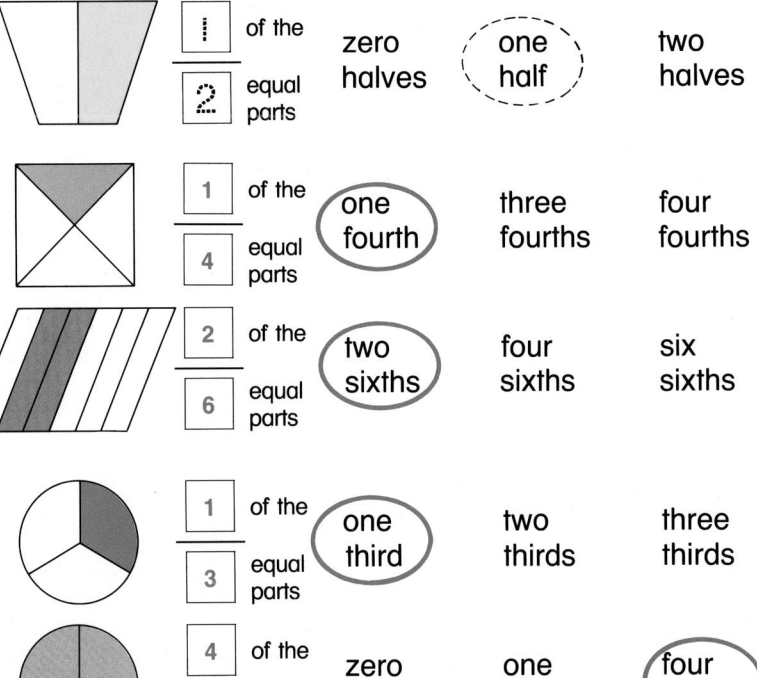

$\frac{1}{2}$ of the equal parts	zero halves	(one half)	two halves
$\frac{1}{4}$ of the equal parts	(one fourth)	three fourths	four fourths
$\frac{2}{6}$ of the equal parts	(two sixths)	four sixths	six sixths
$\frac{1}{3}$ of the equal parts	(one third)	two thirds	three thirds
$\frac{4}{4}$ of the equal parts	zero fourths	one fourth	(four fourths)

AKE AN ESTIMATE

Ring the fraction that tells **about** how long
the carrot is. The carrot is about as long as

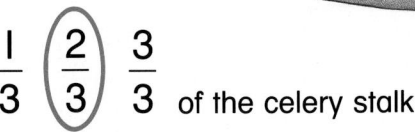

$\frac{1}{3}$ $\left(\frac{2}{3}\right)$ $\frac{3}{3}$ of the celery stalk.

6 (three hundred sixteen)   More Practice, page 426, set A   Chapter 15

LOSE AND ASSESS

HOW WHAT YOU KNOW

ave students use pattern blocks to
d ways to build a hexagon, then
k the following questions: *What
action of a hexagon is 1 green
angle?* ($\frac{1}{6}$) *What fraction of a
xagon is 1 blue parallelogram?* ($\frac{1}{3}$)
hat fraction of a hexagon is 1 red
apezoid?* ($\frac{1}{2}$) Reread the chapter
ory. Have students use their fraction
eces to show how the lettuce,
rnbread, and cake were divided.

QUICK QUIZ

Write a fraction for the shaded part.

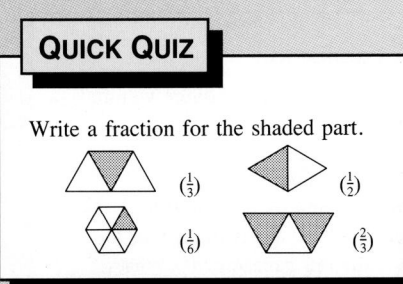

$\left(\frac{1}{3}\right)$ $\left(\frac{1}{2}\right)$

$\left(\frac{1}{6}\right)$ $\left(\frac{2}{3}\right)$

3. PRACTICE AND APPLY

Basic	All
Average	All
Extended	All

PRACTICE

*How will you name the colored part in
each exercise on page 316?* (Possible
answer: Count the colored parts and
write that number above the line. Count
how many equal parts in all and write
that number below the line.)

APPLY

MAKE AN ESTIMATE ▶ **How did
you decide on your answer?** (Possible
answer: The end of the carrot is closest
to the second dashed line.)
▶ **What answer would you ring if the
end of the carrot was close to the first
dashed line?** ($\frac{1}{3}$)
▶ **Write a fraction to show about how
long 2 carrots would be, compared to
the celery stalk.** ($\frac{3}{3}$)

15-2

Chapter 15 Lesson 2   **316**

Modeling and Writing Fractions

OBJECTIVE 15-3   To identify fractions of a whole for eighths

PREBOOK ACTIVITIES

QUICK REVIEW

Continue the pattern.

4, 8, 12, __(16)__ , __(20)__ , __(24)__
4, 7, 10, __(13)__ , __(16)__ , __(19)__
5, 10, 15, __(20)__ , __(25)__ , __(30)__
2, 4, 6, __(8)__ , __(10)__ , __(12)__
35, 30, 25, __(20)__ , __(15)__ , __(10)__

PRIOR KNOWLEDGE

Present the following situation: *You want to share an apple with 3 friends. How many parts should you cut the apple into?* (4) Ask students to act out the situation to check their answer. *If you want this to be a fair share, what do the parts need to be?* (equal; the same size) *How many parts would each friend get?* (1) *What is each part called?* (one fourth)

COMMUNICATION

Reading and Writing in Math   Write the fractions $\frac{1}{3}$, $\frac{2}{3}$, and $\frac{3}{3}$ on the chalkboard. Read each fraction aloud and ask students to explain what it means. (Possible answers: 1 of 3 equal parts; 2 of 3 equal parts; all 3 of the 3 equal parts) Then write the fraction $\frac{1}{4}$ on the chalkboard. *If we are counting by fourths, which fourth should come next?* ($\frac{2}{4}$) *Why?* (because $\frac{1}{4}$ is 1 of 4 parts and $\frac{2}{4}$ is 2 of 4 parts) Ask a student to write $\frac{2}{4}$ on the chalkboard. Continue this procedure to list all fourths, fifths, and sixths.

EXPLORE AND CONNECT

Materials: fraction pieces
Grouping Suggestion: pairs
Write $\frac{1}{8}$, $\frac{2}{8}$, $\frac{3}{8}$, $\frac{4}{8}$, $\frac{5}{8}$, $\frac{6}{8}$, $\frac{7}{8}$, and $\frac{8}{8}$ on the chalkboard. Have students in pairs take turns modeling each fraction. *Which pieces show 8 parts?* (red) *What do you notice about the parts?* (They are equal.) *How can you check to make sure all pieces are equal?* (Possible answer: Put all of the pieces on 1 piece to make sure they match in size.) *Which fraction is the smallest?* ($\frac{1}{8}$) *Which fraction is the largest?* ($\frac{8}{8}$) *What is another way to say $\frac{8}{8}$?* (1 whole) *Which fraction looks like it is one half of the whole?* (*What color pieces would you use to show sixths?* (green) *fourths?* (yellow)
Have students repeat the activity modeling halves, thirds, fourths, and sixths.

CONNECTIONS   Use these anytime.

Problem of the Day

Logic   Draw a picture to help you solve this problem: Kathy, Enzo, and Nima collect stamps. Kathy has 12 stamps. Enzo has half as many stamps as Kathy. Nima has $\frac{1}{3}$ of the number of stamps that Enzo has. How many stamps do Enzo and Nima have together? (8)

Math Connection

Geometry   Build this figure with red and green pattern blocks.

green → ▲ red ▲ ← green

How many green triangles will fit on the red trapezoid? (3) What fraction of the whole is the red trapezoid? ($\frac{3}{5}$) What fraction of the whole are the green triangles? ($\frac{2}{5}$)

Minute Math

Draw a rectangle.   How many ways can you find to divide the rectangle into halves? (Answers may vary.)

CLASSWORK AND HOMEWORK SUPPLEMENTS

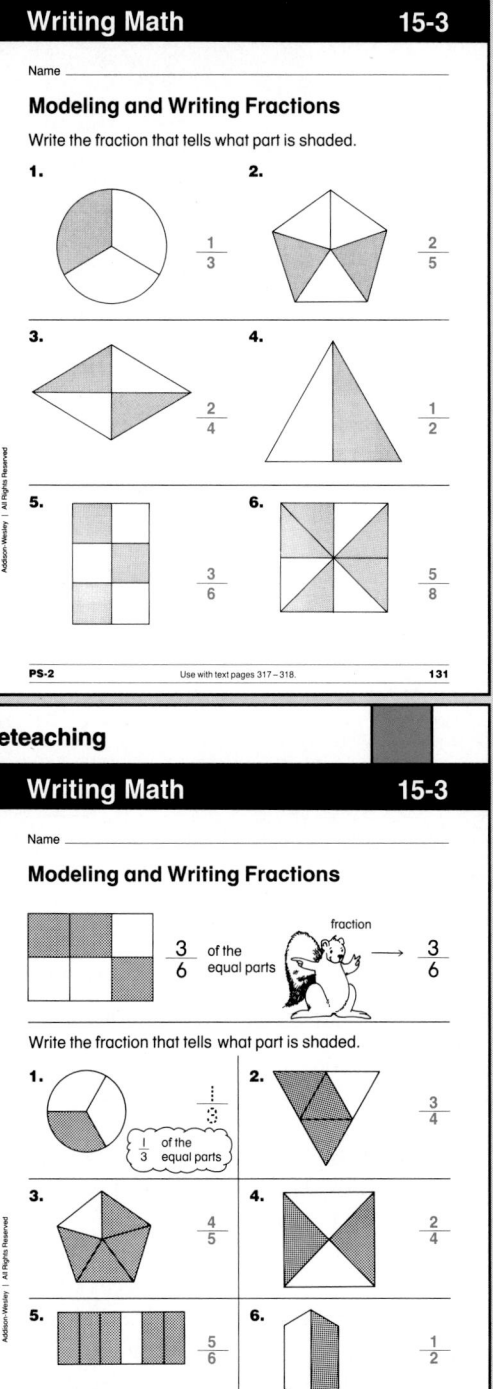

Practice

Writing Math 15-3

Name _____

Modeling and Writing Fractions

Write the fraction that tells what part is shaded.

1. $\frac{1}{3}$

2. $\frac{2}{5}$

3. $\frac{2}{4}$

4. $\frac{1}{2}$

5. $\frac{3}{6}$

6. $\frac{5}{8}$

PS-2   Use with text pages 317–318.   131

Reteaching

Writing Math 15-3

Name _____

Modeling and Writing Fractions

$\frac{3}{6}$ of the equal parts → $\frac{3}{6}$ fraction

Write the fraction that tells what part is shaded.

1. $\frac{1}{3}$ of the equal parts

2. $\frac{3}{4}$

3. $\frac{4}{5}$

4. $\frac{2}{4}$

5. $\frac{5}{6}$

6. $\frac{1}{2}$

RS-2   Use with text pages 317–318.   131

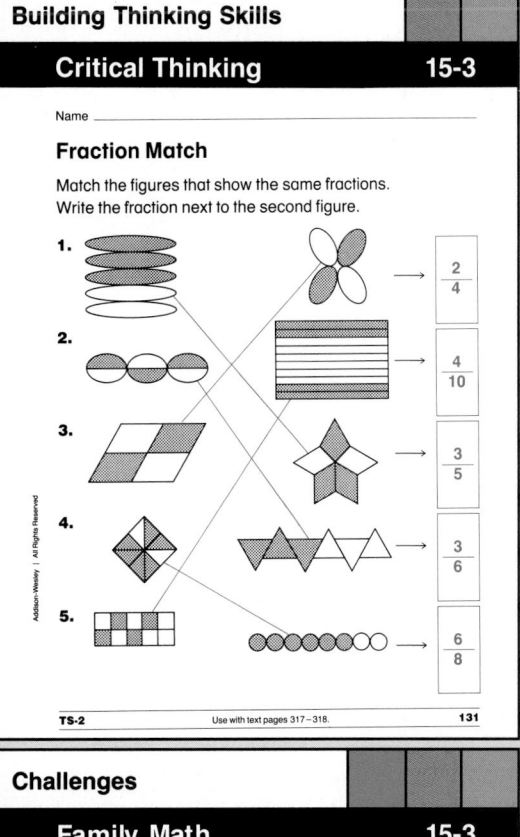

Building Thinking Skills

Critical Thinking 15-3

Name _____

Fraction Match

Match the figures that show the same fractions.
Write the fraction next to the second figure.

1. → $\frac{2}{4}$

2. → $\frac{4}{10}$

3. → $\frac{3}{5}$

4. → $\frac{3}{6}$

5. → $\frac{6}{8}$

TS-2   Use with text pages 317–318.   131

Challenges

Family Math 15-3

Name _____

Follow the Fractions

Dear Family,
Your child has been learning about fractions. Help your child complete the path and have him or her read each fraction aloud.

- Look at each fraction picture as you move down the river.
- Choose the fraction that matches the picture.
- Draw a line to the dot next to the matching fraction.

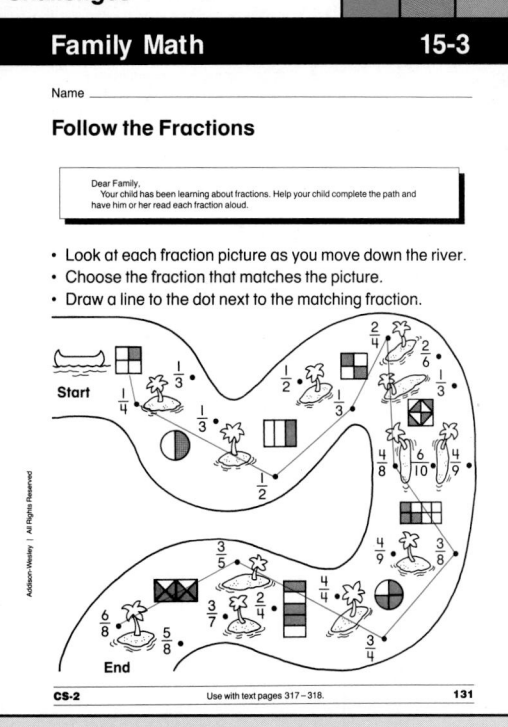

CS-2   Use with text pages 317–318.   131

OPTIONS FOR INDIVIDUAL NEEDS

Basic

Exercises All, Midchapter Review/Quiz
More Practice, p. 426, set B

Supplements
Reteaching 131 or
Practice 131
Challenges 131

Average

Exercises All, Midchapter Review/Quiz
More Practice, p. 426, set B

Supplements
Practice 131
Challenges 131 or
Thinking Skills 131

Extended

Exercises All, Midchapter Review/Quiz

Supplements
Challenges 131
Thinking Skills 131

Other Resources:
Math in Stride, pp. 95-97
Explorations, p. 228
Mathematics Book A, p. 82

15-3

LESSON PLAN 15-3

OBJECTIVE 15-3
To identify fractions of a whole for eighths

Materials: fraction pieces; fraction cards $\frac{1}{6}$, $\frac{3}{6}$, $\frac{5}{6}$, $\frac{1}{8}$, $\frac{2}{8}$ and $\frac{4}{8}$; spinners; TA3 (Centimeter Graph Paper)

Grouping Suggestion: small groups

1. MOTIVATE AND TEACH

LEARN ABOUT IT

Have students use their fraction pieces to model several fractions on the cards. Then have them look at the shapes and spinner on page 317.
▶ **What is the greatest number of equal parts you will be able to color in any of the exercises? Why?** (5; it is the greatest number on the spinner)
▶ **Why will you not be able to color 1 whole in any of the exercises?** (Possible answer: The highest number on the spinner is 5; the whole number of equal parts for each fraction is 6 or 8.)
▶ **What chance would you have of spinning a 1 to make $\frac{1}{8}$ in Exercise 1? Why?** (Possible answer: 1 chance out of 5 because there are 5 numbers on the spinner)
▶ **What is the least fraction you can make?** ($\frac{1}{8}$)
▶ **Write your fractions in order from the smallest to the largest. Check your list by looking at the pictures you colored.** (Fractions will vary.)

2. CHECK UNDERSTANDING

ERROR ALERT Being unable to identify the fraction that names the fractional part of a shape.

Name _____

Modeling and Writing Fractions

I colored 3 of the 8 equal parts. That's three eighths.

Work in a group. Spin and color the number of equal parts. Write the fraction for what you colored. *Answers may vary. Check students' work.*

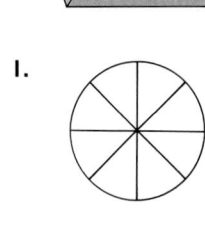

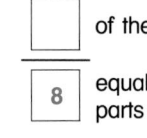 of the

$\frac{}{8}$ equal parts

1.

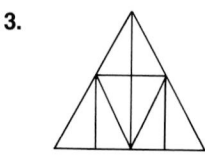

☐ of the

$\frac{}{8}$ equal parts

2.

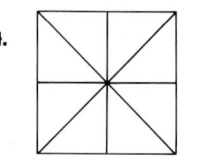

☐ of the

$\frac{}{6}$ equal parts

3.

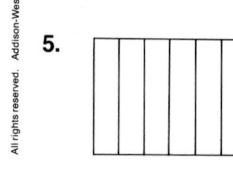

☐ of the

$\frac{}{8}$ equal parts

4.

☐ of the

$\frac{}{8}$ equal parts

5.

☐ of the

$\frac{}{6}$ equal parts

6.

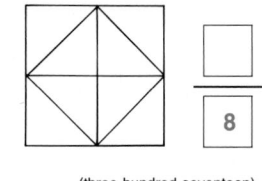

☐ of the

$\frac{}{8}$ equal parts

Chapter 15

(three hundred seventeen) **3**

TEACHING OPTIONS

RETEACHING TIPS Have pairs choose a fraction card. One student outlines on graph paper the number of squares that show the total number of equal parts. The second colors the number of squares that show the fraction shown on the card. Assign Reteaching Supplement 131.

COMPUTER Piece of Cake Math, Springboard Software © 1983 For all to review prerequisite skills. In *Multicake*, students determine how many pieces of cake the baker will have when the cake is cut down and across a given number of times. The recommended game requires 5 minutes.

rite the fraction that tells
hat part is colored.

1.

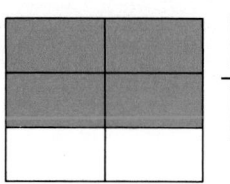 $\dfrac{4}{6}$ of the equal parts

2.

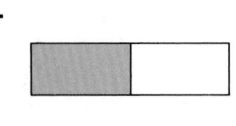 $\dfrac{1}{2}$ of the equal parts

3.

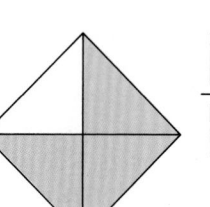 $\dfrac{3}{4}$ of the equal parts

4.

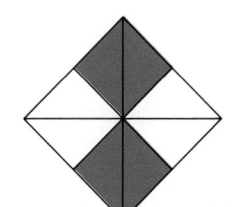 $\dfrac{4}{8}$ of the equal parts

MIDCHAPTER REVIEW/QUIZ

Ring the pictures that show equal parts.

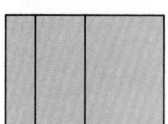 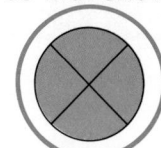 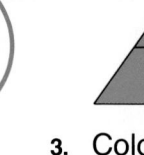 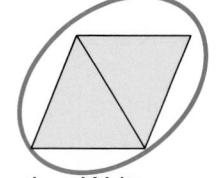

1. Color five sixths. Write the fraction.

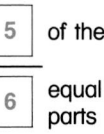 $\dfrac{5}{6}$ of the equal parts

Color any 5 sections.

3. Color two fourths. Write the fraction.

 $\dfrac{2}{4}$ of the equal parts

Color any 2 sections.

More Practice, page 426, set B Chapter 15

---

3. PRACTICE AND APPLY

Basic	All, Midchapter Review/Quiz
Average	All, Midchapter Review/Quiz
Extended	All, Midchapter Review/Quiz

PRACTICE

How will you know which number to write at the bottom of each fraction? (Count the number of equal parts in each shape.) *How will you find the number to write at the top of each fraction?* (Count the number of parts you colored.)

APPLY

▶ **Suppose that you traced the square in Exercise 4 and colored $\frac{1}{2}$ of it. How many eighths would you have colored?** (4)

▶ **Use your fraction pieces to show 6 equal parts. Then show 4 equal parts. Which is greater, $\frac{4}{6}$ or $\frac{3}{4}$?** ($\frac{3}{4}$)

MIDCHAPTER REVIEW/QUIZ The table correlates the Midchapter Review/Quiz items with lesson objectives.

Items	Objectives
1	15-1
2, 3	15-2

15-3

LOSE AND ASSESS

HOW WHAT YOU KNOW

ve pairs of students cut out strips of
aph paper and color them to match
e fraction cards for fourths, sixths,
d eighths. Then have them place the
ction strips and the cards in 2 piles
d take turns drawing 1 strip and 1
rd to try to make a match. When
e fractions match, the students keep
m. Play until all fractions are
tched.

QUICK QUIZ

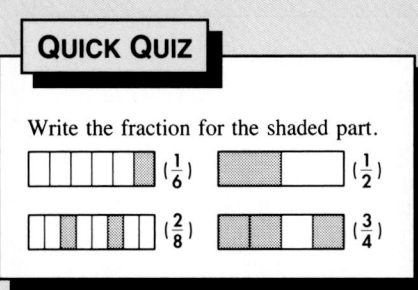

Write the fraction for the shaded part.

$(\frac{1}{6})$ $(\frac{1}{2})$

$(\frac{2}{8})$ $(\frac{3}{4})$

LESSON OPTIONS 15-4

Modeling and Writing Fractions with Sets

OBJECTIVE 15-4   To identify fractions of a set

PREBOOK ACTIVITIES

QUICK REVIEW

Write the number.

6 tens 3 ones (63)	5 tens 6 ones (56)
8 tens 5 ones (85)	3 tens 0 ones (30)
4 tens 0 ones (40)	4 tens 1 one (41)
9 tens 1 one (91)	1 ten 1 one (11)
6 tens 9 ones (69)	2 tens 9 ones (29)

PRIOR KNOWLEDGE

Have all the girls in the classroom stand up. Ask a volunteer to count them. Ask another volunteer to count all the students. *How many students are there in our class? How many are girls?* (Answers will vary.) *How can we show the number of girls as a part of the class?* (Possible answer: Write a fraction.)

COMMUNICATION

Discussing and Writing Math   Write the word *fifths* on the chalkboard. *If I want to show fifths, how many parts do I need?* (5) Have a volunteer write the fractions from $\frac{1}{5}$ to $\frac{5}{5}$ on the chalkboard. Ask 3 boys and 2 girls to stand up at the front of the room. *How many students are standing?* (5) *What fraction tells how many of these students are boys?* ($\frac{3}{5}$) Point to the 5 in the fraction $\frac{3}{5}$. *What does this number tell us?* (how many students in all) Point to 3. *What does this number show?* (the number of boys) *What fraction could we write to show the number of girls standing up?* ($\frac{2}{5}$)

EXPLORE AND CONNECT

Materials: 2-color counters
Grouping Suggestions: pairs
Write the fraction $\frac{1}{4}$ on the chalkboard. *How many 2-color counters will we need in all to model this fraction?* (4) Have students place 4 counters red side up. *How many counters should we turn over to show $\frac{1}{4}$?* (1) Pair students and have them take turns naming fractions in fourths, fifths, sixths, and eighths and modeling them with 2-color counters. Then have each pair demonstrate how to model a fraction of its choice while the other pairs follow the steps with their counters.

CONNECTIONS   Use these anytime.

Problem of the Day

Logic   Draw a picture to help you solve this problem. On my soccer team, $\frac{4}{10}$ of the players are boys. $\frac{2}{6}$ of the girls play forward. How many players are on my team? (10) How many are boys? (4) How many are girls? (6) How many girls play forward? (2)

Math Connection

Fractions   Use 2-color counters to solve this fraction riddle. I have 6 counters. Half of them are red. How many yellow counters do I have? (3) Write a fraction riddle and have a friend find the answer.

Subject Integration

Fine Arts   Draw 9 cars in a parking lot. Color some of the cars red, some blue, and some yellow. Write fractions to show the number of red cars, blue cars, and yellow cars.

CLASSWORK AND HOMEWORK SUPPLEMENTS

OPTIONS FOR INDIVIDUAL NEEDS

Basic

Exercises All, Mixed Review

Supplements
Reteaching 132 or
Practice 132
Thinking Skills 132

Average

Exercises All, Mixed Review

Supplements
Practice 132
Challenges 132 or
Thinking Skills 132

Extended

Exercises All, Mixed Review

Supplements
Challenges 132
Thinking Skills 132

Other Resources:
Explorations, p. 229
Mathematics Book A, p. 82
Mathematics Their Way, pp. 326-342

15-4

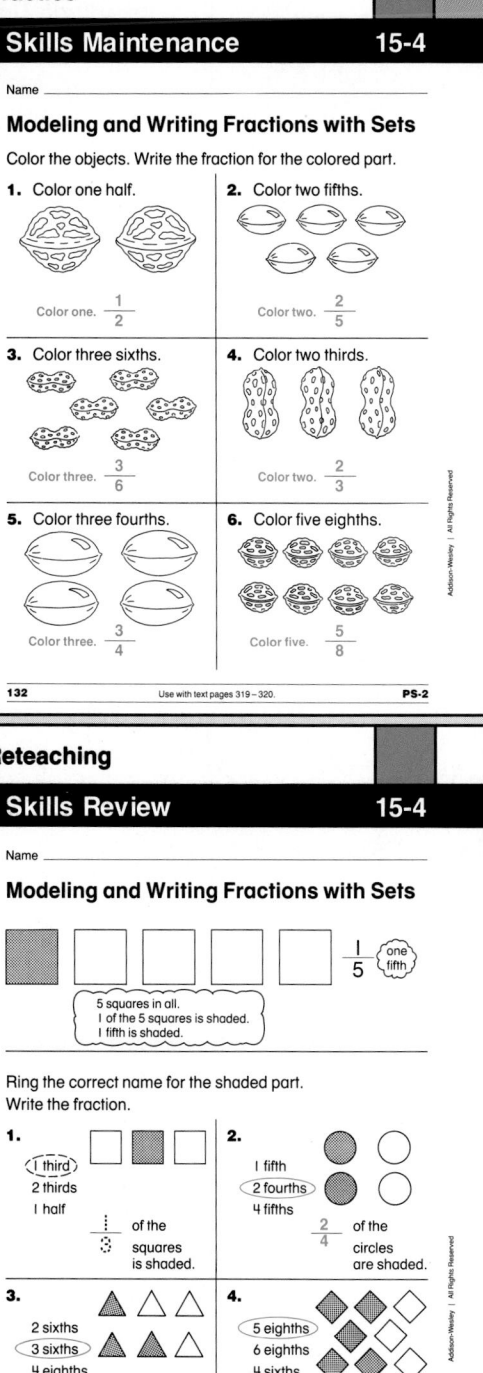

Practice

Skills Maintenance · 15-4

Name ____

Modeling and Writing Fractions with Sets

Color the objects. Write the fraction for the colored part.

1. Color one half.
   Color one. $\frac{1}{2}$

2. Color two fifths.
   Color two. $\frac{2}{5}$

3. Color three sixths.
   Color three. $\frac{3}{6}$

4. Color two thirds.
   Color two. $\frac{2}{3}$

5. Color three fourths.
   Color three. $\frac{3}{4}$

6. Color five eighths.
   Color five. $\frac{5}{8}$

132 · Use with text pages 319–320. · PS-2

Reteaching

Skills Review · 15-4

Name ____

Modeling and Writing Fractions with Sets

$\frac{1}{5}$ (one fifth)

5 squares in all.
1 of the 5 squares is shaded.
1 fifth is shaded.

Ring the correct name for the shaded part.
Write the fraction.

1. (1 third)
   2 thirds
   1 half
   $\frac{\vdots}{\because}$ of the squares is shaded.

2. 1 fifth
   (2 fourths)
   4 fifths
   $\frac{2}{4}$ of the circles are shaded.

3. 2 sixths
   (3 sixths)
   4 eighths
   $\frac{3}{6}$

4. (5 eighths)
   6 eighths
   4 sixths
   $\frac{5}{8}$

132 · Use with text pages 319–320. · RS-2

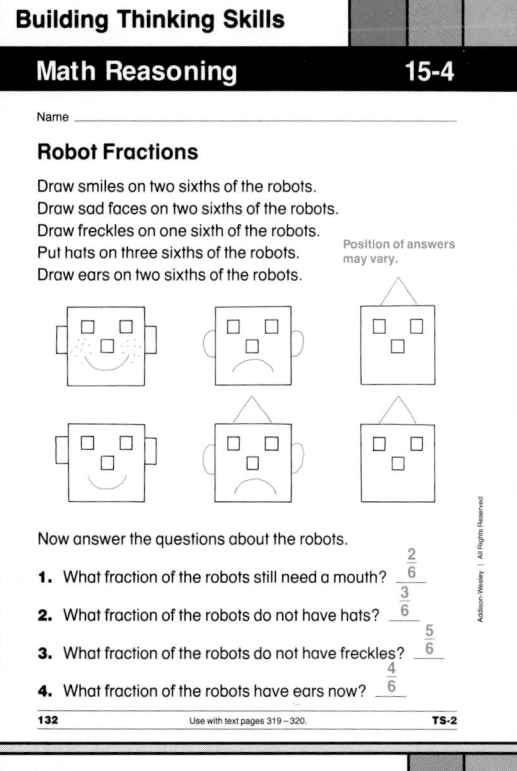

Building Thinking Skills

Math Reasoning · 15-4

Name ____

Robot Fractions

Draw smiles on two sixths of the robots.
Draw sad faces on two sixths of the robots.
Draw freckles on one sixth of the robots.
Put hats on three sixths of the robots.
Draw ears on two sixths of the robots.

Position of answers may vary.

Now answer the questions about the robots.

1. What fraction of the robots still need a mouth? $\frac{2}{6}$

2. What fraction of the robots do not have hats? $\frac{3}{6}$

3. What fraction of the robots do not have freckles? $\frac{5}{6}$

4. What fraction of the robots have ears now? $\frac{4}{6}$

132 · Use with text pages 319–320. · TS-2

Challenges

Cooperative Activities · 15-4

Name ____

Fraction Fun

Play with a partner or in a group. Use a paper clip and a pencil to make the spinner.
Each player gets 8 red counters and 8 yellow counters.
Each puts a marker on the **Start** box.
Take turns. Spin and move your marker that many spaces.
Show the fraction on the space with counters.

For example, to show $\frac{1}{5}$: (Y) (•R) (•R) (•R) (•R)

Tell whether the fraction is for the red part or the yellow part.

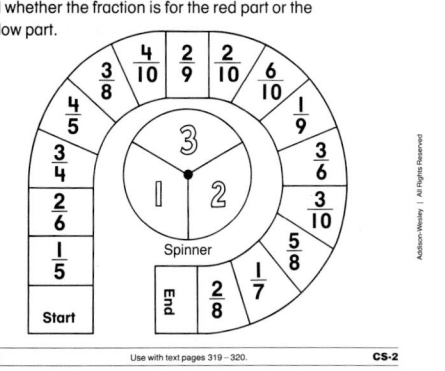

132 · Use with text pages 319–320. · CS-2

OBJECTIVE 15-4
To identify fractions of a set

> **Materials:** 2-color counters
>
> **Grouping Suggestion:** pairs

1. MOTIVATE AND TEACH

LEARN ABOUT IT

Have students carefully spill 5 counters onto their desks and sort them by color. *How many counters are there in all?* (5) *How many are yellow? How many are red?* (Answers will vary.) Have students write fractions to show how many of their set of 5 counters are red and how many are yellow.

▶ **What do you notice about the answers to the exercises on page 319?** (Possible answer: The answers are in order from least to greatest.)

▶ **What is another answer for Exercise 5?** (1; 1 whole set)

▶ **Which pairs of fractions make up 1 whole set?** ($\frac{1}{5}$ and $\frac{4}{5}$; $\frac{2}{5}$ and $\frac{3}{5}$)

▶ **Would you rather have $\frac{2}{5}$ or $\frac{3}{5}$ of something you like? Why?** (Possible answer: $\frac{3}{5}$, because it is more)

2. CHECK UNDERSTANDING

ERROR ALERT Being unable to show a fraction for a part of a set instead of part of a figure.

Name _____

Modeling and Writing Fractions with Sets

Work with a partner. Use 5 two-color counters. Read and show the fractional part. Color to match. Then write the fraction for the red part.

Crisp Apples from the Fruit and Vegetable Group

I of the 5 is red.
one fifth is red.

Fractional Part

Fractio

1. one fifth red
   red   yellow   yellow   yellow   yellow
   $\frac{1}{5}$

2. two fifths red
   Color any 2 red and 3 yellow.
   $\frac{2}{5}$

3. three fifths red
   Color any 3 red and 2 yellow.
   $\frac{3}{5}$

4. four fifths red
   Color any 4 red and 1 yellow.
   $\frac{4}{5}$

5. five fifths red
   red   red   red   red   red
   $\frac{5}{5}$

Chapter 15   (three hundred nineteen)   3

TEACHING OPTIONS

RETEACHING TIPS Have students draw 1 of each of the geometric shapes they know. *How many shapes did you draw in all?* Have them write a fraction to show the triangles as part of the set of shapes. Repeat, having them write fractions for other shapes. Assign Reteaching Supplement 132.

ENRICHMENT **Family Math** Have students ask up to 8 family members and friends to name their favorite kind of juice: apple, orange, or grape. Record the choices with tally marks. Write fractions to show how many in the group preferred each kind of juice and draw a picture to show the result.

Write the fraction for the yellow part. Mark the ○ that is next to the correct name.

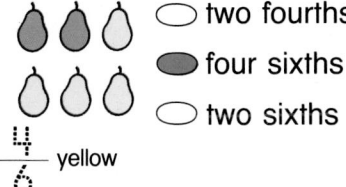 ○ two fourths
● four sixths
○ two sixths

$\frac{4}{6}$ yellow

2. 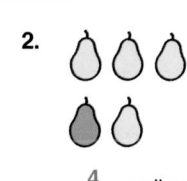 ○ one fifth
● four fifths
○ one fourth

$\frac{4}{5}$ yellow

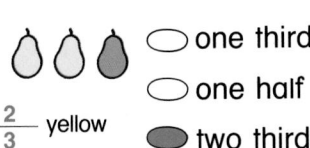 ○ one third
○ one half
● two thirds

$\frac{2}{3}$ yellow

4. 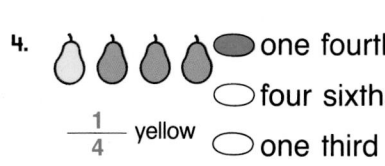 ● one fourth
○ four sixths
○ one third

$\frac{1}{4}$ yellow

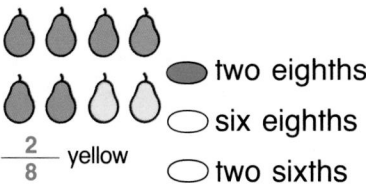 ● two eighths
○ six eighths
○ two sixths

$\frac{2}{8}$ yellow

6. 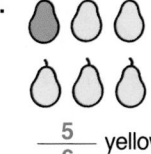 ○ one fifth
○ one sixth
● five sixths

$\frac{5}{6}$ yellow

MIXED REVIEW

Count by 5s. Write the amount.

5　10　15　20　25

$\boxed{25}$ ¢

Count the money.

$\boxed{46}$ ¢

---

3. PRACTICE AND APPLY

Basic	All, Mixed Review
Average	All, Mixed Review
Extended	All, Mixed Review

PRACTICE

How will you decide which circle to mark in each exercise on page 320? (Choose the answer that tells how many parts of the whole group are yellow.) *What do you notice about the fraction you write and the answer next to the circle you mark?* (They both tell how many parts of the whole group are yellow.)

APPLY

▶ **In Exercise 1, what fraction could you write to show the pears that are not yellow?** ($\frac{2}{6}$)
▶ **Compare the fractions you wrote for Exercises 1 and 6. Which is greater? Why?** ($\frac{5}{6}$; more parts of the set are yellow)

MIXED REVIEW
What plan can help you count the coins in exercise 8? (First count the coins of the greatest value, then count the coins of the next greatest value, and so on.)

15-4

CLOSE AND ASSESS

SHOW WHAT YOU KNOW
Reread the chapter story to the class. Ask students to use 2-color counters to show what fraction of the radishes each person in the story received.
Suppose that Roberta's friends brought her 6 balloons and 2 of them were red. Have students show the fraction with their counters. ($\frac{2}{6}$)

QUICK QUIZ

Write the fraction for the shaded part.
●●●○○ ($\frac{3}{5}$)　○○● ($\frac{1}{3}$)
●●○○ ($\frac{2}{4}$)　●●●●○○ ($\frac{4}{6}$)

Problem Solving: Understanding the Operations

OBJECTIVE 15-5 To understand the operation of multiplication by finding a fraction of a number

PREBOOK ACTIVITIES

QUICK REVIEW

Draw a picture of red and green apples to show each fraction
1. 1 sixth red (●○○○○○)
2. 2 eighths red (●●○○○○○○)
3. 4 fifths red (●●●●○)
4. 1 fourth red (●○○○)
5. 5 sixths red (●●●●●○)

PRIOR KNOWLEDGE

When might you use a fraction to describe how much of something you want? (Possible answers: eating $\frac{1}{2}$ of an apple; giving $\frac{1}{4}$ of your balloons to a friend; buying $\frac{3}{4}$ of a pound of vegetables at the grocery store) *Suppose that you have a package of 100 sheets of paper and a friend asks you for $\frac{1}{2}$ of it. How might you decide how much to give your friend?* (Possible answers: Estimate half of the package; count sheets of paper until you each have the same number.)

COMMUNICATION

Discussing and Writing Math *How might you share some grapes equally with a friend?* (Possible answer: Give the friend the same number of grapes; estimate a fair share by looking.) *How would you describe the amount that you and your friend each have?* (Possible answer: We each received half of the grapes.) *Suppose that you are having your friend over for lunch. In your Math Journals write a sentence using the word* estimate *and tell about something you would estimate in order to have the right amount of food.* (Possible answer: I would estimate how much juice my friend might drink or estimate how many sandwiches to make.)

EXPLORE AND CONNECT

COOPERATIVE ACTIVITY

Grouping Suggestion: small groups
Dee and Lee want to share 10 beads equally. How many will each girl get? $\frac{1}{2}$ of 10 = _____
(Each girl will get 5 beads.)

TEACHING ACTIONS

 **BEFORE**
▶ **What do the girls want to do?** (Possible answer: They want to share the beads.)
▶ **Explain what the word *share* tells you about the action in the problem.** (Possible answer: To *share* means to take the whole amount and give an equal part of it to someone else. The whole amount is 10. You need to find a way to divide it equally.)

DURING
▶ **How might you plan how to share the beads equally?** (Possible answer: First estimate how many beads each girl would get. Then act out taking 10 beads and giving 1 to each girl until the beads are all gone.)
▶ **How could you solve this problem using counters?** (Possible answer: Use 10 counters to represent the beads. Share the beads with a partner.)

AFTER
▶ **How could you check that $\frac{1}{2}$ of 10 equals 5?** (Possible answer: Add 2 groups of 5 to see if they equal 10.)
Let students in small groups use counters to act out other problems with total amounts of 4, 6, 8, or 12. Have them say aloud what $\frac{1}{2}$ of each total equals.

CONNECTIONS Use these anytime.

Problem of the Day

Understanding the Operations
Share the fruit equally so each person gets $\frac{1}{2}$.
Write the answer in a sentence.
Naomi and her father shared 14 berries.
How many did they each get?
$\frac{1}{2}$ of 14 = __(7)__
(They each got 7 berries.)

Subject Integration

Art Cut out a picture from a magazine. Cut the picture in 2 **unequal** parts. Paste 1 part of the picture on a piece of paper. Ask a classmate to tell you if more than $\frac{1}{2}$ or less than $\frac{1}{2}$ of the picture is showing. Check the answer by holding the second part next to the first part and comparing their sizes.

Mental Math

Number Sense Answer the riddles.
I am an even number between 5 and 9.
3 is $\frac{1}{2}$ of me.
I am $\frac{1}{2}$ of 12. What number am I? (6)
I am an odd number between 2 and 6.
If you add $\frac{1}{2}$ of 4 to me you get 7. What number am I? (5)

Estimating Fractions

o estimate a fraction of an area

CLASSWORK AND HOMEWORK SUPPLEMENTS

Practice

Problem Solving   15-5

Name _____

Understanding the Operations

Use counters to solve.   Word sentences may vary.
Finish the number sentence.   Sample answers shown.
Then answer the question in a sentence.

1. Two girls shared 6 balloons.
   How many balloons did each girl get? $\frac{1}{2}$ of 6 = __3__

   ___ Each girl got 3 balloons. ___

2. Matt and his brother shared 10 cars.
   How many cars did they each get? $\frac{1}{2}$ of 10 = __5__

   ___ They each got 5 cars. ___

3. Carol has 8 ribbons. She wants to
   share them with Pam.
   How many ribbons should Carol give
   to Pam? $\frac{1}{2}$ of 8 = __4__

   ___ Carol should give 4 to Pam. ___

4. Ted, Ned, and Jed want to share
   9 tennis balls.
   How many tennis balls will Ned get? $\frac{1}{3}$ of 9 = __3__

   ___ Ned will get 3 tennis balls. ___

PS-2   Use with text page 321.   133

Building Thinking Skills

Problem Solving   15-5

Name _____

Recipe Fun

Jan asked 2 friends to come over.
She wants to use this recipe to make a special drink.

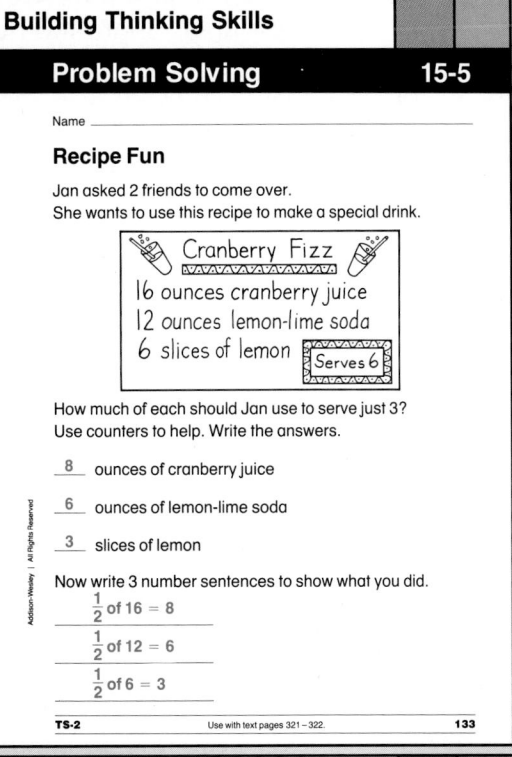

Cranberry Fizz
16 ounces cranberry juice
12 ounces lemon-lime soda
6 slices of lemon   Serves 6

How much of each should Jan use to serve just 3?
Use counters to help. Write the answers.

__8__ ounces of cranberry juice

__6__ ounces of lemon-lime soda

__3__ slices of lemon

Now write 3 number sentences to show what you did.

$\frac{1}{2}$ of 16 = 8

$\frac{1}{2}$ of 12 = 6

$\frac{1}{2}$ of 6 = 3

TS-2   Use with text pages 321–322.   133

Reteaching

Estimation   15-5

Name _____

Estimating Fractions

⬤⬤⬤◯◯◯   3 out of 6 or $\frac{1}{2}$ shaded

⬤⬤◯◯◯◯   ⬤⬤⬤⬤◯◯
less than $\frac{1}{2}$ shaded   more than $\frac{1}{2}$ shaded

Estimate if more than $\frac{1}{2}$ or less than $\frac{1}{2}$ of the circles
are shaded. Use counters to check. Ring your answer.

1. ⬤◯◯◯◯◯   more than $\frac{1}{2}$ shaded
                  (less than $\frac{1}{2}$ shaded)

2. ⬤⬤◯◯⬤◯⬤   (more than $\frac{1}{2}$ shaded)
                  less than $\frac{1}{2}$ shaded

3. ⬤⬤◯ / ⬤⬤◯ / ◯⬤◯   4. ◯◯⬤ / ⬤◯◯ / ◯⬤◯

   (more than $\frac{1}{2}$ shaded)   more than $\frac{1}{2}$ shaded
   less than $\frac{1}{2}$ shaded   (less than $\frac{1}{2}$ shaded)

RS-2   Use with text pages 321–322.   133

Challenges

Estimation   15-5

Name _____

Fraction Math

Estimate without counting which 2 figures in each row show
the same fraction for the shaded part.
Ring those figures.   Estimates will vary.
Then count and write the fractions to check.

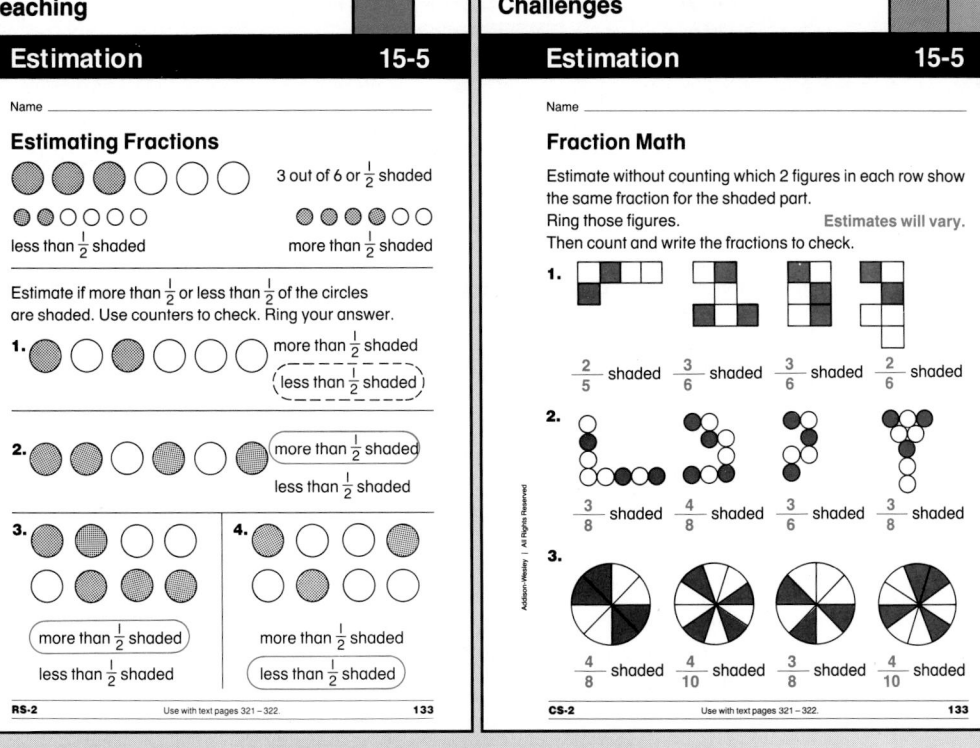

1.
$\frac{2}{5}$ shaded $\frac{3}{6}$ shaded $\frac{3}{6}$ shaded $\frac{2}{6}$ shaded

2.
$\frac{3}{8}$ shaded $\frac{4}{8}$ shaded $\frac{3}{6}$ shaded $\frac{3}{8}$ shaded

3.
$\frac{4}{8}$ shaded $\frac{4}{10}$ shaded $\frac{3}{8}$ shaded $\frac{4}{10}$ shaded

CS-2   Use with text pages 321–322.   133

OPTIONS FOR INDIVIDUAL NEEDS

Basic

Exercises All
More Practice, p. 427, set A

Supplements
Reteaching 133 or
Practice 133

Average

Exercises All
More Practice, p. 427, set A

Supplements
Practice 133
Challenges 133 or
Thinking Skills 133

Extended

Exercises All

Supplements
Challenges 133
Thinking Skills 133

Other Resources:
Math in Stride, p. 95-98
Explorations, pp. 228-229

15-5

Chapter 15 Lesson 5   **321B**

LESSON PLAN 15-5

OBJECTIVE 15-5
To understand the operation of multiplication by finding a fraction of a number; to estimate a fraction of an area

Materials: flannelboard, felt shapes, TA3 (Centimeter Graph Paper)

Grouping Suggestion: pairs

1. MOTIVATE AND TEACH

LEARN ABOUT IT

 **BEFORE** ▶ **Identify the important data in Exercise 1.**
(Possible answer: There are 8 almonds and 2 boys. Each boy gets $\frac{1}{2}$ of the almonds.)

 **DURING** ▶ **How can you use counters to help you find the answer?** (Possible answer: Show 8 counters. Give 1 counter to a partner and 1 counter to yourself until they are gone. Count how many each person has.)

AFTER ▶ **Model a way to check the answer.** (Make a drawing of 8 nuts. Color 4 of them. Count the remaining nuts to see if the same number is left. Then you know that each boy received $\frac{1}{2}$.)
What can you use to act out each situation with a partner? (counters) *How will you share the counters equally?* (Give 1 to yourself, then 1 to your partner, until they are gone.) *What information should be in the sentence you write for each exercise?* (You should tell how many nuts each person got.)

2. CHECK UNDERSTANDING

ERROR ALERT **page 321** Putting unequal parts of the total into 2 groups to show half.
Page 322 Reversing the numbers when writing a fraction.

Name _____

Problem Solving
Understanding the Operations

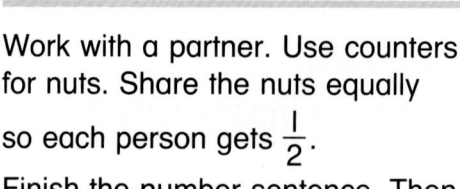
One for you, one for me . . .

Work with a partner. Use counters for nuts. Share the nuts equally so each person gets $\frac{1}{2}$.
Finish the number sentence. Then answer the question in a sentence.

Nuts from the Meat Group

1. Two boys shared 8 almonds. How many almonds did each boy get?

$\frac{1}{2}$ of 8 = ___4___

Word sentences may vary.
Sample answers are shown.

Each boy got _4_ almonds.

2. Susan and her mother shared 12 walnuts. How many walnuts did each get?

$\frac{1}{2}$ of 12 = ___6___

Each got 6 walnuts.

3. Mike and Jeannie want to share 6 peanuts. How many peanuts will Jeannie get?

$\frac{1}{2}$ of 6 = ___3___

Jeannie will get 3 peanuts.

Chapter 15   More Practice, page 427, set A   (three hundred twenty-one) 32

TEACHING OPTIONS

RETEACHING TIPS On a flannelboard, have students show 6, 8, 10, or 12 shapes. Then have them separate the shapes 1 by 1 into 2 distinct areas. When they have finished, have them identify the number that is half of the total. For help in estimating fractions, assign Reteaching 133.

ENRICHMENT Have students design a shape on graph paper, using an even number of squares. Ask them to cut out their design and paste it on a piece of paper. Have them exchange their design with a friend and challenge the friend to color half of the squares. Use counters to check answers.

...nating Fractions

...ate if more than $\frac{1}{2}$

...s than $\frac{1}{2}$ of the tiles are red.

...your estimate. Check by

...ng the tiles. Write a fraction.

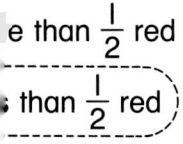

2 red tiles
8 tiles in all

...e than $\frac{1}{2}$ red

...s than $\frac{1}{2}$ red

$\frac{2}{8}$ red

...nates may vary.

...r estimate

...re than $\frac{1}{2}$ red

...s than $\frac{1}{2}$ red

...— red

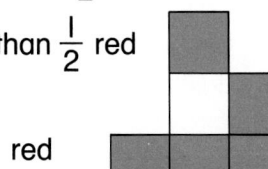

2. Your estimate

more than $\frac{1}{2}$ red

less than $\frac{1}{2}$ red

$\frac{1}{6}$ red

...r estimate

...re than $\frac{1}{2}$ red

...s than $\frac{1}{2}$ red

...— red

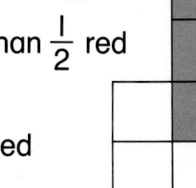

4. Your estimate

more than $\frac{1}{2}$ red

less than $\frac{1}{2}$ red

$\frac{4}{6}$ red

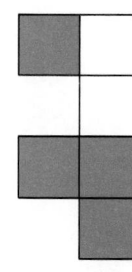

3. PRACTICE AND APPLY

Basic	All
Average	All
Extended	All

▶ **Describe what you will see if more than $\frac{1}{2}$ of the tiles are red.** (Possible answer: When you look at the tiles, you will see more red than white.)

▶ **How will this help you make your estimate?** (Possible answer: You can tell whether there are more red or white tiles before you count them.)

▶ **How will you know how to write the correct fraction?** (Count the number of red tiles and write that number on top. Then count the total number of tiles and write that number below.)

▶ **How could you use the fraction to find out how many white tiles there are in each shape?** (Possible answer: Subtract the top number from the bottom number. You are subtracting the number of red tiles from the total to get the number of white tiles.)

What are you comparing on this page? (numbers of red and white tiles) *What do the numbers in the fraction stand for?* (The top number shows the number of red tiles. The bottom number shows the total number of tiles.)

15-5

...LOSE AND ASSESS

...HOW WHAT YOU KNOW

...mind students of the chapter story. ...ppose that only Roberta and the ...il carrier shared the 4 radishes. ...ow many radishes would they each ...ve gotten? (2) Have students model ...e problem with counters. Then ask ...em to imagine that Roberta also had ...cherries to share with the mail ...rier. *How many would they each ...t?* (4)

QUICK QUIZ

Ring the estimate. Write the fraction.
(more than $\frac{1}{2}$ shaded.)
less than $\frac{1}{2}$ shaded $\left(\frac{6}{8}\right)$

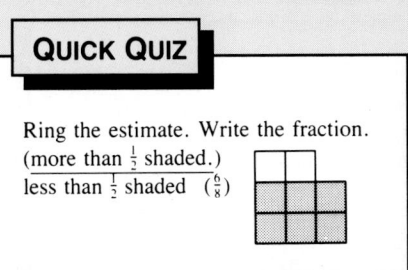

Relating Fractional Parts to the Whole

OBJECTIVE 15-6   To show the relationship between a whole and fractional parts

PREBOOK ACTIVITIES

QUICK REVIEW

Write the amount of money in all.

1. 3 nickels 1 penny   (16¢)   **2.** 1 quarter 1 dime   (35¢)
3. 1 quarter 1 nickel   (30¢)   **4.** 2 quarters 3 dimes   (80¢)
5. 4 dimes 1 nickel   (45¢)   **6.** 3 quarters 2 pennies   (77¢)

PRIOR KNOWLEDGE

Help students recall how to write a fraction for part of a set. Have 2 students wearing gym shoes and 3 who are not wearing gym shoes come to the front of the classroom. *How many students are there?* (5) *How many of these 5 students are wearing gym shoes?* (2) *How many are not wearing gym shoes?* (3) *What fraction could you write to show the number wearing gym shoes?* ($\frac{2}{5}$)

COMMUNICATION

Discussing Math   Write the words *thirds, fifths, sixths, eighths,* and *tenths* on the chalkboard. *You want to share an apple with 2 friends. Which word tells you how many parts to divide the apple into?* *(thirds) Explain how you knew which word to choose.* (Thirds are 3 parts of 1 whole. 3 people would need 3 parts.) Have students complete each sentence.

1. 5 people would divide the apple into   (fifths) .
2. 6 people should divide the apple into   (sixths) .
3. 8 people would divide the apple into   (eighths) .
4. 10 people should divide the apple into   (tenths) .

EXPLORE AND CONNECT

Materials: 1 egg carton cut to show 10 sections, 10 counters per pair
Grouping Suggestion: pairs
Provide each pair of students with a 10-section egg carton and 10 counters. Have one student place 3 counters in 3 sections the egg carton. *How many sections are in the egg carton?* (10 *How many sections have counters?* (3) *What fraction of sections have counters in them?* ($\frac{3}{10}$) Have students take turns performing the following activity. The first student in each pa places a number of counters in the egg-carton sections. The partner names and writes the fraction shown. Then have students cover 1 to 5 sections of the egg carton and repeat the activity to write fractions with different denominators. Remin students to help each other without just giving answers.

CONNECTIONS   Use these anytime.

Problem of the Day

Logic   Students in Mr. Romero's class made a snack. There were 9 ingredients in the snack. Only 1 ingredient was not a vegetable. What fraction of the ingredients were vegetables? ($\frac{8}{9}$)

Math Connection

Geometry
Color 1 half of the rectangle one color and 1 half another color. How did you do it? What other ways might you color the 2 halves? (Answers will vary.)

Subject Integration

Language Arts   What fractional part of these words are vowels?
MATHEMATICS   ($\frac{4}{11}$)
FRACTIONS   ($\frac{3}{9}$ or $\frac{1}{3}$)
PARTS   ($\frac{1}{5}$)
WHOLE   ($\frac{2}{5}$)

CLASSWORK AND HOMEWORK SUPPLEMENTS

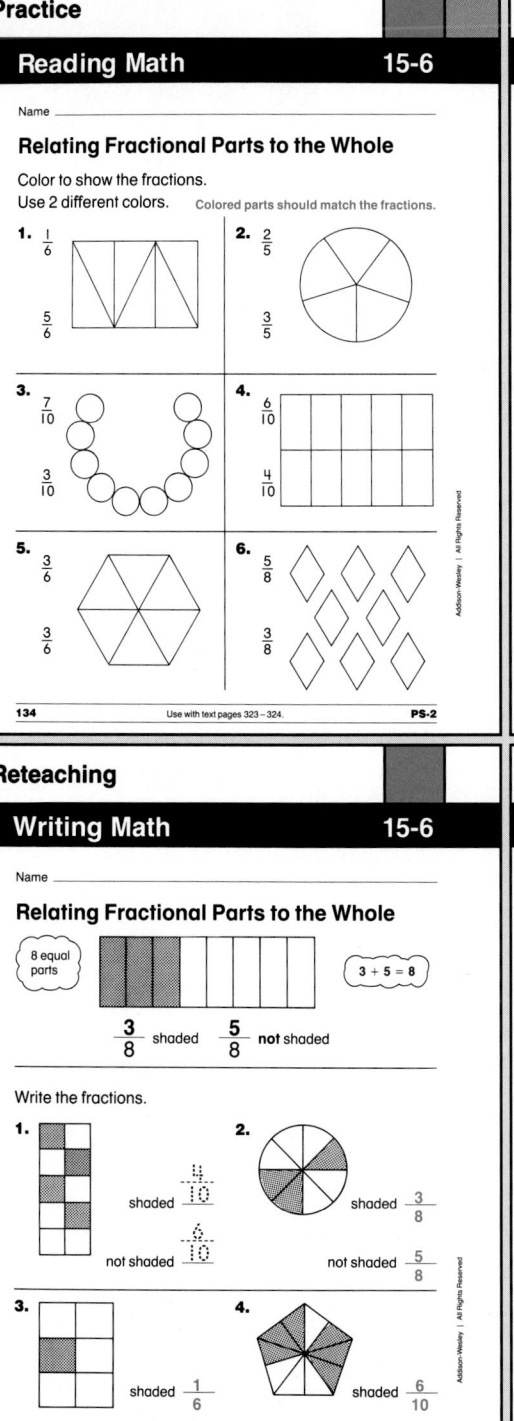

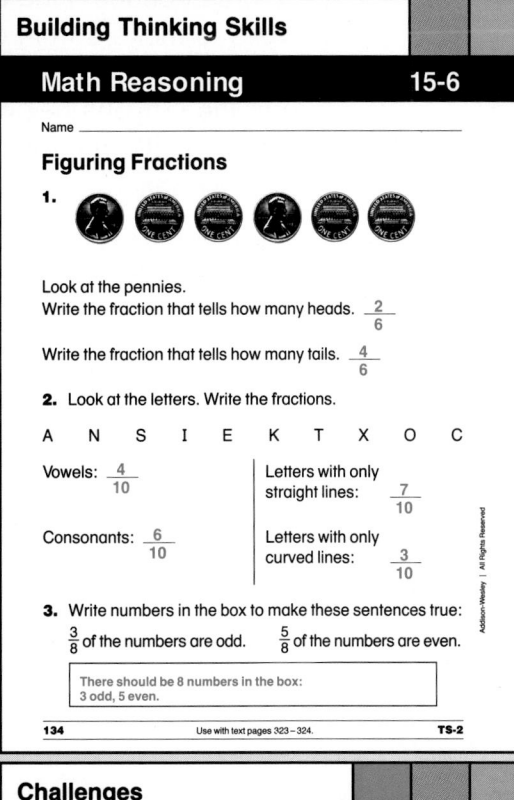

Practice

Reading Math 15-6

Name _____

Relating Fractional Parts to the Whole

Color to show the fractions.
Use 2 different colors. Colored parts should match the fractions.

1. $\frac{1}{6}$ $\frac{5}{6}$

2. $\frac{2}{5}$ $\frac{3}{5}$

3. $\frac{7}{10}$ $\frac{3}{10}$

4. $\frac{6}{10}$ $\frac{4}{10}$

5. $\frac{3}{6}$ $\frac{3}{6}$

6. $\frac{5}{8}$ $\frac{3}{8}$

134   Use with text pages 323–324.   PS-2

Building Thinking Skills

Math Reasoning 15-6

Name _____

Figuring Fractions

1. Look at the pennies.
Write the fraction that tells how many heads. $\frac{2}{6}$

Write the fraction that tells how many tails. $\frac{4}{6}$

2. Look at the letters. Write the fractions.

A N S I E K T X O C

Vowels: $\frac{4}{10}$

Consonants: $\frac{6}{10}$

Letters with only straight lines: $\frac{7}{10}$

Letters with only curved lines: $\frac{3}{10}$

3. Write numbers in the box to make these sentences true:
$\frac{3}{8}$ of the numbers are odd. $\frac{5}{8}$ of the numbers are even.

There should be 8 numbers in the box:
3 odd, 5 even.

134   Use with text pages 323–324.   TS-2

Reteaching

Writing Math 15-6

Name _____

Relating Fractional Parts to the Whole

8 equal parts $3 + 5 = 8$

$\frac{3}{8}$ shaded $\frac{5}{8}$ **not** shaded

Write the fractions.

1. shaded $\frac{4}{10}$ not shaded $\frac{6}{10}$

2. shaded $\frac{3}{8}$ not shaded $\frac{5}{8}$

3. shaded $\frac{1}{6}$ not shaded $\frac{5}{6}$

4. shaded $\frac{6}{10}$ not shaded $\frac{4}{10}$

134   Use with text pages 323–324.   RS-2

Challenges

Creative Thinking 15-6

Name _____

Coloring Fractions   Students may color different sections. Number and color of sections should match fractions.

Color to show the fractions.

1. $\frac{1}{3}$ yellow $\frac{1}{3}$ blue $\frac{1}{3}$ orange

2. $\frac{1}{5}$ red $\frac{2}{5}$ yellow $\frac{2}{5}$ blue

3. $\frac{3}{8}$ red $\frac{1}{8}$ purple $\frac{4}{8}$ orange

4. $\frac{2}{6}$ purple $\frac{2}{6}$ yellow $\frac{2}{6}$ red

5. Make up your own.
Use three different colors to color the boxes.
Write the fractions.   Fractions will vary.

$\overline{12}$ $\overline{12}$ $\overline{12}$

134   Use with text pages 323–324.   CS-2

OPTIONS FOR INDIVIDUAL NEEDS

Basic

Exercises All

Supplements
Reteaching 134 or
Practice 134
Challenges 134

Average

Exercises All

Supplements
Practice 134
Challenges 134 or
Thinking Skills 134

Extended

Exercises All

Supplements
Challenges 134
Thinking Skills 134

Other Resources:
Math in Stride, pp. 95-98
Explorations, p. 229

15-6

LESSON PLAN 15-6

OBJECTIVE 15-6
To show the relationship between a whole and fractional parts

Materials: Cube-A-Links in 2 colors, blank cards, TA3 (Centimeter Graph Paper), pattern blocks

Grouping Suggestions: pairs, individual work

1. MOTIVATE AND TEACH

LEARN ABOUT IT

Write fractions $\frac{2}{10}$, $\frac{5}{10}$, $\frac{7}{10}$, and $\frac{8}{10}$ on the chalkboard. Have students use 10 cubes in 2 colors to model each fraction.

▶ **In the exercises on page 323, what is the smallest fraction you can make with 2 colors?** ($\frac{1}{10}$)

▶ **What is the largest fraction you can make?** ($\frac{9}{10}$)

▶ **How can you know that the bottom number in each fraction will be 10 before you know what color each part will be?** (All the trains have 10 parts in 1 whole.)

▶ **If 1 of your fractions is $\frac{9}{10}$, what will the other one be? Why?** ($\frac{1}{10}$; the 2 colors have to add up to 10.)

▶ **How many different fractions can you write using 10 cubes in 2 colors?** (9: $\frac{1}{10}$, $\frac{9}{10}$; $\frac{2}{10}$, $\frac{8}{10}$; $\frac{3}{10}$, $\frac{7}{10}$; $\frac{4}{10}$, $\frac{6}{10}$; $\frac{5}{10}$)

▶ **If you add 1 more cube to your train, how would the number at the bottom of your fraction change?** (It would be 11.)

2. CHECK UNDERSTANDING

ERROR ALERT Not understanding how 2 fractional parts can be added to make 1 whole.

Name _____

Relating Fractional Parts to the Whole

> There are 10 cu[bes] in the train. Each cube is **one tenth**.

Work in a group. Use two colors of cubes. Find different ways to make a train of 10 cubes. Color the cubes and the crayons below to match. Write the fraction for each color.

$\frac{3}{10}$ $\frac{7}{10}$

Answers may vary. Fractions should match colored cube trains.

1. ⬜⬜⬜⬜⬜⬜⬜⬜⬜⬜ $\overline{10}$ $\overline{10}$

2. ⬜⬜⬜⬜⬜⬜⬜⬜⬜⬜ $\overline{10}$ $\overline{10}$

3. ⬜⬜⬜⬜⬜⬜⬜⬜⬜⬜ $\overline{10}$ $\overline{10}$

4. ⬜⬜⬜⬜⬜⬜⬜⬜⬜⬜ $\overline{10}$ $\overline{10}$

Chapter 15   (three hundred twenty-three) 323

TEACHING OPTIONS

RETEACHING TIPS Draw geometric figures and fold each in 3, 4, 5, 6, 7, 8, 9, or 10 equal parts. Have pairs cut each figure in 2 parts and write a fraction to name each part. Mix up the parts. Challenge students to find matching parts and make 1 whole. Assign Reteaching Supplement 134.

COMPUTER Piece of Cake Math, Springboard Software ©️ 1983 For use with all levels. In *Dividacake*, students help the baker get the right number of pieces. In *The Bakery*, they keep track of the cakes in the bakery, given the number of cakes made and sold. Each lesson requires 5 minutes.

udents may color different sections.
umber of sections colored should match fraction.

olor to show the fraction.

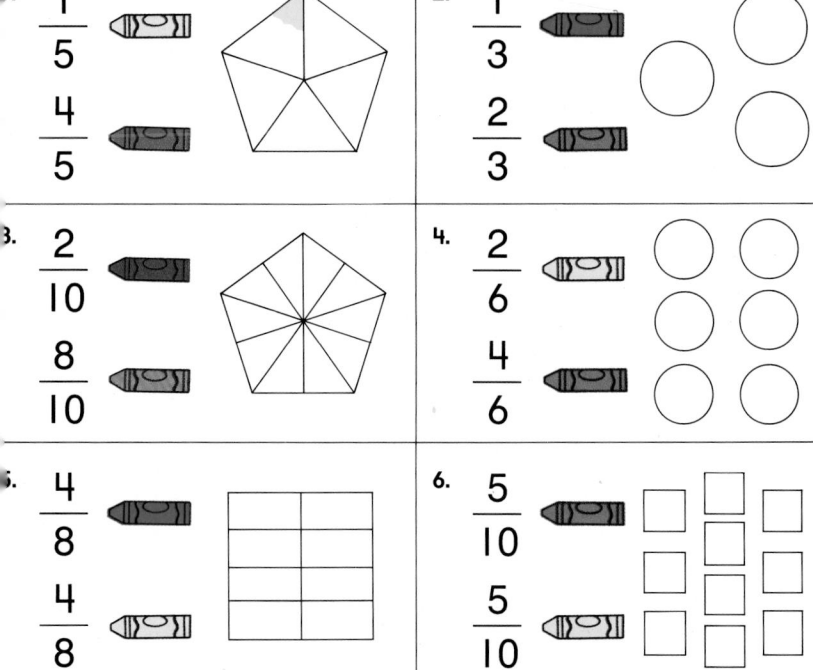

1. $\frac{1}{5}$ $\frac{4}{5}$

2. $\frac{1}{3}$ $\frac{2}{3}$

3. $\frac{2}{10}$ $\frac{8}{10}$

4. $\frac{2}{6}$ $\frac{4}{6}$

5. $\frac{4}{8}$ $\frac{4}{8}$

6. $\frac{5}{10}$ $\frac{5}{10}$

ROBLEM SOLVING

Solve. Use counters to help.
Write the answer in a sentence.

Janet shared 10 oranges with her
sister. Each girl got one half.
How many oranges did each get?

Word sentences may vary. A sample answer is shown.
Each girl got 5 oranges.

4   (three hundred twenty-four)   Chapter 15

---

3. PRACTICE AND APPLY

Basic	All
Average	All
Extended	All

PRACTICE

*How will all the pictures in Exercises 1-6
be similar?* (Possible answer: In each
figure, all the parts will be colored.)

APPLY

PROBLEM SOLVING

▶ **How did you use the counters to
show the oranges Janet shared?**
(Possible answer: Use 10 counters. Put 1
aside for Janet, then 1 aside for her
sister. Continue until you have used all
10.)

▶ **Do you think the sisters shared the
oranges fairly? Why?** (Yes, each got 5
oranges.)

▶ **If Janet had 1 more orange, how
could she share it with her sister?**
(Cut the orange into 2 halves.)

15-6

LOSE AND ASSESS

HOW WHAT YOU KNOW

ake fraction cards for $\frac{1}{5}$, $\frac{3}{5}$, $\frac{4}{5}$, $\frac{3}{7}$, $\frac{6}{7}$, $\frac{5}{8}$,
and $\frac{9}{10}$. Have 1 student in each pair
oose a card and model the fraction
ith pattern blocks. The partner
odels the fraction that, when put
ith the first fraction, will make 1
hole. Have students write the
actions, then outline on graph paper
e squares in their whole. Have them
lor to show the 2 fractions they
ade.

QUICK QUIZ

Draw Xs to show each fraction set.
1. $\frac{1}{6}$ red $\frac{5}{6}$ blue   2. $\frac{1}{4}$ red $\frac{3}{4}$ blue
3. $\frac{3}{8}$ red $\frac{5}{8}$ blue   4. $\frac{1}{3}$ red $\frac{2}{3}$ blue

Problem Solving: Determining Reasonable Answers

OBJECTIVE 15-7   To determine whether answers to problems are reasonable

PREBOOK ACTIVITIES

QUICK REVIEW

Write the fraction for each color.

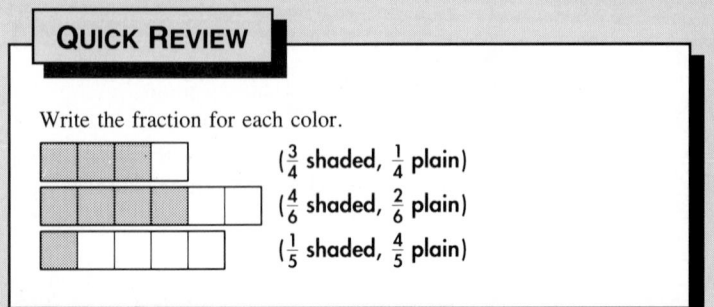

($\frac{3}{4}$ shaded, $\frac{1}{4}$ plain)

($\frac{4}{6}$ shaded, $\frac{2}{6}$ plain)

($\frac{1}{5}$ shaded, $\frac{4}{5}$ plain)

PRIOR KNOWLEDGE

Has anyone ever given you an answer to a question that did not seem quite right? (Answers will vary.) *How did you know the answer was not right?* (Possible answer: It did not make sense; it did not go with what I already knew.) *If you add 10 + 12 and get a sum of 30, is your answer reasonable? How do you know?* (no; you can estimate by adding tens; 10 + 10 = 20)

COMMUNICATION

Reading and Discussing Math   Write the word **reasonable** on the chalkboard. Read it and explain that a reasonable answer is one that makes sense. *What would be a reasonable answer to this question: What time did you get up this morning?* (Possible answers: 6:30, 7:00, 7:30) *What would not be a reasonable answer for that same question?* (noon; 4:00) *Can a whole be divided equally in only one way? Why or why not?* Have students draw pictures to illustrate their answers. (Possible answer: No; 1 whole can be divided equally into different numbers of parts. A square might be divided into halves one time and into fourths another time. As long as the parts are equal in size, it does not matter how many there are.)

EXPLORE AND CONNECT

COOPERATIVE ACTIVITY
Grouping Suggestion: small groups
Mark ate $\frac{2}{8}$ of a fruit salad. Jane ate $\frac{7}{8}$ of a fruit salad. How much did they eat in all? Answer: 1 whole fruit salad
Does the answer make sense? Ring yes or <u>no</u>. If no, ring A or B. A. They ate less than 1 whole fruit salad. <u>B. They ate more than 1 whole fruit salad.</u>

TEACHING ACTIONS

▶ **What are you to decide about this problem** (Possible answer: You decide whether the answer makes sense. If not, you ring the answer that doe make sense.)
▶ **How can the data help you know whether the answer is reasonable?** (Possible answer: The answer is 1 whole fruit salad. You need to ask whether $\frac{2}{8}$ and $\frac{7}{8}$ make 1 whole.)

▶ **What plan can you use to decide if the answer is correct?** (Possible answer: You might picture how many eighths make 1 whole.)
▶ **What questions can you ask yourself to estimate an answer?** (Possible answers: Are there enough eighths to mak 1 whole? Are there too many eighths?

▶ **What can you use to check the answer?** (Possible answer: Put fraction pieces for $\frac{2}{8}$ and $\frac{7}{8}$ together to see if they make 1 whole, more than whole, or less than 1 whole.)
Have students work in small groups and use fraction pieces to solve this and similar problems.

CONNECTIONS   Use these anytime.

Problem of the Day
Understanding the Operations
Finish the number sentence. Then answer the question in a sentence.
Jake and Rick want to share 4 oranges. How many oranges will each boy get?
$\frac{1}{2}$ of 4 = __(2)__
(Each boy will get 2 oranges.)

Subject Integration
Fine Arts   Cut pictures out of a magazine. Fold and cut the pictures into equal pieces, such as fourths. Paste 1 part of the picture on a piece of paper and ask a classmate to finish the puzzle by putting together the other parts to make a whole. Make more puzzles using different numbers of equal pieces.

Minute Math
Fractions   Use different fraction pieces to show amounts that are equal to the ones below.
$\frac{2}{4}$ ($\frac{3}{6}$, $\frac{4}{8}$, $\frac{5}{10}$) $\frac{2}{3}$ ($\frac{4}{6}$)
$\frac{3}{5}$ ($\frac{6}{10}$) $\frac{1}{4}$ ($\frac{2}{8}$)
1 whole (2 halves, 4 quarters, 3 thirds, 5 fifths, 6 sixths, 10 tenths)

Problem Solving Strategy: Use Objects

To solve problems using the strategy Use Objects

CLASSWORK AND HOMEWORK

Practice

Problem Solving   15-7

Name _____

Use Objects

Maria, John, and Linda shared 1 pizza. The pizza was cut into 12 slices. Use your fraction pieces. Finish the fraction in each sentence.

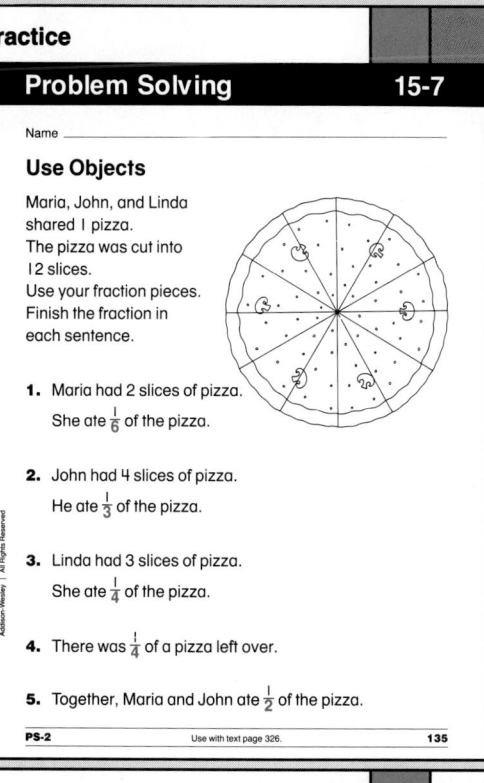

1. Maria had 2 slices of pizza. She ate $\frac{1}{6}$ of the pizza.

2. John had 4 slices of pizza. He ate $\frac{1}{3}$ of the pizza.

3. Linda had 3 slices of pizza. She ate $\frac{1}{4}$ of the pizza.

4. There was $\frac{1}{4}$ of a pizza left over.

5. Together, Maria and John ate $\frac{1}{2}$ of the pizza.

PS-2   Use with text page 326.   135

Building Thinking Skills

Number Sense   15-7

Name _____

More than One Whole

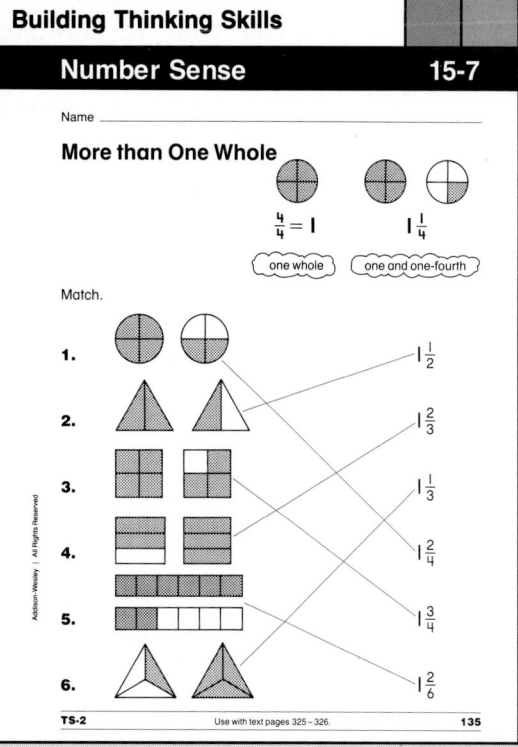

$\frac{4}{4} = 1$ $1\frac{1}{4}$

(one whole)   (one and one-fourth)

Match.

1. $1\frac{1}{2}$

2. $1\frac{2}{3}$

3. $1\frac{1}{3}$

4. $1\frac{2}{4}$

5. $1\frac{3}{4}$

6. $1\frac{2}{6}$

TS-2   Use with text pages 325 – 326.   135

Reteaching

Problem Solving   15-7

Name _____

Determining Reasonable Answers

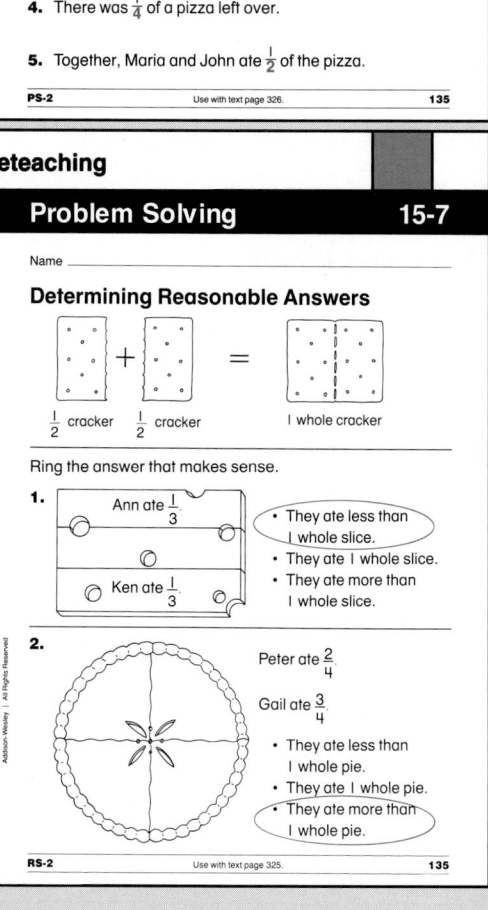

$\frac{1}{2}$ cracker + $\frac{1}{2}$ cracker = 1 whole cracker

Ring the answer that makes sense.

1. Ann ate $\frac{1}{3}$.
   Ken ate $\frac{1}{3}$.
   - They ate less than 1 whole slice.
   - They ate 1 whole slice.
   - They ate more than 1 whole slice.

2. Peter ate $\frac{2}{4}$.
   Gail ate $\frac{3}{4}$.
   - They ate less than 1 whole pie.
   - They ate 1 whole pie.
   - They ate more than 1 whole pie.

RS-2   Use with text page 325.   135

Challenges

Number Sense   15-7

Name _____

Size Them Up

Write > (greater than), < (less than), or = (the same) in each ◯. Use your fraction pieces to help.

1. $\frac{1}{2} > \frac{1}{4}$ 2. $\frac{2}{4} = \frac{4}{8}$

3. $\frac{1}{3} < \frac{1}{2}$ 4. $\frac{2}{8} = \frac{1}{4}$

5. $\frac{3}{8} > \frac{1}{4}$ 6. $\frac{2}{3} < \frac{5}{6}$

7. $\frac{3}{6} = \frac{1}{2}$ 8. $\frac{1}{4} > \frac{1}{6}$

9. $\frac{3}{4} < \frac{7}{8}$ 10. $\frac{1}{3} = \frac{2}{6}$

11. $\frac{2}{3} = \frac{4}{6}$ 12. $\frac{1}{2} < \frac{5}{8}$

CS-2   Use with text pages 325 – 326.   135

OPTIONS FOR INDIVIDUAL NEEDS

Basic

Exercises All

Supplements
Reteaching 135 or
Practice 135

Average

Exercises All

Supplements
Practice 135
Challenges 135 or
Thinking Skills 135

Extended

Exercises All

Supplements
Challenges 135
Thinking Skills 135

Other Resources:
Explorations, pp. 227-229

15-7

LESSON PLAN 15-7

OBJECTIVE 15-7
To determine whether answers to problems are reasonable; to solve problems using the strategy Use Objects

Materials: fraction pieces

1. MOTIVATE AND TEACH

LEARN ABOUT IT

 **BEFORE** ▶ **What do you need to find out about the data in each of these exercises?**
(Possible answer: how much of each whole fruit each person ate)

 **DURING** ▶ **How can you estimate the total amount eaten by both people?** (Possible answer: Picture the fractions that tell how much they ate; think about whether they ate more or less than 1 whole.)

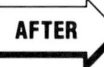 **AFTER** ▶ **How will fraction pieces help you check your answer?** (Possible answer: You can act out each situation with fraction pieces to see if your estimate was correct.)
Where do you show whether you think the answer makes sense? (You ring yes or no next to each exercise.) *If your answer is no, how can you determine whether the amount is more or less than 1 whole?* (Use fraction pieces to model how much each person ate.) *How would your model look if they ate more than 1 whole?* (Your fraction pieces would fill 1 whole and you would have pieces left over.)

2. CHECK UNDERSTANDING

ERROR ALERT **Page 325** Being unable to estimate a reasonable answer to problems involving fractions.
Page 326 Writing $\frac{1}{2}$ for each amount eaten instead the fraction of the total number of pieces.

Name _____

Problem Solving
Determining Reasonable Answers

Does the answer make sense?
Use your fraction pieces to help.
Ring **yes** or **no.** If the answer does not make sense, ring **A** or **B.**

| UNDERSTAND |
| FIND DATA |
| PLAN |
| ESTIMATE |
| SOLVE |
| CHECK |

Jolene ate $\frac{1}{2}$ of a plum.

Ted ate $\frac{1}{2}$ of a plum.

How much did they eat in all?

Answer: 1 whole plum

Does the answer make sense?

(yes)   no

If **no,** ring **A** or **B.**
A They ate less than 1 whole plum.
B They ate more than 1 whole plum.

Brett ate $\frac{2}{4}$ of an apple.

Max ate $\frac{3}{4}$ of an apple.

How much did they eat in all?

Answer: 1 whole apple

Does the answer make sense?

yes   (no)

If **no,** ring **A** or **B.**
A They ate less than 1 whole apple.
(**B**) They ate more than 1 whole apple.

Bing ate $\frac{2}{6}$ of a peach.

Jesse ate $\frac{3}{6}$ of a peach.

How much did they eat in all?

Answer: 1 whole peach

Does the answer make sense?

yes   (no)

If **no,** ring **A** or **B.**
(**A**) They ate less than 1 whole peach.
B They ate more than 1 whole peach

Chapter 15

(three hundred twenty-five) 32

TEACHING OPTIONS

RETEACHING TIPS Draw a 2-by-5 square muffin tin divided in half. Tell students they have eaten 5 muffins, or half. Have them shade 5 squares on 1 half of the tin, and write the fraction to show how much they ate. ($\frac{5}{10}$) For help in finding reasonable answers, assign Reteaching Supplement 135.

ENRICHMENT Have students fold a piece of paper into thirds. In the first third, have them draw a whole fruit or food item. In the middle, draw the same food divided into equal parts. In the last third, draw equal parts with some missing. Then write the fraction for the missing parts.

Problem Solving Strategy
Use Objects

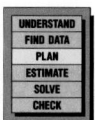

Andrea, Carlos, and Eddie each ordered 1 pizza. Each pizza came cut into a different number of equal parts.

Each person ate $\frac{1}{2}$ of a pizza.

Use your fraction pieces. Fill the empty part of the pizza pan with same-size pieces to show what each person ate. Then write the fraction below.

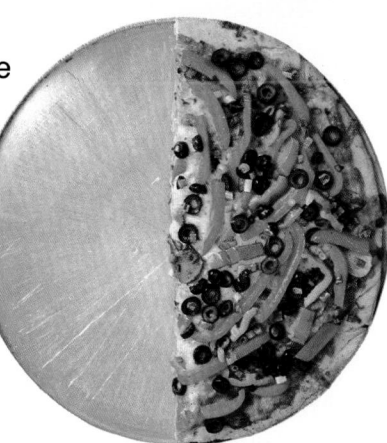

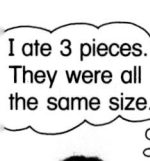
I ate 3 pieces. They were all the same size.

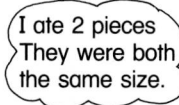
I ate 2 pieces. They were both the same size.

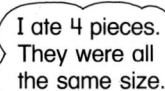
I ate 4 pieces. They were all the same size.

Andrea

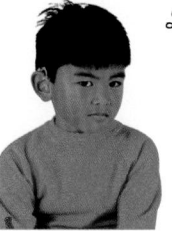
Carlos

Eddie

$\frac{3}{6}$ pizza

$\frac{2}{4}$ pizza

$\frac{4}{8}$ pizza

3. PRACTICE AND APPLY

Basic	All
Average	All
Extended	All

▶ **How could each person eat $\frac{1}{2}$ of a pizza if each of the pizzas were divided into different parts?** (Possible answer: Pizzas can be divided into any number of parts as long as the parts are equal. So each person ate $\frac{1}{2}$ of the total number of parts of a pizza.)

▶ **How can you model how many equal parts were in each pizza?** (Possible answer: If a person ate 3 pieces and that was half of the pizza, then you put 3 pieces on the top half and 3 more pieces on the bottom half.)

▶ **How do you find the bottom number of each fraction?** (Possible answers: Count the total number of equal pieces; double the number of pieces each person ate.) *How can you use the picture on this page to help you solve the problems?* (Use fraction pieces to show how many pieces each person ate and how many were left in the pan.) *What will the top number you write in each fraction stand for?* (the number of pieces of pizza each person ate)

15-7

CLOSE AND ASSESS

SHOW WHAT YOU KNOW

Have small groups act out situations in which 2 students each eat part of some food. A third student narrates what is happening as it is acted out. The narrator then asks the class to tell whether the students ate a whole item, less than a whole, or more than a whole. After the class has given a reasonable answer, the actors can draw pictures to show what they ate and verify the answer.

QUICK QUIZ

Write the fraction for the shaded part.

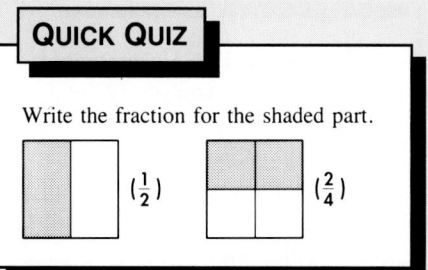

$\left(\frac{1}{2}\right)$ $\left(\frac{2}{4}\right)$

CHAPTER 15

WRAP UP

INTRODUCTION The Wrap Up provides activities emphasizing math language and thinking skills for the chapter.

USING PAGE 327

Math Words ▶ **Which fraction word is different from the others? If you were to make it like the others, how would you change it?** (*halves;* it does not use the ordinal word in the fraction name; possible change: *seconds*)

▶ **What happens to each part of a whole as the fraction name gets larger?** (The size of each part gets smaller.)

Math Reasoning ▶ **Why can you separate a square into 8 equal parts so many different ways?** (All sides are the same length, so it can be separated vertically, horizontally, and diagonally.)

▶ **If you could separate each of the eighths into 2 parts, what fraction would each part be?** (one sixteenth)

Name _____

Wrap Up

MATH WORDS

1. Match each picture to its name. Write the number of equal parts.

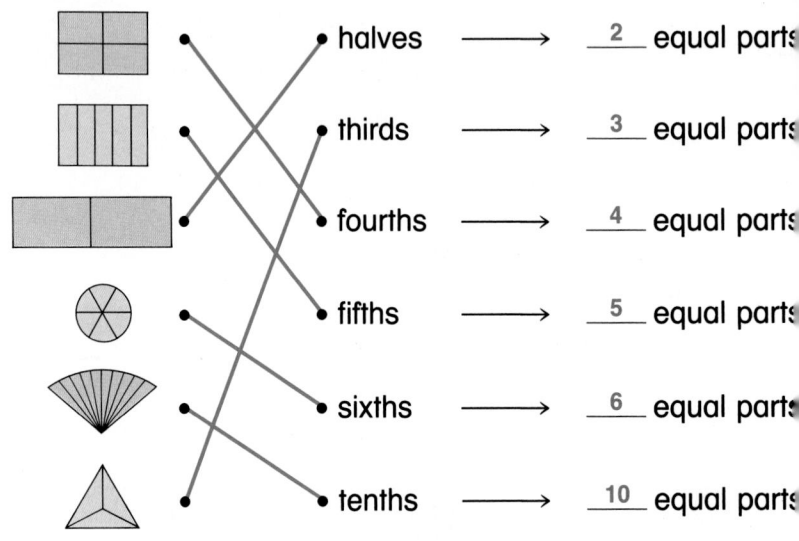

halves $\longrightarrow$ __2__ equal parts

thirds $\longrightarrow$ __3__ equal parts

fourths $\longrightarrow$ __4__ equal parts

fifths $\longrightarrow$ __5__ equal parts

sixths $\longrightarrow$ __6__ equal parts

tenths $\longrightarrow$ __10__ equal parts

MATH REASONING

2. Find as many ways as you can to show a square divided into 8 equal parts. Order may vary.

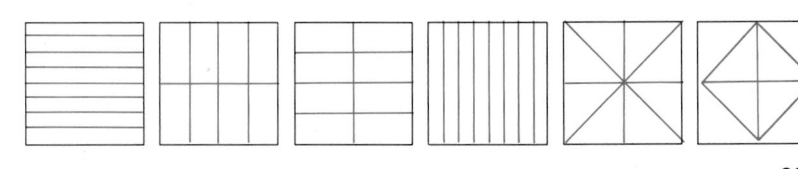

Chapter 15 Wrap Up   (three hundred twenty-seven) 32

TEACHING OPTIONS

ENRICHMENT Have students draw a circle, a square, an oval, a rectangle, and a triangle. Ask them to separate each shape in to 4 equal parts. Then have them color $\frac{1}{4}$ of each shape blue and $\frac{2}{4}$ of each shape red. Display their work.

Name _____

hapter Review/Test

ng the figures that show the equal parts named.

1. halves

2. thirds
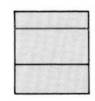 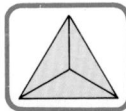

3. fourths
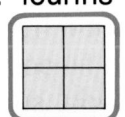 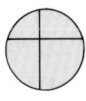

4. Color two thirds.
Write the fraction.

$\frac{2}{3}$ of the equal parts

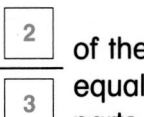

5. Write the fraction that tells what part is red.

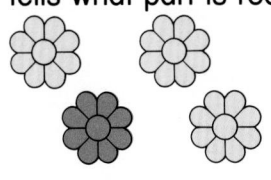

$\frac{1}{4}$

6. Ring the better estimate.

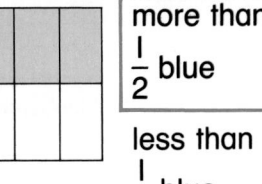

more than $\frac{1}{2}$ blue

less than $\frac{1}{2}$ blue

7. Color to show the fractions.

$\frac{2}{5}$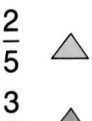

$\frac{3}{5}$

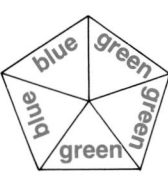

8. Does the answer make sense?
Use your fraction pieces to help.

Ring one. **yes** (**no**)

Ed used $\frac{1}{4}$ jar of paint.

Greg used $\frac{2}{4}$ jar of paint.

How much paint did they use in all?

Answer: I whole jar of paint

If **no**, ring **A** or **B**.

(**A**) They used less than I whole jar of paint.

B They used more than I whole jar of paint.

CHAPTER REVIEW/TEST

INTRODUCTION   The Review/Test is provided to review and evaluate the skills and concepts presented in Chapter 15.

USING PAGE 328
If you prefer to use this page for review, you may want to use the **Multiple-Choice Posttest** (pages 59-60) or the **Free-Response Posttest** (pages 59-60) to evaluate mastery of chapter objectives.

ITEM ANALYSIS   The table below correlates the Chapter Review/Test Items with the lesson objectives.

Items	Objectives
1, 2, 3	15-1
4	15-2
5	15-4, 15-6
6	15-5
7	15-4, 15-6
8	15-7

INFORMAL ASSESSMENT

ing Manipulatives   Have students e their fraction pieces to model, w, and color the following:

5 equal parts, $\frac{2}{5}$ red
3 equal parts, $\frac{1}{3}$ blue
4 equal parts, $\frac{3}{4}$ green
6 equal parts, $\frac{1}{6}$ yellow

mmunication   *Tell what the top d bottom numbers mean in a ction.* (Possible answer: The bottom mber tells the total number of equal rts, the top number tells how many

of the parts are colored.)

Critical Thinking   *When might you use fractions to talk about an amount?* (Possible answers: when you are telling about a recipe; describing part of a group; describing amount of time, such as $\frac{1}{2}$ h)

CHAPTER 15

ENRICHMENT

INTRODUCTION   Reading fractions in a recipe helps students understand the applications of fractions in everyday life.

USING PAGE 329
This Enrichment page is provided for all students. You may wish to use it after they have completed the Chapter Review/Test on page 328.

Help students understand the uses of different measuring tools. Point out that they are all needed for following the recipe.

▶ **Of which ingredient do you need the smallest amount?** (salt)

▶ **Which ingredients require equal amounts?** (wheat and white flour; milk and sugar)

▶ **Why do you think the muffin cups are only $\frac{2}{3}$ full?** (Possible answer: The muffin mix will rise in the oven.)

EXTENSION   Have students think of a trail mix recipe they would like to make using raisins, nuts, dry cereal, and granola. Ask them to write amounts for each ingredient and give directions for making their trail mix. Challenge students to draw pictures showing amounts for each ingredient as well as the preparation process.

Name _____

ENRICHMENT
Data from a Recipe

Follow the recipe. Color to show how you would fill each cup. The egg, sugar, and white flour are in the bowl.

Blueberry Muffins

Mix in a bowl:

1 egg	$\frac{3}{4}$ cup wheat flour
$\frac{1}{2}$ cup milk	$\frac{3}{4}$ cup white flour
$\frac{1}{4}$ cup oil	2 teaspoons baking powder
$\frac{1}{2}$ cup sugar	$\frac{1}{2}$ teaspoon salt
$\frac{1}{3}$ cup blueberries	

Fill muffin cups $\frac{2}{3}$ full.
Bake 20 to 25 minutes at 400°F.
Makes 12 muffins.

1. milk

2. oil

3. wheat flour

4. blueberries

5. X the spoon for baking powder. Ring the spoon for salt.

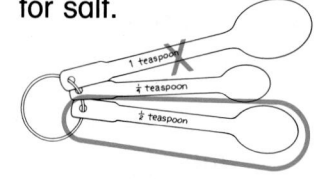

6. Color to show about how far to fill a muffin cup.

muffin cup

Chapter 15   Enrichment: Data from a Recipe

(three hundred twenty-nine)   3

Name _____

umulative Review

Subtract.

64

64 − 30 = ___

- ○ 61
- ● 34
- ○ 44

5. Trade 1 ten for 10 ones.

44

- ○ 4 tens 14 ones
- ● 3 tens 14 ones
- ○ 3 tens 10 ones

hich is the best estimate?

 − 75¢

- ○ more than 50¢
- ● less than 50¢
- ○ 50¢

Subtract.

6.
$$\begin{array}{r} 73 \\ -\ 9 \\ \hline \end{array}$$

- ○ 56
- ○ 71
- ● 64

85
− 21
_____

- ○ about 50
- ● about 60
- ○ about 70

7.
$$\begin{array}{r} 62 \\ -29 \\ \hline \end{array}$$

- ○ 48
- ● 33
- ○ 54

Find how many are left.

Start	Take away	Left
22	15	___

- ○ 5
- ○ 8
- ● 7

8. Which is the add-to-check exercise?

$$\begin{array}{r} 41 \\ -18 \\ \hline 23 \end{array}$$

- ● 18 + 23 = 41
- ○ 18 + 33 = 51
- ○ 41 + 18 = 59

Amy practices the violin 25 minutes each day. She has practiced for 18 minutes already. How many more minutes does she need to practice?

- ○ 10 minutes
- ○ 43 minutes
- ● 7 minutes

CUMULATIVE REVIEW

INTRODUCTION The purpose of this Cumulative Review is to maintain previously taught skills and concepts. The emphasis in this Cumulative Review is on understanding 2-digit subtraction, Chapter 13 and Chapter 14.

ITEM ANALYSIS The table below correlates the Cumulative Review items with the lesson objectives.

Items	Objectives
1	13-2, 13-3
2, 3	13-5, 14-5
4	13-6
5	14-1
6, 7	14-4
8	14-6
9	14-7

Chapter Management

MATHEMATICAL BACKGROUND

Understanding Multiplication

This chapter uses repeated addition to introduce multiplication. This approach, which builds on students' understanding of addition, provides a natural and comfortable starting point for introducing the concept of multiplication in Grade 2.

Because repeated addition is used, considerable attention has been given to developing the idea of same-size or equal groups. Students are taught that multiplication can be used to find the total number of objects when there are several groups, each containing the same number of objects.

Understanding Division

In multiplication, we put together equivalent sets. In division, we form equivalent groups from a given number of objects.

This chapter introduces division through the concepts of *sharing* to make equal groups and *separating* into equal groups. Students use counters and related pictures to learn and practice division.

Problem Solving

In this chapter, students solve problems using data from a pictograph and by using the strategy Choose the Operation.

TIPS FROM TEACHERS

Read a story problem to the class. If the problem requires addition, students hold up a red card. If the problem requires subtraction, they hold up a green card.

**Linda Williams
Quail Run School
Lawrence, KS**

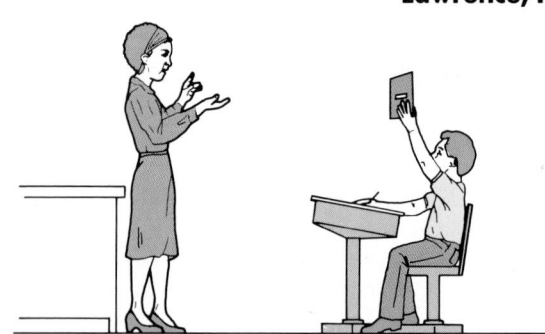

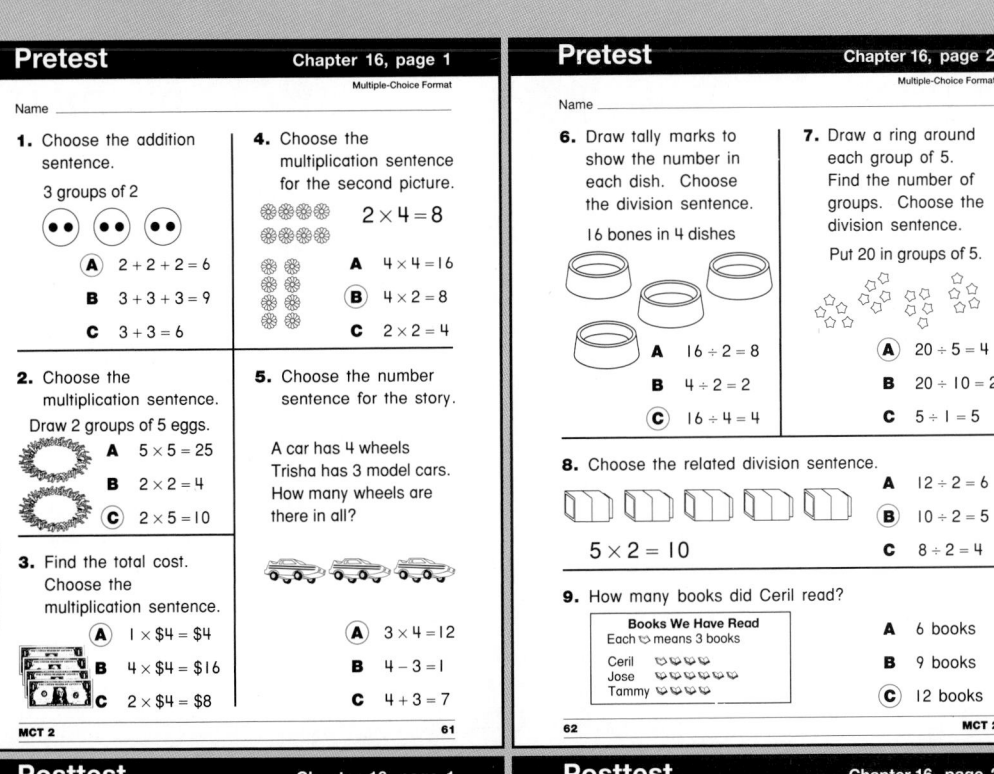

ASSESSMENT

Pretest — Chapter 16, page 1

Multiple-Choice Format

Name _____

1. Choose the addition sentence.

3 groups of 2

A 2 + 2 + 2 = 6
B 3 + 3 + 3 = 9
C 3 + 3 = 6

2. Choose the multiplication sentence.

Draw 2 groups of 5 eggs.
A 5 × 5 = 25
B 2 × 2 = 4
C 2 × 5 = 10

3. Find the total cost. Choose the multiplication sentence.
A 1 × $4 = $4
B 4 × $4 = $16
C 2 × $4 = $8

4. Choose the multiplication sentence for the second picture.

2 × 4 = 8

A 4 × 4 = 16
B 4 × 2 = 8
C 2 × 2 = 4

5. Choose the number sentence for the story.

A car has 4 wheels Trisha has 3 model cars. How many wheels are there in all?

A 3 × 4 = 12
B 4 − 3 = 1
C 4 + 3 = 7

MCT 2   61

Pretest — Chapter 16, page 2

Multiple-Choice Format

Name _____

6. Draw tally marks to show the number in each dish. Choose the division sentence.

16 bones in 4 dishes

A 16 ÷ 2 = 8
B 4 ÷ 2 = 2
C 16 ÷ 4 = 4

7. Draw a ring around each group of 5. Find the number of groups. Choose the division sentence.

Put 20 in groups of 5.

A 20 ÷ 5 = 4
B 20 ÷ 10 = 2
C 5 ÷ 1 = 5

8. Choose the related division sentence.

5 × 2 = 10

A 12 ÷ 2 = 6
B 10 ÷ 2 = 5
C 8 ÷ 2 = 4

9. How many books did Ceril read?

Books We Have Read
Each 📖 means 3 books
Ceril 📖📖📖📖
Jose   📖📖📖📖📖
Tammy 📖📖📖📖

A 6 books
B 9 books
C 12 books

62   MCT 2

Posttest — Chapter 16, page 1

Multiple-Choice Format

Name _____

1. Choose the addition sentence.

4 groups of 3

A 4 + 4 + 4 = 12
B 3 + 3 = 6
C 3 + 3 + 3 + 3 = 12

2. Choose the multiplication sentence.

Draw 3 groups of 2 eggs.
A 3 × 2 = 6
B 2 × 2 = 4
C 3 × 3 = 9

3. Find the total cost. Choose the multiplication sentence.
A 1 × $2 = $2
B 2 × $2 = $4
C 3 × $2 = $6

4. Choose the multiplication sentence for the second picture.

2 × 3 = 6

A 2 × 2 = 4
B 3 × 2 = 6
C 3 × 3 = 9

5. Choose the number sentence for the story.

A skateboard has 4 wheels. Jian has 2 skateboards. How many wheels are there in all?

A 2 + 4 = 6
B 2 × 4 = 8
C 4 − 2 = 2

MCT 2   63

Posttest — Chapter 16, page 2

Multiple-Choice Format

Name _____

6. Draw tally marks to show the number in each dish. Choose the division sentence.

10 bones in 2 dishes

A 12 ÷ 2 = 6
B 2 ÷ 2 = 1
C 10 ÷ 2 = 5

7. Draw a ring around each group of 3. Find the number of groups. Choose the division sentence.

Put 15 in groups of 3.

A 15 ÷ 3 = 5
B 20 ÷ 2 = 10
C 18 ÷ 3 = 6

8. Choose the related division sentence.

5 × 4 = 20

A 20 ÷ 2 = 10
B 20 ÷ 4 = 5
C 10 ÷ 2 = 5

9. How many books did Sue read?

Books We Have Read
Each 📖 means 3 books
Wayne 📖📖📖
Karl
Sue   📖📖📖📖📖

A 3 books
B 9 books
C 15 books

64   MCT 2

ITEM ANALYSIS

Items	Objectives
1	16-1
2	16-2
3	16-3
4	16-4
5	16-5
6	16-6
7	16-7
8	16-8
9	16-9

Note: The item analysis is the same for all pretests and posttests for this chapter.

ALSO AVAILABLE

▶ Free Response Tests
▶ Alternative Tests
▶ Thinking Strategies
▶ Concrete Materials

PROJECT AND BULLETIN BOARD

Introduce readiness for division with this project. Divide the bulletin board into 4 sections and the class into 4 groups. Provide a box with the following materials: 4 plastic detergent bottles, 16 lengths of thick yarn, 8 pieces of fabric, 8 large buttons, 12 rubber bands, and 4 dowel rods or sticks. During each session, have students choose 1 item from the box and ask them to find all like items (all 8 buttons, for example). Explain that 1 section on the bulletin board will belong to each group. Have students divide the buttons (or other items) equally among the 4 groups and attach them to the bulletin board. Continue dividing sets of materials until all are equally distributed. Then have each group use the materials to make a bottle-head puppet, using a bottle for the head, yarn for hair, fabric for clothing, buttons for eyes, a dowel rod to hold the puppet, and rubber bands to hold hair and clothes in place.

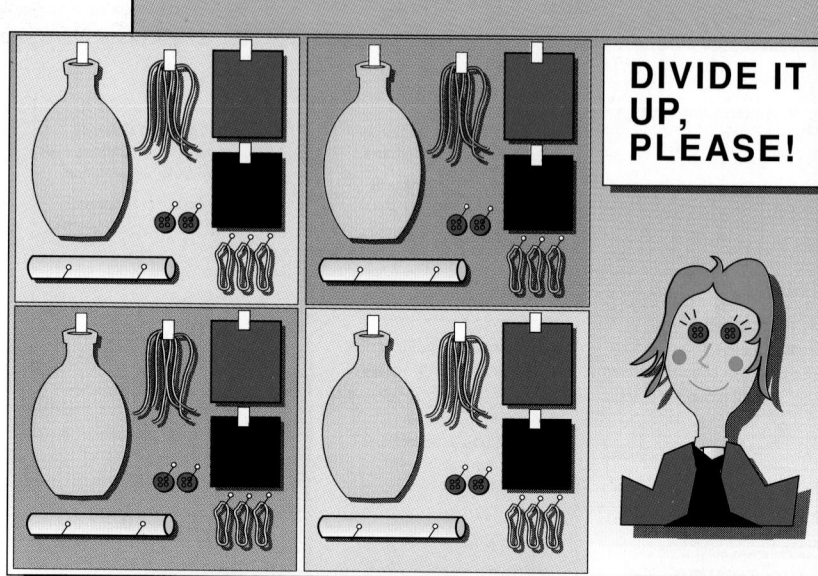

DIVIDE IT UP, PLEASE!

COOPERATIVE LEARNING

Divide the class into 4 groups. Identify the group skill: reaching a group decision. Post a chart similar to the one shown. Have students use the chart and counters to find out how much food each farmer needs to feed his or her animals each day. Have each group solve the problem for 1 farmer. Have individual members of each group multiply using manipulatives to find out how many bones, carrots, ears of corn, apples, or crackers their farmer needs. Record the findings on a class chart. Encourage members of each group to discuss and then decide who should do each task.

You will find grouping suggestions and cooperative learning activities in most lessons throughout this chapter.

Farmer Brad has:	Farmer Gwen has:	Farmer Ed has:	Farmer Cheryl has:
1 dog	3 dogs	5 dogs	2 dogs
1 rabbit	3 rabbits	5 rabbits	2 rabbits
1 horse	3 horses	5 horses	2 horses
1 pig	3 pigs	5 pigs	2 pigs
1 duck	3 ducks	5 ducks	2 ducks

What each animal eats:		
dog – 3 bones	horse – 5 ears of corn	
rabbit – 2 carrots	pig – 4 apples	duck – 1 cracker

LITERATURE

Low, Joseph. *Mice Twice*. New York: Atheneum, 1983.

Cat is so hungry he could eat 47 grasshoppers and more. He decides to invite a mouse to dinner. She accepts only if she can bring a friend, *mice twice*. The story uses the language of multiplication.
Have students draw sets of mice and cats, then multiply. They might also create their own stories using multiplication terms such as *six times as fierce* and *five times as tall*.

Andersen, Hans Christian. *Andersen's Fairy Tales*. New York: Grossett and Dunlap, 1945.

Anno, Masaichiro and Mitsumasa. *Anno's Mysterious Multiplying Jar*. New York: Putnam, 1983.

Carroll, Lewis. *Alice's Adventures in Wonderland*. New York: Dilithium Press, 1988.

de Angeli, Marguerite. *Marguerite de Angeli Book of Nursery and Mother Goose Rhymes*. New York: Doubleday, 1954.

Friskey, Margaret. *Mystery of the Farmer's Three Fives*. New York: Children's Press, 1963.

ENGLISH AS A SECOND LANGUAGE

The ability to visualize the problems in this chapter will be an aid to all students in doing the multiplication. Before using the counters, have students draw what is described in the problem. In general, make sure students hear and understand the synonymous expressions denoting multiplication (*multiplied by, times, 2 groups of 3 eggs, put together, equal groups*) and division (*share, separate, 20 bones in 4 dishes, divide, put 15 in groups of 5*). When teaching the operations, paraphrase often.

When reading the stories aloud, pair an ESL student with a native speaker and have 1 student question the other, repeating the language taught: *Do you need to put together groups? Do you need to share equally?*

Introduce the tongue-twister as a game in which students first recite slowly and then with increasing speed. Tape them and play the tape back. Be sensitive to those students who are not ready or do not want to be taped.

GIFTED

Mathematically talented students may already understand multiplication and division concepts and be able to use the operations readily. They will nevertheless likely be interested in many of the strategies presented in this chapter. You may wish to challenge these students, after they have completed their book work, by showing them how to change a basic recipe to feed a different number of people. For example, after Lesson 2 on multiplication with 2 and 5, write the following recipe for chicken casserole on the chalkboard: Serves 4— 1 medium zucchini; 2 cups diced chicken; 1 cup chopped onion; 3 tablespoons parsley; 2 cups canned tomatoes. Have students multiply to find how much of each ingredient they would need for 8 servings. After Lesson 8 on sharing sets to make equal groups, you might alter the recipe so that it serves 20, then have students find amounts for 4 servings. If this activity appeals to students, encourage them to create their own recipes, then multiply or divide the ingredients to change the number of servings.

STUDENTS AT RISK

The words students say to themselves when they see symbols and numbers guide them as they compute. This is especially true for particular learning-disabled students. Multiplication and division are not new concepts for these students, but the symbols that represent them are. Thus it is essential that teachers model and use words that help children think about what the new symbols mean.

There are a number of ways to do this in multiplication. For example, one may translate the number sentence $2 \times 4 = 8$ as *2 groups with 4 in each group* rather than the traditional *2 times 4*. Practice reading multiplication number sentences aloud and encourage students to translate the operations before they solve them.

Similarly, division can be explained by saying, *Share 6 with 3 different people. How much does each get?* Again, the traditional *6 divided by 3* does not provide enough clues to what the operation means. Encourage students to translate division sentences before they solve them. Careful modeling of language is of significant help to learners who guide their actions with internal *talk*.

You may also use the Reteaching Supplement and the specific Reteaching Tips from each lesson in this chapter.

PICTURE

These pictures and accompanying stories and poems are available as storybooks.

You may want to read and discuss this story with your students before starting the chapter. The first lesson in this chapter includes a question about the story. Lessons 1, 2, 4, 6, and 7 in this chapter have questions in the informal Assessment that refer to the story.

The Magic Multiplier

Bea Bear was enjoying a sunny morning stroll through the woods. As she rounded a curve on the narrow path, she suddenly came upon a large glittering arch. Above the arch, in rainbow colors, a sign read "Storybook Land." Beneath the arch, a gate swung open. Bea could hardly resist. Without a moment's hesitation, she entered this strange and magical land.

Bea shivered with delight. To the right stood a tall beanstalk. Down the road, she could see the three little pigs working on their house of bricks. And to her left, a beautiful table was prepared for the Mad Hatter's tea party. "This is amazing," thought Bea.

At the foot of Jack's beanstalk, Bea spied a curious-looking stick poking up through a pile of empty bean pods. It was perfectly clear, like glass. But when she held it up to the sun's light, it sparkled with glittering particles of sun, moon, and star dust. As Bea was studying this remarkable treasure, the stick slipped through her paws, striking a small bean sprout twice before resting on the ground. To Bea's surprise, the bean sprout, which had had 4 bean pods, was now covered with 8 pods. "How could this be? There must be magic at work," Bea decided. "And the magic must be in this curious-looking stick!"

To test the stick, Bea approached the Mad Hatter's tea table. There were place settings for 10 guests, but only 2 party hats were placed at the center of the table. "Perhaps Mr. Hatter could use a few more hats," she said. She tapped the hats 5 times with the magic stick. And just as she had suspected, the 2 hats became 10 hats.

How excited Bea was! She had discovered the power of the Magic Multiplier. Eager to experiment with her magic stick, Bea gathered 3 acorns and placed them together on the ground. She tapped the acorns 4 times, and they magically multiplied to 12. Four squirrels scampered from the nearby trees and shared the 12 acorns, taking 3 each.

Down the road, Bea Bear neared the construction site of the 3 pigs, but they had gone to lunch. Bea saw 5 bricks piled neatly against the side of the house. "They'll need more than 5 bricks to complete the chimney," she thought.

So she tapped the stack of bricks with her Magic Multiplier 3 times. "Fifteen bricks should be enough to finish the job," Bea said to herself. When the pigs returned, they were surprised to find a stack of 15 bricks. The brothers decided to divide the bricks into 3 equal groups. Each pig took 5 bricks and went happily back to work.

Continuing her stroll, Bea Bear met the muffin man, who had just returned from the fair. He explained that he was very late with a delivery of 16 blueberry muffins to the old woman who lives in the shoe. "I'm afraid I shall never get there in time," sighed the muffin man. "I have only 4 muffins left, so I must hurry home to bake more."

"Maybe I can help," offered Bea. "Let's see. You have 4 muffins and need 16...." Bea tapped the muffin basket 4 times. The muffin man stared in amazement. His basket was suddenly overflowing with muffins. After thanking Bea Bear for her help, he divided the 16 muffins equally into 2 baskets and went merrily on his way.

Just then, from behind a large rock just to the side of the road, Bea heard a soft cry. "Oh dear, oh dear, what ever shall I do?" Peeking behind the rock, Bea Bear was surprised to see a wood sprite.

"Why are you so sad?" asked Bea.

"I've lost my Magic Multiplier, and without it I cannot complete any of my tasks," he moaned. "And everyone here in Storybook Land is counting on me."

"Did this Magic Multiplier have any special power?" Bea asked.

"Well, yes. It has the power to increase the number of objects in a group a specific number of times," replied the sprite. "But why do you ask?"

"Because I've had the Magic Multiplier with me all morning!" exclaimed Bea.

Bea went on to tell the wood sprite all that had happened during the day. "I'm delighted," said the sprite merrily. "I have my Magic Multiplier back, and all my tasks are completed. This is truly an extraordinary day!" And Bea Bear couldn't have agreed more.

Putting Together Equal Groups

OBJECTIVE 16-1   To use models to put together equal groups; to use repeated addition to find the total

PREBOOK ACTIVITIES

QUICK REVIEW

Add.

5	6	9	3	7	1	8
4	3	0	7	2	5	2
+ 1	+ 4	+ 6	+ 9	+ 5	+ 7	+ 2
(10)	(13)	(15)	(19)	(14)	(13)	(12)

PRIOR KNOWLEDGE

Suppose that it is your job to set the table for dinner. How will you know how many sets of silverware you will need? (Possible answer: If there are 4 people at dinner, then I will need 4 sets of silverware.) *If each set has 1 fork, 1 knife, and 1 spoon, how could you find out how many pieces that is in all?* (Possible answer: Add 3 + 3 + 3 + 3 to find the total.)

COMMUNICATION

Listening and Discussing Math   *What does it mean if I ask you to repeat something?* (Say something again exactly the way you said it before.) *If you use repeated addition, you keep adding the same number. As I say a number, hold up the number of fingers that shows the number you would use for repeated addition: 2, 7, 3, 8, 5, 1.*
When might you put things into equal groups? (Possible answer: sharing the same number of apple slices with a friend; putting pennies into equal groups as you count them)

EXPLORE AND CONNECT

Materials: counters
Grouping Suggestions: small groups
Have students put counters into equal groups starting with 3 groups of 5. *Why do we say the groups are equal?* (Possible answer: They all have the same number of counters.) *How can you find out how many cubes there are all together?* (Possible answer: Count by 1s, by 5s, or add 5 at a time.) Ask students to make 3 new groups of 5, 6, and 7 counters. *Compare these groups to the groups you made before. How are they different?* (Possible answer: They do not all have an equal number of counters.) *How can you find out how many counters there are in these groups?* (Possible answer: Count by 1s; add.) Explain that with the equal groups of counters, they could keep adding the same number or use repeated addition to find out how many counters they had. Have students explore other equal groupings of counters.

CONNECTIONS   Use these anytime.

Problem of the Day

Finding Extra Data   Find the answer. Underline the extra data.
Ed picked 48 apples on Monday.
<u>There are 70 trees in the orchard.</u>
He picked 43 apples on Tuesday.
How many apples did he pick in all?
(48 + 43 = 91; he picked 91 apples.)

Subject Integration

Language Arts   Tell a story about an animal who needs to put something into equal groups. Tell what the items are and explain why the animal needs to group them. Draw a picture that shows the items placed in equal groups to go with your story.

Counting Patterns

Skip Counting   Count in your head to find the number you would get if you use repeated addition the number of times shown.
2, 3 times   (2 + 2 + 2 = 6)
5, 2 times   (5 + 5 = 10)
10, 4 times   (10 + 10 + 10 + 10 = 40)
3, 4 times   (3 + 3 + 3 + 3 = 12)
5, 5 times   (5 + 5 + 5 + 5 + 5 = 25)

CLASSWORK AND HOMEWORK SUPPLEMENTS

OPTIONS FOR INDIVIDUAL NEEDS

Basic

Exercises All
Calculator Bank, p. 401

Supplements
Reteaching 136 or
Practice 136

Average

Exercises All
Calculator Bank, p. 401

Supplements
Practice 136
Challenges 136 or
Thinking Skills 136

Extended

Exercises All
Calculator Bank, p. 401

Supplements
Challenges 136
Thinking Skills 136

Practice

Skills Maintenance   16-1

Name _____

Putting Together Equal Groups

How many are there? Group the objects so each container has the same number. Write an addition sentence for each picture.

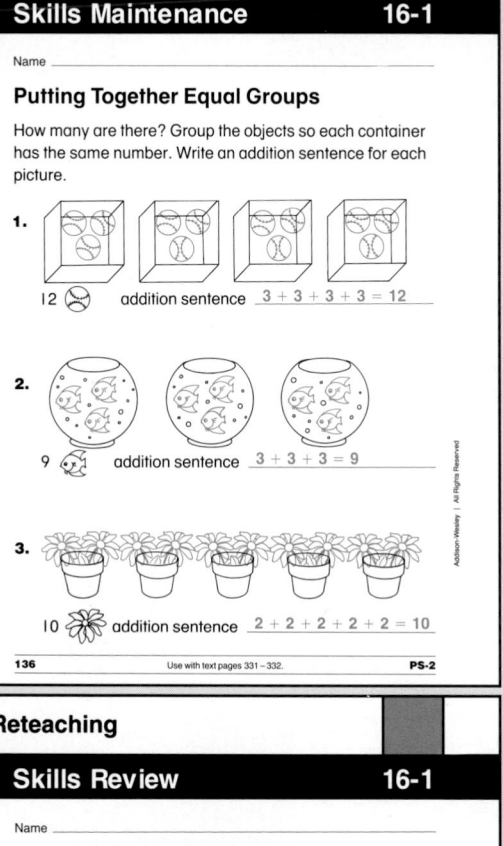

1. 12 addition sentence $3 + 3 + 3 + 3 = 12$

2. 9 addition sentence $3 + 3 + 3 = 9$

3. 10 addition sentence $2 + 2 + 2 + 2 + 2 = 10$

136   Use with text pages 331–332.   PS-2

Building Thinking Skills

Critical Thinking   16-1

Name _____

Show the Ways

Use counters.
Figure out which number in the box you can use to make the different equal groups.
Ring the number. Draw dots to show the ways.

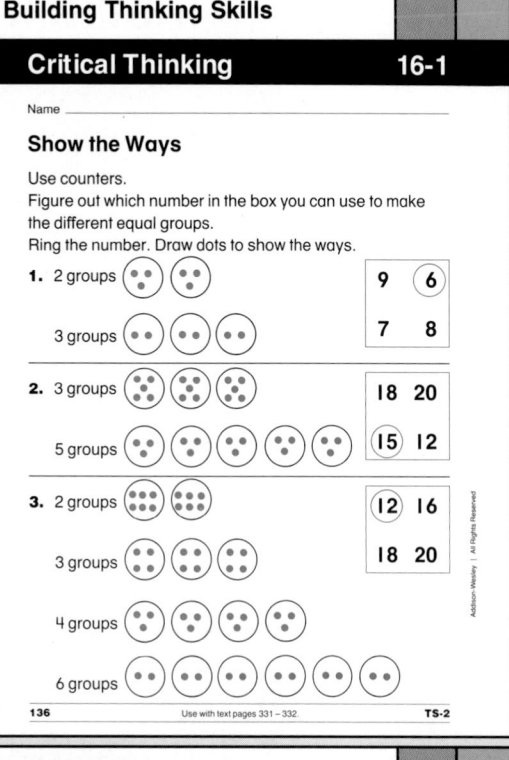

1. 2 groups / 3 groups   9 ⑥ / 7 8
2. 3 groups / 5 groups   18 20 / ⑮ 12
3. 2 groups / 3 groups / 4 groups / 6 groups   ⑫ 16 / 18 20

136   Use with text pages 331–332.   TS-2

Reteaching

Skills Review   16-1

Name _____

Putting Together Equal Groups

 3 groups of 2
$2 + 2 + 2 = 6$

Ring equal groups.
Write an addition sentence to match the picture.

1. 3 groups of 3   (Ring threes.)

$3 + 3 + 3 = 9$

2. 4 groups of 2   (Ring twos.)
$2 + 2 + 2 + 2 = 8$

3. 2 groups of 5   (Ring fives.)
$5 + 5 = 10$

4. 3 groups of 4   (Ring fours.)
$4 + 4 + 4 = 12$

136   Use with text pages 331–332.   RS-2

Challenges

Cooperative Activities   16-1

Name _____

Dot Count

Play with a partner.
Each of you needs a game sheet.
Roll a number cube marked 1 – 6.
Draw that many circles on your scorecard. Roll again. Draw that many dots in each circle.
Skip count or write an addition sentence to find the total.
Take turns. The player with the highest score wins the round.

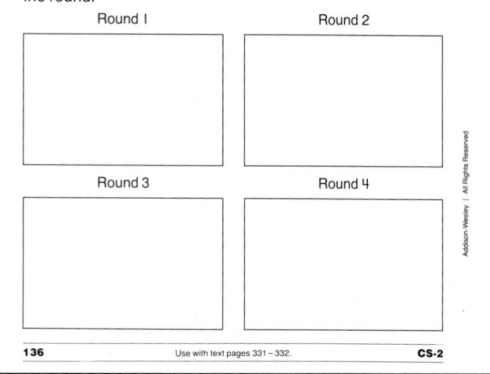
First I rolled a 3. Then I rolled a 4. My score is 12.
$4 + 4 + 4 = 12$

Round 1 / Round 2 / Round 3 / Round 4

136   Use with text pages 331–332.   CS-2

Other Resources:
Mathematics Their Way, pp. 200-201
Explorations, pp. 340-341, 343, 349
Developing Number Concepts With Unifix Cubes, pp. 180-185
Mathematics Book A, p. 39

16-1

OBJECTIVE 16-1

To use models to put together equal groups; to use repeated addition to find the total

Materials: Cube-A-Links, counters, TA3 (Centimeter Graph Paper), number cards 1-9, number cubes labeled 1-6

1. MOTIVATE AND TEACH

LEARN ABOUT IT

Read the chapter story to the class. *How many bean pods were in a group before the Magic Multiplier touched them?* (4) *How many times did the·Magic Multiplier touch them?* (2) Review some of Alice's adventures in the story *Alice in Wonderland,* especially the Mad Hatter's Tea Party. Then have students use counters to act out situations from the party using the place settings on the page.

▶ **Suppose that 3 animals came to the tea party. How many slices of bread would you need if you put 4 slices on each plate? How can you find the answer?** (Possible answer: Use repeated addition; add 3 groups of 4 or $4 + 4 + 4 = 12$.)

▶ **How are 4 + 4 + 4 and 3 groups of 4 the same?** (Possible answer: They both show how many groups there are and how many are in each group.)

▶ **The table shows 4 place settings. How could you show 2 groups of 3?** (Possible answer: Place 3 counters on each of 2 plates and leave 2 plates empty.)

▶ **How is repeated addition like skip counting?** (Possible answer: In both cases, you skip over equal groups of numbers to count. In repeated addition, you are told how many times you are to skip count.)

2. CHECK UNDERSTANDING

ERROR ALERT Confusing the number of groups with the number in each group and reversing them when they count.

16
Understanding Multiplication and Division

TEACHING OPTIONS

RETEACHING TIPS On large sheets of paper, draw groups of 3 and 4 large circles. Ask students to use counters to model groups with equal numbers, such as 3 groups of 4 counters. Have them write a repeated addition sentence to match. Repeat for other numbers. Assign Reteaching Supplement 136.

ENRICHMENT Have students cut out rectangles or squares from graph paper to show groups with equal numbers of squares, such as 2 groups of 4. Tell them to paste cutouts on colored paper and label them, then write addition sentences to match.

For example: ⊞⊞ 2 groups of 4
$4 + 4 = 8$

two groups of 5

utting Together Equal Groups

ork with a partner. Use cubes to
ake equal groups. Draw dots to
how each group. Write an addition
entence to tell how many.

$$5 + 5 = 10$$

3 groups of 4

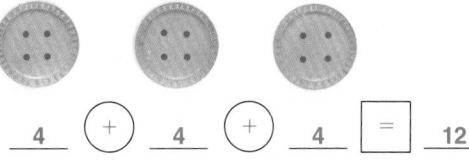

$$4 + 4 + 4 = 12$$

4 groups of 2

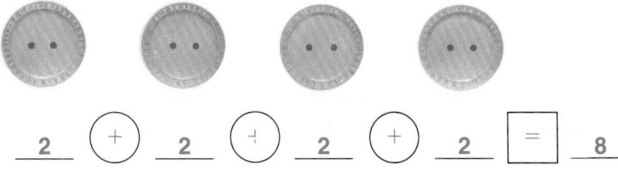

$$2 + 2 + 2 + 2 = 8$$

5 groups of 3

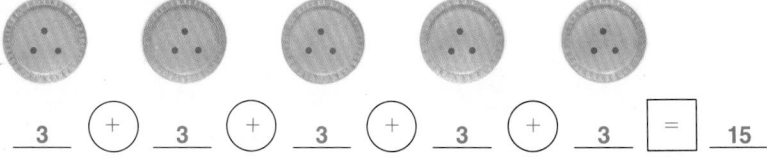

$$3 + 3 + 3 + 3 + 3 = 15$$

SE CRITICAL THINKING

Are three groups of 2 greater than or
the same as two groups of 3? Use
cubes to help. Ring the answer.

greater than

(same as)

2 (three hundred thirty-two)

Chapter 16

3. PRACTICE AND APPLY

Basic	All
Average	All
Extended	All

PRACTICE

What will you use to make equal groups?
(cubes that are snapped together) *How
will you show how many cubes are in
each group?* (Draw the appropriate
number of dots on each plate.) *How will
you write an addition sentence?* (Add the
number of dots shown on each plate.)

APPLY

USE CRITICAL THINKING
► **Estimate the answer for Exercise 4.
Why did you make this estimate?**
(Possible answer: 3 groups of 2 have the
same number as 2 groups of 3 because
there are more groups with fewer in
each.)
► **If you had no cubes, how else
might you compare the groups?**
(Possible answer: Make a drawing
showing the number in each group and
then find the total for each group.)

16-1

LOSE AND ASSESS

HOW WHAT YOU KNOW
ovide each group with number cards
9 and a number cube labeled 1-6.
ave a student pick a number card to
ow the number in each group and
ll the cube to show the number of
oups. Then have another student
odel the groups with counters as a
ird writes an addition sentence to
atch. Encourage students to check
eir work as a group so that they all
ree.

QUICK QUIZ

Draw a picture to show the groups.
Write an addition sentence to match.
3 groups of 4
(xxxx xxxx xxxx)   (4 + 4 + 4 = 12)

Chapter 16 Lesson 1   **332**

Understanding Multiplication

OBJECTIVE 16-2   To model and write multiplication sentences

PREBOOK ACTIVITIES

QUICK REVIEW

Continue the pattern.

2, 4, 6, (8) , (10)   8, 12, 16, (20) , (24)
6, 9, 12, (15) , (18)   42, 40, 38, (36) , (34)
25, 30, 35, (40) , (45)   31, 28, 25, (22) , (19)

PRIOR KNOWLEDGE

Have 4 students come to the front of the classroom. *How many pairs of shoes do you see?* (4) *How many shoes are there in each pair?* (2) Write this on the chalkboard: 2 shoes, 2 shoes, 2 shoes, 2 shoes. *How many shoes are there all together?* (8) Repeat this procedure to explore the number of eyes, ears, hands, and legs that are part of the students at the front of the room.

COMMUNICATION

Discussing Math   Help students discuss multiplication concepts: *Imagine you are having a party for 4 people and yourself. You want to make 2 sandwiches for each person. How many people will be at your party?* (5) *How many sandwiches will each person get?* (2) *How will you know how many sandwiches to make?* (Possible answer: Add 2 five times; 2 + 2 + 2 + 2 + 2 = 10.) On the board, write **multiply** and read it aloud, then write 5 × 2 = 10. *This number sentence can help us understand what multiply means. What does the 5 in this sentence tell us?* (number of people) *What does the 2 tell us?* (number of sandwiches for each person) *What does the 10 mean?* (number of sandwiches we need in all)

EXPLORE AND CONNECT

Materials: counters, paper plates
Grouping Suggestion: small groups
Provide each small group with 15 counters and 5 paper plates. Have students decide together how to separate the counters into equal groups. *How did your group members separate the counters?* (Possible answer: We kept putting 1 counter in each plate until all the counters were used.) *How many groups of counters did your members make?* (5) *How many counters are in each group?* (3) Have students in each group decide how to write an addition sentence to show how they separated the counters. (3 + 3 + 3 + 3 + 3 = 15) Write this on the chalkboard: 5 groups of 3 is 15. Then write 5 × 3 = 15. *What does 5 in this sentence tell us?* (number of equal groups) *What does 3 tell us?* (number of counters in each group) Repeat using 3 or 4 plates and 12 counters.

CONNECTIONS   Use these anytime.

Problem of the Day

Draw a Picture   Make drawings to help you solve this problem.
Mr. Ketch, a science teacher, has 5 cages of white mice. There are 3 white mice in each cage. He also has 4 cages of black mice. There are 2 black mice in each cage. How many mice does Mr. Ketch have? (23)

Math Connection

Geometry   Use pattern blocks. Use the green triangles to make 2 hexagons. Write a multiplication sentence to show the number of triangles you made. (2 × 6 = 12) Next, use blue parallelograms to make 2 hexagons. Write another multiplication sentence to show this. (2 × 3 = 6)

Subject Integration

Science   Draw 2 octopuses. Write a multiplication sentence to show the number of legs on 2 octopuses. (2 × 8 = 16) Choose another group of animals. Draw a picture and write a multiplication sentence for your group. (Answers will vary.)

CLASSWORK AND HOMEWORK SUPPLEMENTS

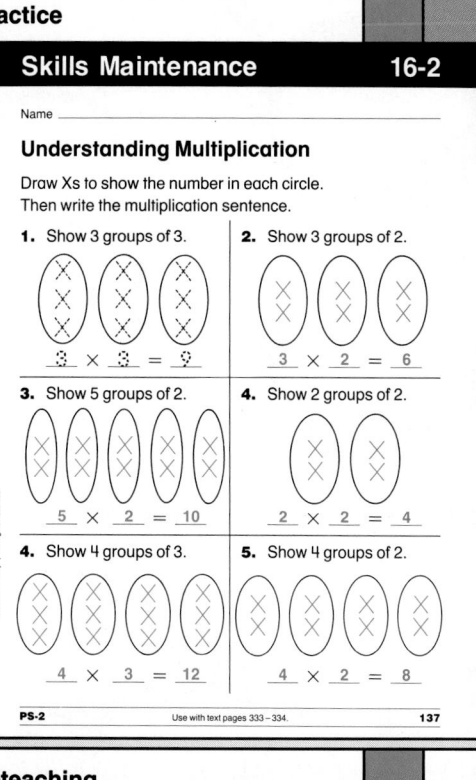

Practice

Skills Maintenance 16-2

Name _____

Understanding Multiplication

Draw Xs to show the number in each circle.
Then write the multiplication sentence.

1. Show 3 groups of 3.

$\underline{3} \times \underline{3} = \underline{9}$

2. Show 3 groups of 2.

$\underline{3} \times \underline{2} = \underline{6}$

3. Show 5 groups of 2.

$\underline{5} \times \underline{2} = \underline{10}$

4. Show 2 groups of 2.

$\underline{2} \times \underline{2} = \underline{4}$

4. Show 4 groups of 3.

$\underline{4} \times \underline{3} = \underline{12}$

5. Show 4 groups of 2.

$\underline{4} \times \underline{2} = \underline{8}$

PS-2   Use with text pages 333–334.   **137**

Building Thinking Skills

Math Reasoning 16-2

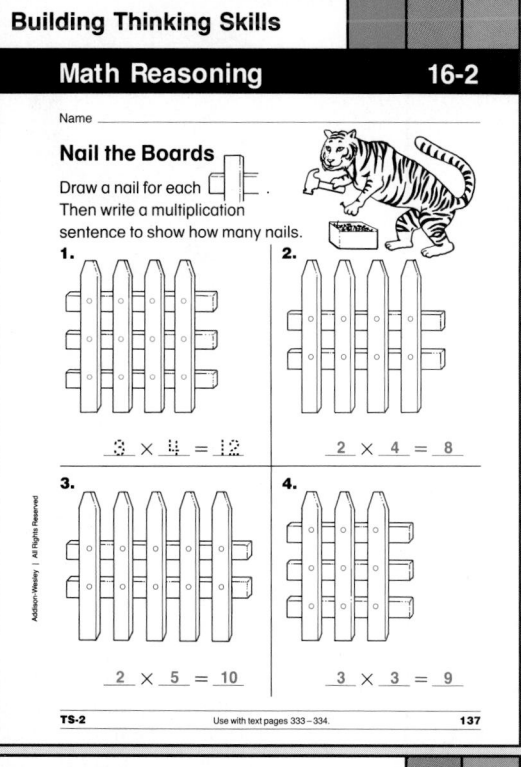

Name _____

Nail the Boards

Draw a nail for each ☐ .
Then write a multiplication
sentence to show how many nails.

1.

$\underline{3} \times \underline{4} = \underline{12}$

2.

$\underline{2} \times \underline{4} = \underline{8}$

3.

$\underline{2} \times \underline{5} = \underline{10}$

4.

$\underline{3} \times \underline{3} = \underline{9}$

TS-2   Use with text pages 333–334.   **137**

Reteaching

Skills Review 16-2

Name _____

Understanding Multiplication

4 twos = 8

4 groups of
2 people

$4 \times 2 = 8$

$2+2+2+2=8$

Ring the groups. Write the total.

1.

$3+3=6$

2 threes

$2 \times 3 = \underline{6}$

2.

$2+2+2+2+2 = 10$

5 twos

$5 \times 2 = \underline{10}$

3.

$2+2+2+2=8$

4 twos

$4 \times 2 = \underline{8}$

4.

$4+4+4 = 12$

3 fours

$3 \times 4 = \underline{12}$

RS-2   Use with text pages 333–334.   **137**

Challenges

Calculators 16-2

Name _____

Skip Counting

Use your ▭ .
Press the keys in order. Write the numbers you see.

1. Skip count by 2s from 0 to 10.

| ON/C | 0 | + | 2 | = | = | = | = | = |

$\underline{2}\quad \underline{4}\quad \underline{6}\quad \underline{8}\quad \underline{10}$

How many times did you press = ? $\underline{5}$

Finish the multiplication sentence: $\underline{2} \times \underline{5} = \underline{10}$

2. Skip count by 3s from 0 to 12.

| ON/C | 0 | + | 3 | = | = | = | = |

$\underline{3}\quad \underline{6}\quad \underline{9}\quad \underline{12}$

How many times did you press = ? $\underline{4}$

Finish the multiplication sentence. $\underline{3} \times \underline{4} = \underline{12}$

3. Skip count by fours from 0 to 16.

| ON/C | 0 | + | 4 | = | = | = | = |

$\underline{4}\quad \underline{8}\quad \underline{12}\quad \underline{16}$

Finish the multiplication sentence. $\underline{4} \times \underline{4} = \underline{16}$

CS-2   Use with text pages 333–334.   **137**

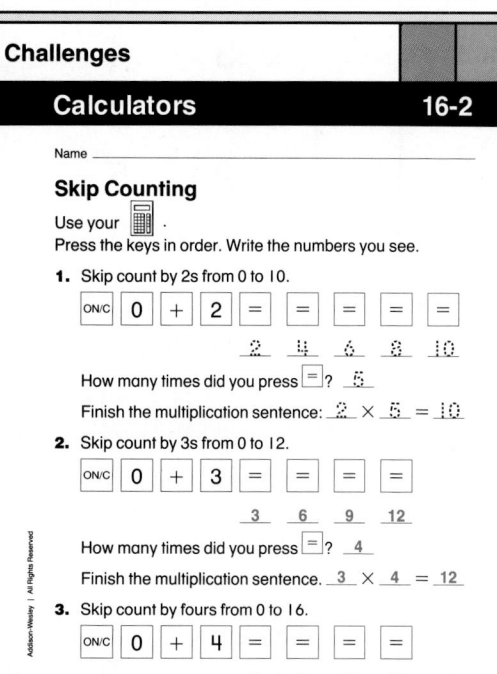

OPTIONS FOR INDIVIDUAL NEEDS

Basic

Exercises All
Calculator Bank, p. 404
Computer Bank, pp. 405-408

Supplements
Reteaching 137 or
Practice 137
Thinking Skills 137

Average

Exercises All
Calculator Bank, p. 404
Computer Bank, pp. 405-408

Supplements
Practice 137
Challenges 137 or
Thinking Skills 137

Extended

Exercises All
Calculator Bank, p. 404
Computer Bank, pp. 405-408

Supplements
Challenges 137
Thinking Skills 137

Other Resources:
Math in Stride, p. 123
Explorations, pp. 340-343, 349
Workjobs II, p. 118
Developing Number Concepts With Unifix Cubes pp. 186-195
Mathematics Book A, pp. 39-40, 42-43

16-2

LESSON PLAN 16-2

OBJECTIVE 16-2
To model and write multiplication sentences

Materials: counters, number cubes 1-5

Grouping Suggestion: pairs

1. MOTIVATE AND TEACH

LEARN ABOUT IT

Read or discuss Hans Christian Andersen's book, *The Ugly Duckling*. Have students use counters to model this problem: *There are 2 mother ducks. Each mother lays 3 eggs. How many eggs are there in all? Write a multiplication sentence to show 2 groups of 3 eggs.* ($2 \times 3 = 6$)

▶ **What plan can you use to complete the exercises on page 333?** (Possible answer: Use counters to show the number of eggs in each nest. Then count and write the number of eggs in all.)

▶ **What is another way you can show 12 eggs?** (Possible answers: 4 nests with 3 eggs or 2 nests with 6 eggs)

▶ **How could you find the number of eggs in all without using multiplication?** (Possible answer: Add the number of eggs in each nest to find the total.)

▶ **Describe how $3 \times 1 = 3$ is different from $1 \times 3 = 3$.** (Possible answer: $3 \times 1 = 3$ means 3 groups of one thing. $1 \times 3 = 3$ means one group of 3 things.)

2. CHECK UNDERSTANDING

ERROR ALERT Misunderstanding the rules for multiplication by 1 and 0—for example, writing $3 \times 1 = 1$ or $4 \times 0 = 4$.

Name _____

Understanding Multiplication

Work with a partner. Use 12 counters.

Find and write the number of eggs in all. Then write the multiplication sentence. Read it to your partner.

This sign means to multiply. Read it as "3 times 4."

Number of nests	Number of eggs in each nest	Number of eggs in all				
1. 3	4	12	3	× 4	=	12
2. 4	2	8	4	× 2	=	8
3. 2	5	10	2	× 5	=	10
4. 1	3	3	1	× 3	=	3

Chapter 16

(three hundred thirty-three) 33

TEACHING OPTIONS

RETEACHING TIPS Have students show 3 groups of 1, by drawing 3 circles and putting 1 counter in each. Have them develop the pattern by saying aloud: *1 + 1 + 1 = 3, 3 ones = 3, 3 groups of 1 = 3, 3 × 1 = 3.* This sequence also can be used for multiplying by 0. Use Reteaching Supplement 137.

ENRICHMENT Have students imagine that they are having a party. Each person at the party will get 2 hot dogs, 1 cup of juice, 4 balloons, and 3 small toys. Challenge students to draw pictures and write multiplication sentences to show how many of each item they need if there are 4 people at the party.

raw eggs to show the number in each
est. Use counters to help. Then
rite the multiplication sentence.

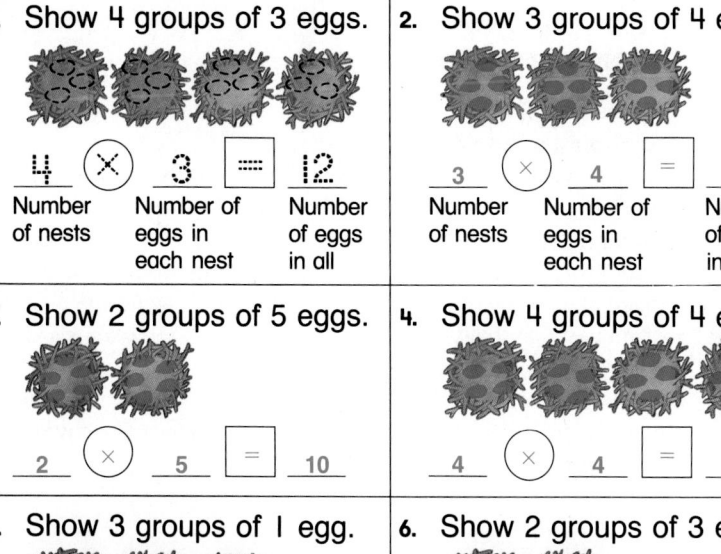

1. Show 4 groups of 3 eggs.	2. Show 3 groups of 4 eggs.
4 ⊗ 3 ⊡ 12	3 ⊗ 4 ☐ 12
Number of nests / Number of eggs in each nest / Number of eggs in all	Number of nests / Number of eggs in each nest / Number of eggs in all
3. Show 2 groups of 5 eggs.	4. Show 4 groups of 4 eggs.
2 ⊗ 5 ☐ 10	4 ⊗ 4 ☐ 16
5. Show 3 groups of 1 egg.	6. Show 2 groups of 3 eggs.
3 ⊗ 1 ☐ 3	2 ⊗ 3 ☐ 6

ALK ABOUT IT

Use counters to show each
multiplication sentence. Tell
why you think the number
in each group is the same as
the number in all. See teaching notes.

Number of groups		Number in each group		Number in all
1	×	2	=	2
1	×	4	=	4
1	×	3	=	3
1	×	5	=	5

3. PRACTICE AND APPLY

Basic	All
Average	All
Extended	All

PRACTICE

What plan do you have for completing the exercises on page 334? (Possible answer: For each sentence, draw the number of eggs on each nest. Multiply the number of nests by the number of eggs in each nest.)

APPLY

TALK ABOUT IT ► **Why is the number in each group the same as the number in all?** (Since there is only 1 group, the number in it must be the number in all.)
► **What would happen to the number in all if you had 2 groups?** (The number in all would be 2 times what it is now.)
► **What do you think the next multiplication sentence in this exercise would be?** ($1 \times 6 = 6$)
► **If you had 5 groups, how many counters would you need in each group to have 5 in all?** (1 in each group)

16-2

CLOSE AND ASSESS

SHOW WHAT YOU KNOW
Review the chapter story with
students. Have them work in small
groups and use counters to show each
multiplication problem in the story.
Then have them write a number
sentence to match the counters for
each problem. Remind students to
listen to each other and make a group
decision about their answers.

QUICK QUIZ

Draw pictures. Write the
multiplication sentence.
2 groups of 3 eggs.   ($2 \times 3 = 6$)
4 groups of 2 eggs.   ($4 \times 2 = 8$)
3 groups of 1 egg.   ($3 \times 1 = 3$)

Multiplying With Money

OBJECTIVE 16-3   To model and write multiplication sentences with money

PREBOOK ACTIVITIES

PRIOR KNOWLEDGE

Draw 4 circles on the chalkboard and label them 10¢, 5¢, 5¢, and 1¢. *How much money is this?* (21¢) Hold up a pencil. *1 pencil costs 5¢. How much do 2 pencils cost?* (10¢) *3 pencils?* (15¢) *4 pencils?* (20¢) *How did you find the answer?* (Possible answer: added 5¢ 4 times) *Is 21¢ enough money to buy 5 pencils?* (no) *How much more money would you need?* (4¢)

COMMUNICATION

Discussing Math   Write a dollar sign on the chalkboard and explain what it means. *Suppose that you save $4/wk. How much would you have in 2 wk?* ($8) *in 3 wk?* ($12) *How do you know?* (Possible answer: Add: 4 + 4 + 4 = 12.) Write 3 × $4 = $12 on the board. *What does the 3 in this sentence mean?* (number of weeks we saved $4) *What is the $12?* (the amount of money we saved in 3 wk) *Why do you think we use multiplication to find the total amount for this problem instead of addition?* (Possible answer: It is faster; the answer is the same, but you do not have to write down so many steps.)

EXPLORE AND CONNECT

Materials: TA15 (Play Money)
Grouping suggestion: small groups
Give each group a supply of $25 in dollar bills. Ask members of each group to take an equal amount of money—for example, 3 students with $5 each. *How many dollar bills does your group have in all?* ($15) Have students in the group work together to write a multiplication sentence showing the amount of money they have in all. *Where do you write dollar signs in your multiplication sentence?* (in 2 places: 3 × $5 = $15) Repeat, having students take amounts from $1-$5 each. Ask them to write a matching multiplication sentence to show the total for each amount.

CONNECTIONS   Use these anytime.

Problem of the Day

Logic   You want to buy a toy that costs $1.74. You have 4 quarters, 8 dimes, and 4 nickels. Do you have enough money to buy the toy? (yes) How could you use 13 coins to pay for the toy? (4 quarters, 6 dimes, and 3 nickels)

Math Connection

Mental Math   1 teddy bear costs $3.99. What is a good way to find out how much 5 teddy bears would cost? *Hint:* Each teddy bear costs 1¢ less than $4. (Possible answer: 5 × $4.00 = $20.00, $20.00 − $0.05 = $19.95)

Minute Math

How many of these multiplication sentences can you complete in 1 min?

2 × $4 = ($8)	3 × $4 = ($12)
3 × $5 = ($15)	4 × $3 = ($12)
4 × $1 = ($4)	2 × $5 = ($10)

CLASSWORK AND HOMEWORK SUPPLEMENTS

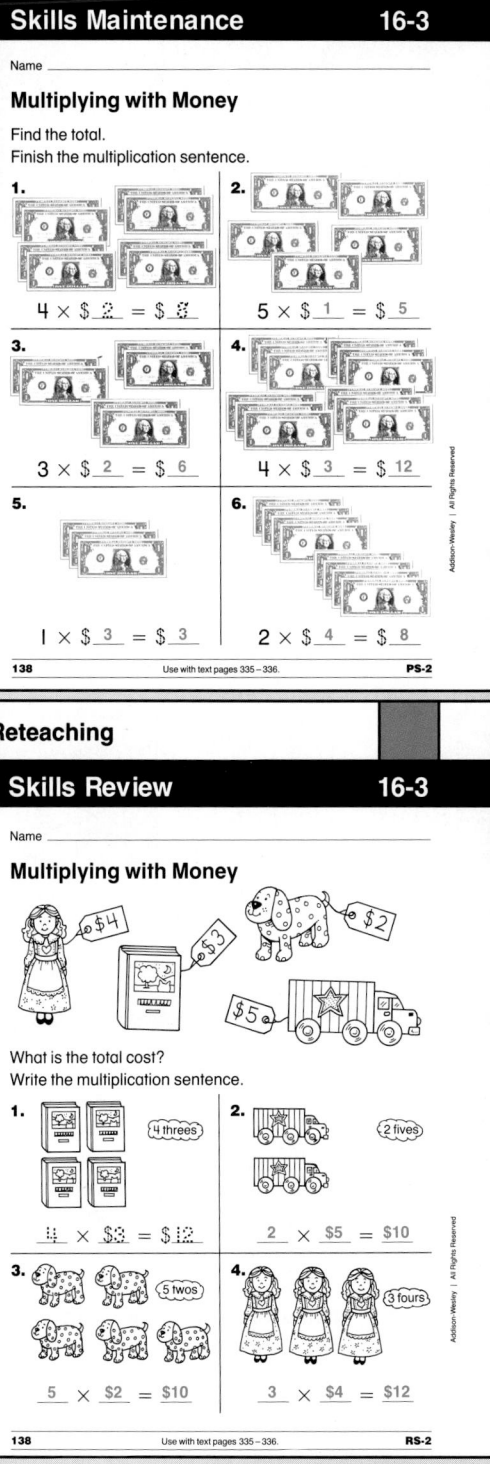

Practice

Skills Maintenance 16-3

Name _____

Multiplying with Money

Find the total.
Finish the multiplication sentence.

1. $4 \times \$\,2 = \$\,8$

2. $5 \times \$\,1 = \$\,5$

3. $3 \times \$\,2 = \$\,6$

4. $4 \times \$\,3 = \$\,12$

5. $1 \times \$\,3 = \$\,3$

6. $2 \times \$\,4 = \$\,8$

138   Use with text pages 335 – 336.   PS-2

Reteaching

Skills Review 16-3

Name _____

Multiplying with Money

What is the total cost?
Write the multiplication sentence.

1. (4 threes) $4 \times \$3 = \$12$

2. (2 fives) $2 \times \$5 = \$10$

3. (5 twos) $5 \times \$2 = \$10$

4. (3 fours) $3 \times \$4 = \$12$

138   Use with text pages 335 – 336.   RS-2

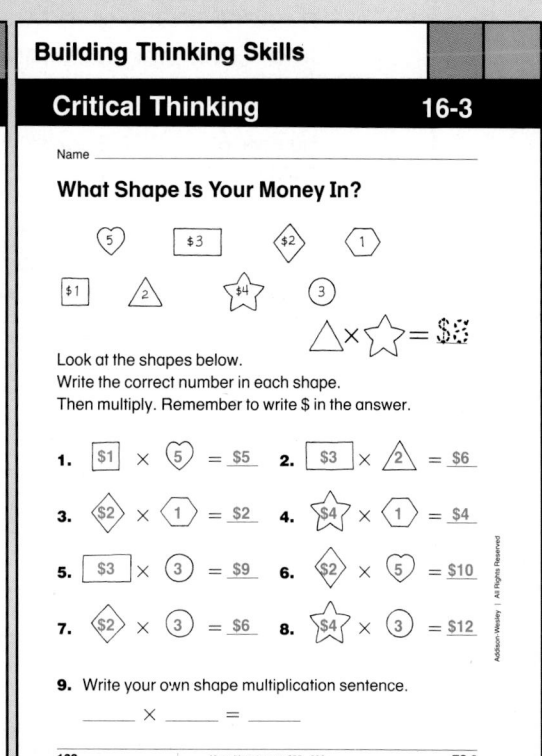

Building Thinking Skills

Critical Thinking 16-3

Name _____

What Shape Is Your Money In?

Look at the shapes below.
Write the correct number in each shape.
Then multiply. Remember to write $ in the answer.

$\triangle \times \bigstar = \$8$

1. $\$1 \times 5 = \$5$ **2.** $\$3 \times 2 = \$6$

3. $\$2 \times 1 = \$2$ **4.** $\$4 \times 1 = \$4$

5. $\$3 \times 3 = \$9$ **6.** $\$2 \times 5 = \$10$

7. $\$2 \times 3 = \$6$ **8.** $\$4 \times 3 = \$12$

9. Write your own shape multiplication sentence.

_____ × _____ = _____

138   Use with text pages 335 – 336.   TS-2

Challenges

Cooperative Activities 16-3

Name _____

Give and Take

You need: 1 or more friends, play money, 1 number cube, and markers.

Rules: Take turns. Put the markers on START.
Ask 1 person to be the Banker.
Roll the number cube and move that many spaces.
Follow the directions on the space.

Take: You get money from the Banker.
Give: You give money to the Banker.

If you land on $, you get $5 from the Banker.
If you do not have enough money to give the Banker,
go back to START.
The player with the most money at FINISH wins.

START	Take 5 × $1.	Take 2 × $2.	Take 4 × $1.	Take 3 × $1 and go again.	$	Go back 3 spaces.	Lose 1 turn.
Take 4 × $3. Give 2 × $4.	$	Go back to start.	Give 3 × $4.	Give 1 × $3.	Take 3 × $2.	Give 1 × $2.	
Go again.	Take 1 × $1.	Take 2 × $5.	Give 3 × $2.	$	Give 3 × $3.	Give 3 × $2. Take 3 × $3.	FINISH

138   Use with text pages 335 – 336.   CS-2

OPTIONS FOR INDIVIDUAL NEEDS

Basic

Exercises All
Data Bank, p. 400

Supplements
Reteaching 138 or
Practice 138
Challenges 138

Average

Exercises All
Data Bank, p. 400

Supplements
Practice 138
Challenges 138 or
Thinking Skills 138

Extended

Exercises All
Data Bank, p. 400

Supplements
Challenges 138
Thinking Skills 138

Other Resources:
Explorations, p. 344
Problem Solving Experiences In Mathematics, p. 155

16-3

OBJECTIVE 16-3
To model and write multiplication sentences with money

> **Materials:** TA15 (Play Money), containers, punchout pennies, spinners, number cubes 1-6
>
> **Grouping Suggestion:** small groups, pairs

1. MOTIVATE AND TEACH

LEARN ABOUT IT

Have students use play money to model and write a multiplication sentence for this problem: *You want to buy 3 books. Each book costs $3. How much money do you need?* ($9)

Have students look at the example at the top of page 335.

▶ **In this multiplication sentence, what do the two numbers with dollar signs mean?** (Possible answer: The first dollar sign shows how much each book costs. The second one shows the total amount.)

▶ **What must happen for you to spend only $1?** (Spin a 1 in Exercise 4.)

▶ **How could you spend more than $8 on *The Ugly Duckling*?** (Spin a 3, 4, or 5.)

▶ **If you buy 5 of one of the books, what is the most money you will spend? Why?** (If you buy 5 copies of *The Three Billy Goats Gruff*, you will spend $25; it is the most expensive book.)

▶ **What is the least possible amount you can spend for any number of books?** ($1)

2. CHECK UNDERSTANDING

ERROR ALERT Confusing the number of groups with the number of objects in each group.

Name _____

Multiplying with Money

Work in a group. Spin to find the number of books to buy. Find the total cost. Use play money to help. Write the multiplication sentence.

Number of books   Book $3

4

4 ⊗ $3 = $12

Answers may vary. Check students' work

1. Number of books   Book $3

___ ◯ $ ___   ☐ $ ___

2. Number of books   Book $2

___ ◯ $ ___   ☐ $ ___

3. Number of books   Book $5

___ ◯ $ ___   ☐ $ ___

4. Number of books   Book $1

___ ◯ $ ___   ☐ $ ___

Chapter 16   (three hundred thirty-five) 3

TEACHING OPTIONS

RETEACHING TIPS Display 4 containers and have students put 3 pennies in each. Then have them tell you the number of containers, the number of pennies in each, and the number of pennies in all as they write a multiplication sentence to match. Assign Reteaching Supplement 138.

ENRICHMENT On the chalkboard, write the following: Pencil = 3¢, Eraser = 2¢, Ruler = 5¢. Tell students they have 15¢ to spend. Have them list as many ways of spending the 15¢ as they can. (Answers may vary.)

se play money. Show these
mounts. Find the total. Finish
e multiplication sentence.

   2.

$3 \times \$4 = \$12$
Dollars in   Dollars
each group   in all

$2 \times \$3 = \$6$
Dollars in   Dollars
each group   in all

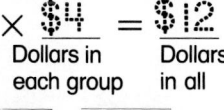   4.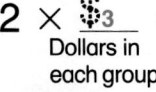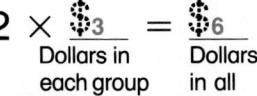

$4 \times \$2 = \$8$ $2 \times \$4 = \$8$

   6.

$3 \times \$1 = \$3$ $1 \times \$5 = \$5$

ND THE DATA   DATA BANK

se mental math to solve.

Joan bought these two dolls. How
much money did she spend?

She spent $\$25$.

Data Bank How much more money
does the Peter Pan tape cost than
the Cinderella tape? (See page 400.)

The Peter Pan tape costs $\$5$ more.

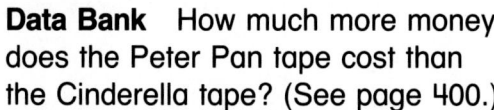

---

3. PRACTICE AND APPLY

Basic	All
Average	All
Extended	All

PRACTICE

*How are Exercises 1-6 on page 336 like
those on page 335?* (They both use
multiplication sentences.) *How will you
find the answer in each exercise?*
(Multiply the number of groups by the
number of $1 bills in each group.)

APPLY

FIND THE DATA ▶ **How did you
find out how much Joan spent on the
2 dolls?** (added $10 + $15)
▶ **How much more does the Alice in
Wonderland doll cost than the Mother
Goose doll?** ($5)
▶ **Which of the 3 tapes is the most
expensive? the least expensive?**
(Peter Pan; Snow White)
▶ **Which 2 tapes together cost the
most?** *(Peter Pan and Cinderella)*

16-3

LOSE AND ASSESS

HOW WHAT YOU KNOW

ave students in pairs take turns
inning the spinner to find a number
groups and rolling the number cube
find how many dollars in each
oup. Then have students write a
ultiplication sentence to show the
tal amount for each pair of numbers.

QUICK QUIZ

Multiply to find the amount of money.
$4 \times \$3 = \underline{(\$12)}$
$3 \times \$2 = \underline{(\$6)}$
$5 \times \$2 = \underline{(\$10)}$
$2 \times \$4 = \underline{(\$8)}$

Multiplying: Finding Turnarounds

OBJECTIVE 16-4 To model and use the commutative property of multiplication

PREBOOK ACTIVITIES

QUICK REVIEW

Multiply.

$1 \times 2 = \underline{(2)}$	$4 \times 1 = \underline{(4)}$
$2 \times 3 = \underline{(6)}$	$3 \times 4 = \underline{(12)}$
$4 \times 2 = \underline{(8)}$	$5 \times 2 = \underline{(10)}$
$2 \times 5 = \underline{(10)}$	$2 \times 4 = \underline{(8)}$

PRIOR KNOWLEDGE

Have 4 students come to the front of the classroom and stand in 2 groups of 2. *How many groups of students are there?* (2) *How many in each group?* (2) *How many in all?* (4) Have the students change positions. *Now how many students are there?* (4) *Does the order in which the students stand change the number of students?* (no)

COMMUNICATION

Discussing Math Write the word **turnaround** and $3 + 2 = 5$ on the chalkboard. *How can you write the turnaround addition fact for $3 + 2 = 5$?* ($2 + 3 = 5$) *If you change the order in which you add the numbers, what will happen to the sum?* (Nothing; the sum stays the same.) Write $4 \times 2 = 8$ on the board. *What do you think will happen to the product if we change the order of the numbers we are multiplying?* (Possible answer: Nothing; you will get the same answer.) Write $2 \times 4 = \underline{\quad}$ on the board and have students use counters or draw pictures to show the answer. (8)

EXPLORE AND CONNECT

Materials: counters, TA13 (Inch Graph Paper)
Provide students with counters and inch graph paper. Have them use counters to make rows with the same number of counters in each row—for example, 3 rows of 4. Ask students to be sure that their rows are placed carefully in the graph-paper squares. *How many rows of counters are there?* (3) *How many counters in each row?* (4) *How many are there in all?* (12) Have a volunteer write on the chalkboard a multiplication sentence to match. ($3 \times 4 = 12$) Show students how to find a column on their graph paper. Draw a ring around each column. *How many columns are there?* (4) *How many in each column?* (3) *How many counters in all?* (12) Write a multiplication sentence to match. ($4 \times 3 = 12$) *How are these 2 multiplication sentences alike?* (They have the same numbers; they have the same answer.) *How are they different?* (The numbers 3 and 4 are in a different order.)

CONNECTIONS   Use these anytime.

Problem of the Day

Logic During summer vacation, Shirley helped her parents plan the family's meals. She made menus for 3 meals a day for 1 wk. How many meals did Shirley plan? (21)

Math Connection

Geometry Use a rubber band to show 3 rows of 4 squares on a geoboard. Use another rubber band to show 4 rows of 3 squares. Write a multiplication sentence to show each group of squares. ($3 \times 4 = 12$, $4 \times 3 = 12$) What do you notice about the number of squares inside each rubber band? (They are the same; there are 12 squares in each.)

Subject Integration

Fine Arts On one half of a sheet of art paper, draw your favorite kind of flowers to show $3 \times 2 = 6$. On the other half, draw flowers to show $2 \times 3 = 6$.

CLASSWORK AND HOMEWORK SUPPLEMENTS

OPTIONS FOR INDIVIDUAL NEEDS

Basic

Exercises All, Midchapter Review/Quiz
Calculator Bank, p. 404
More Practice, p. 427, set B

Supplements
Reteaching 139 or
Practice 139
Thinking Skills 139

Average

Exercises All, Midchapter Review/Quiz
Calculator Bank, p. 404
More Practice, p. 427, set B

Supplements
Practice 139
Challenges 139 or
Thinking Skills 139

Extended

Exercises All, Midchapter Review/Quiz
Calculator Bank, p. 404

Supplements
Challenges 139
Thinking Skills 139

Other Resources:
Explorations, pp. 342-345
Developing Number Concepts With Unifix Cubes, pp. 188-194
Using the Math Explorer Calculator: A Source Book for Teachers, Chapter 14

Practice

Skills Maintenance   16-4

Name _____

Multiplying: Finding Turnarounds

Multiply.

1. $2 \times 5 = \underline{10}$ $2 \times 4 = \underline{8}$
   $5 \times 2 = \underline{10}$ $4 \times 2 = \underline{8}$

2. $4 \times 3 = \underline{12}$ $1 \times 5 = \underline{5}$
   $3 \times 4 = \underline{12}$ $5 \times 1 = \underline{5}$

3. $2 \times 3 = \underline{6}$ $1 \times 3 = \underline{3}$
   $3 \times 2 = \underline{6}$ $3 \times 1 = \underline{3}$

4. $2 \times 1 = \underline{2}$ $2 \times 6 = \underline{12}$
   $1 \times 2 = \underline{2}$ $6 \times 2 = \underline{12}$

5. $1 \times 6 = \underline{6}$ $4 \times 1 = \underline{4}$
   $6 \times 1 = \underline{6}$ $1 \times 4 = \underline{4}$

PS-2   Use with text pages 337–338.   139

Creative Thinking   16-4

Name _____

Flower Power

Color the flowers. The arrow shows the direction of the rows.
1. Color red two rows of five flowers.
2. Color yellow four rows of three flowers.
3. Color pink two rows of three flowers.
4. Color purple five rows of two flowers.
5. Color orange three rows of four flowers.
6. Color blue three rows of two flowers.

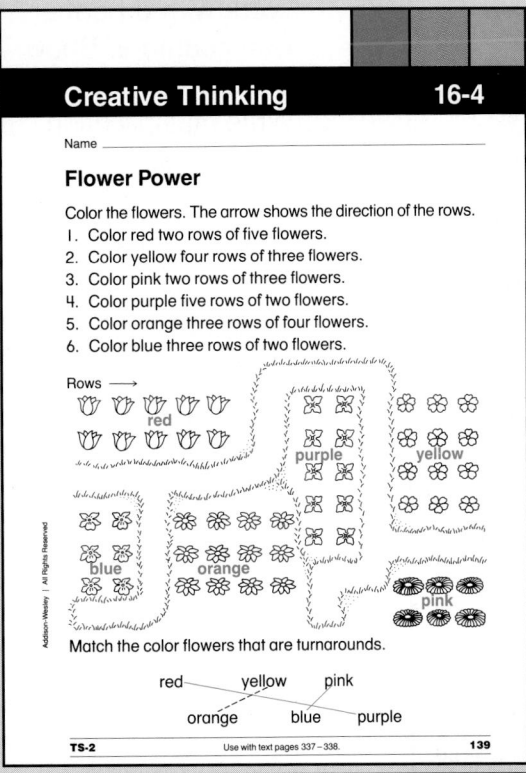

Match the color flowers that are turnarounds.

TS-2   Use with text pages 337–338.   139

Reteaching

Skills Review   16-4

Name _____

Multiplying: Finding Turnarounds

Do both pictures show the same total? __yes__

Does the order of the numbers change the total? __no__

$4 \times 3 = 12$ $3 \times 4 = 12$

Write the multiplication sentences.

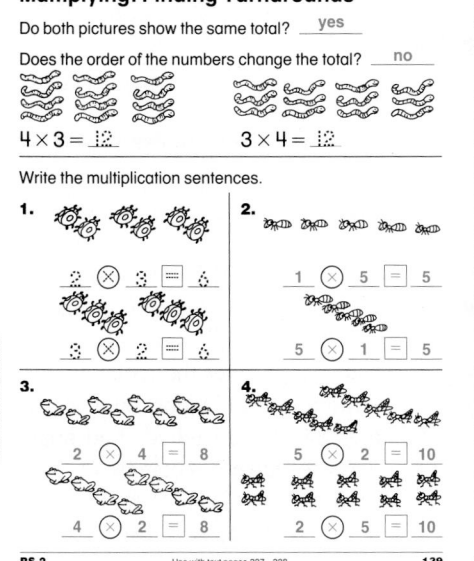

RS-2   Use with text pages 337–338.   139

Challenges

Calculators   16-4

Name _____

Turnarounds

Match the turnarounds.
Use your 🖩 to check.

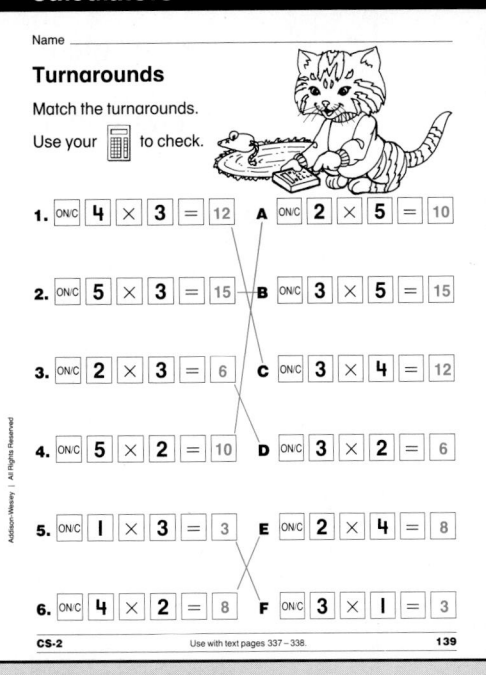

1. ON/C $4 \times 3 = 12$ A ON/C $2 \times 5 = 10$
2. ON/C $5 \times 3 = 15$ B ON/C $3 \times 5 = 15$
3. ON/C $2 \times 3 = 6$ C ON/C $3 \times 4 = 12$
4. ON/C $5 \times 2 = 10$ D ON/C $3 \times 2 = 6$
5. ON/C $1 \times 3 = 3$ E ON/C $2 \times 4 = 8$
6. ON/C $4 \times 2 = 8$ F ON/C $3 \times 1 = 3$

CS-2   Use with text pages 337–338.   139

16-4

OBJECTIVE 16-4
To model and use the commutative property of multiplication

Materials: counters, TA13 (Inch Graph Paper), egg cartons

Grouping Suggestion: pairs

1. MOTIVATE AND TEACH

LEARN ABOUT IT

Have students model these two multiplication sentences: $2 \times 5 = 10$, $5 \times 2 = 10$. *What do you notice about the answers?* (They are the same.) Draw students' attention to page 337.

▶ **In Exercise 2, what are 2 other multiplication sentences that will give you the same answer?** (Possible answer: $2 \times 6 = 12$, $6 \times 2 = 12$)

▶ **What would happen if both numbers in a multiplication sentence were the same?** (The turnaround sentence would be the same as the first sentence.)

▶ **Which would take more space: 2 rows with 3 flowers in each row or 3 rows with 2 flowers in each row?** (Neither; they both take the same amount of space.)

▶ **In what other kind of facts does the order of the numbers not change the answer?** (addition facts)

2. CHECK UNDERSTANDING

ERROR ALERT Forgetting that the product in a turnaround sentence always stays the same and that only the factors change places.

Name _____

Multiplying
Finding Turnarounds

Work with a partner. Use counters. Show the rows of flowers. Write multiplication sentences.

These are turnaround facts.

$2 \times 3 = 6$
$3 \times 2 = 6$

	Rows		Flowers in each row		Flowers in all
1. 2 rows with 3 flowers in each row	2	$\times$	3	=	6
3 rows with 2 flowers in each row	3	$\times$	2	=	6
2. 3 rows with 4 flowers in each row	3	$\times$	4	=	12
4 rows with 3 flowers in each row	4	$\times$	3	=	12
3. 4 rows with 2 flowers in each row	4	$\times$	2	=	8
2 rows with 4 flowers in each row	2	$\times$	4	=	8

Chapter 16

(three hundred thirty-seven) 33

TEACHING OPTIONS

RETEACHING TIPS Break 2 sections from an egg carton. Have students show 5 groups of 2 counters and write a multiplication sentence to match. ($5 \times 2 = 10$) Turn the carton 90 degrees to show that 2 groups of 5 counters is also 10. Assign Reteaching Supplement 139.

ENRICHMENT Have students draw a 6-by-4 rectangle on inch graph paper. Cut out 4 strips of 6 squares to cover the rectangle and write a multiplication sentence. ($4 \times 6 = 24$) Have students find other ways to make a rectangle of 24 squares. (8×3, 3×8, 12×2, 2×12, 24×1, 1×24)

Write a multiplication sentence for each garden.

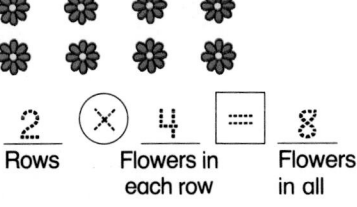

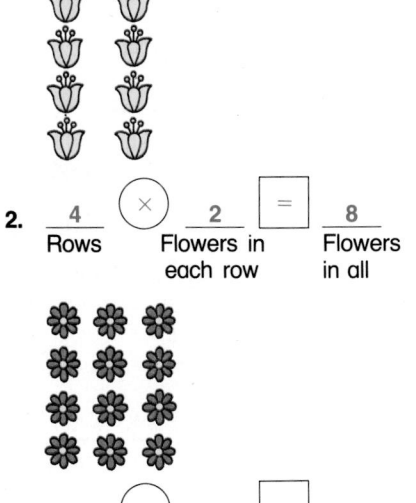

$$\underset{\text{Rows}}{2} \underset{}{\times} \underset{\substack{\text{Flowers in} \\ \text{each row}}}{4} \underset{}{=} \underset{\substack{\text{Flowers} \\ \text{in all}}}{8}$$

2. $\underset{\text{Rows}}{4} \underset{}{\times} \underset{\substack{\text{Flowers in} \\ \text{each row}}}{2} \underset{}{=} \underset{\substack{\text{Flowers} \\ \text{in all}}}{8}$

$$\underset{}{3} \underset{}{\times} \underset{}{4} \underset{}{=} \underset{}{12}$$

4. $\underset{}{4} \underset{}{\times} \underset{}{3} \underset{}{=} \underset{}{12}$

MIDCHAPTER REVIEW/QUIZ

Draw dots to show each group. Use counters to help.

Show 2 groups of 3. Write the addition sentence.

2. Show 4 groups of 1. Write the multiplication sentence.

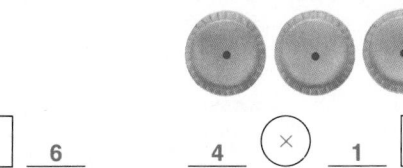

$$\underset{}{3} \underset{}{+} \underset{}{3} \underset{}{=} \underset{}{6}$$

$\underset{}{4} \underset{}{\times} \underset{}{1} \underset{}{=} \underset{}{4}$

Find the total. Use your play money to help. Finish the multiplication sentence.

$3 \times \$2 = \$6$

3. PRACTICE AND APPLY

Basic	All, Midchapter Review/Quiz
Average	All, Midchapter Review/Quiz
Extended	All, Midchapter Review/Quiz

PRACTICE

Look at the 2 groups of flowers in each exercise. What do you notice? (Possible answers: They have the same number of flowers; they are turned around; they match the turnaround multiplication sentences.)

APPLY

▶ **How are the two multiplication sentences in each exercise the same?** (They both have the same numbers.)
▶ **How are they different?** (The order of numbers has changed.)

MIDCHAPTER REVIEW/QUIZ

ITEM ANALYSIS The following table correlates the Midchapter Review/Quiz items with the lesson objectives.

Items	Objectives
1	16-1
2	16-2
3	16-3

16-4

CLOSE AND ASSESS

TELL WHAT YOU KNOW

Discuss with students the events in the chapter story. On the board list the number sentences for each multiplication problem from the story as students say them. Then ask students to say the turnaround number sentence for each number sentence on the board.

QUICK QUIZ

Write a multiplication sentence:
2 rows of 4 $(2 \times 4 = 8)$
4 rows of 2 $(4 \times 2 = 8)$
2 rows of 3 $(2 \times 3 = 6)$
3 rows of 2 $(3 \times 2 = 6)$

Problem Solving: Understanding the Operations

OBJECTIVE 16-5   To understand the operations of addition and multiplication by putting together

PREBOOK ACTIVITIES

QUICK REVIEW

Write the multiplication expression for each repeated addition expression.

$3 + 3$ (2×3)	$2 + 2 + 2 + 2 + 2$ (5×2)
$7 + 7 + 7$ (3×7)	$8 + 8 + 8 + 8$ (4×8)
$6 + 6 + 6 + 6$ (4×6)	$9 + 9 + 9$ (3×9)

PRIOR KNOWLEDGE

Write the heading *Groups of 2* on the chalkboard. Encourage children to notice things about each other that come in groups of 2. Record their observations on the chart. (Possible answers: eyes, ears, hands, arms, feet, legs, socks, shoes) Repeat the procedure for *Groups of 3, Groups of 4,* and *Groups of 5.* Suggest that children search the classroom and think of things in their homes and outdoors.

COMMUNICATION

Reading and Discussing Math   Write the word **algebra** on the chalkboard. Read the word aloud and explain that *algebra* is a type of mathematics in which letters or other symbols are used to take the place of numbers. Then write $5 + * = 8$ on the board. *What makes this an algebra problem?* (It has a star instead of a number.) *How can we find the number that the star stands for?* (Count on from 5 to find the missing addend, 3.)

EXPLORE AND CONNECT

COOPERATIVE ACTIVITY

Grouping Suggestion: small groups
The king has 3 crowns.
He counts 5 jewels in each crown.
How many jewels does the king have?

TEACHING ACTIONS

BEFORE ▶ **What do you need to find out in the story?** (the number of jewels the king has)
▶ **What data is important?** (The king has 3 crowns; each crown has 5 jewels.)

DURING ▶ **Describe a plan you might use to answer the question.**
(Possible answers: Multiply the number of jewels by the number of crowns, 3×5; Add the number of jewels 5 times to find the total jewels in 3 crowns, $5 + 5 + 5$.)
▶ **Estimate how large or small a number the answer might be.** (Answers will vary. Possible answers: It must be greater than 5 or 10; it must be less than 20 or 100.)

AFTER ▶ **What is your plan for checking your answer?** (Possible answers: Use the repeated addition sentence; multiply using the turnaround fact.)
Have students work in small groups to explore ways to illustrate the problem using counters or pictures.

CONNECTIONS   Use these anytime.

Problem of the Day

Understanding the Operations
Princess Mae counted the golden buttons on her 2 royal robes. She had 2 and 20. Her sister, Princess Daisy, had 5 robes with 4 golden buttons on each. Which princess had more golden buttons? How many more? (Mae had $2 + 20$, or 22; Daisy had 5×4, or 20; so Mae had 2 more.)

Math Connection

Algebra   Place up to 9 cubes on one side of a scale. Place the same number of cubes on the other side of the scale but hide some inside a paper bag. Ask a partner to guess how many cubes are hidden in the bag. Let your friend check the guess. Then switch roles and repeat the activity.

Subject Integration

Art   Use toothpicks, buttons, or squares of paper. Make a pattern that shows groups that are repeated in different directions. Glue them to a piece of paper. Then write a multiplication sentence or an addition sentence that matches. Display your design on a wall or bulletin board.

Informal Algebra: Finding the Missing Number

To use informal algebra to find missing numbers

CLASSWORK AND HOMEWORK SUPPLEMENTS

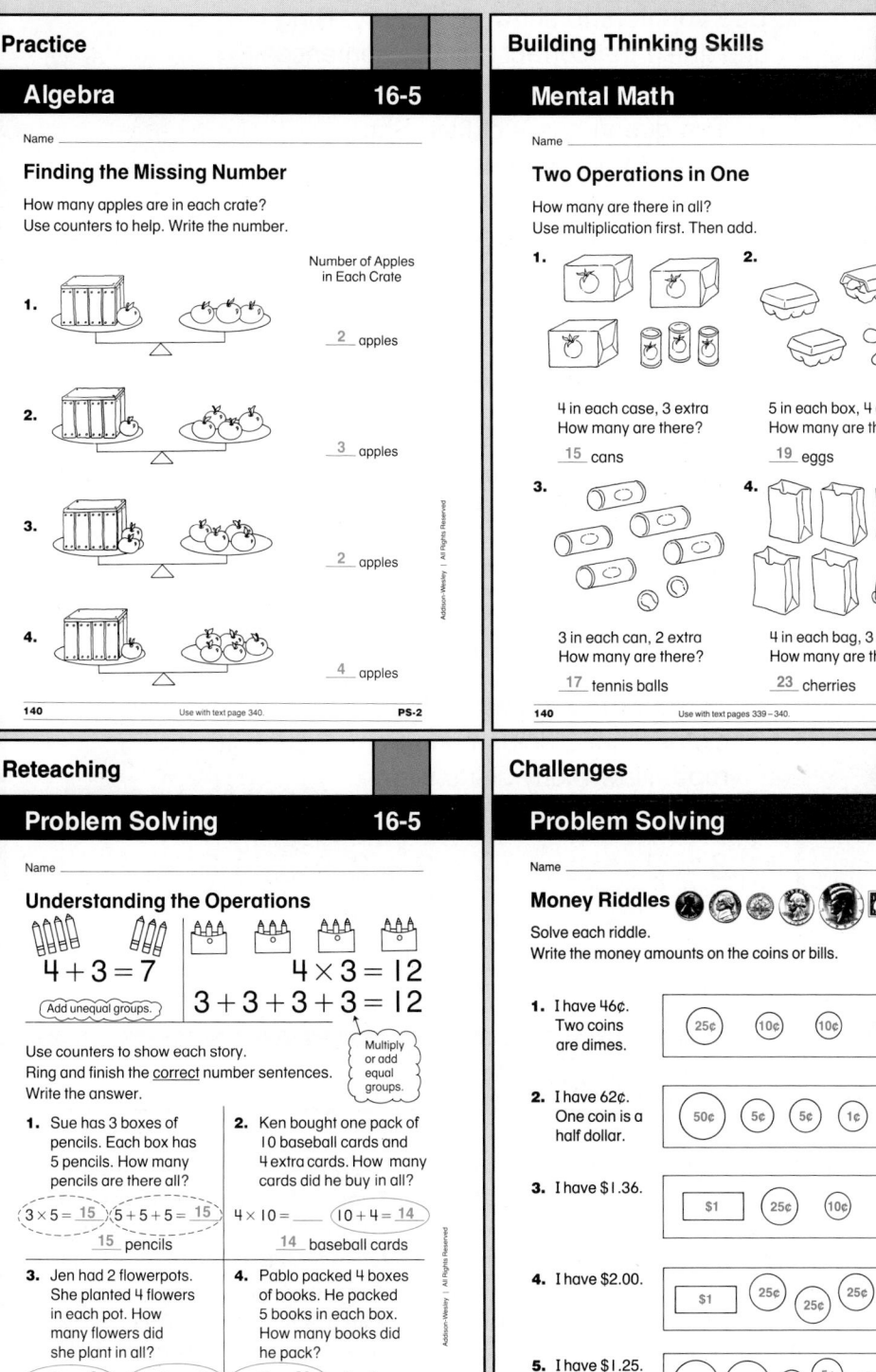

Practice

Algebra 16-5

Name

Finding the Missing Number

How many apples are in each crate?
Use counters to help. Write the number.

Number of Apples in Each Crate

1. __2__ apples

2. __3__ apples

3. __2__ apples

4. __4__ apples

140   Use with text page 340.   PS-2

Building Thinking Skills

Mental Math 16-5

Name

Two Operations in One

How many are there in all?
Use multiplication first. Then add.

1. 4 in each case, 3 extra
How many are there?
__15__ cans

2. 5 in each box, 4 extra
How many are there?
__19__ eggs

3. 3 in each can, 2 extra
How many are there?
__17__ tennis balls

4. 4 in each bag, 3 extra
How many are there?
__23__ cherries

140   Use with text pages 339-340.   TS-2

Reteaching

Problem Solving 16-5

Name

Understanding the Operations

$$4 + 3 = 7$$
(Add unequal groups.)

$$4 \times 3 = 12$$
$$3 + 3 + 3 + 3 = 12$$
(Multiply or add equal groups.)

Use counters to show each story.
Ring and finish the correct number sentences.
Write the answer.

1. Sue has 3 boxes of pencils. Each box has 5 pencils. How many pencils are there all?
$3 \times 5 = $ __15__ $5 + 5 + 5 = $ __15__
__15__ pencils

2. Ken bought one pack of 10 baseball cards and 4 extra cards. How many cards did he buy in all?
$4 \times 10 = $ $10 + 4 = $ __14__
__14__ baseball cards

3. Jen had 2 flowerpots. She planted 4 flowers in each pot. How many flowers did she plant in all?
$2 \times 4 = $ __8__ $4 + 4 = $ __8__
__8__ flowers

4. Pablo packed 4 boxes of books. He packed 5 books in each box. How many books did he pack?
$4 \times 5 = $ __20__ $4 + 5 = $
__20__ books

140   Use with text page 339   RS-2

Challenges

Problem Solving 16-5

Name

Money Riddles

Solve each riddle.
Write the money amounts on the coins or bills.

1. I have 46¢. Two coins are dimes.
25¢   10¢   10¢   1¢

2. I have 62¢. One coin is a half dollar.
50¢   5¢   5¢   1¢   1¢

3. I have $1.36.
$1   25¢   10¢   1¢

4. I have $2.00.
$1   25¢   25¢   25¢   25¢

5. I have $1.25. I do not have any quarters.
50¢   50¢   10¢   5¢   5¢   5¢

140   Use with text pages 339-340.   CS-2

OPTIONS FOR INDIVIDUAL NEEDS

Basic

Exercises All
Computer Bank, pp. 405-408
More Practice, p. 428, set A

Supplements
Reteaching 140 or
Practice 140

Average

Exercises All
Computer Bank, pp. 405-408
More Practice, p. 428, set A

Supplements
Practice 140
Challenges 140 or
Thinking Skills 140

Extended

Exercises All
Computer Bank, pp. 405-408

Supplements
Challenges 140
Thinking Skills 140

Other Resources:
Mathematics Their Way, pp. 202-203, 205, 208, 343-344.
Explorations, pp. 342-343, 349
Developing Number Concepts With Unifix Cubes, p. 189
Mathematics Book A, p. 44

16-5

LESSON PLAN 16-5

OBJECTIVE 16-5

To understand the operations of addition and multiplication by putting together; to use informal algebra to find missing numbers

Materials: counters

1. MOTIVATE AND TEACH

LEARN ABOUT IT

 ► **How can you tell if a problem should be solved using addition or multiplication?** (Read to find out if the problem tells about equal groups.)

 ► **How can you use counters to help you show addition or multiplication?** (Act the problem out. See if the groups are the same size or different sizes.)

► **How many number sentences might tell about one story? Explain.** (Possible answer: One or two, because some number stories can be solved using either addition or multiplication.)

 ► **How will your methods for checking each problem be the same? How will they be different?** (Possible answer: All the problems can be checked using addition; the addition problems should be checked with a turnaround fact.)

2. CHECK UNDERSTANDING

ERROR ALERT

Page 339 Using the incorrect operation to solve.

Page 340 Adding the number of coins shown to find the hidden number of counters.

Name _____

Problem Solving
Understanding the Operations

Word sentences may vary. Sample answers are shown.
Use counters to show each story. Ring and finish the correct number sentences. Write the answer in a sentence.

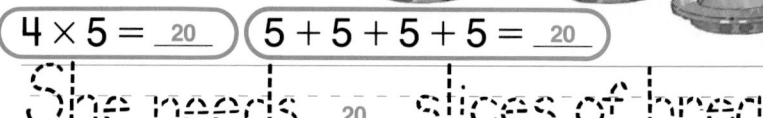

1. The queen has 4 plates. She wants to put 5 slices of bread on each plate. How many slices does she need?

   $\boxed{4 \times 5 = \underline{20}}$ $\boxed{5 + 5 + 5 + 5 = \underline{20}}$

   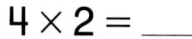 She needs __20__ slices of bread.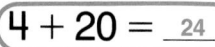

2. There were 4 and 20 flowers all in a row. How many flowers were there altogether?

   $4 \times 2 = \underline{\quad}$ $\boxed{4 + 20 = \underline{24}}$

   ------- There were 24 flowers altogether. -------

3. There were 3 ropes on the clothesline. 2 shirts hung from each rope. How many shirts were hanging on the clothesline?

   $\boxed{3 \times 2 = \underline{6}}$ $\boxed{2 + 2 + 2 = \underline{6}}$

   ------- 6 shirts were hanging. -------

Chapter 16   More Practice, page 428, set A   (three hundred thirty-nine) **33**

TEACHING OPTIONS

RETEACHING TIPS Put an empty bag on one side of a scale and 2 counters in a bag on the other side. Students put 2 counters in the empty bag to prove it balances. Take out 1 counter and put it on the scale pan to see that the scale still balances. For help with problem solving, use Reteaching Supplement 140.

COMPUTER Safari Search, Sunburst Communications © 1985 For use with all levels. In *Intuit the Iguana*, students look for the iguana in a 5-by-5 grid, using an exhaustive search. Discuss the advantages and disadvantages of this method. The recommended game takes 5-10 minutes.

...formal Algebra
...nding the Missing Number

...ow many coins are in the left
...ag? Use counters to help.
...rite the number.

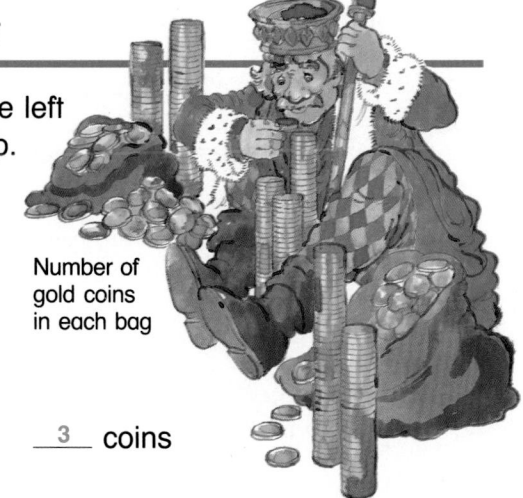

Number of
gold coins
in each bag

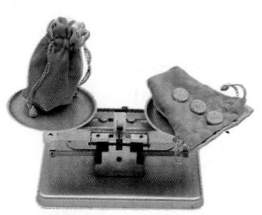

___3___ coins

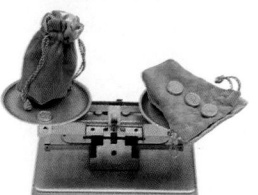

___2___ coins

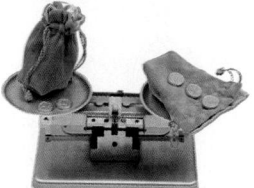

___1___ coin

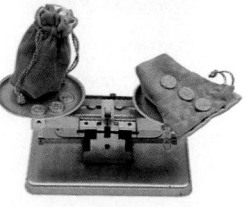

___0___ coins

...0 (three hundred forty)

Chapter 16

Basic	All
Average	All
Extended	All

How will you find the data? (Possible answer: Count the coins on each side of the scale.) *How can you tell there must be the same number of coins on each side of the scale?* (The scale is balanced.)

▶ **What do you have to do in each problem?** (Possible answer: Figure out how many coins are hidden in the bag.)

▶ **How can you use counters to help find out how many coins are in each bag?** (Possible answer: Show with counters the number of coins on each side of the scale; add counters to make the numbers equal. The counters you add tell the number in the bag.)

▶ **Since you cannot check by looking inside the bag, how will you know if your answer is correct?** (Possible answer: Draw the coins inside the bag and count to make sure both sides are equal.)

16-5

...LOSE AND ASSESS

...HOW WHAT YOU THINK

...istribute folded slips of paper with
...ddition or multiplication sentences to
...ch student. Ask students to make up
...story problem to match each number
...ntence. Have students read their
...ories to the class and have the class
...aw pictures or use counters to show
...e solution.

QUICK QUIZ

Write the correct number sentence. The king has 3 birdfeeders for his birds. There are 4 birds in each feeder. How many birds are there in all? 3 + 4 = ?   3 × 4 = (12)

Understanding Division: Sharing

OBJECTIVE 16-6 To model and write division sentences by sharing to make equal groups

PREBOOK ACTIVITIES

QUICK REVIEW

Look at the shapes to see if they have the same number of parts.
Write *yes* or *no*.

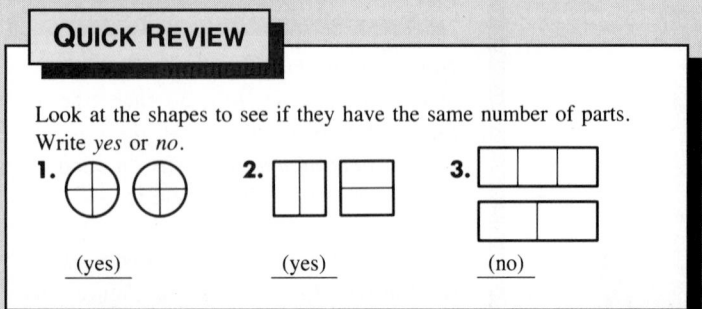

1. (yes)   2. (yes)   3. (no)

PRIOR KNOWLEDGE

Pretend that your grandmother has given you 20 apples. She wants you to share the apples so that all 4 members of your family have the same amount. How will you do this? Encourage students to draw a picture on the chalkboard that shows 4 people. Under each person have them draw an apple until all 20 apples have been shown. *How many apples did each person get?* (5)

COMMUNICATION

Reading and Discussing Math Write **divide, divided by,** and **share equally** on the chalkboard. Read these words aloud to students. *What did your grandmother want you to share equally?* (the apples) *What must you do to the whole group of apples to get smaller groups?* (divide, share equally) *How did we solve the problem?* (20 was divided by 4 to share equally.) Ask volunteers to read each word and use it in a sentence. *What are some things that can be divided and shared equally?* (Possible answer: groups of pennies, pies, space) *Name times when you have been asked to share something equally with someone else. How did you do it?* (Answers will vary.)

EXPLORE AND CONNECT

Materials: counters, containers such as margarine tubs
Grouping suggestion: pairs
Provide each pair with 30 counters and 6 containers. Write these headings on the chalkboard: Number in All, Number of Groups, Number in Each Group. Write 15 under the first heading. *How many counters are in this group?* (15) Write 3 under the second heading. *How many smaller groups do we want to divide 15 into?* (3) *How can we share the 15 counters equally among the 3 groups?* (Possible answer: Place a counter in each container one at a time until all the counters have been used.) *How many counters are in each container?* (5) Write this number sentence: $15 \div 3 = 5$. Read the sentence and point out the division sign. Repeat the activity with numbers of counters that can be shared equally. As students complete each exercise, have them add to the chart and write the number sentence that matches.

CONNECTIONS   Use these anytime.

Problem of the Day

Draw a Picture Draw a picture to solve the problem. Finish the sentence.
There are 8 ladybugs.
They want to fly in groups of 2.
How many groups of 2 are in 8?
There are (4) groups of 2 in 8.

Math Connection

Graphing This week you rode your bike 21 mi. You rode the same distance on each of the 7 days. Make a bar graph that shows how far you rode each day. Label the left side of the graph *Number of Miles.* List the days of the week along the bottom of the graph. Have one square equal one mile.

Counting Patterns

Group Counting Look at the first number in each row. Start with that number and skip count by that number until you reach the second number in each row. How many times did you skip count each time?
3 – 21   (7)   2 – 16   (8)
5 – 25   (5)   4 – 24   (6)

CLASSWORK AND HOMEWORK SUPPLEMENTS

Practice

Skills Maintenance 16-6

Name _____

Understanding Division: Sharing

Find the number of flowers in each flowerpot.
Draw tally marks to show the flowers.
Write the division sentence.

1. Share 16 flowers in 4 pots.

16 ÷ 4 = 4
number of flowers in all / number of flowerpots / number of flowers in each pot

2. Share 12 flowers in 6 pots.

12 ÷ 6 = 2
number of flowers in all / number of flowerpots / number of flowers in each pot

3. Share 12 flowers in 4 pots.

12 ÷ 4 = 3

4. Share 20 flowers in 5 pots.

20 ÷ 5 = 4

5. Share 10 flowers in 5 pots.

10 ÷ 5 = 2

6. Share 15 flowers in 5 pots.

15 ÷ 5 = 3

PS-2   Use with text pages 341–342.   141

Building Thinking Skills

Mental Math 16-6

Name _____

School Trip

We are going to visit a farm!
Each car will hold 3 third graders
     OR 4 second graders
     OR 5 first graders.
Decide how many cars are needed.
Write the division sentence and draw the cars.

1. 15 first graders
need 3 cars.

15 ÷ 5 = 3

2. 20 second graders
need 5 cars.

20 ÷ 4 = 5

3. 12 third graders
need 4 cars.

12 ÷ 3 = 4

4. 20 first graders
need 4 cars.

20 ÷ 5 = 4

TS-2   Use with text pages 341–342.   141

Reteaching

Skills Review 16-6

Name _____

Understanding Division: Sharing

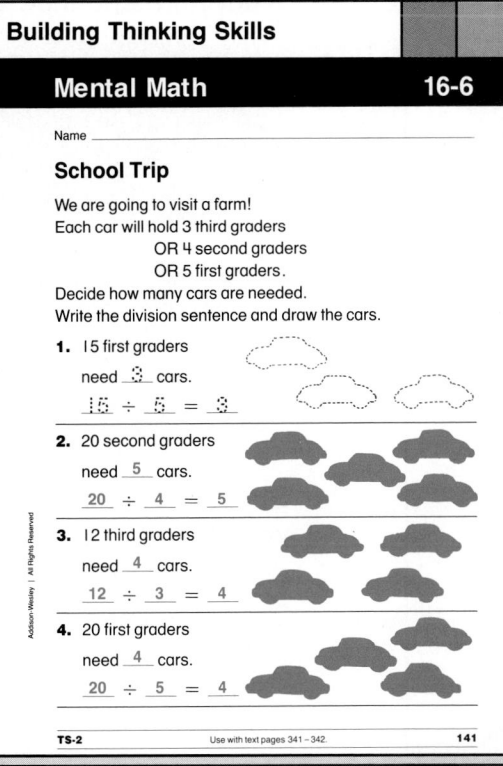

I have 8 plants in all. If I share the plants equally, I will have 4 plants in each garden.

I have 2 gardens.

8 ÷ 2 = 4

Share the plants equally.
Use counters.
Find and write the number of plants in each garden.
Then write the division sentence.

	Number of Plants in All	Number of Gardens	Number of Plants in Each Garden	
1.	20	5	4	20 ÷ 5 = 4
2.	15	3	5	15 ÷ 3 = 5
3.	10	5	2	10 ÷ 5 = 2
4.	12	4	3	12 ÷ 4 = 3
5.	6	2	3	6 ÷ 2 = 3

RS-2   Use with text pages 341–342.   141

Challenges

Writing Math 16-6

Name _____

The Elephant Family

Read the story.
Decide what numbers to
write in the spaces.
Write the numbers and finish
the picture. Use only even
numbers. Write a division
sentence to describe the story.
Then finish writing the story.

Edna and Edward Elephant live in Africa. One day, the
__2__ elephants went for a walk. It was lunchtime.
"Look, Edna!" cried Edward. "Bananas!"
Edna looked up. She saw a tall banana tree with
____ bunches of ripe bananas. The __2__ elephants shook
the tree. One big bunch of bananas fell to the ground.
Edward counted ____ bananas. Edna and Edward shared
the bananas. They each ate ____ bananas for lunch.
After lunch, the elephants ____Additional answers may vary.____

Division sentence: ____Answers will vary.____

CS-2   Use with text pages 341–342.   141

Basic

Exercises All
More Practice, p. 428, set B

Supplements
Reteaching 141 or
Practice 141

Average

Exercises All
More Practice, p. 428, set B

Supplements
Practice 141
Challenges 141 or
Thinking Skills 141

Extended

Exercises All

Supplements
Challenges 141
Thinking Skills 141

16-6

Other Resources:
Explorations, pp. 347-348
Workjobs, pp. 234-235
*Using the Math Explorer
Calculator: A Source Book for
Teachers,* Chapter 14

LESSON PLAN 16-6

OBJECTIVE 16-6
To model and write division sentences by sharing to make equal groups

Materials: Cube-A-Links, counters, flannelboard

Grouping Suggestions: pairs

1. MOTIVATE AND TEACH

LEARN ABOUT IT

Give 12 cubes to each pair. If group sizes vary, be sure the total number of cubes is divisible by the group number.

▶ **How can you divide the cubes so you share them equally?** (Possible answer: Give each person one cube until all the cubes are used.)

Write the sentence $12 \div 2 = 6$ on the chalkboard. Read the sentence aloud.

▶ **How does this sentence relate to the cubes you just shared?** (Possible answer: It shows with numbers how we shared the cubes equally.)

Have students look at the picture at the top of page 341 and say the nursery rhyme *Old Mother Hubbard* aloud with you. *How does this rhyme explain what you will be doing on the page?* (Possible answer: We will be dividing groups of bones into dog dishes.)

▶ **What must you count before you can solve each exercise?** (the number of bones, the number of dishes)

▶ **Why is the number of bones larger?** (Possible answer: This is the whole that you want to separate into parts.)

▶ **How can you explain what the division sentence for Exercise 1 is telling us?** (Possible answer: 12 divided by 4 equals 3; 12 bones divided into 4 dishes equals 3 bones in each dish.)

2. CHECK UNDERSTANDING

ERROR ALERT Writing the parts of a division sentence in incorrect order.

Name _____

Understanding Division
Sharing

Work with a partner. Use 20 counters.

Share the bones equally. Find and write the number of bones in each dish. Then write the division sentence. Read it to your partner.

This sign means to divide. Read it as "12 divided by...

	Number of bones in all	Number of dishes	Number of bones in each dish								
1.	12	4	3	12	÷	4	=	3
2.	8	2	4	8	÷	2	=	4
3.	15	3	5	15	÷	3	=	5
4.	20	4	5	20	÷	4	=	5

(three hundred forty-one) 3

TEACHING OPTIONS

RETEACHING TIPS On a flannelboard, ask students to share 9 birds equally among 3 trees. Ask them to explain their picture by arranging a number sentence in correct sequence. ($9 \div 3 = 3$) Repeat. Assign Reteaching Supplement 141.

ENRICHMENT **Family Math** Have parents ask the student to make pictures with macaroni or other small objects to show the ways that 12 can be shared equally among different numbers of groups. Under each picture, write the division sentence that tells about it.

se counters. Find the number of bones
 each dish. Draw tally marks to show
e bones. Write the division sentence.

1. Share 20 bones
in 4 dishes.

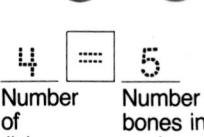

$$\underset{\substack{\text{Number}\\\text{of bones}\\\text{in all}}}{20} \; \div \; \underset{\substack{\text{Number}\\\text{of}\\\text{dishes}}}{4} \; = \; \underset{\substack{\text{Number of}\\\text{bones in}\\\text{each}\\\text{dish}}}{5}$$

2. Share 12 bones
in 3 dishes.

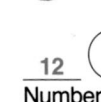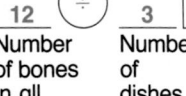

$$\underset{\substack{\text{Number}\\\text{of bones}\\\text{in all}}}{12} \; \div \; \underset{\substack{\text{Number}\\\text{of}\\\text{dishes}}}{3} \; = \; \underset{\substack{\text{Number}\\\text{of bones}\\\text{in each}\\\text{dish}}}{4}$$

3. Share 10 bones
in 2 dishes.

$$\underset{}{10} \; \div \; \underset{}{2} \; = \; \underset{}{5}$$

4. Share 16 bones in
4 dishes.

$$\underset{}{16} \; \div \; \underset{}{4} \; = \; \underset{}{4}$$

HOW WITH COUNTERS

Use counters. Find the
number in each group for
these division sentences.
Did you get 1 each time?
Ring **yes** or **no**.

(yes)　no

Number in all	Number of groups	Number in each group
5 ÷ 5	=	1
4 ÷ 4	=	1
3 ÷ 3	=	1
2 ÷ 2	=	1

3. PRACTICE AND APPLY

Basic	All
Average	All
Extended	All

PRACTICE

*What do the tally marks represent in
Exercises 1-4?* (They stand for the
number of bones that are shared equally
in each dish.) *What do you write under
each picture?* (You write the division
sentence that explains the picture.)

APPLY

SHOW WITH COUNTERS
▶ **What do you notice about all the
division sentences in Exercise 5?**
(Possible answer: The total number and
the number of groups in each sentence
are the same.)
▶ **Why do you think the answer
might be 1 for each sentence?**
(Possible answer: If the total number is
the same as the number of groups, then
you would have enough objects to put
one in each group.)

16-6

LOSE AND ASSESS

HOW WHAT YOU KNOW

eview with students the chapter
ory, *The Magic Multiplier*. Have
dents use counters to act out the
vision problem illustrated by the
ur squirrels in the story. Then have
m write a number sentence for the
oblem. (12 ÷ 4 = 3)

QUICK QUIZ

Share equally. Write the division
sentence for the picture.
○○○○　○○○○
(8) ÷ (2) = (4)

Understanding Division: Separating

OBJECTIVE 16-7 To model and write division sentences by separating into equal groups

PREBOOK ACTIVITIES

QUICK REVIEW

Match the picture to its division sentence.

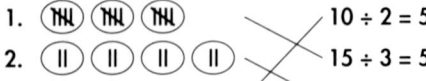

1. $10 \div 2 = 5$
2. $15 \div 3 = 5$
3. $8 \div 4 = 2$

PRIOR KNOWLEDGE

Pretend that you are having a bake sale. You have baked 12 muffins and want to put 2 muffins on each plate. How can you decide how many plates you will need? (Place 2 muffins on each plate until you have used all the muffins.) *How is this method different from sharing equally?* (When you share equally, you know how many groups you have and you place one object in each group until you have used all of them.)

COMMUNICATION

Reading and Discussing Math Write the words **divide** and **separate** on the chalkboard . Read them aloud. Explain that these words are similar in meaning. They both mean **to break apart.** *When you want to find the number of groups, you separate or divide the total number by the number in each group.* Ask students to read the words and use them in sentences as they tell about how they separated the muffins at the bake sale.

Describe other situations when you might need to separate items to find out how many groups you have. (Possible answer: You would separate socks into pairs to see how many pairs you have.)

EXPLORE AND CONNECT

Materials: Cube-A-Links
Alternative Materials: counters
Provide students with 15 linked cubes apiece. Write the following headings on the chalkboard: *Number in All, Number in Each Group, Number of Groups, Number Sentence.* Write *15* under the first heading. *How many cubes do you have in all?* (15) Write 3 under the second heading. *How many cubes are in each group?* (3) *How can you use this information to find out how many groups there are?* (Possible answer: Break off 3 cubes at a time. Count the number of groups.) *How many groups are there?* (5) Write $15 \div 3 = 5$ under the last heading and have students read the division sentence aloud. Repeat the activity. Be sure the total number of cubes can be separated into equal groups. Ask students to fill in the chart on the board and read the division sentence for each exercise.

CONNECTIONS   Use these anytime.

Problem of the Day

Understanding the Operations
Complete the number sentences. Write the answer in a sentence.
Mary has 6 flower pots.
She wants to plant 4 flowers in each pot.
How many flowers does she need?
$6 \times 4 = \underline{(24)}$ $4 + 4 + 4 + 4 + 4 + 4 = \underline{(24)}$ (She needs 24 flowers.)

Creative Thinking

Dividing Make a human division problem. Write a division sentence, such as $20 \div 5 = 4$. Then count 20 students and have them stand. Have 5 separate from the total and strike a pose to make them a separate group. Continue until all students are in separate groups of 5. Read the division sentence aloud and check the answer against the number of groups.

Mental Math

Skip Counting Count back from the first number by the number shown.
20; 5s (20, 15, 10, 5, 0)
12; 2s (12, 10, 8, 6, 4, 2, 0)
15; 3s (15, 12, 9, 6, 3, 0)
 9; 3s (9, 6, 3, 0)
20; 4s (20, 16, 12, 8, 4, 0)
12; 6s (12, 6, 0)

CLASSWORK AND HOMEWORK SUPPLEMENTS

Practice

Skills Maintenance   16-7

Name _____

Understanding Division: Separating

Ring each group of apples.
Find the number of groups.
Write the division sentence.

1. Put 15 in groups of 3.

15 ÷ 3 = 5
in all / number in each group / number of groups

2. Put 8 in groups of 4.

8 ÷ 4 = 2
in all / number in each group / number of groups

3. Put 12 in groups of 4.

12 ÷ 4 = 3

4. Put 20 in groups of 4.

20 ÷ 4 = 5

5. Put 6 in groups of 3.

6 ÷ 3 = 2

6. Put 10 in groups of 2.

10 ÷ 2 = 5

142   Use with text pages 343–344.   PS-2

Building Thinking Skills

Data Analysis   16-7

Name _____

She Sells Seashells by the Seashore

Sheila sells her shells by the bag.
How much does each shell cost?
Write the division sentence.

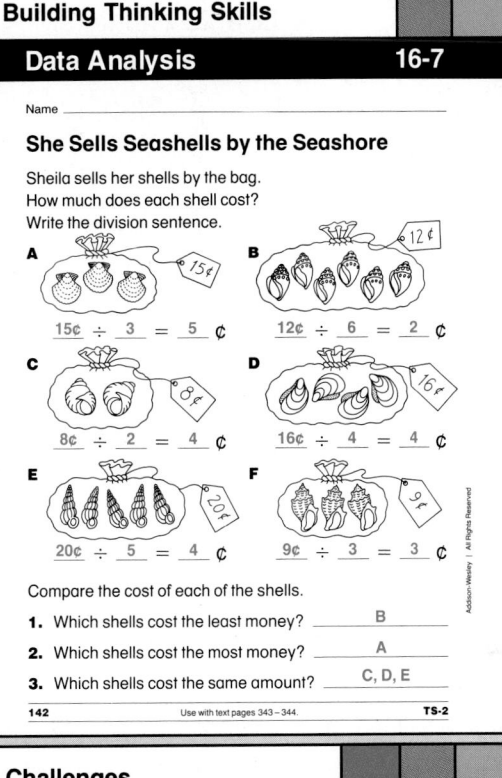

A   15¢ ÷ 3 = 5 ¢

B   12¢ ÷ 6 = 2 ¢

C   8¢ ÷ 2 = 4 ¢

D   16¢ ÷ 4 = 4 ¢

E   20¢ ÷ 5 = 4 ¢

F   9¢ ÷ 3 = 3 ¢

Compare the cost of each of the shells.

1. Which shells cost the least money?   B

2. Which shells cost the most money?   A

3. Which shells cost the same amount?   C, D, E

142   Use with text pages 343–344.   TS-2

Reteaching

Skills Review   16-7

Name _____

Understanding Division: Separating

I have 9 bananas in all.

I have 3 fruit baskets. If I separate the bananas, I will have 3 bananas in each basket.

9 ÷ 3 = 3

Fill one fruit basket at a time.
Find and write the number of baskets you used.
Then write the division sentence.

	Number of bananas in all	Number in each basket	Number of baskets				
1.	12	6	2	12 ÷ 6 = 2
2.	8	4	2	8 ÷ 4 = 2
3.	20	5	4	20 ÷ 5 = 4
4.	16	4	4	16 ÷ 4 = 4
5.	10	5	2	10 ÷ 5 = 2

142   Use with text pages 343–344.   RS-2

Challenges

Family Math   16-7

Name _____

Make It Equal

Dear Family,
Your child is learning about division by separating things into equal groups. For this game you will need 20 paper clips or other small objects, and slips of paper with the numbers 1, 2, 4, 5, and 10 written on them, one number to a card.

Mix up the number cards and put them in a pile.
Take turns. The first player picks a number card and separates the paper clips into that many equal groups.
Together, decide if the task of dividing the paper clips was done correctly. Write the division sentence on the score pad. Put the number card on the bottom of the pile. Each player gets 3 turns.
To find the winner, add the 3 scores.

_____'s Score Pad
(Name)

___ ÷ ___ = ___
___ ÷ ___ = ___
___ ÷ ___ = ___

Total _____

_____'s Score Pad
(Name)

___ ÷ ___ = ___
___ ÷ ___ = ___
___ ÷ ___ = ___

Total _____

142   Use with text pages 343–344.   CS-2

16-7

LESSON PLAN 16-7

OBJECTIVE 16-7
To model and write division sentences by separating into equal groups

> **Materials:** counters; containers, such as margarine tubs
>
> **Grouping Suggestion:** cooperative learning groups of 3

1. MOTIVATE AND TEACH

LEARN ABOUT IT

Write these headings on the chalkboard: *Number in All, Number in Each Group, Number of Groups, Division Sentence.* Ask a student to draw 12 *X*s on the board.

▶ **How can I show that there are 3 in each group?** (Possible answer: Draw a ring around 3 *X*s at a time.)

▶ **How many groups are there?** (4)

▶ **How do you know that the separating has been equal?** (Possible answer: Each group has exactly the same number.)

▶ **What number sentence can you write for the picture?** ($12 \div 3 = 4$)

▶ **In Exercise 1, compare the first two numbers under the headings to the first two numbers in the division sentences. What do you notice?** (Possible answer: The numbers are in the same order, so the first number in the division sentence will be the total number divided by the number in each jar.)

▶ **Describe the procedure for filling up the jars.** (Possible answer: Fill one jar at a time with the correct number of counters before you put counters in the next jar.)

2. CHECK UNDERSTANDING

ERROR ALERT Placing one counter in each jar until there are no counters left instead of filling 1 jar and moving on to the next jar.

4 in this jar.
Then 4 in the next jar.

Name _____

Understanding Division
Separating

Work with a partner.
Use 20 counters.

Fill one jar at a time. Write the number of jars you used. Then write the division sentence. Read it to your partner.

	Number of peppers in all	Number in each jar	Number of jars					
1.	12	4	3	12	÷	4	=	3
2.	8	2	4	8	÷	2	=	4
3.	20	5	4	20	÷	5	=	4
4.	12	3	4	12	÷	3	=	4

Chapter 16

(three hundred forty-three)

TEACHING OPTIONS

RETEACHING TIPS Provide students with counters and small containers. Ask students to model $15 \div 3$ and verbalize each step. *Why must you fill one jar at a time?* (Possible answer: You know how many in each group but not how many groups.) Repeat. Assign Reteaching supplement 142.

COMPUTER Piece of Cake Math, Springboard Software © 1983 For use with students at all levels. In *Dividacake*, students help the baker get the right number of pieces. In *The Bakery*, they keep track of cakes in the bakery, given the number of cakes made and sold. Each lesson requires 15 minutes.

aw a ring around each group of
ppers. Find the number of groups.
rite the division number sentence.

Put 15 in groups of 5.

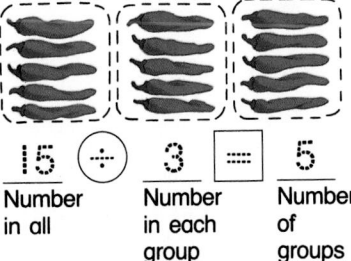

15 ÷ 3 = 5

Number in all	Number in each group	Number of groups

2. Put 12 in groups of 3.

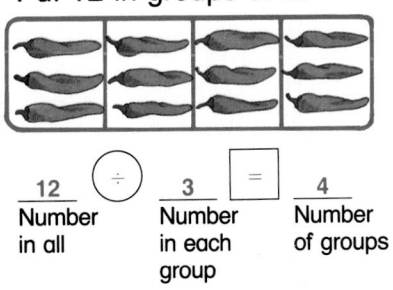

12 ÷ 3 = 4

Number in all	Number in each group	Number of groups

Put 8 in groups of 4.

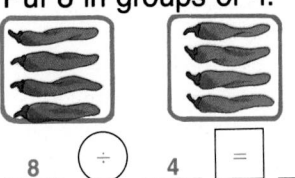

8 ÷ 4 = 2

4. Put 6 in groups of 2.

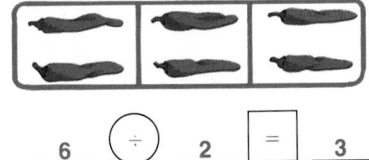

6 ÷ 2 = 3

ROBLEM SOLVING

Solve. Use counters to help.
Ring and finish the correct
number sentence. Write the
answer in a sentence.

Peter had 4 jars of pickled
peppers with 3 peppers in each jar.
How many peppers
were there in all?

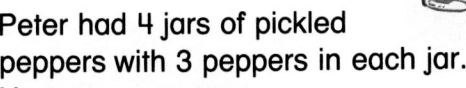

4 + 3 = ___   (4 × 3 = _12_)

Word sentences may vary. Sample answer is shown.
There were 12 peppers in all.

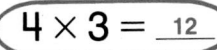

44 (three hundred forty-four)   Chapter 16

---

3. PRACTICE AND APPLY

Basic	All
Average	All
Extended	All

PRACTICE

*Look at Exercise 1 on page 344. How
are the peppers grouped?* (Rings are
drawn around groups of 5.) *How does
the division sentence relate to the
picture?* (It shows with numbers that 15
peppers are divided by 5s into 3 groups.)

APPLY

PROBLEM SOLVING ▶ **Describe
one method you might use to solve
this problem.** (Possible answer: Read
the two number sentences, then model
them using counters. This would show
which number sentence makes sense.)
▶ **If this addition sentence does not
work, can you model an addition
sentence that does?** (Possible answer:
Yes, you could show 3 + 3 + 3 + 3 =
12 to get the answer.)

16-7

CLOSE AND ASSESS

HOW WHAT YOU KNOW Ask
udents to describe the characters in
e chapter story. *Suppose there were
little pigs. If they divided the pile of
5 bricks, how many bricks would
ach one get?* (3) Ask students to use
ounters or make a drawing to show
e answer to the problem.

QUICK QUIZ

Draw a picture for the sentence. Then
write the division sentence. Put 10 in
groups of 5.
Line 1: (TEN) (TEN)
Line 2: _(10)_ ÷ _(5)_ = _(2)_

Relating Multiplication and Division

OBJECTIVE 16-8 To model and write related multiplication and division sentences

PREBOOK ACTIVITIES

Write a multiplication sentence for each picture.

1.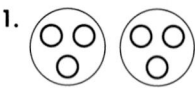

2.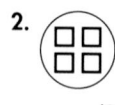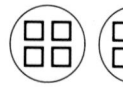

(2) × (3) = (6)   (3) × (4) = (12)

PRIOR KNOWLEDGE

Write these two number sentences on the chalkboard: 5 × 2 = 10 and 10 ÷ 2 = 5. *What do the numbers stand for in the multiplication sentence?* (number of groups times number in each group equals number in all) *What do the numbers stand for in the division sentence?* (number in all divided by number in each group equals number of groups) *How are these two number sentences alike?* (Possible answers: They both have the same three numbers; they both show information about a total number, number of groups, and number in each group.)

COMMUNICATION

Listening and Writing in Math   Write the words **multiplication** and **division** on the chalkboard. Read the following number sentences. Have students raise their left hand for a multiplication sentence, and their right hand for a division sentence. *12 divided by 6 equals 2, 6 times 2 equals 12; 7 multiplied by 2 equals 14, 14 divided by 2 equals 7; 9 divided by 3 equals 3, 3 times 3 equals 9.* Have students complete each sentence in their Math Journals.
1. 2 × 4 = 8 is a (multiplication) sentence.
2. 8 ÷ 4 = 2 is a (division) sentence.

Materials: Cube-A-Links in 2 colors
Grouping Suggestions: small groups
Provide each group with cubes in 2 colors and ask the members to put the cubes in same-color trains of 3 cubes each. *Put your cubes together to show 4 groups of 3. Every other group should be a different color. Can you think of a multiplication sentence that describes these cubes?* Write 4 × 3 = 12 on the chalkboard after students suggest it. *Now separate the long train into short trains again. Break off one short group at a time. Can you think of a division sentence that tells what you did?* Record 12 ÷ 3 = 4 on the board. Repeat this activity and ask students to write the multiplication and division sentences for the following: 2 groups of 3 and 5 groups of 3. If time allows, have students create new trains of 4 cubes and show and write sentences for 3 groups of 4, 5 groups of 4, and 2 groups of 4.

CONNECTIONS   Use these anytime.

Problem of the Day
Understanding the Operations
Solve. Ring and complete the correct number sentence. Then write the answer in a sentence.
Paul had 8 stamps. He put 2 stamps on each letter. How many letters did Paul send? 8 × 2 = (16)   8 ÷ 2 = (4)
(Paul sent 4 letters.)

Subject Integration
Fine Arts   Choose a multiplication sentence, such as 3 × 3 = 9. Clap a rhythm that shows 3 sets of 3 claps. Divide into teams and see if the other team can guess what multiplication sentence matches the rhythm you are clapping.

Creative Thinking
Pattern Blocks   Use pattern blocks to solve. How many red blocks do you need to cover 2 yellow blocks? (4) How many green blocks do you need to cover 4 red blocks? (12) How many yellow blocks can you cover with 18 green blocks? (3)

CLASSWORK AND HOMEWORK SUPPLEMENTS

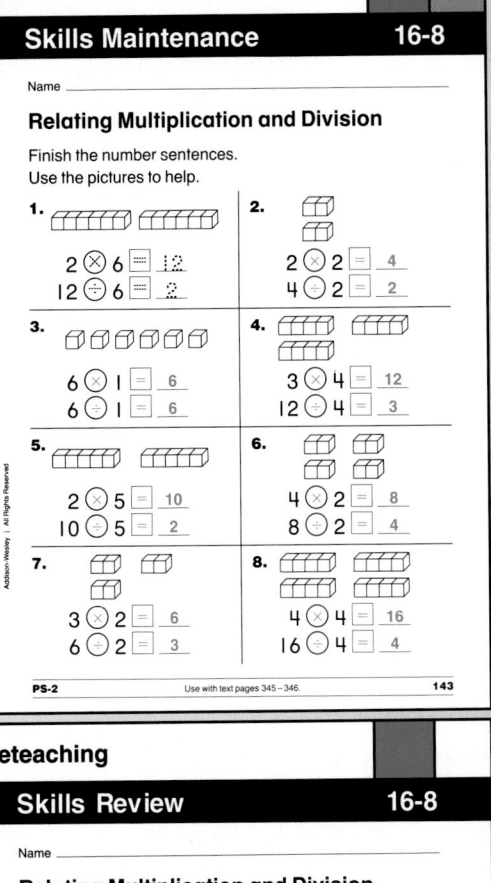

Practice

Skills Maintenance — 16-8

Name

Relating Multiplication and Division

Finish the number sentences.
Use the pictures to help.

1. $2 \otimes 6 = 12$ $12 \oplus 6 = 2$

2. $2 \otimes 2 = 4$ $4 \oplus 2 = 2$

3. $6 \otimes 1 = 6$ $6 \oplus 1 = 6$

4. $3 \otimes 4 = 12$ $12 \oplus 4 = 3$

5. $2 \otimes 5 = 10$ $10 \oplus 5 = 2$

6. $4 \otimes 2 = 8$ $8 \oplus 2 = 4$

7. $3 \otimes 2 = 6$ $6 \oplus 2 = 3$

8. $4 \otimes 4 = 16$ $16 \oplus 4 = 4$

PS-2   Use with text pages 345–346.   143

Building Thinking Skills

Family Math — 16-8

Name

Related Facts

Dear Family,
Your child is learning about the relationship between multiplication and division. Help your child fill in the multiplication tables below. Then together name the related division fact for each multiplication fact.

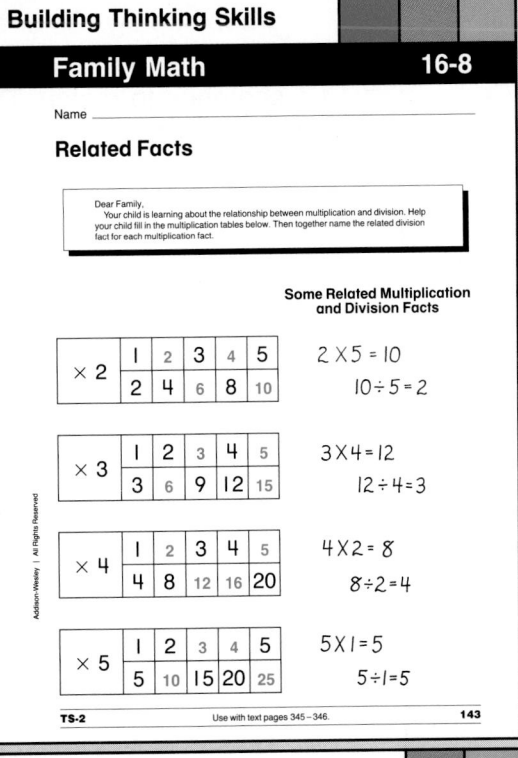

Some Related Multiplication and Division Facts

× 2	1	2	3	4	5
	2	4	6	8	10

$2 \times 5 = 10$
$10 \div 5 = 2$

× 3	1	2	3	4	5
	3	6	9	12	15

$3 \times 4 = 12$
$12 \div 4 = 3$

× 4	1	2	3	4	5
	4	8	12	16	20

$4 \times 2 = 8$
$8 \div 2 = 4$

× 5	1	2	3	4	5
	5	10	15	20	25

$5 \times 1 = 5$
$5 \div 1 = 5$

TS-2   Use with text pages 345–346.   143

Reteaching

Skills Review — 16-8

Name

Relating Multiplication and Division

I have 9 beads.

I can show and write a multiplication sentence and a division sentence.

$3 \times 3 = 9$
number of groups number in each group in all

$9 \div 3 = 3$
in all number in each group number of groups

Write a multiplication sentence to show the groups.
Write a division sentence to show the groups.

1. 3 groups of 2
$3 \otimes 2 = 6$ $6 \oplus 2 = 3$

2. 4 groups of 3
$4 \otimes 3 = 12$ $12 \oplus 3 = 4$

3. 5 groups of 2
$5 \otimes 2 = 10$ $10 \oplus 2 = 5$

4. 2 groups of 4
$2 \otimes 4 = 8$ $8 \oplus 4 = 2$

RS-2   Use with text pages 345–346.   143

Challenges

Family Math — 16-8

Name

Dear Family,
Our class is learning to multiply and divide. This game will help your child understand the relationship between multiplication and division.

Write the numbers 1, 2, or 3 inside a circle on each of 6 cards. Write 2, 3, or 4 inside a square on 6 more cards.
Place the cards facedown in 2 piles.
Take turns. Draw 1 card from each pile.
Write the number on the circle card in the circle below.
Write the number on the square card in the square.
Write the answer in the triangle.
The answer in the triangle is the score.
Write the related division sentence below that.
Each player takes 3 turns. Add up the scores in the triangles.
The player with the highest score wins.

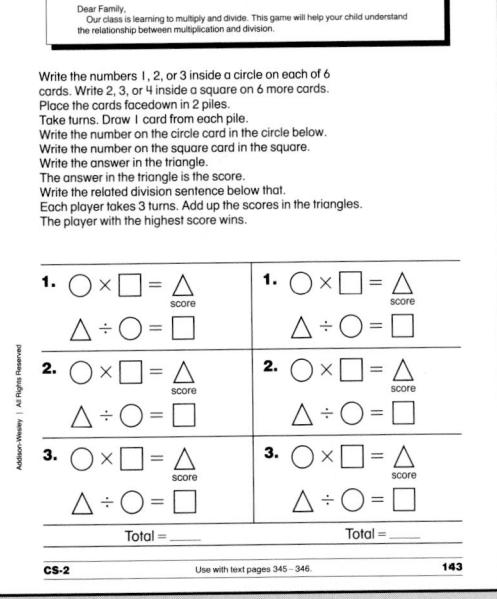

1. $\bigcirc \times \square = \triangle$ score
$\triangle \div \bigcirc = \square$

1. $\bigcirc \times \square = \triangle$ score
$\triangle \div \bigcirc = \square$

2. $\bigcirc \times \square = \triangle$ score
$\triangle \div \bigcirc = \square$

2. $\bigcirc \times \square = \triangle$ score
$\triangle \div \bigcirc = \square$

3. $\bigcirc \times \square = \triangle$ score
$\triangle \div \bigcirc = \square$

3. $\bigcirc \times \square = \triangle$ score
$\triangle \div \bigcirc = \square$

Total = ____   Total = ____

CS-2   Use with text pages 345–346.   143

OPTIONS FOR INDIVIDUAL NEEDS

Basic

Exercises All, Mixed Review
More Practice, p. 428, set C

Supplements
Reteaching 143 or
Practice 143
Thinking Skills 143

Average

Exercises All, Mixed Review
More Practice, p. 428, set C

Supplements
Practice 143
Challenges 143 or
Thinking Skills 143

Extended

Exercises All, Mixed Review

Supplements
Challenges 143
Thinking Skills 143

Other Resources:
Mathematics Book A, p. 55
Using the Math Explorer Calculator: A Source Book for Teachers, Chapter 14

16-8

OBJECTIVE 16-8

To model and write related multiplication and division sentences

---

Materials: colored chalk,
Cube-A-Links in 2 colors; flannelboard,
felt pieces of 2 colors

Grouping Suggestion: small groups

---

1. MOTIVATE AND TEACH

LEARN ABOUT IT

Write this on the chalkboard: *3 groups of 2*. Ask volunteers to come to the board and use chalk in 2 colors to draw 3 groups of 2 squares in a row. *What multiplication sentence matches the picture?* (3 × 2 = 6) Then ask students to draw lines to separate the 3 groups of 2 from the total chain of squares. *What division sentence does the picture show?* (6 ÷ 2 = 3)

▶ **Look at Exercise 1 on page 345. Describe what the row of squares shows.** (Possible answers: The squares show 4 groups of 2; they show the number sentences 4 × 2 = 8 and 8 ÷ 2 = 4.)

▶ **What do you notice about how the squares are colored?** (Possible answer: Each group is either red or yellow.)

▶ **What do you notice about the numbers in both number sentences in Exercise 1?** (Possible answer: They are the same three numbers in different places.)

▶ **How are these number sentences related?** (Possible answer: Both have the same number of groups, number in each group, and number in all.)

2. CHECK UNDERSTANDING

ERROR ALERT Forgetting to alternate colors for each group, making it difficult to separate groups of equal value.

Name _____

Relating Multiplication and Division

Work in a group. Use cubes. Make a train to show the groups below. Color to show your train. Write a multiplication sentence to match. Then snap off each group of cubes. Write a division sentence to match.

Colors may vary.

1. **4 groups of 2**

| 4 | ⊗ | 2 | ▨ | 8 | 8 | ÷ | 2 | ▨ | 4 |

Number of groups   Number in each group   Number in all   Number in all   Number in each group   Number of groups

2. **3 groups of 4**   r r r r y y y y r r r r

   3 ⊗ 4 = 12   12 ÷ 4 = 3

3. **3 groups of 3**   r r r y y y r r r

   3 ⊗ 3 = 9   9 ÷ 3 = 3

4. **2 groups of 5**   r r r r r y y y y y

   2 ⊗ 5 = 10   10 ÷ 5 = 2

Chapter 16   (three hundred forty-five) 3▪

TEACHING OPTIONS

RETEACHING TIPS Have students use a flannelboard and different colors of the same shapes to show both multiplication and division sentences for 4 groups of 3. Students can easily put these shapes together and lift them off to separate them. Have students complete Reteaching Supplement 143.

ENRICHMENT **Family Math** On pieces of paper, have students write labels such as 1 face, 2 eyes; 3 faces, 6 eyes. At home, they find and cut out pictures of faces, then use the cutout faces to illustrate the number in each label. Have them write a multiplication and division sentence for each picture.

inish the number sentences.
se the pictures to help.

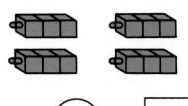

$4 \otimes 3 = 12$

$12 \div 3 = 4$

2.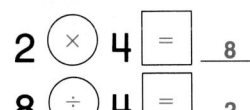

$2 \otimes 4 = 8$

$8 \div 4 = 2$

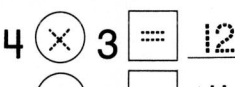

$6 \otimes 2 = 12$

$12 \div 2 = 6$

4.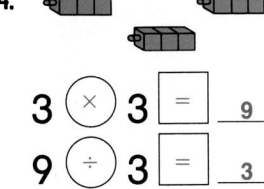

$3 \otimes 3 = 9$

$9 \div 3 = 3$

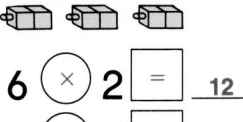

$3 \otimes 2 = 6$

$6 \div 2 = 3$

6.

$5 \otimes 1 = 5$

$5 \div 1 = 5$

MIXED REVIEW

Add or subtract.

$$\begin{array}{r} \overset{1}{23} \\ +18 \\ \hline 41 \end{array} \qquad \begin{array}{r} 39 \\ -32 \\ \hline 7 \end{array} \qquad \begin{array}{r} \overset{7\ 13}{8\cancel{3}} \\ -19 \\ \hline 64 \end{array}$$

8. Count by 3s.

3, 6, _9_,

_12_ , _15_ , _18_

---

3. PRACTICE AND APPLY

Basic	All, Mixed Review
Average	All, Mixed Review
Extended	All, Mixed Review

PRACTICE

How will you complete the two number sentences for each picture? (by deciding whether the sentence should be multiplication or division, writing the sign, then solving the problem)

APPLY

▶ **Look at Exercises 1 and 3 on page 346. Why do the multiplication problems have the same answer but not the division problems?** (There are the same number of cubes in all in both pictures, but not the same number of groups. The answer in a division sentence stands for the number of groups.)

▶ **How can you use multiplication to check division? Give an example.** (Possible answer: Check $16 \div 4 = 4$ by multiplying: $4 \times 4 = 16$.)

MIXED REVIEW   *What should you decide before completing Exercise 7?* (whether you should add or subtract)

16-8

QUICK QUIZ

Write the answers. Then match the related sentences. (**1.** c **2.** a **3.** b)

1. $4 \times 3 = (12)$ **a.** $3 \div 1 = (3)$
2. $3 \times 1 = (3)$ **b.** $8 \times 2 = (16)$
3. $16 \div 2 = (8)$ **c.** $12 \div 3 = (4)$

Problem Solving: Using Data From a Pictograph

OBJECTIVE 16-9   To solve problems using data from a pictograph

PREBOOK ACTIVITIES

QUICK REVIEW

Solve. Use counters to help.

2 × 4 = __(8)__	3 × 2 = __(6)__	6 × 1 = __(6)__
10 ÷ 2 = __(5)__	9 ÷ 3 = __(3)__	8 ÷ 4 = __(2)__
3 × 3 = __(9)__	12 ÷ 3 = __(4)__	5 × 3 = __(15)__

PRIOR KNOWLEDGE

Ask 3 students to come to the front of the classroom. Have the students hold out both hands. *How many hands in all?* (6) *How did you find out?* (Possible answers: Count the hands; count hands by 2s; add 2 + 2 + 2; multiply 3 × 2.)
How many fingers in all? (30) Discuss which of the methods is easiest and which is fastest. Talk about why it is good to know more than one way to find the answer. (Possible answer: You can use one way to solve and another way to check.)

COMMUNICATION

Listening in Math   Read each story aloud. Have students tell whether they would multiply or divide to solve.
1. There are 2 stacks of books and 4 books in each stack. How many books in all? (multiply)
2. There are 8 crayons and 4 students. How many crayons for each student? (divide)
3. There are 10 pencils and 2 pencil cases. How many pencils go in each case? (divide)
4. There are 3 rows of chairs and 5 chairs in each row. How many chairs in all? (multiply)

EXPLORE AND CONNECT

COOPERATIVE ACTIVITY

Grouping Suggestions: small groups

Our Favorite Yogurt Flavors. Each cup means 2 votes.

TEACHING ACTIONS

BEFORE
▶ **What does the pictograph show?** (favorite yogurt flavors)
▶ **In what ways might these data be useful?**
(Possible answer: Yogurt makers and people who sell yogurt may want to know what flavors people like best.)

DURING
▶ **How can you use multiplication to find out how many people voted for each flavor?**
(Possible answer: Multiply each cup by 2, since each cup means 2 votes.)
▶ **What estimates can you make by just looking at the pictograph?** (Possible answers: Vanilla is most popular; banana is least popular.)

AFTER
▶ **Choose a way to check your answers.**
(Possible answers: Use a repeated addition sentence or double the number of cups.)
Have students work in small groups to create their own pictograph showing the class's favorite yogurt flavors.

CONNECTIONS   Use these anytime.

Problem of the Day

Choose the Operation   Write a multiplication or division sentence for the story and solve it.
Roger worked for 5 days. He earned $10. How much did he earn each day? ($10 ÷ 5 = $2; $2 each day)

Math Connection

Make a Pictograph   Work in a group. Ask your classmates to choose their favorite sport. Give 3 choices. Tally the votes and make a pictograph to show the data. Post the graph in class and discuss the results.

Subject Integration

Music   Imagine that you are a drummer in a band. Think of a way to play 20 beats in equal groups. You can show the groups by pausing between groups or by playing the first beat in each group louder than the other beats. Play your beats to a friend. See if your friend can guess your rhythm.

Problem Solving Strategy: Choose the Operation

To solve problems using the strategy Choose the Operation

CLASSWORK AND HOMEWORK SUPPLEMENTS

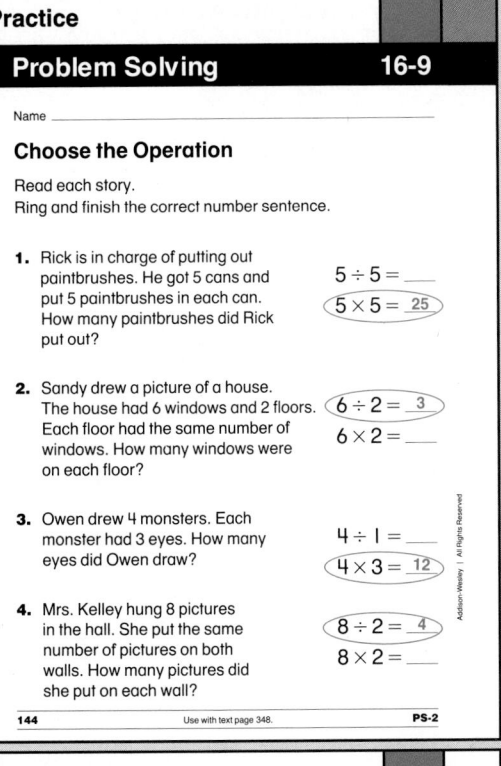

Practice

Problem Solving   16-9

Name _____

Choose the Operation

Read each story.
Ring and finish the correct number sentence.

1. Rick is in charge of putting out paintbrushes. He got 5 cans and put 5 paintbrushes in each can. How many paintbrushes did Rick put out?

$5 \div 5 =$ ___
$\boxed{5 \times 5 = 25}$

2. Sandy drew a picture of a house. The house had 6 windows and 2 floors. Each floor had the same number of windows. How many windows were on each floor?

$\boxed{6 \div 2 = 3}$
$6 \times 2 =$ ___

3. Owen drew 4 monsters. Each monster had 3 eyes. How many eyes did Owen draw?

$4 \div 1 =$ ___
$\boxed{4 \times 3 = 12}$

4. Mrs. Kelley hung 8 pictures in the hall. She put the same number of pictures on both walls. How many pictures did she put on each wall?

$\boxed{8 \div 2 = 4}$
$8 \times 2 =$ ___

144   Use with text page 348.   **PS-2**

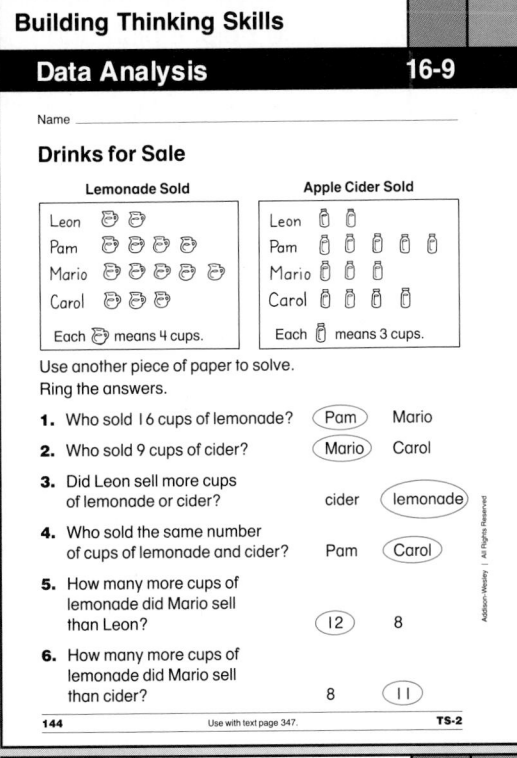

Building Thinking Skills

Data Analysis   16-9

Name _____

Drinks for Sale

Lemonade Sold   Apple Cider Sold

Leon					Leon				
Pam					Pam				
Mario					Mario				
Carol					Carol				

Each 🥤 means 4 cups.   Each 🥛 means 3 cups.

Use another piece of paper to solve.
Ring the answers.

1. Who sold 16 cups of lemonade?   (Pam)   Mario

2. Who sold 9 cups of cider?   (Mario)   Carol

3. Did Leon sell more cups of lemonade or cider?   cider   (lemonade)

4. Who sold the same number of cups of lemonade and cider?   Pam   (Carol)

5. How many more cups of lemonade did Mario sell than Leon?   (12)   8

6. How many more cups of lemonade did Mario sell than cider?   8   (11)

144   Use with text page 347.   **TS-2**

Reteaching

Problem Solving   16-9

Name _____

Using Data from a Pictograph

The 2nd grade had a pencil sale.
They made a graph to show the number of pencils they sold.

Pencils Sold   Each ✏️ means 3 pencils.

Monday	✏️ ✏️
Tuesday	✏️
Wednesday	✏️ ✏️ ✏️ ✏️
Thursday	✏️ ✏️ ✏️
Friday	✏️ ✏️ ✏️ ✏️ ✏️

Finish the multiplication sentences to tell how many pencils were sold each day.

2 ✏️   3 pencils in each ✏️

1. Monday $2 \otimes 3 = 6$ pencils sold

2. Tuesday $1 \otimes 3 = 3$ pencils sold

3. Wednesday $4 \otimes 3 = 12$ pencils sold

4. Thursday $3 \otimes 3 = 9$ pencils sold

5. Friday $5 \otimes 3 = 15$ pencils sold

144   Use with text page 347.   **RS-2**

Challenges

Problem Solving   16-9

Name _____

Spend It on Stamps

2¢   4¢   3¢   5¢

Write a multiplication or a division sentence to solve.

1. Jiro wants to buy 3 baseball stamps. What is the total cost?

$3 \times 4¢ = 12¢$

2. Gwen has 15¢. How many heart stamps can she buy?

$15¢ \div 3¢ = 5$

3. Max has 20¢. How many flag stamps can he buy?

$20¢ \div 5¢ = 4$

4. How much does Paola need to buy 5 flower stamps?

$5 \times 2¢ = 10¢$

5. Megan has 10¢. Can she buy 3 baseball stamps?

$3 \times 4¢ = 12¢;$ no

6. Valerie has 18¢. How many baseball stamps can she buy?

$18¢ \div 4¢ = 4$ with 2¢ left

7. Sam wants to buy 5 flag stamps. How much does he need?

$5 \times 5¢ = 25¢$

8. Ted spent 14¢ on flower stamps. How many did he get?

$14¢ \div 2¢ = 7$

144   Use with text page 348.   **CS-2**

OPTIONS FOR INDIVIDUAL NEEDS

Basic

Exercises All

Supplements
Reteaching 144 or
Practice 144

Average

Exercises All

Supplements
Practice 144
Challenges 144 or
Thinking Skills 144

Extended

Exercises All

Supplements
Challenges 144
Thinking Skills 144

Other Resources:
Mathematics Their Way, pp. 202-203, 205-206, 208, 343-345, 352-353
Explorations, pp. 342-343, 345, 349
Developing Number Concepts with Unifix Cubes, pp. 189, 202, 206
Mathematics Book A, pp. 44, 56

16-9

LESSON PLAN 16-9

OBJECTIVE 16-9
To solve problems using data from a pictograph; to solve problems using the strategy Choose the Operation

> **Materials:** counters, flannelboard, felt squares

1. MOTIVATE AND TEACH

LEARN ABOUT IT

 **BEFORE** ▶ **What information can you get from the graph?** (Possible answer: the number of books read by 4 people)

▶ **What data do you need in order to find out how many books each person read?** (the number of book pictures next to the name and the number of books each picture stands for)

 **DURING** ▶ **How can multiplication help you find the data shown on the graph?** (You can multiply to find the actual number of books each student read.)

▶ **What number will you multiply by each time? Why?** (3, because each picture stands for 3 books)

AFTER ▶ **Suggest a way to check your answers.** (Use turnaround multiplication; use repeated addition; use counters.)

2. CHECK UNDERSTANDING

ERROR ALERT
Page 347 Using the incorrect multiplication sentence to intepret the pictograph data.
Page 348 Choosing the incorrect operation for the story.

Problem Solving
Using Data from a Pictograph

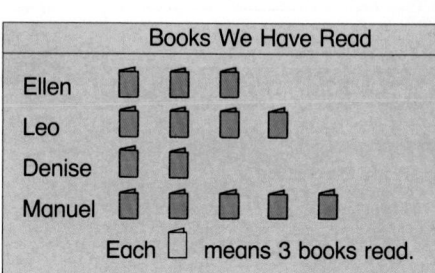

UNDERSTAND
FIND DATA
PLAN
ESTIMATE
SOLVE
CHECK

Solve. Use counters to help. Finish and ring the correct multiplication sentence. Write the answer.

Books We Have Read

Ellen

Leo

Denise

Manuel

Each ▢ means 3 books read.

1. How many books did Denise read?

   Denise read __6__ books.

   $\boxed{2 \times 3 =}$ __6__

   $2 \times 4 =$ ___

2. How many books did Leo read?

   Leo read __12__ books.

   $\boxed{4 \times 3 =}$ __12__

   $3 \times 5 =$ ___

3. How many books did Manuel read?

   Manuel read __15__ books.

   $5 \times 5 =$ ___

   $\boxed{5 \times 3 =}$ __15__

Chapter 16

(three hundred forty-seven) 3▮

TEACHING OPTIONS

RETEACHING TIPS Use felt squares on a flannelboard to make a pictograph about stamp collecting, with 1 square = 2 stamps. Have students use counters to model multiplication sentences about the data. For help in choosing the operation, assign Reteaching Supplement 144.

ENRICHMENT Poll the class to find out which story in their reader they like best. In small groups, have students make pictographs to show the data for the 3 or 4 stories that got the most votes. They decide on a picture to show the stories and on the number of votes each picture stands for.

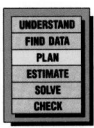

roblem Solving Strategy

hoose the Operation

| UNDERSTAND |
| FIND DATA |
| PLAN |
| ESTIMATE |
| SOLVE |
| CHECK |

sten to the stories. Think
bout the action. Cut and
aste the pictures to match.

Multiplication	Division
Put together equal groups.	Share equally. / Separate into equal groups.
Cheshire Cat and hallway	Mad Hatter's hats and gardeners painting roses

3. PRACTICE AND APPLY

Basic	All
Average	All
Extended	All

Read the following stories to help
students interpret the pictures.

1. Mad Hatter has 6 hats. He wants to
put them on 3 shelves with the same
number of hats on each shelf. How many
hats should he put on each shelf?

2. The Cheshire Cat has 2 rows of teeth
with 6 teeth in each row. How many
teeth does the Cheshire Cat have in all?

3. 3 gardeners were painting the white
roses red on the rose tree. There were 6
white roses. Each gardener painted the
same number of roses. How many roses
did each gardener paint?

4. There is a hallway with 3 doors on
each of the 2 sides. How many doors are
there in all?

▶ **What must you try to understand
as you listen to each story?** (whether
to find the total or the size of each part)

▶ **How can you plan your solution
for each story question?** (Act it out;
decide if you are putting together groups
or sharing or separating.)

▶ **Describe how you would check
your answers.** (Reread the stories. See
if your answers make sense.)

16-9

CLOSE AND ASSESS

AY WHAT YOU THINK Write 2
 3 = 6 and 6 ÷ 3 = 2 on the
halkboard. Ask students to draw
ictures showing one of the number
entences. Have students share their
ictures with the class and ask
lassmates to think of a story that
escribes the picture. Then have
udents identify the number sentence
at matches the picture and story.

QUICK QUIZ

Choose the operation. Then solve.
Karen has 12 seeds. She has 3 pots
and wants to put the same number of
seeds in each. How many seeds should
she put in each pot? (12 ÷ 3 = 4)

CHAPTER 16

WRAP UP

INTRODUCTION   The Wrap Up provides activities emphasizing math language and thinking skills for the chapter.

USING PAGE 349
Math Words ► **What word describes how you combine numbers to multiply?** *(times)*
► **What word describes how you share or separate objects in equal groups?** *(divide)*

Math Reasoning ► **Which 2 operations will you use to make sure that Rosa buys all the toy animals she can for 25¢?** (multiplication and addition)
► **Of which toy animal can Rosa buy the most? Why?** (the spider; it costs the least)

Name _____

Wrap Up

MATH WORDS

Write the correct number sentence.
Use the number sentences below.

| $4 \times 3 = 12$ | $4 \times 2 = 8$ | $12 \div 3 = 4$ | $12 \div 2 = 6$ |

1. What is 4 times 3? $4 \times 3 = 12$

2. What is 12 divided by 3? $12 \div 3 = 4$

3. Divide 12 into 2 groups. $12 \div 2 = 6$

4. Multiply 4 by 2. $4 \times 2 = 8$

MATH REASONING

5. Rosa has 25¢. She can buy 5 toy turtles. Fill in the chart. Find 3 more ways she can spend all her money. Use punchouts coins to help.

			Total
	$5 \times 5¢ = 25¢$		25¢
	$1 \times 5¢ = 5¢$	$5 \times 4¢ = 20¢$	25¢
$5 \times 3¢ = 15¢$	$2 \times 5¢ = 10¢$		25¢
$1 \times 3¢ = 3¢$	$2 \times 5¢ = 10¢$	$3 \times 4¢ = 12¢$	25¢

Chapter 16 Wrap Up   (three hundred forty-nine) 3⁴

TEACHING OPTIONS

ENRICHMENT   Set up a general store in the classroom. Label several classroom objects with prices between 2¢ and 10¢. Tell students they have 50¢ to spend. Have them find as many different ways as they can to spend their money, using the table at the bottom of page 349 as a guide. Have students share and compare their shopping lists.

Name _____

Chapter Review/Test

Draw dots to show each group.

1. Show 2 groups of 3.
   Write the addition
   sentence.

   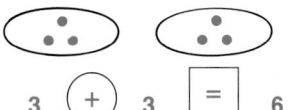

   3 (+) 3 ☐= 6

2. Show 2 groups of 6.
   Write the multiplication
   sentence.

   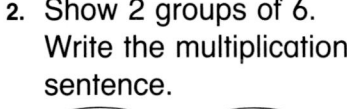

   2 (×) 6 ☐= 12

3. Draw dots. Share 12 balls
   in 3 groups. Write the
   division sentence.

   12 (÷) 3 ☐= 4

   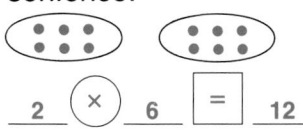

4. Put 8 in groups of 2.
   Ring the groups. Write
   the division sentence.

   8 (÷) 2 ☐= 4

5. Finish the number sentences.

   4 (×) 4 ☐= 16   16 (÷) 4 ☐= 4

6. Ring and finish the correct number sentence.
   Write the answer in a sentence.

   The class had 4 fish bowls.
   There were 2 fish in each bowl.
   How many fish did the class have?

   (2 × 4 = _8_)

   2 + 2 + 2 = ____

   The class had 8 fish.

CHAPTER REVIEW/TEST

INTRODUCTION   The Review/Test is
provided to review and evaluate the skills
and concepts presented in Chapter 16.

USING PAGE 350
If you prefer to use this page for review,
you may want to use the
Multiple-Choice Posttest (pages 63-64)
or the **Free-Response Posttest** (pages
63-64) to evaluate mastery of chapter
objectives.

ITEM ANALYSIS   The table below
correlates the Chapter Review/Test Items
with the lesson objectives.

Items	Objectives
1	16-1
2	16-2
3	16-6
4	16-7
5	16-8
6	16-5

INFORMAL ASSESSMENT

Using Manipulatives   Give student
pairs number cards 1-5 and 20
counters. Students choose a card and
use the numbers to write
multiplication sentences. Have the
first student use counters to model the
multiplication, while the second solves
the sentence using paper and pencil or
mental math. After they compare
answers, have them change tasks and
repeat for other number pairs.

Communication   *Explain what each
number means in a multiplication
sentence.* (Possible answer: The first
number tells the number of groups;
the second tells the amount in each
group. The third, which is highest,
tells how many in all.)

Critical Thinking   *Name all the ways
you can arrange 12 counters into
equal groups.* (2 groups of 6; 6
groups of 2; 3 groups of 4; 4 groups
of 3)

Chapter 16 Chapter Review/Test   **350**

ENRICHMENT

INTRODUCTION Multiplying by using a number line helps students understand multiplication as repeated addition.

USING PAGE 351

This Enrichment page is provided for all students. You may wish to use it after they have completed the Chapter Review/Test on page 350.

Help students see that multiplication can be shown on a number line by using several jumps of the same size.

▶ **What does the first number in the multiplication sentence tell you?** (the number of jumps)

▶ **What does the second number tell you?** (how many in each jump)

▶ **What would happen if there were no jumps?** (Possible answer: The answer would be zero.)

EXTENSION

Provide student pairs with TA 16 (Number Lines). Students write a multiplication sentence and exchange it with their partners. Partners solve the problem using the number line. Next, have students write a division sentence. Direct partners to work backward from the first number in the sentence, taking jumps back equal to the second number until they reach zero. The number of jumps tells the answer.

Name _____

Enrichment
Using a Number Line to Multiply

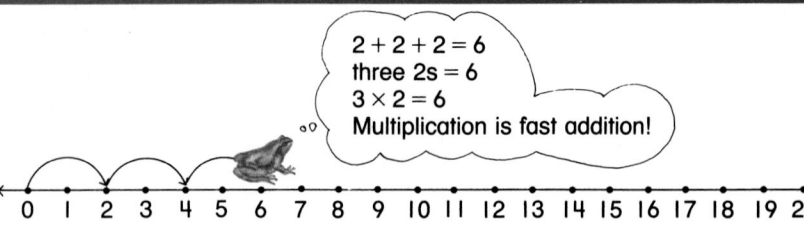

> $2 + 2 + 2 = 6$
> three 2s = 6
> $3 \times 2 = 6$
> Multiplication is fast addition!

Try this one.

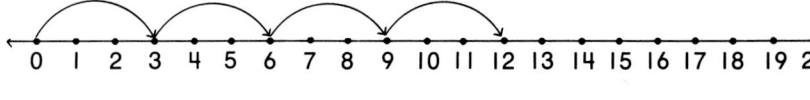

$3 + 3 + 3 + 3 = \underline{12}$

four 3s = 12

$4 \times 3 = \underline{12}$

Use the number to multiply.

1. $4 \times 2 = \underline{8}$ $3 \times 3 = \underline{9}$ $5 \times 4 = \underline{20}$

2. $3 \times 1 = \underline{3}$ $6 \times 2 = \underline{12}$ $2 \times 3 = \underline{6}$

3.
$$\begin{array}{r} 3 \\ \times 5 \\ \hline 15 \end{array} \qquad \begin{array}{r} 2 \\ \times 6 \\ \hline 12 \end{array} \qquad \begin{array}{r} 5 \\ \times 2 \\ \hline 10 \end{array} \qquad \begin{array}{r} 1 \\ \times 3 \\ \hline 3 \end{array} \qquad \begin{array}{r} 4 \\ \times 4 \\ \hline 16 \end{array}$$

Chapter 16 Enrichment: Using a Number Line to Multiply   (three hundred fifty-one) 3

Name _____

ᴜMULATIVE Rᴇᴠɪᴇᴡ

ꞁdd or subtract.

63
− 27

○ 81
○ 47
● 36

28
+ 16

○ 12
● 44
○ 53

71
− 35

● 36
○ 42
○ 56

49
+ 17

● 66
○ 32
○ 75

What part is colored?

5.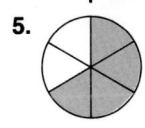

○ $\frac{3}{6}$ ● $\frac{4}{6}$ ○ $\frac{3}{5}$

6.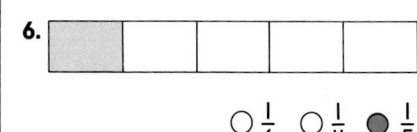

○ $\frac{1}{6}$ ○ $\frac{1}{4}$ ● $\frac{1}{5}$

7.

○ $\frac{3}{4}$ ● $\frac{2}{3}$ ○ $\frac{1}{2}$

Which picture shows
equal parts?

A   B   C

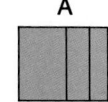 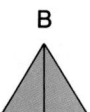 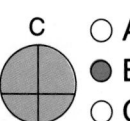

○ A
● B
○ C

How many more miles
is it to Spring Lake
than to Bay City?

○ 13 miles
○ 29 miles
● 15 miles

Bay City   28 miles

Spring Lake   43 miles

CUMULATIVE REVIEW

INTRODUCTION   The purpose of this
Cumulative Review is to maintain
previously taught skills and concepts.
The emphasis in this Cumulative Review
is on addition of 2-digit numbers,
Chapter 11; subtraction of 2-digit
numbers, Chapter 14; and on fractions,
Chapter 15.

ITEM ANALYSIS   The table below
correlates the Cumulative Review items
with the lesson objectives.

Items	Objectives
1, 3	14-4, 14-6
2, 4	11-4, 11-6
5	15-1
6, 7	15-2, 15-3
8	15-4
9	14-7

OVERVIEW

Lesson	Pages	Objectives	Subject Integration	Strand Integration
Recording Hundreds, Tens, and Ones	353-354	17-1 To group and write hundreds, tens, and ones	language arts: following directions	calculator
Modeling Hundreds, Tens, and Ones	355-356	17-2 To model hundreds, tens, and ones	fine arts: cut & paste	number
Modeling and Writing 3-Digit Numbers	357-358	17-3 To model and write 3-digit numbers	social studies: collections, hobbies	problem solving
Counting Patterns	359-360	17-4 To count on by ones	health and fitness: marbles	place value, patterns
Modeling and Writing Numbers Before, After, and Between	361-362	17-5 To model and write numbers before, after, and between	language arts: books	patterns, number, computation
Problem Solving: Understanding the Operations/Mental Math	363-364	17-6 To use addition, subtraction, and multiplication; to use mental math	language arts: writing	patterns, money
Comparing 3-Digit Numbers	365-366	17-7 To compare 3-digit numbers using > and <	social studies: stamps	number, data analysis
Counting Dollars and Cents	367-368	17-8 To count money beyond $1	social studies: group skills	consumer math, money
Problem Solving: Writing a Story/Problem Solving Strategy: Act It Out	369-370	17-9 To write a story; to use the strategy Act It Out	language arts: writing	computation, logical thinking

MATHEMATICAL BACKGROUND

3-Digit Place Value
A solid understanding of place value is essential to the development of computational skills. The introduction to reading and writing 2-digit numbers in Chapter 7 is extended in this chapter to 3-digit numbers. Before beginning this chapter, students should have a firm grasp of the following concepts:
- 1 ten is the same as 10 ones
- The place value of a digit in a 2-digit number tells the value of the digit.

These concepts were introduced with 2-digit place value and can now be extended to include the following:
- 1 hundred is the same as 100 ones
- 1 hundred is the same as 10 tens.

In particular, students should recognize how each place represents groups of 10. The idea that the place of a digit tells its value should be applied to 3-digit place value. Students will need many opportunities to experience these three forms for representing numbers: model, expanded form, standard form.

Problem Solving
In this chapter, students solve problems by writing a story and by using the strategy Act It Out.

TIPS FROM TEACHERS

To help students learn number facts, record groups of facts on a tape with the answers. Play the fact and then pause 5-7 seconds before playing the answer. Students write and check their own answers. Students enjoy making their own tapes, too.

Ann Riemer
Lakeshore Elementary School
Rochester, NY

ASSESSMENT

ITEM ANALYSIS

Items	Objectives
1	17-1
2	17-2
3	17-3
4	17-4
5	17-5
6	17-6
7	17-7
8	17-8
9	17-9

Note: The item analysis is the same for all pretests and posttests for this chapter.

Pretest — Chapter 17, page 1

Multiple-Choice Format

Name _____

1. Choose the number of hundreds, tens, and ones.

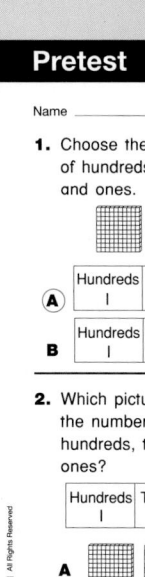

(A)
Hundreds	Tens	Ones
1	2	4

B
Hundreds	Tens	Ones
1	4	2

2. Which picture shows the number of hundreds, tens, and ones?

Hundreds	Tens	Ones
1	3	8

A

B

(C)

3. How many rocks are in the collection?

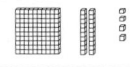

A   530 rocks

(B)   350 rocks

4. Choose the numbers to count on.
409, 410, 411, ?, ?, ?

(A)   412, 413, 414

B   408, 409, 410

C   401, 391, 381

5. Choose the numbers to count on.
845, ?, ?, 848

(A)   846, 847

B   844, 843

MCT 2   65

Pretest — Chapter 17, page 2

Multiple-Choice Format

Name _____

6. Choose the number sentence.

Omar had 142 fish. He bought 3 more fish. Then how many did he have?

A   142 + 0 = 142

B   142 − 3 = 139

(C)   142 + 3 = 145

7. Choose > or < for the ○.

457 ○ 546

A   >

(B)   <

9. Choose the letters for the cars to show the order.

The jeep (J) is first in line.
The station wagon (S) is between the jeep and the van (V).
The truck (T) is behind the van and in front of the race car (R).

J	S		T	
first	second	third	fourth	last

(A)   J S V T R   First   Last

B   J S T R V   First   Last

C   J S R T V   First   Last

8. Count the money.

A $1.71

B $1.28

(C) $1.46

66   MCT 2

Posttest — Chapter 17, page 1

Multiple-Choice Format

Name _____

1. Choose the number of hundreds, tens, and ones.

A
Hundreds	Tens	Ones
5	3	5

(B)
Hundreds	Tens	Ones
2	3	5

2. Which picture shows the number of hundreds, tens, and ones?

Hundreds	Tens	Ones
1	6	5

(A)

B

C

3. How many shells are in the collection?

(A)   420 shells

B   402 shells

4. Choose the numbers to count on.
377, 378, 379, ?, ?, ?

A   389, 399, 409

B   376, 375, 374

(C)   380, 381, 382

5. Choose the numbers to count on.
723, ?, ?, 726

A   722, 721

(B)   724, 725

MCT 2   67

Posttest — Chapter 17, page 2

Multiple-Choice Format

Name _____

6. Choose the number sentence.

Al had 232 rocks. He found 6 more. Then how many did he have?

(A)   232 + 6 = 238

B   232 − 6 = 226

C   232 + 8 = 240

7. Choose > or < for the ○.

923 ○ 879

(A)   >

B   <

9. Choose the letters for the cars to show the order.

The van (V) is first in line.
The station wagon (S) is between the van and the truck (T).
The jeep (J) is behind the truck and in front of the race car (R).

V	S		J	
first	second	third	fourth	last

A   V S T R J   First   Last

(B)   V S T J R   First   Last

C   V S R J T   First   Last

8. Count the money.

(A) $1.42

B $1.57

C $1.12

68   MCT 2

ALSO AVAILABLE

▶ Free Response Tests
▶ Alternative Tests
▶ Thinking Strategies
▶ Concrete Materials

Optional Chapter Activities

PROJECT AND BULLETIN BOARD

Introduce numbers to 1,000 with this project. On the bulletin board, hang a shopping bag filled with edge strips from computer paper. Attach a 100-hole strip to the board and label it *100*. Use the strip as a model for estimating. Draw a box under each of the heads *Guess How Many* and *Count How Many*. Draw 6 boxes under the head *Show*, and write in the boxes: *100 more, 200 more, 10 less, 50 less, 10 more, same number*. Display a second strip with more than 100 holes. Have students estimate and record how many holes the strip has. Have volunteers count the holes and record the number. Use the leftover strips in the shopping bag to show 100 more holes on the displayed strip. Continue to add and remove strips as indicated by the boxes on the board. On subsequent days, display new strips with from 50-1,000 holes. Repeat the estimating, counting, and adding or subtracting process.

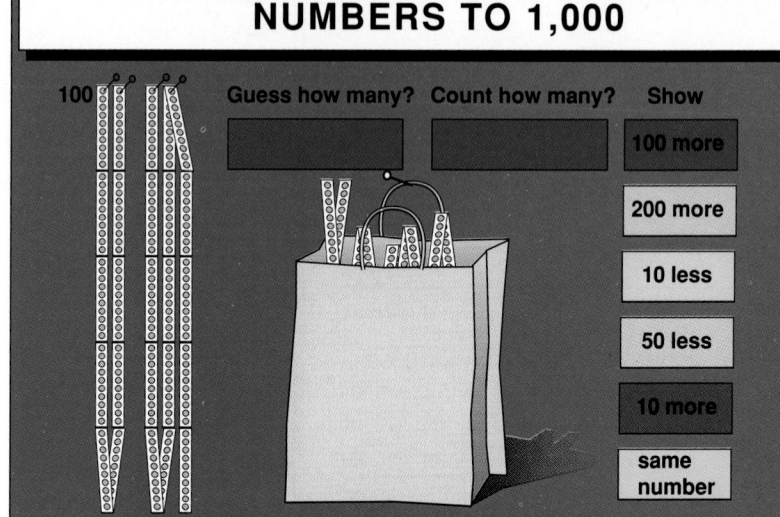

NUMBERS TO 1,000

100 | Guess how many? | Count how many? | Show

100 more

200 more

10 less

50 less

10 more

same number

COOPERATIVE LEARNING

Divide the class into groups of 3. Identify the group skill: treating each other with respect. Assist each group in making a spool spinner to show place value (see illustration). Write the numbers 0-9 around the middle of 3 empty spools so that they can be read when the spools are turned sideways. Run a pencil or plastic drinking straw through the centers of the spools. The spools should spin freely around the pencil.

Have students show place value using base-ten blocks or toothpicks. The first member of each group will spin the spools to show a number of hundreds, tens, and ones. A second group member will model the number, and a third will write the number and read it aloud. Remind students to treat each other with respect. Repeat, having students take turns.

You will find grouping suggestions and cooperative learning activities in most lessons throughout this chapter.

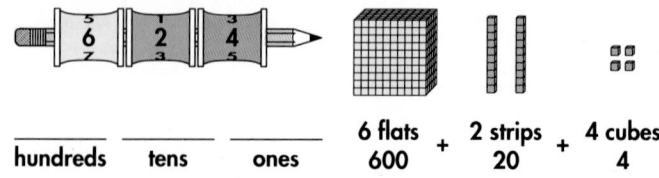

hundreds	tens	ones	6 flats	2 strips	4 cubes
			600	+ 20	+ 4

LITERATURE

Barrett, Judi. *Cloudy With a Chance of Meatballs.* New York: Macmillan, 1978.

What if food fell from the sky like rain? In this story it does!
Have students make up numbers for the things falling from the sky. Then ask them to write 3-digit numbers.

Leodhas, Sorche Nic. *Always Room for One More.* New York: Henry Holt, 1965.

Mack, Stan. *10 Bears in My Bed.* New York: Pantheon Books, 1974.

ENGLISH AS A SECOND LANGUAGE

Make the distinction between the number 100 and the place value hundreds. Have students read 3-digit numbers in a circle game in which the teacher calls out a number and students count on.

The chapter uses a variety of grammatical structures such as the present-future conditional, the passive voice, and *there are*. While accepting simple numerical answers, try to elicit complete sentences that reuse the grammar in the questions.

Have students design their own data hunts and write the problems. Collect problems and use them at a later date as a game, review or quiz.

Writing a Story is a good collaborative activity. Have students create their own word banks and stories. Encourage native speakers to help ESL students. Use this opportunity to informally evaluate ESL students' problem areas and have them read the stories on tape.

GIFTED

Mathematically talented students may already understand how place value is extended to the thousands place. They will nevertheless likely be interested in many of the strategies presented in this chapter. You may wish to challenge these students to model and write 4-digit numbers. For example, after Lesson 5 on counting patterns, write 1,000 on the chalkboard. Explain that just as ones and tens grow by tens, so do hundreds. One thousand is the same as 10 hundreds. Use place value models if necessary. Ask students to read and write several 4-digit numbers with 1 in the thousands place, then challenge them to complete the exercises in their books after they add 1 thousand to each number. Have students work in pairs and compare answers. If this appeals to your students, you may wish to use the technique throughout the chapter and allow them to add any digit to the thousands place.

STUDENTS AT RISK

This chapter is an extension and elaboration of much of what has been done earlier in the year. It will help all students, especially those who are very concrete, if the materials used earlier in the year are extended to include the ideas presented in this chapter. For example, the hundred chart and hundred number line (see page 1D) can be extended up to and past 1,000. (It would be more feasible to do this with the worksheet-size grids and number lines.) This is an excellent cooperative class project.

With the new thousand chart, students can play an extended version of the Travel Game (see page 137D). Change the spinner to include moves such as + 100, − 101, and + 200. A thousand number line game might use toy cars that travel from the city at number dot 203 to the town at dot 303.

Similarly, the manipulatives used to represent ones, tens, and hundreds in Chapter 10 may now be extended to 1,000. Reintroduce the Trading Game (see page 207D) with the goal of reaching 1,000.

You may also use the Reteaching Supplements and the specific Reteaching Tips from each lesson in this chapter.

Storybook

PICTURE

These pictures and accompanying stories and poems are available as storybooks.

You may want to read and discuss this story with your students before starting the chapter. The first lesson in this chapter includes a question about the story. Lessons 1, 2, and 7 in this chapter have questions in the informal Assessment that refer to the story.

Maggie's Hobby

The wind whistled through the trees as Maggie Mouse huffed and puffed up the hill dragging a bag of fabric scraps behind her. The chill in the air worried Maggie. Winter was nearly here, and the weather would soon turn colder. She wondered how she and her friends would stay warm. "I must hurry," she thought, as she climbed over the last log near her burrow. She looked up and saw her neighbors Barnie Badger and Greta Gopher.

"Good morning, Maggie. Where have you been so early in the morning?" inquired Barnie.

Maggie pointed to the bag behind her and replied, "I was down at the houses by the lake collecting for my hobby."

That was all Barnie and Greta needed to hear to start another argument about their own hobbies.

"I still think stamp collecting is the best hobby," claimed Barnie. "Stamps have such beautiful pictures."

"No, Barnie," replied Greta. "You can't play with stamps. Marble collecting is the best hobby because you can play with the marbles while you collect them."

Although the two neighbors disagreed about whose hobby was best, they both felt that Maggie's hobby of collecting fabric pieces was silly. "Maggie," said Barnie, "wouldn't you like to have a better hobby—one that would be more fun and more interesting?"

Maggie had heard the arguments before and wanted no part of them. "I'm quite happy with my hobby, just as you are with yours," she said, and then dragged her bag into her burrow. She stayed there for the next two days working on her hobby. On the third day, the weather turned bitterly cold, and the first snow fell on the ground. It was so cold that night that Barnie and Greta could not sleep. In the middle of the night they went to Maggie's burrow to see how she was doing.

They knocked, and then called to the sleeping mouse. "Maggie, are you asleep? Can we come in? Brrrrrrr. Aren't you cold, too?" they both asked.

Maggie welcomed her friends into her home, saying, "I've been expecting you." And that's when Greta saw the beautiful warm quilt on Maggie's bed. It was a patchwork design made from little squares that Maggie had cut from her fabric pieces and had sewn in rows. There were 10 rows with 10 fabric squares in each row. That made 100 squares in all.

"Maggie," she said, "your hobby isn't collecting pieces of fabric after all. You make quilts."

"Yes," said Maggie, with a sparkle in her eye. And then she pointed to two wrapped packages, one for each of her friends. When Barnie and Greta opened the boxes, they could scarcely believe their eyes. Maggie had made each of them a 100-square patchwork quilt just like hers.

Greta was the first to realize how poorly they had treated Maggie when they had made fun of her hobby. She carefully wrapped the magnificent quilt around her shoulders and said, "Maggie your hobby isn't silly or useless. You created something beautiful, and your hobby is going to keep us warm all winter long."

Barnie thought about his stamps and about Greta's marbles. Then he gave Maggie a big thank-you hug, saying, "Maggie, I think your hobby is wonderful after all."

Recording Hundreds, Tens, and Ones

OBJECTIVE 17-1   To group and write hundreds, tens, and ones

PREBOOK ACTIVITIES

QUICK REVIEW

Give the number of tens and ones in each number.

54 _(5)_ tens _(4)_ ones		98 _(9)_ tens _(8)_ ones
12 _(1)_ tens _(2)_ ones		77 _(7)_ tens _(7)_ ones
29 _(2)_ tens _(9)_ ones		40 _(4)_ tens _(0)_ ones
2 _(0)_ tens _(2)_ ones		65 _(6)_ tens _(5)_ ones
81 _(8)_ tens _(1)_ ones		10 _(1)_ tens _(0)_ ones

PRIOR KNOWLEDGE

Help students recall what they know about grouping tens and ones. *Suppose that you must carry drinking cups for 10 groups of 10 children at summer camp. How could you group the cups to make this job easier for yourself?* (Possible answers: 10 groups of 10 equals 100; buy 1 bag of 100 cups and carry it by myself; ask 10 friends to each carry 1 stack of 10 cups.)

COMMUNICATION

Discussing and Writing Math   *Why might you want to trade 10 ones for 1 ten?* (Possible answer: The amounts are equal, but 10 ones are harder to count then 1 ten.) *What are some different ways you could group 100 ones?* (Possible answer: Group 100 ones into 10 groups of 10 or 1 group of 100.) Ask students to copy and complete these sentences in their Math Journals.

1. I can trade 10 ones for 1 ___(ten)___ .
2. I can trade 10 tens for 1 ___(hundred)___ .

EXPLORE AND CONNECT

Materials: toothpicks, twist ties, rubber bands
Grouping Suggestions: small groups
Ask students in each group to count sets of 10 toothpicks and bundle them with twist ties. Then have them show how many bundles of 10 it takes to show 100. Encourage students to count aloud by tens up to 100 as they display the bundles. *How many tens does it take to make 150? 200?* (15, 20) Give students time to explore and count other amounts of tens. *What problem might you have when you show large numbers using groups of 10?* (Possible answer: You need to use many groups of 10; they are hard to handle and count.) *How could you show groups of 100?* (Trade 10 tens for 1 hundred.) Have students use rubber bands to bundle 10 tens into hundreds and model numbers such as 170 and 220. *Why are groups of 100 easier to count when you are showing large numbers?* (There are fewer groups to count.)

CONNECTIONS   Use these anytime.

Problem of the Day

Estimating   Ring the best answer.
There are 33 people on the red team.
There are 42 people on the blue team.
About how many people are on both teams?
about 60 people
about 70 people
about 80 people

Subject Integration

Fine Arts   Design a city using a piece of graph paper with 1000 squares. Cut the paper into groups of hundreds, tens, and ones and arrange them in the shapes of buildings, houses, and streets. When you have finished, trade papers with a friend to compare how the same number of squares can be grouped and arranged differently.

Mental Math

Number Sense   Write the numbers in order from smallest to largest. Use base-ten blocks if you need to.
289, 430, 521, 167, 305
(167, 289, 305, 430, 521)

CLASSWORK AND HOMEWORK SUPPLEMENTS

Basic

Exercises All
Calculator Bank, p. 401
More Practice, p. 429, set A

Supplements
Reteaching 145 or
Practice 145

Average

Exercises All
Calculator Bank, p. 401
More Practice, p. 429, set A

Supplements
Practice 145
Challenges 145 or
Thinking Skills 145

Extended

Exercises All
Calculator Bank, p. 401

Supplements
Challenges 145
Thinking Skills 145

Other Resources:
Mathematics Their Way, pp. 308-309
Explorations, pp. 241, 244-248

Practice

Skills Maintenance — 17-1

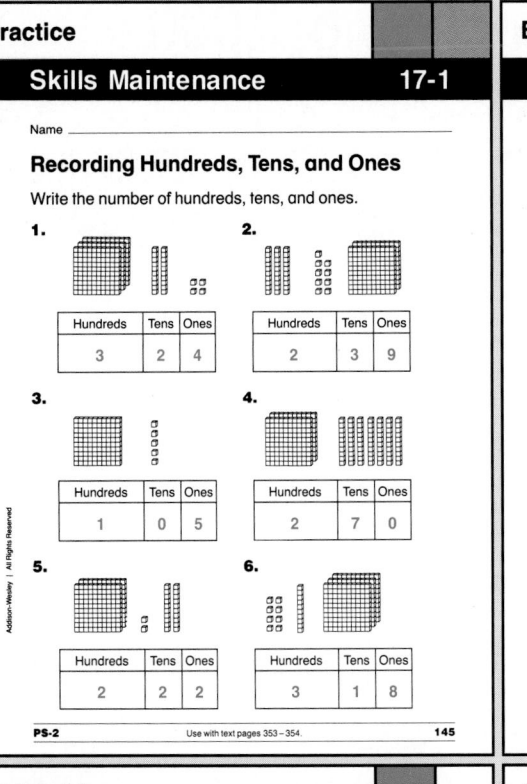

Building Thinking Skills

Number Sense — 17-1

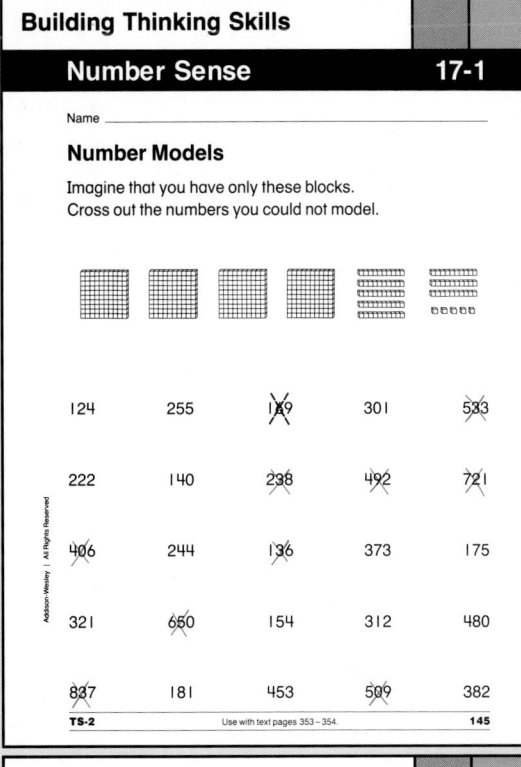

Reteaching

Skills Review — 17-1

Challenges

Reading Math — 17-1

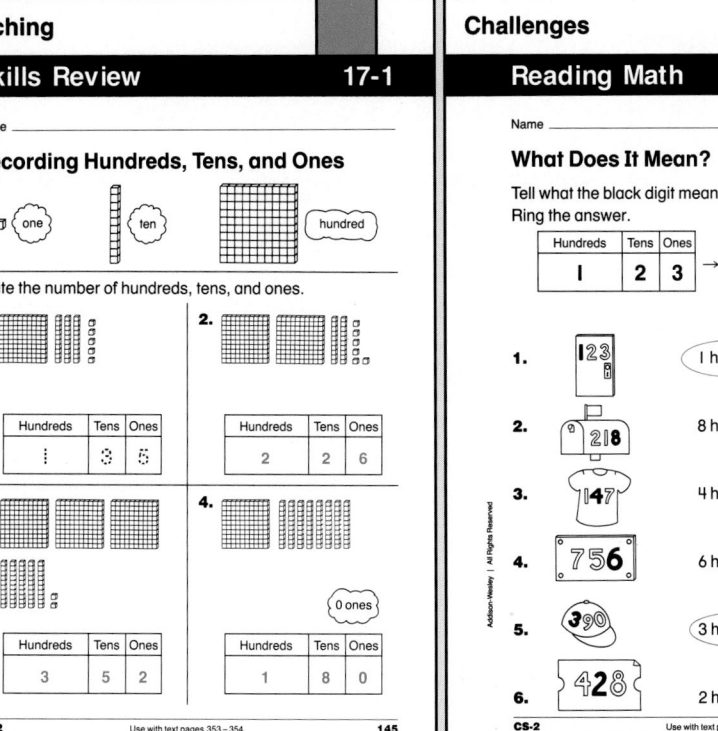

17-1

OBJECTIVE 17-1

To group and write hundreds, tens, and ones

> **Materials:** punchout number cards, base-ten blocks, TA3 (Centimeter Graph Paper), TA17 (Place Value Chart)
>
> **Grouping Suggestions:** cooperative groups of 3

1. MOTIVATE AND TEACH

LEARN ABOUT IT

Read the chapter story. *How many squares were there in 1 quilt?* (100) Have students show 10 rows of 10 with tens sticks, then trade 10 tens for 1 hundred block. Then draw their attention to the book cover on page 353. Have them model 3-digit numbers with base-ten blocks, and place the number cards on the lines to show the corresponding numeral.

▶ **What can you do with the blocks and number cards after you show 10 tens?** (Possible answer: Trade 10 tens for 1 hundred, change the 10 in the tens column to 1 in the hundreds column.)

▶ **Describe the blocks you would use to show the number 253.** (Possible answer: You could use 2 hundreds, 5 tens, and 3 ones.)

▶ **Explain why you need to change the number in the tens column after you trade 10 tens for 1 hundred.** (Possible answer: After the trade, you have 0 tens left, but you have 1 hundred.)

2. CHECK UNDERSTANDING

ERROR ALERT Writing the number in the wrong place value column.

17
Place Value
Numbers to 1,000

TEACHING OPTIONS

RETEACHING TIPS Use graph paper cutouts to model hundreds, tens, and ones. Ask students to count the number of each set and write the result in a place value chart. Then write a 3-digit number and ask students to model the hundreds, tens, and ones. Assign Reteaching Supplement 145.

ENRICHMENT Have students make up number riddles like the one below. Tell them to exchange riddles with a friend and solve them. Ring the number. It has a 4 in the tens place. It has a 5 in the ones place.

465   246   574   <u>345</u>   935

me _____

Recording Hundreds, Tens, and Ones

se 5 hundreds, 5 tens, and
ones blocks. Take away
) blocks. Write the number of
undreds, tens, and ones. Try
gain with I0 different blocks.
nswers may vary.

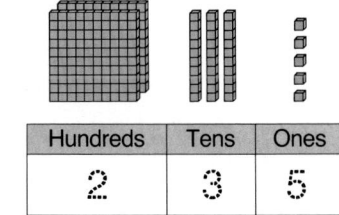

Hundreds	Tens	Ones
2	3	5

Hundreds	Tens	Ones

2.

Hundreds	Tens	Ones

ook at the pictures.
Vrite the number of hundreds, tens, and ones.

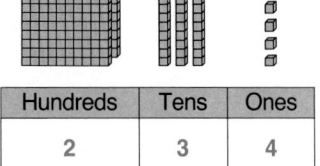

Hundreds	Tens	Ones
2	3	4

4.

Hundreds	Tens	Ones
3	0	2

RY A CALCULATOR

Press ON/C 100 + 100 =.

Keep pressing = until you see [1000].
Write the numbers the calculator shows.

100 , 200 , 300 , 400 , 500 ,

600 , 700 , 800 , 900 , 1000

---

3. PRACTICE AND APPLY

Basic	All
Average	All
Extended	All

PRACTICE

*Why will the answers be different in
Exercises 1 and 2?* (Each time you
remove a different group of blocks, the
digit will change in at least 1 column.)
*What do you notice about how the blocks
are arranged in Exercises 3 and 4?* (The
hundreds, tens, and ones are not always
shown in order.)

APPLY

TRY A CALCULATOR ▶ **Compare
the numbers 100 and 1,000. How are
they the same and how are they
different?** (Possible answer: Both are
shown by writing a 1 with zeros; but
1,000 has 3 zeros and 100 only has 2
zeros; 1,000 is made up of ten 100s.)
▶ **What digits will stay the same as
you keep pressing the equal sign on
the calculator? Which digit will
change?** (Possible answer: The zeros in
the tens and ones places will stay the
same; the digit in the hundreds place will
get larger.)

17-1

LOSE AND ASSESS

HOW WHAT YOU KNOW
ave students work in cooperative
arning groups of 3. The first student
kes 2 handfuls of base-ten blocks.
ne second arranges the blocks in
undreds, tens, and ones and makes
propriate trades. The third student
ecks the results and writes the
digit number shown by the blocks.
ave students exchange tasks and
peat.

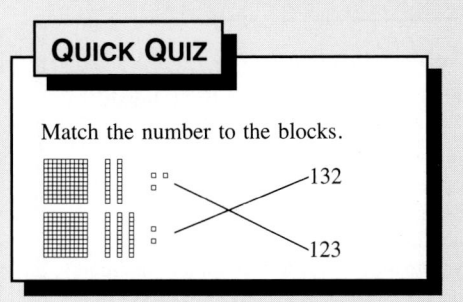

Modeling Hundreds, Tens, and Ones

OBJECTIVE 17-2   To model hundreds, tens, and ones

PREBOOK ACTIVITIES

QUICK REVIEW

Write the number of tens and ones for each number.

1. 67 __(6)__ tens __(7)__ ones   **2.** 43 __(4)__ tens __(3)__ ones
3. 9 __(0)__ tens __(9)__ ones   **4.** 12 __(1)__ tens __(2)__ ones
5. 22 __(2)__ tens __(2)__ ones   **6.** 95 __(9)__ tens __(5)__ ones
7. 10 __(1)__ ten __(0)__ ones   **8.** 89 __(8)__ tens __(9)__ ones
9. 15 __(1)__ ten __(5)__ ones   **10.** 60 __(6)__ tens __(0)__ ones

PRIOR KNOWLEDGE

Ask students to name 2-digit numbers that they are familiar
with. Suggest that they think of their address or the age of
someone they know. Have students take turns recording these
numbers on the chalkboard and reading them aloud. Point out
the place each digit holds as students follow these directions:
*Circle the number in the tens place. Put a square around the
number in the ones place.*

COMMUNICATION

Reading and Writing in Math   Write the words **Hundreds,
Tens,** and **Ones** on the chalkboard. Read the words aloud.
What do these words have in common? (They are all words
that show place value.) Write the following sentence. Have
students copy and complete the sentence in their Math Journals,
then read it aloud: *A 3-digit number has a _____ place, a tens
place, and a ones place.* (hundreds)
Next, draw on the board a place value chart that has a space
for hundreds, tens, and ones. Have students copy the chart and
write the words that go at the top of the chart. Check students'
work to make sure they have written the words in the correct
order.

EXPLORE AND CONNECT

Materials: hundreds, tens, and ones blocks
Draw a place value chart on the chalkboard, similar to the one
on page 355. Fill in the headings at the top and draw models
each place in the chart. *How many hundreds are there? Show
the number of hundreds using your blocks.* Allow students tim
to group the appropriate number of hundreds blocks on the lef
side of their work space. *How many tens are there? Show the
number of tens using the blocks.* Again, students group the
correct number of tens and place them next to the hundreds.
Repeat this activity for the ones in the number. Have students
say the number of hundreds, tens, and ones they have
modeled. Ask a volunteer to record the numbers in the chart
under your pictures. Continue this activity with other numbers
until students feel comfortable working with hundreds. Include
3-digit numbers that have zeros in the tens and ones places.

CONNECTIONS   Use these anytime.

Problem of the Day

Modeling Hundreds   Write a
number sentence and the answer.
  Bill put 4 hundreds blocks on the
  chart.
  Then he put down 2 more hundreds.
  How many hundreds did he show?
(4 hundreds + 2 hundreds = 6 hundreds)

Subject Integration

Fine Arts   Make a collage of 3-digit
numbers. Cut out numbers from
magazines and newspapers. Paste them
on a piece of paper. Try to find as many
3-digit numbers as possible. When you
are finished, count how many numbers
you found and write that number on your
paper. Display your collage in class.

Mental Math

Numeration   Find Jill's room
number.
It has 6 tens.
It has 3 hundreds.
631   613   316   163
361   136   336   636
(361)

CLASSWORK AND HOMEWORK SUPPLEMENTS

Basic

Exercises All

Supplements
Reteaching 146 or
Practice 146

Average

Exercises All

Supplements
Practice 146
Challenges 146 or
Thinking Skills 146

Extended

Exercises All

Supplements
Challenges 146
Thinking Skills 146

Other Resources:
Mathematics Their Way, pp. 308-310
Explorations, pp. 241, 244-248

17-2

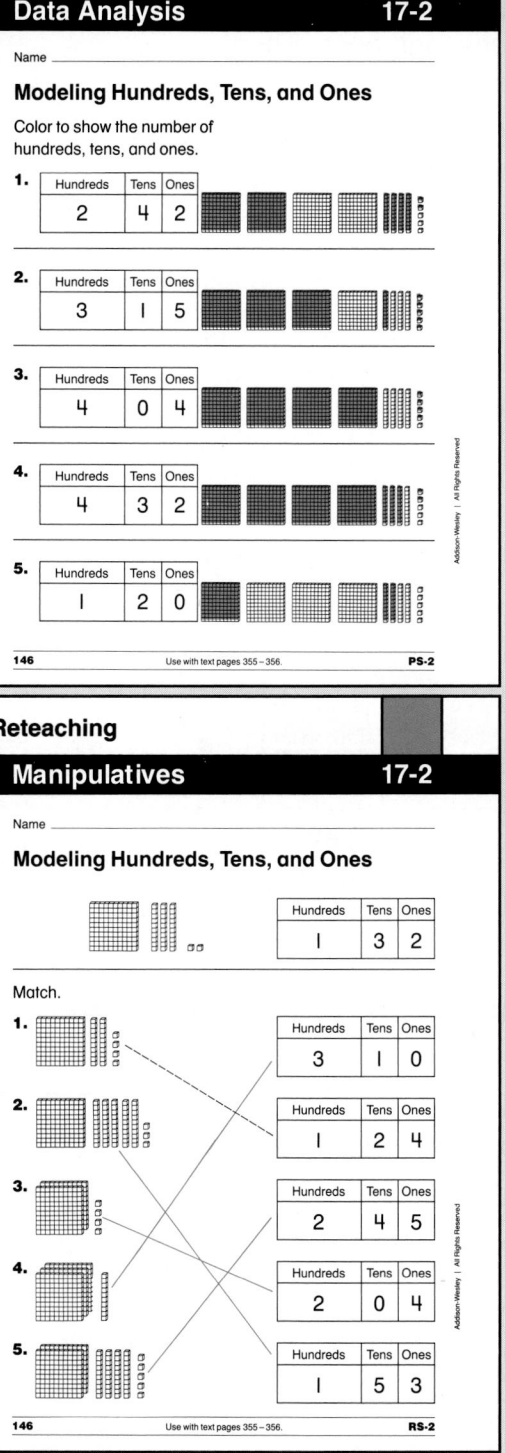

Practice

Data Analysis   17-2

Name

Modeling Hundreds, Tens, and Ones

Color to show the number of hundreds, tens, and ones.

1.
Hundreds	Tens	Ones
2	4	2

2.
Hundreds	Tens	Ones
3	1	5

3.
Hundreds	Tens	Ones
4	0	4

4.
Hundreds	Tens	Ones
4	3	2

5.
Hundreds	Tens	Ones
1	2	0

146   Use with text pages 355 – 356.   PS-2

Reteaching

Manipulatives   17-2

Name

Modeling Hundreds, Tens, and Ones

Hundreds	Tens	Ones
1	3	2

Match.

1.
Hundreds	Tens	Ones
3	1	0

2.
Hundreds	Tens	Ones
1	2	4

3.
Hundreds	Tens	Ones
2	4	5

4.
Hundreds	Tens	Ones
2	0	4

5.
Hundreds	Tens	Ones
1	5	3

146   Use with text pages 355 – 356.   RS-2

Building Thinking Skills

Critical Thinking   17-2

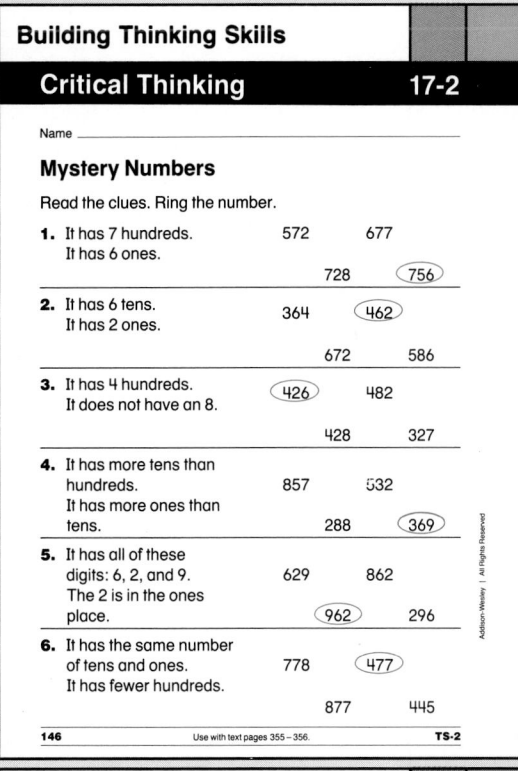

Name

Mystery Numbers

Read the clues. Ring the number.

1. It has 7 hundreds.
   It has 6 ones.   572   677   728   (756)

2. It has 6 tens.
   It has 2 ones.   364   (462)   672   586

3. It has 4 hundreds.
   It does not have an 8.   (426)   482   428   327

4. It has more tens than hundreds.
   It has more ones than tens.   857   532   288   (369)

5. It has all of these digits: 6, 2, and 9.
   The 2 is in the ones place.   629   862   (962)   296

6. It has the same number of tens and ones.
   It has fewer hundreds.   778   (477)   877   445

146   Use with text pages 355 – 356.   TS-2

Challenges

Estimation   17-2

Name

Building Blocks

Use your base-ten blocks.
Estimate how many hundreds, tens, and ones will cover the book.   Answers will vary.
Then cover each book and count.

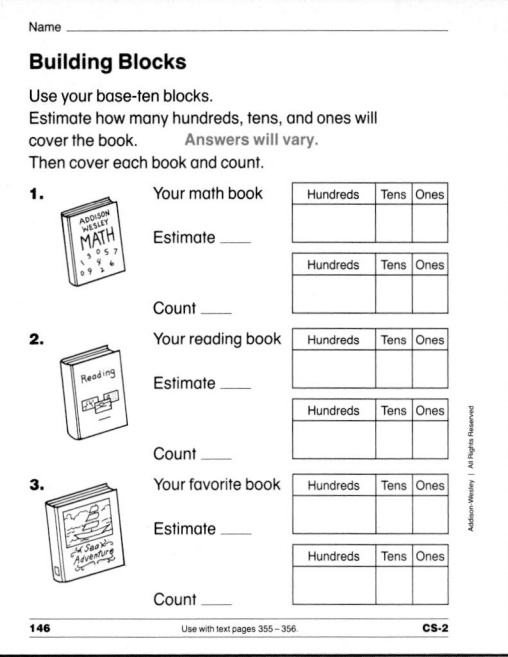

1. Your math book

Estimate ____

Hundreds	Tens	Ones

Count ____

Hundreds	Tens	Ones

2. Your reading book

Estimate ____

Hundreds	Tens	Ones

Count ____

Hundreds	Tens	Ones

3. Your favorite book

Estimate ____

Hundreds	Tens	Ones

Count ____

Hundreds	Tens	Ones

146   Use with text pages 355 – 356.   CS-2

LESSON PLAN 17-2

OBJECTIVE 17-2
To model hundreds, tens, and ones

Materials: flannelboard; felt shapes to represent hundreds, tens, and ones; base-ten blocks, number cubes

Grouping Suggestions: individual work, small groups

1. MOTIVATE AND TEACH

LEARN ABOUT IT

Cut out shapes to represent hundreds, tens, and ones on the flannelboard. Write a 3-digit number in a place value chart on the chalkboard. *How can you show this number using the pictures on the flannelboard?* Ask a volunteer to arrange the pictures for each digit and discuss the results.

Direct students' attention to the top of page 355.

▶ **What is a quick way to tell the difference between 4 hundreds and 4 tens?** (The hundreds are pictured in squares; the tens are pictured in strips.)

▶ **What are some things to think about before you paste the number of hundreds, tens, and ones in Exercises 1-4?** (Possible answer: When you match the blocks, be sure you have them in the correct order.)

▶ **Look at the number of ones in each exercise. Now look at the ones pictures. Will you use all of the ones pictures?** (No, you will not use the picture with one 1; none of the exercises have only one 1 in that place.)

▶ **What do you notice about the tens place in Exercise 1? What does that mean?** (Possible answer: There is a zero in the tens place, so you will not have to paste anything in that box.)

2. CHECK UNDERSTANDING

ERROR ALERT Arranging and pasting the pictures in the incorrect place value order.

Name _____

Modeling Hundreds, Tens, and Ones

Hundreds	Tens	Ones
2	1	4

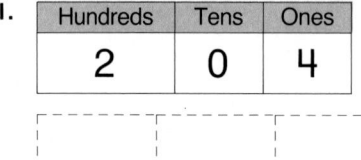

Cut out the pictures below. Match the number of hundreds, tens, and ones. Then paste in the boxes. Watch for extras.

1.

Hundreds	Tens	Ones
2	0	4

Paste 2 hundreds and 4 ones

2.

Hundreds	Tens	Ones
4	3	2

Paste 4 hundreds, 3 tens, and 2 ones

3.

Hundreds	Tens	Ones
3	4	0

Paste 3 hundreds and 4 tens

4.

Hundreds	Tens	Ones
1	2	3

Paste 1 hundred, 2 tens, and 3 ones

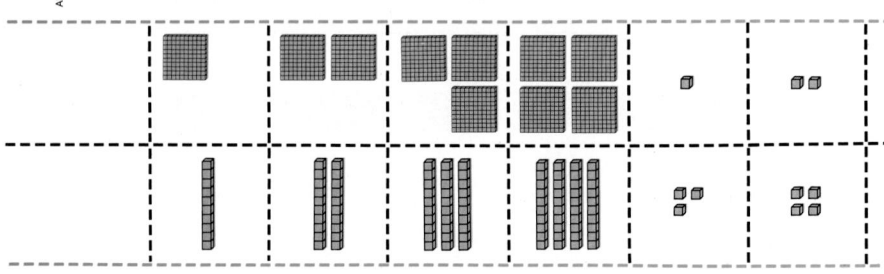

Chapter 17   (three hundred fifty-five) 3

TEACHING OPTIONS

RETEACHING TIPS Write a 3-digit number on the board. Have 3 students each represent hundreds, tens, or ones, standing in the correct order and holding the appropriate number of hundreds, tens, or ones blocks. Have each say their number beginning with hundreds. Assign Reteaching Supplement 146.

ENRICHMENT Have students model 3-digit numbers using base-ten blocks and clues such as:
1. 2 tens; 3 more hundreds than tens, 2 fewer ones than tens (520)
2. 7 hundreds; 5 fewer ones than hundreds, 3 more tens than ones (752)

Color to show the number of
hundreds, tens, and ones.

Color 3 hundreds, 4 tens, 2 ones.

Hundreds	Tens	Ones
3	4	2

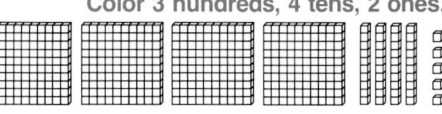

Color 4 hundreds, 5 ones.

Hundreds	Tens	Ones
4	0	5

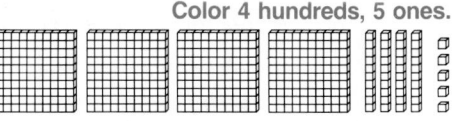

Color 2 hundreds, 2 tens, 3 ones.

Hundreds	Tens	Ones
2	2	3

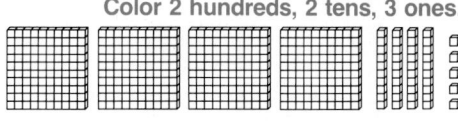

Color 4 hundreds, 3 tens, 1 one.

Hundreds	Tens	Ones
4	3	1

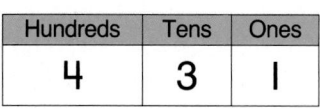

Color 1 hundred, 3 tens.

Hundreds	Tens	Ones
1	3	0

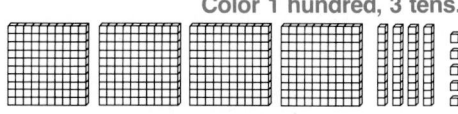

Color 3 hundreds, 1 ten, 4 ones.

Hundreds	Tens	Ones
3	1	4

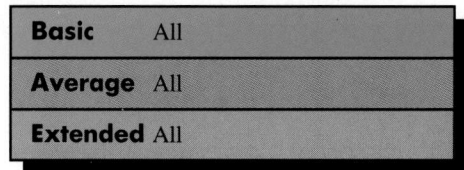

3. PRACTICE AND APPLY

Basic	All
Average	All
Extended	All

PRACTICE

How will you show the number of hundreds, tens, and ones on page 356? (Color the amount shown by the number in the place value chart.) *What do you notice about the number in the tens place in Exercise 2?* (It is a zero.) *How will you show tens?* (Do not color any tens.)

APPLY

▶ **When coloring blocks to show hundreds, tens, and ones, would it matter if you colored the ones first? Explain.** (no, as long as you color the correct number of ones)

▶ **What is the largest 3-digit number you could model using hundreds, tens, and ones blocks?** (999)

▶ **What is the smallest 3-digit number that you could model?** (100)

17-2

CLOSE AND ASSESS

SHOW WHAT YOU KNOW Talk about how Maggie made her quilts in the chapter story. *If you make a quilt with 10 squares in each row and 15 rows, how many quilt squares do you need?* (150) Have students use tens blocks and then trade 10 tens for 1 hundred to show how many squares are needed.

QUICK QUIZ

How many hundreds, tens, and ones?

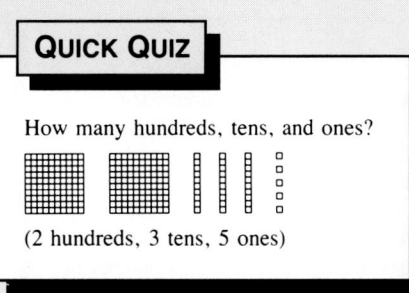

(2 hundreds, 3 tens, 5 ones)

Modeling and Writing 3-Digit Numbers

OBJECTIVE 17-3 To model and write 3-digit numbers

PREBOOK ACTIVITIES

QUICK REVIEW

Write numbers for the blocks shown on the overhead projector (or chalkboard.)

3 tens 4 ones	5 tens 1 one	7 tens	1 ten 6 ones
8 tens 9 ones	2 tens 7 ones	3 ones	1 ten 8 ones

(34; 51; 70; 16; 89; 27; 3; 18)

PRIOR KNOWLEDGE

Review with students what they know about recording hundreds, tens, and ones. Display base-ten blocks on the chalkboard ledge: 3 hundreds, 2 tens, 6 ones. Draw a place value chart and ask students to tell you how to fill it in. *How many hundreds?* (3) *How many tens?* (2) *How many ones?* (6) Then write the number 326 below the chart. *What does the first digit mean?* (3 hundreds) *What does the second digit mean?* (2 tens) *What does the third digit mean?* (6 ones) *Does this number match the numbers in the chart?* (yes) *In what order did I write the digits?* (in the same order as on the chart: first hundreds, then tens, then ones)

COMMUNICATION

Reading in Math Write the following 3-digit numbers on the chalkboard: 116, 247, 320, 456, 288, 307. *How do we read these numbers? When you see a number with 3-digits, say the first digit and* hundred, *then say the 2-digit part you already know.* Read 116 as 1 hundred 16. Emphasize that you do not say *1 hundred and 16.* Then have the students read the other numbers. Point out that if the tens digit is 0, they read the hundreds and then the ones digit, as in *3 hundred 7.*

EXPLORE AND CONNECT

Materials: base-ten blocks (hundreds, tens, ones)
Grouping Suggestion: pairs
Write sixteen 3-digit numbers on the chalkboard in 4 rows (4 per row). Have students play *Find My Number.* One student in each pair chooses a number and tells his or her partner its location—for example, third row, second number; first row, fourth number. Remind students to treat each other with respect as they work together. Have partners raise their hands when they agree on the number. Call on a pair to read the number and tell its location to the class. Have all students model the number with base-ten blocks. Continue by having other pairs present their numbers for the class to model.

CONNECTIONS   Use these anytime.

Problem of the Day

Number Sense Carrie had 257 stickers in her sticker book. Shelly gave her 5 more. Does Carrie have more or less than 300 stickers now? (less)

Math Connection

Place Value Use hundreds, tens, and ones blocks to cover your math book. Start with the hundreds blocks and use smaller units when you need to. Write the number of hundreds, tens, and ones you used. Then write the total number of squares. Compare your 3-digit number to that of another student.

Life Skills

Finding Pages in a Book Use your math book. Write the name of the lesson found on these pages.
1. page 103 (Fact Families)
2. page 235 (Addition Practice)
3. page 335 (Multiplying with Money)
4. page 271 (Subtracting Tens)
5. page 359 (Counting Patterns)
6. page 147 (Dimes and Pennies)

CLASSWORK AND HOMEWORK SUPPLEMENTS

Practice

Writing Math   17-3

Name _____

Modeling and Writing 3-Digit Numbers

How many are there? Write the number.

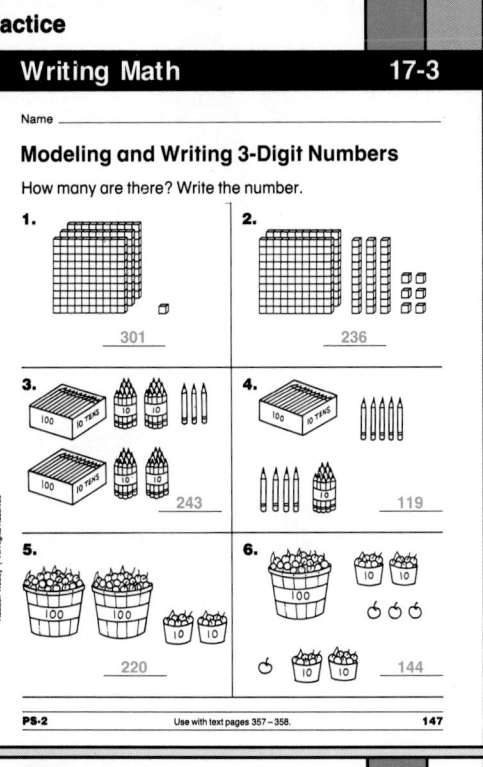

1. 301
2. 236
3. 243
4. 119
5. 220
6. 144

PS-2   Use with text pages 357–358.   **147**

Building Thinking Skills

Math Reasoning   17-3

Name _____

Make a Number

Make number cards for 3 8 4 .
Move the cards around to make six 3-digit numbers.
Write the numbers.

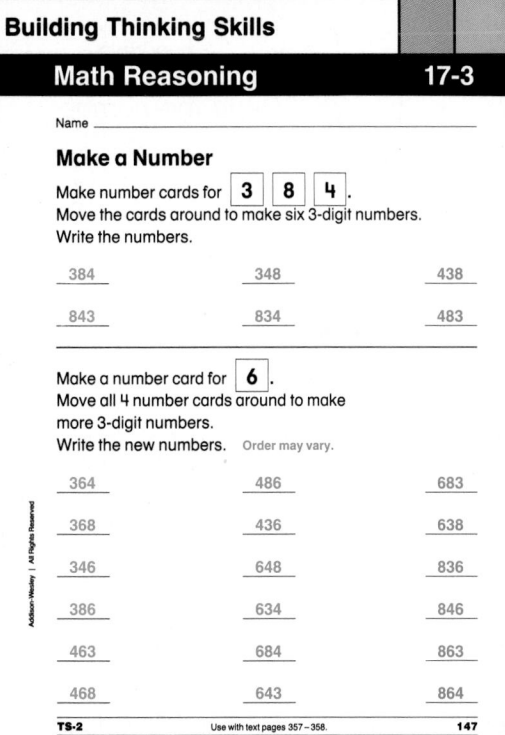

| 384 | 348 | 438 |
| 843 | 834 | 483 |

Make a number card for 6 .
Move all 4 number cards around to make
more 3-digit numbers.
Write the new numbers.   Order may vary.

364	486	683
368	436	638
346	648	836
386	634	846
463	684	863
468	643	864

TS-2   Use with text pages 357–358.   **147**

Addison-Wesley | All Rights Reserved

Reteaching

Writing Math   17-3

Name _____

Modeling and Writing 3-Digit Numbers

How many are there? Write the number.

1. 2 hundreds 5 tens 6 ones   0 ones   170
2.
3. 135
4. 305
5. 228
6. 169

RS-2   Use with text pages 357–358.   **147**

Challenges

Cooperative Activities   17-3

Name _____

Flip It!

Play with a partner.
Flip 6 counters onto the board.
Record your score. Take turns.

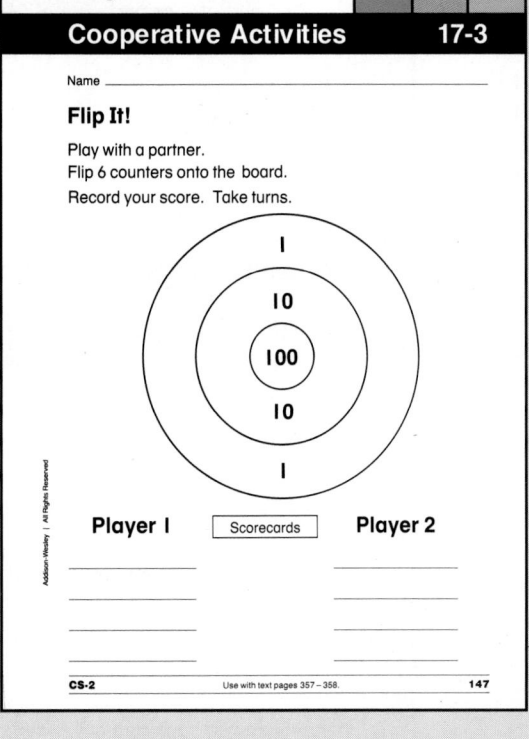

Player I   Scorecards   Player 2

CS-2   Use with text pages 357–358.   **147**

Exercises All
More Practice, p. 429, set B

Supplements
Reteaching 147 or
Practice 147
Challenges 147

Average

Exercises All
More Practice, p. 429, set B

Supplements
Practice 147
Challenges 147 or
Thinking Skills 147

Extended

Exercises All

Supplements
Challenges 147
Thinking Skills 147

Other Resources:
Mathematics Their Way, pp. 308-310
Explorations, pp. 249-251, 302
Using the Math Explorer Calculator: A Source Book for Teachers, Chapter 14

17-3

LESSON PLAN 17-3

OBJECTIVE 17-3
To model and write 3-digit numbers

Materials: 1 set of large number cards 0-9; TA17 (Place Value Chart), base-ten blocks, punchout number cards

Grouping Suggestions: individual work, cooperative learning groups of 4

1. MOTIVATE AND TEACH

LEARN ABOUT IT

Have students practice reading 3-digit numbers by displaying large number cards to show the number 416. *Say the first digit and* hundred, *then say the 2-digit part you already know,* sixteen. *Read 416 as* four hundred sixteen. Repeat for several other numbers. Have students look at the example at the top of page 357.

▶ **Look at the models and write over the 3-digit number. What does the first digit stand for?** (hundreds) **What does the second digit stand for?** (tens) **In what order do we write 3-digit numbers?** (from left to right, starting with the digit with the greatest value)

▶ **What if the picture of the bags of 100s was shown last? Would that change how many marbles there are?** (No, there are still 325.) **What if we changed the order of the digits and wrote 253? Would this number still match the picture?** (No; you would have a different amount: 2 hundreds, 5 tens, and 3 ones.)

2. CHECK UNDERSTANDING

ERROR ALERT Exercises 2 and 4: Miscounting tens and ones and/or writing the numbers without regard to place value. Exercise 3: Forgetting to use zero as a place holder.

Name _____

Modeling and Writing 3-Digit Numbers

3 hundreds   2 tens   5 ones

My collection has 325 marbles in it.

Read the number
"three hundred twenty-five."

325

Work with a partner. How many are in each collection? Write the number. Then read it to your partner.

1. Button Collection

_412_ buttons

2. Rock Collection

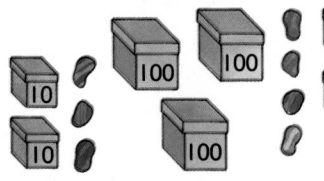

_347_ rocks

3. Shell Collection

_503_ shells

4. Coin Collection

_634_ coins

Chapter 17   (three hundred fifty-seven)

TEACHING OPTIONS

RETEACHING TIPS Model 360 with blocks on a place value chart. Have students record, write, and read the number. *If you forgot to write the 0, how would you read the number?* (36) Replace the 6 tens with 6 ones. Have students write and read it. Assign Reteaching Supplement 147.

COMPUTER Galaxy Math Facts Game, Random House ©️ 1985 For use with all levels of students. In *Place Value*, students must fill their rockets with fuel, load torpedoes, and energize their space bomb for a journey. Students may set the level of difficulty. The lesson takes 25 minutes to complete.

The numbers tell how many are in each collection. Color hundreds, tens, and ones to show each number.

321 Color 3 hundreds, 2 tens, 1 one.

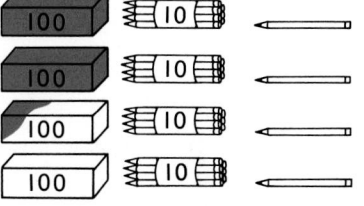

2. **203** Color 2 hundreds, 3 ones.

130 Color 1 hundred, 3 tens.

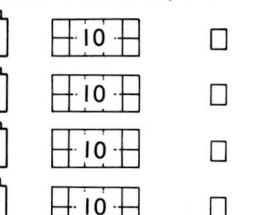

4. **424** Color 4 hundreds, 2 tens, 4 ones.

PROBLEM SOLVING

Solve. Use your punchout number cards 3 8 5 to help.

Kelly's father makes house numbers from wood. What different 3-digit numbers can he make with these numbers? Write them.

358	385	538
583	835	853

Order of answers may vary.

---

3. PRACTICE AND APPLY

Basic	All
Average	All
Extended	All

PRACTICE

Call students' attention to Exercises 2 and 3 on page 358. *How is zero shown when you are coloring to show a number?* (by coloring nothing in that group)

APPLY

PROBLEM SOLVING ▶ **How can you list all the numbers?** (Possible answer: Start with one number, arrange and rearrange the other two numbers; then begin with another number and repeat.)

▶ **How can you check to see if your list is complete?** (Possible answer: List the numbers in a different way and compare the lists.)

▶ **If zero was used as one of the numbers, how would the list change?** (Two of the numbers would be 2-digit numbers.)

17-3

LOSE AND ASSESS

HOW WHAT YOU KNOW

ovide each group of 4 with base-ten ocks and punchout number cards 9. Three students draw cards and ace them beside each other to form 3-digit number, then tell the place d value of the number they picked. e fourth student reads the number d models it with base-ten blocks. mind students to treat each other th respect as they work operatively.

QUICK QUIZ

Write each number that I model with base-ten blocks. Read each number to your partner. Tell how many hundreds, tens and ones.
261 124 307 500 315 430

Chapter 17 Lesson 3   **358**

PREBOOK ACTIVITIES

QUICK REVIEW

Write the next three numbers.

56 ____, ____, ____   (57, 58, 59)
39 ____, ____, ____   (40, 41, 42)
60 ____, ____, ____   (61, 62, 63)
74 ____, ____, ____   (75, 76, 77)
18 ____, ____, ____   (19, 20, 21)

PRIOR KNOWLEDGE

Ask students to listen to the following story: *Mrs. Squirrel had never collected so many nuts! She was counting as her children left for school—32, 33, 34, 35, . . .—and she was* still *counting when they came home—432, 433, 434, ... Mrs. Squirrel asked her children if they knew how to find the next number. What do you think they said?* (Encourage all responses. Some students may suggest thinking of the number that comes after 34 and adding 4 hundreds to it. Others may suggest modeling the number 434 and adding one more block.)

COMMUNICATION

Listening and Writing in Math   Have students number a sheet of paper from 1-8. Have them write each number as you say it aloud. Pause between numbers to give students enough time. Then repeat the number so students can check what they wrote. Use these numbers: 4 hundred 22, 4 hundred 23, 4 hundred 24, 4 hundred 25, 4 hundred 26, 4 hundred 27, 4 hundred 28, 4 hundred 29. Have students look at the numbers. *Which digit changed?* (the ones digit) *What is the pattern?* (one more each time)

EXPLORE AND CONNECT

Materials: base-ten blocks
Grouping Suggestion: pairs
Have a student in each pair model a 2-digit number with tens and fewer than 6 ones blocks. Have the other student record the number. Then have partners take turns adding 1 unit to the model, reading and writing the new number each time. After students have written 4 new numbers, have them model the original number and then add several hundreds blocks to it. Have them record the new 3-digit number below the first 2-digit number, then take turns adding ones and recording 4 new numbers. Be sure students treat each other with respect. *Read the numbers you wrote. What is the pattern?* (counting ones) *Which numbers in the second row are the same as the first row?* (The tens and ones are the same.) *Why did the tens and hundreds stay the same in each number in the second row?* (We added only ones but not enough ones to make another ten)

CONNECTIONS   Use these anytime.

Problem of the Day

Number Patterns   Sally has to count the beans in a jar. She counted to 371. Then she counted 5 more beans and stopped. On which number did Sally stop? (376)

Minute Math

Answer Patterns   Copy the exercises. Then add or subtract. How many can you complete in 1 minute?

36	88	45	62
+42	−9	+35	+19
(78)	(79)	(80)	(81)

97	99	57
−13	−17	+26
(84)	(82)	(83)

Math Connection

Calculator   Count on from a 3-digit number as your press keys on your calculator. To count on from 350, press these numbers.
3 5 0 + 1 = = . . .
Say and write each new number. Read your pattern to a friend.

CLASSWORK AND HOMEWORK SUPPLEMENTS

Basic

Exercises All
Calculator Bank, p. 401
Computer Bank, pp. 405-408
More Practice, p. 430, set A

Supplements
Reteaching 148 or
Practice 148
Thinking Skills 148

Average

Exercises All
Calculator Bank, p. 401
Computer Bank, pp. 405-408
More Practice, p. 430, set A

Supplements
Practice 148
Challenges 148 or
Thinking Skills 148

Extended

Exercises All
Calculator Bank, p. 401
Computer Bank, pp. 405-408

Supplements
Challenges 148
Thinking Skills 148

Other Resources:
Mathematics Their Way, pp. 309-310
Explorations, pp. 244-245, 302, 334
Mathematics Book A, p. 10

Practice

Patterns   17-4

Name _____

Counting Patterns

Finish each row. Follow the pattern.

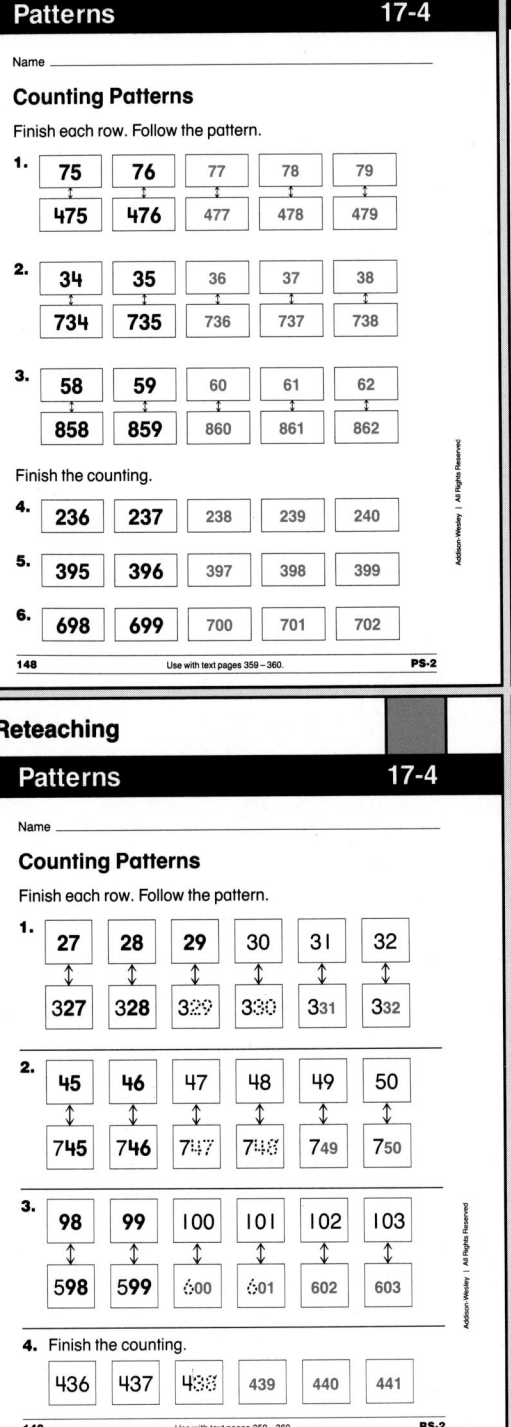

1.

75	76	77	78	79
475	476	477	478	479

2.

34	35	36	37	38
734	735	736	737	738

3.

58	59	60	61	62
858	859	860	861	862

Finish the counting.

4.

236	237	238	239	240

5.

395	396	397	398	399

6.

698	699	700	701	702

148   Use with text pages 359 – 360.   PS-2

Building Thinking Skills

Patterns   17-4

Name _____

A-maze-ing Patterns

Follow the trails from the top of the chart to the bottom.
Use blue for the trail that counts by 1s.
Use red for the trail that counts by 10s.
Predict which path will end at the highest number.

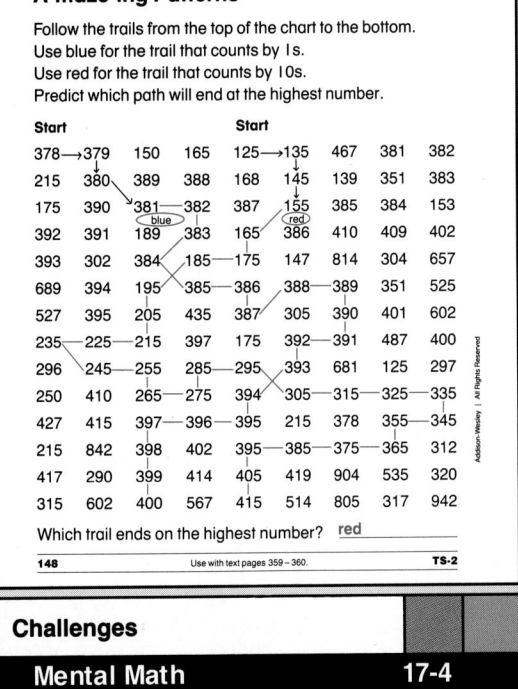

Start				Start				
378→379	150	165	125→135	467	381	382
215	380	389	388	168	145	139	351	383
175	390	381—382	387	155	385	384	153
392	391	189 blue 383	165	386 red	410	409	402
393	302	384	185—175	147	814	304	657
689	394	195	385—386	388—389	351	525
527	395	205	435	387	305	390	401	602
235—225—215	397	175	392—391	487	400
296	245—255	285—295	393	681	125	297
250	410	265—275	394	305—315—325—335
427	415	397—396—395	215	378	355—345
215	842	398	402	395—385—375—365	312
417	290	399	414	405	419	904	535	320
315	602	400	567	415	514	805	317	942

Which trail ends on the highest number? __red__

148   Use with text pages 359 – 360.   TS-2

Reteaching

Patterns   17-4

Name _____

Counting Patterns

Finish each row. Follow the pattern.

1.

27	28	29	30	31	32
327	328	329	330	331	332

2.

45	46	47	48	49	50
745	746	747	748	749	750

3.

98	99	100	101	102	103
598	599	600	601	602	603

4. Finish the counting.

436	437	438	439	440	441

148   Use with text pages 359 – 360.   RS-2

Challenges

Mental Math   17-4

Name _____

Number Paths

Complete the path by writing numbers in each shape as you go. Use the code.

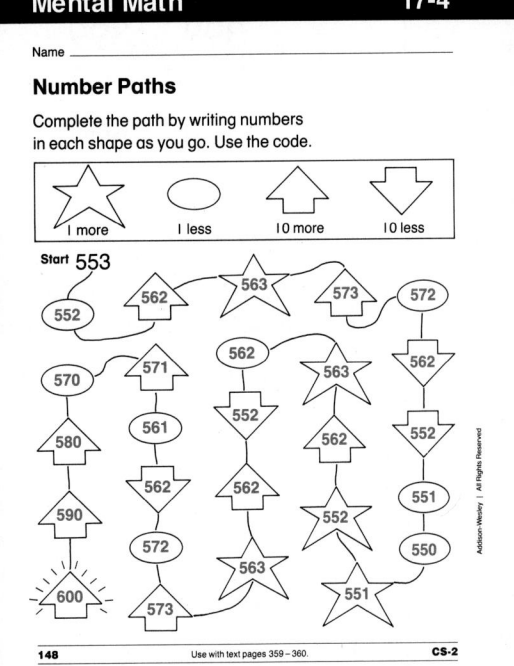

☆	⬭	⬆	⬇
1 more	1 less	10 more	10 less

Start 553
552, 562, 563, 573, 572
570, 571, 562, 563, 562
580, 561, 552, 562, 552
590, 562, 563, 551
572, 563, 552, 550
600, 573, 551

148   Use with text pages 359 – 360.   CS-2

LESSON PLAN 17-4

OBJECTIVE 17-4
To count on by ones

Materials: TA 7 (Blank Hundred Chart) labeled 201-300; yellow crayons; base-ten blocks; counters, number cubes labeled 1-6

Grouping Suggestions: individual work, cooperative learning groups of 4

1. MOTIVATE AND TEACH

LEARN ABOUT IT

Practice counting on 3-digit numbers by starting a number chain. Begin with 331. Emphasize that you say *three hundred thirty-one;* not *three hundred* and *thirty-one.* Ask a student to say the next number, then call another student's name. That student says the next number and another student's name. Continue until all students have had a chance to say a number.

Call student's attention to the picture and first exercise at the top of page 359.
▶ **How are the numbers in the first two rows alike? How are they different?** (They have the same number of tens and ones; the second row has hundreds.)
▶ **In Exercise 5, what is the last number? Why does it have 3 places?** (Possible answers: 100; after 99, you need another place to show the next number; you trade 10 tens for 100.)
▶ **Why does the last number in Exercise 6 have 4 digits?** (Possible answer: 999 is the last hundreds number; you need another place to show the next number; you trade 10 hundreds for 1,000.)

2. CHECK UNDERSTANDING

ERROR ALERT Increasing the number by 100 instead of by 1, as in 725, <u>825</u>.

Name _____

Counting Patterns

... 23, 24, 25, 26, ...

Write the numbers as you count on. Follow the patterns.

1. 23, 24, 25, <u>26</u>, <u>27</u>, <u>28</u>, <u>29</u>

2. 723, 724, 725, <u>726</u>, <u>727</u>, <u>728</u>, <u>729</u>

---

3. 46, 47, 48, 49, <u>50</u>, <u>51</u>, <u>52</u>

4. 646, 647, 648, <u>649</u>, <u>650</u>, <u>651</u>, <u>652</u>

---

5. 94, 95, 96, 97, <u>98</u>, <u>99</u>, <u>100</u>

6. 994, 995, <u>996</u>, <u>997</u>, <u>998</u>, <u>999</u>, <u>1000</u>

---

7. 98, 99, 100, 101, <u>102</u>, <u>103</u>, <u>104</u>

8. 398, 399, <u>400</u>, <u>401</u>, <u>402</u>, <u>403</u>, <u>404</u>

9. 598, 599, <u>600</u>, <u>601</u>, <u>602</u>, <u>603</u>, <u>604</u>

Chapter 17   (three hundred fifty-nine) 3

TEACHING OPTIONS

RETEACHING TIPS Give students counters and a hundred chart showing 201-300. Have them place a counter on 227 and find the number that comes next by moving the counter one square to the right. (228) Continue counting by ones to 235. Assign Reteaching Supplement 148.

ENRICHMENT Family Math Have students and a family member fill a jar with 200-300 beans or other small objects. Students guess the number of beans before counting them. Then, have them count on or back by ones, tens, or hundreds from their guess to the actual number.

Write the numbers as you count on.

836, 837, __838__, __839__, __840__, __841__, __842__

118, 119, __120__, __121__, __122__, __123__, __124__

906, 907, __908__, __909__, __910__, __911__, __912__

594, 595, __596__, __597__, __598__, __599__, __600__

Count on from 198. Color a yellow path to the marble ring.

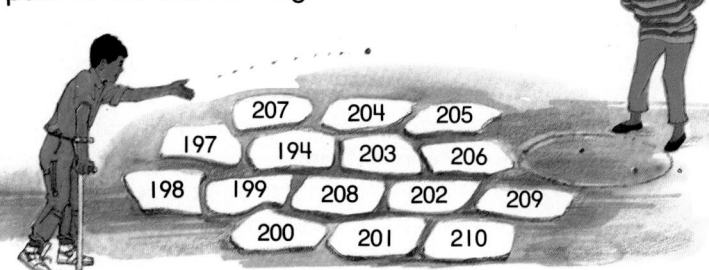

198, 199, 200, 201, 202, 203, 204, 205

SHOW WITH BLOCKS

Use blocks to show the numbers.

Put down 3 more tens. Count on for each ten. Write the numbers.

255	382	970
265	392	980
275	402	990
285	412	1,000

7. Pick up 3 tens. Count back for each ten. Write the numbers.

441	780	285
451	790	295
461	800	305
471	810	315

---

3. PRACTICE AND APPLY

Basic	All
Average	All
Extended	All

PRACTICE

Call students' attention to Exercise 5 on page 360. *What will happen in the hundreds place as you count on from 198?* (After 199, you must start with a new hundred, or 200.)

APPLY

SHOW WITH OBJECTS ► **How are the counting patterns different in Exercises 6 and 7 from the patterns in Exercises 1-5?** (They show counting on and back by tens instead of by ones.)
► **In the middle column of Exercise 6, how did you get from 392 to the next number?** (by adding a ten and trading 10 tens for 1 hundred to get 402)
► **In counting on from which number in Exercise 6 did you have to trade two times?** (from 990 to 1,000: trading tens and hundreds)

17-4

CLOSE AND ASSESS

SHOW WHAT YOU KNOW

Provide groups of 4 with base-ten blocks and 3 number cubes labeled 1-6. One student rolls the cubes and arranges them to make a 3-digit number. The second models the number with blocks. The third writes the next 3 numbers, counting on by ones, and the fourth writes the next 3 numbers, counting on by tens.

QUICK QUIZ

Complete the patterns.
567, 568, _(569)_, _(570)_, _(571)_
798, _(799)_, _(800)_, 801, _(802)_
457, 467, _(477)_, _(487)_, _(497)_

Modeling and Writing Numbers Before, After, and Between

OBJECTIVE 17-5   To model and write numbers before, after, or between

PREBOOK ACTIVITIES

QUICK REVIEW

Write the number that is one more and the number that is one less.
35 52 63 19 24   (34, 36; 51, 53; 62, 64; 18, 20; 23, 25)
89 77 30 13 26   (88, 90; 76, 78; 29, 31; 12, 14; 25, 27)

PRIOR KNOWLEDGE

Help students recall writing numbers before, after, and between. *If you know one number, how can you find the number that comes after?* (Possible answers: Add 1; count on 1; say the next number.) *How can you find the number that comes before?* (Possible answers: Subtract 1; count back 1.) *How can you find the number that is between two other numbers?* (Possible answers: Count on or add 1 from the first number; count back or subtract 1 from the last number.) *Why do you think you can find 3-digit numbers before, after, and between the same way?* (Possible answer: 3-digit numbers have the same patterns as 2-digit numbers, so the strategies are the same.)

COMMUNICATION

Writing in Math   Write the following number sequence on the chalkboard: 76, 77, 78, 79, 80, 81. Tell students to use the words **before, after,** and **between** to complete each sentence in their Math Journals.
1. The number 77 is _(before)_ 78.
2. The number that comes _(after)_ 76 is 77.
3. The number 79 is _(after)_ 78.
4. The number 80 is _(between)_ 79 and 81.

EXPLORE AND CONNECT

Materials: base-ten blocks, TA7 (Blank Hundred Chart) labeled 201–300; peephole cards (3-by-5 cards with hole cut i center just large enough to show one number)
Grouping Suggestion: pairs
Provide each pair of students with base-ten blocks, a hundred chart, and a peephole card. One student moves the peephole card to show one number on the hundreds chart and models t number with base-ten blocks. The partner must add a unit, pu it back and then take away a unit to show the numbers **befor** and **after.** The peephole card is removed to check the student work. Have students switch roles and repeat the activity. Encourage students to treat each other with respect as they work cooperatively.

CONNECTIONS   Use these anytime.

Problem of the Day

Logic   Sarina's book came apart. After page 182 came page 187. How many pages were missing? (4) How did you find out? (Possible answer: by counting on from 182, then counting only the numbers between 182 and 187: 183, 184, 185, 186)

Subject Integration

Language Arts   Work with a partner. Pick a word in the dictionary. Write down the word, what it means, and the page you found it on. Ask your partner to find your mystery word. Give a clue about where to find the word by telling the page that comes before or after. Then give a clue telling what the word means. Take turns.

Life Skills

Money   Use punchout coins. Make a money collection that totals less than $1.00. Write the amount of the collection. Now add a penny. What is the new amount? Take a penny away from your original amount. What is the new amount? What amount is between the two new amounts? Write the amounts from least to greatest.

CLASSWORK AND HOMEWORK SUPPLEMENTS

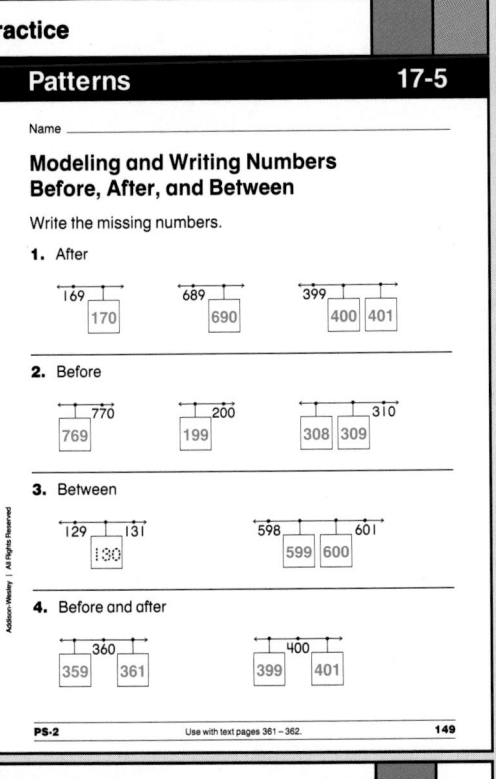

Practice

Patterns   17-5

Name _____

Modeling and Writing Numbers Before, After, and Between

Write the missing numbers.

1. After

| 169 | → 170 | | 689 | → 690 | | 399 | → 400 | 401 |

2. Before

| 769 | 770 | | 199 | 200 | | 308 | 309 | 310 |

3. Between

| 129 | 130 | 131 | | 598 | 599 | 600 | 601 |

4. Before and after

| 359 | 360 | 361 | | 399 | 400 | 401 |

PS-2   Use with text pages 361 – 362.   149

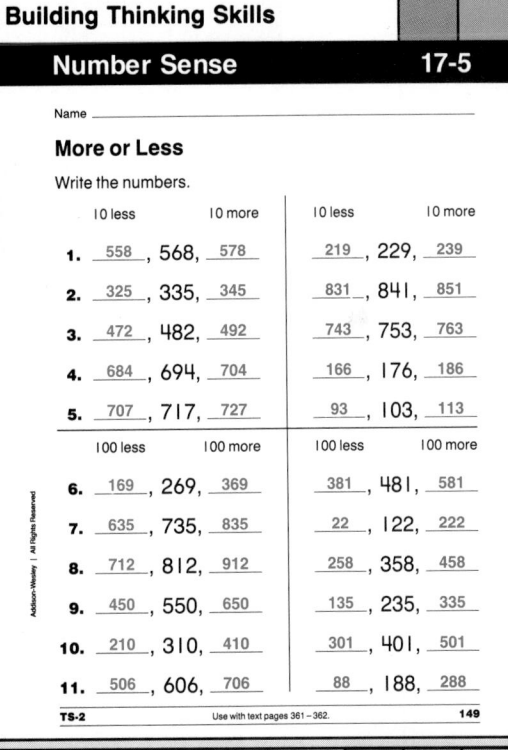

Building Thinking Skills

Number Sense   17-5

Name _____

More or Less

Write the numbers.

	10 less		10 more		10 less		10 more
1.	558	568,	578		219	229,	239
2.	325	335,	345		831	841,	851
3.	472	482,	492		743	753,	763
4.	684	694,	704		166	176,	186
5.	707	717,	727		93	103,	113

	100 less		100 more		100 less		100 more
6.	169	269,	369		381	481,	581
7.	635	735,	835		22	122,	222
8.	712	812,	912		258	358,	458
9.	450	550,	650		135	235,	335
10.	210	310,	410		301	401,	501
11.	506	606,	706		88	188,	288

TS-2   Use with text pages 361 – 362.   149

Reteaching

Manipulatives   17-5

Name _____

Modeling and Writing Numbers Before, After, and Between

218	**219**	**220**
218 comes before 219.	219 comes between 218 and 220.	220 comes after 219.

Show the number in the box with place value blocks.
Take away a one. It is the number that comes **before**.
Put the one back. Now add one more.
It is the number that comes **after**.

	Before			**After**	
1.	126 (one less than 127)	**127**		128 (one more than 127)	
2.	234	**235**		236	
3.	428	**429**		430	
4.	189	**190**		191	

5. Tell what number comes between the numbers you wrote.

RS-2   Use with text pages 361 – 362.   149

Challenges

Family Math   17-5

Name _____

Before, After, Between

> Dear Family,
> Your child is learning about 3-digit numbers. Play this game to review numbers before, after, and between.

Make cards for each of these numbers:
    355 through 375.
Shuffle and deal the cards.
The player with card 365 goes first.

Play continues around the table until all cards are played.

CS-2   Use with text pages 361 – 362.   149

17-5

OBJECTIVE 17-5
To model and write numbers before, after, or between

Materials: base-ten blocks, number cards for 231-235; index cards labeled *before, after;* 3-digit number cards

Grouping Suggestions: individual work, pairs

1. MOTIVATE AND TEACH

LEARN ABOUT IT

Write a series of 3-digit numbers on the chalkboard, such as 741, 742, 743, 744, 745. Have students tell which number comes after 741, which number comes before 744, and which numbers are between 742 and 745. (742; 743; 743, 744)

Ask students to look at the books at the top of page 361.

▶ **Which digits stay the same in the first pair of numbers? Which digit changes? Why?** (The hundreds and tens stay the same; the ones change because the next number is 1 more.)

▶ **Why are all 3 digits different in the second pair of numbers?** (200 is the first number in a new hundred.)

▶ **How can you use blocks to show the number that comes after? before?** (Add one block to show the number that comes after, take away one block to show the number that comes before.)

▶ **In Exercise 7, how can you show the numbers that come between?** (Add one block to the first number, take away one block from the last number.)

2. CHECK UNDERSTANDING

ERROR ALERT Writing the number *after* when asked for the number *before*.

Name _____

Modeling and Writing Numbers
Before, After, and Between

Use blocks to show each page number.

Show and write the number that comes after.

1. 314 | 315   2. 469 | 470   3. 299 | 300

Show and write the number that comes before.

4. 203 | 204   5. 399 | 400   6. 329 | 330

Show and write the numbers that come between.

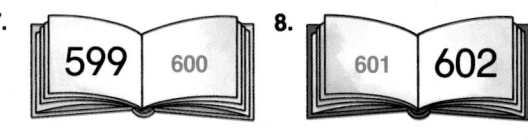

7. 599 | 600   8. 601 | 602

Chapter 17   (three hundred sixty-one) 361

TEACHING OPTIONS

RETEACHING TIPS Use cards for 231-235. Have students read the numbers aloud, model the last one with blocks, and place the blocks below 235. Next, they remove 1 unit, move the blocks 1 number to the left, and say the number that comes before. (234) Assign Reteaching Supplement 149.

ENRICHMENT Place 3 *before* and 2 *after* cards in one pile, and 10 3-digit number cards in another. Students take turns drawing 1 card from each pile and naming the number that comes before or after. If correct, they keep the number card. If not, the card goes to the bottom of the pile.

Write the numbers that come after, before, or between. Use blocks to check.

 after 304, <u>305</u>, <u>306</u>   412, <u>413</u>, <u>414</u>

278, <u>279</u>, <u>280</u>   599, <u>600</u>, <u>601</u>

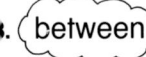 before <u>245</u> <u>246</u>, 247   <u>383</u>, <u>384</u>, 385

<u>189</u>, <u>190</u>, 191   <u>399</u>, <u>400</u>, 401

between 462, <u>463</u>, <u>464</u>, 465

649, <u>650</u>, <u>651</u>, 652

398, <u>399</u>, <u>400</u>, 401

MIDCHAPTER REVIEW/QUIZ

Write the number of hundreds, tens, and ones.

Hundreds	Tens	Ones
2	1	4

2.

Hundreds	Tens	Ones
3	0	5

How many are there? Write the number.

450
beads

Write the numbers as you count on.

4. 739, <u>740</u>, <u>741</u>   5. 998, <u>999</u>, <u>1,000</u>

---

3. PRACTICE AND APPLY

Basic	All; Midchapter Review/Quiz
Average	All; Midchapter Review/Quiz
Extended	All; Midchapter Review/Quiz

PRACTICE

How can you use blocks to check your answers to the exercises at the top of page 362? (Model the number given and add blocks to check after and between, or subtract blocks to check before.)

APPLY

▶ **In what other ways could you check your answers to the exercises?** (Possible answers: Use a hundred chart or number line; use a big book and look at the page numbers.)

MIDCHAPTER REVIEW/QUIZ

ITEM ANALYSIS The table correlates the Midchapter Review/Quiz items with the lesson objectives.

Items	Objectives
1-2	17-1
3	17-3
4-5	17-4

17-5

CLOSE AND ASSESS

SHOW WHAT YOU KNOW

Have student pairs make a tic-tac-toe grid. One partner writes a 3-digit number in the middle square. Students then take turns writing numbers in the squares, trying to complete a row with numbers in sequence. Remind students to be polite while working together.

QUICK QUIZ

Write the number that comes before, after, or between.
782, <u>(783)</u> <u>(684)</u>, 685
423, <u>(424)</u>, 425
899, <u>(900)</u> 598, <u>(599)</u>, 600

Problem Solving: Understanding the Operations/Mental Math

OBJECTIVE 17-6 To understand the operations of addition, subtraction, and multiplication by putting together or

PREBOOK ACTIVITIES

QUICK REVIEW

Write the number of hundreds, tens, and ones for each number.
375 (3 hundreds, 7 tens, 5 ones)
609 (6 hundreds, 0 tens, 9 ones)
750 (7 hundreds, 5 tens, 0 ones)
419 (4 hundreds, 1 ten, 9 ones)
 29 (0 hundreds, 2 tens, 9 ones)

PRIOR KNOWLEDGE

Tell students to imagine that they have a sticker collection. Ask them to pretend that each of the following situations happens. Have students tell whether they could use an addition, subtraction, multiplication, or division sentence to describe the situation.
1. You buy 4 pages of stickers with 5 stickers on each page. (multiplication)
2. You shared your stickers equally with 3 of your friends. (division)
3. You get 2 more stickers in a cereal box. (addition)
4. You compare the number of stickers you and your friends have. (subtraction)

COMMUNICATION

Listening in Math Have students listen as you say each set of numbers. Have them say the next number in the pattern.
1. 10, 20, 30, 40, _(50)_
2. 44, 54, 64, 74, _(84)_
3. 16, 26, 36, 46, _(56)_
4. 89, 79, 69, 59, _(49)_
5. 52, 42, 32, 22, _(12)_

EXPLORE AND CONNECT

COOPERATIVE ACTIVITY

Grouping Suggestion: Small groups
Choose and finish the correct number sentences.
Florrie invites 3 friends to her house.
She gives each of her friends 4 fuzzy stickers.
How many fuzzy stickers does Florrie give away?
$3 + 4 =$ _____ $3 \times 4 =$ _(12)_ $4 - 3 =$ _____

TEACHING ACTIONS

BEFORE ▶ **Describe what is happening in the story.** (Florrie gives her friends some stickers.)
▶ **Find the important data in the story.** (There are 3 friends; each friend gets 4 stickers.)

DURING ▶ **Which number sentence is correct? How do you know?** ($3 \times 4 =$ _____; the story asks how many Florrie gives away, so you have to mulitply the number of friends by the number of stickers she gave each friend.)
▶ **Which calculation method would you choose to solve the number sentence: blocks, paper and pencil, calculator or mental math? Explain your answer.** (Answers will vary. Discuss students' choices.)

AFTER ▶ **What sentence can you give to answer the question in the story?** (Possible answer: Florrie gave away 12 stickers.)
▶ **How can you check your answer?** (Possible answers: Use a turnaround multiplication sentence or repeated addition sentence; use another calculation method.)
Have students work in small groups to solve the problem.

CONNECTIONS   Use these anytime.

Problem of the Day

Logic Lauren is saving her money to buy a new doll that costs $5.00. She has $3.75 already. If she saves 10¢ a day, in how many days will she have enough to buy the doll? (13)

Minute Math

Multiplication Write the problems and answers to these multiplication facts. How many can you solve in 1 min?

3	5	2	4	3	2	5
×2	×3	×4	×2	×3	×5	×4
(6)	(15)	(8)	(8)	(9)	(10)	(20)

4	2	5	6	2	3	7
×4	×3	×2	×2	×7	×5	×2
(16)	(6)	(10)	(12)	(14)	(15)	(14)

Math Connection

Money Use punchout dimes to solve. Brandon earns 10¢ for every newspaper he sells. He sold 9 papers on Sunday and 5 papers on Monday. How much more money did he earn on Sunday? (40¢)

•y comparing; to use mental math to count on and back by tens

CLASSWORK AND HOMEWORK SUPPLEMENTS

Basic

Exercises All
Calculator Bank, p. 401
More Practice, p. 430, set B

Supplements
Reteaching 150 or
Practice 150

Practice

Patterns   17-6

Name _____

Mental Math

Count on or back by tens.
Write the missing numbers.

1.
244
254
264
274
284

2.
349
359
369
379
389

3.
506
516
526
536
546

4.
260
270
280
290
300

5.
636
646
656
666
676
686
696

6.
397
407
417
427
437
447
457

7.
755
765
775
785
795
805
815

8.
472
482
492
502
512
522
532

150   Use with text page 364.   PS-2

Building Thinking Skills

Mental Math   17-6

Name _____

Think Fast

Count on or back by tens or hundreds to solve.
Write the answers.

1. 237 people were on the plane. 30 people got off in Kansas City. How many people were left on the plane?

   __207__ people

2. 186 people were on the plane. 20 more people got on in Denver. How many people were on the plane then?

   __206__ people

3. Two planes left for Miami. One plane had 345 people, the other had 300 people. How many people went to Miami in all?

   __645__ people

4. 550 people bought tickets to New York. 300 people bought tickets to Los Angeles. How many more people were going to New York?

   __250__ people

5. If a jet can travel 500 miles in one hour, how many miles can it travel in 2 hours?

   __1,000__ miles

6. From Boston it is 400 miles to Buffalo and 551 miles to Cleveland. How much farther is it to Cleveland?

   __151__ miles

150   Use with text pages 363 – 364.   TS-2

Average

Exercises All
Calculator Bank, p. 401
More Practice, p. 430, set B

Supplements
Practice 150
Challenges 150 or
Thinking Skills 150

Reteaching

Problem Solving   17-6

Name _____

Understanding the Operations

$144 + 3 =$ ___ $80 - 32 =$ ___

Use mental math.   Use paper and pencil.

(144, 145, 146, 147)

Ring and finish the correct number sentence.
Use mental math or paper and pencil to solve.
Write the answer.

1. 156 oranges were in the bag. Gary picked 3 more and put them in. How many oranges were in the bag then?

   (Find the total.)

   ($156 + 3 = 159$)
   $156 - 3 =$

   __159__ oranges

2. 40 trees had red apples and 26 trees had yellow apples. How many more trees had red apples?

   (Compare.)

   $40 + 26 =$
   ($40 - 26 = 14$)

   __14__ more red

3. There were 4 bunches of bananas. Each bunch had 5 bananas. How many bananas were there in all?

   $5 + 4 =$
   ($5 \times 4 = 20$)

   __20__ bananas

150   Use with text page 363.   RS-2

Challenges

Problem Solving   17-6

Name _____

Play Time

Decide which operation you will use.
Choose a calculation method and solve.
Write the answer in a sentence.

Word sentences and calculation methods may vary. Sample answers shown.

1. The Hawks scored 32 points in the first half of the basketball game. They scored 28 points in the second half. What was the total score?

   addition, mental math, $32 + 28 = 60$
   The total score was 60 points.

2. 80 students signed up for soccer. 50 students signed up for softball. How many more students will play soccer?

   subtraction, mental math, $80 - 50 = 30$
   30 more students will play soccer.

3. 20 children ran in relay races. There were 4 teams. How many children were on each team?

   division, blocks, $20 \div 4 = 5$
   There were 5 children on each team.

4. 240 fans watched the game. The gym has 300 seats in all. How many seats were empty?

   subtraction, calculator, $300 - 240 = 60$
   60 seats were empty.

150   Use with text pages 363 – 364.   CS-2

Extended

Exercises All
Calculator Bank, p. 401

Supplements
Challenges 150
Thinking Skills 150

Other Resources:
Mathematics Their Way, pp. 307-309
Mathematics Book A, pp. 32-33
Explorations, pp. 277-278, 280-281, 292, 299, 342, 345

17-6

OBJECTIVE 17-6

To understand the operations of addition, subtraction, and multiplication by putting together or by comparing; to use mental math to count on and back by tens

Materials: base-ten blocks, calculators, TA7 (Blank Hundred Chart)

1. MOTIVATE AND TEACH

LEARN ABOUT IT

 **BEFORE** ► **Read Exercise 1. Describe what is happening in the story.**
(Jake has 197 pennies and gets 3 more.)

 **DURING** ► **Describe and explain your plan for solving the problem.** (Possible answer: Use mental math to count on 3 more from 197.)
► **Why might your plan be different for the other problems on the page?** (Possible answer: How you solve each problem will depend on the numbers and operations involved.)

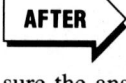 **AFTER** ► **How can you check your answers?** (Read the problem again and make sure the answer sentence makes sense.)

2. CHECK UNDERSTANDING

ERROR ALERT **Page 363**
Choosing the incorrect operation and number sentence to solve a problem.
Page 364 Failing to see the counting-on-10 and counting-back-10 patterns in the chart.

Name _____

Problem Solving
Understanding the Operations

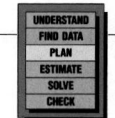

Use blocks, paper and pencil, mental math, or to solve. Ring and finish the correct number sentence. Write the answer in a sentence.

Calculation methods may vary.
Word sentences may vary.
Sample answers are shown.

1. Jake collects coins. He has 197 pennies. How many will Jake have if he gets 3 more?

    $\boxed{197 + 3 =}$ ___200___

    $197 - 3 =$ _____

    Jake will have 200 pennies.

2. Jake has a book of silver dollars. The book has 5 pages. There are 4 silver dollars on each page. How many silver dollars are in the book?

    $5 + 4 =$ _____

    $\boxed{5 \times 4 =}$ ___20___

    There are 20 silver dollars in the book.

3. Jake has 80 nickels and 60 dimes. How many more nickels than dimes does he have?

    $80 + 60 =$ _____

    $\boxed{80 - 60 =}$ ___20___

    He has 20 more nickels.

Chapter 17   More Practice, page 430, set B   (three hundred sixty-three) 36

TEACHING OPTIONS

RETEACHING TIPS Have students write 347 and model it with base-ten blocks. Students add ten-sticks and record the new numbers, one at a time, until they reach 397. Count back by tens to check. For help in problem solving, use Reteaching Supplement 150.

ENRICHMENT On a blank hundred chart, have students write the numbers starting with 10 and ending with 1,000, counting by 10s. Start by completing the top row from 10 to 100 and the bottom row from 910 to 1,000. Then finish the chart.

Mental Math

Count on or back by 10s. Write the missing numbers in the yellow boxes.

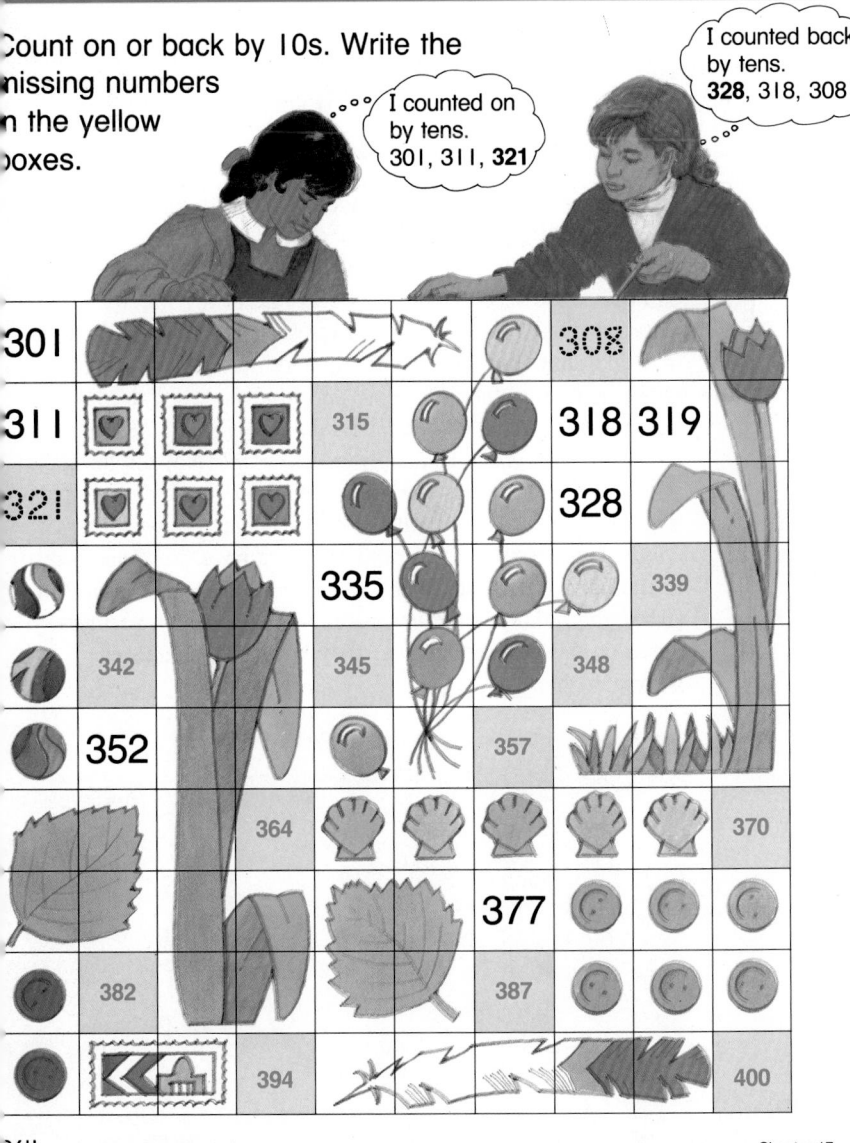

I counted on by tens.
301, 311, **321**

I counted back by tens.
328, 318, 308

301					**308**	
311			315		**318**	**319**
321					**328**	
		335			339	
	342		345		348	
352				357		
		364				370
			377			
	382			387		
		394				400

364 (three hundred sixty-four)

Chapter 17

3. PRACTICE AND APPLY

Basic	All
Average	All
Extended	All

Direct students' attention to the number chart on page 364. How will you decide which numbers go in the boxes? (Look at the numbers above or below the number and count on or back by tens.)
▶ **What do you have to do to complete the number chart?** (Fill in the missing numbers in the yellow boxes.)
▶ **How can mental math help you find the missing numbers?** (Possible answer: You can look at the numbers above or below the yellow box, then count on or back by tens to identify the missing number.)
▶ **How can you examine your chart to make sure your answers are correct?** (Possible answer: Count by ones from 301 to 400 to see if the numbers are correct.)

17-6

CLOSE AND ASSESS

SHOW WHAT YOU KNOW
Write the following exercises on the chalkboard: 45 + 28, 319 + 2, 90 − 20, 3 × 2. Have students choose mental math, pencil and paper, calculator, or base-ten blocks to solve each one. Ask students to share their answers and calculation methods for solving the exercises. Have students make up stories to match.

QUICK QUIZ

Jake and Louise compare their coin collections. Jake has 75 buffalo nickels; Louise has 45. How many more buffalo nickels does Jake have? (30)

LESSON OPTIONS 17-7

Comparing 3-Digit Numbers

OBJECTIVE 17-7   To compare 3-digit numbers using > and <

PREBOOK ACTIVITIES

PRIOR KNOWLEDGE

Help students recall what they know about comparing 2-digit numbers. *How can you find the number that is greater?* (Look at the tens place. The number with more tens is greater. If both have the same number of tens, the number with more ones is greater.) *What symbols do you use to compare numbers?* (> and <) Write the symbols > and < on the chalkboard. *How do you know which way to place the symbol?* (Possible answers: The open side of the symbol faces the larger number; the pointed side points to the smaller number.) *Do you think 3-digit numbers might be compared in the same way as 2-digit numbers? Why?* (Accept all reasonable answers.)

COMMUNICATION

Discussing and Writing Math   Ask students to tell about times when they have compared 2-digit numbers. *Can you think of times when you might need to compare 3-digit numbers?* Help students brainstorm by offering topics such as comparing money amounts; comparing boys and girls in school; and comparing collections of marbles, stamps, or stickers. Have students choose one topic and draw a captioned illustration.

EXPLORE AND CONNECT

Materials: base-ten blocks, index cards with 3-digit numbers
Grouping Suggestion: pairs
Provide each pair of students with base-ten blocks and 2 number cards. Each student models one of the numbers with base-ten blocks. Students place the cards one below the other, with like units aligned. They compare models by looking first at the hundreds, then the tens, and finally ones if necessary. *If one number has more hundreds, does it matter which number has more tens and ones? Why or why not?* (No, the number with more hundreds is the greater number, because hundreds have the highest place value.) *When would you have to compare the tens?* (when both numbers have the same number in the hundreds place) *When would you have to compare ones?* (when the hundreds and tens are the same) When partners agree on the greater number, they write two sentences: _____ is greater than _____; _____ is less than _____.

CONNECTIONS   Use these anytime.

Problem of the Day

Draw a picture   I am a 3-digit number with 3 different digits. All my digits are written with straight lines only. My tens digit is greater than my hundreds digit but less than my ones digit. What number am I? (147)

Number Sense

Estimation   Look at this jar of beans. How many beans do you think there are? Write your guess on a piece of paper. Compare your guess with a neighbor. Which guess is higher? Compare with other neighbors. Which guess is highest of all? Which is the lowest? Count the beans. Which guess was closest?

Math Connection

Numeration   How many different comparisons can you make with these numbers? Use the symbols > and <.
314   355   426
(314 < 355, 355 > 314, 314 < 426, 426 > 314, 355 < 426, 426 > 355)

CLASSWORK AND HOMEWORK SUPPLEMENTS

Basic

Exercises All
More Practice, p. 431, set A

Supplements
Reteaching 151 or
Practice 151
Thinking Skills 151

Average

Exercises All
More Practice, p. 431, set A

Supplements
Practice 151
Challenges 151 or
Thinking Skills 151

Extended

Exercises All

Supplements
Challenges 151
Thinking Skills 151

Other Resources:
Mathematics Their Way, pp. 311-312
Explorations, pp. 255-256, 263, 302
Problem Solving Experiences In Mathematics, p. 144
Using the Math Explorer Calculator: A Source Book for Teachers, Chapter 14

Practice

Number Sense — 17-7

Name ____

Comparing 3-Digit Numbers

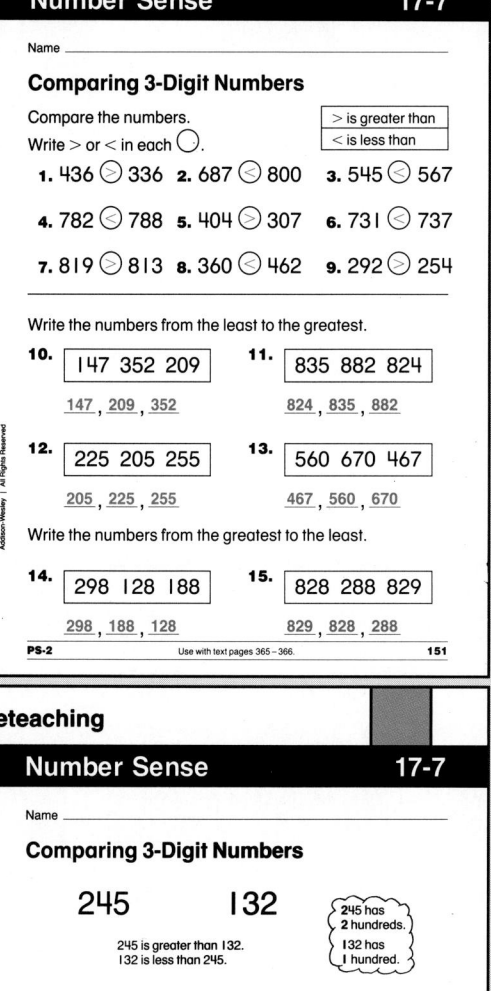

Building Thinking Skills

Critical Thinking — 17-7

Name ____

Heavy Weights

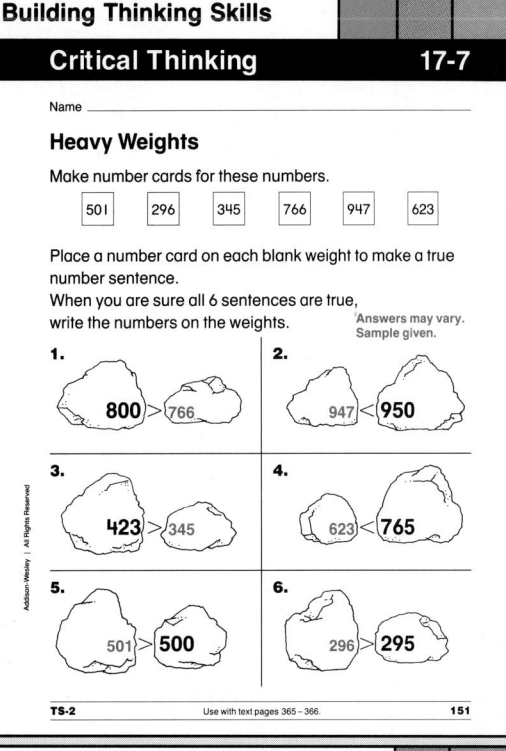

Reteaching

Number Sense — 17-7

Name ____

Comparing 3-Digit Numbers

Challenges

Cooperative Activities — 17-7

Name ____

Graph-a-Game

17-7

Chapter 17 Lesson 7 **365B**

OBJECTIVE 17-7

To compare 3-digit numbers using > and <

Materials: base-ten blocks, sand, small shallow boxes, index cards with 3-digit numbers, 1-in. by 4-in. paper strips

Alternative Materials: salt, sugar

Grouping Suggestions: pairs, individual work, cooperative learning groups of 3

---

1. MOTIVATE AND TEACH

LEARN ABOUT IT

Give each pair of students a shallow box with sand covering the bottom, and two 3-digit number cards. Have students write the numbers in the sand. Then ask them to shape their hands like an open mouth with the open mouth facing the greater number. Have one student trace the sign in the sand between the two numbers while the partner checks. Ask them to read the sentence two ways, using > in one sentence and < in the other. Direct students' attention to the top of page 365.

▶ **How can you compare the two numbers?** (Look at the place of greatest value, the hundreds.)

▶ **Why can two sentences be written about the same two numbers?** (One sentence tells which number is greater, the other tells which number is less.)

▶ **In Exercises 2 and 3, why do you compare tens or ones to find the answer?** (You compare hundreds first, then the tens if the hundreds are the same, then the ones if the hundreds and the tens are the same.)

▶ **For which exercise are the numbers closest in value? Why?** (The numbers are closest in Exercise 3 because the number of hundreds and tens are equal; the difference between the numbers is only some ones.)

2. CHECK UNDERSTANDING

ERROR ALERT Reversing the inequality symbol.

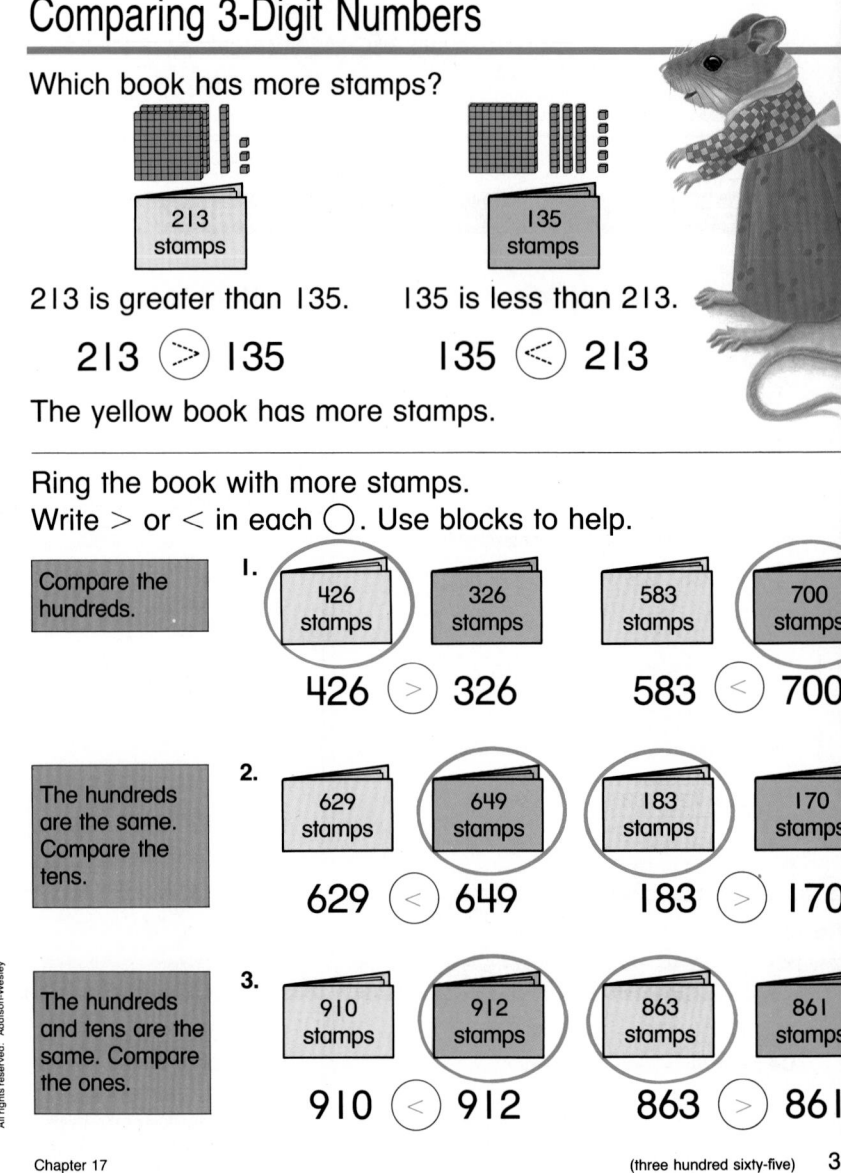

Name _____

Comparing 3-Digit Numbers

Which book has more stamps?

213 stamps   135 stamps

213 is greater than 135.   135 is less than 213.

213 ⊙> 135   135 ⊙< 213

The yellow book has more stamps.

Ring the book with more stamps.
Write > or < in each ◯. Use blocks to help.

Compare the hundreds.

1. 426 stamps   326 stamps   583 stamps   700 stamps

426 ⃝> 326   583 ⃝< 700

The hundreds are the same. Compare the tens.

2. 629 stamps   649 stamps   183 stamps   170 stamps

629 ⃝< 649   183 ⃝> 170

The hundreds and tens are the same. Compare the ones.

3. 910 stamps   912 stamps   863 stamps   861 stamps

910 ⃝< 912   863 ⃝> 861

Chapter 17   (three hundred sixty-five) 3

TEACHING OPTIONS

RETEACHING TIPS Use base-ten blocks and paper strips. Have students model and write 2 numbers, such as 752 and 757, and find the greater number. Students fold the paper strip, point it toward the smaller number, and say *Less than (<) points to the left*. Assign Reteaching Supplement 151.

ENRICHMENT Have students choose 4 digits and write as many different 3-digit numbers as they can using those 4 digits. Ask them to ring the greatest number on their list and draw a box around the smallest number. Finally, ask them to write the numbers in order from least to greatest.

Compare the numbers. Write > or < in each ◯.

1.
| 537 |
| 438 |

537 ⟨>⟩ 438

2.
| 730 |
| 750 |

730 ⟨<⟩ 750

3.
| 425 |
| 428 |

425 ⟨<⟩ 428

4.
| 659 |
| 509 |

659 ⟨>⟩ 509

5.
| 183 |
| 235 |

183 ⟨<⟩ 235

6.
| 213 |
| 225 |

213 ⟨<⟩ 225

7.
| 979 |
| 972 |

979 ⟨>⟩ 972

8.
| 611 |
| 618 |

611 ⟨<⟩ 618

Ring the greatest number in each box.

9.
683   ⟨917⟩   635

10.
734   ⟨786⟩   781

Ring the least number in each box.

11.
⟨335⟩   353   533

12.
200   ⟨198⟩   228

FIND THE DATA

13. **Data Hunt**   Find the number of
pages in your math book and in your reading
book. Write the numbers.
Which book has more pages? Ring it.
Answers may vary.

_____   _____

your math book   your reading book

CLOSE AND ASSESS

SHOW WHAT YOU KNOW
Review with students the chapter
story. *Suppose there are 3 quilts. One
quilt has 135 squares, the second has
227 squares, and the third has 214
squares. Which quilt has the most
squares? Which has the fewest
squares?* Have students use base-ten
blocks to find the answer.

QUICK QUIZ

Complete each sentence with < or >.
357 ◯ 425   (<)   583 ◯ 783   (<)
631 ◯ 628   (>)   295 ◯ 289   (>)
247 ◯ 249   (<)   423 ◯ 420   (>)

---

3. PRACTICE AND APPLY

Basic	All
Average	All
Extended	All

PRACTICE

Have students look at Exercises 9 and 10
on page 366. *How will you find the
greatest number in each box?* (Compare
two numbers, then compare the greater
of those with the third number.)

APPLY

<u>FIND THE DATA</u>   ▶ **How might
you estimate which book contains
more pages?** (Possible answer: Look at
the thickness of each book.)
▶ **How can you find the actual
number of pages in your math and
reading books?** (Look at the last page
of each book.)
▶ **How could you find out how many
more pages the longer book has?**
(Possible answer: Count on from the
smaller number to the larger number.)

17-7

Counting Dollars and Cents

OBJECTIVE 17-8   To count money beyond $1

PREBOOK ACTIVITIES

QUICK REVIEW

Use coin punchouts. Write the total amount in cents.

1. 2 dimes	**2.** 1 dime	**3.** 2 dimes	**4.** 1 quarter
1 nickel	2 nickels	3 nickels	1 dime
2 pennies	4 pennies		2 nickels
(27¢)	(24¢)	(35¢)	(45¢)

PRIOR KNOWLEDGE

Help students recall counting groups of coins up to 99¢. Begin by holding up each coin and asking volunteers to identify the coin and state its value. *How do you count a group of coins?* (Group like coins together, then skip count by the value of the coin.) *In what order do you count a group of coins?* (from the coin of greatest value to the coin of least value)

COMMUNICATION

Reading and Discussing Math   Write the word **dollar** on the chalkboard. Read the word aloud with students. Next, show students a dollar bill (real or model). *This is a one-dollar bill. It is worth one dollar. One dollar is equal to 100 cents. How many pennies would you need to trade for one dollar?* (100) *How do you know?* (One dollar equals 100¢; each penny equals 1¢.) *How can you find out how many nickels you would need to trade for one dollar?* (Count by fives.) Have students count by the value of each coin to find out how many nickels, dimes, and quarters are needed to make one dollar. (20, 10, 4) *Does it take more dimes or quarters to make a dollar? Why?* (more dimes because dimes are worth less than quarters)

EXPLORE AND CONNECT

Materials: punchout money–dollar bills and coins; index card with money amounts between $1.00 and $2.00
Alternative Materials: TA14, TA15 (Play Money)
Grouping Suggestion: pairs

Write 100¢ = $1.00 on the chalkboard. Explain that for amounts of money more than 100¢, we use dollar bills and write the amount with a dollar sign ($) and a decimal point. Display a dollar bill and add a quarter to the amount. On the board write $1.25. *Which part shows the number of dollars?* (the number to the left of the decimal point) *Which part shows how many cents more?* (the numbers to the right) Read the amount aloud: *One dollar and twenty-five cents.* Next, provide each pair of students with coin and bill punchouts and a money amount card. Partners read the amount together and each models it with a bill and coins. Have students compare collections and check each other's work.

CONNECTIONS   Use these anytime.

Problem of the Day

Adding Money   Harry has 100¢. He earns 75¢ for raking the yard. How much does Harry have now? Write the amount in two ways. (175¢, $1.75)

Life Skills

Making Purchases   You have 1 dollar, 1 quarter, 2 dimes. Which thing can you buy? Use punchout money.

(the car or the book)

Math Connection

Place Value   Show these amounts using base-ten blocks.
1. 75¢   (7 tens, 5 ones)
2. $1.40   (1 hundred, 4 tens)
3. $1.05   (1 hundred, 5 ones)
4. $1.91   (1 hundred, 9 tens, 1 one)
5. $2.20   (2 hundreds, 2 tens)

CLASSWORK AND HOMEWORK SUPPLEMENTS

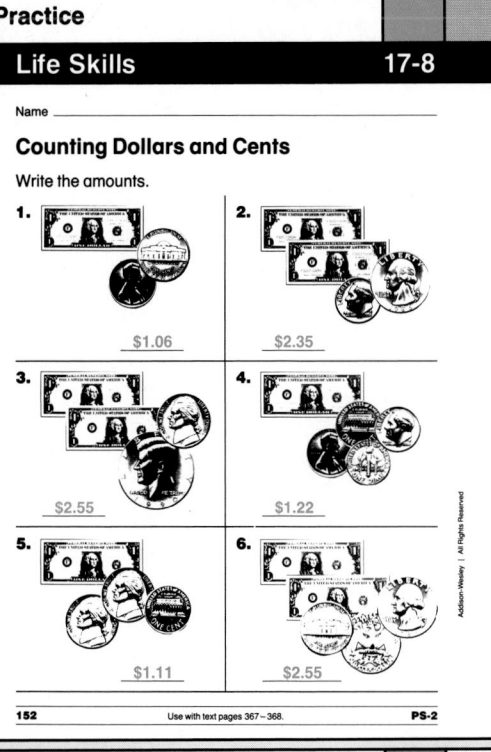

Practice

Life Skills 17-8

Name

Counting Dollars and Cents

Write the amounts.

1. $1.06
2. $2.35
3. $2.55
4. $1.22
5. $1.11
6. $2.55

152   Use with text pages 367–368.   PS-2

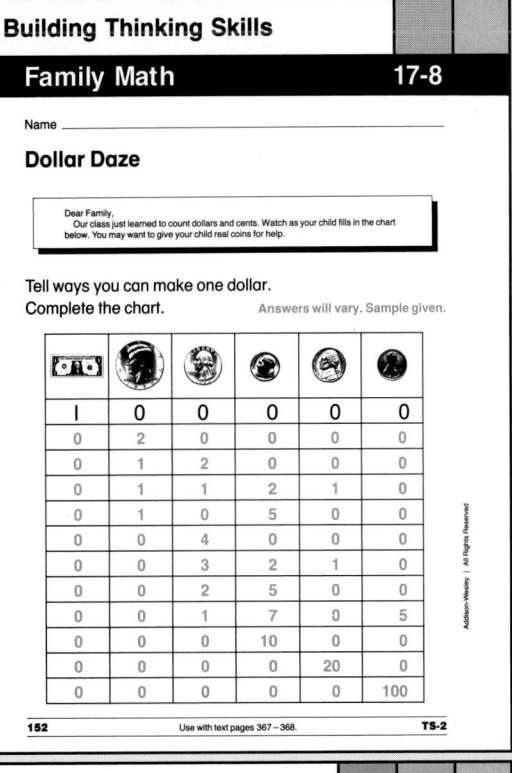

Building Thinking Skills

Family Math 17-8

Name

Dollar Daze

Dear Family,
Our class just learned to count dollars and cents. Watch as your child fills in the chart below. You may want to give your child real coins for help.

Tell ways you can make one dollar.
Complete the chart.   Answers will vary. Sample given.

$1	50¢	25¢	10¢	5¢	1¢
1	0	0	0	0	0
0	2	0	0	0	0
0	1	2	0	0	0
0	1	1	2	1	0
0	1	0	5	0	0
0	0	4	0	0	0
0	0	3	2	1	0
0	0	2	5	0	0
0	0	1	7	0	5
0	0	0	10	0	0
0	0	0	0	20	0
0	0	0	0	0	100

152   Use with text pages 367–368.   TS-2

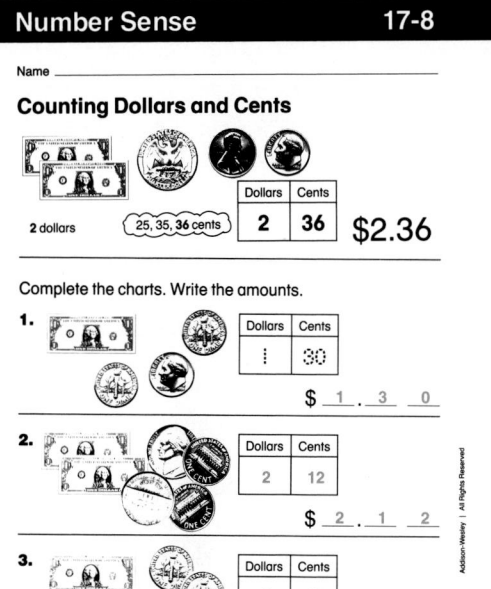

Reteaching

Number Sense 17-8

Name

Counting Dollars and Cents

2 dollars   25, 35, 36 cents | Dollars 2 | Cents 36 | $2.36

Complete the charts. Write the amounts.

1. | Dollars | Cents |
   | | 30 |
   $ 1 . 3 0

2. | Dollars | Cents |
   | 2 | 12 |
   $ 2 . 1 2

3. | Dollars | Cents |
   | 1 | 41 |
   $ 1 . 4 1

152   Use with text pages 367–368.   RS-2

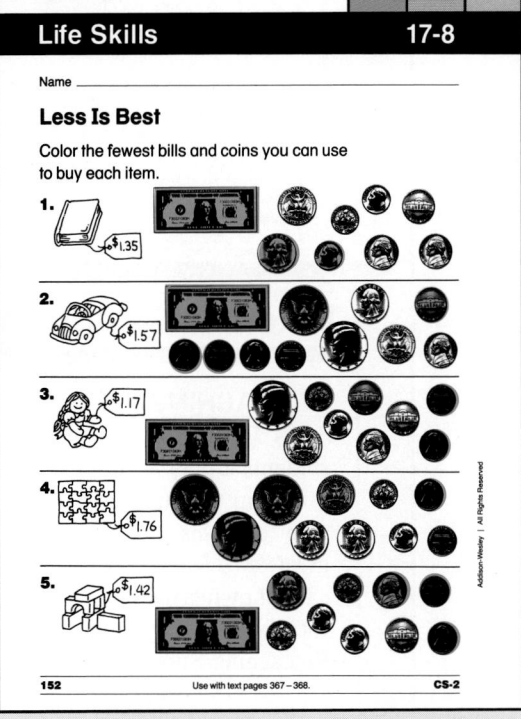

Challenges

Life Skills 17-8

Name

Less Is Best

Color the fewest bills and coins you can use to buy each item.

1. $1.35
2. $1.57
3. $1.17
4. $1.76
5. $1.42

152   Use with text pages 367–368.   CS-2

OPTIONS FOR INDIVIDUAL NEEDS

Basic

Exercises All, Mixed Review

Supplements
Reteaching 152 or
Practice 152
Challenges 152

Average

Exercises All, Mixed Review

Supplements
Practice 152
Challenges 152 or
Thinking Skills 152

Extended

Exercises All, Mixed Review

Supplements
Challenges 152
Thinking Skills 152

Other Resources:
Mathematics Their Way, pp. 312-313, 317
Explorations, pp. 235, 258-261
Problem Solving Experiences In Mathematics, pp. 119, 150

17-8

LESSON PLAN 17-8

OBJECTIVE 17-8
To count money beyond $1

> **Materials:** punchout bills and coins; paper bag; number cards 50, 25, 10, 5, 1; money amount cards, $1.00-$2.00
>
> **Alternative Materials:** TA14, TA15 (Play Money)
>
> **Grouping Suggestions:** individual work, cooperative learning groups of 3

1. MOTIVATE AND TEACH

LEARN ABOUT IT

Place some play money in a paper bag. Have students begin with a dollar, then draw one coin at a time from the bag and say each new total. For example, if the student draws a dime, the total would be one dollar and ten cents.
Have students look at the bills and coins at the top of page 367.
▶ **How can you find the total amount?** (Begin with the one-dollar bill, then count on the value of the coins, one coin at a time, beginning with the coins of the greatest value.)
▶ **Which amounts could you show using a dollar bill and only one coin?** ($1.25, a dollar and a quarter; $1.50, a dollar and a half-dollar)
▶ **Which amount could you show without using any coins?** ($2.00, 2 one-dollar bills)
▶ **Which coins could you use to equal a one-dollar bill?** (Possible answers: 2 half dollars; 1 half dollar and 5 dimes; 1 half dollar and 2 quarters)

2. CHECK UNDERSTANDING

ERROR ALERT Using the wrong value when skip counting coins.

Name _____

Counting Dollars and Cents

$1.00 or 100¢ — This is a one-dollar bill.

This is one dollar and 25 cents.

There a many w to show $1.25.

$1.25
dollars cents

Work in a group. Use this play money.

| 2 one-dollar bills | 2 half dollars | |
| 3 quarters | 5 dimes | 5 nickels |

Find two different ways to show each amount. Mark an X for each bill or coin you would use. Answers may vary. Sample answers are shown.

1.	$1.25	1st way	X			XX	X
		2nd way		XX	X		
2.	$1.50	1st way	X	X			
		2nd way			XXXX	XXXX	XX
3.	$1.75	1st way	X		XXX		
		2nd way	X	X	X		
4.	$2.00	1st way	X	XX			
		2nd way	X		XX	XXXX	XX

Chapter 17   (three hundred sixty-seven) 36

TEACHING OPTIONS

RETEACHING TIPS Label cards *50, 25, 10, 5,* and *1.* Give students a play $1 bill and coins and ask them to count the $1 bill first, then the coins in order of value, greatest to least. Have them place a card showing the coin's value under each coin as they count it. Assign Reteaching Supplement 152.

ENRICHMENT Have groups make a chart with headings *Less Than $1.00* and *More Than $1.00.* Have them cut pictures of items from newspapers and paste them under the appropriate headings. Have them choose 1 item and show the fewest money units they could use to buy it.

ount the money. Write each amount.

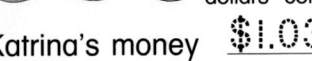

dollars cents

Katrina's money **$1.03**

2.

dollars cents

Nat's money ___$1.17___

dollars cents

Frieda's money ___$1.46___

4.

dollars cents

Dick's money ___$2.00___

. Who has enough money to buy the beads?
Ring the names.

Katrina   Nat   (Dick)   (Frieda)

 $1.30

Mixed Review

Add or subtract.

. $45 - 5 =$ _40_ $33 + 40 =$ _73_ $86 - 24 =$ _62_

. Ring the fraction that is colored.

       ⬤⬤⬤⬤⬤

$\frac{1}{3}$ $\left(\frac{1}{4}\right)$ $\frac{1}{6}$ $\left(\frac{1}{3}\right)$ $\frac{2}{3}$ $\frac{1}{2}$ $\frac{2}{3}$ $\left(\frac{3}{5}\right)$ $\frac{2}{5}$

---

3. Practice and Apply

Basic	All, Mixed Review
Average	All, Mixed Review
Extended	All, Mixed Review

PRACTICE

Have students examine the exercises on page 368. *What must you do before you can answer Exercise 5?* (Find the total amount for each person in Exercises 1-4.)

APPLY

▶ **In Exercise 1, why is there a zero to the right of the decimal point?** (Possible answer: to show that there are no tens in the amount of money)

▶ **Can you estimate an amount of money by just counting the number of coins? Why or why not?** (No, the coins' values are different. Each coin must be counted according to its value.)

▶ **When might you need to count money?** (Possible answers: to count money saved in a piggy bank; to count lunch or milk money in school; to count change)

MIXED REVIEW *How can you find the fractions in Exercise 7?* (Count the number of colored parts, then count the total number of parts.)

17-8

Close and Assess

SHOW WHAT YOU KNOW Give each group of 3 money amount cards and punchout money. Have one student choose a money amount card. The other two students each show a way to make the amount using coins or a bill and coins. The first student verifies the accuracy of the others' work by counting each amount.

QUICK QUIZ

Use punchouts to show the money.
Write the total amount.
1 dollar, 1 quarter, 2 dimes   ($1.45)
1 dollar, 1 half dollar,   ($1.50)
1 dollar, 3 quarters, 2 nickels   ($1.85)

Problem Solving: Writing a Story

OBJECTIVE 17-9   To solve problems by writing a story

PREBOOK ACTIVITIES

QUICK REVIEW

Write the sums.

40	60	20	10	70	80	50	30	40	50
+20	+10	+50	+70	+20	+10	+40	+20	+40	+30
(60)	(70)	(70)	(80)	(90)	(90)	(90)	(50)	(80)	(80)

PRIOR KNOWLEDGE

Write the following story on the chalkboard to help students recall solving addition problems.

Lucy did 20 sit-ups the first minute of the race.
She did 30 more the second minute.
How many sit-ups did Lucy do in all?

What words tell you that this problem can be solved using addition? Explain your answer. (*how many . . . in all;* because those words mean to combine, or join, two groups) *What other words are sometimes used when groups are to be added?* (Possible answers: *all together, total*) List students' responses on the chalkboard.

COMMUNICATION

Listening in Math   Ask students to place the following items on their desks: a pencil, a crayon, their math book, their reading book, and a ruler. Tell them to listen carefully and follow your directions. *Place the objects in a row. Place the math book first. Place the reading book second. Place the ruler third. Place the pencil fourth. Place the crayon last. Which words told you the order in which to arrange the objects?* (*first, second, third, fourth, last*)

EXPLORE AND CONNECT

COOPERATIVE ACTIVITY

Grouping Suggestion: small groups

Have students work in small groups to write a story for 20 + 50. One member can record the story that the group creates. Another can write the addition question for the story. A third can write the answer in a sentence. Encourage students to treat each other with respect as they check each other's writing.

TEACHING ACTIONS

 ► **What kind of story are you going to write?** (an addition story)
► **What data will you use to write the story?** (20 and 50)

 ► **What should you discuss as you plan your story?** (You should think of a situation for which you might need to add 20 and 50.)
► **Suppose you have 20 of one thing. What are some ways you might get 50 more?** (Possible answers: You might buy them, find them, save them, or get them as a gift.)
► **What are some phrases you could use in an addition question?** (Possible answers: *how many in all, how many now*)

 ► **How will you solve the problem?** (Use mental math or pencil and paper to add 20 + 50, then write the answer in a complete sentence.)
► **How can you check your story and answer?** (Possible answers: Read them to other groups and have them solve; use another calculation method.)

CONNECTIONS   Use these anytime.

Problem of the Day

Act It Out   Use pattern blocks. Arrange the blocks on your desk this way: The red block is first. The blue block is behind the yellow block. The green block is between the red block and the yellow block. The orange block is behind the blue block. Compare your block arrangements with a neighbor's to check.

Calculator

Logical Reasoning   Use the calculator keys ③, ④, ⑤, ⊠, ⊟, and ⊟. Use each key only once. Use no other key. Make your calculator read 17.
(4 × 5 − 3 =) or (5 × 4 − 3 =)

Subject Integration

Language Arts   Make up a fantasy story about a magic kingdom. Include an addition problem in your story. Illustrate your story, solve the addition problem, and display your story on a bulletin board to share with the class.

Problem Solving Strategy: Act It Out

To solve problems using the strategy Act It Out

CLASSWORK AND HOMEWORK SUPPLEMENTS

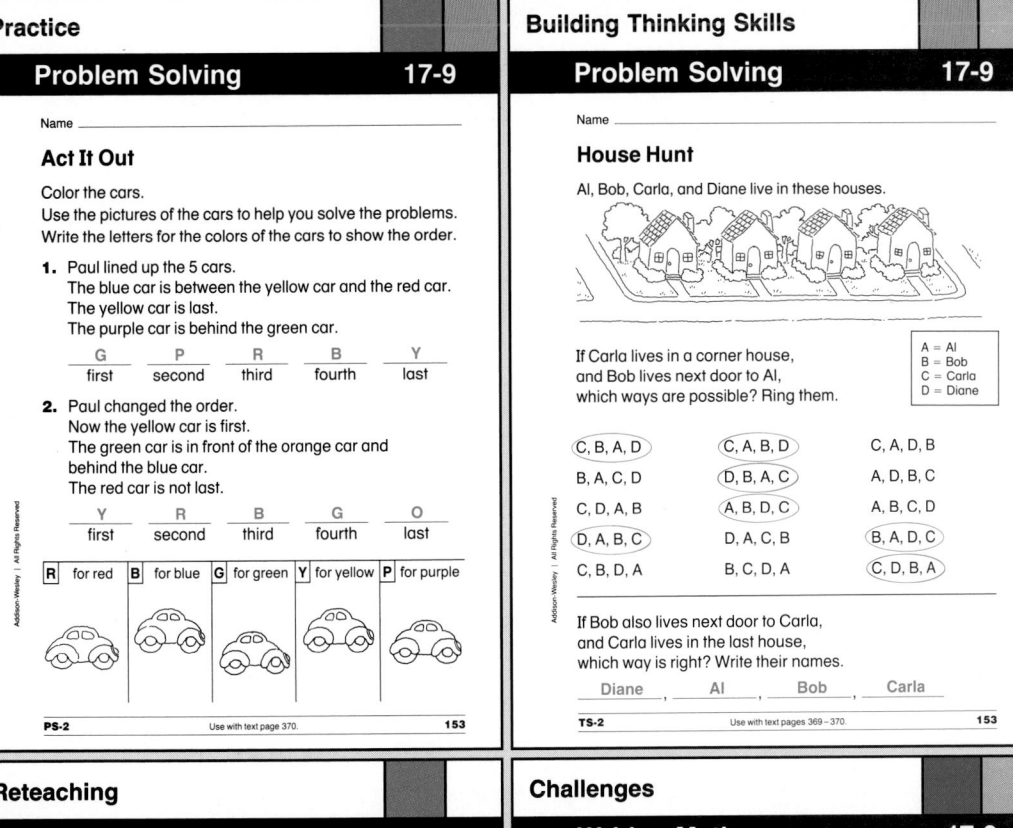

Practice

Problem Solving — 17-9

Name _____

Act It Out

Color the cars.
Use the pictures of the cars to help you solve the problems.
Write the letters for the colors of the cars to show the order.

1. Paul lined up the 5 cars.
   The blue car is between the yellow car and the red car.
   The yellow car is last.
   The purple car is behind the green car.

G	P	R	B	Y
first	second	third	fourth	last

2. Paul changed the order.
   Now the yellow car is first.
   The green car is in front of the orange car and behind the blue car.
   The red car is not last.

Y	R	B	G	O
first	second	third	fourth	last

   | R for red | B for blue | G for green | Y for yellow | P for purple |

PS-2   Use with text page 370.   153

Building Thinking Skills

Problem Solving — 17-9

Name _____

House Hunt

Al, Bob, Carla, and Diane live in these houses.

If Carla lives in a corner house,
and Bob lives next door to Al,
which ways are possible? Ring them.

A = Al
B = Bob
C = Carla
D = Diane

(C, B, A, D)	(C, A, B, D)	C, A, D, B
B, A, C, D	(D, B, A, C)	A, D, B, C
C, D, A, B	(A, B, D, C)	A, B, C, D
(D, A, B, C)	D, A, C, B	(B, A, D, C)
C, B, D, A	B, C, D, A	(C, D, B, A)

If Bob also lives next door to Carla,
and Carla lives in the last house,
which way is right? Write their names.

Diane ____ Al ____ Bob ____ Carla

TS-2   Use with text pages 369–370.   153

Reteaching

Problem Solving — 17-9

Name _____

Writing a Story

Finish writing the story for 20 + 30 = _____

1. Finish the sentence to tell how many shells Pat found.
2. Finish the sentence to tell how many shells Kate found.
3. Finish the question to ask how many shells they found in all.
4. Finish the answer sentence.

The Shell Story

Pat and Kate collected shells.

Pat found 20 shells

Kate found 30 shells

How many shells did they find in all ____?

They found 50 shells

RS-2   Use with text page 369.   153

Challenges

Writing Math — 17-9

Name _____

Choose Your Own

Choose one of the titles.   Stories will vary.
Write an addition story or a subtraction story.
Use 2-digit numbers.
Write question and answer sentences. Share your story.

| A Sticker Story | A Bus Trip Story |
| A Picnic | A Zoo Story |

CS-2   Use with text pages 369–370.   153

OPTIONS FOR INDIVIDUAL NEEDS

Basic

Exercises All
Computer Bank, pp. 405-408

Supplements
Reteaching 153 or
Practice 153

Average

Exercises All
Computer Bank, pp. 405-408

Supplements
Practice 153
Challenges 153 or
Thinking Skills 153

Extended

Exercises All
Computer Bank, pp. 405-408

Supplements
Challenges 153
Thinking skills 153

Other Resources:
Explorations, pp. 100,
135-136, 280, 292, 298, 342
*Problem Solving Experiences
In Mathematics,* pp. 77, 89,
107, 111-113, 125, 153
Mathematics Book A, pp.
15-16

17-9

OBJECTIVE 17-9

To solve problems by writing a story; to solve problems using the strategy Act It Out

Grouping Suggestions: individual work; small groups

1. MOTIVATE AND TEACH

LEARN ABOUT IT

BEFORE ▶ **What data will you use in your story?** (70 + 30)

DURING ▶ **How will you make sure that you write an addition story?** (Write about putting together 70 and 30; ask an addition question such as *How many in all?*)

AFTER ▶ **Explain how you can check your story problem and its solution.** (Possible answer: Read it to the class. See if your problem is clear enough to be solved by your classmates.)

2. CHECK UNDERSTANDING

ERROR ALERT

Page 369   Using subtraction clue words to ask an addition question.

Page 370   Misunderstanding the position words *between, in front of,* and *behind.*

Name _____

Problem Solving
Writing a Story

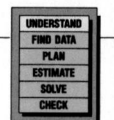

Finish writing the story for 70 + 30 = ____.
Use the Word Bank to help.   70 + 30 = 100

Word Bank			
bought	how many	gave	wants
friend	more	in all	found

Ask an addition question in your story.
Then answer the question in a sentence. Stories may vary.

The Toy Car Story

Gina collects toy cars.

_____

Chapter 17   (three hundred sixty-nine) 369

TEACHING OPTIONS

RETEACHING TIPS   Have students put 5 crayons in this order: red, yellow, green, blue, brown. Have them use *behind, in front of,* and *between* to tell the order of the crayons. *(Yellow is behind red.)* For help in writing a story, assign Reteaching Supplement 153.

COMPUTER   **Safari Search, Sunburst Communications © 1985** Problem solving practice for all students. In *Find the Flamingo,* students find the bird in a 5-by-5 grid. A clue is given after each guess. Encourage students to plan using paper and pencil. The game takes 5-10 minutes.

Problem Solving Strategy
Act It Out

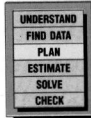

UNDERSTAND
FIND DATA
PLAN
ESTIMATE
SOLVE
CHECK

Work in a group. Act out each problem to solve it. Write the letters for the cars to show the order.

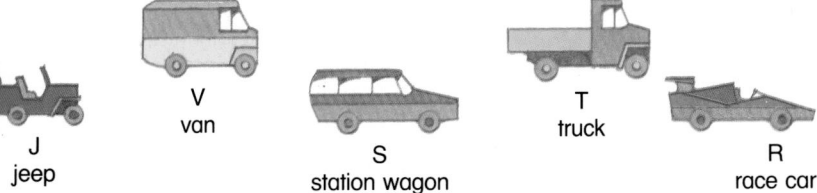

J
jeep

V
van

S
station wagon

T
truck

R
race car

1. Gina put 5 toy cars in a line. The jeep is first in line. The station wagon is between the jeep and the van. The truck is behind the van and in front of the race car. What cars are 2nd, 3rd, 4th, and 5th in line?

J	S	V	T	R
first	second	third	fourth	fifth

2. Joel put the cars in a different order. The truck is last in line. The jeep is between the truck and the van. The station wagon is in front of the van. The station wagon is behind the race car. What cars are 1st, 2nd, 3rd, and 4th in line?

R	S	V	J	T
first	second	third	fourth	fifth

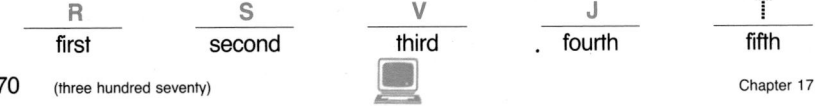

Chapter 17

17-9

3. PRACTICE AND APPLY

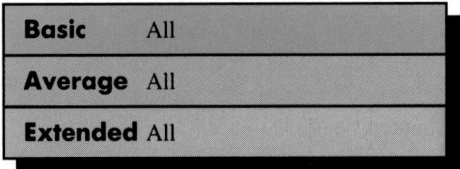

Basic	All
Average	All
Extended	All

Have students work in groups of 5. *How will you act out the problems on this page?* (Possible answer: Students will pretend to be cars. They will stand in the order that the problem states.) *What will you write on the lines at the bottom of each problem?* (The letters that match the names of the cars, in the order that the problem describes.)

▶ **Look at Exercise 1. Describe what is happening in this story.** (Possible answer: Gina is putting 5 toy cars in a line, in a special order.)

▶ **Where can you find the data to solve the problem?** (Read the clues to find the position for each car.)

▶ **Construct a plan for acting out the problem.** (Each student can be one of the cars and hold up a piece of paper with the letter of the car; students can line up as each clue is read.)

▶ **How can you check your solution?** (Reread the problem. Make sure the order matches each clue.)

CLOSE AND ASSESS

SHOW WHAT YOU KNOW Ask small groups to act out a circus parade with each child portraying an animal or a clown. Have a member of the group ask the class questions such as *Who comes between the clown and the elephant?* Then ask students to write an addition or a subtraction story problem about what was acted out.

QUICK QUIZ

Write the answer in a sentence.
James has 40 stamps. He needs 10 stamps to mail a package. How many stamps will he have left? (James will have 30 stamps left.)

CHAPTER 17

WRAP UP

INTRODUCTION The Wrap Up provides activities emphasizing math language and thinking skills for the chapter.

USING PAGE 371

Math Words ▶ **If a number is greater than another number, what do you know about both numbers?** (The greater number is farther from zero; the lesser number is closer to zero.)

▶ **To name the numbers between 235 and 239, do you name the numbers 235 and 239?** (No, you name the numbers after 235 and before 239—236, 237, 238.)

Math Reasoning ▶ **What is the same about the number of beans in all 3 jars?** (All the numbers contain the same digits—4, 5, and 9.)

▶ **How can you decide if each answer is correct?** (Read the description again to see if the number matches it; the greatest number will have the greatest hundreds digit; the least number will have the least hundreds digit.)

Wrap Up

MATH WORDS

Choose a word from the box.
Write it in the correct sentence.

tens	before	less
greater	hundreds
between	after

1. 252 comes ___before___ 253.

2. 749 comes ___after___ 748.

3. 548 comes ___between___ 547 and 549.

4. If you say 453, 463, 473, you are

   counting on by ___tens___

5. 965 is ___greater___ than 896.

MATH REASONING

Find the number of beans in each jar. Each number uses these three digits. | 5 | 4 | 9 |

Write the number on the jar.

6. 954   This jar has the greatest possible number of beans.

7. 459   This jar has the least possible number of beans.

Chapter 17 Wrap Up

(three hundred seventy-one) 37

TEACHING OPTIONS

ENRICHMENT Have students work in groups of 3. Each student chooses a number between 1 and 9. Students work together to make as many 3-digit numbers as possible and order them from least to greatest. Then challenge students to make up riddles about the numbers, similar to Exercise 9 on page 371.

Allow time for them to read them to each other and solve.

Name _____

CHAPTER REVIEW/TEST

1. How many are there? Write the number.

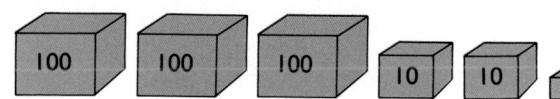

                               323

2. Write the numbers as you count on.

352,   353,   354,   355,   356,   357,   358

Write the numbers after, before, or between.

3.  (after) 172, _173_, _174_   680, _681_, _682_

4. (before) _184_, _185_, 186   _576_, _577_, 578

5. (between) 498, _499_, _500_, 501

6. Count on by tens.   7. Count back by tens.

   340, _350_, _360_, _370_   231, _221_, _211_, _201_

8. Write > or < in each ◯.

846 (>) 648   292 (>) 229   438 (<) 483

9. Ring and finish the correct number sentence.
Write the answer in a sentence.

Glenda has 50 dimes and 90 nickels. How many more nickels than dimes does she have?

(90 − 50 = _40_)   50 + 90 = ___

She has 40 more nickels.

CHAPTER REVIEW/TEST

INTRODUCTION The Review/Test is provided to review and evaluate the skills and concepts presented in Chapter 17.

USING PAGE 382
If you prefer to use this page for review, you may want to use the **Multiple-Choice Posttest** (pages 67-68) or the **Free-Response Posttest** (pages 67-68) to evaluate mastery of chapter objectives.

ITEM ANALYSIS The table below correlates the Chapter Review/Test Items with the lesson objectives.

Items	Objectives
1	17-3
2	17-4
3, 4, 5	17-5
6, 7	17-6
8	17-7
9	17-6

INFORMAL ASSESSMENT

Using Manipulatives Provide students with base-ten blocks. Say a -digit number and have students model it with blocks. Ask them to identify the place and value of each digit.

Communication *Compare the money values in dollars and cents with place values of hundreds, tens, and ones.* (Possible answer: Dollars are equivalent to hundreds; dimes are equivalent to tens; pennies are equivalent to ones.)

Critical Thinking *How can you remember how to place the less than (<) and greater than (>) signs between 2 numbers?* (Answers will vary. Possible answers: The pointed part of the arrow points to the smaller number; the "mouth" opens to the larger number.)

CHAPTER 17

ENRICHMENT

INTRODUCTION Reading temperatures on a thermometer helps students apply what they know about number values to everyday situations.

USING PAGE 373
This Enrichment page is provided for all students. You may wish to use if after they have completed the Chapter Review/Test on page 372.

▶ **How does the temperature change as the number marked on the thermometer gets larger?** (The temperature becomes warmer.)

▶ **Why do you think thermometers are marked in units of 10?** (Possible answers: They are easier to read than they would be if every number were shown; there is not enough space to show every number.)

▶ **What would the temperature be if the line were between 50° and 60°?** (Accept 55° or all temperatures between 50° and 60°.)

EXTENSION Provide students with a thermometer and empty paper cups. Have them pour cold water into one cup and warm water into another cup. First have students read and record the temperature shown on the thermometer (to the nearest 10°). Then have students place the thermometer into the cup with cold water. Ask them to read and record the temperature (to the nearest 10°). Have them repeat the procedure for the warm water. Have students compare their temperatures and describe their results.

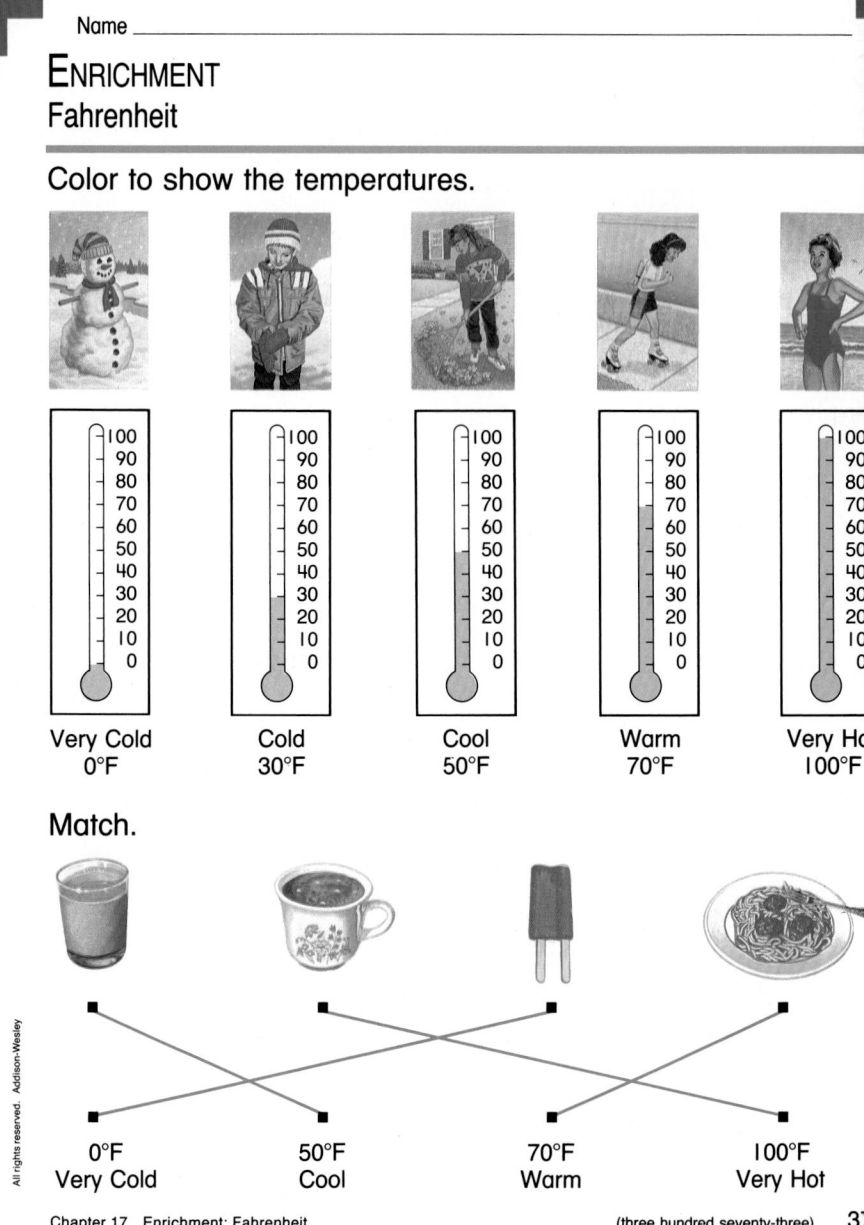

Name _____

ENRICHMENT
Fahrenheit

Color to show the temperatures.

| Very Cold 0°F | Cold 30°F | Cool 50°F | Warm 70°F | Very Hot 100°F |

Match.

0°F Very Cold   50°F Cool   70°F Warm   100°F Very Hot

Chapter 17 Enrichment: Fahrenheit   (three hundred seventy-three) 37

Name _____

CUMULATIVE REVIEW

What part is colored?

1.

- ● $\frac{3}{5}$
- ○ $\frac{1}{4}$
- ○ $\frac{2}{3}$

2.
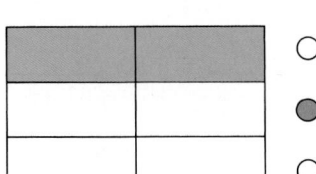
- ○ $\frac{1}{4}$
- ● $\frac{2}{6}$
- ○ $\frac{3}{5}$

3.
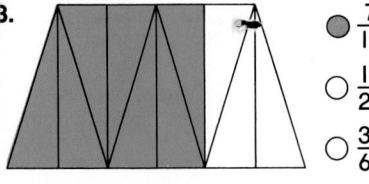
- ● $\frac{7}{10}$
- ○ $\frac{1}{2}$
- ○ $\frac{3}{6}$

4.
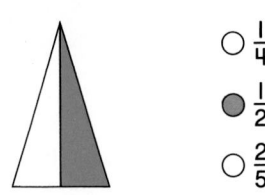
- ○ $\frac{1}{4}$
- ● $\frac{1}{2}$
- ○ $\frac{2}{5}$

Which number sentence matches the picture?

5.
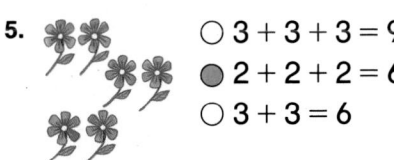
- ○ $3 + 3 + 3 = 9$
- ● $2 + 2 + 2 = 6$
- ○ $3 + 3 = 6$

6.
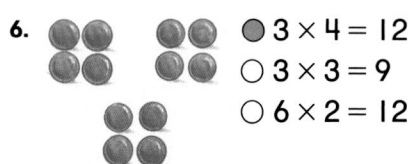
- ● $3 \times 4 = 12$
- ○ $3 \times 3 = 9$
- ○ $6 \times 2 = 12$

7.
- ● $2 \times \$4 = \$8$
- ○ $2 \times \$1 = \$2$
- ○ $4 \times \$1 = \$4$

8.

- ○ $4 \times 3 = 12$
- ● $2 \times 5 = 10$
- ○ $2 \times 6 = 12$

9. Evan and Beth shared 6 whistles.

Each got $\frac{1}{2}$ of them.

How many whistles did each get?

- ● 3 whistles
- ○ 5 whistles
- ○ 6 whistles

CUMULATIVE REVIEW

INTRODUCTION The purpose of this Cumulative Review is to maintain previously taught skills and concepts. The emphasis in this Cumulative Review is on fractions, Chapter 15; and on understanding multiplication and division, Chapter 16.

ITEM ANALYSIS The table below correlates the Cumulative Review items with the lesson objectives.

Items	Objectives
1	15-4
2, 3, 4	15-2, 15-3
5	16-1
6	16-2
7	16-3
8	16-2
9	15-5

Chapter Management

OVERVIEW

Lesson	Pages	Objectives	Subject Integration	Strand Integration
Adding: Trading 10 Ones for 1 Ten	375-376	18-1 To trade 10 ones for 1 ten	science: seeds	problem solving
Trading 10 Tens for 1 Hundred	377-378	18-2 To trade 10 tens for 1 hundred	social studies: partner skills	mental math
Adding: Trading 10 Tens for 1 Hundred	379-380	18-3 To add, trading 10 tens for 1 hundred if needed	language arts: verbal skills	computation, place value
Problem Solving: Understanding the Operations/Data Analysis: Organizing Data	381-382	18-4 To add and subtract; to make and read a bar graph	language arts: writing	graphing
Subtracting: Trading 1 Ten for 10 Ones	383-384	18-5 To subtract, trading 1 ten for 10 ones if needed	language arts: following directions	number, place value
Trading 1 Hundred for 10 Tens	385-386	18-6 To trade 1 hundred for 10 tens	fine arts: cut & paste	critical thinking, number
Subtracting: Trading 1 Hundred for 10 Tens	387-388	18-7 To subtract, trading 1 hundred for 10 tens if needed	language arts: following directions	mental math
Adding and Subtracting Money	389-390	18-8 To add and subtract 3-digit numbers with money	life skills: making purchases	consumer math
Problem Solving: Problems with Two Questions/Problem Solving Strategy: Make a Table	391-392	18-9 To solve 2-question problems; to use the strategy Make a Table	science: gardening	consumer math, patterns

MATHEMATICAL BACKGROUND

Adding and Subtracting 3-Digit Numbers
Since students' formal introduction to trading occurs in Grade 2, a major focus of this book is on the development of an understanding of and facility with trading. Chapters 10 and 11 (addition) and Chapters 13 and 14 (subtraction) involved operations with 2-digit numbers requiring trading between ones and tens.

Trading from tens to hundreds for addition and from hundreds to tens for subtraction is a new skill introduced with 3-digit numbers.

The foundation for understanding trading tens and hundreds is in the place-value work with hundreds. When students are introduced to place value through the hundreds place, they should begin to develop a general understanding of place value, recognizing that 10 ones make 1 ten (and 1 ten makes 10 ones) and that 10 tens make 1 hundred (and 1 hundred makes 10 tens). This understanding is essential for trading with hundreds. When students manipulate concrete objects, they are better able to see the reasonableness of the algorithm steps that involve trading.

Problem Solving
In this chapter, students solve problems with two questions and use the strategy *Make a Table*.

TIPS FROM TEACHERS

Collect cash register receipts. Highlight two 3-digit amounts and write + or − on each one. Have students write and illustrate an addition or subtraction story using the amounts and the operation sign indicated on the receipt.

Debra Perellis
Bloom Elementary School
Louisville, KY

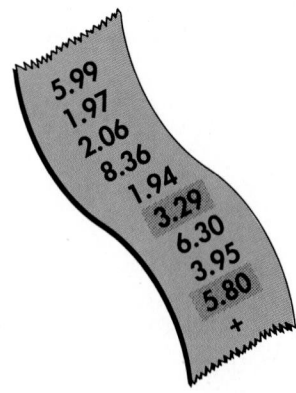
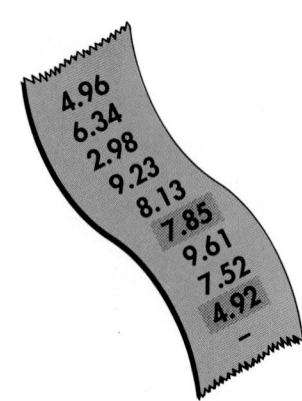

ASSESSMENT

Pretest — Chapter 18, page 1

Multiple-Choice Format

Name _____

1. Add. Trade 10 ones for 1 ten if you need to.

$$146 + 27$$

(A) 173
B 163
C 121

2. Add. Ring 10 tens to make 1 hundred.

$$50 + 60$$

(A) 110
B 140
C 100

3. Add.

$$152 + 271$$

← Trade

A 412
B 523
(C) 423

4. Jack wants 26 model cars. He has 19 model cars. How many more does he need?

A 45 more
(B) 7 more
C 35 more

5. Subtract. Trade 1 ten for 10 ones if you need to.

$$142 - 25$$

A 107
(B) 117
C 127

6. Subtract. Trade 1 ten for 10 ones if you need to.

$$245 - 27$$

A 272
B 228
(C) 218

MCT 2   69

Pretest — Chapter 18, page 2

Multiple-Choice Format

Name _____

7. Trade 1 hundred for 10 tens. Choose the new numbers.

Hundreds	Tens	Ones
☐ 2	☐ 6	6

(A)
Hundreds	Tens	Ones
1	16	6

B
Hundreds	Tens	Ones
2	16	6

8. Subtract. Trade 1 hundred for 10 tens.

$$317 - 142$$

Trade →

A 165
B 275
(C) 175

9. Add.

$$\$5.92 + 1.75$$

A $6.67
B $4.17
(C) $7.67

10. If Alice buys 3 packs of bows, how many bows will she have? Finish the table.

1 Pack 4 Bows

1 Pack	2 Packs	3 Packs
4 bows	___ bows	___ bows

(A) 12 bows
B 4 bows
C 3 bows

70   MCT 2

Posttest — Chapter 18, page 1

Multiple-Choice Format

Name _____

1. Add. Trade 10 ones for 1 ten if you need to.

$$137 + 18$$

A 145
B 119
(C) 155

2. Add. Ring 10 tens to make 1 hundred.

$$40 + 70$$

A 100
B 130
(C) 110

3. Add.

$$225 + 194$$

← Trade

(A) 419
B 411
C 519

4. Elona wants 38 ribbons. She has 29 ribbons. How many more does she need?

A 67 more
(B) 9 more
C 19 more

5. Subtract. Trade 1 ten for 10 ones if you need to.

$$153 - 35$$

A 188
B 128
(C) 118

6. Subtract. Trade 1 ten for 10 ones if you need to.

$$262 - 36$$

A 236
(B) 226
C 298

MCT 2   71

Posttest — Chapter 18, page 2

Multiple-Choice Format

Name _____

7. Trade 1 hundred for 10 tens. Choose the new numbers.

Hundreds	Tens	Ones
☐ 2	☐ 1	4

A
Hundreds	Tens	Ones
2	11	4

(B)
Hundreds	Tens	Ones
1	11	4

8. Subtract. Trade 1 hundred for 10 tens.

$$325 - 163$$

Trade →

A 262
(B) 162
C 152

9. Add.

$$\$3.83 + 1.35$$

A $4.18
(B) $5.18
C $2.48

10. If Boris buys 3 packs of bows, how many bows will he have? Finish the table.

1 Pack 5 Bows

1 Pack	2 Packs	3 Packs
5 bows	___ bows	___ bows

A 12 bows
B 9 bows
(C) 15 bows

72   MCT 2

ITEM ANALYSIS

Items	Objectives
1	18-1
2	18-2
3	18-3
4	18-4
5, 6	18-5
7	18-6
8	18-7
9	18-8
10	18-9

Note: The item analysis is the same for all pretests and posttests for this chapter.

ALSO AVAILABLE

▶ **Free Response Tests**
▶ **Alternative Tests**
▶ **Thinking Strategies**
▶ **Concrete Materials**

PROJECT AND BULLETIN BOARD

Reproduce the nomograph on the bulletin board. Be sure to line up the number lines exactly as they are shown. Explain to students that a *nomograph* has three sets of number lines. Draw a straight line from a number in the top row to a number in the bottom row. The sum of the two numbers should be the number crossed on the second line. Demonstrate with 47 + 23. Start on the top number line. Wrap a piece of yarn around a thumbtack on 47. Pull the yarn straight down and wrap it around a tack on 23 on the bottom line. *Through which number on the middle number line does the yarn pass?* (70) 47 + 23 = 70. During sessions that follow, have students experiment with adding 2-digit numbers on the nomograph.

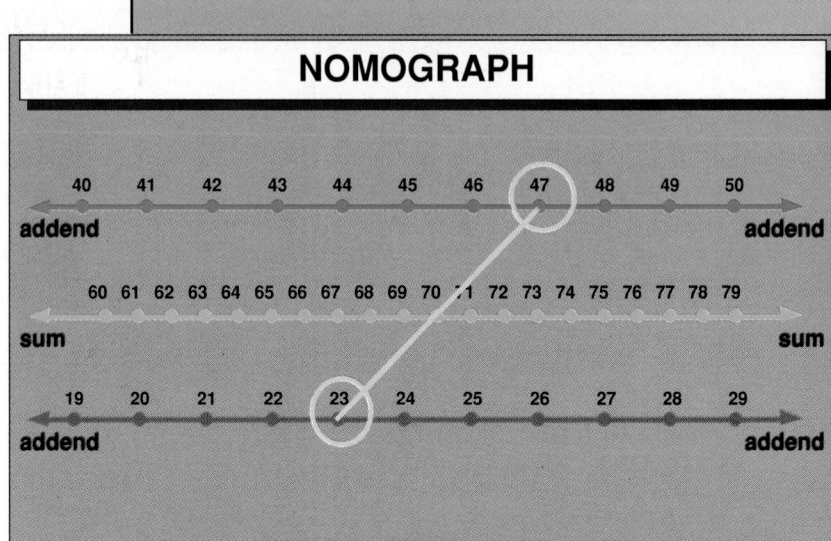

NOMOGRAPH

| 40 | 41 | 42 | 43 | 44 | 45 | 46 | 47 | 48 | 49 | 50 |

addend   addend

60 61 62 63 64 65 66 67 68 69 70 71 72 73 74 75 76 77 78 79

sum   sum

| 19 | 20 | 21 | 22 | 23 | 24 | 25 | 26 | 27 | 28 | 29 |

addend   addend

COOPERATIVE LEARNING

Divide the class into 4 groups. Identify the group skill: building on the strengths in each other's ideas rather than the weaknesses. Suggest to students that they start a lemonade stand. List the following supplies and their prices: lemonade, $3.25; ice, $.79; big cups, $2.50; small cups, $.85; napkins, $.57; pitcher, $2.18; sign, $.99; tablecloth, $4.86; straws, $1.11. Tell students to buy the items they will need to set up their stand. Instruct them to keep a record of the money they spend. Have each group start with $9.99. In turn, have each member of the group choose an item, record the price in the record book, and then subtract to show the amount of money left. As members choose an item to buy, the group may question the necessity for the item, or discuss better alternatives if money is running low. If a purchase is questioned, encourage students to listen to the good points suggested by the member, and then come to a group decision on whether to make the purchase. Continue until all of the money is spent or all of the items are purchased.

You will find grouping suggestions and cooperative learning activities in most lessons throughout this chapter.

LITERATURE

Gag, Wanda. *Millions of Cats.* New York: Coward, McCann & Geoghegan, 1977.

A little old man goes in search of just one cat to please an old woman. He comes home with hundreds of cats, thousands of cats, millions of cats. See what happens! Have students use events in the story to count on and back by ones, tens, and hundreds.

Jacobs, Allan D. and Leland B. Jacobs. *Arithmetic in Verse and Rhyme.* Champaign, Illinois: Garrard Publishing, 1971.

Schwartz, David M. *How Much Is A Million?* New York: Lothrop, Lee, & Shepard, 1985.

Youldon, Gillian. *Numbers.* New York: Franklin Watts, 1979.

ENGLISH AS A SECOND LANGUAGE

Transform the word problems into real-life situations by having students act them out. This will provide opportunities for functional, communicative language practice as well as problem solving. Tape the students as they act out problems and play back the tape so that they can judge the effectiveness of their communication skills. If ESL students had trouble accomplishing this task, this will provide feedback for them and the opportunity to discuss their problems.

Since the passive voice is used extensively in these problem solving activities, contrast it with the active voice by having students paraphrase and by writing pairs of sentences on the chalkboard. Ask students to enter these verb forms on flash cards and add them to their files.

GIFTED

Mathematically talented students may already be able to add and subtract 2- and 3-digit numbers. They will nevertheless likely be interested in many of the strategies presented in this chapter. You may wish to challenge these students, after they have completed their book work, by having them shop in a toy catalog. Explain that they may purchase as many toys as they wish, up to a total of $10.00. To extend subtraction concepts, ask students to compare the costs of the least and most expensive toys on their list. Artistically gifted students may wish to create their own toy catalogs, with price tags of no more than $5.00 for any one toy. Original catalogs may be exchanged with a friend for more shopping experiences. If this idea appeals to students, have them repeat the activity using other kinds of catalogs or different totals.

STUDENTS AT RISK

Prepare a small chart like the following with a washable acetate overlay.

100s	10s	1s
3	4	9
2	6	0

Make the lines separating columns very dark or textured. Point out to students the importance of lining up numbers in the correct place value columns. Dictate several 3-digit numbers and have students practice writing them using the correct columns. They can cross out and show regrouping as well.

Later on, dictate 3-digit addition or subtraction exercises for more practice in writing and lining up the numbers according to place value. Have students write the addition or subtraction sign, but do not have them solve the exercises at this time.

You may also use the Reteaching Supplements and the specific Reteaching Tips from each lesson in this chapter.

PICTURE

These pictures and accompanying stories and poems are available as storybooks.

You may want to read and discuss this story with your students before starting the chapter. The first lesson in this chapter includes a question about the story. Lessons 1, 5, and 7 in this chapter have questions in the informal Assessment that refer to the story.

How the Peacock Got Its Tail Feathers

Long, long ago, there was a time when peacocks were rather plain-looking birds. There was one old peacock who loved beautiful, bright colors. He had a beautiful flower garden. People would laugh at him because he was so plain, but they did not laugh at his wonderful garden. In it, he grew 125 pansies and 155 snapdragons. He knew because he counted them each and every day as he carefully watered and weeded the rows of the garden.

One morning when the old peacock awakened, he remembered that it was the Queen's birthday. He decided to go to his garden and cut some flowers to make a bouquet for the Queen. But when he got out to the garden, the old peacock found 28 holes in the ground where flowers had been before. He checked all around, but found no signs that gophers, caterpillars, or grasshoppers were eating his flowers. He went inside to think about this mystery. When he came back to the garden, he found 48 more holes in the ground where flowers had been before.

The old peacock thought some more and decided to find out what was happening to his garden. He flew up into a large oak tree at the edge of his garden and waited and watched.

He didn't have to wait long until he saw a little man coming into the garden pulling an empty cart behind him. The man went straight to the flowers and dug out another 25 plants from the ground, placed them in his cart, and started up the road with the cart behind him.

The old peacock followed the man, who soon turned off the road and into a meadow. There, spread out on the ground, was a large fan. On the fan, someone had started to make a beautiful design of green, purple, and blue.

As the old peacock watched from behind a tree, the little man carefully removed the leaves from each stem and the petals from each flower. He wove them together onto the fan until at last the design was finished. The old peacock had never seen anything so magnificent. He thought the fan was even more beautiful than his garden.

Then, as the old peacock watched, the little man looked at him, winked, and disappeared into thin air.

The old peacock didn't quite know what to think. He decided that for some reason the little man had left the fan for him. "Why, it is fit for the Queen." he said. And then he remembered. It was the Queen's birthday. He would give the fan to the Queen.

He cradled the wondrous fan in his arms and hurried to the palace. Once inside, he was escorted to the courtyard where many people were also presenting the Queen with their presents. The people laughed at him because he was so plain. But when he bowed to the Queen and gave her the fan with the exquisite pattern and colors, they stopped laughing and said how beautiful the old peacock's gift was.

The Queen was delighted with such a beautiful and unique gift. "And where does the fan get such beautiful colors?" she asked the old peacock. When he told her that it had been made from the flowers in his garden, she was even more pleased. She told the old peacock that she would give him a gift in return.

"Because you have pleased others with your beautiful garden, from this day forward, you shall be as beautiful as your garden." The royal magician then said some words of magic over the peacock. Suddenly the old peacock's feathers changed from brown to green, purple, and blue. Then, quite unexpectedly, the peacock started to grow a large and beautiful tail with a design that looked just like the magnificent fan. People oohed and aahed and said that the peacock was as beautiful as his garden and as the fan.

PREBOOK ACTIVITIES

QUICK REVIEW

Tell whether the underlined digit in each number represents hundreds, tens, or ones.

2<u>4</u>5 (tens)   <u>4</u>98 (hundreds)   <u>4</u>0 (ones)
53<u>1</u> (ones)   <u>3</u>1 (tens)   <u>3</u>87 (hundreds)
10<u>9</u> (tens)   <u>5</u>44 (hundreds)   50<u>0</u> (ones)
<u>1</u>26 (hundreds)   <u>5</u> (ones)   2<u>3</u>8 (tens)

PRIOR KNOWLEDGE

What happens when you trade something? (Possible answer: You exchange something for something else.) *When you trade something, do you usually get something more valuable in return? Why or why not?* (Possible answer: No, trades are usually even exchanges.)

COMMUNICATION

Discussing and Writing Math   *When do you need to trade in addition problems?* (Possible answer: When you have 10 or more ones, you trade them for 1 ten.) *What would happen if you did not trade ones for tens in an addition exercise that needed a trade?* (Possible answer: your answer would be wrong because you cannot have more than 9 ones in the ones column.) *Fill in the blanks below to show the trade: 1 ten and 14 ones is the same as (2) tens and (4) ones.*

EXPLORE AND CONNECT

Materials: base-ten blocks
Grouping Suggestions: small groups
Review adding two 2-digit numbers with sums less than 100. Have students use base-ten blocks to add 25 + 39. As they work, write the steps on the chalkboard. Then write 75 + 108 on the board. *How is this exercise different from the first one?* (Possible answer: It adds a 3-digit number and a 2-digit number.) *How is it the same?* (Possible answer: You need to trade 10 ones for 1 ten.) Have students use blocks to add this and similar exercises as you record the steps on the board. Include 2-digit plus 3-digit, 3-digit plus 3-digit, and 3-digit plus 1-digit exercises that have no trading or trading ones for tens. Remind students to build on the strengths in each other's ideas.

CONNECTIONS   Use these anytime.

Problem of the Day

Extra Data   Write a number sentence and the answer. Then underline the extra data.
There were 325 cows at the state fair. <u>There were 241 rabbits.</u> There were 128 horses. How many cows and horses were at the fair? (325 + 128 = 453; there were 453 cows and horses.)

Math Connection

Addition   Complete the table.

+36	
104	(140)
227	(263)
521	(557)
949	(985)
306	(342)

Mental Math

Number Sense   Add 10 to each of the following numbers.

45	(55)	37	(47)
213	(223)	876	(886)
100	(110)	636	(646)
405	(415)	989	(999)
56	(66)	280	(290)

CLASSWORK AND HOMEWORK SUPPLEMENTS

Practice

Skills Maintenance   18-1

Name _____

Adding: Trading 10 Ones for 1 Ten

Add. Trade if you need to.

1.
```
□ 1          □          □ 1          □ 1
  239        125         78          719
 +131       + 64        +215        +156
  370        189         293         875
```

2.
```
□          □ 1          □ 1          □ 1
247        539         625          135
+212       +132        + 49        +648
459        671         674          783
```

3.
```
□ 1          □ 1          □ 1          □
216        233         438          722
+726       +458        + 42        +134
942        691         480          856
```

4.
```
□ 1          □ 1          □ 1          □
327        555         236          51
+ 68       +437        +635        +828
395        992         871          879
```

154   Use with text pages 375–376.   PS-2

Building Thinking Skills

Mental Math   18-1

Name _____

Hundreds of Things

Solve each problem. Ring the correct pictures.

1. Jack bought 600 seeds. He bought 2 packs. One pack had fewer than 200 seeds.

2. Sharon had 700 pennies. She had 3 banks.

3. Hector had 2 jars of beans. Each jar had more than 300 beans. He had 900 beans in all.

4. Val read 3 books. She read 800 pages. Two books had the same number of pages.

154   Use with text pages 375–376.   TS-2

Reteaching

Skills Review   18-1

Name _____

Adding: Trading 10 Ones for 1 Ten

```
Add the ones.      Add the tens.    Add the
Trade if you can.                   hundreds.

 1   6+7=13    1   1+2+3=6    1   1+1=2
              Trade 10
 126  ones for  126           126
+137   1 ten.  +137          +137
   3             63           263
```

Add. Trade 10 ones for 1 ten if you can. Use blocks to help.

1.
```
□ 1                      □
238  8+4=12      562  2+5=7
+144  Trade.    +135  No trade.
382              697
```

2.
```
□           □ 1          □
325         458         523
+247        + 33        +230
572         491         753
```

3.
```
□ 1          □ 1          □
236         726         665
+ 18        +  6        +122
254         732         787
```

154   Use with text pages 375–376.   RS-2

Challenges

Number Sense   18-1

Name _____

Find the Addends

Use the numbers in the box.
Write the addends that make each sum.
Clues: 1. Add the ones.
       2. See if there is a trade.

```
106   122
27    133
    219
```

Order of addends may vary.

1.
```
□           1           1
106         133         219
+133        + 27        +122
239         160         341
```

2.
```
1           □           □
106         122         122
+ 27        +133        +106
133         255         228
```

3.
```
1           1           1
219         27          133
+106        +219        +219
325         246         352
```

154   Use with text pages 375–376.   CS-2

Basic

Exercises All
Calculator Bank, p. 402
More Practice, p. 431, set B

Supplements
Reteaching 154 or
Practice 154

Average

Exercises All
Calculator Bank, p. 402
More Practice, p. 431, set B

Supplements
Practice 154
Challenges 154 or
Thinking Skills 154

Extended

Exercises All
Calculator Bank, p. 402

Supplements
Challenges 154
Thinking Skills 154

Other Resources:
*Problem Solving Experiences
In Mathematics*, p. 165

18-1

OBJECTIVE 18-1
To trade 10 ones for 1 ten

Materials: base-ten blocks, toothpicks, twist ties, rubber bands

1. MOTIVATE AND TEACH

LEARN ABOUT IT

Read the chapter story about how the peacock got its feathers. *What is the total number of flowers that the old peacock originally had in his garden?* (280) Have students use blocks to help them. As students look at the picture on page 375, explain that a greenhouse is a building where plants can grow all year long. Tell them that this greenhouse belongs to a school and that the classes take turns caring for the plants. Aloud, read story problems involving 2-digit plus 3-digit, 3-digit plus 3-digit, and 3-digit plus 1-digit addition with no trading of ones for tens. Have students use the page as a mat for the blocks as they find the sums.

▶ **What are you trying to find out about the plants in the greenhouse?** (Possible answer: the total number of plants)

▶ **What is a good way to use the base-ten blocks to model an addition problem?** (Possible answer: Start by adding the blocks in the ones column. If you need to, trade 10 ones for 1 ten. Then add the tens and the hundreds. Write the steps as you do them.) Have students make up and solve problems of their own.

2. CHECK UNDERSTANDING

ERROR ALERT Not being able to tell when trading is necessary.

18
Adding and Subtracting 3-Digit Numbers

TEACHING OPTIONS

RETEACHING TIPS Write addends such as 426 + 249 on the chalkboard. Have students use bundled toothpicks to model the addition. When there are more than 10 ones, group 10 and add the ten to the tens column. Have them write the exercise to match. Assign Reteaching Supplement 154.

ENRICHMENT Have students solve these exercises, then make up their own to exchange with classmates.

2 3 (7)	4 (5) 4	3 4 6
+4 0 6	+3 4 5	+5 0 (4)
6 4 3	7 9 9	8 5 0

Name _____

Adding

Trading 10 Ones for 1 Ten

Add 128 and 144. Use blocks to help.

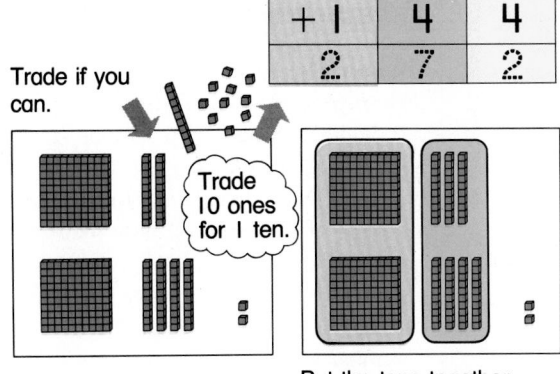

Hundreds	Tens	Ones
	1	
1	2	8
+1	4	4
2	7	2

Put the ones together.

Trade if you can.

Trade 10 ones for 1 ten.

Put the tens together.
Put the hundreds together.

Use blocks to help find the sums.
Trade 10 ones for 1 ten if you can.

1.

Hundreds	Tens	Ones
	1	
	5	6
+2	3	4
290		

2.

Hundreds	Tens	Ones
	1	
1	3	5
+1	2	8
263		

PROBLEM SOLVING

3. Al bought 700 seeds. He bought 2 packs. Each pack had more than 200 seeds. Ring the 2 packs he bought. See teaching notes.

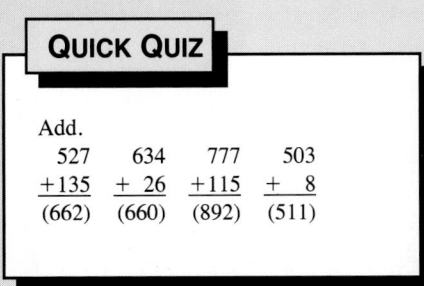

More Practice, page 431, set B
Chapter 18

CLOSE AND ASSESS

SAY WHAT YOU THINK Provide students with base-ten blocks and several 3-digit addition exercises that require trading 10 ones for 1 ten. Have them choose 2 exercises to model and solve. Then ask them to write the exercises to match the models.

QUICK QUIZ

Add.

527	634	777	503
+135	+ 26	+115	+ 8
(662)	(660)	(892)	(511)

---

3. PRACTICE AND APPLY

Basic	All
Average	All
Extended	All

Look at the last picture at the top of this page. How do you show that you need to trade 10 ones for 1 ten? (You write a small 1 above the tens column before you write the answer in the ones column.)

APPLY

PROBLEM SOLVING ▶ **Which methods can you use to solve this problem?** (Guess and Check: pick 2 numbers and add to see if they total 700; Logical Reasoning: think carefully about which combinations of packs will work and which ones will not)

▶ **What should you think about if more than 1 pair of packs total 700?** (Possible answer: Check to see if both packs in each pair have more than 200 seeds.)

18-1

Trading 10 Tens for 1 Hundred

OBJECTIVE 18-2   To trade 10 tens for 1 hundred

PREBOOK ACTIVITIES

QUICK REVIEW

Find the sums.

60	10	20	40	50	30	70
+30	+40	+50	+40	+30	+10	+20
(90)	(50)	(70)	(80)	(80)	(40)	(90)

PRIOR KNOWLEDGE

Help students recall what they have learned about adding with and without trading. *When you are finding the sum for 2 numbers, what do you add first?* (ones) *How do you know if you need to trade?* (You trade if there are 10 or more ones.) *What happens to the traded ones?* (They become a ten and the ten is added with the other tens.) *What do you think would happen if there were 10 or more tens? Why?* (Possible answer: Trade 10 tens for a hundred, because 10 tens equal 1 hundred.)

COMMUNICATION

Discussing and Writing Math   Tell students that just as we can trade 10 ones for 1 ten, we can trade 10 tens for 1 hundred. Write **10 tens, 1 hundred, 100.** *Do these all stand for the same amount?* (Yes; they all mean 100.) *What if we had 11 tens? How many hundreds and extra tens would we have?* (1 hundred, 1 ten) *What number would that be?* (110) Have students write each of the following in hundreds and tens and as a number.

1. 12 tens   (1 hundred, 2 tens; 120)
2. 15 tens   (1 hundred, 5 tens; 150)
3. 19 tens   (1 hundred, 9 tens; 190)

EXPLORE AND CONNECT

Materials: base-ten blocks
Grouping Suggestion: pairs
Provide each pair with 18 tens sticks and 1 hundred block. Each student selects a number of tens from 1 to 9 and counts out that many tens sticks to match. Have them combine their groups of tens and tell how many tens in all—for example, 3 tens plus 9 tens equal 12 tens. Ask pairs to trade 10 tens for 1 hundred if they can. Make sure students recall that 10 tens equal 100. Have students restate their sentences, using only number words. For 3 tens and 9 tens, students will say *30 plus 90 equals 120.* List students' addition sentences on the chalkboard and have the class read the completed list aloud. Have students repeat the activity several times for different amounts.

CONNECTIONS   Use these anytime.

Problem of the Day

Use Logical Reasoning   Seth and Shea are adding their tens together. They have exactly enough to trade for 1 hundred. Seth has 2 more tens than Shea. How many tens do Seth and Shea each have? (Seth has 6, Shea has 4.)

Minute Math

Addition   Copy and solve.

130	245	315	409
+ 45	+ 127	+ 234	+ 165
(175)	(372)	(549)	(574)

37	128	212	388
+ 137	+ 208	+ 365	+ 6
(174)	(336)	(577)	(394)

Number Sense

Numeration   How many ways can you make a hundred using 2 of these numbers? Use tens sticks to help.

10	20	30	40
60	70	80	90

(10 + 90; 20 + 80; 30 + 70; 40 + 60) Can you think of a way to make a hundred using 3 of these numbers? (10 + 20 + 70; 60 + 30 + 10)

CLASSWORK AND HOMEWORK SUPPLEMENTS

Practice

Skills Maintenance 18-2

Name _____

Trading 10 Tens for 1 Hundred

Use the pictures to help you find the sums.
Ring 10 tens to make 1 hundred if you can.
Write the number of hundreds, tens, and ones.

	Hundreds	Tens	Ones
1. 50 + 60	1	1	0
2. 40 + 70	1	1	0
3. 50 + 30		8	0
4. 60 + 70	1	3	0
5. 70 + 50	1	2	0

PS-2   Use with text pages 377 – 378.   155

Building Thinking Skills

Reading Math 18-2

Name _____

Graphic Details

The first, second, and third graders raised money for a community project. Each grade made greeting cards. They sold the cards at the winter and spring school fairs. The first grade sold 60 cards in the winter and 70 in the spring. The second grade sold 80 cards at each fair. The third grade sold 70 cards at the first fair and 40 cards at the second one.
Use the numbers in the story to fill in the graph.

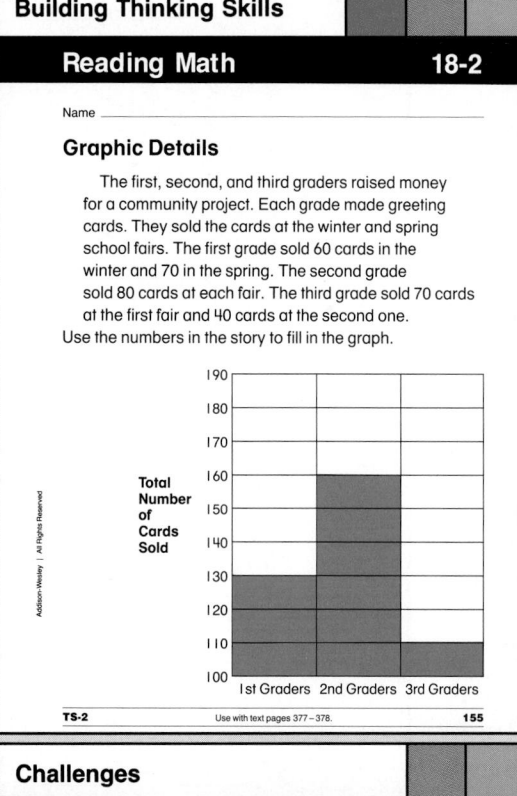

Total Number of Cards Sold

1st Graders   2nd Graders   3rd Graders

TS-2   Use with text pages 377 – 378.   155

Reteaching

Skills Review 18-2

Name _____

Trading 10 Tens for 1 Hundred

	Can you trade?	Hundreds	Tens	Ones
70 + 70	yes no	1	4	0
40 + 20	yes no		6	0

Can you trade 10 tens for 1 hundred?
Ring **yes** or **no**.
Write the number of hundreds, tens, and ones.

	Can you trade?	Hundreds	Tens	Ones
1. 60 + 50	yes no	1	1	0
2. 40 + 80	yes no	1	2	0
3. 30 + 40	yes no		7	0
4. 20 + 90	yes no	1	1	0
5. 70 + 50	yes no	1	2	0
6. 60 + 90	yes no	1	5	0
7. 10 + 60	yes no		7	0
8. 50 + 80	yes no	1	3	0
9. 30 + 50	yes no		8	0

RS-2   Use with text pages 377 – 378.   155

Challenges

Writing Math 18-2

Name _____

Initial Scores

An initial is the first letter of a word.
Write your first and last name initials. ____
Ring the number that goes with each of your initials.

A	B	C	D	E	F	G	H	I	J	K	L	M	N
30	40	50	60	70	80	90	30	40	50	60	70	80	90

O	P	Q	R	S	T	U	V	W	X	Y	Z
30	40	50	60	70	80	90	30	40	50	60	70

Answers will vary.

Add to find your score. ____ + ____ = ____

Pick 5 friends.
Write their first names on the chart.
Write their first and last name initials.
Find the points for each letter.
Add the points to find the score.

Name	Initials	Points	Score
1. _____	_____	____ + ____	= ____
2. _____	_____	____ + ____	= ____
3. _____	_____	____ + ____	= ____
4. _____	_____	____ + ____	= ____
5. _____	_____	____ + ____	= ____

CS-2   Use with text pages 377 – 378.   155

Basic

Exercises All
Calculator Bank, p. 402

Supplements
Reteaching 155 or
Practice 155
Thinking Skills 155

Average

Exercises All
Calculator Bank, p. 402

Supplements
Practice 155
Challenges 155 or
Thinking Skills 155

Extended

Exercises All
Calculator Bank, p. 402

Supplements
Challenges 155
Thinking Skills 155

Other Resources:
Explorations, p. 274
Using the Math Explorer Calculator: A Source Book for Teachers, Chapter 14

18-2

OBJECTIVE 18-2
To trade 10 tens for 1 hundred

Materials: base-ten blocks, spinners, TA17 (Place Value Chart), TA18 (Practagons), number cubes marked 30-80

Grouping Suggestions: pairs, cooperative learning groups of 3

1. MOTIVATE AND TEACH

LEARN ABOUT IT

Provide each pair of students with 10 tens sticks and 1 hundred block. One student places tens sticks on top of the hundreds block until the block is completely covered. The partners then trade 10 tens for 1 hundred.
Call students' attention to the groups of tens sticks at the top of page 377.

▶ **How do you know that you will need to trade 10 tens for 1 hundred?** (because 8 tens plus 7 tens equal 15 tens, and 15 tens is greater than 100)

▶ **Why do you always need 10 tens to trade for 100?** (because exactly 10 tens equal 100)

▶ **When will you circle *no* for the trading question? Why?** (when the sum is less than 100, because you cannot trade unless you have 10 tens, or 100)

▶ **Will you trade if you spin 50 and 30?** (no) **Will you trade if you spin 50 and 70?** (yes)

2. CHECK UNDERSTANDING

ERROR ALERT Recording the number of hundreds and tens in the tens place.

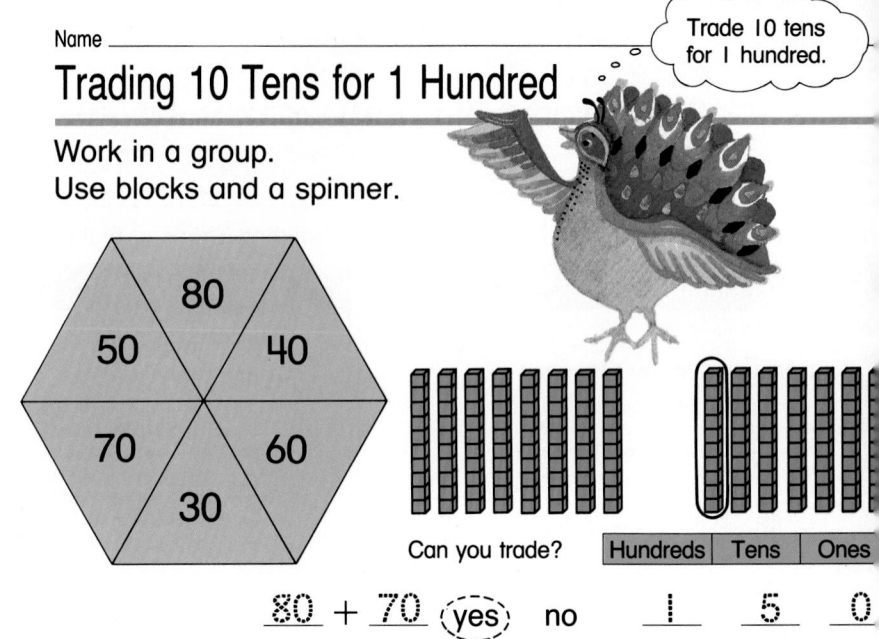

Name _____

Trading 10 Tens for 1 Hundred

Trade 10 tens for 1 hundred.

Work in a group.
Use blocks and a spinner.

| 80 |
| 50 | 40 |
| 70 | 60 |
| 30 |

Can you trade?

		Hundreds	Tens	Ones

$\underline{80} + \underline{70}$ (yes) no $\underline{1}$ $\underline{5}$ $\underline{0}$

Spin two times and write the numbers. Show the amounts with blocks. Can you trade 10 tens for 1 hundred? Ring **yes** or **no**. Write the number of hundreds, tens, and ones. Answers may vary. Check students' wor

	Can you trade?		Hundreds	Tens	Ones
1. ____ + ____	yes	no	____	____	____
2. ____ + ____	yes	no	____	____	____
3. ____ + ____	yes	no	____	____	____
4. ____ + ____	yes	no	____	____	____
5. ____ + ____	yes	no	____	____	____

Chapter 18   (three hundred seventy-seven) **37**

TEACHING OPTIONS

RETEACHING TIPS Use base-ten blocks and a place value chart. Students add 2 numbers, such as 70 and 60, by placing tens sticks in the tens place in the chart. When the chart holds 10 tens, they trade the tens for a hundred block. Then they write the sum. Assign Reteaching Supplement 155.

ENRICHMENT Have students fill in the middle sections of blank practagons with multiples of ten from 10 to 90 and write 50 in the center. Challenge them to calculate the sums mentally and write them in the outer sections. Have them color sums up to 100 blue and color sums 100 and greater red.

10 tens to make I hundred if you
Write the number of hundreds,
, and ones.

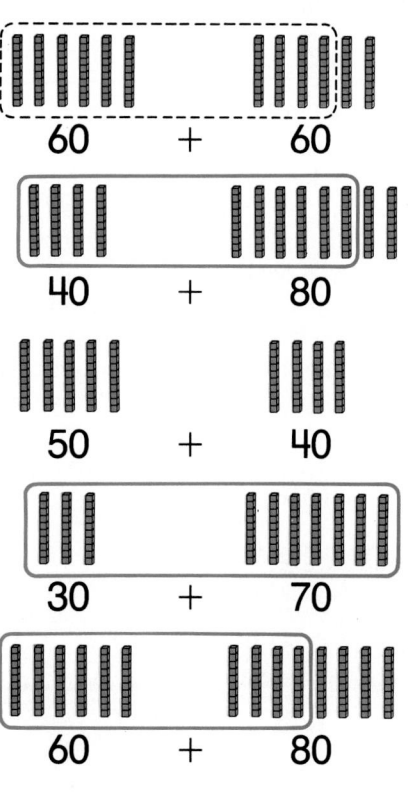

Hundreds	Tens	Ones

60 + 60   1   2   0

40 + 80   1   2   0

50 + 40   ___ 9   0

30 + 70   1   0   0

60 + 80   1   4   0

MENTAL MATH

Use basic facts to help find the sums.

$4 + 8 = \underline{12}$ | $6 + 9 = \underline{15}$ | $7 + 4 = \underline{11}$

$40 + 80 = \underline{120}$ | $60 + 90 = \underline{150}$ | $70 + 40 = \underline{110}$

3. PRACTICE AND APPLY

Basic	All
Average	All
Extended	All

PRACTICE

How will you count 10 tens? (Draw a
ring around them.) *How will you show
the trade in your answer?* (Write a 1 in
the hundreds place.)

APPLY

USE MENTAL MATH ► **How can
you compare each basic fact with the
addition exercise beneath it?** (The
basic fact uses ones; the addition exercise
uses tens.)
► **How can the basic fact help you
find the sum for the addition
exercise?** (Possible answer: (You can
add the tens as though you were adding
the basic fact.)
► **Can you think of another exercise
that has a sum of 120? Think of the
basic addition facts you know.** (60 +
60, 50 + 70, 90 + 30, 20 + 100, 110
+ 10)

CLOSE AND ASSESS

SHOW WHAT YOU KNOW

Provide each group of 3 with tens
sticks, a hundred block, and a number
cube labeled 30-80. The number cube
is rolled twice to make an addition
exercise that one student records. A
second student solves the exercise
mentally and writes the sum. The
third checks the sum by combining
tens sticks and trading 10 tens for 1
hundred if necessary.

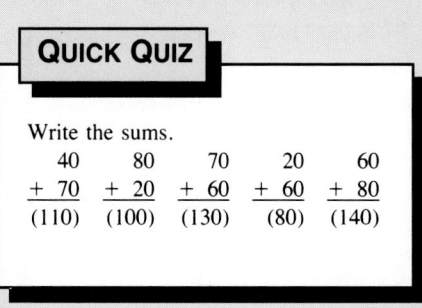

QUICK QUIZ

Write the sums.

40	80	70	20	60
+ 70	+ 20	+ 60	+ 60	+ 80
(110)	(100)	(130)	(80)	(140)

18-2

LESSON OPTIONS 18-3

Adding: Trading 10 Tens for 1 Hundred

OBJECTIVE 18-3   To model 3-digit addition problems, trading 10 tens for 1 hundred if needed

PREBOOK ACTIVITIES

QUICK REVIEW

Look at the numbers in the ones place. As I point to each exercise, raise your hand if you need to trade 10 ones for 1 ten.

345	206	123	631	246	218
+219	+686	+321	+109	+405	+411
(yes)	(yes)	(no)	(yes)	(yes)	(no)

PRIOR KNOWLEDGE

Write the heading *Things We Know About . . .* and the subheadings *Numbers, Place Value,* and *Addition* on the chalkboard. *Imagine that you are a teacher, teaching a class to add two 3-digit numbers. What things do your students need to know first?* (Possible answers: *Numbers:* how to read and write 3-digit numbers; what 3-digit numbers mean; *Place Value:* that 10 ones equal 1 ten and 10 tens equal 1 hundred; *Addition:* that addition means joining groups; how to trade ones for tens and tens for hundreds) Have students explain their answers. Write their responses under the appropriate headings.

COMMUNICATION

Discussing and Writing Math   Use flannelboard numbers to write 228 + 134 vertically on a flannelboard. Ask a student to show the numbers with base-ten blocks. Have another student add the ones and hold up the flannelboard numbers to show the total. (12) *Where do the numbers 1 and 2 go in the problem?* (The 2 goes below the ones place, and the 1 goes above the tens place.) *Why?* (The 1 means 1 ten and the 2 tells the number of ones left.) Have another student add the tens and hundreds to show the sum. (362)

EXPLORE AND CONNECT

Materials: base-ten blocks, TA17 (Place Value Chart)
Grouping Suggestions pairs
Provide students with a place value chart and base-ten blocks. Write the following numbers on the chalkboard: 235, 8, 73, 410, 39, 83, 136, 346, 281. Each student chooses a different number and models it with blocks on the place value chart. Write addition exercises from pairs' numbers vertically on the board. Have students use the blocks to add the ones, tens, and hundreds, trading when necessary, and record each step on the board as they complete it. Encourage students to build on the strengths in each other's ideas rather than to focus on the weaknesses. Allow time for partners to switch roles and repeat the activity several times with different numbers.

CONNECTIONS   Use these anytime.

Problem of the Day

Estimation   Lorada is making a ribbon wreath. She needs 187 in. of blue ribbon and 152 in. of white ribbon. Will Lorada's wreath need closer to 300 in. or 400 in. of ribbon? (400)

Life Skills

Nutrition   Choose 2 items from the chart for lunch.

Food	Calories
Apple	80
Sandwich	337
Milk	135
Carrot sticks	47
Corn chips	125

Find the total number of calories.

Math Connection

Calculator   Which step do you think has a sum over 500? Use your calculator to find out. Keep doubling the sum. Keep track of the number of steps you take.

Step 1	Step 2	Step 3	Step 4
1	2	4	8
+1	+2	+4	+8
2	4	8	16

(Step 9: 512)

CLASSWORK AND HOMEWORK SUPPLEMENTS

Practice

Skills Maintenance 18-3

Name _____

Adding: Trading 10 Tens for 1 Hundred

Add. Trade if you need to.

1.
$$\begin{array}{r}\boxed{1}\\3\ 8\ 1\\+4\ 8\ 6\\\hline 867\end{array}\quad\begin{array}{r}\boxed{1}\\6\ 8\ 2\\+\ \ 5\ 5\\\hline 737\end{array}\quad\begin{array}{r}\boxed{1}\\5\ 5\\+4\ 9\ 1\\\hline 546\end{array}\quad\begin{array}{r}\boxed{1}\\3\ 3\ 6\\+5\ 9\ 3\\\hline 929\end{array}$$

2.
$$\begin{array}{r}\boxed{1}\\3\ 7\ 1\\+4\ 3\ 2\\\hline 803\end{array}\quad\begin{array}{r}\boxed{1}\\4\ 7\ 1\\+4\ 4\ 5\\\hline 916\end{array}\quad\begin{array}{r}\boxed{1}\\4\ 4\ 2\\+1\ 6\ 2\\\hline 604\end{array}\quad\begin{array}{r}\boxed{\ }\\2\ 5\ 2\\+3\ 3\ 7\\\hline 589\end{array}$$

3.
$$\begin{array}{r}\boxed{1}\\5\ 9\ 3\\+1\ 2\ 1\\\hline 714\end{array}\quad\begin{array}{r}\boxed{1}\\1\ 9\ 5\\+4\ 3\ 4\\\hline 629\end{array}\quad\begin{array}{r}\boxed{1}\\1\ 6\ 3\\+7\ 5\ 5\\\hline 918\end{array}\quad\begin{array}{r}\boxed{1}\\2\ 8\ 5\\+4\ 2\ 4\\\hline 709\end{array}$$

4.
$$\begin{array}{r}\boxed{1}\\4\ 9\ 2\\+2\ 5\ 7\\\hline 749\end{array}\quad\begin{array}{r}\boxed{\ }\\5\ 4\ 3\\+2\ 5\ 6\\\hline 799\end{array}\quad\begin{array}{r}\boxed{1}\\4\ 8\ 4\\+3\ 5\ 5\\\hline 839\end{array}\quad\begin{array}{r}\boxed{1}\\4\ 6\ 3\\+4\ 6\ 6\\\hline 929\end{array}$$

5.
$$\begin{array}{r}\boxed{1}\\2\ 5\ 1\\+2\ 5\ 2\\\hline 503\end{array}\quad\begin{array}{r}\boxed{1}\\4\ 6\ 3\\+\ \ 9\ 3\\\hline 556\end{array}\quad\begin{array}{r}\boxed{1}\\2\ 7\ 1\\+6\ 7\ 7\\\hline 948\end{array}\quad\begin{array}{r}\boxed{\ }\\5\ 3\ 4\\+2\ 3\ 2\\\hline 766\end{array}$$

156   Use with text pages 379–380.   **PS-2**

Building Thinking Skills

Mental Math 18-3

Name _____

What's the Missing Digit?

Write the missing digit in the box.

1.
$$\begin{array}{r}1\ \boxed{7}\ 3\\+3\ 4\ 6\\\hline 5\ 1\ 9\end{array}\quad\begin{array}{r}3\ 2\ 3\\+1\ \boxed{8}\ 1\\\hline 5\ 0\ 4\end{array}\quad\begin{array}{r}2\ \boxed{9}\ 2\\+3\ 4\ 5\\\hline 6\ 3\ 7\end{array}$$

2.
$$\begin{array}{r}6\ \boxed{8}\ 2\\+1\ 7\ 4\\\hline 8\ 5\ 6\end{array}\quad\begin{array}{r}3\ 9\ 7\\+4\ \boxed{3}\ 0\\\hline 8\ 2\ 7\end{array}\quad\begin{array}{r}6\ \boxed{6}\ 5\\+2\ 9\ 1\\\hline 9\ 5\ 6\end{array}$$

3.
$$\begin{array}{r}3\ \boxed{6}\ 2\\+4\ 6\ 6\\\hline 8\ 2\ 8\end{array}\quad\begin{array}{r}1\ 2\ 7\\+3\ \boxed{9}\ 1\\\hline 5\ 1\ 8\end{array}\quad\begin{array}{r}5\ \boxed{8}\ 1\\+2\ 9\ 8\\\hline 8\ 7\ 9\end{array}$$

156   Use with text pages 379–380.   **TS-2**

Reteaching

Skills Review 18-3

Name _____

Adding: Trading 10 Tens for 1 Hundred

| Add the ones. Trade if you need to. | → | Add the tens. Trade if you need to. | → | Add the hundreds. |

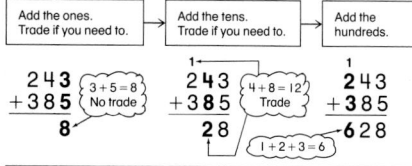

$$\begin{array}{r}2\ 4\ 3\\+3\ 8\ 5\\\hline 8\end{array}\ \left(\begin{array}{c}3+5=8\\\text{No trade}\end{array}\right)\quad\begin{array}{r}\overset{1}{2}\ 4\ 3\\+3\ 8\ 5\\\hline 2\ 8\end{array}\ \left(\begin{array}{c}4+8=12\\\text{Trade}\end{array}\right)\quad\begin{array}{r}\overset{1}{2}\ 4\ 3\\+3\ 8\ 5\\\hline 6\ 2\ 8\end{array}\ \left(1+2+3=6\right)$$

Add. Trade if you need to.

1.
$$\begin{array}{r}5\ 7\ 7\\+1\ 5\ 2\\\hline 7\ 2\ 9\end{array}\ \left(\begin{array}{c}7+5=12\\\text{Trade}\end{array}\right)\quad\begin{array}{r}4\ 8\ 2\\+1\ 5\ 3\\\hline 6\ 3\ 5\end{array}\ \left(\begin{array}{c}8+5=13\\\text{Trade}\end{array}\right)$$

2.
$$\begin{array}{r}2\ 4\ 6\\+3\ 6\ 2\\\hline 608\end{array}\quad\begin{array}{r}6\ 7\ 5\\+\ \ 5\ 1\\\hline 726\end{array}\quad\begin{array}{r}1\ 7\ 6\\+7\ 7\ 2\\\hline 948\end{array}\quad\begin{array}{r}4\ 5\ 6\\+1\ 5\ 1\\\hline 607\end{array}$$

3.
$$\begin{array}{r}1\ 7\ 5\\+1\ 9\ 3\\\hline 368\end{array}\quad\begin{array}{r}2\ 6\ 4\\3\ 8\ 4\\\hline 648\end{array}\quad\begin{array}{r}4\ 4\ 5\\+2\ 8\ 2\\\hline 727\end{array}\quad\begin{array}{r}4\ 7\ 6\\+3\ 4\ 3\\\hline 819\end{array}$$

156   Use with text pages 379–380.   **RS-2**

Challenges

Creative Thinking 18-3

Name _____

Treasure Hunt

Look at the treasure map.
Finish each set of directions.

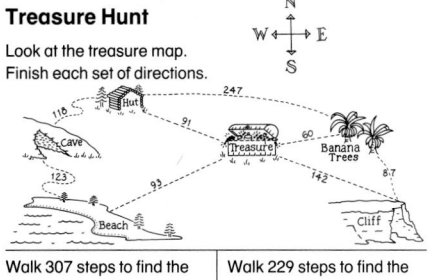

Walk 307 steps to find the treasure. Start at the hut. Walk 247 steps to the ___banana trees___. Go _60_ steps to the treasure.	Walk 229 steps to find the treasure. Start at the banana trees. Walk _87_ steps to the cliff. Go _142_ steps to the treasure.
Walk 216 steps to find the treasure. Start at the cave. Walk 123 steps to the ___beach___. Go _93_ steps to the treasure.	Walk 209 steps to find the treasure. Start at the cave. Walk _118_ steps to the hut. Go _91_ steps to the treasure.

156   Use with text pages 379–380.   **CS-2**

OPTIONS FOR INDIVIDUAL NEEDS

Basic

Exercises All
Calculator Bank, p. 402

Supplements
Reteaching 156 or
Practice 156
Challenges 156

Average

Exercises All
Calculator Bank, p. 402

Supplements
Practice 156
Challenges 156 or
Thinking Skills 156

Extended

Exercises All
Calculator Bank, p. 402

Supplements
Challenges 156
Thinking Skills 156

Other Resources:
Developing Number Concepts with Unifix Cubes, p. 178
Using the Math Explorer Calculator: A Source Book for Teachers, Chapter 14

18-3

OBJECTIVE 18-3

To model 3-digit addition problems, trading 10 tens for 1 hundred if needed

---

Materials: base-ten blocks, overhead projector, punchout number cards 0-9, spinners labeled 0-9

Grouping Suggestions: individual work, cooperative learning groups of 4

---

1. MOTIVATE AND TEACH

LEARN ABOUT IT

On the chalkboard, write an addition exercise, such as 345 + 262, in vertical form. Ask students to model the numbers with base-ten blocks on the overhead projector. Have volunteers combine the groups of blocks, trading where necessary, as you guide them through the problem on the chalkboard.
Call students' attention to Exercise 1 on page 379.

▶ **How will you know if you can trade for another ten or another hundred?** (The total number of ones or tens will be 10 or more.)

▶ **Why do you always start from the ones place when adding?** (So you can trade to a higher value, if it is necessary.)

2. CHECK UNDERSTANDING

ERROR ALERT Exercise 1: Failing to trade or to record the trade. Writing the sum as 2,125 or 125.

Name _____

Adding
Trading 10 Tens for 1 Hundred

Find the sum of 143 and 82. Use blocks to help.

1. Add the ones. Can you trade?　　yes　　(no)

What you do.　　　　　　　　　What you write.

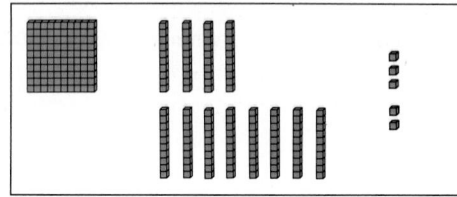

Hundreds	Tens	Ones
□	□	
1	4	3
+	8	2
		5

2. Add the tens. Can you trade?　　(yes)　　no

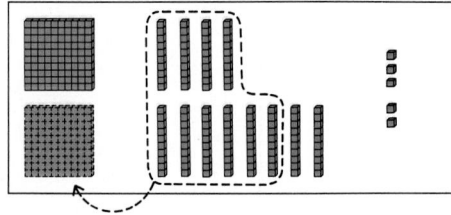

Hundreds	Tens	Ones
1	□	
1	4	3
+	8	2
	2	5

3. Add the hundreds.

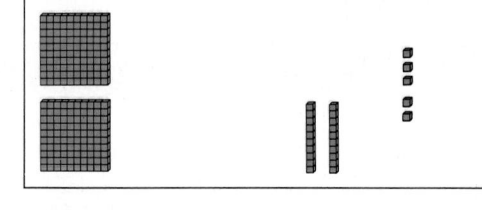

Hundreds	Tens	Ones
1	□	
1	4	3
+	8	2
2	2	5

Chapter 18　　　　　　　　　　　　　　　　(three hundred seventy-nine) 37

TEACHING OPTIONS

RETEACHING TIPS Have students use number cards to add 278 + 91 vertically. Have them add ones, then tens and show 16 tens by placing the 1 above the hundreds column and the 6 in the tens column. Then add the hundreds. Assign Reteaching Supplement 156.

ENRICHMENT Have students write 6 addition problems using the numbers: 63, 146, 79, 212. Then have them label the problems No Trade, Trade Ones, Trade Tens, or Trade Ones and Tens. Have students exchange problems and solve.

se blocks to find the sum. Trade if you can.

Hundreds	Tens	Ones
⋮	☐	
1	4	3
+1	6	2
3	0	5

Hundreds	Tens	Ones
1	☐	
1	7	5
+	7	1
2	4	6

Hundreds	Tens	Ones
☐	☐	
2	0	8
+1	3	1
3	3	9

Hundreds	Tens	Ones
1	☐	
1	9	0
+	7	0
2	6	0

$$\begin{array}{r}\overset{1}{1}5\\+391\\\hline 406\end{array}\qquad\begin{array}{r}372\\+\ \ 25\\\hline 397\end{array}\qquad\begin{array}{r}\overset{1}{8}5\\+306\\\hline 391\end{array}$$

$$\begin{array}{r}\overset{1}{1}80\\+220\\\hline 400\end{array}\qquad\begin{array}{r}78\\+\ \ 80\\\hline 158\end{array}\qquad\begin{array}{r}\overset{1}{\ }9\\+223\\\hline 232\end{array}$$

ALK ABOUT IT

Add. Make two trades for each of these
problems. Use blocks to help.
Tell what trades you made. See teaching notes.

$175 + 25 =$ _200_ $154 + 168 =$ _322_ $92 + 8 =$ _100_

CLOSE AND ASSESS

HOW WHAT YOU KNOW

ovide each group of 4 with base-ten
ocks and 3 spinners, each marked
9. Students spin to create an
dition exercise with two 3-digit
mbers. Have students take turns
cording the numbers, using the
ocks to model the addition, and
cording the sum.

QUICK QUIZ

Copy and add. Use base-ten blocks to
help.

246	147	382	95	207
+172	+ 29	+104	+142	+ 9
(418)	(176)	(486)	(237)	(216)

---

3. PRACTICE AND APPLY

Basic	All
Average	All
Extended	All

PRACTICE

*Why is there a box above the tens and
hundreds places?* (You write a 1 in it if
you trade.) *How are Exercises 3 and 4
different from Exercises 1 and 2?* (The
numbers are not written in a place value
chart.)

APPLY

TALK ABOUT IT ▶ **What happens
to the tens place when you trade 10
ones?** (The tens place has 1 more.)
▶ **What happened in the first exercise
as a result of having an extra ten?**
(There were enough tens to trade 10 tens
for another hundred.)
▶ **How could you check to see if your
answers are correct?** (Possible
answers: Use a calculator; count on for
92 + 8; add the numbers in reverse
order.)

18-3

Problem Solving: Understanding the Operations

OBJECTIVE 18-4   To understand the operations of addition and subtraction by putting together, by finding how

PREBOOK ACTIVITIES

QUICK REVIEW

Add or subtract.

35	48	52	66	137	142
+ 20	+ 16	− 24	− 30	+ 21	+ 173
(55)	(64)	(28)	(36)	(158)	(315)

PRIOR KNOWLEDGE

Tell students that 2 of their friends are collecting money for a new radio. Explain that Nat has $2.97 and Pat has $1.59. Ask students to decide whether Nat and Pat should add or subtract their money amounts for each question below.
How much do Nat and Pat have together? (add)
How much more does Nat have than Pat? (subtract)
Nat has $1.38 more than Pat. How much does Nat have? (add)
Nat spends $1.38. How much does he have left? (subtract)

COMMUNICATION

Reading and Discussing Math   Write the following Word Bank and incomplete sentences on the chalkboard. Have students read each sentence with the correct word, then write the sentences in their Math Journals.

   data   tally   bar graph   survey

1. You can take a __(survey)__ to find out what people think about something.
2. You make a __(tally)__ to keep track of the votes.
3. The results of the survey are called the __(data)__.
4. A __(bar graph)__ shows the data in a way that makes the information easy to compare.

EXPLORE AND CONNECT

COOPERATIVE ACTIVITY

Grouping Suggestion: cooperative learning groups of 3
Use blocks, paper and pencil, or a calculator to solve.
Mrs. Bush planted 325 tulips and 219 daffodils. She wondered how many bulbs she planted all together.

TEACHING ACTIONS

BEFORE
▶ **What does Mrs. Bush want to know?** (the total number of bulbs she planted)
▶ **What is the data in the story?** (325 tulip bulbs and 219 daffodil bulbs)

DURING
▶ **Should Mrs. Bush plan to add or subtract? Why?** (Add to find the total.)
▶ **How can you use mental math to estimate the sum? What estimate can you make?** (You can add the hundreds. 3 hundreds and 2 hundreds is 5 hundreds, so you can estimate about 500.)
▶ **What are three methods for solving the problem?** (Use blocks, paper and pencil, or a calculator.)

AFTER
▶ **How can you check your answer?** (Possible answers: Add the numbers in reverse order; use a different calculation method and compare answers.)

Have students work in groups of 3. Each student can solve the problem using a different calculation method. Have them decide as a group which method is most efficient. Ask students to share their ideas with the class.

CONNECTIONS   Use these anytime.

Problem of the Day

Choose the Operation   Solve.
Then write the answer in a sentence.
Jason had 54 baseball cards.
33 of them were pictures of home team players.
How many were not pictures of home team players?
(54 − 33 = 21; 21 were not home team players.)

Math Connection

Graphing   Ask 20 students to tell whether they walk to school, ride a bus, ride a bike, or ride in a car. Tally the results on a chart. Then use the chart to make a bar graph.

Number Sense

Mental Math   Use mental math to solve. Write only the answers.

40	80	63	74
+ 50	− 30	+ 20	− 10
(90)	(50)	(83)	(64)

235	144	382	289
+ 30	− 20	− 2	− 3
(265)	(124)	(380)	(286)

Data Analysis: Organizing Data

many more are needed, or by finding part; to make and read a bar graph

CLASSWORK AND HOMEWORK SUPPLEMENTS

Practice

Problem Solving 18-4

Name _____

Understanding the Operations

Use blocks, ✏️, mental math, or 🧮 to solve.
Write the answer in a sentence. Calculation methods and word sentences may vary. Sample answers shown.

1. Jack needs 50 box tops to get a baseball glove. So far he has 35 box tops. How many more does he need? _____

   He needs 15 more box tops.

2. Fran collected empty bottles. She collected 125 bottles in July and 148 in August. How many bottles did Fran collect in the two months? _____

   She collected 273 bottles.

3. Jorge earned $62. He earned $16 mowing lawns. The rest he earned washing cars. How much did he earn washing cars? _____

   He earned $46 washing cars.

PS-2   Use with text page 381.   **157**

Building Thinking Skills

Data Analysis 18-4

Name _____

Bake Sale

Nicole kept a tally of the goods sold at the bake sale.

🧁 ||||| ||||| ||||| ||||| ||||| |||||
🍪 ||||| ||||| ||||| ||||| ||||| ||||| ||||| ||||| |||||
🍊 ||||| ||||| ||||| ||||| ||||| ||||| |||||
🥧 ||||| ||||| |||||

1. Color the bar graph to show the data.

Use the graph to answer the questions.

2. How many more cookies were sold than muffins?

   _15_ more cookies

3. How many fewer pieces of pie were sold than rolls?

   _20_ fewer pieces of pie

4. How many baked goods were sold in all?

   _125_ baked goods

Baked Goods Sold

TS-2   Use with text pages 381 – 382.   **157**

Reteaching

Data Analysis 18-4

Name _____

Organizing Data

| means I vote ||||| means 5 votes

The students in Mr. Nelson's class took a vote to find out what kind of instrument each student wanted to play.

Instrument Votes

🎷 ||||| ||||| ||
🥁 ||||| |||
🎻 ||||
🎺 ||||| |

1. Count the tally marks. Write the total for each instrument.

🎷 __12__   🥁 __8__   🎻 __4__   🎺 __6__

2. Color the graph to match the data. Color I box for each vote.

Instrument Votes

3. How many more students chose recorder than drums? __4__ more students

RS-2   Use with text page 382.   **157**

Challenges

Problem Solving 18-4

Name _____

Puzzle Problems

Choose a calculation method and solve. Write the answer in a sentence.

Word sentences and calculation methods may vary. Sample answers shown.

1. Denise just finished a jigsaw puzzle that had 300 pieces. She is starting a new puzzle that has 450 pieces. How many more pieces does the new puzzle have? _____

   It has 150 more pieces.

2. Lonny's model airplane has 95 pieces. So far he has put together 46 pieces. How many pieces does he still have to put together? _____

   He has 49 pieces to put together.

3. Andrea has two dinosaur kits. The Stegosaurus has 42 pieces. The Tyrannosaurus has 68 pieces. How many more pieces does the Tyrannosaurus have? _____

   The Tyrannosaurus has 26 more pieces.

4. Brian's father collects model boats. He has 137 sailboats and 154 power boats. How many model boats does he have altogether? _____

   He has 291 model boats.

CS-2   Use with text pages 381 – 382.   **157**

OPTIONS FOR INDIVIDUAL NEEDS

Basic

Exercises All
Calculator Bank, p. 402
Computer Bank, pp. 405-408

Supplements
Reteaching 157 or
Practice 157

Average

Exercises All
Calculator Bank, p. 402
Computer Bank, pp. 405-408

Supplements
Practice 157
Challenges 157 or
Thinking Skills 157

Extended

Exercises All
Calculator Bank, p. 402
Computer Bank, pp. 405-408

Supplements
Challenges 157
Thinking Skills 157

Other Resources:
Explorations, pp. 196-200, 280-281, 292, 299, 327-329
Problem Solving Experiences In Mathematics, pp. 93, 105, 117, 123, 135, 159, 165
Mathematics Book A, p. 57

18-4

Chapter 18 Lesson 4   **381B**

OBJECTIVE 18-4

To understand the operations of addition and subtraction by putting together, by finding how many more are needed, or by finding the missing part; to make and read a bar graph

Materials: base-ten blocks, calculators

1. MOTIVATE AND TEACH

LEARN ABOUT IT

 **BEFORE** ▶ **In Exercise 1, what does Josh want to find out?** (how many more roses he needs to have 25) *What must you plan before you solve each problem?* (the operation and the method you will use to find the solution)

 **DURING** ▶ **Why might you use different calculation methods to solve different problems?** (Possible answer: It depends on the numbers in the story and the operation involved.)

AFTER ▶ **If you used paper and pencil to solve, how might you check your answer?** (Possible answers: Use blocks or a calculator.)

2. CHECK UNDERSTANDING

ERROR ALERT   Page 381

Choosing an inappropriate calculation method.

Page 382 Coloring the incorrect number of boxes to represent the tallies on the chart.

Name _____

Problem Solving
Understanding the Operations

Use blocks, paper and pencil, mental math, or to solve. Write the answer in a sentence.

1. Josh wants 25 roses for a present. He already has 10 roses. How many more does he need?

   He needs 15 more roses.
   Calculation methods may vary. Word sentences may vary.

2. Elsie sold tulip bulbs to earn money. She sold 134 bulbs one week and 82 bulbs the next week. How many bulbs did she sell in the two weeks?

   She sold 216 bulbs.

3. Mr. Gomez bought 48 iris bulbs There were 12 purple iris bulbs. The rest were yellow iris bulbs. How many yellow iris bulbs did he buy?

   He bought 36 yellow iris bulbs.

Chapter 18   (three hundred eighty-one) 38

TEACHING OPTIONS

RETEACHING TIPS Write addition and subtraction problems on the board. Include multiples of 10 and 100, 2- and 3-digit addition, and 2-digit subtraction. Have students solve them using mental math, pencil and paper, or a calculator. For help with bar graphs, assign Reteaching Supplement 157.

COMPUTER Math Rabbit, Learning Company © 1984 For use with all levels of students. Students practice addition facts by using problem solving skills. In *Circus Train,* they produce a sequence of + and − steps to load animals on the train. The game takes 5-15 minutes to complete.

Data Analysis
Organizing Data

Kenji's class is going to plant a flower garden. They took a survey to find out what kind of flower each student wanted to plant.

Finish the bar graph to show the data.

1. Write a title above the graph.
2. Write the numbers below the graph.
3. Color the graph to show the data.

Flower Survey

🌹	rose	~~IIII~~ I
🌸	pansy	~~IIII~~ ~~IIII~~
🌷	tulip	IIII
🌼	daisy	~~IIII~~ ~~IIII~~ II

> I means I vote.
> ~~IIII~~ means 5 votes.

Titles may vary.

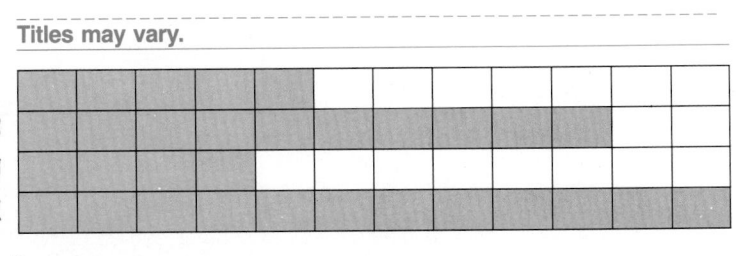

0 1 2 3 4 5 6 7 8 9 10 11 12

Use the graph to answer the questions.

4. How many more students chose pansies than chose roses? ___5___ more students

5. How many more students chose daisies than chose tulips? ___8___ more students

6. How many students voted in the survey? ___31___ students

3. PRACTICE AND APPLY

Basic	All
Average	All
Extended	All

Direct students' attention to the tally chart on page 382. What does each tally mark stand for? (1 vote) *What will you write on the line above the graph?* (a title for the graph)

▶ **What did each student vote on?** (the kind of flower they wanted to plant most)

▶ **Where can you find the data you will show on the bar graph?** (Look at the chart that shows the tally for each kind of flower.)

▶ **Describe your plan for completing the bar graph.** (Possible answer: Color one kind of flower at a time; color one square for every tally mark.)

▶ **What can you do with the results of the bar graph?** (Possible answer: Find other data by analyzing the graph, such as favorite flowers or the number of students surveyed.)

CLOSE AND ASSESS

SHOW WHAT YOU KNOW

Write the names of 3 games on the board and ask students to place a tally mark under the game they like best. Have them construct a bar graph using the data and ask questions using the graph. Then have student pairs make up a story problem using the game theme and tell how they would solve it.

QUICK QUIZ

Choose a calculation method and solve. There are 135 rose gardens in Rose, Maine. Red roses grow in 72 of the gardens. How many gardens grow roses of other colors? (63)

18-4

Chapter 18 Lesson 4   **382**

Subtracting: Trading 1 ten for 10 ones

OBJECTIVE 18-5   To model 3-digit subtraction problems, trading 1 ten for 10 ones if needed

PREBOOK ACTIVITIES

QUICK REVIEW

Copy and find the differences.

1. 84	**2.** 29	**3.** 46	**4.** 62	**5.** 90	**6.** 56	**7.** 89
−15	−12	−38	−25	−46	−35	−28
(69)	(17)	(8)	(37)	(44)	(21)	(61)

For which exercises did you trade 1 ten for 10 ones? (Exercises 1, 3, 4, 5)

PRIOR KNOWLEDGE

Help students recall what they know about subtracting 2-digit numbers. *When do you need to trade in 2-digit subtraction?* (Possible answer: when the number you are subtracting has more ones than the number you are subtracting from) *What do you do?* (Trade 1 ten for 10 ones.)

COMMUNICATION

Reading and Writing Math   Write the following sentences on the chalkboard. In their Math Journals, have students copy the sentences in the order that they would model 2-digit subtraction using base-ten blocks.
1. Take away the ones.
2. Take away the tens.
3. Look at the ones in the take-away number. Trade 1 ten for 10 ones if you need to.
4. Show the short number with tens and ones blocks.
(4, 3, 1, 2)

EXPLORE AND CONNECT

Materials: base-ten blocks
Grouping Suggestion: pairs
Provide each pair of students with base-ten blocks. Write 85 − 8 and 85 − 26 vertically on the chalkboard. *How do you know whether a trade is needed in each exercise?* (There are not enough ones to take away.) *What will you trade?* (1 ten for 10 ones) Have 1 student use blocks to model the subtraction as the partner writes and solves the exercise on paper. (77; 59) Next, write 283 − 145 vertically on the board. *Are there enough ones to take 5 away?* (no) *What can you do?* (Trade 1 ten for 10 ones.) Have students change roles and solve. (138) *How is subtracting 2-digit numbers the same as subtracting 3-digit numbers? How is it different?* (Both may require trading 1 ten for 10 ones; with 3-digit numbers, you must also subtract hundreds.) Encourage students to build on the strengths in each other's ideas rather than to focus on the weaknesses.

CONNECTIONS   Use these anytime.

Problem of the Day

Show with Objects   Use punchout money to solve.
Jane had $1. She bought a can of juice for 65¢. Jane got 3 coins as change. What 3 coins did she get? (1 quarter and 2 nickels)

Number Sense

Estimation   Which problems will have a difference over 200? Copy the problems and ring your guesses. Then use your calculator to check.

356	275	872	654	521
−125	− 99	−544	−501	−316
(231)	(176)	(328)	(153)	(205)

Math Connection

Measurement   Cut a string 95 cm long. Cut the string into 2 pieces. Measure 1 piece. How can you find the length of the other piece without measuring? (Subtract the length of the piece from 95; answers will vary.)

CLASSWORK AND HOMEWORK SUPPLEMENTS

Basic

Exercises All, Midchapter
Review/Quiz
Calculator Bank, p. 403
More Practice, p. 431, set C

Supplements
Reteaching 158 or
Practice 158
Challenges 158

Average

Exercises All, Midchapter
Review/Quiz
Calculator Bank, p. 403
More Practice, p. 431, set C

Supplements
Practice 158
Challenges 158 or
Thinking Skills 158

Extended

Exercises All, Midchapter
Review/Quiz
Calculator Bank, p. 403

Supplements
Challenges 158
Thinking Skills 158

Other Resources:
Mathematics Book A, pp.
26-27
Explorations, p. 287

Practice

Skills Maintenance — 18-5

Name _____

Subtracting: Trading 1 Ten for 10 Ones

Subtract. Trade if you need.

1.
$$\begin{array}{r}6\ 12\\ 6\ 7\ 2\\ -2\ 1\ 4\\ \hline 458\end{array}\quad\begin{array}{r}5\ 14\\ 9\ 6\ 4\\ -4\ 3\ 9\\ \hline 525\end{array}\quad\begin{array}{r}7\ 16\\ 9\ 8\ 6\\ -5\ 5\ 9\\ \hline 427\end{array}\quad\begin{array}{r}3\ 14\\ 7\ 4\ 4\\ -1\ 3\ 8\\ \hline 606\end{array}$$

2.
$$\begin{array}{r}\square\square\\ 8\ 5\ 6\\ -6\ 3\ 6\\ \hline 220\end{array}\quad\begin{array}{r}8\ 13\\ 7\ 9\ 3\\ -3\ 8\ 9\\ \hline 404\end{array}\quad\begin{array}{r}4\ 15\\ 6\ 5\ 5\\ -4\ 2\ 7\\ \hline 228\end{array}\quad\begin{array}{r}5\ 11\\ 4\ 6\ 1\\ -3\ 5\ 6\\ \hline 105\end{array}$$

3.
$$\begin{array}{r}4\ 12\\ 7\ 5\ 2\\ -4\ 1\ 5\\ \hline 337\end{array}\quad\begin{array}{r}\square\square\\ 9\ 9\ 9\\ -1\ 9\ 3\\ \hline 806\end{array}\quad\begin{array}{r}6\ 13\\ 5\ 7\ 3\\ -4\ 5\ 8\\ \hline 115\end{array}\quad\begin{array}{r}\square\square\\ 8\ 9\ 7\\ -1\ 6\ 7\\ \hline 730\end{array}$$

4.
$$\begin{array}{r}2\ 11\\ 9\ 3\ 1\\ -2\ 2\ 2\\ \hline 709\end{array}\quad\begin{array}{r}2\ 10\\ 6\ 3\ 0\\ -\ \ \ \ 9\\ \hline 621\end{array}\quad\begin{array}{r}8\ 14\\ 8\ 9\ 4\\ -3\ 7\ 8\\ \hline 516\end{array}\quad\begin{array}{r}6\ 15\\ 6\ 7\ 5\\ -5\ 6\ 6\\ \hline 109\end{array}$$

5.
$$\begin{array}{r}8\ 17\\ 3\ 9\ 7\\ -1\ 6\ 8\\ \hline 229\end{array}\quad\begin{array}{r}\square\square\\ 9\ 8\ 8\\ -7\ 2\ 8\\ \hline 260\end{array}\quad\begin{array}{r}1\ 11\\ 7\ 2\ 1\\ -5\ 1\ 3\\ \hline 208\end{array}\quad\begin{array}{r}7\ 12\\ 6\ 8\ 2\\ -6\ 7\ 6\\ \hline 6\end{array}$$

158 · Use with text pages 383 – 384. · PS-2

Building Thinking Skills

Math Reasoning — 18-5

Name _____

Grading Janet's Paper

Put an X on each incorrect answer.
Correct each problem Janet missed.

Name __Janet__

1.
$$\begin{array}{r}3\ 6\ 2\\ -1\ 2\ 4\\ \hline 238\end{array}\quad\begin{array}{r}6\ 8\ 6\\ -2\ 3\ 8\\ \hline 448\end{array}\quad\begin{array}{r}5\ 7\ 4\\ -1\ 2\ 7\\ \hline \cancel{453}\\ 447\end{array}\quad\begin{array}{r}6\ 4\ 5\\ -1\ 3\ 5\\ \hline 510\end{array}$$

2.
$$\begin{array}{r}9\ 5\ 1\\ -1\ 2\ 5\\ \hline \cancel{827}\\ 826\end{array}\quad\begin{array}{r}7\ 6\ 0\\ -6\ 0\ 2\\ \hline 158\end{array}\quad\begin{array}{r}4\ 8\ 2\\ -\ \ 4\ 9\\ \hline 433\end{array}\quad\begin{array}{r}8\ 5\ 3\\ -2\ 1\ 8\\ \hline \cancel{634}\\ 635\end{array}$$

3.
$$\begin{array}{r}8\ 9\ 4\\ -3\ 3\ 5\\ \hline 559\end{array}\quad\begin{array}{r}6\ 8\ 3\\ -6\ 5\ 5\\ \hline \cancel{32}\\ 28\end{array}\quad\begin{array}{r}7\ 4\ 5\\ -1\ 2\ 3\\ \hline \cancel{612}\\ 622\end{array}\quad\begin{array}{r}5\ 7\ 0\\ -1\ 3\ 9\\ \hline 431\end{array}$$

158 · Use with text pages 383 – 384. · TS-2

Reteaching

Skills Review — 18-5

Name _____

Subtracting: Trading 1 Ten for 10 Ones

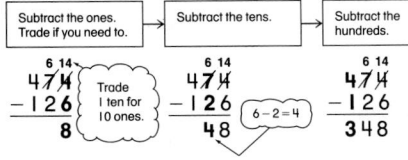

Subtract the ones. Trade if you need to. → Subtract the tens. → Subtract the hundreds.

$$\begin{array}{r}6\ 14\\ 4\ 7\ 4\\ -1\ 2\ 6\\ \hline 8\end{array}\ \text{Trade 1 ten for 10 ones.}\quad\begin{array}{r}6\ 14\\ 4\ 7\ 4\\ -1\ 2\ 6\\ \hline 48\end{array}\ 6-2=4\quad\begin{array}{r}6\ 14\\ 4\ 7\ 4\\ -1\ 2\ 6\\ \hline 348\end{array}$$

Subtract. Trade if you need to.

1.
$$\begin{array}{r}4\ 12\\ 5\ 5\ 2\\ -1\ 2\ 6\\ \hline 426\end{array}\ \text{1 less ten, 10 more ones}\quad\begin{array}{r}5\ 15\\ 3\ 6\ 5\\ -\ \ 2\ 7\\ \hline 338\end{array}\ \text{Trade.}\quad\begin{array}{r}4\ 10\\ 4\ 5\ 0\\ -1\ 1\ 8\\ \hline 332\end{array}\ \text{Trade.}$$

2.
$$\begin{array}{r}6\ 5\ 2\\ -2\ 2\ 6\\ \hline 426\end{array}\quad\begin{array}{r}4\ 4\ 5\\ -1\ 2\ 4\\ \hline 321\end{array}\quad\begin{array}{r}5\ 2\ 8\\ -2\ 1\ 9\\ \hline 309\end{array}\quad\begin{array}{r}3\ 7\ 6\\ -1\ 5\ 8\\ \hline 218\end{array}$$

3.
$$\begin{array}{r}7\ 8\ 0\\ -5\ 1\ 6\\ \hline 264\end{array}\quad\begin{array}{r}4\ 3\ 6\\ -\ \ \ \ 9\\ \hline 427\end{array}\quad\begin{array}{r}8\ 4\ 6\\ -5\ 1\ 5\\ \hline 331\end{array}\quad\begin{array}{r}2\ 2\ 8\\ -\ \ 1\ 9\\ \hline 209\end{array}$$

158 · Use with text pages 383 – 384. · RS-2

Challenges

Family Math — 18-5

Name _____

Dear Family,
We are learning to subtract with trading 1 ten for 10 ones. Help your child practice.
You will need 12 slips of paper with the numbers below written on them.

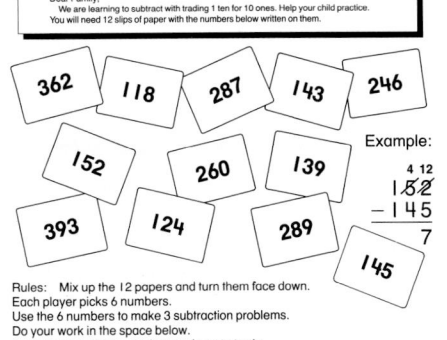

362 · 118 · 287 · 143 · 246
152 · 260 · 139
393 · 124 · 289

Example:
$$\begin{array}{r}4\ 12\\ 1\ 5\ 2\\ -1\ 4\ 5\\ \hline 7\end{array}$$

145

Rules: Mix up the 12 papers and turn them face down.
Each player picks 6 numbers.
Use the 6 numbers to make 3 subtraction problems.
Do your work in the space below.
Arrange the numbers so that you have to trade.
Subtract the smaller numbers from the larger ones.
If you did not trade, your score is 5 points for each.
If you traded 1 ten for 10 ones, your score is 10 points for each.

158 · Use with text pages 383 – 384. · CS-2

18-5

LESSON PLAN 18-5

OBJECTIVE 18-5
To model 3-digit subtraction problems, trading 1 ten for 10 ones if needed

---

Materials: base-ten blocks, TA17 (Place Value Chart), index cards with 2- and 3-digit subtraction exercises

Grouping Suggestions: individual work, cooperative learning groups of 4

---

1. MOTIVATE AND TEACH

LEARN ABOUT IT

Write 465 − 134 in vertical form on the chalkboard. Ask a volunteer to model the top number with base-ten blocks. Invite other students to complete the subtraction process as you guide them through the steps on the chalkboard. Call students' attention to Exercise 1 on page 383.

▶ **How will you know if you need to trade 1 ten for 10 ones?** (There will not be enough ones to take away.)

▶ **Suppose you were subtracting 145-37. What would the difference in the tens place be. Why?** (There would be a 0 in the tens place because 1 ten would be taken from the 4 tens when you traded, leaving only 3 tens; 3 tens − 3 tens equals 0 tens.)

2. CHECK UNDERSTANDING

ERROR ALERT Neglecting to subtract all the columns.

Name _____

Subtracting
Trading 1 Ten for 10 Ones

Subtract 135 from 264. Use blocks to help.

1. Look at the ones. Do you need to trade? **(yes)** no
   Subtract the ones. Draw and cross out blocks to show it.

   What you do.   What you write.

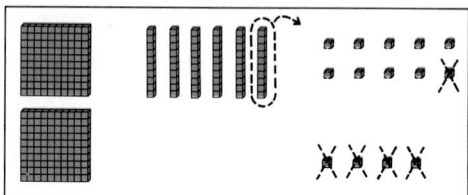

Hundreds	Tens	Ones
	⑤	⑭
2	6̸′	4̸
− 1	3	5
		9

2. Subtract the tens. Cross out to show it.

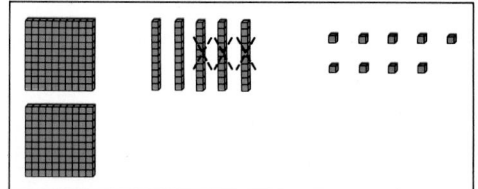

Hundreds	Tens	Ones
	5	14
2	6̸	4̸
− 1	3	5
	2	9

3. Subtract the hundreds. Cross out to show it.

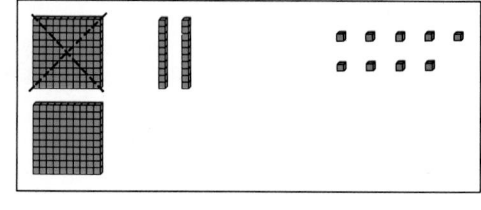

Hundreds	Tens	Ones
	5	14
2	6̸	4̸
− 1	3	5
1	2	9

Chapter 18   (three hundred eighty-three) 38

TEACHING OPTIONS

RETEACHING TIPS Have students write 450 − 35 vertically and use blocks to model 450 on a place value chart. As students find the difference for each place value, they make a check above it on the written problem and record the difference. Assign Reteaching Supplement 158.

ENRICHMENT On cards, write 4 subtraction exercises and their solutions. Cut to separate the exercises from the solutions to make 2-piece puzzles, and mix the pieces. Have students solve each exercise to match the puzzle pieces.

Use blocks to find the difference.
Trade 1 ten for 10 ones if you need to.

Hundreds	Tens	Ones
	1̶	1̶5̶
3	2̶	5̶
−1	1	7
2	0	8

Hundreds	Tens	Ones
	3	16
1	4̶	6̶
−	2	8
1	1	8

2.

```
  0 17
  3̶/7̶
−108
 209
```

```
  3 10
 1̶4̶0̶
−135
    5
```

```
 386
− 42
 344
```

3.

```
  5 14
 2̶6̶4̶/
− 39
 225
```

```
 226
−205
  21
```

```
  0 10
 3̶1̶0̶/
−206
 104
```

MIDCHAPTER REVIEW/QUIZ

Add. Use blocks to help.

1.

```
 1
 208
+ 55
 263
```

```
 1
 127
+ 91
 218
```

```
 70
+60
130
```

```
 211
+214
 425
```

```
 460
+212
 672
```

2.

```
 314
+311
 625
```

```
  1
 226
+183
 409
```

```
 40
+50
 90
```

```
  1
 162
+ 53
 215
```

```
  1
 214
+ 29
 243
```

384 (three hundred eighty-four)   More Practice, page 431, set C   Chapter 18

---

3. PRACTICE AND APPLY

Basic	All, Midchapter Review/Quiz
Average	All, Midchapter Review/Quiz
Extended	All, Midchapter Review/Quiz

PRACTICE

How will you show the trades in the exercises at the top of page 384? (Write the number that is 10 more above the ones place; write the number that is 1 less ten above the tens place.)

APPLY

▶ **For subtraction exercises such as these, in which box might you write a number greater than 10? Why?** (above the ones place; you trade 1 ten for 10 ones and must add them to the ones already in the ones place)

MIDCHAPTER REVIEW/QUIZ The table correlates the Midchapter Review/Quiz items with the lesson objectives.

Items	Objectives
1-2	18-1, 18-2, 18-3, 18-5

CLOSE AND ASSESS

SHOW WHAT YOU KNOW

Review with students the chapter story, *How the Peacock Got Its Tail Feathers*. How many flowers were left in the peacock's garden after the little man took the first batch of flowers? (280 − 28 = 252) Have pairs of students work together and use blocks to solve the problem.

QUICK QUIZ

Copy and solve. Use blocks to help.

```
 497      325      133      470
−148     −205     − 29     −342
(349)    (120)    (104)    (128)
```

18-5

Chapter 18 Lesson 5   **384**

LESSON OPTIONS 18-6

Trading 1 Hundred for 10 Tens

OBJECTIVE 18-6   To trade 1 hundred for 10 tens

PREBOOK ACTIVITIES

QUICK REVIEW

Tell the number of hundreds, tens, and ones in each number.

365   (3 hundreds, 6 tens, 5 ones)
405   (4 hundreds, 0 tens, 5 ones)
170   (1 hundred, 7 tens, 0 ones)
 92   (0 hundreds, 9 tens, 2 ones)
800   (8 hundreds, 0 tens, 0 ones)

PRIOR KNOWLEDGE

Help students recall that they traded 10 ones for 1 ten in addition and 1 ten for 10 ones in subtraction. *Why were you able to make these trades?* (because 1 ten equals 10 ones) *What other trades were you able to make when adding 3-digit numbers?* (10 tens could be traded for 1 hundred.) *Why?* (because 10 tens equals 1 hundred) *Do you think you could trade 1 hundred for 10 tens?* (yes) *Why?* (Possible answer: Because if you can trade one way, you should be able to reverse the trade.)

COMMUNICATION

Listening and Discussing Math   Tell students that you will read sentences that contain a mystery word. Explain that you will say *buzz* every time the mystery word occurs in the sentence. Challenge students to identify the mystery word.
1. Sometimes you need to *buzz* in addition and subtraction.
2. You can *buzz* 10 ones for 1 ten or *buzz* 1 ten for 10 ones.
3. In addition, you can *buzz* 10 tens to make 1 hundred.
4. In subtraction, you can *buzz* 1 hundred for 10 tens.
What is the mystery word? (trade) Reread the sentences using the word **trade** in place of *buzz*.

EXPLORE AND CONNECT

Materials: base-ten blocks
Grouping Suggestion: pairs
Provide each pair with base-ten blocks and paper. The first student writes the number 248 on the paper. The partner models the number with blocks. *How many hundreds, tens, and ones does your number have?* (2 hundreds, 4 tens, 8 ones) *Trade 1 hundred for 10 tens. How many hundreds, tens, and ones do you have after the trade?* (1 hundred, 14 tens, 8 ones) *Is it the same total amount as before the trade?* (yes) *How can you show the trade in writing?* (Cross out the 4, write 14; cross out the 2; write 1.) Demonstrate on the chalkboard how to record the numbers in boxes as shown on page 385 of this lesson. Allow time for students to switch roles and repeat the activity several times, making up their own 3-digit numbers. As students work, encourage them to build on the strengths of each other's ideas rather than to focus on the weaknesses.

CONNECTIONS   Use these anytime.

Problem of the Day

Write a Question   Write a subtraction question that can be answered using this data. Then answer the question.
Peter is reading a book.
He is on page 143.
The book has 319 pages.
(How many more pages does Peter have left to read? 176)

Math Connection

Place Value   Trade 10 tens for 1 hundred. Write the 3-digit number.
1. 3 hundreds, 13 tens, 5 ones (435)
2. 16 tens, 6 ones (166)
3. 2 hundreds, 18 tens (380)
4. 4 hundreds, 10 tens, 6 ones (506)
5. 5 hundreds, 11 tens, 2 ones (612)
6. 1 hundred, 19 tens, 9 ones (299)

Life Skills

Money   Imagine that you have a roll of 20 dimes. You see this sign:
Toy car $1.50
Doll $1.80
Ball $1.20
Write the name and price of the toy you would choose. Tell how many dimes you would need to pay for the toy. (car, 15 dimes; doll, 18 dimes; ball, 12 dimes)

CLASSWORK AND HOMEWORK SUPPLEMENTS

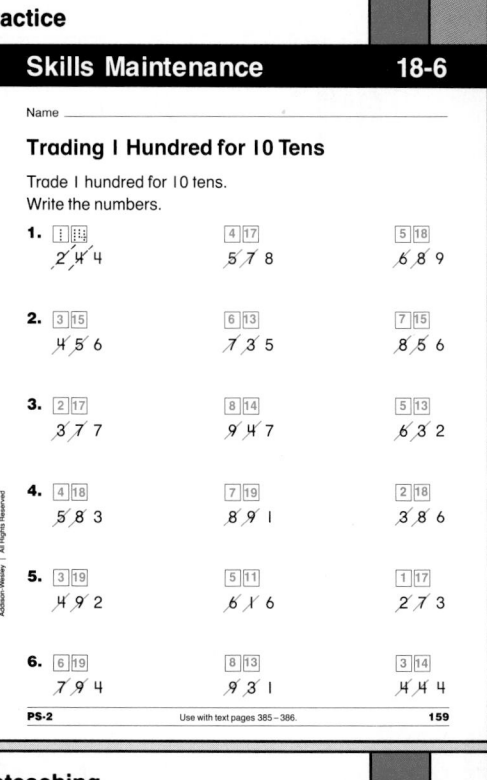

Practice

Skills Maintenance   18-6

Name _____

Trading 1 Hundred for 10 Tens

Trade 1 hundred for 10 tens.
Write the numbers.

1. | 1 | 14 | 4 | 17 | 5 | 18 |
   2 4 4   5 7 8   6 8 9

2. | 3 | 15 | 6 | 13 | 7 | 15 |
   4 5 6   7 3 5   8 5 6

3. | 2 | 17 | 8 | 14 | 5 | 13 |
   3 7 7   9 4 7   6 3 2

4. | 4 | 18 | 7 | 19 | 2 | 18 |
   5 8 3   8 9 1   3 8 6

5. | 3 | 19 | 5 | 11 | 1 | 17 |
   4 9 2   6 1 6   2 7 3

6. | 6 | 19 | 8 | 13 | 3 | 14 |
   7 9 4   9 3 1   4 4 4

PS-2   Use with text pages 385 – 386.   159

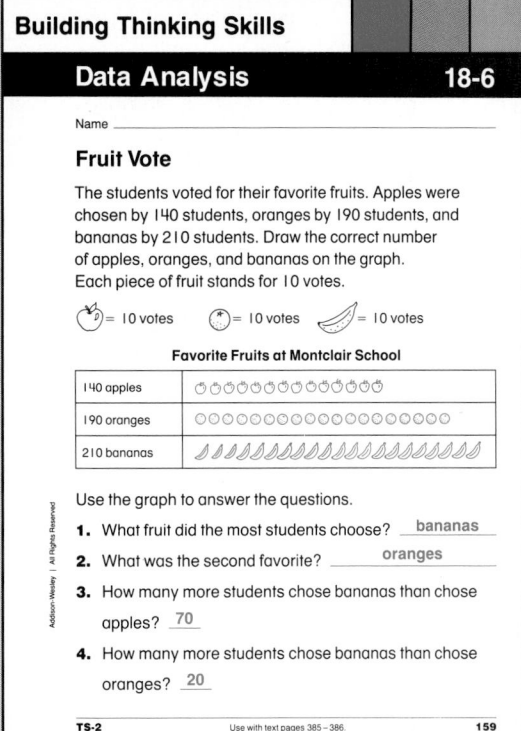

Building Thinking Skills

Data Analysis   18-6

Name _____

Fruit Vote

The students voted for their favorite fruits. Apples were chosen by 140 students, oranges by 190 students, and bananas by 210 students. Draw the correct number of apples, oranges, and bananas on the graph. Each piece of fruit stands for 10 votes.

= 10 votes   = 10 votes   = 10 votes

Favorite Fruits at Montclair School

140 apples	○○○○○○○○○○○○○○
190 oranges	○○○○○○○○○○○○○○○○○○○
210 bananas	///////////////////////

Use the graph to answer the questions.

1. What fruit did the most students choose? **bananas**

2. What was the second favorite? **oranges**

3. How many more students chose bananas than chose apples? **70**

4. How many more students chose bananas than chose oranges? **20**

TS-2   Use with text pages 385 – 386.   159

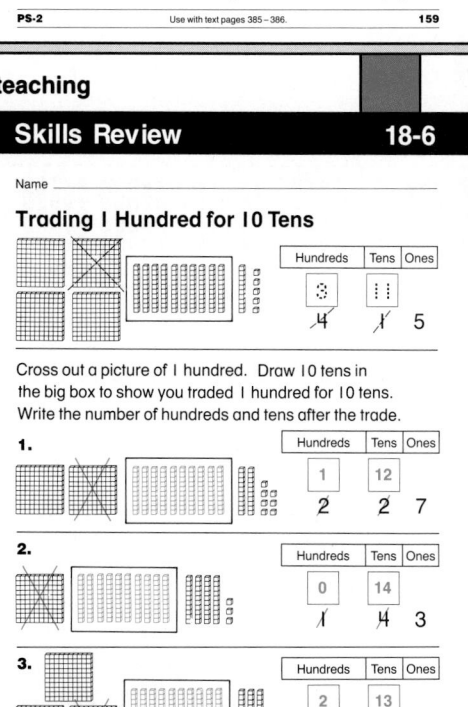

Reteaching

Skills Review   18-6

Name _____

Trading 1 Hundred for 10 Tens

Hundreds	Tens	Ones
3	1	5
4	1	5

Cross out a picture of 1 hundred. Draw 10 tens in the big box to show you traded 1 hundred for 10 tens. Write the number of hundreds and tens after the trade.

1. | Hundreds | Tens | Ones |
   |---|---|---|
   | 1 | 12 | 7 |
   | 2 | 2 | 7 |

2. | Hundreds | Tens | Ones |
   |---|---|---|
   | 0 | 14 | 3 |
   | 1 | 4 | 3 |

3. | Hundreds | Tens | Ones |
   |---|---|---|
   | 2 | 13 | 6 |
   | 3 | 3 | 6 |

RS-2   Use with text pages 385 – 386.   159

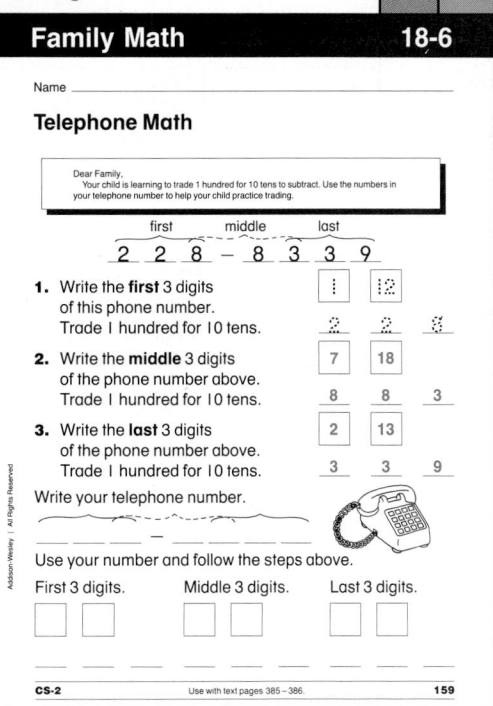

Challenges

Family Math   18-6

Name _____

Telephone Math

Dear Family,
  Your child is learning to trade 1 hundred for 10 tens to subtract. Use the numbers in your telephone number to help your child practice trading.

first   middle   last
2 2 8 – 8 3 3 9

1. Write the **first** 3 digits of this phone number. Trade 1 hundred for 10 tens.
   | 1 | 12 |
   2 2 8

2. Write the **middle** 3 digits of the phone number above. Trade 1 hundred for 10 tens.
   | 7 | 18 |
   8 8 3

3. Write the **last** 3 digits of the phone number above. Trade 1 hundred for 10 tens.
   | 2 | 13 |
   3 3 9

Write your telephone number.

_____ — _____

Use your number and follow the steps above.

First 3 digits.   Middle 3 digits.   Last 3 digits.

CS-2   Use with text pages 385 – 386.   159

OPTIONS FOR INDIVIDUAL NEEDS

Basic

Exercises All
Calculator Bank, p. 403

Supplements
Reteaching 159 or
Practice 159
Thinking Skills 159

Average

Exercises All
Calculator Bank, p. 403

Supplements
Practice 159
Challenges 159 or
Thinking Skills 159

Extended

Exercises All
Calculator Bank, p. 403

Supplements
Challenges 159
Thinking Skills 159

Other Resources:
Mathematics Book A, pp. 26-27

18-6

OBJECTIVE 18-6
To trade 1 hundred for 10 tens

> **Materials:** paste, scissors, base-ten blocks, punchout number cards 0-9, number cubes 1-6
>
> **Grouping Suggestions:** individual work, cooperative learning groups of 4

1. MOTIVATE AND TEACH

LEARN ABOUT IT

Give students 3-digit numbers to model with base-ten blocks. Have them trade 1 hundred for 10 tens and tell how many hundreds, tens, and ones there are after the trade. *How do you know that the amounts before and after the trade are equal?* (You know 1 hundred equals 10 tens; you can count blocks to check.) Call students' attention to the trade in Exercise 1.

▶ **How does the place value chart show the trade from 1 hundred to 10 tens?** (The 5 is changed to 15 in the tens place; the 3 is changed to 2 in the hundreds place.)

▶ **Why does the hundreds place get smaller by 1 and the tens place get larger by 10?** (because 1 hundred equals 10 tens; so when you trade 1 hundred, you get 10 tens)

▶ **In Exercise 3, why does the tens place have only 10 tens after the trade?** (because there were no tens before the trade)

2. CHECK UNDERSTANDING

ERROR ALERT Failing to add 10 to the digit in the tens place after trading. Failing to subtract 100 from the hundreds place.

Name _____

Trading 1 Hundred for 10 Tens

Cut out the tens. Trade by pasting 10 tens over 1 hundred. Write the numbers of hundreds and tens.

1.
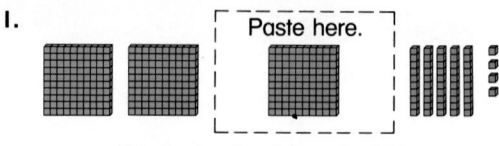
Students should paste 10 tens.

Hundreds	Tens	Ones
2̶ 3̶	1̶5̶ 5̶	4

2.
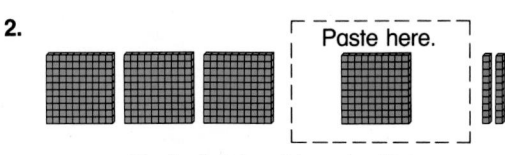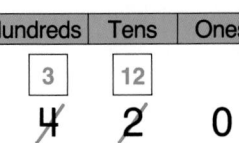
Students should paste 10 tens.

Hundreds	Tens	Ones
3̶ 4̶	12̶ 2̶	0

3.
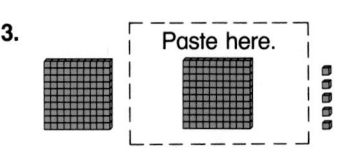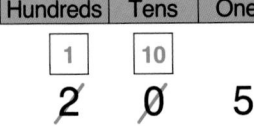
Students should paste 10 tens.

Hundreds	Tens	Ones
1̶ 2̶	10̶ 0̶	5

4.
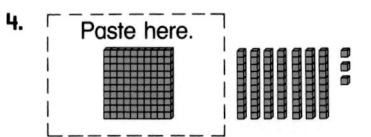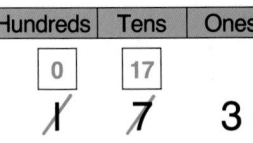
Students should paste 10 tens.

Hundreds	Tens	Ones
0̶ 1̶	17̶ 7̶	3

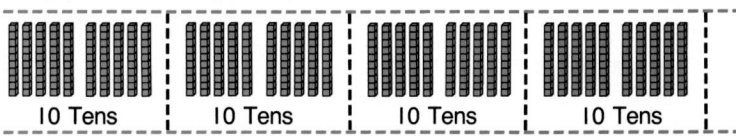

| 10 Tens | 10 Tens | 10 Tens | 10 Tens |

Chapter 18   (three hundred eighty-five) **385**

TEACHING OPTIONS

RETEACHING TIPS Have students model 1 hundred and 5 tens with blocks and place number cards 1 and 5 below them. As they trade the hundred for 10 tens, they move the 1 to the tens place and place a 0 in the hundreds place. Repeat for other numbers. Assign Reteaching Supplement 159.

ENRICHMENT Have students make up subtraction exercises involving 3-digit numbers with one trade from the hundreds to the tens place. Have them exchange exercises with a classmate and show the trades by crossing out numbers and writing new ones. Check the trades with base-ten blocks.

rade 1 hundred for 10 tens. Write
ne numbers. Use blocks to help.

2 hundreds, 3 tens is the same as 1 hundred, 13 tens.

| 1 | 13 |
2̸ 3̸ 0

| 2 | 18 | | 1 | 15 | | 4 | 10 | | 3 | 11 |
3̸ 8̸ 6   2̸ 5̸ 1   5̸ 0̸ 2   4̸ 1̸ 7

| 1 | 17 | | 5 | 10 | | 2 | 12 | | 0 | 14 |
2̸ 7̸ 4   6̸ 0̸ 0   3̸ 2̸ 0   1̸ 4̸ 6

| 3 | 19 | | 1 | 12 | | 0 | 17 | | 2 | 16 |
4̸ 9̸ 2   2̸ 2̸ 5   1̸ 7̸ 0   3̸ 6̸ 1

| 2 | 10 | | 1 | 18 | | 4 | 13 | | 0 | 10 |
3̸ 0̸ 0   2̸ 8̸ 9   5̸ 3̸ 0   1̸ 0̸ 0

SE CRITICAL THINKING

Suppose you have these blocks.

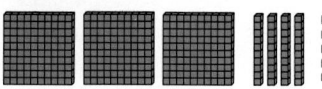

Ring the amounts you could pick up without trading. Use blocks to check.

250 (234) 328 (345)

3. PRACTICE AND APPLY

Basic	All
Average	All
Extended	All

PRACTICE

How can you show that a trade has been made? (Cross out the numbers and write the new amounts in the boxes above.) *What number would you write in the hundreds box after a trade if there were only 1 hundred to start with?* (0)

APPLY

USE CRITICAL THINKING ▶ **How can you tell if an amount can be picked up without trading?** (The number in each place will be the same or less than the number of each kind of block shown.)
▶ **What trade would you need to make to take away 250 from the blocks? How do you know?** (Trade 1 hundred for 10 tens; there are not enough tens to take away 5 tens.)
▶ **How could you cross out to subtract 234 from the blocks shown?** (Cross out 2 hundreds, 3 tens, and 4 ones.) **What 3-digit number tells how many are left?** (111)

CLOSE AND ASSESS

HOW WHAT YOU KNOW
rovide each cooperative learning roup of 4 with a number cube beled 1-6 and base-ten blocks. One udent rolls the number cube 3 times nd writes a 3-digit number. Another udent models the number with ocks. The third trades 1 hundred ith the fourth student, who replaces e hundred with 10 tens. The first udent records the trade.

QUICK QUIZ

Trade 1 hundred for 10 tens. Show the trade by crossing out and writing above the original numbers.
345 719 143 928 360 200
(2/14; 6/11; 0/14; 8/12; 2/16; 1/10)

18-6

Subtracting: Trading 1 Hundred for 10 Tens

OBJECTIVE 18-7 To model 3-digit subtraction problems, trading 1 hundred for 10 tens if needed

PREBOOK ACTIVITIES

QUICK REVIEW

Use blocks. Trade 1 ten for 10 ones. Tell how many hundreds, tens, and ones.

413 4/0/13)   277 (2/6/17)   840 (8/3/10)   574 (5/6/14)

Use blocks. Trade 1 hundred for 10 tens. Tell how many hundreds, tens, and ones.

742 (6/14/2)   613 (5/11/3)   902 (8/10/2)   216 (1/11/6)

PRIOR KNOWLEDGE

Provide a situation such as the following to help students recall subtraction with trading 1 ten for 10 ones.

Christie's aunt lives 455 miles away.
Christie has traveled 237 miles so far.
How can we find out how many more miles Christie has to travel to get to her aunt's house? (Subtract 237 from 455.) Write 455 − 237 in vertical form on the chalkboard. *Are there enough ones to subtract?* (no) *What do you need to do?* (Trade 1 ten for 10 ones.) Have a student make the trade, then complete the problem. *How many more miles does Christie have to travel?* (218 mi)

COMMUNICATION

Discussing Math   Display base-ten blocks to show the number 357. Write 246, 319, and 185 on the board. *Which number could be subtracted from 357 with no trades?* (246) *Which number could be subtracted from 357 with a trade of 1 ten for 10 ones?* (319) *How could you subtract 185 from 357?* (Trade 1 hundred for 10 tens.) *How do you know?* (There are not enough tens to take 8 tens away. You get 10 more tens if you trade 1 hundred.)

EXPLORE AND CONNECT

Materials: base-ten blocks, number cubes labeled 1-6 and 4-9
Grouping Suggestion: pairs
Provide each pair with base-ten blocks and 2 number cubes. The first student models 299 with blocks. The second student rolls the number cubes to make a 2-digit number, then takes away that many blocks from the pile, trading when necessary. The first student now rolls the number cubes and takes away from the remaining amount. Students continue to roll and take away blocks until there are no blocks or there are not enough to subtract the rolled number. Encourage students to help each other when questions arise. Students should build on the strengths in each other's ideas rather than focus on the weaknesses.

CONNECTIONS   Use these anytime.

Problem of the Day

Writing a Story   Finish writing the story for 427 − 165 = _____. Ask a subtraction question in your story. Use blocks to solve. Write the answer in a sentence to end your story.
Eddie had 427 stickers.
(Stories will vary but should include a subtraction question and the answer, 262, in a sentence.)

Math Connection

Subtraction Patterns   Finish the patterns.
1. Subtract 100.
699, 599, (499), (399), (299), (199)
2. Subtract 11.
788, 777, (766), (755), (744), (733)
3. Subtract 110.
760, 650, (540), (430), (320), (210)

Number Sense

Estimation   Renée has 275 yellow counters and some red counters, too. She knows that she has between 575 and 600 counters in all. What is the least number and the greatest number of red counters that she could have? (300, 325)

CLASSWORK AND HOMEWORK SUPPLEMENTS

Practice

Skills Maintenance 18-7

Name _____

Subtracting: Trading 1 Hundred for 10 Tens

Subtract.

1.
$\overset{7\;|13}{8\,3\,4} - 680 = 154$
$\overset{6\;|14}{7\,4\,6} - 476 = 270$
$\overset{4\;|13}{5\,3\,6} - 275 = 261$
$\overset{3\;|10}{4\,0\,7} - 384 = 23$

2.
$\overset{5\;|18}{6\,8\,5} - 595 = 90$
$\overset{8\;|10}{9\,0\,5} - 742 = 163$
$\overset{3\;|12}{4\,2\,3} - 260 = 163$
$\overset{6\;|14}{7\,4\,5} - 663 = 82$

3.
$\overset{7\;|12}{8\,2\,4} - 172 = 652$
$\overset{4\;|13}{5\,4\,5} - 180 = 365$
$\overset{8\;|11}{9\,1\,7} - 387 = 530$
$\overset{3\;|13}{4\,3\,2} - 160 = 272$

4.
$\;9\,5\,8 - 850 = 108$
$\overset{4\;|11}{5\,1\,9} - 369 = 150$
$\overset{7\;|17}{8\,7\,9} - 791 = 88$
$\overset{5\;|13}{6\,3\,2} - 391 = 241$

5.
$\overset{3\;|16}{4\,6\,8} - 394 = 74$
$\overset{5\;|16}{6\,6\,1} - 281 = 380$
$\overset{8\;|14}{9\,4\,9} - 652 = 297$
$\overset{7\;|15}{8\,5\,7} - 381 = 476$

160   Use with text pages 387–388.   PS-2

Addison-Wesley | All Rights Reserved

Reteaching

Skills Review 18-7

Name _____

Subtracting: Trading 1 Hundred for 10 Tens

| Subtract the ones. Trade if you need to. | Subtract the tens. Trade if you need to. | Subtract the hundreds. |

$536 - 182$ $6 - 2 = 4$ No trade → 4

$\overset{4\;|13}{5\,3\,6} - 182$ Trade 1 hundred for 10 tens. → $5\,4$

$\overset{4\;|13}{5\,3\,6} - 182 = 354$

Subtract. Trade if you need to.

Finish subtracting.

1.
$\overset{5\;|12}{4\,6\,2} - 237 = 225$ *1 less ten, 10 more ones*
$\overset{5\;|10}{6\,0\,5} - 172 = 433$ *1 less hundred, 10 more tens*
$\overset{6\;|13}{7\,3\,3} - 281 = 452$

2.
$\overset{2\;|13}{3\,3\,7} - 164 = 173$
$\overset{4\;|10}{5\,0\,9} - 44 = 465$
$\overset{4\;|12}{4\,5\,2} - 317 = 135$
$8\,6\,3 - 241 = 622$

3.
$\overset{8\;|16}{9\,6\,3} - 82 = 881$
$\overset{2\;|10}{3\,0\,1} - 70 = 231$
$\overset{3\;|12}{4\,2\,8} - 195 = 233$
$\overset{0\;|13}{5\,1\,3} - 305 = 208$

160   Use with text pages 387–388.   RS-2

Addison-Wesley | All Rights Reserved

Building Thinking Skills

Critical Thinking 18-7

Name _____

Walking to School

Read the story.

Anita, Wendy, Juan, and Joaquin live on Park Lane. Wendy walks 315 steps to get to school. She lives the farthest away from school. Anita lives next to Wendy. Anita is 35 steps closer to school than Wendy. Juan lives between Joaquin and Anita. Juan lives 160 steps closer to school than Wendy. Joaquin walks 72 steps to get to Juan's house.

Write **Anita, Wendy, Juan,** or **Joaquin** to identify each child's house.

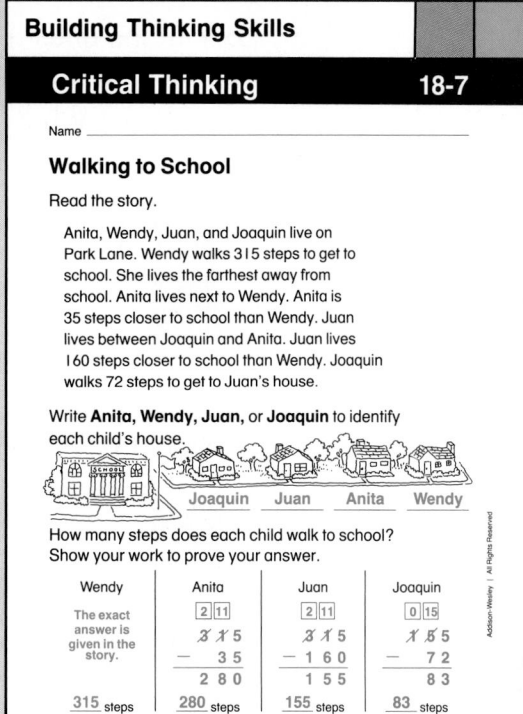

Joaquin   Juan   Anita   Wendy

How many steps does each child walk to school? Show your work to prove your answer.

Wendy	Anita	Juan	Joaquin
The exact answer is given in the story.	$\overset{2\;|11}{3\,\cancel{1}\,5} - 35 = 280$	$\overset{2\;|11}{3\,\cancel{1}\,5} - 160 = 155$	$\overset{0\;|15}{\cancel{1}\,5\,5} - 72 = 83$
315 steps	280 steps	155 steps	83 steps

160   Use with text pages 387–388.   TS-2

Addison-Wesley | All Rights Reserved

Challenges

Number Sense 18-7

Name _____

Crossnumber Puzzle Fun

Solve the puzzle.

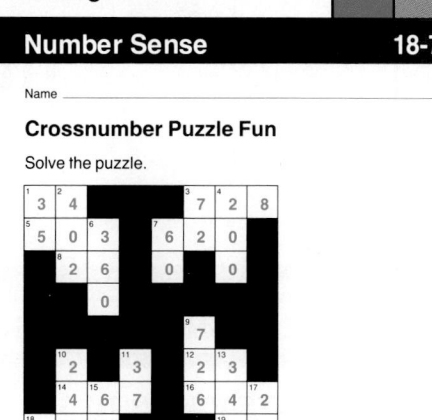

Across
1. 17 + 17
3. 862 − 134
5. 5 hundreds, 3 ones
7. 415 + 205
8. 560 − 534
12. 3 ones, 2 tens
14. 180 + 287
16. 771 − 129
18. 590 − 1
19. 77, 78, 79, □

Down
1. 20, 25, 30, □
2. 540 − 138
3. 27 + 45
4. the number after 199
6. 357, 358, 359, □
7. 59 + 1
9. 617 + 109
10. 385 − 137
11. 40 − 3
13. 4 tens, 8 ones, 3 hundreds
15. 70 − 1
17. 17, 18, 19, □

160   Use with text pages 387–388.   CS-2

Addison-Wesley | All Rights Reserved

OPTIONS FOR INDIVIDUAL NEEDS

Basic

Exercises All
Calculator Bank, p. 403

Supplements
Reteaching 160 or
Practice 160
Challenges 160

Average

Exercises All
Calculator Bank, p. 403

Supplements
Practice 160
Challenges 160 or
Thinking Skills 160

Extended

Exercises All
Calculator Bank, p. 403

Supplements
Challenges 160
Thinking Skills 160

Other Resources:
Mathematics Book A, pp. 26-27

18-7

LESSON PLAN 18-7

OBJECTIVE 18-7
To model 3-digit subtraction problems, trading 1 hundred for 10 tens if needed

Materials: base-ten blocks, TA17 (Place Value Chart), punchout number cards 0-9

Grouping Suggestions: individual work, small groups

1. MOTIVATE AND TEACH

LEARN ABOUT IT

Have students model 325 with base-ten blocks as you write the number on the chalkboard. Ask them to trade 1 hundred for 10 tens and have a volunteer show the trade on the board above the original numbers. (2/12) Repeat for other numbers if necessary.

Call students' attention to the first exercise on page 387.

▶ **Why do you not need to trade 1 ten for 10 ones?** (There are enough ones to take away 6.)

▶ **How is trading 1 ten for 10 ones similar to trading 1 hundred for 10 tens?** (Possible answers: You get more from the place to the left; you get 10 more from trading 1.)

2. CHECK UNDERSTANDING

ERROR ALERT Failing to decrease the hundreds digit by 1 after trading. Failing to increase the tens digit by 10.

Name _____

Subtracting
Trading 1 Hundred for 10 Tens

Subtract 126 from 219. Use blocks to help.

1. Look at the ones. Do you need to trade? yes n⊘
   Subtract the ones. Cross out to show it.

   What you do.

   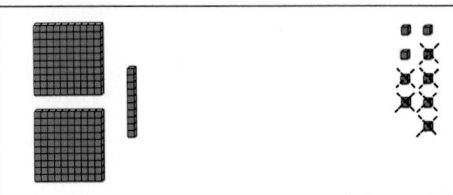

   What you write.

   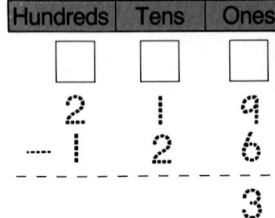

2. Look at the tens. Do you need to trade? (yes) n
   Subtract the tens. Draw and cross out to show it.

   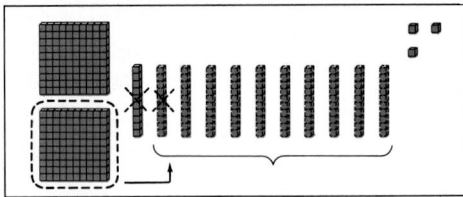

   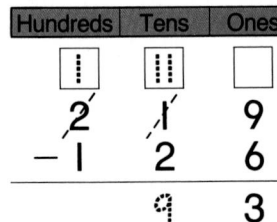

3. Subtract the hundreds. Cross out to show it.

   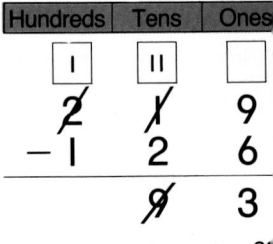

Chapter 18

(three hundred eighty-seven) 3⊘

TEACHING OPTIONS

RETEACHING TIPS
Clarification for Reteaching: Have students subtract 325 − 192 with blocks on a place value chart. As they trade 1 hundred for tens they count and record the new hundreds and tens. Show the subtraction with the blocks and write the difference. Use Reteaching Supplement 160.

COMPUTER Subtraction Puzzles, MECC © 1985 For review with all levels. In *Name that Creature*, students subtract 1- and 2-digit numbers from 2-digit numbers or multiples of ten with trading. Students may earn a turn at a guessing game. The recommended lesson takes 15 minutes.

se blocks to find the differences.
rade if you need to.

Hundreds	Tens	Ones
1	10	
2̸	0̸	5
−1	6	3
	4	2

Hundreds	Tens	Ones
2	11	
3̸	1̸	8
−1	5	0
1	6	8

257
−132
_____
125

²308
−175
_____
133

⁰¹³1̸3̸2
− 70
_____
62

⁴¹⁰250
−125
_____
125

⁰¹⁶1̸6̸2
− 91
_____
71

se blocks to add or subtract.

¹138
+215
_____
353

¹275
+130
_____
405

²¹¹3̸1̸8
−224
_____
94

⁰¹⁵31̸5̸
− 7
_____
308

⁰¹⁴1̸4̸9
− 99
_____
50

¹ 98
+251
_____
349

⁴¹⁰25̸0̸
−118
_____
132

¹¹⁰2̸0̸0̸
− 80
_____
120

¹ 78
+ 51
_____
129

256
−100
_____
156

SE MENTAL MATH

'se basic facts to help find the sums.

4 + 5 = __9__

400 + 500 = __900__

6. 2 + 6 = __8__

200 + 600 = __800__

38 (three hundred eighty-eight) Chapter 18

3. PRACTICE AND APPLY

Basic	All
Average	All
Extended	All

PRACTICE

How will you show each trade? (by writing the new numbers above the hundreds and tens digits) *What do you have to look for in Exercises 3 and 4?* (the operation signs)

APPLY

USE MENTAL MATH ▶ How is each basic fact like the addition exercise below it? (They have the same numbers, but they are in the ones place instead of in the hundreds place.)
▶ **How can you use mental math to find these sums?** (Add the numbers in the same way that you add the facts, but show the answers in hundreds.)
▶ **What other methods could you use to find the sums?** (Possible answers: Show with base-ten blocks; count on by hundreds from the first number.)
▶ **What hundreds addends can you think of with the sum of 600?** (100 + 500, 200 + 400, 300 + 300, 400 + 200, 500 + 100)

LOSE AND ASSESS

RITE WHAT YOU KNOW Ask dents to describe what happens in e chapter story. *Suppose there were 5 flowers in the garden and the tle man took 23 of them. How many ould be left?* (182) Encourage dents to use blocks to help them d the answer and build on each her's strengths as they work gether.

QUICK QUIZ

Use blocks to add or subtract.

319	562	296	612	940
−193	−149	+310	+179	−216
(126)	(413)	(606)	(791)	(724)

18-7

Chapter 18 Lesson 7   **388**

Adding and Subtracting Money

OBJECTIVE 18-8   To add and subtract 3-digit numbers with money

PREBOOK ACTIVITIES

QUICK REVIEW

Read each money amount aloud.
$2.45 $3.91 $4.09 $6.78 $0.34 $9.98 $6.16 $5.40
(Two dollars and forty-five cents; three dollars and ninety-one cents; four dollars and nine cents; six dollars and seventy-eight cents; thirty-four cents; nine dollars and ninety-eight cents; six dollars and sixteen cents; five dollars and forty cents)

PRIOR KNOWLEDGE

Help students recall adding and subtracting 3-digit numbers with and without trading. *When do you need to trade in addition? How do you trade?* (when there are 10 or more ones or tens in all; trade 10 ones to make another 10 and 10 tens to make another 100) *When do you need to trade in subtraction? How do you trade?* (when there are not enough ones or tens to take away; trade 1 ten for 10 ones or 1 hundred for 10 tens)

COMMUNICATION

Writing and Discussing Math   Display base-ten blocks and punchout dollars, dimes, and pennies. Write the following on the board and have students copy and match.

hundreds   dimes
tens   pennies
ones   dollars

Why are pennies like ones? (Pennies are worth 1¢.) *How do you know that dimes are the same as tens?* (Possible answers: 10 pennies equal 1 dime just as 10 ones equal 1 ten; dimes are worth 10¢.) *How are dollars and hundreds the same?* (A dollar is worth 100¢, 100 pennies, or 10 dimes.)

EXPLORE AND CONNECT

Materials: punchout dollars, dimes, and pennies
Grouping Suggestion: pairs
Provide each pair with punchout dollars, dimes, and pennies and have them model $4.29 and $1.38. Then ask partners to combine the punchout money to find the sum as you record the steps on the chalkboard. *What is the sum?* ($5.67) *What trade did you have to make?* (10 pennies for 1 dime) *How are the steps for adding money the same as for adding 3-digit numbers? How are they different?* (Possible answers: The steps are the same because you start at the right to add the smallest value and move to the left to add the largest value; you trade pennies, dimes, and dollars the same way you trade ones, tens, and hundreds; the difference is that when you add money, you have to write the decimal point and the dollar sign.)
Have students use money to model the subtraction of $4.29 − $1.38 as you record the steps. ($2.91)

Photo: 2-18-8-1-1

CONNECTIONS   Use these anytime.

Problem of the Day

Choose the Operation   Decide whether to add or subtract. Use punchout money to solve.
Kim has $2.25 in her wallet.
She has $5.67 in her piggy bank.
How much money does Kim have?
(Add: $2.25 + $5.67 = $7.92)

Life Skills

Making Purchases   Look at the ad.

Pen Sale
$0.62 each
2 for $1.00

How much will you save on each pen if you buy 2? (You will save $0.12 on each pen. If they are 2 for $1.00, each is $0.50, which is $0.12 less than $0.62.)

Number Sense

Estimation   Find 2 amounts that add up to about $7.00.
$5.32 $4.21 $6.10
$3.09 $9.75 $1.39
($4.21 and $3.09, $6.10 and $1.39, $5.32 and $1.39)

CLASSWORK AND HOMEWORK SUPPLEMENTS

Practice

Skills Maintenance 18-8

Name _____

Adding and Subtracting Money

Add or subtract. Trade if you need to.

1.
$3.27 + 4.27 = $7.54
$1.95 + 7.93 = $9.88
$7.74 − 6.61 = $0.53
$2.86 + 3.33 = $6.19

2.
$4.67 + 4.14 = $8.81
$5.39 − 4.85 = $0.54
$2.44 + 4.85 = $7.29
$5.26 + 1.55 = $6.81

3.
$4.77 − 2.58 = $2.19
$1.52 + 2.54 = $4.06
$4.35 − 3.61 = $0.74
$2.39 + 5.35 = $7.74

4.
$6.19 + 2.18 = $8.37
$8.17 − 6.74 = $1.43
$1.65 + 3.61 = $5.26
$6.55 − 4.62 = $1.93

5.
$9.81 − 7.29 = $2.52
$3.17 + 3.26 = $6.43
$7.89 − 3.31 = $4.58
$4.68 + 1.26 = $5.94

PS-2   Use with text pages 389–390.   161

Building Thinking Skills

Life Skills 18-8

Name _____

Reading a Menu

Menu			
Bean soup	$1.50	Green Salad	$2.00
Noodle soup	$1.70	Chicken salad	$2.50
		Shrimp salad	$3.00

1. Jean had soup and salad. She spent $4.50. What did she have?

   bean soup and shrimp salad

2. Bill had soup and salad. He spent $3.50. What did he have?

   bean soup and green salad

3. Patty had soup and salad. The salad was $1.00 more than the soup. What did she have?

   bean soup and chicken salad

4. Ted had soup and salad. The salad was $1.30 more than the soup. What did he have?

   noodle soup and shrimp salad

5. Sue and Jerry each had a bowl of soup. They spent $3.00 in all. What did they have?

   They each had a bowl of bean soup.

6. Joe had two different salads. He spent $5.00. What did he have?

   green salad and shrimp salad

TS-2   Use with text pages 389–390.   161

Reteaching

Skills Review 18-8

Name _____

Adding and Subtracting Money

Sale			
Crayons	$1.29	Chalk	$1.50
Scissors	$1.09	Paint	$1.65
Paper	$1.65	Clay	$1.42

Read the sale prices.

1. Crayons cost _$1.29_   2. Paint costs _$1.65_

3. What costs $1.09? _scissors_

Solve.

4.
Crayons	$1.29
Paper	+1.65
	$2.94

What is the total cost?   (Add to find the total.)

5.
Chalk	$1.50
Scissors	−1.09
	$0.41

How much more does the chalk cost?   (Subtract to compare.)

6.
Paint	$1.65
Clay	+1.42
	$3.07

How much is it for both?

7.
Paper	$1.65
Scissors	−1.09
	$0.56

How much more does the paper cost?

RS-2   Use with text pages 389–390.   161

Challenges

Manipulatives 18-8

Name _____

To Market

You need: 2 players, markers, a number cube, punchout money, and newspapers.

Rules: Find ads in the newspaper for the foods on the game board. Write the prices of the foods on the spaces. Write other foods and their prices on any blank spaces.
To start, each player gets $10 to spend. Estimate what you can buy and make a shopping list.
Roll the cube and move that many spaces.
Buy the item on the space.
Use the punchout money to make change.
Play until your money is spent or you reach the exit. The player who bought the most items on his or her list wins.

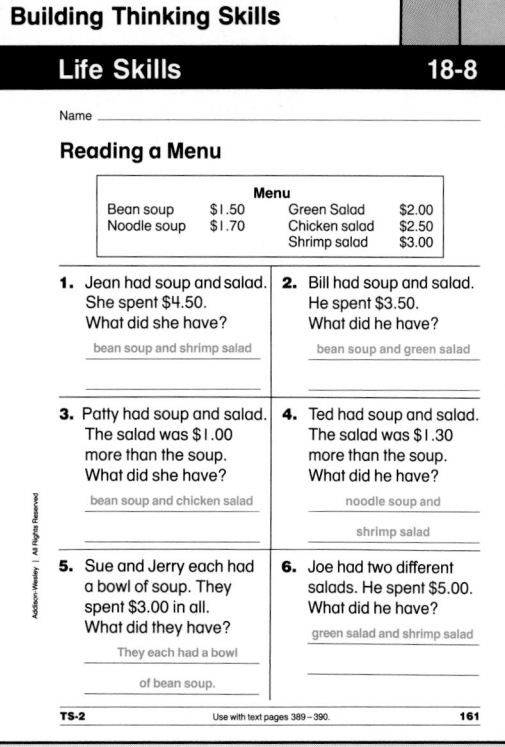

CS-2   Use with text pages 389–390.   161

OPTIONS FOR INDIVIDUAL NEEDS

Basic

Exercises All, Mixed Review
Calculator Bank, p. 402
More Practice, p. 432, set A

Supplements
Reteaching 161 or
Practice 161
Challenges 161

Average

Exercises All, Mixed Review
Calculator Bank, p. 402
More Practice, p. 432, set A

Supplements
Practice 161
Challenges 161 or
Thinking Skills 161

Extended

Exercises All, Mixed Review
Calculator Bank, p. 402

Supplements
Challenges 161
Thinking Skills 161

Other Resources:
Explorations, pp. 259-261
Problem Solving Experiences In Mathematics, pp. 119, 150
Mathematics Book A, pp. 26-27
Using the Math Explorer Calculator: A Source Book for Teachers, Chapter 14

18-8

OBJECTIVE 18-8
To add and subtract 3-digit numbers with money

> **Materials:** punchout dollars, dimes, and pennies; base-ten blocks, TA17 (Place Value Chart), index cards with money amounts from $0.05 to $4.99
>
> **Grouping Suggestions:** individual work, cooperative learning groups of 4

Have students make a collection of $2.25 using 1 dollar, 12 dimes, and 5 pennies. Ask them to trade 10 dimes for 1 dollar. Then, working from $2.25, have students trade 1 dime for 10 pennies and ask how many pennies they have now. (15) Repeat if needed for other numbers and trades. Call students' attention to the example at the top of page 389.

▶ **Why do you add to solve this problem?** (You must find the total cost for both flower pots.)

▶ **In this problem, you trade 10 dimes for 1 dollar. What if there were 10 or more pennies instead?** (You would trade 10 pennies for 1 dime.) Ask students to look at the example on the lower half of page 389.

▶ **Why do you subtract to find the change?** (Possible answer: You are finding the amount, or part, left from the amount you had to start.)

▶ **Explain why a trade is needed to subtract the dimes but not the pennies.** (There are no pennies to take away, so you do not need any. There are 6 dimes to take away and there are 0 dimes to start, so you need to trade 1 dollar to get 10 dimes.)

2. CHECK UNDERSTANDING

ERROR ALERT Misunderstanding the conversion of written money amounts to dollars, dimes, and pennies or hundreds, tens, and ones.

Name _____

Adding and Subtracting Money

How much money will it cost to buy a red flower pot and a blue flower pot?

$$\begin{array}{r} \$2.45 \\ +\ 1.60 \\ \hline \$4.05 \end{array}$$

Trade 10 dimes for 1 dollar.

It will cost __$4.05__ for the pots.

Add. Use punchout money to help. Trade when you need to.

1.
$$\begin{array}{r} \$1.67 \\ +\ 1.28 \\ \hline \$2.95 \end{array}$$ Trade 10 pennies for 1 dime.

$$\begin{array}{r} \$0.75 \\ +\ 3.50 \\ \hline \$4.25 \end{array}$$

$$\begin{array}{r} \$1.50 \\ +\ 1.50 \\ \hline \$3.00 \end{array}$$

$$\begin{array}{r} \$1.05 \\ +\ 0.85 \\ \hline \$1.90 \end{array}$$

You want to buy the blue flower pot. You give the clerk $2.00. How much change will you get back?

$$\begin{array}{r} \$2.00 \\ -\ 1.60 \\ \hline \$0.40 \end{array}$$

Trade 1 dollar for 10 dimes. Then take away.

You will get __$0.40__ back.

Subtract. Use punchout money to help. Trade when you need to.

2.
$$\begin{array}{r} \$3.24 \\ -\ 1.16 \\ \hline \$2.08 \end{array}$$ Trade 1 dime for 10 pennies.

$$\begin{array}{r} \$2.53 \\ -\ 0.72 \\ \hline \$1.81 \end{array}$$

$$\begin{array}{r} \$5.00 \\ -\ 1.40 \\ \hline \$3.60 \end{array}$$

$$\begin{array}{r} \$4.08 \\ -\ 3.56 \\ \hline \$0.5 \end{array}$$

Chapter 18   (three hundred eighty-nine) 38

TEACHING OPTIONS

RETEACHING TIPS Write $2.39 + $1.47 ($3.86) and $4.75 − $2.49 ($2.26) on the board. Have students use base-ten blocks to combine or remove blocks to show addition or subtraction. Then have them write the matching number sentences. Use Reteaching Supplement 161.

ENRICHMENT **Family Math** Tell students they have $10 to spend on gifts for 2 relatives. Ask a family member for a store catalog or newspaper ads so they can choose the gifts. Students add to make sure the total cost is under $10, then subtract to find out how much they will have left.

dd or subtract. Use play money or blocks
help. Look at the sums and differences
each row. What is the pattern? Ring it.

				Pattern
¹ $0.78 + 0.51 $1.29	² ¹⁰ $3.09 − 0.80 $2.29	¹ $1.34 + 1.95 $3.29	⁸ ¹⁰ $5.90 − 1.61 $4.29	(+ $1.00) + $0.01 − $1.00
³ ¹⁵ 345 − 128 217	¹ 208 + 7 215	295 − 82 213	² ¹⁰ 301 − 90 211	+ 20 (− 2) − 1
³ ¹⁴ $4.45 − 0.95 $3.50	¹ $3.16 + 0.24 $3.40	¹ $1.60 + 1.70 $3.30	⁴ ¹¹ $5.12 − 1.92 $3.20	(− $0.10) + $0.10 − $1.00
¹ 70 + 80 150	346 − 146 200	¹ 125 + 125 250	¹ 270 + 30 300	+ 10 + 5 (+ 50)

MIXED REVIEW

Write > or < in each ◯.

123 (>) 103   458 (<) 532   775 (<) 777

Ring the fraction that tells how much is colored.

 $\dfrac{1}{3}$ $\left(\dfrac{1}{2}\right)$ $\dfrac{2}{2}$ 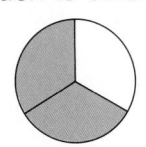 $\dfrac{1}{3}$ $\left(\dfrac{2}{3}\right)$ $\dfrac{3}{3}$

90   (three hundred ninety)   More Practice, page 432, set A   Chapter 18

---

3. PRACTICE AND APPLY

Basic	All, Mixed Review
Average	All, Mixed Review
Extended	All, Mixed Review

PRACTICE

What will you need to do before you identify the pattern? (Complete all the exercises in the row and look at the answers.)

APPLY

▶ **What operation sign would the exercises in a pattern show if the answers got larger? smaller?** (+, −)
▶ **How can understanding money patterns help you if you save money in a savings account?** (Possible answer: You will be able to keep track of your own money if you put the same amount in your bank each week.)

MIXED REVIEW *How will you find out what fraction tells how much is colored?* (Count the number of parts shaded for the top number; count the total number of parts for the bottom number.)

18-8

CLOSE AND ASSESS

SHOW WHAT YOU KNOW

Provide each group of 4 with punchout money and index cards with money amounts from $0.05 to $4.99. Cards are placed face down in a deck. Then 2 students draw cards and write an addition or subtraction sentence using the amounts shown on the cards. As they solve the exercise on paper, the 2 other students use punchout money to solve. Students compare answers.

QUICK QUIZ

Use punchout money to solve.

$4.59 + 1.38 ($5.97)	$5.18 − 2.95 ($2.23)	$3.65 + 4.50 ($8.15)	$2.85 − 0.69 ($2.16)

Problem Solving: Problems with Two Questions

OBJECTIVE 18-9   To solve problems with two questions

PREBOOK ACTIVITIES

QUICK REVIEW

Write each money amount. Use the dollar sign and decimal point.
Three dollars and forty-nine cents ($3.49)
Seven dollars and ninety cents ($7.90)
Six dollars and four cents ($6.04)
Eight dollars ($8.00)
Seventy-nine cents ($0.79)

PRIOR KNOWLEDGE

Help students recall shopping in a grocery store. Tell them to imagine that they are at the cashier, ready to pay for the food they have bought. *When does the cashier need to use addition?* (when finding the total for all the groceries bought; the cashier adds the prices to find the amount you need to pay) *When might the cashier need to use subtraction?* (If you give the cashier more than the total amount, the cashier must subtract to find the amount of change to give you.)

COMMUNICATION

Reading and Discussing Math   Write the following table on the chalkboard:

Packs of Pencils	1	2	3	4
Number of Pencils	5	10	15	20

Discuss the table. *How many pencils are in one pack?* (5) *How many pencils are in 2 packs?* (10) *What is the pattern in the table?* (The number increases by 5 with each additional pack.) *How could you find out how many pencils are in 6 packs?* (Continue the table for 5 and 6 packs; count on by 5s.)

EXPLORE AND CONNECT

COOPERATIVE ACTIVITY

Grouping Suggestion: small groups
Have students write number sentences and solve them.
Beth buys a spade for $1.05 and a hoe for $3.08.
What is the total cost of her purchase? ($4.13)
How much change will she get if she pays $4.50? ($0.37)

TEACHING ACTIONS

BEFORE ▶ **What is happening in this story?** (Possible answer: Beth buys a spade and a hoe. She gets change from $4.50)
▶ **What data do you need to answer the questions?** (Possible answer: the prices of the spade and hoe; the amount of money Beth gives the cashier)

DURING ▶ **Why do you need to make two plans for this problem?** (Possible answer: You need to find the total cost of the spade and the hoe; then you must find the amount of money Beth will have left.)
▶ **Tell how you can solve the problems.** (Possible answer: Add to find the total cost; subtract the total cost from $4.50, the amount of money Beth has.)

AFTER ▶ **How can you check your answers?** (Possible answers: Use a calculator or play money.)
Have students work in small groups to solve and check each step of the problem. Have each student use a different method for checking and ask them to compare methods and results.

CONNECTIONS   Use these anytime.

Problem of the Day

Make a List   Wendy buys a plant for $3.50. She pays with a five-dollar bill. How much change will Wendy get? ($1.50) In how many ways can the cashier give Wendy change? Make a list. (Answers will vary. All coin collections must be equivalent to $1.50.)

Counting Patterns

Continue each number pattern.
2; 4; 6; ____; ____.   (8; 10)
20; 40; 60; ____; ____.   (80; 100)
200; 400; 600; ____; ____.   (800; 1,000)
Compare the patterns. Tell how they are the same and how they are different. (Each pattern is the same, using 2, 4, 6, 8, 10. The difference is the digit where the pattern is being continued.)

Math Connection

Money   Sarah has $3.49. Susan has $1.25 more than Sarah. How much money does Susan have? ($4.74). If Susan wants to buy a basket for $5.85, how much more money does she need? ($1.11)

roblem Solving Strategy: Make a Table

solve problems using the strategy Make a Table

CLASSWORK AND HOMEWORK SUPPLEMENTS

Practice

Problem Solving 18-9

Name _____

Make a Table

Finish the tables. Use the tables to solve the problems.
Write the answers in a sentence. Word sentences may vary.
Sample answers shown.

1 ride	2 rides	__3__ rides	__4__ rides
20 ¢	40 ¢	60 ¢	80 ¢

1 ride	2 rides	__3__ rides	__4__ rides
25 ¢	50 ¢	75 ¢	$1.00

Merry-go-Round 20¢

Ferris Wheel 25¢

1. Sandy went on 4 merry-go-round rides. How much did she spend?

She spent 80¢.

2. Joel has $1.00. How many Ferris wheel rides can he buy?

He can buy 4 rides.

3. Abdul spent 75¢ on 3 rides. Which ride did he go on?

He went on the Ferris wheel.

162   Use with text page 392.   PS-2

Building Thinking Skills

Problem Solving 18-9

Name _____

Time Tables

Solve. Make tables to help.

1. Belinda picked 2 baskets of berries in the morning and 3 baskets of berries in the afternoon. Each basket had 30 berries. How many berries did she pick in all?

__150__ berries

2. Neil can pack 15 boxes in 2 hours. How long will it take him to pack 75 boxes?

__10__ hours

3. Carey does 20 sit-ups each day. How many sit-ups does he do in one week?

__140__ sit-ups

4. Anna can walk a mile in 20 minutes. How many miles can she walk in 1 hour?

__3__ miles

5. Jody spends $2 a month on soap and $1 a month on toothpaste. How much does she spend on soap and toothpaste in 1 year?

$36

6. A play was performed each day from Monday through Friday. Each day the auditorium was full. The auditorium holds 150 people. How many people saw the play?

__750__ people

162   Use with text pages 391 – 392.   TS-2

Reteaching

Problem Solving 18-9

Name _____

Problems with Two Questions

Ring the letter that tells the correct steps.

1. 17 boys were on the bus. 15 girls were on the bus. How many children were on the bus? *(Add to find the total.)*

  A Add 17 and 15. Then add 6.

6 children got off at the corner. How many children were still on the bus? *(Subtract to take away.)*

  (B) Add 17 and 15. Then subtract 6.

2. 25 crayons were in the the box. 6 were broken. How many crayons were not broken?

  A Subtract 6 from 25. Then add 10.

10 of the crayons not broken were used. How many were not used?

  (B) Subtract 6 from 25. Then subtract 10.

3. Kerry saved 45¢ last week and 28¢ this week. How much money did she save altogether?

  (A) Add 45 and 28. Then subtract 25.

She bought an old book for 25¢. How much money did she have left?

  B Add 45 and 28. Then add 25.

162   Use with text page 391.   RS-2

Challenges

Problem Solving 18-9

Name _____

At the Store

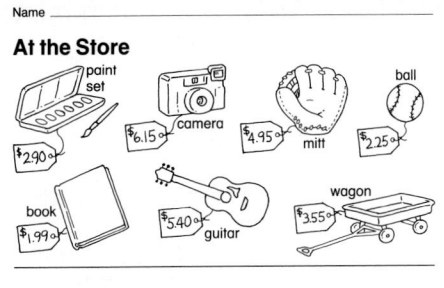

paint set, camera $6.15, mitt $4.95, ball $2.25, book $1.99, guitar $5.40, wagon $3.55, $2.90

Solve.

1. Ramon had $7.50. He bought a paint set and a wagon. How much money does he have left?

$1.05

2. Andy bought a mitt and 2 balls. How much did he spend?

$9.45

3. Jenny had $3.50. She earned $2.75 more. How much will she have left after she buys the camera?

$0.10

4. Luanna wants to buy a book and a guitar. She has $6.25 now. How much more does she need?

$1.14

162   Use with text pages 391 – 392.   CS-2

OPTIONS FOR INDIVIDUAL NEEDS

Basic

Exercises All
Computer Bank, pp. 405-408
More Practice, p. 432, set B

Supplements
Reteaching 162 or
Practice 162

Average

Exercises All
Computer Bank, pp. 405-408
More Practice, p. 432, set B

Supplements
Practice 162
Challenges 162 or
Thinking Skills 162

Extended

Exercises All
Computer Bank, pp. 405-408

Supplements
Challenges 162
Thinking Skills 162

Other Resources:
Problem Solving Experiences In Mathematics, pp. 22-23, 52-53, 58-59, 88, 106, 124, 130, 136-137, 142, 148, 154-155, 160, 162, 166
Mathematics Book A, pp. 59-61

18-9

OBJECTIVE 18-9

To solve problems with two questions; to solve problems using the strategy Make a Table

---

Materials: play money, calculators, base-ten blocks

---

1. MOTIVATE AND TEACH

LEARN ABOUT IT

BEFORE ▶ **Describe what Tran is doing in Exercise 1.** (He buys a hoe, finds how much money he has left, and then buys plant food.)

▶ **Why do these problems require two operations to solve them?** (Possible answer: You need to find an answer for each of the two questions.)

DURING ▶ **Why must you answer each question in order, one step at a time?** (You need the answer for the first question in order to answer the second question.)

AFTER ▶ **How can you check your answers?** (Possible answer: Add the price of the plant food to the remaining amount and add the price of the hoe to that amount; work backward by adding.)

2. CHECK UNDERSTANDING

ERROR ALERT

Page 391 Reversing the order of operations.

Page 392 Incorrectly identifying and continuing the number pattern.

Name _____

Problem Solving
Problems with Two Questions

| UNDERSTAND |
| FIND DATA |
| PLAN |
| ESTIMATE |
| SOLVE |
| CHECK |

Solve. Use a 🖩 or play money to help.

1. Tran had $4.70. He bought a hoe. Later he bought some plant food. How much money was left after he bought the hoe? $2.45

   How much money was left after Tran bought plant food? $1.35

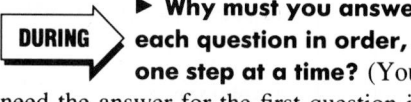
hoe   plant food
$2.25

$$\begin{array}{r} 6\,10 \\ \$4.\!\!\not7\!0 \\ -\,2.25 \\ \hline \$2.45 \end{array}$$

$$\begin{array}{r} \$2.4 \\ -\,1.1 \\ \hline \$1.3 \end{array}$$

2. Kristen wants to buy a hose and a watering can. She has $5.60 now. What is the total cost of the hose and the watering can? $6.74

   How much more money does Kristen need? $1.14

hose   watering
$5.25

$$\begin{array}{r} \$5.25 \\ +\,1.49 \\ \hline \$6.74 \end{array}$$

$$\begin{array}{r} \$6.74 \\ -\,5.60 \\ \hline \$1.14 \end{array}$$

3. Paco wants to buy some potting soil. He has $1.80 in his pocket. He has $1.75 in his piggy bank. How much money does Paco have in all? $3.55

   How much money will he have left after he buys the potting soil? $0.30

potting soil
$3.25

$$\begin{array}{r} \$1.80 \\ +\,1.75 \\ \hline \$3.55 \end{array}$$

$$\begin{array}{r} \$3.55 \\ -\,3.25 \\ \hline \$0.30 \end{array}$$

Chapter 18   More Practice, page 432, set B   (three hundred ninety-one)

TEACHING OPTIONS

RETEACHING TIPS Have students make a row of blocks with 1, 2, 3, and 4 ones. Place a matching number of tens under each ones unit and write the pattern for both rows. Repeat, placing 2 tens, then 1 hundred under each ones unit. For two-question problems, use Reteaching Supplement 162.

ENRICHMENT Have students gather data to use for subtraction problems. Find out how many days there are from the beginning of the school year to the end. Find out the number of weekend days and holidays in the school year. Subtract to find out how many days are spent in school.

Problem Solving Strategy
Make a Table

UNDERSTAND
FIND DATA
PLAN
ESTIMATE
SOLVE
CHECK

Finish the table to solve the problem.
Write the answer.

1. Jessica and Steven bought 4 packs of tomato seeds. How many plants can they grow?

TOMATOES
30 SEEDS

Pack	1	2	3	4
Plants	30	60	90	120

Word sentences may vary. Sample answers are shown.
They can grow 120 tomato plants.

2. How many pumpkin plants can they grow with 4 packs of seeds?

PUMPKINS
15 SEEDS

Pack	1	2	3	4
Plants	15	30	45	60

They can grow 60 pumpkin plants.

3. They want to plant 600 carrot plants. How many seed packs do they need to buy?

CARROTS
200 SEEDS

Pack	1	2	3	4
Plants	200	400	600	800

They need 3 seed packs.

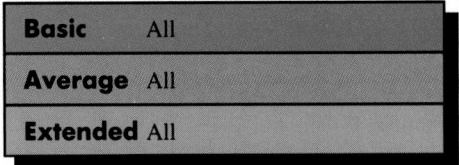

3. PRACTICE AND APPLY

Basic	All
Average	All
Extended	All

How will you know which numbers to use to complete each table? (Identify and continue the number pattern.) *What will you write on the line below each table?* (The answer to the question in a complete sentence.) *How is Exercise 3 different?* (The answer is not in the last section of the table.)

▶ **Why do you need to know how many seeds are in each pack?** (Possible answer: so you will know how many seeds you are buying in all if you buy more than 1 pack)

▶ **How will you plan to complete each table?** (Possible answer: Add the number of seeds per pack each time for every additional pack.)

▶ **In what ways could you check the data in your table?** (Possible answers: Write repeated addition sentences; add on the calculator; analyze the number pattern in the table.)

CLOSE AND ASSESS

SHOW WHAT YOU KNOW
Display 5 classroom objects priced from $0.79 to $1.95 at the front of the room. Tell students that they have $4.79 to spend. Have them name 2 items, write their prices, and find the total amount. Then ask them to find how much money they would have left after purchasing the items. Have students check their work with a calculator.

QUICK QUIZ

Continue the patterns.

1 box	2 boxes	3 boxes	4 boxes
40	(80)	(120)	(160)
1 box	2 boxes	3 boxes	4 boxes
25	(50)	(75)	(100)

18-9

Chapter 18 Lesson 9   **392**

CHAPTER 18

WRAP UP

INTRODUCTION The Wrap Up provides activities emphasizing math language and thinking skills for the chapter.

USING PAGE 393

Math Words ▶ **For which operation might you need to trade 10 ones for 1 ten? When?** (addition; when you add in the ones place, you must trade if there are 10 or more ones)

▶ **How is trading 1 hundred for 10 tens like trading 1 ten for 10 ones?** (Possible answer: You trade 1 large unit for 10 smaller units; you trade 1 hundred for 10 tens or 1 ten for 10 ones when you are subtracting.)

Math Reasoning ▶ **What clues can you use to help you guess which items go together to make $1.00?** (Possible answer: The numbers in the ones place will total 10; the numbers in the tens place will total 10.)

▶ **What will you do if the sum of 2 tags is over $1.00?** (Possible answer: Change 1 of the toys for a toy that has a lower price.)

Name _____

Wrap Up

MATH WORDS

Match.

1. You trade 10 ones for 1 ten.

2. You trade 10 tens for 1 hundred.

3. You trade 1 ten for 10 ones.

4. You trade 1 hundred for 10 tens.

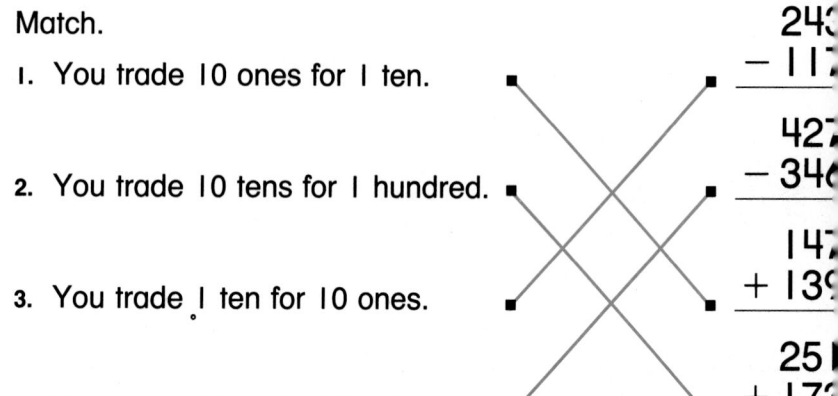

$$24?$$
$$-11?$$

$$42?$$
$$-34?$$

$$14?$$
$$+139$$

$$25?$$
$$+173$$

MATH REASONING

5. Color pairs of tags that add to $1.00 (100¢) the same color. Use a different color for each pair. **Colors may vary.**

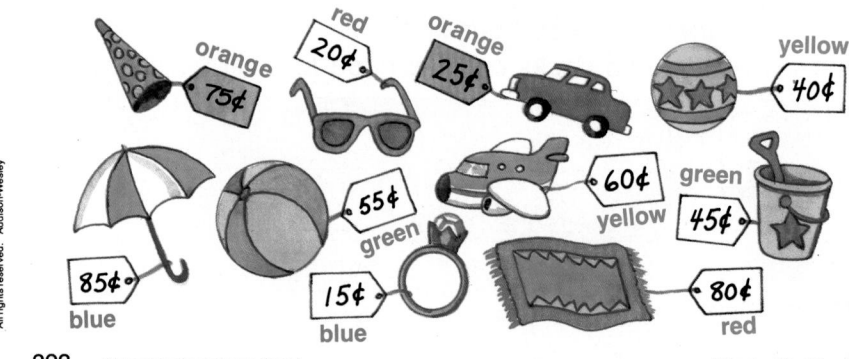

orange 75¢
red 20¢
orange 25¢
yellow 40¢
blue 85¢
green 55¢
green 60¢
yellow 45¢
blue 15¢
red 80¢

Chapter 18 Wrap

TEACHING OPTIONS

ENRICHMENT Provide students with magazines, scissors, and glue. Have them cut out pictures for their own store and paste them onto a piece of paper. Ask students to price items as follows: 5¢, 15¢, 25¢, 30¢, 40¢, 45¢, 60¢, 70¢, 85¢. Have students find pairs or groups of 3 items that total $1.00 and ring them in the same color. (Possible combinations: 15¢, 85¢; 5¢, 25¢, 70¢; 25¢, 30¢, 45¢)

Name _____

CHAPTER REVIEW/TEST

Add or subtract. Use blocks to help.

$$\begin{array}{r} \overset{1}{1}46 \\ +\ 27 \\ \hline 173 \end{array} \qquad \begin{array}{r} \overset{1}{2}19 \\ +135 \\ \hline 354 \end{array} \qquad \begin{array}{r} 130 \\ +143 \\ \hline 273 \end{array} \qquad \begin{array}{r} 427 \\ +\ 61 \\ \hline 488 \end{array} \qquad \begin{array}{r} \overset{1}{3}08 \\ +\ 46 \\ \hline 354 \end{array}$$

$$\begin{array}{r} \overset{1}{\ }50 \\ +80 \\ \hline 130 \end{array} \qquad \begin{array}{r} \overset{1}{\ }40 \\ +70 \\ \hline 110 \end{array} \qquad \begin{array}{r} \overset{1}{1}53 \\ +\ 61 \\ \hline 214 \end{array} \qquad \begin{array}{r} \overset{1}{\$}1.72 \\ +\ 1.84 \\ \hline \$3.56 \end{array} \qquad \begin{array}{r} \overset{1}{\$}2.70 \\ +\ 1.65 \\ \hline \$4.35 \end{array}$$

$$\begin{array}{r} \overset{8\ 14}{1\cancel{9}\cancel{4}} \\ -\ 76 \\ \hline 118 \end{array} \qquad \begin{array}{r} \overset{6\ 11}{2\cancel{7}\cancel{1}} \\ -129 \\ \hline 142 \end{array} \qquad \begin{array}{r} 199 \\ -\ 28 \\ \hline 171 \end{array} \qquad \begin{array}{r} \overset{3\ 10}{4\cancel{4}0} \\ -127 \\ \hline 313 \end{array} \qquad \begin{array}{r} \overset{6\ 12}{3\cancel{7}2} \\ -148 \\ \hline 224 \end{array}$$

$$\begin{array}{r} \overset{1\ 12}{2\cancel{2}6} \\ -\ 71 \\ \hline 155 \end{array} \qquad \begin{array}{r} \overset{3\ 10}{4\cancel{0}\cancel{0}} \\ -\ 60 \\ \hline 340 \end{array} \qquad \begin{array}{r} \overset{1\ 13}{2\cancel{3}9} \\ -\ 95 \\ \hline 144 \end{array} \qquad \begin{array}{r} \overset{2\ 14}{\$3.\cancel{4}8} \\ -\ 1.64 \\ \hline \$1.84 \end{array} \qquad \begin{array}{r} \overset{2\ 11}{\$3.\cancel{1}7} \\ -\ 1.53 \\ \hline \$1.64 \end{array}$$

Kory wants to buy a book and a plant.
She has $5.25. What is the total cost of

the book and plant? <u>$4.52</u>

How much money will

Kory have left? <u>$0.73</u>

$3.25

$1.27

$$\begin{array}{r} \overset{1}{\$}3.25 \\ +\ 1.27 \\ \hline \$4.52 \end{array} \qquad \begin{array}{r} \overset{4\ 12}{\$\cancel{5}.\cancel{2}5} \\ -\ 4.52 \\ \hline \$0.73 \end{array}$$

CHAPTER REVIEW/TEST

INTRODUCTION The Review/Test is provided to review and evaluate the skills and concepts presented in Chapter 18.

USING PAGE 394
If you prefer to use this page for review, you may want to use the
Multiple-Choice Posttest (pages 71-72) or the **Free-Response Posttest** (pages 71-72) to evaluate mastery of chapter objectives.

ITEM ANALYSIS The table below correlates the Chapter Review/Test Items with the lesson objectives.

Items	Objectives
1	18-1
2	18-2, 18-3, 18-8
3	18-5
4	18-6, 18-7, 18-8
5	18-9

INFORMAL ASSESSMENT

Using Manipulatives Provide students with punchout bills and coins. Students draw 2 pictures of their favorite toys and price them between $1.01 and $4.99. Have students use punchout dollars, dimes, and pennies to find the total cost of both toys and the difference in their cost.

Communication Have students write step-by-step directions telling how to solve a 3-digit addition or

subtraction problem and read them to a partner. Have partners follow the directions and help each other make changes if necessary. (Answers will vary.)

Critical Thinking *If you wanted to buy 3 things, how would you find out how much money you had left from $5.00?* (Possible answer: Find the sum of the 3 items first, then subtract the total from $5.00.)

CHAPTER 18

ENRICHMENT

INTRODUCTION Solving problems that have more than 1 solution helps students understand and extend the process of creative thinking.

USING PAGE 395

This Enrichment page is provided for all students. You may wish to use it after they have completed the Chapter Review/Test on page 394.

Help students appreciate that some problems may be solved in a variety of ways, and that more than 1 answer may be correct. Point out that zero will not appear in the table, since there is at least 1 shell of each color in the collection.

▶ **What is the same about all the ways you could describe the shells?** (Possible answer: All answers will have total of 9 shells.)

▶ **What patterns do you see in the table you completed?** (Possible answer: As the number of pink shells get larger, the number of gray shells got smaller.)

▶ **How could using objects or drawing a picture help you solve the problem another way?** (Possible answer: You could organize the solutions in a different way; you could see other patterns.)

EXTENSIONS Provide pairs of students with a collection of pennies, nickels, and dimes and a paper bag. The first student places up to 10 coins in the bag and tells his or her partner how many pennies there are. The second student has 3 guesses to find the number of nickels and dimes hidden in the bag. If 1 of the guesses is correct, the student wins a point. Students exchange roles and repeat the activity. Play continues until 1 student accumulates 3 points.

Name _____

Enrichment
Finding Another Solution

Josh collected 9 shells. Some shells were white, some were pink, and some were gray.

Suppose 3 of the shells were white. What colors could the others be? Fill in the table to show it.

Now do the problem another way.

Josh's Shells			
White	Pink	Gray	Total
3	1	5	9
3	2	4	9
3	3	3	9
3	4	2	9
3	5	1	9

Draw a picture.	or	Use objects.

Did you get the same answers? **Check students' work.**

Ring one.   yes   no

Chapter 18   Enrichment: Finding Another Solution   (three hundred ninety-five)   3

Name _____

Cumulative Review

Multiply or divide.

1.
○ 2
● 8
○ 12

$2 \times 4 =$ ___

2.
○ 6
○ 3
● 4

$12 \div 3 =$ ___

3.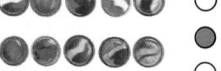
○ 6
● 5
○ 4

$10 \div 2 =$ ___

4. Which number sentence is related?
$3 \times 3 = 9$
○ $9 \div 1 = 19$
● $9 \div 3 = 3$
○ $3 \times 6 = 18$

5. How many are there?
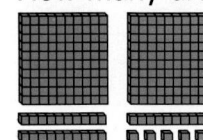
○ 233
○ 600
● 235

6. What number comes after?
533, 534, ___
● 535
○ 536
○ 350

7. What number comes between?
710, ___, 712
○ 713
○ 709
● 711

8. Count the money.
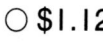

● $1.21
○ $1.12
○ $1.03

9. The book has 4 pages. There are 4 pictures on each page. How many pictures are in the book? Which number sentence would you use to solve the problem?

○ $4 + 4 = 8$
○ $4 \times 3 = 12$
● $4 \times 4 = 16$

CUMULATIVE REVIEW

INTRODUCTION The purpose of this Cumulative Review is to maintain previously taught skills and concepts. The emphasis in this Cumulative Review is on understanding multiplication and division, Chapter 16; and on place value—numbers to 1,000, Chapter 17.

ITEM ANALYSIS The table below correlates the Cumulative Review items with the lesson objectives.

Items	Objectives
1	16-2
2	16-6
3	16-7
4	16-8
5	17-3
6, 7	17-5
8	17-8
9	16-5

Resource Bank and Glossary

Contents   397

Data Bank

Swim Meet Ribbons

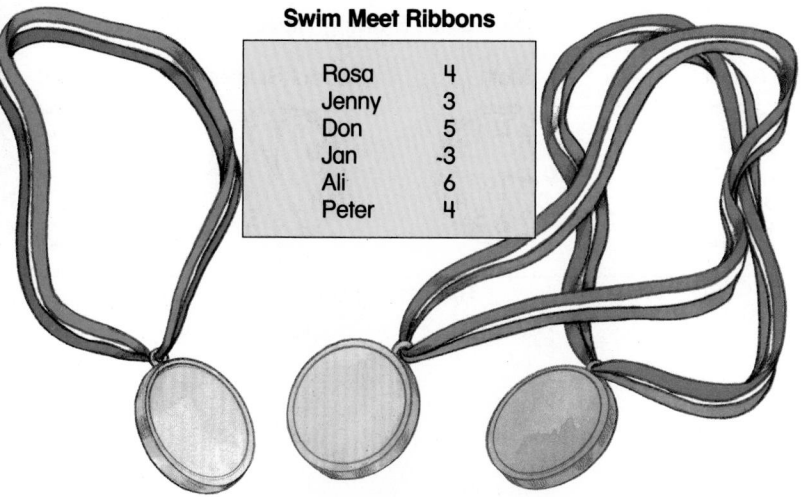

Rosa	4
Jenny	3
Don	5
Jan	-3
Ali	6
Peter	4

Moon Walkers

Trip	Number of Americans
1st	4
2nd	0
3rd	4
4th	4

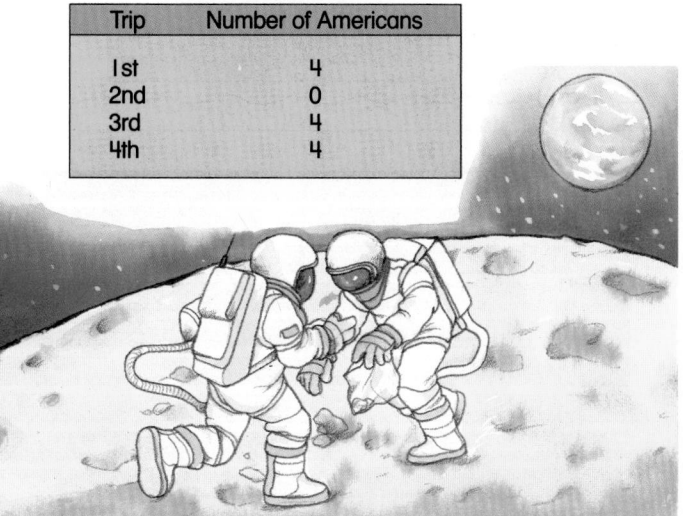

DATA BANK

Data Bank

Rex's Class Starting Times

Reading	Math	Social Studies	Art

Theater Seating

Row	Seats
1	19
2	27
3	31
4	31
5	31
6	31
7	31
8	31
9	31

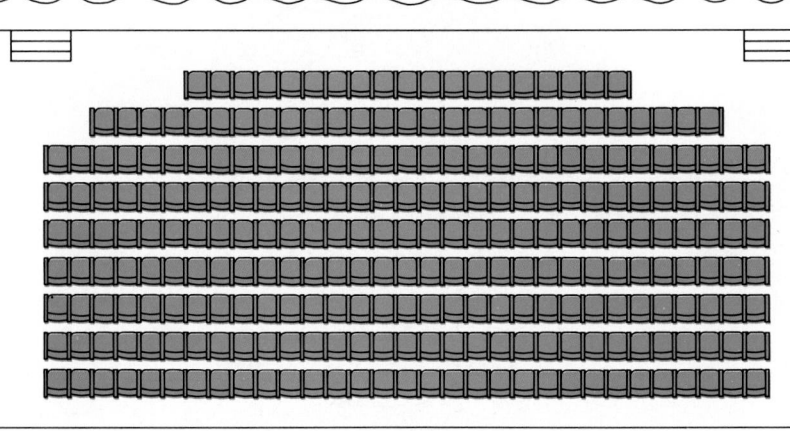

Data Bank

Football Scores

| Beetles | 18 |
| Groundhogs | 25 |

| Bulldogs | 35 |
| Whales | 21 |

| Bulldogs | 28 |
| Groundhogs | 34 |

Videotape Prices

Peter Pan	$25
Snow White	$18
Cinderella	$20

CALCULATOR BANK

Calculator Bank

Name _____

Counting On and Back

1. Start at 0. Count on by 2s. Write the numbers.

   Press [ON/C] 0 [+] 2 [=] [=] [=] [=]

   _2_, _4_, _6_, _8_

2. Start at 100. Count on by 25s. Write the numbers.

   Press [ON/C] 100 [+] 25 [=] [=] [=] [=]

   _125_, _150_, _175_, _200_

3. Start at 30. Count back by 3s. Write the numbers.

   Press [ON/C] 30 [−] 3 [=] [=] [=] [=]

   _27_, _24_, _21_, _18_

4. Start at 400. Count back by 100s. Write the numbers.

   Press [ON/C] 400 [−] 100 [=] [=] [=] [=]

   _300_, _200_, _100_, _0_

ACTIVITY

Find the rule for each number pattern.
Write the three numbers that come next.

5.   3,   8,   13,   18, _23_, _28_, _33_

6. 122, 117, 112, 107, _102_, _97_, _92_

7. 66, 166, 266, 366, _466_, _566_, _666_

Rules
Count on by 100s.
Count back by 5s.
Count on by 5s.

Calculator Bank   (four hundred one) 40

Calculator Bank

me _____

dding Whole Numbers

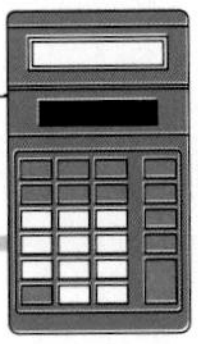

ay each addition sentence as you
ress the keys. Write the sum.

Say		"Seven	plus	four	equals"	
Press	ON/C	7	+	4	=	11

Say		"Fourteen	plus	twenty-three	equals"	
Press	ON/C	14	+	23	=	37

Say		"Six	plus	nine	plus	five	equals"	
Press	ON/C	6	+	9	+	5	=	20

Say		"Nine	plus	eleven	plus	two hundred	equals"	
Press	ON/C	9	+	11	+	200	=	220

CTIVITY

Which tools did each person buy?

Tools

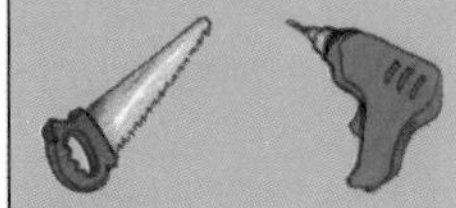

Plane	$49
Saw	$26
Grinder	$72
Sander	$180
Drill	$149

Anne bought 2 tools. She paid $98.

grinder   saw

Walt bought 2 tools. He paid $198.

plane   drill

Mark bought 3 tools. He paid $401.

drill   sander   grinder

2   (four hundred two)

Calculator Bank

Name _____

Subtracting Whole Numbers

Say each subtraction sentence as you press the keys. Write the difference.

1. Say   "Eight minus five equals"

   Press | ON/C | 8 | − | 5 | = | 3

2. Say   "Forty-six minus eighteen equals"

   Press | ON/C | 46 | − | 18 | = | 28

3. Say   "One hundred twelve minus eighty equals"

   Press | ON/C | 112 | − | 80 | = | 32

4. Say   "Five hundred minus two hundred equals"

   Press | ON/C | 500 | − | 200 | = | 300

ACTIVITY

5. Write two numbers from the box that make the difference.

| 66 | 17 | 55 | 9 | 200 |

17	66	200	55
− 9	− 55	− 17	− 9
8	11	183	46

Calculator Bank

Name _____

Multiplying Whole Numbers

Here are some ways you can find the total number in 3 groups of 5.

```
X X X X X
X X X X X
X X X X X
```

Count by 5s.
Press [ON/C] 0 [+] 5 [=] [=] [=] | 15 |

Add 3 fives.
Press [ON/C] 5 [+] 5 [+] 5 [=] | 15 |

Multiply 5 by 3.
Press [ON/C] 3 [×] 5 [=] | 15 |

Use your calculator. Write each answer.

1. 4 twos | 8 | 2. 4 times 3 | 12 |

3. 3 fours | 12 | 4. 2 times 5 | 10 |

ACTIVITY

| 1 | 1 | 2 | 2 | 3 | 3 | 4 | 4 | 5 | 5 |

5. Make cards like these.
Play this game with a partner. Use counters and take turns. Mix the cards. Put them face down. Draw two cards and find the product. Put a counter on that number on the board. Then your partner takes a turn. Continue taking turns. The person with four markers in a row is the winner.

5	12	8	25
16	10	2	15
3	12	6	20
1	15	4	9

Calculator Bank

COMPUTER BANK

This program is available on disk.

Computer Bank

Name _____

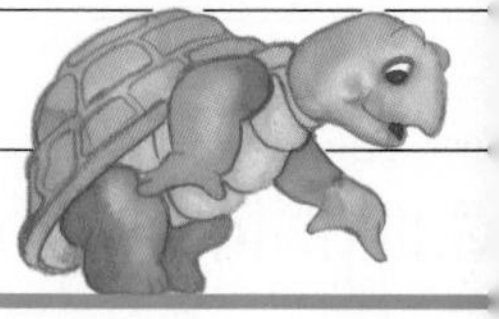

Turtle Travels

Cut out the turtle. Put it in the HOME box. Follow
each set of instructions. Find where the turtle will land.

1. HOME
   FORWARD 1 (box)
   (turn) RIGHT
   FORWARD 2
   Color this
   box [crayon].

2. HOME
   FORWARD 2
   (turn) RIGHT
   FORWARD 2
   (TURN) RIGHT
   FORWARD 4
   Draw a flower
   in this box.

3. HOME
   (turn) RIGHT
   FORWARD 1
   (turn) RIGHT
   FORWARD 1
   (turn) RIGHT
   FORWARD 3
   Draw a star
   in this box.

4. HOME
   (turn) RIGHT
   FORWARD 2
   (turn) RIGHT
   FORWARD 2
   (turn) RIGHT
   FORWARD 4
   (turn) RIGHT
   FORWARD 3
   Draw a fish
   in this box.

fish				green
		 HOME		
star				
				flower

Computer Bank

(four hundred five) 405

This program is available on disk.

Computer Bank

ame _____

Get Turtle Home

The turtle is lost. Help it get to the front door of
its home. Cut out the turtle. Connect the dots.
Follow these instructions:

RT 90   ⌐ FD 7   ⌐ RT 90
FD 5   │ RT 90   │ FD 2
RT 90   ⌐ FD 3   ⌐

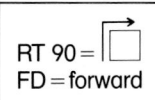

RT 90 = ⌐→▢
FD = forward

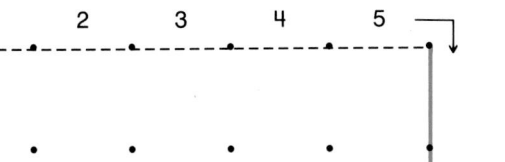

1   2   3   4   5

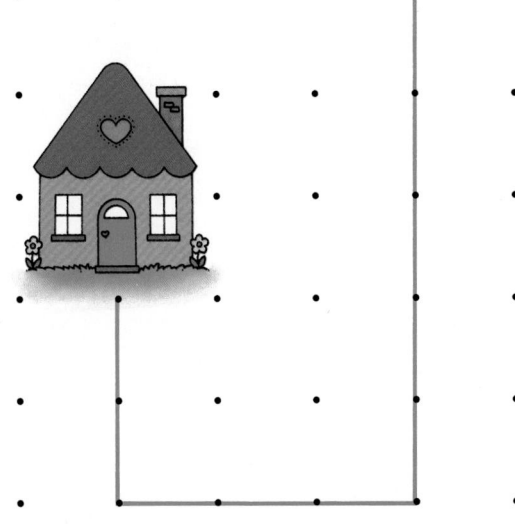

06 (four hundred six)   Computer Bank

COMPUTER BANK

This program is available on disk.

Computer Bank

Name _____

My Logo Drawing

Connect the dots to draw a picture. Use the instructions FORWARD, BACK, RIGHT 90, LEFT 90, HOME. Draw a △ at the start. Write your program on another sheet of paper.

Answers may vary.

Computer Bank   (four hundred seven) 40

This program is available on disk.

Computer Bank

Name _____

Surprise Program

Put together a surprise program. Copy each instruction onto a card. Shuffle the cards. Choose any number of cards. Put these instructions into a surprise program to use on the computer.

Answers may vary.

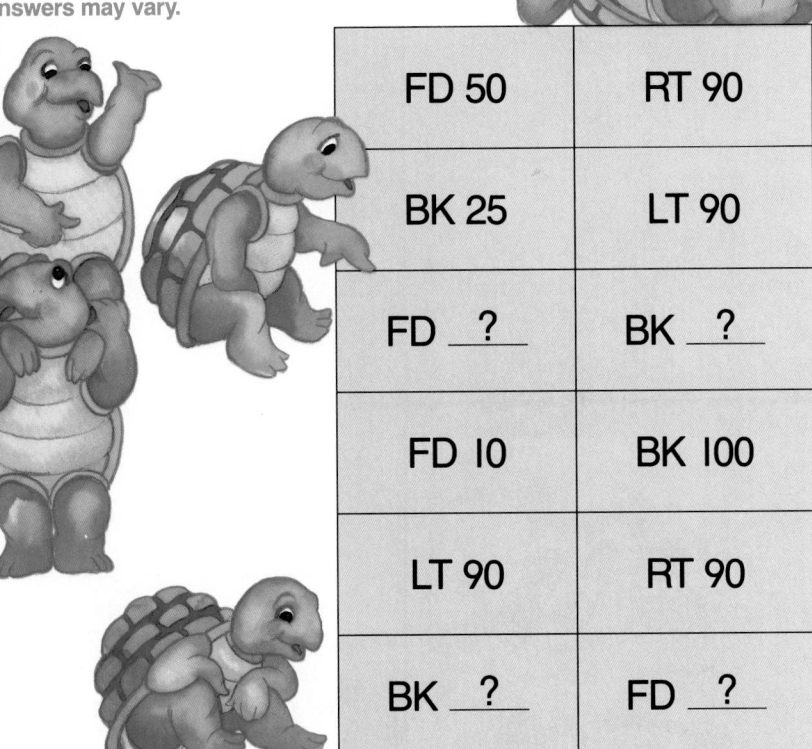

FD 50	RT 90
BK 25	LT 90
FD __?__	BK __?__
FD 10	BK 100
LT 90	RT 90
BK __?__	FD __?__

Computer Bank

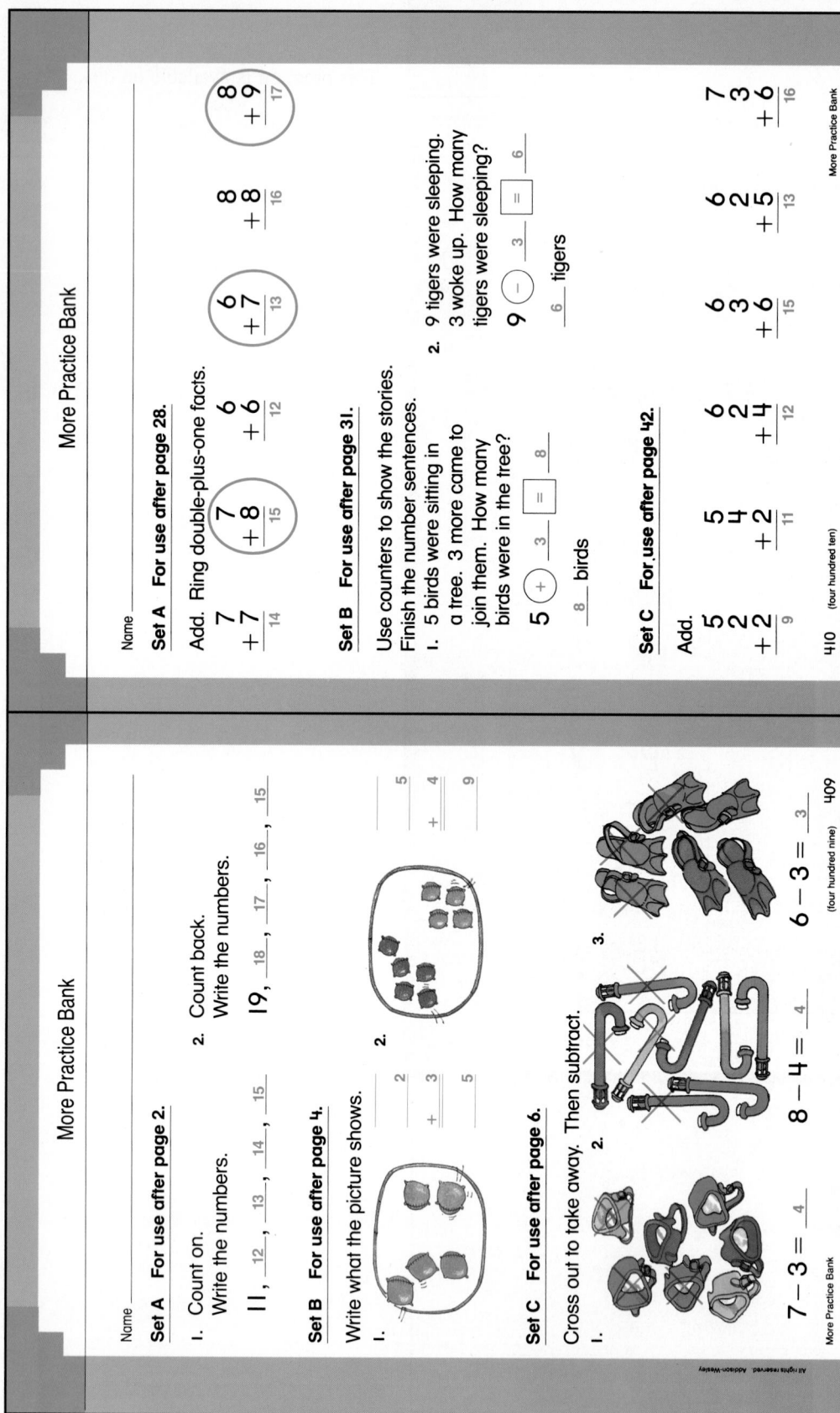

More Practice Bank

Name _____

Set A For use after page 2.

1. Count on. Write the numbers.

11, _12_ , _13_ , _14_ , _15_

2. Count back. Write the numbers.

19, _18_ , _17_ , _16_ , _15_

Set B For use after page 4.

Write what the picture shows.

1. $+\;\begin{array}{r}2\\3\\\hline5\end{array}$

2. $+\;\begin{array}{r}5\\4\\\hline9\end{array}$

Set C For use after page 6.

Cross out to take away. Then subtract.

1. $7 - 3 = \_4\_$

2. $8 - 4 = \_4\_$

3. $6 - 3 = \_3\_$

409 (four hundred nine)

More Practice Bank

More Practice Bank

Name _____

Set A For use after page 28.

Add. Ring double-plus-one facts.

$\begin{array}{r}7\\+7\\\hline14\end{array}$ (7+8=15 ringed) $\begin{array}{r}7\\+8\\\hline15\end{array}$ $\begin{array}{r}6\\+6\\\hline12\end{array}$ (6+7=13 ringed) $\begin{array}{r}6\\+7\\\hline13\end{array}$ $\begin{array}{r}8\\+8\\\hline16\end{array}$ (8+9=17 ringed) $\begin{array}{r}8\\+9\\\hline17\end{array}$

Set B For use after page 31.

Use counters to show the stories. Finish the number sentences.

1. 5 birds were sitting in a tree. 3 more came to join them. How many birds were in the tree?

$5 + 3 = \boxed{8}$

_8_ birds

2. 9 tigers were sleeping. 3 woke up. How many tigers were sleeping?

$9 - 3 = \boxed{6}$

_6_ tigers

Set C For use after page 42.

Add.

$\begin{array}{r}5\\2\\+2\\\hline9\end{array}$ $\begin{array}{r}5\\4\\+2\\\hline11\end{array}$ $\begin{array}{r}6\\2\\+4\\\hline12\end{array}$ $\begin{array}{r}6\\3\\+6\\\hline15\end{array}$ $\begin{array}{r}6\\2\\+5\\\hline13\end{array}$ $\begin{array}{r}7\\3\\+6\\\hline16\end{array}$

410 (four hundred ten)

More Practice Bank

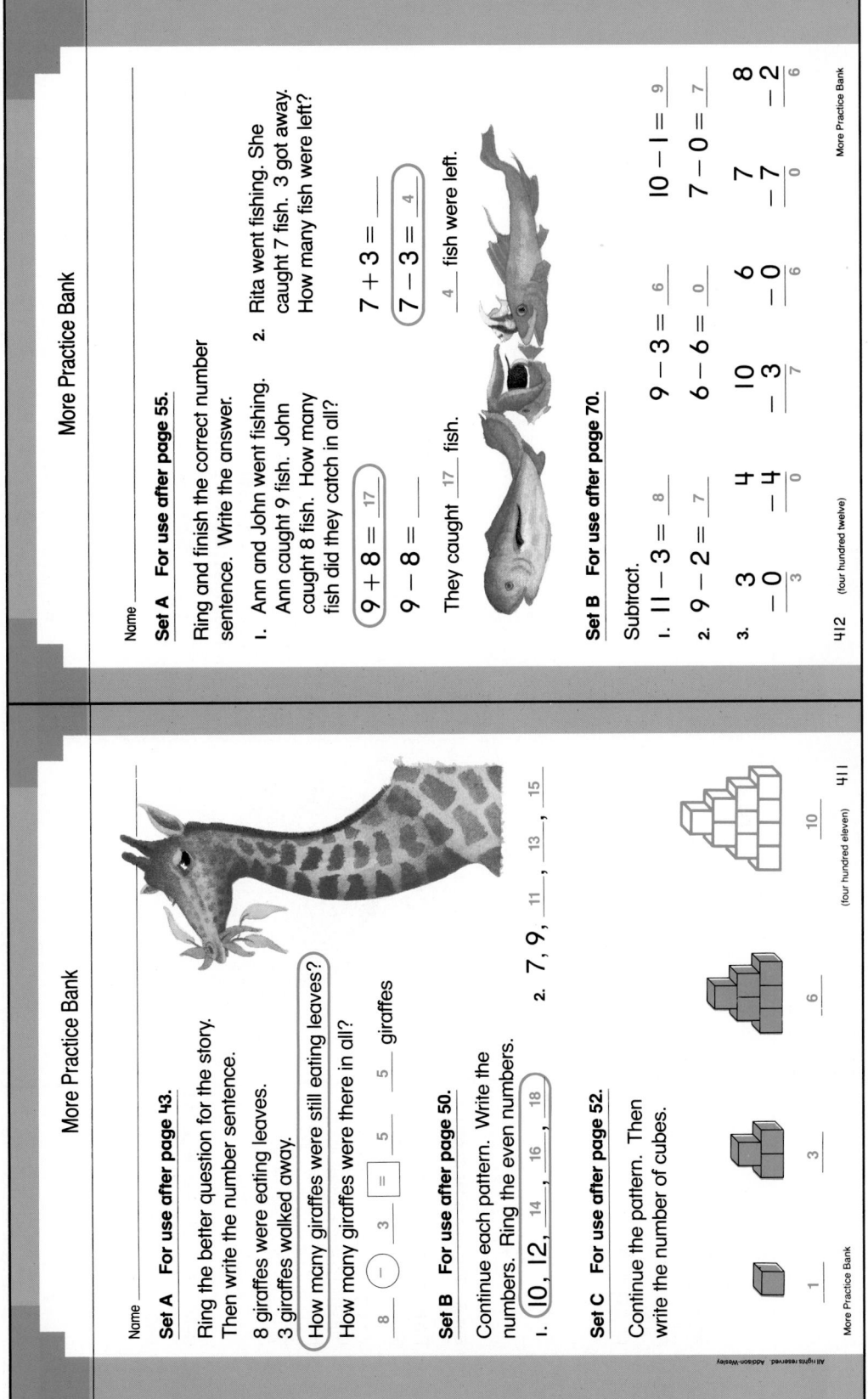

More Practice Bank

Name _____

Set A   For use after page 43.

Ring the better question for the story.
Then write the number sentence.

8 giraffes were eating leaves.
3 giraffes walked away.

(How many giraffes were still eating leaves?)

How many giraffes were there in all?

$8 - 3 = 5$ __5__ giraffes

Set B   For use after page 50.

Continue each pattern. Write the
numbers. Ring the even numbers.

1. ⑩, ⑫, __14__ , __16__ , __18__

2. 7, 9, __11__ , __13__ , __15__

Set C   For use after page 52.

Continue the pattern. Then
write the number of cubes.

__1__   __3__   __6__   __10__

More Practice Bank

(four hundred eleven)   411

More Practice Bank

Name _____

Set A   For use after page 55.

Ring and finish the correct number
sentence. Write the answer.

1. Ann and John went fishing.
   Ann caught 9 fish. John
   caught 8 fish. How many
   fish did they catch in all?

   (9 + 8 = __17__)

   9 − 8 = ___

   They caught __17__ fish.

2. Rita went fishing. She
   caught 7 fish. 3 got away.
   How many fish were left?

   7 + 3 = ___

   (7 − 3 = __4__)

   __4__ fish were left.

Set B   For use after page 70.

Subtract.

1. $11 - 3 = $ __8__ $9 - 3 = $ __6__ $10 - 1 = $ __9__

2. $9 - 2 = $ __7__ $6 - 6 = $ __0__ $7 - 0 = $ __7__

3.
$$\begin{array}{r} 3 \\ -0 \\ \hline 3 \end{array} \quad \begin{array}{r} 4 \\ -4 \\ \hline 0 \end{array} \quad \begin{array}{r} 10 \\ -3 \\ \hline 7 \end{array} \quad \begin{array}{r} 6 \\ -0 \\ \hline 6 \end{array} \quad \begin{array}{r} 7 \\ -7 \\ \hline 0 \end{array} \quad \begin{array}{r} 8 \\ -2 \\ \hline 6 \end{array}$$

412   (four hundred twelve)

More Practice Bank

More Practice Bank   **T14**

More Practice Bank

Name ___

Set A For use after page 84.

Add and subtract to finish the fact families.

1. 5 + 9 = 14
2. 8 + 6 = 14
3. 7 + 6 = 13

   9 + 5 = 14   6 + 8 = 14   6 + 7 = 13

   14 − 5 = 9   14 − 8 = 6   13 − 7 = 6

   14 − 9 = 5   14 − 6 = 8   13 − 6 = 7

Set B For use after page 85.

Draw more or cross out to match the story.
Finish the number sentence.

7 frogs were on a rock.
4 frogs hopped away.
How many frogs were left?

7 − 4 = 3

3 frogs

Set C For use after page 102.

Write the differences.

11	15	13	12	17	14
−6	−6	−8	−5	−8	−9
5	9	5	7	9	5

(four hundred thirteen) 413

More Practice Bank

More Practice Bank

Name ___

Set A For use after page 105.

Write a story for 12 − 8 = ___.
Use the Word Bank to help.
Stories may vary. 12 − 8 = 4.

Word Bank

bought broke ate
were left had
sold gave away in all

Set B For use after page 114.

Estimate each length.
Then measure to the nearest inch. Estimates may vary.

1.  estimate: ___ inches   measure: 2 inches

2.  estimate: ___ inches   measure: 5 inches

414 (four hundred fourteen)

More Practice Bank

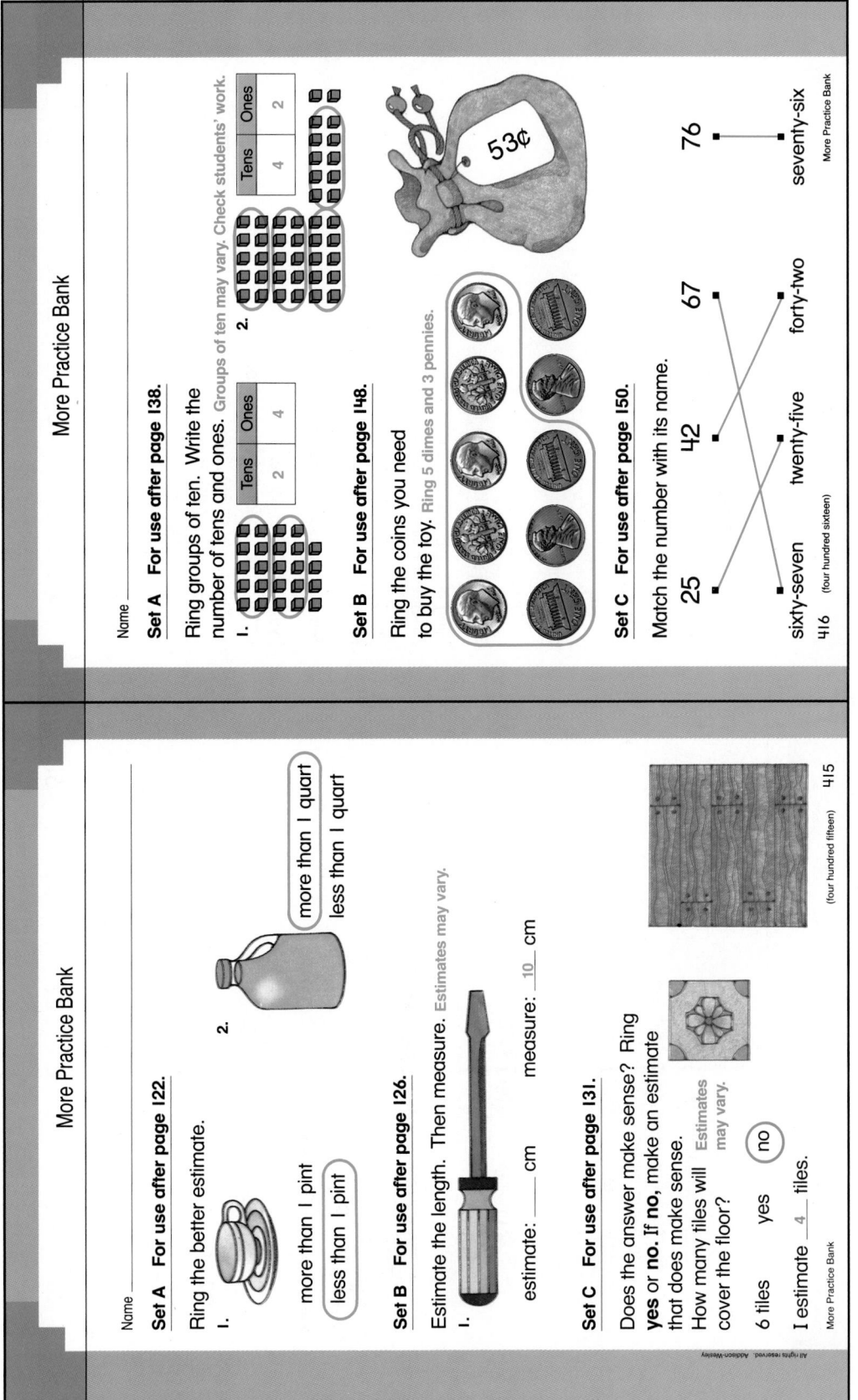

More Practice Bank

Name _____

Set A For use after page 122.

Ring the better estimate.

1.

more than 1 pint

(less than 1 pint)

2.

(more than 1 quart)

less than 1 quart

Set B For use after page 126.

Estimate the length. Then measure. Estimates may vary.

1.

estimate: _____ cm   measure: __10__ cm

Set C For use after page 131.

Does the answer make sense? Ring **yes** or **no**. If **no**, make an estimate that does make sense.

How many tiles will cover the floor?

Estimates may vary.

6 tiles   yes   (no)

I estimate __4__ tiles.

More Practice Bank   (four hundred fifteen) 415

More Practice Bank

Name _____

Set A For use after page 138.

Ring groups of ten. Write the number of tens and ones. Groups of ten may vary. Check students' work.

1.

Tens	Ones
2	4

2.

Tens	Ones
4	2

Set B For use after page 148.

Ring the coins you need to buy the toy. Ring 5 dimes and 3 pennies.

53¢

Set C For use after page 150.

Match the number with its name.

25   42   67   76

sixty-seven   twenty-five   forty-two   seventy-six

416 (four hundred sixteen)   More Practice Bank

More Practice Bank   **T16**

More Practice Bank

Name _____

Set A   For use after page 152.

Write how many hundreds, tens, and ones. Then write the number.

1.

Hundreds	Tens	Ones
1	0	6

____106

2.

Hundreds	Tens	Ones
1	1	0

____110

3.

Hundreds	Tens	Ones
1	1	5

____115

Set B   For use after page 160.

1. Write the number after.

37, _38_

79, _80_

2. Write the number before.

_25_, 26

_66_, 67

3. Write the number between.

29, _30_, 31

37, _38_, 39

Set C   For use after page 166.

Write > or < in each ◯.

1. 28 (>) 23

2. 35 (>) 27

3. 59 (<) 61

(four hundred seventeen)   417

More Practice Bank

Name _____

Set A   For use after page 170.

Write the missing numbers.

1. Count by 3s.

45, 48, 51, 54, 57, 60, 63, 66, 69

2. Count by 4s.

54, 58, 62, 66, 70, 74, 78, 82, 86

Set B   For use after page 174.

Ring the second, eighth, twelfth, nineteenth, and twenty-third letters.

A (B) C D E F G (H) I J K (L) M
N O P Q R (S) T U V (W) X Y Z

Set C   For use after page 175.

Write a number sentence and the answer. Draw a line under the extra data.

1. There are 12 cats and 9 dogs. 6 of the dogs are eating. How many more cats than dogs are there?

$12 - 9 = 3$

There are _3_ more cats.

2. Joan had 14 pens. She had 7 pencils. She lost 8 pens. How many pens does she have left?

$14 - 8 = 6$

She has _6_ pens left.

418   (four hundred eighteen)

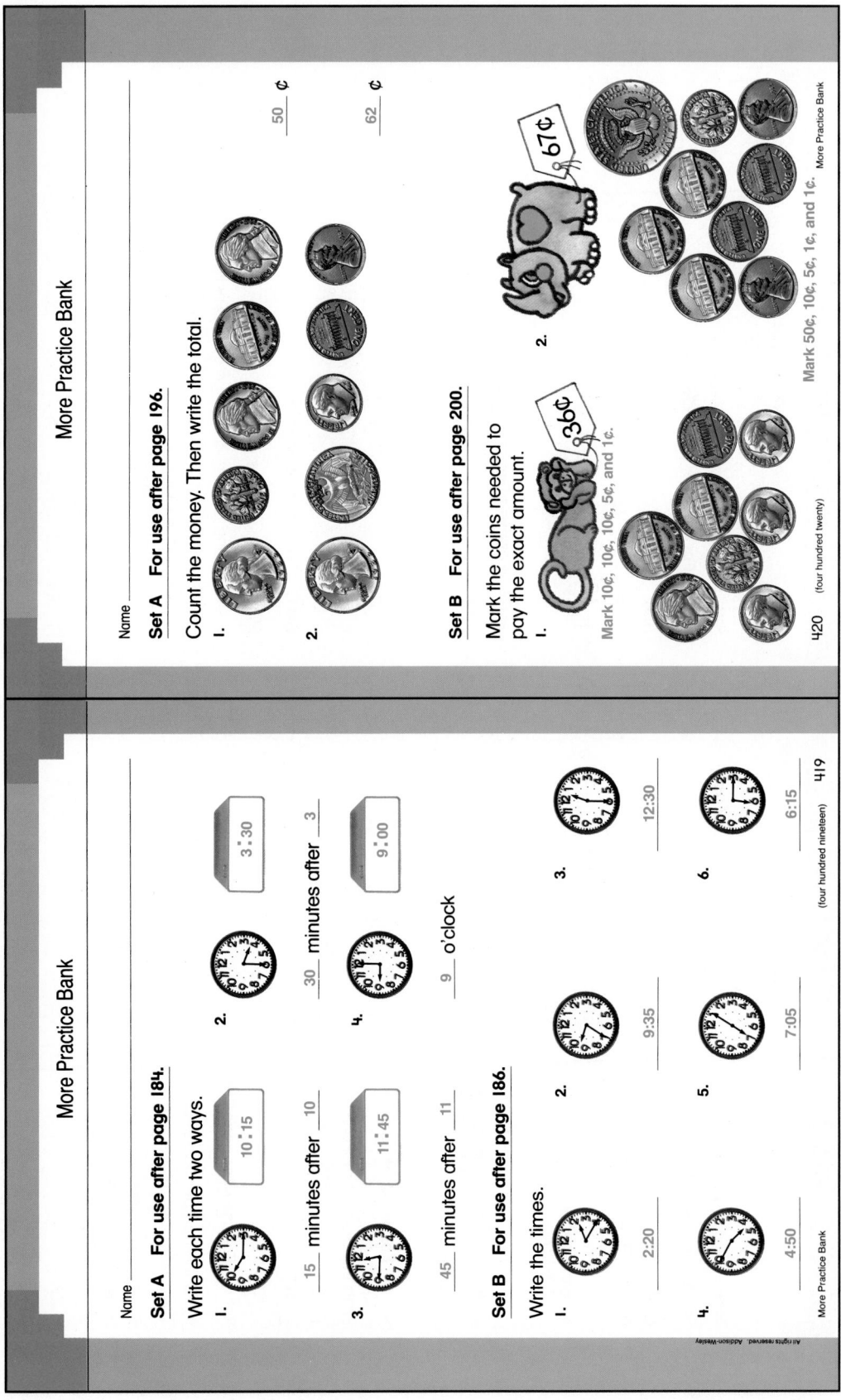

More Practice Bank

Name _____

Set A For use after page 184.

Write each time two ways.

1. [clock] 10:15
   15 minutes after 10

2. [clock] 3:30
   30 minutes after 3

3. [clock] 11:45
   45 minutes after 11

4. [clock] 9:00
   9 o'clock

Set B For use after page 186.

Write the times.

1. [clock] 2:20

2. [clock] 9:35

3. [clock] 12:30

4. [clock] 4:50

5. [clock] 7:05

6. [clock] 6:15

More Practice Bank

(four hundred nineteen) 419

More Practice Bank

Name _____

Set A For use after page 196.

Count the money. Then write the total.

1. [coins] 50 ¢

2. [coins] 62 ¢

Set B For use after page 200.

Mark the coins needed to pay the exact amount.

1. 36¢ [coins] Mark 10¢, 10¢, 5¢, and 1¢.

2. 67¢ [coins] Mark 50¢, 10¢, 5¢, 1¢, and 1¢.

420 (four hundred twenty)

More Practice Bank

More Practice Bank

Name _____

Set A For use after page 236.
Add.

77 +18 = 95	¹45 +19 = 64	¹37 +53 = 90	¹66 +9 = 75	16¢ +18¢ = 34¢
				¹21¢ +17¢ = 38¢

Set B For use after page 242.
Add.

23 16 +33 = 72	¹46 18 +22 = 86	¹33 3 +14 = 50	11 6 +3 = 20	51 7 +3 = 61	¹32 19 +20 = 71

Set C For use after page 243.
Ring the best estimate.

1. The band bought 22 orange flags and 24 green flags. About how many flags did they buy in all?
   - **about 40 flags** (circled)
   - about 60 flags
   - about 80 flags

2. There are 33 girls and 34 boys in the band. About how many students are in the band?
   - about 40 students
   - **about 60 students** (circled)
   - about 80 students

422 (four hundred twenty-two) More Practice Bank

More Practice Bank

Name _____

Set A For use after page 214.
Can you make another ten? Ring **yes** or **no**. Write the number in all.

1. 14 20   Another ten? yes (**no**)   How many in all? 34

2. 17 14   (**yes**) no   31

Set B For use after page 218.
Ring the ways to make each sum.

1. 63   (20 + 43)   (31 + 32)   37 + 18
2. 47   (22 + 26)   22 + 25   (15 + 32)

Set C For use after page 219.
Write the number sentence.
Then write the answer in a sentence.   *Word sentences may vary. Sample answer is shown.*

9 girls and 6 boys went on a hike.
How many children went on a hike?

9 + 6 = 15

15 children went on a hike.

421 (four hundred twenty-one)

More Practice Bank

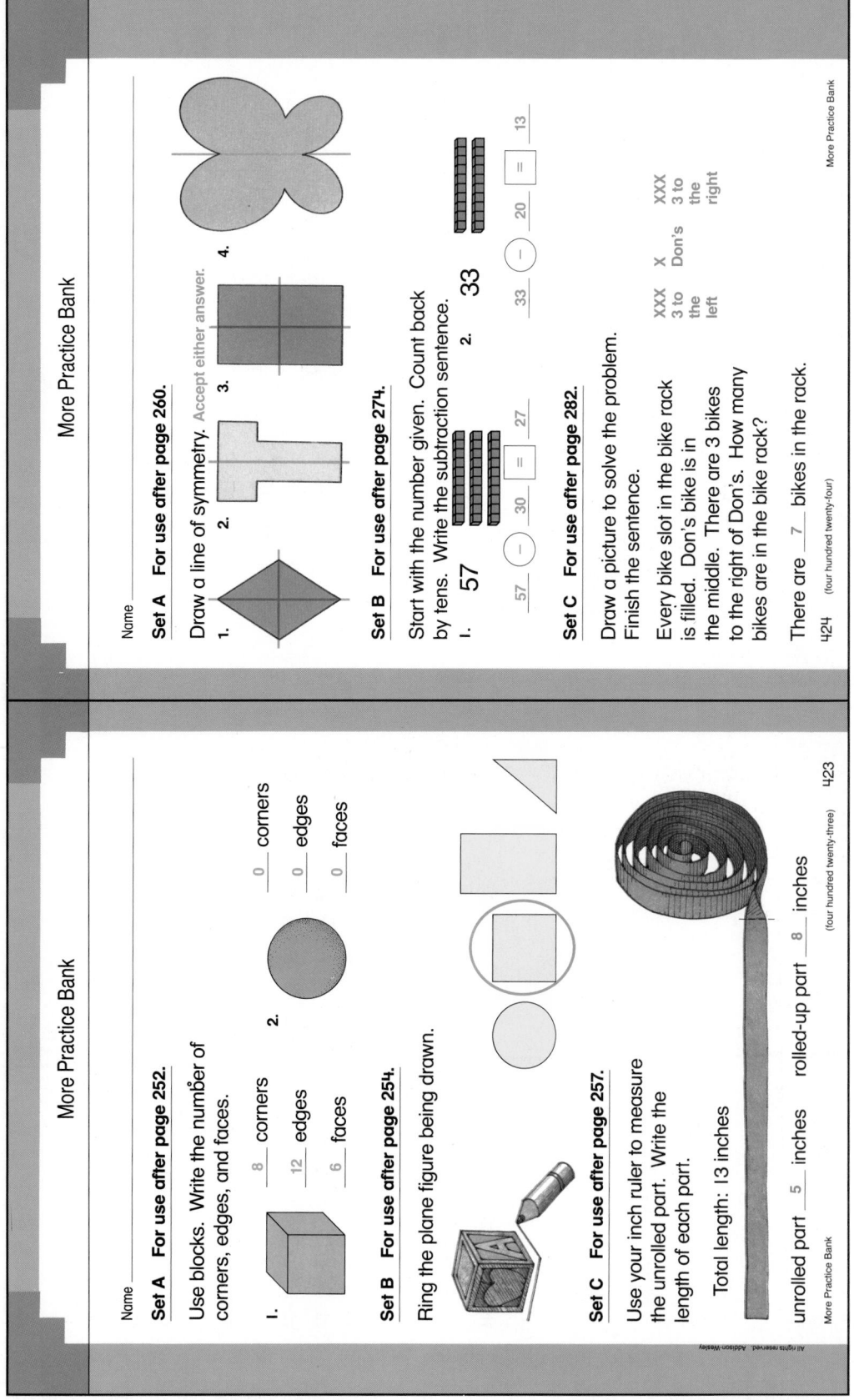

More Practice Bank

Name _____

Set A For use after page 252.

Use blocks. Write the number of corners, edges, and faces.

1.
8 corners
12 edges
6 faces

2.
0 corners
0 edges
0 faces

Set B For use after page 254.

Ring the plane figure being drawn.

Set C For use after page 257.

Use your inch ruler to measure the unrolled part. Write the length of each part.

Total length: 13 inches

unrolled part __5__ inches   rolled-up part __8__ inches

More Practice Bank

Name _____

Set A For use after page 260.

Draw a line of symmetry. Accept either answer.

1.   2.   3.   4.

Set B For use after page 274.

Start with the number given. Count back by tens. Write the subtraction sentence.

1. 57   57 (−) 30 = 27

2. 33   33 (−) 20 = 13

Set C For use after page 282.

Draw a picture to solve the problem. Finish the sentence.

Every bike slot in the bike rack is filled. Don's bike is in the middle. There are 3 bikes to the right of Don's. How many bikes are in the bike rack?

XXX X XXX
3 to the left Don's 3 to the right

There are __7__ bikes in the rack.

MORE PRACTICE BANK

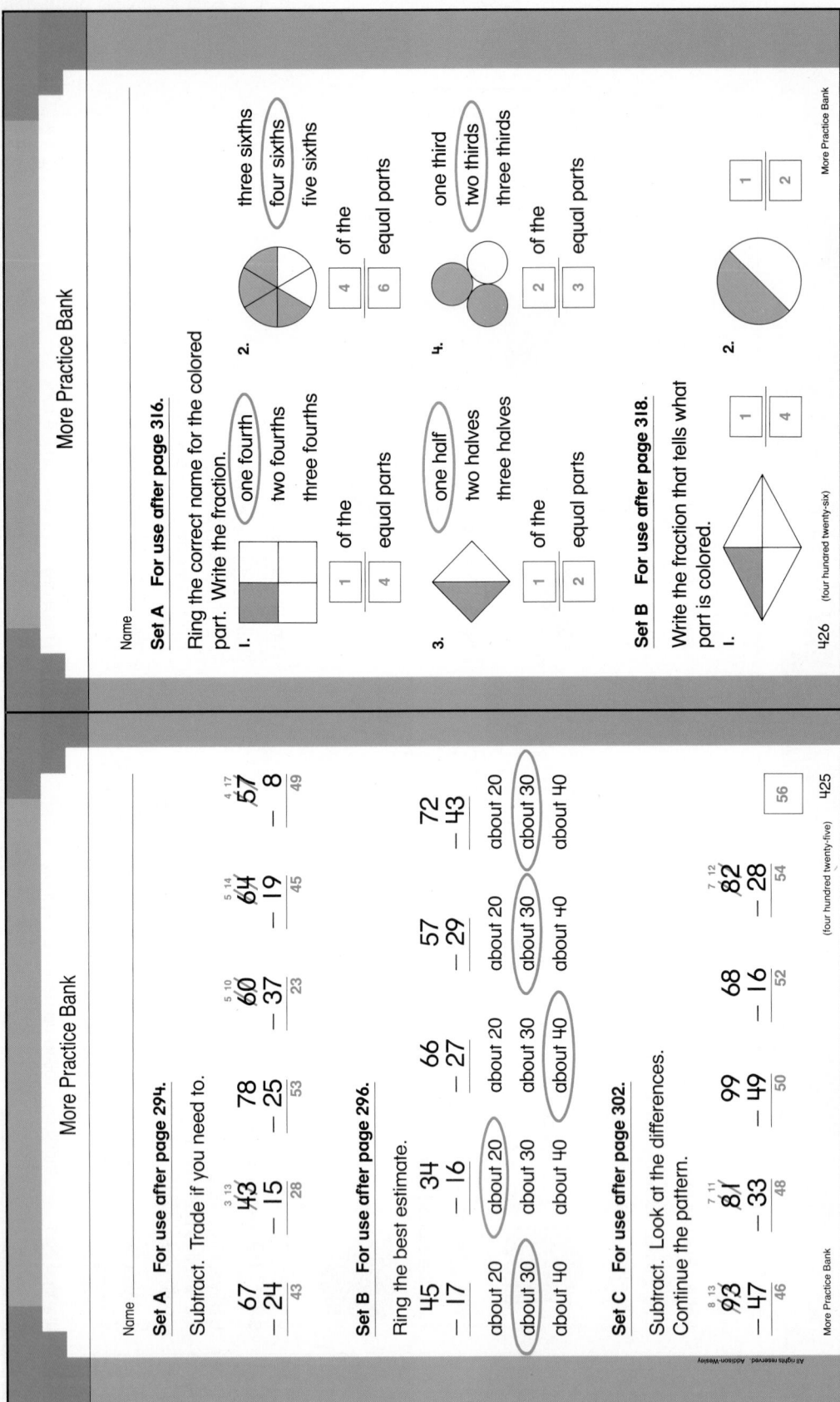

More Practice Bank

Name _____

Set A For use after page 294.

Subtract. Trade if you need to.

$$67 - 24 = 43$$

$$\overset{3\ 13}{43} - 15 = 28$$

$$78 - 25 = 53$$

$$\overset{5\ 10}{60} - 37 = 23$$

$$\overset{5\ 14}{64} - 19 = 45$$

$$\overset{4\ 17}{57} - 8 = 49$$

Set B For use after page 296.

Ring the best estimate.

45 − 17   about 20   (about 30)   about 40

34 − 16   (about 20)   about 30   about 40

66 − 27   about 20   about 30   (about 40)

57 − 29   about 20   (about 30)   about 40

72 − 43   about 20   (about 30)   about 40

Set C For use after page 302.

Subtract. Look at the differences. Continue the pattern.

$$\overset{8\ 13}{93} - 47 = 46$$

$$\overset{7\ 11}{81} - 33 = 48$$

$$99 - 49 = 50$$

$$68 - 16 = 52$$

$$\overset{7\ 12}{82} - 28 = 54$$

56

(four hundred twenty-five)   425

More Practice Bank

Name _____

Set A For use after page 316.

Ring the correct name for the colored part. Write the fraction.

1. (one fourth)   two fourths   three fourths
   1 of the 4 equal parts

2. three sixths   (four sixths)   five sixths
   4 of the 6 equal parts

3. (one half)   two halves   three halves
   1 of the 2 equal parts

4. one third   (two thirds)   three thirds
   2 of the 3 equal parts

Set B For use after page 318.

Write the fraction that tells what part is colored.

1. $\frac{1}{4}$

2. $\frac{1}{2}$

426   (four hundred twenty-six)

More Practice Bank

Name _____

Set A For use after page 321.

Finish the number sentence. Then answer the question in a sentence.

1. Timmy, Kris, and Mia shared 9 nuts. Each got the same number. How many nuts did each get?

$\frac{1}{3}$ of $9 = $ _3_

Each got 3 nuts.

2. Alan and Carrie shared 12 nuts. Each got the same number. How many nuts did Alan get?

$\frac{1}{2}$ of $12 = $ _6_

Alan got 4 nuts.

Set B For use after page 338.

Write a multiplication sentence for each garden.

1. $2 \times 5 = 10$

2. $5 \times 2 = 10$

427 (four hundred twenty-seven)

More Practice Bank

More Practice Bank

Name _____

Set A For use after page 339.

Ring and finish the correct number sentence. Write the answer in a sentence. Word sentences may vary. Sample answer is shown.

There were 3 bowls on the table. Each bowl had 4 apples in it. How many apples were there in all?

$3 + 4 = $ _____

$(3 \times 4 = 12)$

There were 12 apples in all.

Set B For use after page 342.

Find the number of carrots on each plate. Draw tally marks to show them. Write the division sentence.

1. Share 18 carrots on 3 plates.

$18 \div 3 = 6$

2. Share 12 carrots on 4 plates.

$12 \div 4 = 3$

Set C For use after page 346.

Finish the number sentences. Use the pictures to help.

1. $2 \times 3 = 6$

$6 \div 3 = 2$

2. $3 \times 6 = 18$

$18 \div 6 = 3$

428 (four hundred twenty-eight)

More Practice Bank

MORE PRACTICE BANK

More Practice Bank

Name _____

Set A   For use after page 354.

Look at the pictures. Write the number
of hundreds, tens, and ones. Then
write the number.

1.

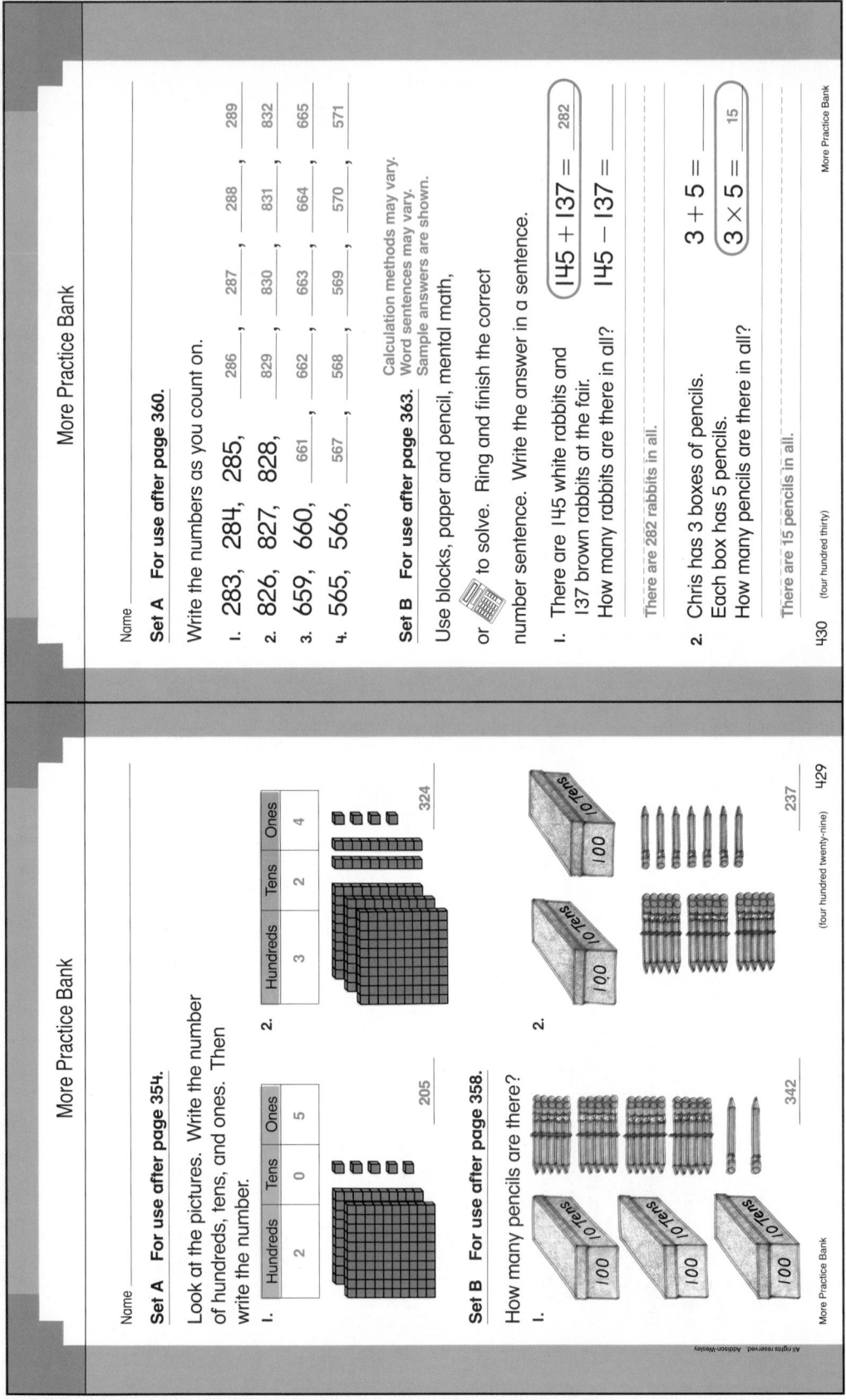

Hundreds	Tens	Ones
2	0	5

___205___

2.

Hundreds	Tens	Ones
3	2	4

___324___

Set B   For use after page 358.

How many pencils are there?

1.

___342___

2.

___237___

More Practice Bank

Name _____

Set A   For use after page 360.

Write the numbers as you count on.

1. 283, 284, 285, ___286___, ___287___, ___288___, ___289___

2. 826, 827, 828, ___829___, ___830___, ___831___, ___832___

3. 659, 660, ___661___, ___662___, ___663___, ___664___, ___665___

4. 565, 566, ___567___, ___568___, ___569___, ___570___, ___571___

Set B   For use after page 363.

Calculation methods may vary.
Word sentences may vary.
Sample answers are shown.

Use blocks, paper and pencil, mental math,
or to solve. Ring and finish the correct
number sentence. Write the answer in a sentence.

1. There are 145 white rabbits and
137 brown rabbits at the fair.
How many rabbits are there in all?

$(145 + 137 =$ ___282___$)$

$145 - 137 =$

There are 282 rabbits in all.

2. Chris has 3 boxes of pencils.
Each box has 5 pencils.
How many pencils are there in all?

$3 + 5 =$

$(3 \times 5 =$ ___15___$)$

There are 15 pencils in all.

More Practice Bank

More Practice Bank

Name _____

Set A For use after page 366.

Write > or < in each ◯.

1. 426 ◯ 326   583 ◯ 783   927 ◯ 627
2. 635 ◯ 645   318 ◯ 308   629 ◯ 649

Set B For use after page 376.

Add. Trade 10 ones for 1 ten if you can.

```
  243     115     176      48      59     227
+  28   + 156   +  18   +  32   + 336   + 315
-----   -----   -----   -----   -----   -----
  271     271     194      80     395     542
```

Set C For use after page 384.

Find the difference. Trade 1 ten for 10 ones if you need to.

```
1.  694     381     414     798     263     655
  - 405   - 162   - 209   - 589   -  42   - 347
   -----   -----   -----   -----   -----   -----
    289     219     205     209     221     308

2.  395     880     653     791     544     407
  - 207   - 448   - 142   - 353   - 316   - 201
   -----   -----   -----   -----   -----   -----
    188     432     511     438     228     206
```

(four hundred thirty-one)   431

More Practice Bank

Name _____

Set A For use after page 390.

Add or subtract. Use play money to help.
Look at the sums and differences in each row.
Ring the amount to continue the pattern.

```
1.  $2.25     $4.90     $1.70     $7.39   +  $0.25
  + 1.25    - 1.65    + 1.30    - 4.64   - ($0.25)
   ------     -----     -----     -----   - $25.00
   $3.50     $3.25     $3.00     $2.75

2.  $1.66     $5.35     $2.16     $7.91   + ($0.01)
  + 2.73    - 0.85    + 2.25    - 3.49   +  $0.10
   ------     -----     -----     -----   +  $1.00
   $4.39     $4.50     $4.41     $4.42
```

Set B For use after page 391.

Solve. Use a 🖩 or play money to help.

1. Vicki had $5.23. She bought a shovel and a packet of seeds. She spent $4.15.

   How much money did the seeds cost? _____ $1.05

   How much money does Vicki have left? _____ $1.08

```
$3.10

  $5.23      $4.15
- 4.15      - 3.10
 ------      ------
  $1.08      $1.05
```

432   (four hundred thirty-two)

Glossary

Add

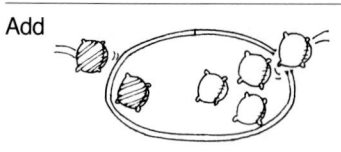

$$2 + 4 = 6$$

Addend

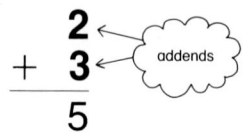

Addition sentence

$$3 + 5 = 8$$

After

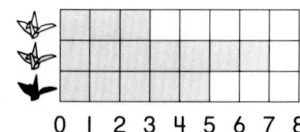

Bar graph

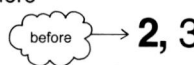

Number of Birds Made

0 1 2 3 4 5 6 7 8

Before

Between

2, **3**, 4

Calendar

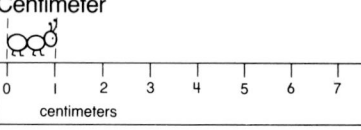

MAY

Sun.	Mon.	Tue.	Wed.	Thu.	Fri.	Sat.
	1	2	3	4	5	6
7	8	9	10	11	12	13
14	15	16	17	18	19	20
21	22	23	24	25	26	27
28	29	30	31			

Centimeter

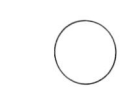

Circle

Cone

Congruent figures

Corner

Cube

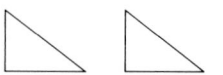
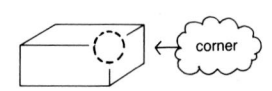
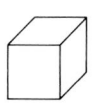

Glossary

(four hundred thirty-three) 43

Glossary

up

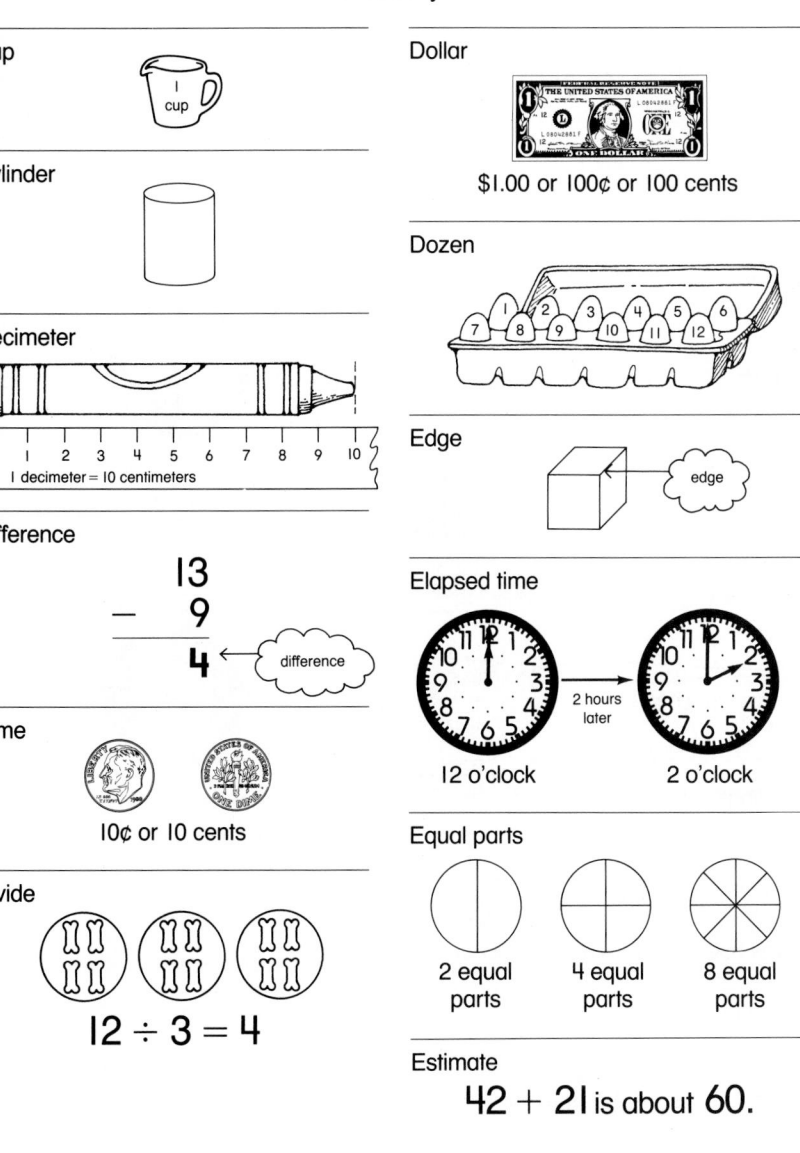

ylinder

ecimeter

1 decimeter = 10 centimeters

fference

$$
\begin{array}{r}
13 \\
-\ \ 9 \\
\hline
4
\end{array}
$$

difference

me

10¢ or 10 cents

ivide

$12 \div 3 = 4$

Dollar

$1.00 or 100¢ or 100 cents

Dozen

Edge

edge

Elapsed time

2 hours later

12 o'clock   2 o'clock

Equal parts

2 equal parts   4 equal parts   8 equal parts

Estimate

$42 + 21$ is about 60.

Glossary

Even numbers

$$2, 4, 6, 8, 10, \ldots$$

Face

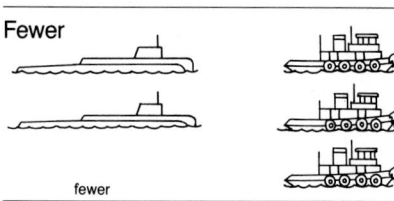

Fact family

$$2 + 4 = 6 \qquad 6 - 4 = 2$$
$$4 + 2 = 6 \qquad 6 - 2 = 4$$

Fewer

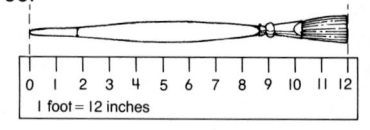

fewer

Foot

1 foot = 12 inches

Fractions

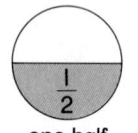 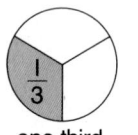 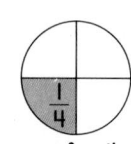

$\frac{1}{2}$ one half $\frac{1}{3}$ one third $\frac{1}{4}$ one fourth

Greater than

$$17 > 13$$
17 is **greater than** 13.

Half dollar

50¢ or 50 cents

Half hour

12:00 to 12:30

Hour

2:00 to 3:00

Inch

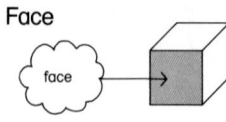

inches

Glossary

(four hundred thirty-five) 43

Glossary

...gram

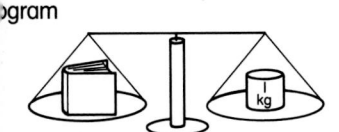

...ss than

$$13 < 17$$
13 is **less than** 17.

...e of symmetry

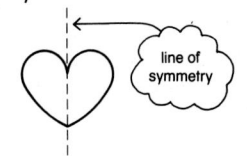

line of symmetry

...er

...ter

about 1 meter

Minute

1 minute

More

more

Multiply

$$3 \times 4 = 12$$

Nickel

5¢ or 5 cents

Number sentence

$$3 + 5 = 8 \text{ or } 7 - 4 = 3 \text{ or}$$
$$3 \times 3 = 9 \text{ or } 12 \div 3 = 4$$

Odd numbers

$$1, 3, 5, 7, 9, \ldots$$

INDEX

Teacher's Edition References are in italics.

A

Addition
associative property of, 267
with calculator, 30, 238, 354, 402, 404
to check subtraction, 72, 94, 244, 292, 297-98, 402
column, 1- and 2-digit numbers, 41-42, 47, 241-42, 267, 332, 402
commutative property of (turnaround facts), 38, 209-10, 214, 267
concept using models, 3-4, 9-10, 47, 55
counting on from 2-digit numbers, 208, 211-12
fact families, 15-16, 83-84, 103-04
fact strategies, 25-28
facts through 18, 3-4, 9-10, 11-12, 15-16, 17, 18, 21, 24, 25-26, 27-28, 29-30, 33-34, 35-36, 37-38, 39-40, 55, 83-84, 85, 97, 98, 99, 103-04, 339
mental math, 24, 25-26, 37-38, 70, 98, 210, 336, 378, 388
with money, 10, 33-34, 36, 86, 201, 216, 263, 336, 389-90, 391, 402
and multiplication, 332, 339, 363, 404
properties, 24, 25-26, 39-40, 209-10, 267
related to subtraction, 93-94, 99-100
special sums with multiples of 10, 209-10, 378, 388
with three addends, 41-42, 241-42, 332, 402
of 2-digit numbers, one trade, 227-28, 230, 231-32, 235-36, 239-40, 242, 263, 267, 281, 292, 311, 376
of 3-digit numbers, one trade, 377-78
of 3-digit numbers, two trades, 379-80, 389-90
trading, 213-14, 227-28, 229-30, 231-32, 235-36, 239-40, 263, 267, 281, 311, 376, 377-78, 379-80, 389-90
understanding, 1, 3-4, 9-10, 47, 97, 207, 215
using symbols 3-4, 9-10, 17, 63, 217-18, 231-32, 332, 339

Algebra readiness
coordinate graphing 263
exploring algebra, 21, 60, 168, 340
missing numbers in equations 17, 21, 33-34, 60, 340

Algorithm lessons
addition 231-32, 379-80
subtraction 293-94, 387-88

Analyzing data. *See* Data collection and analysis.

Answers
determining reasonable, 131, 325
estimating, 118, 216, 243, 307

Area, 131, 322

Assess. See Close and Assess throughout the Teacher Edition, for example 3, 5, 7, 9, 11, 13, 15, 17.

Assessment. See also Assess; Quick Review.
alternative, 19, 45, 65, 87, 107, 155, 177, 203, 221, 245, 265, 283, 309, 327, 349, 371, 393
Chapter Review/Test, 20, 46, 66, 88, 108, 133, 134, 156, 178, 204, 222, 246, 266, 284, 310, 328, 350, 372, 394
Cumulative Review, 22, 48, 68, 90, 110, 136, 158, 180, 206, 224, 248, 268, 286, 312, 330, 352, 374, 396
Midchapter Review/Quiz, 12, 34, 58, 78, 100, 124, 166, 190, 214, 233-34, 254, 274, 298, 304, 318, 338, 362, 384

Associative property of addition, 267

B

Bar graphs. *See* Graphs.
Blocks. *See also* Cubes.
place value, as manipulatives, 288, 354, 361-62, 387-88
Breaking apart numbers, 279-80
Bulletin Boards, 1C, 23C, 49C, 69C, 91C, 111C, 137C, 159C, 181C, 207C, 225C, 249C, 269C, 287C, 313C, 331C, 353C, 375C. See also Projects.

C

Calculator
activities, 401-05
as a calculation method, 239-40, 363
using, 30, 238, 294, 300, 354, 402-05
Calculator Bank, 401-04
Calendar, 8, 189-90
Capacity, 121, 122, 129, 329
Celsius scale, 157
Centimeter, 125-26
measuring to nearest, 125-26
Change. *See* Money.
Choose the Operation, 215, 348
Choosing a calculation method, 239-40, 303-04, 363, 381
Charts. *See* Tally charts; Data from a chart.
Circle, 253-54, 255-46
Clocks. *See* Manipulatives; Time.
Coins. *See* Manipulatives; Money.
Collecting data. *See also* Data collection and analysis. 32, 114, 164, 366
Communication, 4, 92, 112, 120, 138, 188, 196, 230, 250, 334, 380

Commutative property
of addition, 209-10, 267
of multiplication, 332, 337-38
Comparing whole numbers, 32, 57-58, 82, 145, 146, 148, 165-66, 365-66, 37? 382
Computer activities. See Computer Bank; *Computer Software.*
Computer Bank, 405-08
Computer Software, 5, 11, 35, 43, 55, 6? 73, 79, 97, 101, 113, 123, 143, 145, 169, 175, 185, 199, 215, 217, 233, 24? 255, 259, 261, 271, 281, 293, 307, 31? 323, 339, 343, 357, 369, 381, 387
Cone, 249, 250, 251-52
Congruent figures, 261-62
Constant, 354, 404
Consumer applications. *See* Money.
Cooperative group activities, 121-22, 127-28, 141-42, 176, 179, 199-200, 217-18, 235-36, 275-76, 297-98, 323-24, 345-46, 367-68, 370
Cooperative Learning, 1C, 23C, 49C, 69C, 91C, 111C, 137C, 159C, 181C, 207C, 225C, 249C, 269C, 287C, 313C, 331C, 353C, 375C
Coordinate geometry, 263
Counters, as manipulatives, 3-4, 5-6, 7, 9-10, 31, 33-34, 35-36, 37-38, 55, 73-74, 75, 92, 97, 216, 319-20, 324, 333-34, 337-38, 339, 340, 341-42, 343-44, 347
Counting
back from 2-digit numbers, 163-64, 166 274, 296
counting on and counting back, 2, 24, 7? 74, 146, 161-64, 182, 185-86, 195-96, 208, 211-12, 236, 255-56, 258, 270, 273-74, 296, 359-60, 364, 373, 401
money, 14, 36, 193-98, 367-68
odd and even numbers, 50, 179
1-100, 161-62
on from 2-digit numbers, 163-64
patterns, 152, 159, 169-70, 171-72, 179 359-60
skip count, 152, 163-64, 179, 185-86, 193-94, 212, 320, 346, 362, 401
whole numbers, 2, 12, 16, 77-78, 163-6? 173-74, 270, 273-74, 359-60, 362, 364
Counting patterns. See Connections throughout the Teacher Edition, for example, 1G, 9A, 13A, 15A.
Creative Thinking. See Connections throughout the Teacher Edition, for example, 3A.
Critical thinking
lessons, 8, 56, 146, 258
using, 10, 24, 50, 74, 96, 160, 182, 22? 290, 332, 386

Acknowledgments

Illustrations

ALEX BLOCH 307
LISA BONFORTE 30, 36B, 38, 39
KATHY BOTTORFF 76, 85, 207, 353, 357, 361, 362, 368, 376, 382, 392
BRUCE BOWLES 101, 182T, 193, 196, 202
ELIZABETH CALLEN 115T, 118T, 125
CHI CHUNG 333B, 335T, 337L, 341B
CYNDIE CLARK-HUEGEL 8, 87, 88, 115B, 127T, 133, 135, 177, 198, 221T, 236, 244, 316, 329, 334, 344T, 351
ROBERTA COLLIER 77, 81
GWEN CONNELLY 377, 386
JULIE DOWNING 308, 412, 413
CHIYORI FILION 25, 27T, 45, 296
LAURIE FRY 250T, 253, 255, 259, 263L
ROGER GRAHAM punchouts
KATE BRENNAN HALL 90T, 246, 266, 283
DENNIS HOCKERMAN 1, 2T, 3, 5T, 13, 24, 26, 28, 36T, 69, 70, 72, 73, 74, 79, 83, 84, 137, 161, 165, 166T, 172, 339T, 340, 341T, 343, 344B, 406, 407, 408, 420, 427, punchouts
ANN IOSA 294, 305, 306
SUSAN JAEKEL 9B, 11, 155, 178, 192, 223
CHRISTA KIEFFER 375, 380, 381, 384
RALPH LAO punchouts
DORA LEDER 272, 274, 279
TOM LEONARD 91, 355, 365, 367
RICHARD LOEHLE 373
DIANA MAGNUSON 71, 182B, 185, 187, 188, 210T, 226, 233B, 239, 257T, 278R, 321, 332B
KATHLEEN McCORD 92T, 94, 96, 98
LYLE MILLER 314, 319, 322, 324
TERRA MUZICK 9T, 21B, 57, 58, 63, 64, 65, 66, 67, 68, 89B, 162, 166B, 175, 176, 263R, 335B, 337R, 339B, 347, 405T, punchouts

MARK NAGATA 113; 116; 118B; 121; 122; 124; 141; 142; 143B; 147B; 148; 149; 150B; 151TL, B; 152T; 156; 158; 159; 221B; 249; 265; 332T; 338; 342
JAMES NEEDHAM 29
SHARRON O'NEIL 27, 40, 41, 44, 173R, 174, 210B, 213, 218, 287, 336
JENNIE OPPENHEIMER 75, 254T, 331, 348
TOM LAPADULA 310, 393, 394
HEATHER PRESTON 23, 53, 59T, 61
JAN PYK 358, 364B, 370
MATHEW REY 6, 12, 20, 22, 49, 54, 55, 59B, 62, 78, 82, 110, 131, 152B, 190, 220, 228, 250B, 254B, 270, 271, 278L, 349, 352
PHYLLIS ROCKNE 48, 109, 183, 184, 191, 201
DOUG ROY 415T, M; punchouts
ED SAUK 395
SALLY SHIMIZU 371
DJ SIMISON 52, 92B, 117, 127B, 129
JAMES STAGG 269, 313
ANDREA TACHIERA 233T, 237, 309, 312, 374, 396
DIANA THEWLIS 5B, 7, 17, 47, 106, 138, 143, 144, 145, 146, 147T, 150T, 151TR, 167, 173L, 211, 215, 219
BUD THON 111, 225
COCO THORPE 181, 227, 230, 235, 333T
MEL WILLIGES 288, 295, 299, 360, 364T

Photography

MIRIAM AUSTERMAN/ANIMALS ANIMALS 43M
E. R. DEGGINGER/ANIMALS ANIMALS 31MT
CURT FISCHER iii, v, vi, vii, viii, ix, 10, 14, 18, 25, 27, 45, 303, 357, 358, 359, 361, 362, 389
STEPHEN FRISCH 86T, 95, 112B, 134, 172, 176, 180 (pencil, door, book), 206, 236, 240, 268
STEPHEN J. KRASEMANN/DRK PHOTO 43T
ZIG LESZCZYNSKI/ANIMALS ANIMALS 43B, 47B
BERT MURRAY/ANIMALS ANIMALS 47T
ALAN NELSON/ANIMALS ANIMALS 31MB
NICK PAVLOFF 2, 4, 12, 15, 16, 32, 33, 35, 37, 42, 50, 56, 61, 62, 63, 64, 85, 86B, 99, 100, 102, 103, 104, 107, 112T, 114, 119, 120, 121, 123, 124, 125, 126, 128, 130, 132, 139, 153, 154, 163, 168, 169, 171, 180 (pail), 194, 197, 199, 200, 205, 208, 209, 216, 217, 231, 241, 251, 256, 261, 264, 270, 273, 275, 277, 280, 314, 315, 317, 323, 325, 326, 340, 343, 345
MARTY STOUFFER PRODUCTIONS/ ANIMALS ANIMALS 31T
PETER VEIT/DRK PHOTO 31B

Technical Art

CYNDIE CLARK-HUEGEL, TERRA MUZICK, SALLY SHIMIZU, MARTHA TUESCHER

PHOTO CREDITS

Lillian Gee: pp. 1D, 23D, 27A, 49D, 53A, 69D, 91D, 111D, 119A, 137D, 149A, 159D, 173A, 181D, 197A, 207D, 207G, 217A, 225D, 229A, 231A, 235A, 249D, 253A, 261A, 269D, 287D, 291A, 295A, 313D, 313G, 331D, 333A, 341A, 343A, 353D, 355A, 359A, 365A, 375D.
Michael Heron: pp. 5A, 15A, 23G, 25A, 29A, 39A, 41A, 61A, 101A, 121A, 139A, 161A, 227A, 251A, 323A, 347A, 367A.
Ken Karp: pp. 3A, 9A, 11A, 49G, 51A, 57A, 59A, 69G, 71A, 73A, 79A, 83A, 91G, 103A, 111G, 113A, 115A, 123A, 125A, 127A, 129A, 137G, 141A, 143A, 147A, 151A, 163A, 165A, 171A, 189A, 193A, 195A, 199A, 209A, 211A, 213A, 225G, 233A, 241A, 255A, 259A, 275A, 279A, 287G, 293A, 301A, 305A, 315A, 317A, 319A, 331G, 335A, 337A, 345A, 353G, 357A, 361A, 375G, 377A, 379A, 383A, 385A, 387A, 389A.

ART CREDITS

Electronic Publishing Center, Inc.: pp. 1G, 13A, 33A, 35A, 37A, 77A, 81A, 93A, 95A, 99A, 159G, 181G, 183A, 185A, 187A, 249A, 271A, 273A, 289A, 297A.
Networkgraphics: pp. 1A, 49A, 49C, bottom left, 49G, 52, 53A, 54, 61A, 62, 69A, 69C, bottom left, 69D, 77, 85A, 91A, 91C, bottom left, 104, 111A, 111C, bottom left, 118, 137A, 137C, bottom left, 137D, 138, 139A, 143A, 143, 147A, 147, 153A, 159A, 181A, 181C, bottom left, 181D, 183A, 184, 185A, 193, 207A, 225A, 225C, bottom left, 239A, 245, 249A, 249G, 250, 251A, 253A, 254, 255A, 255, 256, 259A, 260, 261A, 263A, 269A, 269C, bottom left, 273A, 287A, 287C, bottom left, 291A, 311, 313A, 313C, bottom left, 313D, 253A, 253C, 314, 315, 316, 317A, 318, 322, 325A, 326, 331A, 331C, bottom left, 341A, 343A, 344, 345A, 347A. 353A, 353C, bottom left, 354, 356, 367A, 375A, 375C, bottom left, 375D.

PLACEMENT TEST

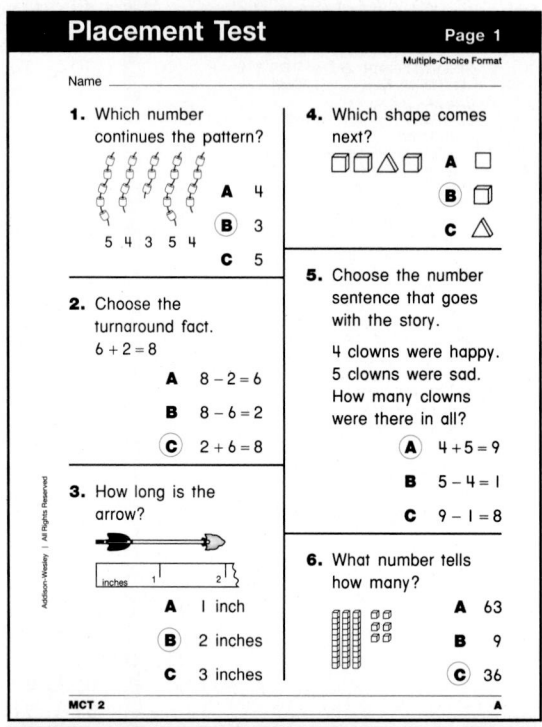

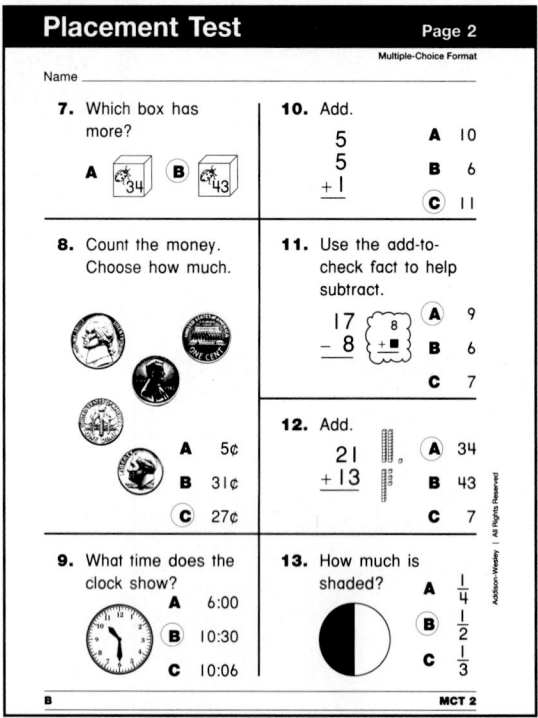

ASSESSMENT

Mid-Year Test — Chapters 1-9, page 1

Multiple-Choice Format

Name _____

1. Choose the fact that belongs to the family.

$$\begin{array}{cc} 8 & 2 \\ +2 & +8 \\ \hline 10 & 10 \end{array}$$

$$\begin{array}{cc} 10 & \\ -2 & \\ \hline 8 & \end{array}$$

A $\begin{array}{r} 10 \\ -8 \\ \hline 2 \end{array}$

B $\begin{array}{r} 8 \\ -2 \\ \hline 6 \end{array}$

2. Add.

$$\begin{array}{r} 4 \\ 2 \\ +3 \\ \hline \end{array}$$

A 6
B 9
C 5

3. Are these numbers odd or even?

5, 7, 9, 11

A odd
B even

4. Which cube continues the pattern?

A □
B ■

5. One night, Lou saw 8 stars. Tina saw 3 stars. How many more stars did Lou see than Tina?

A 10 more stars
B 11 more stars
C 5 more stars

6. Subtract. Choose the add-to-check fact.

$$\begin{array}{r} 16 \\ -7 \\ \hline \end{array}$$

A 7 + 2 = 9
B 7 + 16 = 23
C 7 + 9 = 16

7. Measure to the nearest inch.

inches 1   2

A 3 inches
B 2 inches
C 1 inch

MCT 2 — 73

Mid-Year Test — Chapters 1-9, page 2

Multiple-Choice Format

Name _____

8. Choose the word name for 85.

A eighty-five
B fifty-eight
C eight-five

9. Choose > or < for the ○.

57 ○ 75

A >
B <

10. Count on by 2's. What number comes next?

14, 16, 18

A 12
B 19
C 20

11. Count on by 5's. What number comes next?

55, 60, 65

A 50
B 70
C 65

12. Choose the place in line of the shaded moon.

○ ○ ○ ● ○
first   last

A fourth
B third
C fifth

13. Choose the time.

A 5:45
B 9:25
C 9:05

14. Count the money.

A 31¢
B 16¢
C 36¢

74 — MCT 2

End-of-Year Test — Chapters 1-18, page 1

Multiple-Choice Format

Name _____

1. Which fact completes the family?

$$\begin{array}{cc} 4 & 3 \\ +3 & +4 \\ \hline 7 & 7 \end{array}$$

$$\begin{array}{cc} 7 & \\ -4 & \\ \hline 3 & \end{array}$$

A $\begin{array}{r} 4 \\ -3 \\ \hline 1 \end{array}$

B $\begin{array}{r} 7 \\ -3 \\ \hline 4 \end{array}$

2. Add.

$$\begin{array}{r} 5 \\ 4 \\ +3 \\ \hline \end{array}$$

A 9
B 12
C 7

3. Which cube continues the pattern?

A ■
B □

4. Subtract. Choose the add-to-check fact.

$$\begin{array}{r} 14 \\ -6 \\ \hline \end{array}$$

A 6 + 8 = 14
B 6 + 2 = 8
C 6 + 14 = 20

5. Measure to the nearest inch.

inches 1   2   3

A 3 inches
B 2 inches
C 1 inch

6. Choose the word name for 63.

A thirty-six
B six-three
C sixty-three

7. Choose the place in line of the shaded bug.

first   last

A fourth
B second
C fifth

MCT 2 — 75

End-of-Year Test — Chapters 1-18, page 2

Multiple-Choice Format

Name _____

8. Choose the time.

A 7:20
B 7:10
C 2:35

9. Count the money.

A 40¢
B 31¢
C 36¢

10. Add.

$$\begin{array}{r} 63 \\ +29 \\ \hline \end{array}$$

A 92
B 70
C 65

11. Draw a triangle. How many corners does it have?

A 3 corners
B 4 corners
C 5 corners

12. Subtract.

$$\begin{array}{r} 62 \\ -27 \\ \hline \end{array}$$

A 35
B 25
C 89

13. What part is shaded?

A 1 fourth
B 1 half
C 3 fourths

14. Choose > or < for the ○.

444 ○ 333

A >
B <

15. Jorge wants 36 fish. He has 18 fish. How many more does he need?

A 18 more
B 20 more
C 54 more

76 — MCT 2

ITEM ANALYSIS

Items	Objectives
1	1-8
2	2-10
3	3-1
4	3-3
5	4-4
6	5-5
7	6-2
8	7-7
9	8-4
10	8-6
11	8-7
12	8-8
13	9-3
14	9-8

ITEM ANALYSIS

Items	Objectives
1	1-8
2	2-10
3	3-3
4	5-2
5	6-2
6	7-7
7	8-8
8	9-3
9	9-8
10	11-4
11	12-4
12	14-4
13	15-4
14	17-7
15	18-4

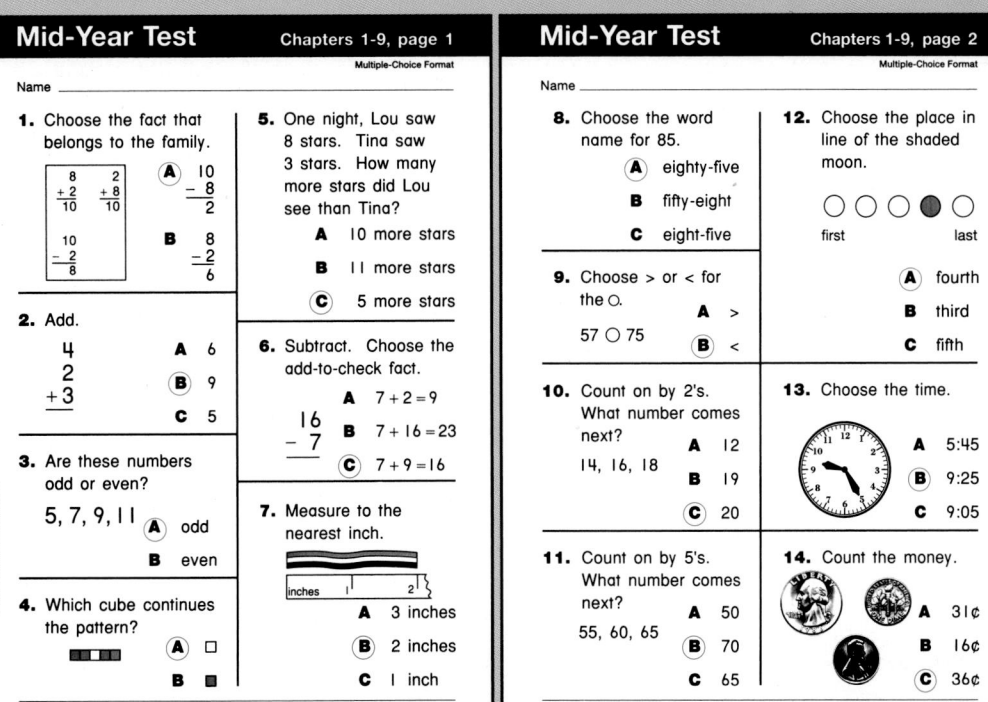

BASIC FACTS TESTS

Basic-Facts Test — Addition Facts Test 1

Emphasis on facts from first half of Chapter 1

Name _____

Add.

	A	B	C	D	E	F
1.	5 + 5 = 10	2 + 5 = 7	6 + 7 = 13	8 + 3 = 11	0 + 6 = 6	4 + 5 = 9
2.	6 + 3 = 9	7 + 2 = 9	7 + 7 = 14	5 + 0 = 5	6 + 1 = 7	8 + 7 = 15
3.	9 + 8 = 17	3 + 9 = 12	1 + 7 = 8	6 + 5 = 11	0 + 9 = 9	6 + 6 = 12
4.	8 + 0 = 8	5 + 4 = 9	2 + 3 = 5	6 + 2 = 8	8 + 9 = 17	4 + 3 = 7
5.	8 + 8 = 16	5 + 1 = 6	5 + 6 = 11	3 + 5 = 8	2 + 6 = 8	4 + 4 = 8
6.	7 + 6 = 13	0 + 4 = 4	4 + 4 = 8	2 + 9 = 11	7 + 8 = 15	9 + 9 = 18

MCT 2   77

Basic-Facts Test — Addition Facts Test 2

Emphasis on facts from second half of Chapter 1

Name _____

Add.

	A	B	C	D	E	F
1.	5 + 7 = 12	6 + 4 = 10	8 + 5 = 13	3 + 7 = 10	1 + 9 = 10	3 + 9 = 12
2.	0 + 3 = 3	7 + 4 = 11	2 + 8 = 10	9 + 6 = 15	7 + 6 = 13	8 + 6 = 14
3.	2 + 9 = 11	8 + 9 = 17	0 + 9 = 9	3 + 4 = 7	4 + 9 = 13	7 + 0 = 7
4.	4 + 7 = 11	9 + 1 = 10	3 + 8 = 11	5 + 8 = 13	6 + 6 = 12	9 + 7 = 16
5.	5 + 9 = 14	4 + 5 = 9	8 + 9 = 17	5 + 5 = 10	6 + 8 = 14	7 + 5 = 12
6.	4 + 8 = 12	3 + 3 = 6	8 + 3 = 11	6 + 9 = 15	8 + 4 = 12	7 + 3 = 10

MCT 2   79

Basic-Facts Test — Subtraction Facts Test 1

Facts introduced in Chapter 4

Name _____

Subtract.

	A	B	C	D	E	F
1.	11 − 2 = 9	14 − 7 = 7	7 − 3 = 4	5 − 5 = 0	9 − 0 = 0	10 − 4 = 6
2.	10 − 9 = 1	9 − 1 = 8	6 − 3 = 3	11 − 8 = 3	9 − 3 = 6	11 − 3 = 8
3.	9 − 2 = 7	8 − 3 = 5	10 − 6 = 4	7 − 2 = 5	16 − 8 = 8	12 − 9 = 3
4.	8 − 4 = 4	9 − 5 = 4	10 − 8 = 2	7 − 7 = 0	12 − 3 = 9	10 − 5 = 5
5.	6 − 4 = 2	9 − 8 = 1	11 − 9 = 2	8 − 0 = 8	10 − 3 = 7	9 − 4 = 5
6.	9 − 6 = 3	12 − 6 = 6	10 − 2 = 8	10 − 7 = 3	18 − 9 = 9	9 − 7 = 2

MCT 2   81

Basic-Facts Test — Subtraction Facts Test 2

Emphasis on facts introduced in Chapter 5

Name _____

Subtract.

	A	B	C	D	E	F
1.	14 − 6 = 8	15 − 8 = 7	18 − 9 = 9	14 − 8 = 6	13 − 7 = 6	12 − 9 = 3
2.	11 − 9 = 2	13 − 5 = 8	16 − 7 = 9	9 − 9 = 0	13 − 8 = 5	15 − 9 = 6
3.	11 − 7 = 4	13 − 9 = 4	11 − 6 = 5	14 − 5 = 9	10 − 7 = 3	13 − 4 = 9
4.	11 − 8 = 3	12 − 3 = 9	11 − 4 = 7	17 − 9 = 8	12 − 5 = 7	17 − 8 = 9
5.	16 − 9 = 7	12 − 4 = 8	10 − 9 = 1	12 − 7 = 5	16 − 8 = 8	11 − 5 = 6
6.	15 − 7 = 8	10 − 8 = 2	15 − 6 = 9	13 − 6 = 7	14 − 9 = 5	12 − 8 = 4

MCT 2   83

OOKS FOR THE TEACHER

ratta-Lorton, Mary. *Mathematics Their Way.* Menlo Park, CA: Addison-Wesley, 1976.

———. *Workjobs.* Menlo Park, CA: Addison-Wesley, 1972.

———. *Workjobs II—Number Activities for Early Childhood.* Menlo Park, CA: Addison-Wesley, 1979.

———. *Workjobs for Parents—Activity-Centered Learning in the Home.* Menlo Park, CA: Addison-Wesley, 1975.

rnett, Carne and Sharon Young. *Teaching Kids Math: Problem-Solving Activities to Help Young Children Learn and Enjoy Mathematics.* Englewood Cliffs, NJ: Prentice-Hall, 1982

lstein, R., S. Libeskind and J. Lott. *A Problem-Solving Approach to Mathematics for Elementary School Teachers, Second Edition.* Menlo Park. CA: Addison-Wesley.

ter, Gary G. and Jerald L. Mikesell. *Sourcebook for Teachers Using the TI-12 Math Explorer Calculator.* Menlo Park, CA: Addison-Wesley, 1989.

rton, Grace. *Towards a Good Beginning: Teaching Early Childhood Mathematics.* Menlo Park, CA: Addison-Wesley.

rruthers, C. *Open the Lights: ESL Activities for Young Children.* Menlo Park, CA: Addison-Wesley.

arles, R. et al. *Problem-Solving Experiences in Mathematics.* Menlo Park, CA: Addison-Wesley, 1985.

amot, A. and J.M. O'Malley. *Mathematics Book A: Learning Strategies for Problem Solving.* Menlo Park, CA: Addison-Wesley, 1988.

ark, C., B. Carter, and B. Sternberg. *Math in Stride.* Menlo Park CA: Addison-Wesley, 1988/89.

burn, T. *How to Teach Mathematics Using a Calculator: Activities for Elementary and Middle School.* Reston, VA: National Council of Teachers of Mathematics, 1987.

ombs, B. et al. *Explorations for Early Childhood.* Menlo Park, CA: Addison-Wesley, 1988.

———. *Explorations 1 and 2.* Menlo Park, CA: Addison-Wesley, 1988.

vidson, N., editor. *Small Group Cooperative Learning in Mathematics: A Handbook for Teachers.* Menlo Park, CA: Addison-Wesley, 1990.

ll, Jane M., editor. *Geometry for Grades K-6.* Reston, VA: National Council of Teachers of Mathematics, 1987.

use, Peggy, editor. *Providing Opportunities for the Mathematically Gifted, K-12.* Reston, VA: National Council of Teachers of Mathematics, 1987.

obs, Harold R. *Mathematics: A Human Endeavor.* San Francisco: Freeman, 1976.

binowicz, E. *Learning From Children.* Menlo Park, CA: Addison-Wesley.

———. *The Piaget Primer.* Menlo Park, CA: Addison-Wesley.

son, J., L. Burton and K. Stacey. *Thinking Mathematically.* Menlo Park, CA: Addison-Wesley.

National Council of Teachers of Mathematics. *Curriculum and Evaluation Standards for School Mathematics.* Reston, VA: National Council of Teachers of Mathematics, 1989.

———. *Computers in Mathematics Education, 1984 Yearbook.* Reston, VA: NCTM, 1984.

———. *Mathematics Learning in Early Childhood, 37th Yearbook.* Reston, Va: NCTM, 1975.

———. *Measurement in School Mathematics, 1976 Yearbook.* Reston, VA: NCTM, 1976.

———. *New Directions for Elementary School Mathematics.* Reston, VA: NCTM, 1989.

———. *Problem Solving in School Mathematics, 1980 Yearbook.* Reston, VA: NCTM, 1980.

———. *The Agenda in Action, 1983 Yearbook.* Reston, VA: NCTM, 1983.

———. *The Ideas of Algebra, K-12, 1988 Yearbook.* Reston, VA: NCTM, 1988.

Nelson, Doyal and Joan Worth. *How to Choose and Create Good Problems for Primary Children.* Reston, VA: National Council of Teachers of Mathematics, 1983.

Richardson, K. *Developing Number Concepts Using Unifix Cubes.* Menlo Park, CA: Addison-Wesley.

Shimabukuro, G. *Thinking in Logo: A Sourcebook for Teachers.* Menlo Park, CA: Addison-Wesley, 1988.

Shoecraft, P. and T. Clukey. *The Mad Minute.* Menlo Park, CA: Addison-Wesley, 1981.

Stenmark, J., V. Thompson and R. Cossey. *Family Math.* Berkeley, CA: Lawrence Hall of Science, 1986.

Thornburg, D. *Exploring Logo Without a Computer.* Menlo Park, CA: Addison-Wesley.

Thornton, Carol, et al. *Teaching Mathematics to Children With Special Needs.* Menlo Park, CA: Addison-Wesley, 1983.

Veitch, B. and T. Harms. *Cook and Learn—Pictorial Single-Portion Recipes: A Child's Cookbook.* Menlo Park, CA: Addison-Wesley, 1981.

Walker, M. *Addison-Wesley ESL Program.* Menlo Park, CA: Addison-Wesley, 1989.

Westley, J. and M. Randolph. *Windows on Mathematics.* Sunnyvale, CA: Creative Publications, 1987.

Williams, E.M. and H. Shuard. *Elementary Mathematics Today: A Teacher Resource, 2nd ed.* Reading, MA: Addison-Wesley, 1976.

Young, Sharon. *Mathematics in Children's Books.* Palo Alto, CA: Creative Publications, 1979.

RECOMMENDED PERIODICALS

Arithmetic Teacher. Reston, VA: National Council of Teachers of Mathematics.

Instructor. New York: Instructor Publications, Inc.

Mathematics Teacher. Reston, VA: National Council of Teachers of Mathematics.

BIBLIOGRAPHY

BOOKS FOR THE STUDENT

Allen, Pamela. *Who Sank the Boat?* New York: Coward, McCann, 1982.

Andersen, Hans Christian. *Andersen's Fairy Tales*. New York: Grossett & Dunlap, 1945.

Anno, Masaichiro and Mitsumasa. *Anno's Mysterious Multiplying Jar*. New York: G.P. Putnam, 1983.

Anno, Mitsumara. *Anno's Alphabet*. New York: Thomas Y. Crowell, 1975.

_____. *Anno's Counting Book*. New York: Harper & Row, 1977.

_____. *Anno's Counting House*. New York: Philomel Books, The Putnam Publishing Group, 1982.

_____. *The King's Flower*. Cleveland, OH: William Collins Publishers, 1979.

Baba, Noboru. *Eleven Hungry Cats*. Minnesota: Carolrhoda Books, 1988.

Bang, Molly. *Ten, Nine, Eight*. New York: Picture Puffins Books, Penguin, 1985.

Barrett, Judi. *Cloudy With a Chance of Meatballs*. New York: Aladdin Books, Macmillan Publishing, 1978.

Bayley, Nicola. *One Old Oxford Ox*. New York: Atheneum. 1977.

Blos, Joan. *Martin's Hats*. New York: Morrow, 1984.

Boynton, Sandra. *Hippos Go Berserk*. Chicago: Recycled Paper Press, 1977.

Brandenberg, Franz. "Flags for Sale," from *Leo and Emily's Big Ideas*. New York: Greenwillow Books, 1982.

Breiter, Herta S. *Time and Clocks*. Read About Science Series. Milwaukee, WI: Raintree, 1978.

Brenner, Barbara. *The Five Pennies*. New York: Alfred A. Knopf, 1963.

Bridgman, Elizabeth. *All the Little Bunnies*. New York: Atheneum, 1977.

Brown, Marc. *One Two Three: An Animal Counting Book*. Boston: Little Brown, 1976.

Brown, Marcia. *Listen to a Shape*. New York: Franklin Watts, 1979.

Burningham, John. *Mr. Grumpy's Outing*. New York: Thomas Y. Crowell, 1976.

_____. *The Shopping Basket*. New York: Thomas Y. Crowell, 1980.

Carroll, Lewis. *Alice's Adventures in Wonderland*. New York: Dilithium Press/Children's Classics, 1988.

Cretan, Gladys T. *Ten Brothers With Camels*. New York: Western Publishing Co., 1975.

Crowther, Robert. *The Most Amazing Hide-and-Seek Counting Book*. New York: Viking, 1981.

de Angeli, Marguerite. *Marguerite de Angeli Book of Nursery and Mother Goose Rhymes*. New York: Doubleday and Company, 1954.

de Paola, Tomie. *Pancakes for Breakfast*. New York: Harcourt, Brace, Jovanovich, 1978.

Dodd, Lynley. *The Nickle Nackle Tree*. New York: Macmillan, 1978.

Emberley, Barbara. *Drummer Hoff*. New York: Simon & Schuster, 1967.

Friskey, Margaret. *Mystery of the Farmer's Three Fives*. New York: Children's Press, 1983.

Froman, Robert. *The Greatest Guessing Game*. New York: Thomas Y. Crowell, 1978.

Gag, Wanda. *Millions of Cats*. New York: Coward, McCann & Geoghegan, 1977.

Galdone, Paul. *Henny Penny*. New York: Seabury Press, 1968.

Gerstein, Mordical. *Roll Over*. New York: Crown Publishers, 1984.

_____. *The House that Jack Built*. New York: McGraw Hill, 1961.

Goeller, Lee. *How to Make an Adding Machine: That Even Adds Roman Numerals*. New York: Harcourt Brace Jovanovich, 1979.

Greenaway, Kate. *A-Apple Pie*. New Jersey: Castle Books, 1979.

Hawkins, Colin. *One More and One Less*. New York: Crown, 1974.

_____. *Take Away Monsters*. New York: G.P. Putnam's Sons, 1984.

Hoban, Tana. *Big Ones, Little Ones*. New York: William Morrow, 1976.

Holl, Adelaide. *Let's Count*. Reading, MA: Addison-Wesley, 1976.

Huff, Vivian. *Let's Make Paper Dolls*. New York: Harper & Row, 1978.

Hutchins, Pat. *Clocks and More Clocks*. New York: Macmillan, 1970.

Kellogg, Steven. *Much Bigger Than Martin*. New York: Dial, 1976.

Jacobs, Allan D. and Leland B. Jacobs. *Arithmetic in Verse and Rhyme*. Champaign, IL: Garrard Publishing, 1971.

Kirn, Ann. *Nine in a Line*. New York: Grosset & Dunlap, 1966.

Korr, David. *The Day the Count Stopped Counting*. New York: Golden Press, 1977.

Kotzwinkle, William. *The Day the Gang Got Rich*. New York: Viking Press, 1970.

_____. and Joe Servello. *The Ants Who Took Away Time*. New York: Doubleday, 1978.

Leodhas, Sorche Nic. *Always Room for One More*. New York: Henry Holt & Co., 1965.

Leonni, Leo. *Pezzettino*. New York: Pantheon, 1975.

Low, Joseph. *Mice Twice*. New York: McElderry Book, Atheneum, 1983.

Mack, Stan. *10 Bears in My Bed*. New York: Pantheon Books, 1974.

Maestro, Betsey. *Harriet Goes to the Circus*. New York: Crown, 1977.

Magill, David. *I Can Tell Time*. New York: Dandelion Press, 1979.

Mahy, Margaret. *17 Kings and 42 Elephants*. New York: Dial Press, 1987.

Manley, Deborah. *Animals One to Ten*. Milwaukee, WI: Raintree, 1979.

Mathews, Louise. *Bunches and Bunches of Bunnies*. New York: Dodd, Mead and Company, 1978.

_____. *Gator Pie*. New York: Dodd, Mead & Co., 1979.

_____. *The Great Take-Away*. New York: Dodd, Mead & Co., 1980.

Mayer, Mercer. *Just For You*. New York: Golden Press, 1975.

Nentl, Jerolyn Ann. *The Gram Is*. Mankato, MN: Crestwood House, 1976.

_____. *The Liter Is*. Mankato, MN: Crestwood House, 1976.

_____. *The Meter Is*. Mankato, MN: Crestwood House, 1976.

_____. *The Metric System Is*. Mankato, MN: Crestwood House, 1976.

Olney, Ross & Patricia. *How Long? To Go, To Grow, To Know*. New York: William Morrow & Co., 1984.

Ormerod, Jan. *101 Things to do With a Baby*. New York: Lothrop, 1984.

Peppe, Rodney. *Humphrey the Number Horse*. New York: Viking, 1975.

Pienkowski, Jan. *Shapes*. New York: Harvey House, 1975.

Quackenbush, Robert. *Too Many Lollipops*. New York: Golden Press, 1987.

Raskin, Ellen. *Twenty-two, Twenty-three*. New York: Atheneum, 1976.

Reit, Seymour. *All Kinds of Signs*. New York: Western Publishing, 1970.

Rice, Jean. *Computers are Fun*. Minneapolis, MN: Dennison, 1981.

Rockwell, Anne. *The Old Woman and Her Pig*. New York: Thomas Y. Crowell, 1979.

_____. "The Travels of a Fox," from *The Old Woman and Her Pig and 10 Other Stories*. New York: Thomas Y. Crowell, 1975.

Ross, Pat. *M and M and the Big Bag*. New York: Pantheon Books, Random House, 1981.

Sazer, Nina. *What Do You Think I Saw? A Nonsense Number Book*. New York: Pantheon, 1976.

Schwartz, David M. *How Much is a Million?* New York: Lothrop, Lee, & Shepard, 1985.

Seuss, Dr. *The Shape of Me and Other Stuff*. New York: Beginner Books, Random House, 1973.

Shannon, George. *Beanboy*. New York: Greenwillow Books, William Morrow & Co., 1984.

Sharmat, Mitchell. *The Seven Sloppy Days of Phineas Pig*. New York: Harcourt Brace Jovanovich.

Shaw, Charles G. *It Looked Like Spilt Milk*. New York: Harper & Row, 1947.

Testa, Fulvio. *Leaves*. New York: Peter Bedrick Books, distributed by Harper & Row, 1980.

Thurber, James. *The Thirteen Clocks*. New York: Simon & Schuster, 1950.

Viorst, Judith. *Alexander, Who Used to Be Rich Last Sunday*. New York: Aladdin Books, Macmillan Publishing Company, 1978.

Walter, Marion. *Look at Annette*. New York: M. Evans, 1972.

_____. *Make a Bigger Puddle, Make a Smaller Worm*. New York: M. Evans, 1972.

Weiks, Erika. *Count the Cats*. New York: Doubleday, 1976.

Wells, Rosemary. *Max's Toys: A Counting Book*. New York: Dial, 1979.

Yolen, Jane. *An Invitation to the Butterfly Ball*. New York: Parents' Magazine Press, 1976.

Zemach, Margot. *It Could Always Be Worse*. New York: Farrar, Straus, & Giroux, 1976.

SOFTWARE

Addition Magician (Apple II series; Commodore 64; IBM PC/PCjr and PS/2; Tandy 1000; color monitor desirable). The Learning Company, 1984.

Arithmetic Critters (Apple II series; color monitor required). MECC, 1986.

Blockers and Finders (Apple II series; Commodore 64; color monitor desirable). Sunburst Communications, 1987.

Challenge Math (Apple II series; Commodore 64). Sunburst Communications, 1984.

Clock (Apple II series). Hartley Courseware, 1985.

MacKids: Coinworks (Apple Macintosh). Nordic Software, 1986.

Conservation and Counting (Apple II series; requires color monitor). Hartley Courseware, 1985.

Creature Creator (Apple II series; Atari 400, 800, XL; Commodore 64; IBM PC/PCjr and PS/2; Tandy 1000). Designware, 1983.

Fish Scales (Apple II series). DLM, 1985.

Galaxy Math Facts (Apple II series). Random House.

How to Weigh an Elephant (Apple II series). Learning Technologies, 1985.

Learning About Numbers (Apple II+, e, c). C & C Software, 1985.

Logo Works: Lessons in Logo (Apple II series). Terrapin, 1985.

BIBLIOGRAPHY

Math Practice Level I (IBM PC/PCjr and PS/2; requires color monitor). IBM Educational Systems, 1985.

Math Rabbit (Apple II series) The Learning Company, 1984.

Milt's Math Drills (Apple II series). Hartley Courseware, 1986.

Moptown Parade (Apple II series; Atari; Commodore 64; IBM PC/PCjr and PS/2; Tandy 1000; requires color monitor). Addison-Wesley, 1985.

Number Munchers (Apple II series; color monitor desirable). MECC, 1986.

Path Tactics (Apple II series; Commodore 64; IBM PC/PCjr and PS/2; Tandy 1000; color monitor desirable). MECC, 1986.

Piece of Cake Math (Apple II series). Springboard Software, 1983.

Safari Search (Apple II series). Sunburst Communications, 1985.

Subtraction Defenders (Apple II series). Gamco Industries, 1985.

Subtraction Puzzles (Apple II series). MECC, 1985.

Trap-A-Zoid (Apple II series; Atari 400, 800; Commodore 64; IBM PC/PCjr and PS/2; Tandy 1000). Designware, 1983.

TEACHER'S NOTES